NATURAL RESOURCES IN SCOTLAND

Natural Resources in Scotland

Symposium

AT

The Royal Society of Edinburgh

24 George Street, Edinburgh

31st October to 2nd November 1960

Symposium Chairman

L. A. ELGOOD, Esq., O.B.E., M.C., D.L., J.P., C.A.

SCOTTISH COUNCIL (DEVELOPMENT AND INDUSTRY)

1961

Printed in Great Britain by
T. & A. Constable Ltd.
Hopetoun Street, Edinburgh

COMMITTEE ON NATURAL RESOURCES IN SCOTLAND

Chairman

L. A. ELGOOD, Esq., O.B.E., M.C., D.L., J.P., C.A.,
Director of Royal Bank of Scotland; Williams Deacon's Bank Ltd.;
United Glass Ltd. (chmn.); Westclox Ltd. (chmn.); Forteviot Trust Ltd.

Members

Land—A. B. STEWART, Esq., M.A., B.SC., PH.D., F.R.I.C., F.R.S.E.,
Director, The Macaulay Institute for Soil Research, Aberdeen.

Water—Professor W. FRAZER, B.SC., PH.D., A.R.C.S.T., A.M.I.C.E., A.M.I.MECH.E.,
Department of Mechanical, Civil and Chemical Engineering,
The Royal College of Science and Technology, Glasgow.

Fuel and Energy—J. L. WARRANDER, Esq.,
Senior Scottish Officer, Ministry of Power.

Minerals—ROBERT H. S. ROBERTSON, Esq., M.A.(CANTAB.), F.G.S.,
Consultant in Raw Material Development, Pitlochry.

Fish and Wildlife—F. FRASER DARLING, Esq., D.SC., PH.D., N.D.A., LL.D., F.R.S.E.,
The Conservation Foundation, New York.

Forestry—A. H. H. ROSS, Esq., C.B.E.,
lately Director of Forestry for Scotland, Ford, Midlothian.

Human Resources—Professor C. MACRAE, C.B.E., D.PHIL.,
Department of Industrial Administration,
The Royal College of Science and Technology, Glasgow.

General Procedure—F. N. WOODWARD, Esq., C.B.E., B.SC., PH.D., F.R.S.E.,
Director, Arthur D. Little Research Institute, Inveresk;
Scientific Attaché to E.P.A. of O.E.E.C.; Member—Board of Management,
Institute of Seaweed Research; Member—International Seaweed Symposia,
Standing Committee; 1948—U.K. representative, UNSCCUR Preparatory Committee;
1949—U.K. delegate, UNSCCUR, Lake Success, N.Y.

Development—B. RAISTRICK, Esq., B.SC., PH.D., F.R.I.C., M.I.CHEM.E., F.R.S.E.,
(co-opted), Director, Associated Chemical Companies, Stockton-on-Tees.

Secretary

H. M. WILSON, Esq., B.SC., A.M.I.MECH.E., A.M.I.E.E.,
Technical Secretary, The Scottish Council (Development and Industry), Edinburgh.

Attendance at the Symposium

The list below gives the names of persons attending the Symposium and, where appropriate, the organisations which they represented. For convenience these names have been grouped into categories. Within the categories the names of bodies represented have been placed in alphabetical order. The names of Chairmen, Deputy Chairmen, Reporters, Authors, are not included, since they are mentioned separately elsewhere.

DEPARTMENTS OF H.M. GOVERNMENT

Admiralty

Eng. Rear-Admiral B. J. H. Wilkinson, C.B., C.B.E.

Board of Trade

C. J. A. Whitehouse, O.B.E.

Department of Agriculture and Fisheries for Scotland

A. J. Aglen
O. J. Beilby, M.A., B.LITT.
Miss I. F. Haddow
E. E. Hunter
R. H. Law
A. Paton, B.SC.(AGR.), N.D.A., N.D.D.
W. Russell
W. H. Senior, F.R.S.E.
A. Tomter

Department of Health for Scotland

J. C. O. Burns, C.B.E., B.A., M.I.C.E.
Mrs. M. J. Earley
R. Grieve, A.M.I.C.E., M.T.P.I., A.M.I.MUN.E.

Department of Scientific and Industrial Research

N. G. Kennedy, B.SC., A.M.I.MECH.E.

Ministry of Agriculture, Fisheries and Food

Maj.-General L. F. de Vic Carey, C.B.E. (Director General, Ordnance Survey)
E. G. B. Gooding, M.A., M.I.BIOL.

Ministry of Aviation

S. P. Dobbs
G. M. Macintosh, O.B.E.

Ministry of Labour

J. A. Diack, C.B.E.
Miss I. Robertson, O.B.E.

Ministry of Power

J. L. Warrander
F. A. Williams, M.SC., PH.D., A.R.I.C., M.INST.F.

Ministry of Works

W. V. Wastie, O.B.E.

Office of the Minister of Science

G. J. Spence

Scottish Home Department

Miss M. K. Macdonald
J. E. Stark
H. H. A. Whitworth, M.B.E.

Scottish Office

Sir William S. Murrie, K.B.E., C.B.

UNIVERSITIES AND COLLEGES

University of Aberdeen

Department of Forestry

Professor H. M. Steven, C.B.E., M.A., B.SC., PH.D., F.R.S.E.

Department of Geography

R. E. H. Mellor, B.A., F.R.G.S.
K. Walton, M.A., PH.D.

University of Edinburgh

Sir Edward Appleton, G.B.E., K.C.B., M.A., D.SC., SC.D., LL.D., LITT.D., F.R.C.S.E., F.R.S.E., F.R.S., Principal

Department of Architecture

Professor R. H. Matthew, C.B.E., M.A., A.R.S.A., F.R.I.B.A., F.R.I.A.S.

Department of Political Economy

P. Pearse, M.A., B.S.F.

Department of Geology

Professor F. H. Stewart, B.SC., PH.D., F.R.S.E.

Department of Geography

Professor J. W. Watson, M.A., PH.D., F.R.S.C.
D. R. Macgregor, M.A.

Institute of Animal Genetics

Professor C. H. Waddington, C.B.E., M.A., SC.D., D.SC., F.R.S.

UNIVERSITY OF GLASGOW

Department of Geography

Professor Ronald Miller, M.A., PH.D., F.R.S.E., F.R.S.G.S.

J. S. Keates

Department of Zoology

Professor C. M. Yonge, C.B.E., PH.D., D.SC., F.R.S.

H. D. Slack, B.SC., PH.D.

UNIVERSITY OF ST. ANDREWS

Department of Botany

D. G. N. Spence, B.SC., PH.D.

HERIOT-WATT COLLEGE, EDINBURGH

Hugh Nisbet, PH.D., D.SC., A.H.-W.C., F.R.I.C., F.R.S.E., Principal

Department of Chemical Engineering

Professor P. H. Calderbank, PH.D., B.SC., A.M.I.CHEM.E.

Department of Mining Engineering

Professor R. McAdam, PH.D., B.SC., M.I.MIN.E., F.R.S.E.

IMPERIAL COLLEGE OF SCIENCE AND TECHNOLOGY, LONDON

Department of Public Health Engineering

F. E. Bruce

ROYAL COLLEGE OF SCIENCE AND TECHNOLOGY, GLASGOW

Department of Biology

Miss Blodwen Lloyd, M.SC., PH.D., M.I.BIOL.

Department of Mechanical, Civil and Chemical Engineering

Professor A. S. T. Thomson, D.SC., PHD., A.R.C.S.T., M.I.C.E., M.I.MECH.E.
Professor A. S. Scott, B.SC., PH.D., A.R.C.S.T., M.I.MECH.E., M.I.CHEM.E.
Robert White, B.SC., A.M.I.C.E.

EDINBURGH AND EAST OF SCOTLAND COLLEGE OF AGRICULTURE

A. M. Smith, PH.D., D.SC., F.R.I.C., F.R.S.E.

NORTH OF SCOTLAND COLLEGE OF AGRICULTURE

M. A. H. Tincker, M.A., D.SC., F.L.S., F.R.S.E., Principal

WEST OF SCOTLAND COLLEGE OF AGRICULTURE

Professor Hugh Nicol, M.SC., PH.D., F.R.I.C., F.R.S.E.

ASSOCIATIONS, OFFICIAL AND SEMI-OFFICIAL BODIES AND NATIONALISED INDUSTRIES

Advisory Panel on Highlands and Islands

Gordon Chalmers

The Council of Scottish Chambers of Commerce

T. D. Bruce

Counties of Cities Association

Bailie Sydney Fyfe
Councillor Lawrence S. Miller, M.A., LL.B., S.S.C.

Crofters Commission

Sir Robert Urquhart, K.B.E., C.M.G.

Federation of Scottish Junior Chambers of Commerce

James A. Macreadie

Forestry Commission

Andrew Watt, B.A.(FOR.)

Geological Survey of Great Britain

Dr. G. H. Mitchell, F.R.S.

Herring Industry Board

H. H. Goodwin

International Centre for Regional Planning and Development

P. E. Johnson-Marshall
P. D. McGovern

National Coal Board

R. W. Parker, C.B.E., Chairman, Scottish Division

J. Anderton
L. E. Bourke
J. B. Caldwell
W. Macleod
L. R. Milligan
D. Skidmore
R. W. Taylor
A. M. Wandless

The Nature Conservancy

E. M. Nicholson, C.B.

National Farmers' Union of Scotland

D. S. Johnston
G. Milne
W. B. Swan

The National Trust for Scotland

P. Sked

New Zealand Scientific Liaison Office

B. W. Collins, M.SC.

North of Scotland Hydro-Electric Board

J. C. N. Baillie, M.S.M.A., M.I.B.A.E., M.AMER.S.A.E.

River Purification Boards

Ayrshire: J. L. Campbell
Clyde: J. H. Spencer
Forth: W. F. Collett
Lothians: R. W. Covill
D. Hammerton
R. W. Hershey
Councillor Bruce L. Russell
Solway: C. P. James
Tay: J. A. Rangeley
Tweed: J. T. Waddington

Scottish Agricultural Organisation Society Ltd.

C. J. M. Cadzow
Prophet Smith

Scottish Board for Industry

D. Fraser

Scottish Country Industries Development Trust

Sir John Gilmour, Bt., D.S.O., T.D., D.L.
Col. I. D. N. Leslie, O.B.E.
Ewing McGruer

Scottish Gas Board

H. R. Hart, T.D.

Scottish Landowners' Federation

His Grace the Duke of Buccleuch and Queensberry, K.T., P.C., K.C.V.O.

Scottish Peat and Land Development Association

T. B. L. Thomson

South of Scotland Electricity Board

E. Hywel Jones, M.I.E.E.

Scottish Woodland Owners' Association

A. F. Wallace of Candacraig

Town and Country Planning Association (Scottish section)

John L. Kinloch

White Fish Authority

J. R. D. Murray, M.A., LL.B.
Sir John Ure Primrose, D.L., J.P.

RESEARCH ESTABLISHMENTS AND ASSOCIATIONS

Agricultural Research Council

The Director, Poultry Research Centre
A. A. Rutherford, Unit of Statistics

Animal Diseases Research Association

The Director

Arthur D. Little Research Institute

F. N. Woodward, C.B.E., B.SC., PH.D., F.R.S.E.

British Iron and Steel Research Association

G. E. Davies

Department of Scientific and Industrial Research—Water Pollution Research Laboratory

Dr. M. C. Dart

Hill Farming Research Organisation

Dr. R. F. Hunter
Dr. J. King
I. A. Nicholson

Macaulay Institute for Soil Research

A. B. Stewart, M.A., B.SC., PH.D., F.R.I.C., F.R.S.E.

National Institute of Agricultural Engineering, Scottish Section

The Director

Oceanographic Laboratory (Department of Agriculture and Fisheries)

The Director

Rowett Research Institute
Dr. D. P. Cuthbertson

Scottish Horticultural Research Institute
T. Swarbrick, M.SC., PH.D.

Scottish Plant Breeding Station
The Director

Stanford Research Institute
W. L. White

The Water Research Association
J. L. Robinson

PROFESSIONAL AND LEARNED BODIES

Institute of Fuel, London
Dr. A. C. Dunningham

Institution of Mining Engineers
R. A. Moore, President

Royal Caledonian Horticultural Society
J. Forbes, President

Royal Philosophical Society of Glasgow
Professor Esmond Wright, M.A.

Royal Scottish Forestry Society
Major S. F. Macdonald Lockhart

Royal Scottish Geographical Society
C. W. A. Allan, President

Royal Society of Edinburgh
Professor E. L. Hirst, C.B.E., LL.D., F.R.S.

The Town Planning Institute (Scottish Branch)
Andrew Wilson

INDIVIDUALS AND REPRESENTATIVES OF FIRMS

Bailie George Simpson Barron
D. P. Bickmore, The Clarendon Press
John Boyd, Scottish Diatomite Ltd.
J. G. M. Bremner, M.A., B.SC., D.PHIL., Scottish Agricultural Industries Ltd.
W. E. Bryden, George Scott & Son (London) Ltd.
W. D. Burnett, The Distillers Co. Ltd.
J. M. Caldwell, Scottish Oils Ltd.
W. A. Cooper, I.C.I. Ltd.
Captain James Craig
Professor R. Ruggles Gates, F.R.S.
Lt.-Col. Robert Gayre of Gayre and Nigg, K.C.M.M., M.A.
Rt. Hon. Lord Glentanar, D.L., J.P.
W. Guthrie, Messrs. Strain & Robertson
T. G. N. Haldane, Messrs. Merz & McLellan
S. W. F. Hanson
S. George Henderson
C. H. Huddleston, M.I.C.E.
David Jenkins, M.A., M.R.C.V.S.
P. Jones, United Glass Ltd.
J. Gibson Kerr, W.S., F.R.S.E.
W. A. W. Krebs, Arthur D. Little Inc.
David Lowe, C.B.E.
James Macaulay, M.B.E., Messrs. James Macaulay & Son
A. G. MacGregor, M.C., D.SC., F.R.S.E., F.G.S.
Murray Macgregor, M.A., D.SC.
B. G. McLellan, F.R.I.C., M.I.CHEM.E.
N. S. Main, LL.B., Messrs. Glen & Henderson
Frank Nugent, MacFisheries Ltd.
Dr. W. B. Peutherer, B.P. Refinery (Grangemouth) Ltd.
F. A. B. Preston, M.I.MUN.E., M.T.P.I., F.R.S.E.
Dr. Magnus Pyke, The Distillers Co. Ltd.
J. E. Richey, M.C., B.A., SC.D., F.R.S.
John Rollo, Rollo Industries Ltd.
W. Scholes, Transport and General Workers' Union
Dr. F. R. Smith, T. & H. Smith Ltd.
A. A. Templeton, C.B.E., J.P.
Adam Watson, PH.D., B.SC.
D. Blair Watt, British Hydrocarbon Chemicals Ltd.
T. D. Weatherhead, Hunting Surveys Ltd.
J. L. Williamson

REPRESENTATIVES OF JOURNALS

Colliery Guardian (the Editor)
Farming News and North British Agriculturist (the Editor)
The Gas World (the Editor)
The Journal of Industrial Economics (R. G. L. McCrone, University of Glasgow)
The Journal of the Institute of Water Engineers (E. W. Denholm)
The Timber Trades Journal (A. J. Meldrum)
Town and Country Planning (Miss E. B. Mitchell)

FOREWORD

Most of us have a good appreciation of one Resource or another—possibly not so many are so fortunate as to see where the dependence of one Resource upon another is so important. These transactions are published to help those who would be well informed on an integrated approach to Resource development, but I hope they will also be of interest and service to those who wish to be acquainted with the current state of specific Resource development and knowledge. I believe the transactions comprise valuable factual presentation of these and the thinking thereon.

The Symposium was part of a larger remit which covered enquiry into, with recommendations concerning, integrated Resource development.

The Committee decided to have the framework of its enquiry on the three main supports: (1) Basic Resource Facts, (2) Utilisation of Resources, and (3) Resource Administration and Development, and to assemble Authorities in one place at one time for discussion, followed by sifting of the issues by various Working Parties. The attendance on each of the three days of the Symposium was entirely satisfactory.

It is understandable that in such a short period of the Symposium a number of important subjects were only skimmed, but even so the number of issues raised in a thoroughly practical manner showed there is an urgent need to make a broader approach to Resource use and development.

I hope these transactions will help to maintain a well informed public to help further social and economic objectives to be achieved.

None of this work would have been possible without the willing co-operation of all who made up the Symposium and of the Press who commented so fully thereon. My Committee are most grateful to all who gave help and encouragement.

I should also like to thank the staff of the Scottish Council for arranging the transactions for publication and further to express appreciation to Mr. R. H. McNab who carried out the recording and subsequent editing.

L. A. ELGOOD.

COMMITTEE ON NATURAL RESOURCES IN SCOTLAND,
THE SCOTTISH COUNCIL (DEVELOPMENT AND INDUSTRY),
1 CASTLE STREET,
EDINBURGH, 2.

September, 1961.

FIRST DAY

BASIC RESOURCE FACTS

PROGRAMME

Opening of the Symposium

The Rt. Hon. LORD POLWARTH, T.D., C.A.
The Rt. Hon. J. GREIG DUNBAR, Lord Provost of Edinburgh
The LORD CRAIGTON, C.B.E.

Introduction

BASIC RESOURCE FACTS
E. P. HUDSON, M.A., F.R.S.E., *Chairman, First Day*

Deputy Chairman

E. P. HUDSON, M.A., F.R.S.E.
Managing Director, Scottish Agricultural Industries Ltd.

Deputy Chairman

Professor W. H. PEARSALL, D.SC., F.R.S.
Chairman, Scientific Policy Committee, Nature Conservancy

ADDRESS BY THE RT. HON. LORD POLWARTH, T.D., C.A.

My Lord Provost, My Lords, Ladies and Gentlemen: May I say how glad we are to see that we have some ladies with us. Could I express a very warm welcome on behalf of the Scottish Council to all who have come here today? There has been a wonderful turnout and a great response to our invitation, and I hope that as a result of that great response you will not find yourselves too cramped or uncomfortable. For the benefit of those who don't know, I should say that the Scottish Council (Development and Industry), which has sponsored this Conference, is an entirely voluntary body which exists with the one object of helping the Scottish economy, and we are entirely voluntary. We represent all sides of industry and those interested in industrial development, and we have no dependence on outside sources although we work in close collaboration with H.M. Government, and we are particularly pleased that the Minister of State for Scotland, Lord Craigton, has seen fit to come along with us this morning. This is not the time to say thank you—that will come at the end—but I do think that at the start we should express our appreciation of all the preparatory work which has gone into making this Conference. I, myself, have had very little to do with it because I have been able to devolve the whole of it on to Mr. Elgood and his Committee, and I know how much they have done, and his staff, and all those who have produced the papers for the Conference. An immense amount of work has gone into all of this and we of the Scottish Council are immensely grateful to you all.

Particularly we are glad to welcome to this Conference those who have come very great distances, some of you from the other side of the Atlantic. This is a Symposium, and I seem to remember that a Symposium in Greek meant a get-together over a very big meal. This is in fact a three-day fact-finding meeting and I think that it is probably unique not only in Scotland and Great Britain but almost in the world: because while there have been one or two other conferences of this kind, I believe this is the first that has been sponsored entirely by private enterprise. I am a layman in matters of natural resources, but one thing strikes me, and that is the subject inspires not only intense interest, but arouses strong passions in the breasts of some of those interested. I know that there are people on one extreme who maintain that Scotland is rich in natural resources and that it is just a question of getting down to development, and I know equally that on the other hand there are those who say she is poor in natural resources and there are not many resources worth developing. As is so often the case, I would hazard the guess that the truth lies somewhere in between these extremes, and we are here with the object of discovering just where that truth lies; and I hope that at the end of three days we will be a good deal wiser than we are at present. In a country as small as Scotland inevitably there is competition for the use of resources to the best advantage. We have one example of a clash before us at the moment with the proposal for a certain hydro-electric development and the objections to it on the grounds of the amenity, of the preserving of our countryside, and also on the grounds that there would be more economic ways of developing power. I would be the last person to prejudge that issue, but that is the kind of thing for which we want the information which will come out of this Conference. We also have a terrific variety of resources very much cheek by jowl and close to each other. I spent Saturday shooting grouse in among the worked-out mines of the Leadhills area on the borders of Lanarkshire and Dumfriesshire. Well, those mines once brought considerable wealth to Scotland; at present they don't, but one day again they may. On the other hand grouse go on, and grouse and wildlife in general are just as much a natural resource of Scotland as are the others.

I am particularly glad we are not only considering the traditional resources such as minerals and timber, but rather going into the land, our wildlife, and so on. It is not just a question of the economic return from them in farming, in forestry, in sport, or in tourism. All of these are important, but there is a much more subtle and profound aspect of these sides of our resources as *we* know who have been in close contact with them. In industrial society I believe it is more and more necessary to go back to these basic things and to refresh not only the body but mind and soul, and in Scotland we are very fortunate to have these resources so very close to our great industrial centres, and I believe that that is one of the major attractions for industry coming to Scotland.

I am glad to see we are including human resources—our Scots men and our Scots women, because they are not only our greatest resource—they are also, and some regret this, our greatest export. Now, there are those who moan about this. Well, I am not one of those, because I believe that as a result of Scots men and Scots women going out into the world, Scotland has left a more profound mark on the world than she would have done if they had stayed at home.

Speaking of Scotsmen, I wonder if I may strike a personal note and say how much we mourn the loss of one of Scotland's greatest sons—Sir Cecil Weir. I will not go over his career—he was too well known for that—but you will all remember his work in mounting the Empire Exhibition in Glasgow in 1938, his work for Scotland and Britain throughout the war, and afterwards with the European Community, and latterly as Chairman of the London Committee of the Council and in many other public services. I remember five months ago going with him on a mission of the Dollar Exports Council to the Pacific coast of North America. Not only did he throw himself into the work with a vigour that was astounding for a man of his years, but he threw himself into the play and amusement side with every bit as much vigour. I think he died as he would have wished—in harness; he was only ill for three short days and he died in his sleep the night before last. In view of his great services, not only to Scotland but to the country, I would ask you, if you would be so good, to stand for a brief moment.

Ladies and Gentlemen, this Conference is only a beginning. Undoubtedly it must be followed up when it is finished, but if it is to be followed up we must have one particular resource in sufficiency, and that is finance. No doubt that will be turned to when these three days are over. I hope that not only will we follow it up, but that it will point the way for other countries, some of them less developed than ourselves, to examine their own resources with a view to turning them to their good.

And so, Mr. Elgood, I wish you and your Committee and all members every good wish for a highly successful three days.

ADDRESS BY THE RT. HON. J. GREIG DUNBAR

Lord Provost of Edinburgh

Mr. Chairman, My Lords, Ladies and Gentlemen: First of all, sir, may I say what a great pleasure it is for me as Lord Provost to be here this morning, and I particularly want to extend a warm welcome to the city to those of you from other parts, particularly to those from abroad. I hope that your stay with us will be not only pleasurable in that you will derive benefit from this important Conference, but that there may be an opportunity for you to see something of our city. I notice Lord Polwarth skirted very cleverly over this Symposium definition. I do not know what dictionary he was looking at. I looked at one just to make sure I knew what a Symposium was, and I noticed that it started off with a drinking party. Now, I am quite certain that this is not the type of Symposium that you are going to have here.

I very much regret that it has never been possible for me in public life to take an active interest in the Scottish Council. It is quite obvious to me, reading the papers, of the valuable work this body is doing for Scotland, and this Conference is one more example of the value of that work to Scotland.

In your letter of invitation, sir, one point which you kindly gave me when giving some indication of the technical nature of the discussion which is about to take place: I would like to make a plea for the ordinary chap who may not claim to be an expert but may provide the equivalent in sound common sense. It must be clear to all that the development of manufacturing industry upsets the balance of population. It stimulates a flow of people into an area where centres of communication meet, and where the older resources such as coal and water first stimulated the new developments. The introduction of new companies to Scotland does not substantially put a brake on this trend. So some other means seem to be needed to help the economy of the northern and southern parts of Scotland. I have no doubt that those industries settling in Central Scotland are the right industries for Central Scotland. I understand we are a bit puzzled concerning the right industries for the Highlands and Borders. If it is part of the design of this Symposium to help local activity throughout Scotland to be more enterprising, to go ahead on a basis of self-help, then I think someone has the right idea and Mr. Elgood must be given every help in his difficult job of drawing useful pointers from this meeting.

Now, much can be done by local people for themselves. In the old days local authorities were towers of strength in arranging trading agreements for their people in connection with the product of their respective community. While the world is a little more complicated now, and some activities tend to be centralised in Chambers of Commerce, and the Scottish Council, and in federations of companies, only local authorities can focus fully on local resources and opportunities. A very great deal of thought has been given to the injection of new industry into Scotland from outside. It is not so clear that the equivalent weight has been given to getting new basic facts about our native resources. Such new facts may illumine opportunities natural to people in country areas, and the communication in these areas. No doubt it may be costly to obtain these facts, but it may be costlier in the long run if the appropriate surveys are not put in hand soon. Perhaps the views of this meeting will provide the substance to points which I can only put to you as personal impressions. That I think would be a good place for me to hope that the discussions which you are going to have will throw some light on some of these points. I look forward to meeting some of you this evening when I am to be your guest, and I look forward to meeting you tomorrow night when you will be the guests of Edinburgh Corporation. In the meantime I wish your Conference every possible success.

ADDRESS BY THE LORD CRAIGTON, C.B.E.

Mr. Elgood, My Lord Provost, My Lords, Ladies and Gentlemen: We in Scotland have very much for which to thank the Scottish Council, and it is with the greatest sincerity that I congratulate them now on their vision in the conception of this Symposium. So much has been said in general terms in recent years about the natural resources in Scotland and their proper development. But, as you gentlemen know better than I do, the subject is vast and diverse, and over the last years discussion has tended to lose its way. We all realise the need to halt; to survey the area thoroughly; to take fresh bearings so that further progress can become more sure and can proceed in the right direction. That is just what the Scottish Council have set out to do, and today sees the completion of the first part of their work. Now, I say "work" advisedly, because it is one thing to form an imaginative conception of this kind and quite another to bring it to a point of reality. I must give a double congratulation, firstly to the Scottish Council for entrusting the proceedings of these three days' sittings to Mr. Elgood and his Committee; and secondly I must congratulate on behalf of the Scottish Office Mr. Elgood himself and his colleagues for the way in which they have carried out their task. This is an enormous subject, and to bring it within a three-day compass can only have been achieved by a combination of patient organisation and clear thinking; and the gentlemen who brought us together have these qualities in good measure.

For your three days' feast you have three volumes of papers provided by experts in their own fields—from a distance that ranges from Scotland to Puerto Rico. On this, our first thought must be to express our thanks and gratitude to you busy men who have willingly given up time and effort to write these papers and to attend here and discuss them here. We in Scotland are deeply in your debt. So impressive has been the response that I hope that Scotland will feel as I do, that it is due in no small measure to the high reputation of the Scottish Council and to the members the Council so wisely appointed to the Committee.

It is proper that these acknowledgments should be made. But where does the central Government stand? The interest of the Secretary of State in this Symposium goes further than saying thank you to those concerned. You will observe that among the papers circulated for consideration and discussion during the next few days are four or five by officers of the Secretary of State's departments on both technical and general subjects. Many others are by writers who belong to bodies and institutions who have ties with St. Andrew's House. I mention this to make the point that in addition to our general interest in all the Scottish Council does—I echo what Lord Polwarth said—we work very closely together—the subject-matter is one in which we in St. Andrew's House have active interests already and a very considerable stake.

To clarify the Government's interest I can't do better than to anticipate the third day and quote from the general Scottish Office paper: "So far as concerns the use of natural resources the Secretary of State and his Departments are directly responsible in the central administration for many factors affecting the use in Scotland of land—agriculture and forestry of course in particular—and water (in connection with fisheries, industry, hydro-electricity and public health) and are also responsible for physical planning and to take natural resources in the human sphere, for education, welfare and public order." I mentioned land and water. I suppose I could go on to claim some stake in all the elements if I mentioned the fire service and clean air.

We at the Scottish Office are vitally concerned in this subject you are discussing, the natural resources of Scotland. But I must not stake out too wide a claim. The Government is by no means the only body concerned in these matters, and in some matters the Government's responsibility can only be minimal. Perhaps our greatest direct responsibility is in forestry, where the Forestry Commission does play a major executive part—acquires land, plants trees and looks after them and in that way uses and develops one of the most important natural resources in Scotland. But that is an exception. For the most part we rely on, and must continue to rely on, various agencies and authorities, private individuals and business concerns to supply the interest and enterprise needed to make the best of what we have. I am sure this is right and inevitable. Governments can control; Governments can co-ordinate; they can provide facilities or assist others to provide them. There is certainly a wide scope in the public field, but it is a limited scope, and to succeed in such endeavours any Government help that should be properly given must be supported by the drive of private initiative and personal interest. That is why I am so heartened by this Symposium. You have gathered together those of you who are concerned and informed on this subject. The response you have obtained shows that the interest is live and active. That augurs well for practical steps which we need for the future. I know you will have a stimulating and successful three days' discussion and at the end of it I feel sure you will keep this interest up and consolidate your gains, and, I hope, achieve another step forward in the well-being of all the Scottish people.

BASIC RESOURCE FACTS

SOIL AND MINERALS

The Soil Survey of Scotland

R. GLENTWORTH, B.S.A., PH.D.
The Macaulay Institute for Soil Research, Aberdeen

Systematic soil surveys are now being made in Scotland which aim at covering the whole country. The work is being conducted by the Department of Soil Survey of the Macaulay Institute for Soil Research, Aberdeen. Areas completed, and at present under survey, are shown on a map. An account is given of the organisation of the survey, methods and definitions used in describing soils, the soil classification system, the Major Soil Groups found in Scotland and some of the processes which are responsible for their development. The rate of progress and some of the uses of the soil survey and the reasons for making it are dealt with.

While most people are aware that terrestrial life springs from or is dependent on soil, few people have any true appreciation of what soil is, or know how to define it. For many years while the fundamental sciences were in process of rapid development the complexity of soil deterred the application of science. During the past forty years, however, the scientific study of soil in all its branches has become of universal importance.

Everyone who has had any dealing with soil knows that many different kinds of soils can occur in one district and even on one farm. Soils are difficult objects to describe and Anderson,[1] in the late eighteenth century, stated that "few things are more difficult than to give a description of soils, as to convey any accurate ideas to those for whom it was intended", pointing out that we do not have sufficient words to describe the many shades of difference between them. An eighteenth-century contributor to the Statistical Account commented that if a hundred persons were asked to describe a soil they would give a hundred different answers. The long-felt need for soil surveys is evidenced by the fact that they are now being conducted in virtually every country.

On scientific and economic grounds the value of the systematic study of rocks carried out by the Geological Survey is unquestioned, and this applies equally to the study of that important class of natural objects, the soils developed on drifts overlying the rocks. Soil survey is in effect making an inventory of a very precious asset, and without the standardisation of description and mapping which it provides, knowledge of the properties of a soil must necessarily remain of local and prescribed interest. The need for information about the nature and distribution of the main soil types has long been felt, especially by those responsible for agricultural planning and advisory work, where future progress is dependent on field experimentation. To make the results of field trials widely applicable, it is essential to know the extent and distribution of the soil on which the trials have been carried out.

Soil is a natural body occurring at the surface of the earth. It contains mineral and organic matter, air, water and organisms, and is capable of supporting life. Its character is determined by the action of biological, chemical and physical weathering processes on the geological substratum, which may be referred to as the parent material. The kind of soil formed is conditioned by the time the parent material has been exposed and the influence of climate, vegetation, hydrologic conditions and relief. In Scotland soil formation has been proceeding since the end of the last Glacial Period, or for approximately 11,000 years. By contrast, in territories south of the glaciated regions the development of soils may have been proceeding for over a million years. Soils are not all of the same age and this must be taken into consideration in surveying together with any climatic changes which may have occurred.

THE SOIL SURVEY ORGANISATION

The systematic soil survey of Great Britain came into being officially in 1946 when the Soil Survey Research Board was set up under the aegis of the Agricultural Research Council, but several persons, notably the late Professor G. W. Robinson[2] and associates in Wales, D. A. Osmond,[3] F. F. Kay,[4] W. M. Davies and G. Owen[5] in England and A. Muir[6] and R. Glentworth[7] in Scotland, had previously made soil surveys for special purposes. The Soil Survey of England and Wales, although based on the Rothamsted Experimental Station, is a separate organisation with a staff of approximately thirty persons. The Soil Survey of Scotland is a department of the Macaulay Institute for Soil Research. It has a staff of sixteen (honours graduates in either geology, botany, geography, chemistry or agriculture), consisting of the Head of Survey, Deputy Head, Correlator, Ecologist responsible for botanical surveys of the surveyed areas, six senior surveyors, six assistant surveyors and one cartographer. The surveyors normally work in teams of two, one team to a sheet, and are distributed two teams to each of the advisory provinces in the west, east and north of Scotland. The chemical and physical analyses of soil survey profile samples are undertaken by the Departments of Pedology and Spectrochemistry of the Macaulay Institute.

METHODS AND DEFINITIONS

The soil profile refers to the different layers of horizons which are exposed in the face of a pit, and the physical examination of soils is made by digging an inspection hole about one foot in diameter to a depth of 18 in. to 2 ft. Stoniness generally makes the use of the soil auger impracticable. Advantage is taken of available exposures in quarries, gravel pits, road cuttings, etc. Frequency of examination depends on the complexity of the soil pattern and on the scale of mapping; 2·5 in. to 1 mile Ordnance Survey Maps are used as base maps for the systematic survey; and the published maps are on a scale of 1 in. to 1 mile. The sheet numbers (see Fig. 1) are those of the 3rd Edition of the Ordnance Survey Maps where the projection is that of the Geological Survey Maps. When necessary, selected areas are surveyed in more detail on a scale of 6 in. to 1 mile. This scale and that of 25 in. to 1 mile are used for special surveys, for experimental farms, Forestry Commission lands, etc.

The lithological composition of the subsoil is examined. In Scotland the soil parent material is of glacial origin except on the higher hills and certain steep slopes where the soil is developing on shattered bedrock and the soils are formed *in situ*. Glacial deposits are of two kinds; (1) glacial till or boulder clay (which is another name for till), a non-sorted material consisting of boulders, stones, sand, silt and clay and (2) fluvioglacial deposit, water-sorted material, which may vary from gravel to clay depending upon the speed of flow of the water from which it was deposited.

The nature of the rock from which the parent material has been derived is of great importance in soil development, and a large number of glacial tills have been recognised depending upon the rocks from which they were formed. Sometimes the till is derived predominantly from one rock, but more often it contains a mixture of two or more rocks. In valleys the till is thicker and of finer texture than on thc valley sides. The amount of silt and clay in the till and in the soil is important in aiding the retention of water and plant nutrients.

Depending upon topographical position and on texture, the hydrologic conditions in soils may vary and five drainage classes are distinguished, namely (1) excessively freely drained, (2) freely drained, (3) imperfectly drained, (4) poorly drained and (5) very poorly drained. These terms refer to natural drainage and not to artificial drainage systems.

The colour of a soil is related to the inherent colour of the parent material which is more particularly reflected in the freely drained soils. When excess water, whether periodic or permanent, is present, grey and ochreous mottling is found, and the colours for waterlogged soils are blue-grey and dark grey. Soil colour is assessed by standard Munsell Colour Charts.

The texture of the soil is judged by the feel of the moistened soil between the fingers and gives an indication of the amount of sand, silt, clay and organic matter present; sand, loamy sand, sandy loam, loam, sandy clay loam, silt loam, silt, clay loam, and clay are some of the textural classes distinguished.

Soil structure—the size, shape and arrangement of soil particles—is determined by observing the way a soil breaks when a clod is dropped.

The consistence of a soil means the way in which the structural units cohere and are bound together, and such terms as loose, firm, hard, friable, soft and plastic are used to describe soil in a particular moisture condition, the terms being dependent on whether the soil is dry, moist or wet.

The nature of the transition from one horizon to another—it may, for instance, be merging or sharp—the sequence of the horizons, and other features such as stoniness, roots and earthworms are noted.

RATE OF PROGRESS

Of Scotland's total area of almost 30,000 square miles approximately two-thirds lie at above 1,000 ft., the altitude around which agriculture stops. The soil survey has completed the mapping of about 4,300 square miles, which as mapping is done on a sheet basis, include some high ground. With roughly 6,700 square miles of low ground still to be covered, and estimating that six survey teams map 400 square miles per year, the survey will take at least 16 years to complete. Allowing for the mapping of the high ground which has to be included with the low when surveying on a sheet basis, for difficulties of access to remote districts and similar eventualities, a more realistic estimate would be about 25 years.

THE SOILS OF SCOTLAND

The cool, humid climate of Scotland gave rise to a native vegetation of open coniferous forest on the hill flanks and broad-leaved forest at lower altitudes where temperature is higher and parent materials generally richer in plant nutrients. The summits have probably always been under heath and moor. Under coniferous forest a well-drained soil develops with three or four inches of organic litter, known as the A horizon, on top and underneath this a layer (the A_2 horizon) which is grey in colour. This horizon develops because organic acids, produced by microbial activity in the surface layer and carried down by the rain water, wash iron and aluminium compounds and clay out of the grey layer, leaving it relatively higher in silica. The iron and aluminium compounds are redeposited in the yellow-brown layer below, which is known as the B horizon, the horizon of accumulation. The underlying parent material, the C horizon, is only slightly affected by soil-forming processes. Many varieties of this profile are known on the wooded hills and on the heather-covered high ground. Such soils are known as Podzol Soils, the name given them by the Russians, who were first to point out the correlation between climate and soils. Well-developed grey A_2 ashy layers are usually found on the higher hill slopes where the temperature is lower, the rainfall higher and the rock material high in silica.

On the lower ground, which is now mainly arable but formerly carried deciduous forest, the horizon differences in the profiles are generally less marked. Some low-ground soils have relatively uniform brown layers without much surface litter accumulation, and these soils are known as Brown Forest Soils. Many of the arable soils, particularly in the north-east, have however been derived from podzol soils. Good, freely drained arable soils tend to be of medium texture and can retain sufficient moisture for good plant growth. Only after prolonged rain are the soils waterlogged, and then only for a short period. Such soils have moderate to deep topsoils and brown, red or yellow-brown subsurface B horizons. In poorly drained soils, which are known as Gley Soils, the periodic presence of excess moisture in the subsurface horizons—often through the months October to May—interferes with the downward movement of mobile constituents and the physical and chemical weathering process is strongly modified. As a result, instead of the uniform brown, red-brown or yellow subsoils of the well-drained soils, we find mottled grey, ochre and blue-grey colours—indicating reducing conditions—and often a more clayey texture. Such poorly drained soils usually occur on flattish sites with an extensive catchment area of sloping ground behind. They also are found where the texture is clay loam or clay in high rainfall areas, particularly in the south-west (Ayrshire), on slopes which one might reasonably expect to be perfectly freely drained. In concave depressions, the wettest position of all, peat is formed because anaerobic conditions have retarded the decomposition of plant remains. The subsoils of these soils may be a dull grey or blue-grey with bright ochreous tubes encircling root channels. These soils are known as Peaty Gley Soils. In Scotland three broad altitudinal soil zones can be recognised:

(1) Soils of the mountains above 2,500 ft.
(2) Soils of the mountains and foothills between 1,000 and 2,500 ft.
(3) Soils of the lowlands below 1,000 ft.

In the upper zone frost action and wind erosion, together with high precipitation, results in the formation of bare rock pavements, boulder fields, scree slopes and, on some of the high plateaux, shattered frost debris on which Alpine Humus Soils are developed. These soils occur under a pavement of small stones and sparse stunted vegetation and have a dark brown mineral and organic A horizon passing into a brown stony coarse sandy loam B horizon which overlies shattered rock. Associated with these soils are frost phenomena of stone polygons and stone stripes, features common to a tundra-like climate.

In the intermediate zone hill peat (distinguished as such when over 12 in. deep) is widespread, due to high rainfall and humidity; it occupies plateaux and gentle slopes. Hill and basin peats are estimated to cover an area of about 2,600 square miles, and are being studied and surveyed by the Peat Section of the Department of Agriculture for Scotland in collaboration with the Macaulay Institute. The work is under the general supervision of the Moss Survey Group of the Scottish Peat Committee.

Associated with the peat is the Peaty Podzol Soil, which has a peaty surface 6 to 12 in. thick followed by a distinct grey mineral A_2 horizon of some 6 to 9 in. Underneath this is a thin iron pan $\frac{1}{8}$ in. thick which forms a continuous sheet and acts as a barrier to root penetration. This checks the downward movement of water, which is forced to flow laterally across the pan. The B and C horizons, which are freely drained, are thus effectively sealed off from the profile above the iron pan. As a result of the pan, the grey A_2 and the peaty surface horizons become saturated with water for long periods of the year, and it is often the accumulation of organic matter on these soils which leads to the formation of hill peat sometimes to a depth of 8 to 9 ft. The peaty podzol supports a moorland vegetation in which *Calluna vulgaris*, *Erica tetralix*, *Tricophorum caespitosum*, *Sphagnum* spp. and other wet moorland species are abundant. The wetness and strong acidity (pH 3·5 to 4·5) provide poor conditions for tree growth. Although estimated to be as much as 80 years old, many specimens of Scots pine found on peaty podzol soils have shown only stunted growth—5 to 6 ft. tall and $1\frac{1}{2}$ in. in diameter. Nevertheless, this soil type is being extensively planted by the Forestry Commission after ploughing to a depth of 12 in. at a spacing of 5-ft. intervals, a procedure which has the effect of disrupting the iron pan in places with a consequent improvement in drainage. By this method, together with the use of phosphate fertiliser, a satisfactory growth of pine can be obtained on this soil. The peaty podzol extends down to sea-level on acid and coarse textured parent materials. On the steeper slopes Iron Podzol Soils occur. These have a humus surface, and a grey quartzose A_2 underlain by a yellow-brown B horizon. They are admirably suited to conifers, which in many instances they no doubt at one time supported, this being the native vegetation.

In the lowland region Brown Forest and Iron Podzol Soils are common on well-drained sites. The Brown Forest Soil, which is usually found on parent materials moderately rich in nutrients, has a profile which is essentially of a uniform brown colour, with a mull surface (i.e. mixed mineral and organic material). An earthworm population brings about the intermixing of mineral and organic material and the soil may be said to have a high biological activity. The Iron Podzol mentioned above, and intergrades between it and the Brown Forest Soil, are found associated with Gley Soils of poor drainage and Peaty Gley Soils of very poor drainage. A third soil which is extensive in the lowland region, particularly in the area from Kincardineshire to the Forth and between the Forth and Tweed estuaries, is a Brown Forest Soil with gleyed B and C horizons. This soil, which has imperfect drainage (intermediate between free drainage and poor), is developed on parent materials often of a sandy clay loam texture derived from moderately base rich rocks. It provides some of the best and most extensive farmland in Scotland. Soils of this group tend to have a higher clay content in the B horizon than in the A or C. Some mottling, which decreases with depth, is evident in the B and C horizons. Although not necessarily grey-brown in colour—the Scottish soils are mostly reddish brown—these soils may be equated to the Grey Brown Podzolic Soils of eastern U.S.A.

SOIL CLASSIFICATION

Podzol, Brown Forest, Gley and Peaty Gley are names given to what are known as Major Soil Groups. Each term conveys a broad general picture of a soil, of the climatic region in which it occurs, and of the genetic processes involved in its formation.

In the systematic soil survey of Scotland the surveyor is particularly concerned not only with the genetic soil group but also with changes in parent material and drainage class. The mapping units distinguished are called soil series. A soil series while being representative of a Major Soil Group, is restricted to a specific geological parent material. In Scotland, soil series are grouped on a parent material basis into Soil Associations. A Soil Association contains all the soil series derived from similar rocks or combinations of rocks. Names are given to each series and the Soil Association is named after the dominant series contained within it. Thus, although it contains a range of soil series differing in major soil group and drainage class, the Countesswells Association—a group of soils developed on granitic till—is named after the freely drained member, an iron podzol, which is the most extensive series.

Table I is an extract from a key to a coloured soil map. Shades of brown indicate brown forest soils and shades of red podzol soils. Blue denotes gley soils and green peaty gley soils, whilst purple signifies peat and yellow alluvial soils. The soil series are named and distinguished on the map by appropriate symbols.

PUBLICATIONS

Four Soil Survey Memoirs, complete with soil maps, have been published by Her Majesty's Stationery Office:

1. The Soils of the Country round Banff, Huntly and Turriff. Sheets 86 and 96.
2. The Soils of the Country round Jedburgh and Morebattle. Sheets 17 and 18.
3. The Soils of the Country round Kilmarnock. Sheets 22 and part of 21.
4. The Soils of the Country round Kelso and Lauder. Sheets 25 and 26.

A typescript memoir entitled The Soils of the Country round Elgin has been produced for local use, and the soil map for Sheet 95 (Elgin) has been published.

Figure 1 shows the progress of the Soil Survey to 1960.

USES OF THE SOIL SURVEY

Obviously a soil survey—and its related chemical studies—consists of an inventory of the soils of a region, classifying and describing them and showing their distribution

Table I

Soil Classification

EXPLANATION OF SYMBOLS AND COLOURS

Major Soil Groups		Brown Forest Soil (low base status)		Iron Podzol		Peaty Podzol	Non Calcareous Gley	Peaty Gley
		Soil Series						
Association	Parent Material	Freely Drained	Imperfectly Drained	Freely Drained	Imperfectly Drained	Freely Drained below B_1	Poorly Drained	Very Poorly Drained
Countesswells	Till derived from granite and granitic-gneiss	RM. Raemoir		CW. Countess-wells	DS. Dess	CR. Charr	TV. Terryvale	DM. Drumlassie
Tarves	Till derived from mixed acid-igneous, acid-meta-morphic and basic rocks	TR. Tarves	TL. Thistlyhill	TN. Tillypronie		PS. Pressendye	PD. Pitmedden	PK. Pettymuck

on a map. The value of this information can be envisaged in relation to administrative, planning, advisory and fundamental soil research work. In Scotland the use of soil survey for planning purposes is still restricted, as systematic surveying has not progressed beyond certain areas in the north-east, south-east and south-west. Soil information applicable to the whole country cannot yet be given, but soil data for advisory and research purposes are becoming increasingly available.

Perhaps the greatest benefit from soil survey will be in connection with recommendations for fertiliser application. In Scotland, where rainfall is abundant and nutrients are leached out of the soil, the application of manures and fertilisers almost invariably produces a noticeable response in crops. It is possible to build up the fertility of a naturally poor soil (provided its drainage is reasonably good) until it becomes quite productive, but the annual fertiliser dressing required to maintain a naturally poor soil in "good heart" will be greater than the maintenance dressing required to keep a naturally good soil in a similar condition. In arriving at lime and fertiliser recommendations, the agricultural advisory chemist is guided by management factors and by chemical analyses correlated with observed responses from experimental fertiliser trials in the field. The information thus gained applies only to the soil series involved in the actual test plots, and to extend this information to other areas without knowledge of the soils involved would be to presuppose a similarity in soil types which might not exist. Soil survey information should be a guide to the advisory chemist in his choice of sites for field trials, enabling him to decide upon the proper fertiliser recommendation for each soil series. Without the soil survey information his problem is much more difficult with the range of soil series unknown and undefined and the extent of the area to which the field trial results will apply likewise unestablished.

The systematic mapping, sampling and analysis of soil profiles encountered in the course of soil survey have revealed many clearly defined trends in the distribution down the profile of several macro- and micro-nutrients in the soil which indicate consistent differences between the genetic soil groups and drainage classes. Detailed investigation of some of these differences is providing a better understanding of soil properties and of the relation of soil to plant and animal nutrition.

The information about soils, parent materials and drainage contained in a soil map is of practical use in connection with building, road construction, and the laying of, for instance, pipe-lines. Collaborative work between the Soil Survey of Scotland and the Road Research Laboratory has yielded useful information about the suitability of certain soils (brown forest soils and gleys) and the unsuitability of others (podzols) for direct stabilisation for soil cement.

In conclusion, it can be said that when soil surveys were first undertaken it was not known whether the different soils mapped on the basis of their morphological characters had any real meaning in terms of fertility and other properties, but it can now be positively stated that the units—the soil series—distinguished by the Soil Survey on a morphological basis are valid and that they differ in physical and chemical properties.

REFERENCES

1. Anderson, J. (1794). General view of the agriculture, etc., of the County of Aberdeen. Edinburgh.
2. Robinson, G. W. (1934). The Soils of Wales. *Emp. J. exp. Agric.*, **2**, 258.

3. Osmond, D. A., *et al.* (1949). A survey of the soils and fruit in the Vale of Evesham, 1926-1934. *Bull. Minist. Agric.*, No. 116. H.M.S.O.

4. Kay, F. F. A soil survey of the eastern portion of the Vale of the White Horse, 1934. *Bull. Fac. Agric. Reading*, xlviii.
——A soil survey of the strawberry district of South Hampshire, 1939. *Bull. Fac. Agric. Reading*, lii.

5. Davies, W. M., and Owen, G. Soil survey of North Shropshire, 1934. *Emp. J. exp. Agric.*, **2**, 178.

6. Muir, A., and Fraser, G. K. The soils and vegetation of the Bin and Clashindarroch Forests, 1939. *Trans. roy. Soc. Edinb.*, **9**, Part 1, 223.

7. Glentworth, R. Studies on the soils developed on basic igneous rocks on central Aberdeenshire. *Trans. roy. Soc. Edinb.*, **61**, Part 1, 162.

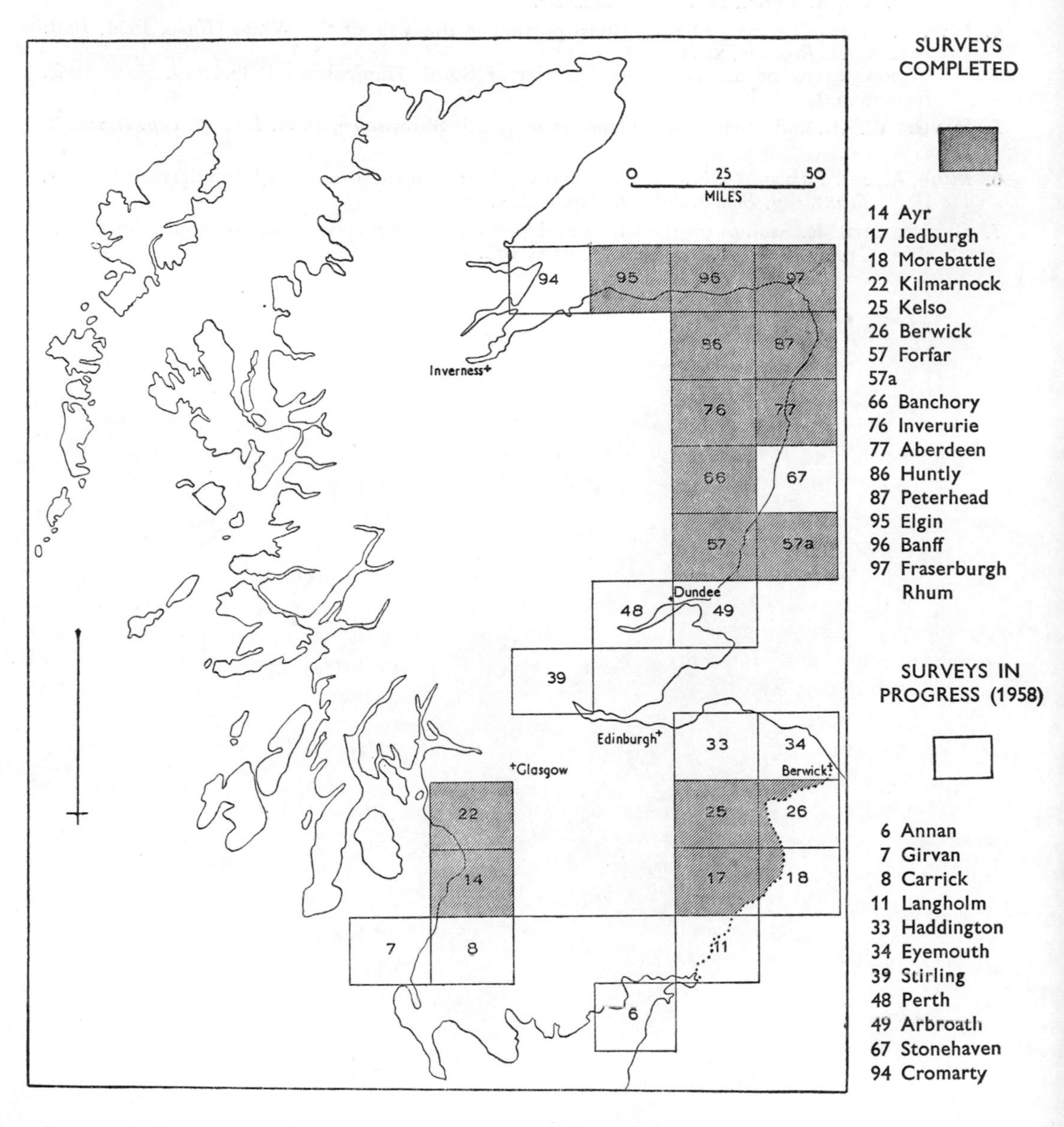
0
25
50
MILES
94
95
96
97
86
87
Inverness
76
77
66
67
57
57a
Dundee
48
49
39
Edinburgh
33
34
Glasgow
Berwick
22
25
26
14
17
18
7
8
11
6
SURVEYS COMPLETED
14 Ayr
17 Jedburgh
18 Morebattle
22 Kilmarnock
25 Kelso
26 Berwick
57 Forfar
57a
66 Banchory
76 Inverurie
77 Aberdeen
86 Huntly
87 Peterhead
95 Elgin
96 Banff
97 Fraserburgh
Rhum
SURVEYS IN PROGRESS (1958)
6 Annan
7 Girvan
8 Carrick
11 Langholm
33 Haddington
34 Eyemouth
39 Stirling
48 Perth
49 Arbroath
67 Stonehaven
94 Cromarty

Fig. 1. Soil Survey of Scotland—Sheet Index

Work of the Geological Survey

G. H. MITCHELL, D.SC., PH.D., D.I.C., F.R.S., F.R.S.E.
Assistant Director, Geological Survey of Great Britain, Edinburgh

A bricf account is given of the history of the Geological Survey in Scotland and the scope and progress of its work. The various types and scales of geological maps and the range of memoirs, bulletins, handbooks and pamphlets are described. The latter include publications dealing with the general geology of large districts; others which give detailed accounts of areas depicted on 1-in. maps; special volumes dealing with coalfields, oil-shale fields and occurrences of metallic and non-metallic minerals and their ores; as well as those describing particular types of rock such as limestone, sand and gravel, fireclay, brick-clay, peat and slate. A set of pamphlets is devoted to details of underground water supplies. An abridged bibliography is appended of the publications of the Geological Survey which are specially concerned with mineral resources.

The Geological Survey of Great Britain, the first official or Government Survey of any country, was formed in 1835, with Sir Henry Thomas De la Beche as Director, and has since operated continuously. In 1841 the Museum of Economic Geology was opened. These two closely integrated institutions are the direct ancestors of the Geological Survey of Great Britain and the Museum of Practical Geology, which is the official title of the body, with headquarters in Exhibition Road, South Kensington, which is now responsible for the geological survey of Great Britain. The organisation forms part of the Department of Scientific and Industrial Research.

The geological mapping of Scotland commenced in 1854 when A. C. Ramsay, later Sir Andrew Ramsay the third Director of the Geological Survey of Great Britain, began work in the Lothians. The Scottish office was established in Edinburgh in 1867. The present office is situated in Grange Terrace.

By 1880 practically the whole of Lowland Scotland had been mapped and the results were published on hand-coloured 1 in. to 1 mile maps with small accompanying explanatory memoirs. For the mining areas 6 in. to 1 mile maps were also published.

Since that date the work has been steadily continued until now all the Scottish mainland has been mapped in detail except for some 1,400 square miles around Loch Cluanie in Inverness-shire; all the islands have been so covered except for the Outer Hebrides. 1 in. to 1 mile maps and a large number of explanatory memoirs have been published.

From 1901 onwards, because of the accumulation of large amounts of new information, it was found necessary to remap much of the Lowland mining areas on the 6 in. scale, and at the present time a further revision is in progress.

The Geological Survey in Scotland had the advantage of 6 in. to 1 mile Ordnance Survey Maps from the start, and this scale has since been used throughout Scotland as the standard field map. The clean copies of the field maps are deposited for reference in the library of the Geological Survey, and in some districts such as mining areas, where detail is important for economic reasons, they have been published. The standard published map is, however, on the scale of 1 in. to 1 mile and it is customary to produce a "solid" edition, showing only the rock formations which occur at surface or below the cover of superficial deposits, and a "drift" edition which shows formations actually exposed at surface whether superficial or solid. 1-in. maps are usually accompanied by an explanatory memoir. Maps on smaller scales, notably ¼ in. to 1 mile, approximately 10 miles to 1 in., and 25 miles to 1 in. are also published.

To date, 102 1-in. maps, many with both solid and drift editions, 10 ¼-in. maps and some 72 explanatory volumes known as General, District and Sheet memoirs have been published. The results of particular research problems are in some cases described in papers in the *Bulletin of the Geological Survey*, which is published as required, and an account of the current Survey activities is given annually in the Summary of Progress.

In this account it is not proposed to give details of the important scientific results of the Survey's work over the last hundred years, some of which, such as descriptions of the structure of the North-West Highlands and the Southern Uplands, or the very detailed investigations of the ancient volcanic centres of Mull, Skye and Ardnamurchan, have profoundly affected geological thought. Details of this work are summarised in the Handbooks of British Regional Geology published by the Geological Survey for five of the great natural regions of Scotland—the Northern Highlands, the Grampian Highlands, the Tertiary Volcanic Districts, the Midland Valley and the South of Scotland. In these volumes copious references to other more detailed work, published both by the Geological Survey and by other authors, are given.

Here it is intended to focus attention on the Survey's work which has a direct connection with mineral resources. This, however, is not easy to do because it can happen that certain rocks or minerals which in the past may have been recorded as of little worth subsequently have acquired great value in human affairs.

There are separate lists of Geological Survey maps and memoirs which may be purchased at the present time (see Bibliography, p. 25). Both lists show only a fraction of the total number of maps and memoirs which have been produced in the past, for many are now out of print largely because the stock was destroyed by enemy action during the last war. It has been one of the Survey's major post-war tasks to replace these, and considerable progress has been made, especially in the reprinting of maps. With maps, as with memoirs, it is still necessary in some cases to have recourse to out-of-print editions to be found only in libraries. In 1937 the last full list of maps and memoirs was published (see Bibliography, p. 27), and this list is a useful compilation for anyone desirous of becoming acquainted with available information.

The memoirs are of various kinds, the two most numerous being the Sheet memoirs, which are explanations of 1-in. sheets, and the District memoirs, which deal with somewhat larger areas having a geological unity.

It was early found that certain of the latter called for special treatment because of the importance in them of particular branches of mining such as the oil-shale, coal or bauxite industries. So special attention was paid to this by preparing memoirs with the emphasis on the mining information, the so-called Economic Memoirs. Prominent among these are "The Oil-Shales of the Lothians" which ran to three editions, "The Ayrshire Bauxitic Clay" and some nineteen memoirs devoted to the Central, Ayrshire, Fife,

Stirling-Clackmannan, Sanquhar and Midlothian coalfields. Many of the latter were for convenience of description divided into smaller areas, with separate volumes comprising only a part of the coalfield concerned. Recently two supplements to the geology of the Clackmannan-Fife Coalfield have been published as Coalfield Papers.

During the 1914-18 War detailed investigations were undertaken into a large number of mineral deposits in Great Britain. Of reports on these, three volumes were devoted entirely to Scotland, namely those dealing with "The Iron Ores of Scotland", "The Lead, Zinc, Copper and Nickel Ores of Scotland", and "Cannel Coals, Lignite and Mineral Oils in Scotland". To these have since been added volumes on "The Granites of Scotland", "Limestones of Scotland", "The Cambro-Ordovician Limestones and Dolomites of the Ord and Torran areas, Skye and the Kishorn area, Ross-shire" and a small volume entitled "Synopsis of the Mineral Resources of Scotland". In the case of the reports dealing with tungsten and manganese, barytes and witherite, fluorspar, ganister, silica-rock and dolomite, mineral oil, fireclays, arsenic and antimony, rockwool, the Scottish occurrences are described in the same volume as the rest of Great Britain.

Further detailed surveys for special minerals were undertaken during the 1939-45 War. The results of much of this work were incorporated in a series of Wartime Pamphlets, of which thirty-six dealt with Scottish mineral resources including barytes, brick-clay, chromite, coal, diatomite, dolomite, feldspar, gravel, limestone, mica, oil-shale, olivine-rock, peat, sand, serpentine, silica-rock, slate and talc. One part deals specially with the Lothians in all aspects of its mineral resources.

As well as minerals, a survey of the underground water resources of Scotland was undertaken and eight Wartime Pamphlets devoted to details of the nature of strata encountered in wells and boreholes and water-levels were published.

This account has so far dealt mainly with published geological material, but in the course of its history the Scottish office of the Geological Survey, in common with other offices, has accumulated a great mass of information, comprising many thousands of borehole and shaft records, innumerable records of temporary exposures and a vast quantity of mining information. These details, some confidential, have been acquired in part by the courtesy of companies, boards and individuals, sometimes in exchange for geological information and latterly as a result of the Mining Industry, 1926, Petroleum (Production), 1918, 1939, and Water (Scotland), 1946, Acts, which made it compulsory to notify borings and sinkings to the Geological Survey. This great stock of information has enabled Survey officers, already equipped with the knowledge gained from detailed surveys of the ground, effectively to assist countless enquirers in their geological problems, be they concerned with mining, water supply, foundations, quarrying, dam sites, hydro-electric schemes or the like. The proportion of geologists' time which is occupied with such enquiries is considerable.

The Chemical Laboratory of the Geological Survey in London, staffed by the Government Chemist, carries out analyses of rocks and minerals, many of which have been quoted in memoirs. Nearly 900 of these analyses have been collected in two volumes entitled "Chemical Analyses of Igneous Rocks, Metamorphic Rocks and Minerals" published in 1931 and 1956 respectively; analyses also appear annually in the Summary of Progress. A volume entitled "Attrition Tests of British Roadstones" was published in 1929.

Recently the Geological Survey has increased its geophysical work. Some thirty years ago a gravitational survey was carried out across the line of the Pentland Fault near Portobello. Since 1945 a geophysical department of the Geological Survey has been instituted. Recent special investigations have included the geophyscial surveying of deep boreholes and of igneous masses mapped as vents likely to present obstacles to mining as well as instances of faulting concealed by superficial deposits. In 1959 an airborne magnetic survey was conducted over southern Scotland in northward continuation of aero-magnetic surveys in previous years in England and Wales.

Since the last war a considerable programme of deep boring by the Geological Survey has been carried out in Great Britain, including two deep boreholes drilled in Scotland, the one at Rashiehill in Lanarkshire to explore a possible extension of the West Lothian Oil-shale field, and the other at Archerbeck near Canonbie in Dumfriesshire. This latter was designed to prove the Carboniferous succession and reached the record depth at that time of 4,604 ft.

Another important branch of Survey work is that of the Atomic Energy Division, which, as part of a large programme of work all over the world, has investigated occurrences of radioactive minerals in Scotland.

Apart from the Geophysical and Atomic Energy Divisions, which work from London, the Scottish Survey is based on Edinburgh. The staff comprises an Assistant Director, three District Geologists, seventeen Geologists (including both Palaeontological and Petrographical specialists) and eight Experimental Officers and Assistants together with Drawing and Clerical staff. For the purposes of the survey the staff is divided into the Highland unit and the North and South Lowland units. In addition to their researches into all aspects of the geology of their respective areas, the first-named is heavily involved in geological work concerned with hydro-electric schemes, the two others between them are concerned with by far the greater part of the minerals which play so important a part in the industrial activity of Scotland, including almost all the coal, fireclay and brick fields and the Lothian oil-shale field. The other industries such as quarrying, lime works and the like, which when added together make a formidable total, are widely scattered throughout the three areas, as are also a large number of other minor mineral ventures, some still working but others at the moment dormant.

Among examples of mineral exploitation directly resulting from Geological Survey work or knowledge may be mentioned the bauxite refractory clay in Ayrshire, low-grade iron-ore in Raasay, magnetite in Shetland, high-grade glass sand in Morvern, high-grade muscovite-mica in Knoydart and elsewhere, and feldspar in Harris. Most of these developments took place because of wartime shortages, but the Geological Survey is continuously in the closest touch with the National Coal Board, the North of Scotland Hydro-Electric Board and with the major mining and the principal quarrying firms in the country. Survey Officers serve on the several committees dealing with the exploitation of mineral resources. Among these may be mentioned the Committee set up in 1942 by the Secretary of State for Scotland to consider the Scottish Coalfields and the Committee set up in 1946 to enquire into minerals in Great Britain and Northern Ireland other than coal, oil, bedded ironstone and substances of widespread occurrence.

BIBLIOGRAPHY

A list of the principal publications of the Geological Survey which deal with mineral resources is given below. The list does not include the numerous maps, and Sheet and District memoirs, mentioned in the paper. Most of these memoirs contain at least a summary of mineral resources within the areas described. Volumes marked with an asterisk are out of print, but can be consulted at the library of the Geological Survey, 19 Grange Terrace, Edinburgh, 9. Latest editions are quoted in each case.

Memoirs

(1) *Special Reports on the Mineral Resources of Great Britain*

*Vol. I Tungsten and Manganese Ores. 3rd edition, 1923.
*Vol. II Barytes and Witherite. 3rd edition, 1922.
*Vol. V Potash-Feldspar, Phosphate of Lime, Alum Shales, Plumbago or Graphite, Molybdenite, Chromite, Talc and Steatite, Diatomite. 2nd edition, 1917.
*Vol. VI Refractory Materials: Ganister and Silica-Rock, Sand for Open-Hearth Steel Furnaces, Dolomite. 2nd edition, 1920.
*Vol. XI Iron Ores of Scotland. 1920.
*Vol. XIV Refractory Materials: Fireclays. 1920.
*Vol. XV Arsenic and Antimony Ores. 1920.
*Vol. XVI Refractory Materials: Ganister and Silica-Rock, Sand for Open-Hearth Steel Furnaces, Dolomite. Petrography and Chemistry. 1920.
*Vol. XVII Lead, Zinc, Copper and Nickel Ores of Scotland. 1921.
*Vol. XXIV Cannel Coals, Lignite and Mineral Oil in Scotland. 1922.
Vol. XXVIII Refractory Materials: Fireclays. Analyses and Physical Tests. 1924.
Vol. XXXII Granites of Scotland. 1939.
Vol. XXXIII Synopsis of Mineral Resources of Scotland. 1940.
Vol. XXXIV Rock Wool. 2nd edition, 1949.
Vol. XXXV Limestones of Scotland. 1949.
Vol. XXXVI Cambro-Ordovician Limestones and Dolomites of Skye and Kishorn. 1954.
Vol. XXXVII Limestones of Scotland, Chemical Analyses and Petrography. 1956.

(2) *Economic Geology of the Scottish Coalfields*

Central Coalfield:
Area I Kilsyth and Kirkintilloch. 1937.
*Area II Denny, Plean, Falkirk. 1917.
Area III Bo'ness and Linlithgow. 1933.
*Area IV Paisley, Barrhead and Glasgow West. 1920.
Area V Glasgow East, Coatbridge and Airdrie. 2nd edition, 1926.
Area VI Bathgate and Wilsontown. 1923.
*Area VII Rutherglen, Hamilton and Wishaw. 1920.
Area VIII East Kilbride and Quarter. 1917.
*Area IX Carluke, Strathaven and Larkhall. 1921.

Ayrshire Coalfields:
Area I Kilbirnie, Dalry and Kilmaurs. 1925.
Area II Kilmarnock Basin. 1925.
Area III Ayr, Mauchline and Muirkirk. 1930.
Area IV Dailly, Patna, Dalmellington and New Cumnock. 1932.

Fife Coalfields:
Area I Dunfermline and West Fife. 1931.
*Area II Cowdenbeath and Central Fife. 1934. (2nd edition *in press.*)
Area III Markinch, Dysart and Leven. 1954.

Stirling-Clackmannan Coalfield. 1932.

Sanquhar Coalfield. 1936.

Midlothian Coalfield. 1958.

Certain coalfields are not yet included in this series, but much economic information regarding them is contained in the following general memoirs:
*Geology of East Lothian. 1910.
*Geology of the Country around Golspie. 1925. (Brora Coal.)

(3) *Other Economic Memoirs*

Oil-Shales of the Lothians. 3rd edition, 1927.
The Ayrshire Bauxitic Clay. 1922.

(4) *General Memoirs*

*Attrition Tests of British Road-Stones. 1929.
Chemical Analyses of Igneous Rocks, Metamorphic Rocks and Minerals. *1931; also 1931-54. 1956.

Coalfield Papers

Stirling and Clackmannan. Area North of River Forth. 1956.
Stirling and Clackmannan. Area South of River Forth. 1959.

Bulletins

For recent information regarding Douglas Coalfield see Bulletin No. 15 (1958); for Ayrshire and Fife Coalfields see Bulletin No. 16 (1960).

Wartime Pamphlets

*No. 2 British Sources of Alkali Feldspar. 1940.
Supplement 1941.
*No. 5 Diatomite. 1940.
*No. 6 Dolomite and Brucite-marble in the Scottish Highlands. 1940.
Supplements 1 and 2 (1941).
No. 7 High-Grade Silica Rocks of the Scottish Highlands and Islands. 1945.
*No. 9 Talc, other Magnesian Minerals and Chromite, associated with British Serpentines. 1946.
Supplement No. 1. Glen Lochay. 1949.
No. 13 Limestones of Scotland. Areas I-VIII. 1942-45.
(See later memoir under (1) above.)
No. 24 Limestone Coal Group of Glasgow. 1942.
No. 27 Oil-Shales of Lothians:
Area I West Calder. 1942.
Area II Pumpherston. 1942.
Area IV Philipstoun. 1943.
No. 30 Sands and Gravels of Scotland:
I Elgin-Banff-Aberdeen. 1943.
II Stonehaven-Perth-Dundee. 1945.
Supplement to I and II. 1948.
III Glasgow and West Central Scotland. 1946.
IV Fife-The Lothians-Berwickshire. 1948.
No. 34 Commercial Mica in Scotland:
I Characteristics. 1943.
II North of Great Glen. 1943.
No. 36 Peat Deposits of Scotland:
I General Account. 1943.
II Aberdeenshire, Banffshire and Morayshire. 1948.
No. 38 Barytes in Central Scotland. 1944.
No. 40 Scottish Slates. 1944.
No. 42 Canonbie Coalfield. 1945.
No. 44 Scottish Sources of Alkali Feldspar. 1945.
*No. 45 The Mineral Resources of the Lothians. 1945.
No. 47 Brick Clays of North-East Scotland:
I Occurrences.
II Analyses and Physical Tests. 1946.

Wartime Pamphlets dealing with Water Supply from underground sources:

*No. 28 South-east Scotland:
 I Fife and Kinross. 1942.
 II Lothians. 1942.
 III Peebles, Selkirk, Galashiels, Dunbar, Eyemouth, North Berwick. 1943.

No. 29 South-west Scotland:
 I Girvan, Dumfries, Lockerbie, Hawick, Jedburgh. 1946.
 II Stranraer to Annan. 1945.

*No. 37 Central Scotland, Dundee to Stonehaven westwards. 1943.

No. 39 Glasgow and adjacent areas:
 II Loch Lomond, Stirling, Clackmannan. 1944.
 V North Arran, Kilmarnock, Hamilton, Lanark. 1955.

A List of Memoirs, Maps, Sections, etc., published by the Geological Survey, was formerly revised from time to time, but the latest, dated 1937, is now out of print. It can be consulted at the office of the Geological Survey and gives a complete list of publications to the end of 1936 including items out of print.

Government Publications, Sectional List No. 45 (1960) gives details of publications of the Geological Survey and Museum (other than maps and Wartime Pamphlets) available for purchase.

A List of Geological Survey Maps on sale on 29th April 1960 is also available.

Both of the current lists may be obtained from the Government Bookshops of which the address in Edinburgh is 13a Castle Street, Edinburgh, 2.

A few Wartime Pamphlets are still available. Applications should be addressed to the Geological Survey Office, 19 Grange Terrace, Edinburgh, 9.

Economic Minerals in Scotland

T. NEVILLE GEORGE, D.SC., D.-ÈS-SC., F.R.S.E., F.G.S.
Professor of Geology in the University of Glasgow; Chairman of the Mineral Resources Panel

The geological structure of Scotland, expressed in the three contrasted areas of the Highlands, the Midland Valley, and the Southern Uplands, determines a sharply defined distribution in economic minerals that is reflected in the present-day concentrations of industry.

In the Highlands are to be found mainly the kinds of minerals associated with metamorphic and igneous rocks: they include serpentine and talc, chromite and magnetite, feldspar, garnet, sillimanite and kyanite. In the Highlands also occur the deposits of high-grade dolomite and quartzite that run from north Sutherland to Skye, and that are potentially of inexhaustible industrial use; and the more restricted pockets of diatomite.

The Midland Valley contains the younger rocks of the Old Red Sandstone and the Carboniferous formations, which provide 90 per cent. of the presently exploited mineral deposits, including almost all the coals. The belt will probably continue to be the major scene of mineral use for many years to come in supplying not only coal but limestones, ganisters, fireclays and (if they should be needed) iron-ores—not to mention the small flows of petroleum.

The Southern Uplands, apart from the Sanquhar basin, are relatively impoverished except in ores of the lead-zinc suite, which may continue richly in depth beyond their present known development.

It is commonly supposed that many Scottish minerals are near-marginal in quality or otherwise not worth exploiting. But to dismiss them as industrially negligible is to make two assumptions. One is that present-day techniques, with their demand for prescribed "standard" materials, will continue indefinitely to determine exploitation and process: whereas advance is likely to come by improvements in adapting techniques to available minerals. The other is that free-market prices are the sole criterion for judging a mineral to be economic or not: whereas in such a country of mixed economy as Scotland, especially rural Scotland, enterprise in technical methods and in social integration might well turn apparent loss into real profit, as judged less in financial than in social terms.

While it is highly unlikely that any large deposits of exceptionally valuable minerals remain to be discovered, there yet is widespread ignorance of the kind and quantity and distribution of each potentially useful mineral in Scotland; and a systematic economic survey, complementary to the work of the Geological Survey, is a major need to remedy this ignornace and to prelude further economic advance. Such a survey, whose proportionate cost would be small, would begin in the field, but it would lead on to laboratory studies in mineral processing, usage and beneficiation, and to a review of industrial techniques.

I. ORIGIN AND DISTRIBUTION

(*a*) Economic Minerals

Minerals have economic significance only when they are found to be useful: they are not endowed by nature with intrinsic properties, like their crystal form or their chemical composition, that define a hierarchy of desirability or need in making some economically more valuable than others. It is a platitude to say that minerals become economic minerals in contexts of evolving social organisation; and there are inevitably rhythms of increasing and declining use that reflect technical practice, intricately complex in its detail, in the changing cultural context. Any and every mineral is thus potentially an economic mineral; and no part of Scotland (or of any other country) is without rich resources that could be worked if they were sufficiently needed. Moreover, the variety of minerals is legion over a great part of Scotland, and the urge to economic exploitation at any moment is controlled less by scarcity (though some minerals are scarce) than by social cost.

In an assessment of Scottish economic minerals it is then not enough merely to list occurrences in terms of current and temporary industrial demand: the occurrences must be set in a geographical environment that includes the human and political factors of exploitation as well as the abstract technical requirements of industrial process. The social cost of getting the minerals should not be measured in restrictedly commercial or financial terms alone: amongst its items should be included the importance of the getting in an integrated economy that subsumes initial market value under a broader-based social and political coherence. The primary demand for the minerals may be industrial; but where the minerals are worked and how they are processed are determined only in part by the geologist and the chemical engineer—they are also the concern of the social economist, the regional planner, and the local and central government officer.

It is necessary to stress this aspect of mineral use since many Scottish minerals are considered for one reason or another to be "uneconomic" at current market values: they are relatively inaccessible and costly to transport; they are widely or thinly dispersed in a worthless rock-matrix, or do not occur in sufficiently large concentrated masses to cover overhead costs (including the costs of housing a labour force) in modern bulk-use plant; they are contaminated by "impurities" and fail to reach industrial specification; they are recalcitrant in physical and chemical composition and not readily processed by present-day techniques. In consequence, they are commonly dismissed as marginal or submarginal in quality or availability, and as unable to compete in the open market with equivalent minerals got elsewhere in Britain or Europe or the world.

To dismiss many Scottish minerals as not worth exploiting is, however, to make two assumptions. One is that present-day techniques, inertial in some industries, specialised in others, are to continue indefinitely as the arbiters of exploitation and process. While techniques no doubt evolve, sometimes fast, they usually presuppose the traditional use of "standard" materials whose quality is known and whose availability is determined by free-market supplies; whereas in reverse approach advances in industrial use could as well begin with available "sub-standard" materials and convert them to standard, bring them up to "specification", either by improving primary techniques or by inventing subsidiary techniques of beneficiation. The other assumption is that free-market costs are the sole criterion for judging a mineral deposit to be economic or not. While such a measure is in the main taken for granted as axiomatic by economists and industrialists, there are many parts of Scotland (and elsewhere) in which costs of getting and processing as judged simply in commercial terms would seem to be prohibitive, but where enterprise in technical methods and in social integration might well turn probable loss into probable profit, as judged in social terms.

Scottish economic minerals are thus to be surveyed in relation to present and prospective industrial needs, and to the communities who exploit them: they become economic minerals not because they consist of coal or dolomite or galena but because they are exploited; and in a real sense their distribution (as economic minerals) is determined by their use.

At the same time it need scarcely be said that there is great variation in the abundance, the quality, the availability and the kinds of potential economic minerals in different parts of Scotland; and the working of a deposit is justified on a nice balance of many factors of which mode of geological occurrence is a primary. Thus although feldspar is very widely distributed in many Scottish rocks, the scattered grains common in the Carboniferous sandstones of Muirkirk or Broxburn would be absurdly uneconomic (on a simple book-keeping basis of social cost) as a source of a mineral that can be got far more richly and easily from the pegmatites of Ross or Harris; and the manufacture of high-grade quartz glass by a cleaning of the haematite-filmed grains of Mauchline Sandstone even more absurd when untreated Loch Aline sand is amply pure. Nevertheless, given sufficient need, feldspar could be got from Carboniferous sandstones, clean quartz from Permian, if other richer sources were not available: so poorer-quality but more readily accessible coals from existing pits continue to be minded when shafts to seams at depth remain forbiddingly expensive, until such time as worked-out measures compel the deeper sinkings—unless oil or Polish coal or nuclear power meanwhile proves to be "cheaper".

(*b*) Geological Habitat

What is known of the distribution of Scottish economic minerals is very largely the result of the activities of the Geological Survey; and in broad conspectus, though not always in the detail required for modern industrial practice, the publications of the Survey provide descriptions of most of the principal deposits of the principal economic minerals.

It is now thoroughly established that in Scotland (as in other countries of comparable geological complexity) the origin and the correlated distribution of the main kinds of economic minerals are systematically related to, and depend on, the mode of formation of the country rock in which the minerals are found and the geological changes it has undergone; and there tends to be a limitation of mineral species to one or other type that excludes the likelihood of agates being found in coal-seams, or coal in volcanic lavas. Minerals in sedimentary rocks thus have different habitats from those in igneous, and both kinds from the minerals formed by high temperature or pressure in metamorphic rocks. After it is deposited or emplaced, any kind of rock may be internally transformed in a diagenesis arising from ground-water migration and other modes of chemical exchange, by which its redistributed or reconstructed constituents may be segregated in economically valuable concentrates; or it may be subjected to prolonged weathering and decay, to give rise to suites of secondary minerals as residual deposits. There are complementary differences in the technical means of getting the minerals, and of processing or beneficiating the minerals when they are got—particularly when the minerals may be diffusely distributed or locally concentrated, when they may lie in ground simple in geological structure or much deformed, when they may be uniform in quality or patchily "contaminated" and variable.

Since Scotland has an honoured place in the history of geology precisely because it has many kinds of rocks that have followed an eventful course—its strata range in age from Pre-Cambrian to Tertiary and it carries the signs of three or four major phases of volcanic activity and as many of earth-movement—generalised statements about its mineral deposits are thus not likely to be very informative. In more or less degree each deposit is unique in its geological context, and requires individual examination before its potential uses in industry can be ascertained: much of what follows suffers from a vagueness, expressed in generalisation, that is a measure of the need for more knowledge of most of the Scottish ores.

Sedimentary rocks are mainly detrital in origin, and commonly consist of a great variety of minerals mixed in the processes of sedimentation. They range from the widespread unconsolidated sands and clays (the "drift") of Glacial age, found as a veneer on the "solid" rocks over a great part of Scotland, to the highly indurated and partly altered quartzites and marbles of the Highlands; and they include shales, fire-clays, brick-clays, cementstones, coals and oil-shales, almost all limestones, sandstones, ganisters and diatomite. Because of the conditions of their formation they are rarely so "pure" as to be monomineralic; though mechanical and chemical sorting and winnowing of their constituents during transport or deposition sometimes achieve a high degree of separation of individual kinds of mineral species, so that some Scottish carbonate-rocks may contain over 99 per cent. of calcite or dolomite, and some sandstones as high a proportion of quartz. But while it may not be "pure", a sedimentary rock characteristically has wide extension even when it is thin—some individual coal-seams in the Midland Valley cover hundreds of square miles—and usually its properties tend to change laterally comparatively slowly: if it proves of industrial use, therefore, its reserves may be indefinitely large and the limits of its being worked are likely to be imposed less by intrinsic than by external or accidental factors (including the vicissitudes of its geological history). Behaving like the sedimentary rocks in which they occur, nodular and sheeted segregations of secondary minerals are sometimes found following the bedding—notably the clay-ironstones of the Carboniferous system.

The minerals found in igneous rocks are of very different origin: they are usually directly the product of crystallisation from molten magma, and occur commonly as interlocked grains in a mosaic of crystals of different species and of different chemical composition. Their nature and their relative concentrations depend on a variety of factors including the chemical composition of the parental fluid (magma) and the physcial environment of cooling and crystallisation. Rapidly chilled magma is generally characterised (as in basalt) by small and intimately mixed crystals not easily separated; and a similar fine-grained rock is produced when solidification of even very large slow-cooling masses (like granite) takes place in a chemical environment approaching eutectic composition. On the other hand, even when the bulk of the rock is cooled and solidified, tongues of residual fluid, often rich in "water" as a flux, may form segregates of ore in which late-freezing and comparatively rare minerals are strongly concentrated, or in which exceptionally largy crystals of the more common minerals separate out. Such hydrothermal ore-shoots, injected under the high pressures of igneous intrusion, usually follow planes of weakness (joints or faults of bedding-planes) in the country rock, and their distribution is then closely controlled by a regional geological structure—often when they occupy corrosion cavities bitten into the wall rocks defined in a pattern of pods or lenticles.

In the nature of their formation, masses of igneous rock tend to be diffuse but to be sharply self-contained and separated from neighbouring country rock. The injected ore-shoots and veins similarly form precisely delimited bodies of restricted extension, though locally they may riddle a close-jointed host. Granites are the largest of the igneous masses in Scotland, but although they contain much feldspar they are mostly without important segregates of economic minerals, and in them crystal interlocking is usually not readily undone by mechanical crushing and sorting. The related pegmatite veins and dykes, on the other hand, usually coarse-grained, are important for the variety and size of the minerals they contain; and the comparable metalliferous veins (not always with known roots in a parental intrusion) are the extreme end-products of such igneous injection.

Some of the granites of the Highlands crop out over many square miles of country, and the bosses in the south-western part of the Southern Uplands are comparable in size; but they have a far less widespread extension on the surface than the sedimentary or metamorphic rocks in which they are emplaced. The dykes and sills and smaller veins are almost always proportionately very narrow, and though they may run across country for long distances they sharply reflect the variant physical characters of the country rock into which they were injected—they thin and thicken, they split into strings of veinlets, they are pinched out or locally fail to reach the present surface, they do not always remain constant in mineral composition, and they are often "lost" or abruptly truncated when they meet a fault.

Metamorphic rocks in Scotland are the products of the transformation of both sedimentary and igneous rocks. A few of them form shells of thermal alteration (aureoles) in the country rock immediately surrounding the larger igneous intrusions; but the vast majority owe their origin to regional earth-movements when physical and chemical changes, brought about by intense compressive and shearing stresses probably at high temperatures under a thick (but now-vanished) rock cover, included both the imposition of a cleavage and a schistosity and the reconstitution of mineral structure. The cleaved rocks include the slates, not much altered; the reconstituted rocks with "new" mineral assemblages include the phyllites, schists and gneisses, in which micas, garnets and other metamorphic minerals may be common. The kinds of chemical recrystallisation that occurred during the metamorphism were dependent on a number of factors not all of which may now be recognised—the composition and grain size of the parent rock (ranging from shale or sandstone to granite or basalt), the depth of burial and the "mobilisation" of the rock substance during the changes, the chances of ionic migration, and the availability of "water" in the synthesis of hydrous minerals; but it is clear that the intensity of the metamorphic process was a major factor in determining the species of "new" minerals formed, which fall into a series of metamorphic zones of changing mineral composition. Metamorphic rocks as now seen at the surface inevitably show great structural complexity: they are intensely folded into sharp, often overturned, anticlines and synclines, and broken by large thrusts and faults. They offer formidable obstacles to easy exploitation even when they are rich in economic minerals, partly because of the intimate intergrowth of the minerals and the matrix, but particularly because of the changes in kind and quality of rock that take place where fold axes or major dislocations occur.

A few relatively unimportant minerals are not readily classified as falling to one or other of the three main groups. They include the manganese oxide forming a "pan" in the superficial deposits associated with the raised beaches of Galloway, which is probably an evaporite from solutions held up in conditions of stagnancy by an impervious floor; the alluvial gold—strictly a constituent of a sedimentary rock—found as sluiced residues in pot-holes of Highland stream-beds, and doubtless transported from upstream outcrops of auriferous vein-quartz; and the agates ("Scotch pebbles"), which were formed as siliceous gels, now represented in banded chalcedony, in the gas-cavities of solidified volcanic lavas, notably in the Old Red Sandstone of Ayrshire.

Anomalous "minerals" also include the petroleum and gas proved and worked particularly in the Lothians: strictly sedimentary in origin, in being the products of anaerobic decay of organic debris in shales and limestones, they are distributed and preserved underground through the accidental availability of suitable source rocks, suitable routes of migration, and suitable reservoir rocks capped by an impervious cover. In the nature of the country rock there is little probability of their being found in the Southern Uplands, and none in the Highlands. Where they occur in the Midland Valley and how best they are tapped are problems—obscured by a usual lack of all direct surface evidence—that demand a refinement in geological analysis and a recondite skill in the interpretation of stratigraphy and structure, and that can be settled (and then only partially) by the pragmatic test of drilling. The indications so far obtained are that (as elsewhere in Britain) Scottish supplies are never likely to be great, though there is no reason to suppose that the modest fields so far discovered are the only or even the largest that occur. In a present-day economy the search for oil is justified not only when oil is found but also when (in an exploratory husbandry) it is not found—unless we are to suppose that (like Polish coal) foreign oil will always be cheaper and always there to be got.

(*c*) Structural Context

The links between mineral types and mineral distribution on the one hand and geological context on the other are very well illustrated in the structural pattern of Scotland. The three main regions of the country are tectonically defined by the abrupt dislocations of the Highland Boundary fault and the Southern Uplands fault, both of which transect the country from the North Sea to the Atlantic and form almost absolute partitions between the complex horst of the Highlands to the north, the broken half-anticline of the Southern Uplands to the south, and the down-faulted rift of the Midland Valley between. Sediments dominate the rock succession in all three areas, but for the most part they are utterly contrasted in their nature because of their different ages and the different accidents of change they have suffered. The Lewisian, Moinian and Dalradian sediments of the Highlands, "old" rocks that have been subjected to intense crustal pressures during three or four phases of major earth-movement, are now intensely metamorphosed schists, gneisses and granulites which retain few of their original constituents or textural features unaltered. The Lower Palaeozoic strata of the Southern Uplands escaped the most severe episodes of metamorphism, but were caught up in the Caledonian orogeny and are composed of acutely folded and partly cleaved shales and sandstones in which (as it happens) few sedimentary minerals of economic value occur. The Upper Palaeozoic rocks of the Midland Valley, on the other hand, most deposited after the decline of the Caledonian stresses, are relatively gently deformed and not greatly faulted, and are the main repositories in Scotland of "normal" sediments changed only by slight diagenesis.

There are few areas outside the Midland Valley of comparable "normal" sediments. Cambrian and Ordovician rocks that overlie the Lewisian gneisses on the leeward side of the Moine thrust in the North-West Highlands are not much altered, nor is the Old Red Sandstone around the borders of the Moray Firth. Fringe deposits of Mesozoic rocks seen in small outcrops along both the eastern and the western seaboards of the Highlands carry several kinds of economic minerals of sedimentary origin; and the outlying Machrihanish coalfield beyond the Highland Boundary fault in Kintyre is of importance. Nevertheless, the present Highland surface is essentially a surface in metamorphic rocks veneered only to a tenth or less of its area by these "normal" strata. The slates and greywackes of the Southern Uplands similarly are without extensive cover of younger rocks except along their southern borders; and only in the small Sanquhar and Thornhill basins, where Carboniferous sediments are found, and in the residual pockets of New Red Sandstone about Dumfries, Lockerbie, Moffat and Stranraer are there signs in the heart of the Uplands of a former unconformable veneer now mostly stripped from the deformed rocks beneath.

Igneous rocks of many kinds are to be found throughout the greater part of Scotland, but they show significant differences in their distribution from one province to another. Little-altered lavas, ashes and tuffs, products of widespread volcanicity, are interbedded with normal sediments in rocks of Ordovician, Devonian, Carboniferous and Permian age; and, still in the freshness of relatively recent (Tertiary) extrusion, occur over wide areas in the north-west, notably in Sky and Mull. Of greater bulk and wider distribution, especially in the older rocks of the Highlands, are intrusive igneous masses, usually granitic, that form stocks and bosses emplaced amongst the schists and gneisses. Intrusions of similar type are found in the Southern Uplands; but there are none of equivalent size cutting the younger rocks of the Midland Valley, where on the contrary smaller sills and dykes, mostly doleritic in composition, are outstandingly common.

Rocks in Scotland thus fall into a two-fold grouping—of kind, depending on manner of formation, and of distribution, depending on structural context.

There are correspondingly well-defined provinces of economic minerals. It is futile to search for coal or oil-shale in the Grampians, talc in the coalfields, kyanite in Galloway. On a smaller scale, each kind of geological terrain has its special mineral suite, and although there is some overlap in distribution, and some minerals may form secondary concentrates when transported from the area of their primary occurrence to contribute to deposits elsewhere, a regional compartmentalisation of mineral ranges is a first discovery in the economic geology of Scotland.

II. MINERALS OF SEDIMENTARY ORIGIN

(*a*) Coals and Oil-Shales

With the exception of the Brora "brown coal" of Jurassic age, of some importance in local use, the carbonaceous rocks of Scotland are almost exclusively of Carboniferous age, and correspondingly are limited in their distribution to the Midland Valley and to the small outlying coalfields of south Kintyre (a remnant of deposits formerly continuous with, and composed of much the same stratal sequence as, the coal measures of Ayrshire) and the Sanquhar basin (linked in comparable sequence with the New Cumnock coal-field). The Canonbie coalfield is also geographically in Scotland, but in lying on the southern flanks of the Southern Uplands near the English border it is geologically more closely linked with the Cumbrian coal measures than with the main Scottish measures.

Empirical knowledge derived from centuries of mining, and in recent decades the systematised knowledge got from the admirably combined exploratory work of the National Coal Board and the Geological Survey, provide a very full understanding of the geological context in which the deposits lie. The main coal-seams are all of Upper Carboniferous age, and at original accumulation spread over a great part of the area of the Midland Valley and its flanks: they are lithified peats, products of thick forest growth in a swamp environment. The oil-shales on the other hand are of Lower Carboniferous age, were deposited in a restricted basin in the region of the Lothians, and consist dominantly of detrital shales and clays (with many intervening sandstone bands) in which there are thin layers charged with masses of resinous plant cells (the oil-shales proper). They display rapid lateral changes (and a corresponding decline in "oil" content) as they are followed toward the margins of the depositional basin, and workings in them are concentrated over a small area.

The principal coal-seams fall into two groups of strata, the Limestone Coal Group and the Productive Coal Measures, which are separated by many hundreds of feet (locally some thousands of feet) of almost barren beds. There has thus been some independence in the mining of the two groups, and a tendency in the past for the lower group to be neglected where it descends to depths far below the Coal Measures proper. Moreover, Upper Carboniferous rocks now have a fragmented outcrop through the accidents of folding and erosion, and occupy isolated basins in not all of which is the full sequence preserved: some of the basins are shallow, so that the lowest seams have not been regarded as inaccessible, but others are acutely downfolded (notably the submarine basin beneath the Forth) and exhaustive mining is rendered more difficult and costly. Some ground in the coalfields is rendered secondarily barren by shattering and faulting; and in many places igneous intrusions cutting the measures have "burnt" the coals over wide areas and made them industrially useless. Most of the coals are bituminous in rank, and some are good coking coals; a few are cannels; none is a true anthracite, though occasionally a coal baked by a dyke or sill is low in volatile matter. While a number of the seams have a very wide lateral extent, some are impersistent in quality or thickness; and towards the margins of the main basin of deposition, in south Ayrshire for instance and in Kintyre, some of the coal-forming peats may not have grown at all.

These various geological controls impose limits on practicable mining in Scotland—limits that ultimately compel a mine, however profitable, to be abandoned. They point a lesson of general application: economic minerals are a wasting asset, never replenishable, never therefore to be squandered either in their use or in the manner of their working. Economic exploitation, conditioned by natural occurrence, is itself a process that transforms its own economy: industrial communities founded on local mineral resources must be prepared to acknowledge with a stout realism that the greater their success in exploitation the faster comes their decline: the "ghost towns" of Californian gold must inevitably have their counterparts sooner or later in the derelict mining villages of Scottish coalfields, and Lanarkshire and Ayrshire decline while Fife thrives. Whatever may be the emotional bonds of a citizen to his community, there is a certain social perversity in deploring what is in the nature of things, and in exploiting not only coal but a foreseeable communal future.

Moreover, while Scottish coal reserves may be indefinitely large in bulk—perhaps large enough to give a "life" at present rates of working of 100 to 200 years—the exhaustion of the thicker or more accessible or more easily mined seams (intensified in the past by a carelessly uneconomical practice that almost wholly neglected the advantages of mining any one field in a unitary operation) will steadily increase the relative costs of getting the coal and put Scottish coal increasingly at a disadvantage with Polish coal or other sources of "cheap" power. Only on autarchic grounds (which might well be justified so long as world economy continues on a national basis) could the industry then be maintained. Not least of the (fully appreciated) responsibilities of the National Coal Board is the need for conservation, as an obverse facet of well-considered exploitation.

There are several reasons for the decline virtually to extinction of the oil-shale industry during recent years, but amongst them is not to be counted an exhaustion of resources or increasing geological difficulties in mining: a prospective "life" of the fields, based on a very modest estimate of reserves of the richer oil-yielding layers, and on average output of the past decade, is not less than 100 years; and the folds and faults that in the Midland Valley are the normal hazards of mining are no more severe now than they ever have been. The decline, on the contrary, is a measure of diminishing momentum in an industry using near-marginal raw materials: the oil-shales, until some fifty years ago, were worked as much as a source of various chemicals (ammonium salts the chief) as of oil (which was almost a by-product). The oil itself had multiple use, as a lubricant, as a cleanser, only to a degree as a source of fuel. When with changing techniques in chemical manufacture the production of chemicals ceased to be profitable, emphasis was shifted to oil itself as a principal product of oil-shale distillation. But (except to the people of Broxburn and Pumpherston) imported petroleum products proved to be far more "amenable" in national economy than the Scottish oils; nor (as measured by social effort) could the Scottish oils "compete" with other sources of primary power, including Scottish coals. It is very doubtful if the industry, except on a small scale, would ever have grown as it did if its sole end had been oil for fuel; and in the improvement of industrial methods and the discovery of new resources it has gone the way of many similar palaeotechnic processes—perhaps rightly gone on a dispassionate assessment of present gains through present effort, perhaps wrongly in a long view of planned mineral use.

(*b*) Limestones and Dolomites

All the carbonate rocks of Scotland are of sedimentary origin, the vast majority of them marine. They occur in all systems from Lewisian to Cretaceous, but only those of

Cambro-Ordovician and Carboniferous age are of great significance. Being sedimentary rocks, they are widespread in suitable terrain over much of Scotland, and their utilisation depends less on the supplies available, which in many parts are indefinitely large, than on their physical and chemical properties, the purposes for which they are wanted, and their accessibility.

Limestones in the Lewisian and Moinian rocks. The general environment of sedimentation of both the Lewisian and the Moinian groups of sandstones was mostly unsuitable for the formation of limestone, and there are only two or three localities where calcareous concentrations are of any importance. The few limestones that occur are generally highly impure, with carbonates rarely reaching 90 per cent. of the rock and commonly falling towards 50 per cent. The rocks are much sheared, and any one deposit has no great extension, being useful at best but for agricultural lime. A great part of the central and northern Highlands may then be ruled out as a source of industrial carbonate rocks.

Limestones of Dalradian Age. Through much of the central and southern Highlands extending into Islay, and again in rocks of the same age in Shetland, several beds of limestone of the Dalradian system run for many miles, but not unbrokenly across country. They have received a number of local names, partly reflecting local occurrence or local lithological differences, but probably there are no more than three major beds of which the principal labels are the Ballachulish Limestone, the Blair Atholl Limestone and the Loch Tay Limestone. The uncertain regional correlation reflects the fragmentation and strong deformation the limestones (and associated sediments) suffered notably during the Caledonian earth-movements: they commonly functioned as a lubricant under stress, they are almost completely recrystallised, and they are locally thinned out to disappearance or are piled up on themselves into fat internally sheared lenticles. There is also much variation in contained "impurities", which may be detrital (and therefore original) or may be due to secondary infiltration (as at Duror, where the Appin Limestone contains thin seams of secondary quartz); and the limestones are variably dolomitised—even in a single short outcrop, as in the neighbourhood of Ballachulish, the magnesian content may have a range of 4 to 46 per cent. of $MgCO_3$. There appears to be no consistency in the little that is known of the regional variations in the rocks, and what is needed is systematic study of lateral change in relation to structural setting. The rocks have been quarried where obtrusive outcrops have attracted local attention; but a review of the chemistry should be accompanied by an assessment of sites and reserves.

Durness Limestone. It is possible that in part the Durness Limestone, of Cambro-Ordovician age, is approximately contemporaneous with some of the Dalradian limestones, the difference in quality and persistence being due to the differences in their orogenic history of the central and the north-west Highlands. Lying in the "foreland" region beyond the Moine thrust, the Durness Limestone is comparatively undeformed along much of its outcrop, and is little metamorphosed except in the neighbourhood of igneous intrusions; and it is very much more thickly developed and more uniform than any of the Dalradian beds. It is found in a belt, discontinuous because of shearing-out along the zone of the Moine thrust, extending from the north coast at Durness south-westwards to Skye. In several layers it gives clear signs of its marine origin in the occurrence of fossil molluscs and trilobites, and inferentially it was originally a normal organic limestone. At the present time, however, much of it is an almost pure dolomite, though the upper members of the group show alternations of dolomite and calcite. It forms one of the principal sources of dolomite in Scotland, and is of high potential value.

These, however, are general statements. They need to be qualified by evidence, obtained in those small parts of the outcrop that have been fairly closely studied, of variations in composition arising through several causes. In the limestones forming the mid members of the group the ratio of magnesium to calcium appears to be uniformly high and to indicate molecular proportions of true dolomite—that is, over the greater part of the outcrop the (secondary) dolomitisation appears to be complete. But with the magnesium may also be found aluminium and iron oxide—not in high proportion but sometimes reaching as much as 4 or 5 per cent. together: they appear to be mainly of detrital origin and to contaminate significantly only a few bands to which they are confined. Silica is a more pernicious impurity when high-grade dolomite is needed: some of it is recognisably detrital quartz, confined to a few thin layers, and then avoidable in quarrying; but there also occur nodules and ribs of secondary chert, introduced under the control of migrant siliceous waters and then unpredictable and "random" in amount and extent. The chert seams may be almost pure silica, of which bulk analyses of a mass of alternating dolomite and chert beds may show as much as 10 or more per cent. This local contamination is not a cause for condemning the rock as a whole, however, which in many parts and for considerable thicknesses may be almost silica free: but it is a warning that some bulk prospecting is needed to prove quality—prospecting that has not been begun over the greater part of the outcrop.

In places, especially in the neighbourhood of the major thrusts, the Durness Limestone has been splintered by faulting, and wedges of it may be trapped between non-calcareous rocks of several kinds: a warning that the structural context of the rock needs to be examined no less than the chemical composition to determine suitable sites for quarrying.

Ordovician Limestones in Ayrshire. Thick deposits of limestone in the Stinchar valley and its neighbourhood have been worked for many years as a source of lime and road-stone. There are still probably large reserves, but the rock, though mostly with low magnesia, is very impure, with $CaCO_3$ commonly falling below 85 per cent. and with a high proportion of detrital quartz and clay minerals.

Cornstones in the Upper Old Red Sandstone. The bands of cornstone in the Old Red Sandstone, sometimes reaching a thickness of 20 or 30 ft. and probably produced by a secondary leaching and a migration of carbonate in contemporaneous soils, are variable in composition where leaching was incomplete; but in their purer layers the proportion of $CaCO_3$ may exceed 98 per cent. and persist at this high level for long distances. The little that is known about them has been got from old workings now abandoned, but they extend (under an overburden) far beyond the limits of the old workings, as shallow drilling would prove.

Carboniferous Limestones. The many carbonate rocks of the Carboniferous system range from coarse-grained pure organic limestones to calmy limestones and cement-stones—a range that reflects the changing conditions of sedimentation under which the rocks were formed, and consequently the extent, manner of occurrence, composition, uniformity and possible uses of the several beds.

Many of the carbonate rocks in the lower part of the Calciferous Sandstone Series are thin-bedded argillaceous dolomites, the "cementstones" of the geologist. They vary widely in composition, but may contain 25 per cent. or more of non-carbonate material (of which the greater part is clay minerals and fine-grained quartz): the $CaCO_3$ content sometimes falls to less than 50 per cent., and the $MgCO_3$ may rise to 38 per cent., the $FeCO_3$ to 17 per cent. Moreover, they are interbedded with non-calcareous layers of shale and sandstone which themselves lack uniformity in thickness and composition, bulk analysis for any one outcrop may not be constant, and the rock association (despite the labelling of the carbonate beds as cementstones) is not readily worked as a unit in cement manufacture. Of the several limestones in the Oil-Shales development of the Calciferous Sandstone Series, the Burdiehouse Limestone—like most of its associates of non-marine origin—is relatively thick and persistent: it usually carries more than 90 per cent. of $CaCO_3$, though it may be strongly bituminous and contain carbonaceous partings and thin coals.

The carbonate rocks in the Upper Sedimentary Group of the Calciferous Sandstone Series, and at higher horizons notably in the Lower Limestone Group and the Upper Limestone Group, are dominantly richly fossiliferous marine beds in which most of the calcareous matter is composed of shell fragments. Where the accumulation of fossil detritus was rapid and deposition took place in fairly clear waters, the composition may show a very high proportion of $CaCO_3$—over 98 per cent. in places—but in the majority of the beds the individual limestone ribs carry much argillaceous and finely quartzitic contamination, and are interlayered with calcareous shales. They are also thin—rarely more than 20 ft.—and cannot compare in bulk or quality (as a source rock in lime manufacture for instance, or in chemical industry) with the much more massive beds (like the Buxton Limestone) of the Carboniferous Limestone of England and Wales.

The limestones have been worked, sometimes extensively, in many local quarries, but not enough is known of their regional variations, or of their place with beds above and below in rock associations that might be of bulk use in industry. They are gently folded and faulted, sometimes forming wide flat-lying outcrops easily worked, sometimes plunging underground with steep dip and a rapidly thickening overburden; and often they occur in urbanised areas where quarrying or mining must be carefully planned. A critical survey of their occurrence is a pre-requisite to any extensive systematic development in working them.

Many of the Carboniferous limestones are dolomitised, but generally in a variable patchiness or in vein contamination. The Carham and Barjarg outcrops in the Southern Uplands are exceptional in revealing rocks that throughout are almost pure dolomite. The first is the poorer in being riddled by veins of secondary chert not readily sorted either in quarrying or crushing. The second is free of quartz (except as a constituent of the insoluble residue—about 2 per cent.—of the rock) and otherwise is not unpromising as a source of high-grade dolomite: the quarries and small mine of former workings tapped only a very small part of the resources, but whether the rock persists with little change in composition and thickness along its outcrop, whether faults interrupt its continuity, and whether mining down-dip would result in flooding are unknown and wait on exploratory shallow drilling.

Jurassic Limestones. Both in east Sutherland and along the west coast in Argyll and Skye the Jurassic rocks contain many beds of limestone. They are mostly thin, however, and although in aggregate thickness they form very large reserves they are relatively impure (usually with less than 90 per cent. of $CaCO_3$ and more than 10 per cent. of clay minerals and silty quartzes). Some of the beds in the Lias, worked with associated calcareous shales, might well be suitable for cement manufacture on a large scale.

(*c*) Quartz Rocks and Diatomite

Sandstones and similar rocks are exceedingly common in the Scottish succession in all members from Lewisian quartzites to Glacial sands and gravels and recent alluvial and dune deposits. They vary widely in physical and chemical properties, and in most regions of Scotland one kind or another is usually available to meet the needs of industry in all its cruder demands—for building stone, for concrete aggregate, for roadstone, and (less often) for abrasives and for moulding sands. High-grade silica rocks are much more restricted in occurrence, and although they also are to be found in quantity they require some discriminating selection in their use as refractories or as glass-making sands, and perhaps some processing to attain standard. Sands of different geological ages display broad distinctions in lithological properties that have tended to encourage sweeping generalisations about their possible industrial uses; but what emerges from a conspectus of their known characteristics is that they are more varied and more amenable than they at first appear, and may be far more selectively used than their generalised qualities suggest. Much remains to be done to integrate the geological with the physico-chemical evidence, and a great deal more to place the main resources in a comprehensive industrial field.

Thus the sandstones belonging to the Moinian and Dalradian series, in cumulative thickness reaching many thousands of feet and in outcrop covering a large part of the Highlands, have been much affected by the metamorphism the whole region has suffered, and as they are now seen they are mostly altered to crystalline quartzites. In many of them the quartz grains are commonly accompanied by accessory minerals, some of which are original detrital constituents, others metamorphic in origin. The "impurities" are distributed through the mass of the rock in an interlocked crystal mosaic; they are not easily separated from the quartz by either physical or chemical means, and they reduce the value of the rock for specialised purposes. Nevertheless, the initial purity of the rock has not everywhere been significantly altered by metamorphism: for instance, in the Scaraben Quartzite (Sutherland) of the Moinian group and in the Binnein Quartzite (Argyll) of the Dalradian, the rock may have a bulk composition of more than 98 per cent. of silica.

Similarly, sandstones of Cambrian age, in a rock-group (the Eireboll Quartzite) underlying the Durness Limestone and running with it for many miles across the north-western Highlands, have been diagenetically altered by secondary recrystallisation, though they were little touched by the Caledonian metamorphism that altered and contaminated the Moinian and Dalradian rocks. They may contain original contaminant detritus (including aluminous feldspars); and locally they may be infiltrated along joints and faults by mineralising solutions, some of them iron-charged, that give the rock a pink or rusty tinge. But many of them have a silica content exceeding 98 per cent., an alumina content below 1 per cent.; and while this high degree of purity is not consistently maintained in all layers and at all localities, the rock as a whole shows little lateral change along a hundred miles of outcrop and is of the order of 200 to 500 ft. thick. What systematic variations occur in the greater part of this enormous mass are unknown and need study.

There is equal untidiness in detailed knowledge of the high-grade ganisters, containing more than 98 per cent. of silica, that are sources of refractories in the Carboniferous rocks, notably the Millstone Grit. Many of them have been used for many years for various kinds of furnace work: but it is unknown whether sufficient of them, if any, reach the highest "super-duty" grade, comparable with the best Hirwaun stone of South Wales (with a bulk composition of silica more than 99·5 per cent., alumina less than 0·3 per cent.); or, if they do not, whether industry can adapt itself to the use of inferior materials (of Carboniferous or Cambrian or Pre-Cambrian age) when, as is inevitable, there is decline and final exhaustion of practicable British sources of silica rock outside Scotland.

The Upper Cretaceous sands of Morven and Skye are exceptional in their purity, usually running to 99·5 per cent., or more of SiO_2. They are of approximately the same age as the Upper Greensand of England, but are almost free of contamination by metallic compounds and contain no green glauconite or iron oxides derived from it (though along a few joint faces there is a secondary infiltration of rusty limonite). They were deposited later than the major crustal movements that affected Scotland, are deformed only by gentle warping and slight faulting, and occur in an area where thick overlying flows of basalt form a nearly horizontal and very strong roof for protection. They thus combine high purity in silica content with almost ideal conditions for mining. Unless the basalt is strongly transgressive, for which there is no evidence, they extend for several miles to the north and west; and as now worked at Loch Aline they have an indefinitely long "life". Their uses in refined processes, notably in the manufacture of optical glass, make them unique in Scotland; and the main disadvantages from which they suffer are social and geographical rather than geological and industrial.

Diatomite as a siliceous deposit differs in its properties from normal detrital sands, and, being used for different purposes, is measured in different terms. Its qualities lie in its very fine grain and the hardness of its individual particles; peculiarly adapted to use as an abrasive, it is not in the same class of demand as refractories. The special circumstances under which it has formed in Scotland make it a mineral of highly restricted distribution. Unlike most other silica rocks it is an organic deposit, formed of an accumulation in clear still waters of myriads of minute skeletons of algal diatoms; and it is contaminated when it is mixed with transported detritus even of clear quartz grains. There are few areas of normal drainage where lake or pond waters are sufficiently undisturbed by stream flow to allow the rain of diatom skeletons to accumulate uninterruptedly as a thick and uniform deposit; and fewer where silt and clay minerals are not being transported into basins of sedimentation. The characteristic localities for diatomaceous accumulation are therefore on the one hand the lochans (like Loch Cuithir in Skye), often relatively deep but replenished only by short clear-water runnels, that occupy the floors of enclosed stepp-walled corries, and on the other the isolated ponds trapped in the hollows of moundy ground moraine (like the now-dry Muir of Dunnet). But although the topographical controls rarely allow the diatomaceous deposits to be either very thick or very extensive, the appropriate circumstances of deposition are not rare in the Highlands; and the half-dozen localities where deposits have been worked in the past are no more than examples of what might be expected in similar contexts elsewhere. Comparable deposits must occupy the floors of many mountain lochans: a probing to discover them would be no great task: a greater barrier to their being worked—a reflection of their topographical setting—might be the limited quantities to be got from any one occurrence in relation to remoteness and inaccessibility.

(*d*) Clays

The fireclays complement the ganisters as sources of refractory raw material in the Carboniferous sediments of the Midland Valley. They are widespread in occurrence both in area and in rock sequence; but their present workings are limited to seams and to localities in which traditionally high-quality material is known to be available. This limitation is understandable when some clays and shales may be impersistent or variable in composition for one reason or another; but it leads to an unbalanced use of possible resources in a progressive exhaustion of worked seams without a compensating search (in field and laboratory) for others. It also results in an inertia tending to make the relatively few clays that are worked all-purpose in their application, whereas refinement in selection might well allow each kind to be used to better advantage, and so less to limit technical improvements. The refractory bauxitic clays—most of them residual deposits rather than truly detrital—have also been worked concentratedly at a few centres, though they are extensively developed (with varying quality) in the region of outcrop of the Clyde Plateau Lavas.

Similar comments apply to the calcareous clays, as widespread and abundant as the fireclays in the Carboniferous sequence: a systematic study of their fuller and more discriminating use particularly in cement manufacture might not be amiss, nor further exploration into the practicalities of variable composition obtained in mixtures with suitable limestone.

(*e*) Bedded Ironstones

Bedded ironstones are strongly developed in two major groups of rocks in Scotland —the clayband and blackband ores of the Carboniferous rocks in the Midland Valley and the Jurassic ore of Raasay. The growth of the iron industry during the nineteenth century was mainly based on the exploitation of the Carboniferous ores, in the order of tens of millions of tons: the Jurassic ores have been worked only intermittently during the present century. The decline of the use of Scottish ores has followed not from an exhaustion of supplies but from their replacement by imported ores with which for several reasons they are not able to "compete". Enormous reserves of the clay-ironstones remain in the coalfields, and an estimated 10 million tons of the Raasay ore.

The iron that impregnates the shales of the coal measures occurs as scattered nodules or continuous bands generally associated with coal-seams. The nodules commonly may be seen to be embedded in shale whose laminae appear to be moulded to the nodular outline, and then to give the appearance of secondary concentrates grown after initial sedimentation. This is probably true of the diagenetic origin of the siderite of which they are dominantly composed; but some nodules clearly show the laminae to run through their centres, and the iron may well have been introduced into the sediments as a gel at the time of sedimentation, the congelate being nucleated in incipient nodular form or extending as a more or less continuous layer to form a blackband. The whole rock association in which the ironstones are found suggests a de-oxygenated environment of deposition conducive to the formation of iron-rich gels; and the ironstones are thus to be looked upon as primary and syngenetic in source material, though secondary as they now appear. Their recurrence in well-defined bands of the coal measures is thus systematic, and any one productive band is likely to have wide extent and some constancy in yield.

The nodules and bands vary in their "purity", but they rarely contain more than 40 per cent. of iron, the siderite always incorporating silica-rich and alumina-rich particles as primary constituents. Moreover, the bands are normally thin—occasionally as much as 2 ft., commonly less than 1 ft.—and the quarrying or the mining of them necessarily includes the working of associated worthless shale. In such circumstances they continue (in relation to imported ores) to be of economic worth only when they are conveniently worked in association with and accompanying a much more valuable coal-seam.

The greatest reserves, probably much exceeding 100 million tons, lie in the Ayrshire coalfield—a coalfield in which coal mining is not in the ascendant.

The Raasay ore is an oolitic ironstone of the Upper Lias. It is sideritic-chamositic in composition, containing about 25 per cent. of iron, and it is comparable in origin and in physical and chemical properties with some of the Yorkshire ores. Unlike the Carboniferous siderites, the ore is a member of a series of marine sediments; and presumably the environment of deposition was one of stagnant and de-oxygenated waters in which some rocking allowed ooliths to grow. Whatever the precise mode of its formation, the ore is likely to be uniformly developed over its whole extent. The ore is low-grade, contains relatively high phosphorus, is only 8 ft. thick, and except at outcrop is overlain by thicknesses of younger rock that compel it to be mined: although the bulk of the deposit still remains to be worked, there is no great encouragement to exploitation except in circumstances of shortage: at the same time the comparable English ores of Jurassic age are "economic", partly because they can be worked in bulk by dragline excavation in opencast quarries.

III. MINERALS IN IGNEOUS ROCKS

(*a*) Feldspars

The difficulties attending the exploitation of dispersed minerals in an igneous matrix are well illustrated by the feldspars—a family abundantly represented in all Scottish igneous rocks except the ultrabasic periodotites. The detailed mineralogy of cooled magmas, that are often contaminated by collapsed roof and wall rock and internally reorganised by differential crystallisation, is exceedingly complex, being a function of initial magmatic composition, manner of emplacement and conditions of cooling. A score or more of chemical elements in highly variable proportion commonly occur in most magmas, and in permutative combination form on freezing a host of mineral species some of which (like the feldspars) are in isomorphous series. Characteristically the igneous mineral association is an intergrown mixture from which the individual species is not easily separated. Prospecting for industrial feldspar (of use notably in ceramics) then becomes a search for large reserves of crystals of the desired composition and amenable to ready extraction.

The established needs of the ceramic industry are of high-potash feldspar, typified by orthoclase, in a rock almost free from iron (which stains the ware). The coarser-textured igneous rocks with large feldspar crystals are the granites and their kin, found as stocks and bosses in the Highlands and the Southern Uplands, and as pegmatite veins mainly in the Highlands. Some of the granites, like the Corennie granite, contain only small amounts of iron, but offset that favourable feature in a closely intimate "graphic" intergrowth of quartz with the feldspar which is correspondingly not amenable to easy sorting. Others like the Loch Borolan and Ben Loyal masses, syenitic in composition with little free quartz, are fouled by too much iron.

Very large individual feldspar (and other) crystals are found in some of the pegmatites, which abound especially in Sutherland and Wester Ross and are important in Harris. They are superior to most of the granite feldspars in the ease with which they may be extracted and in being less contaminated by iron (though sometimes as at Sletteval in Harris streaks of ferriferous mica are a major defect in a rock that otherwise would be of high quality). Nevertheless, despite the success with which they were worked for several years in the forties, they continue to be regarded as inferior to the imported Scandinavian feldspars partly because they contain a higher proportion of plagioclase and a lower of potash. (It is also true, but as a domestic problem, that each pegmatite band is usually narrow—the intrusion at Chaipaval in Harris, containing perhaps the best-quality industrial feldspar in Scotland, is only some 20 ft. wide—and the reserves at any one locality are not great, even if its situation is not too remote and inaccessible for easy working.)

The significance of this rejection of Scottish feldspars lies in the setting of an industrial standard by the properties of imported material to which industry has become accustomed. It might well be that as used in existing plant Scandinavian feldspar is superior to Scottish; but defective natural products can be remedied either by beneficiating them and bringing them to standard or by processing them in different ways. The rejection of the Scottish resources has in some aspects the appearance of passive practice likely to lead to technical stagnation—an antecedent assumption is that the materials must suit the process, not the process the materials.

(*b*) Serpentine and Talc

Amongst the larger igneous masses of the Highlands and Shetland the intrusions of serpentine, with which or in which occur seams of talc, have been desultorily worked from time to time, but they invite a far more sustained interest as possible sources of raw material in a variety of industrial applications.

The serpentine is usually a hydrated and partly reconstituted magnesium silicate occurring as an alteration product of ultrabasic periodites rich in olivine. The pure olivine rock, dunite, is comparatively rare at least in surface outcrops in the Highlands, partly because of the metamorphic and metasomatic changes it has undergone, but its physical properties are not wholly lost in its derivatives, particularly its resistance to high temperature. Commonly serpentine is looked upon as almost worthless, "country rock" or "matrix", but it is worthless only because it is not used: much of it no doubt would prove to be commercially unattractive, but without critical study it is not to be lightly discarded as a source of refractory bricks and moulding sands to supplement and improve upon the quartz-based materials.

Talc is a derivative of serpentine through partial silicification—usually brought about by dynamo-thermal metamorphism and then tending to be concentrated in zones of thrusting. The bulk of the Scottish talc is too impure to be used as a cosmetic base, but in most other uses where purity is not identified with whiteness it is a thoroughly suitable raw material—in fire-bricks, in furnace-linings, in some ceramic ware, in foundry bonding-sands. Nowhere is it abundant, and at most localities it is found in association with other minerals, especially bruennerite, that may for some purposes "contaminate" it; but a combined working with adjacent serpentine has obvious economic possibilities.

These possibilities, tested in Scotland on any scale only at Queyhouse in Unst, are no more than prognostic when they rest only on the slender evidence of field observation; but if they are neglected they will serve as yet another instance of the indifference and lack of enterprise that mark much of Scottish economic geology when no immediate return for expended effort appears to be forthcoming: it is not to be assumed that there ever will certainly be a return, but until the rocks are thoroughly assessed there is never likely to be.

(*c*) Chromite

A number of the basic and ultrabasic igneous intrusions in Scotland show a banding of mineral segregates in which feldspars or olivine-rock (serpentine) alternate with iron or other heavy-metal minerals. The lighter bands may be of no economic importance, but the darker may show sufficient concentrations to justify exploitation. Amongst the metallic ores, chromite in layered granules is not unusual. The chromite in Unst and in Skye has this particular form of occurrence, and is a pointer to possible occurrences elsewhere.

Characteristically the banding of the Unst intrusion is never sharply clean-cut—it is indicated by a merging of dunite and periodite serpentines along an ill-defined junction curved in outcrop—and the chromite occupies no precisely defined zone that can be identified as a sheeted ore body. On the contrary, the mineral grains are scattered in ribbon-banded concentration through the rock, and their possible economic use depends not on their mere occurrence but on their concentration. The rhythmic bands of ore grains are repeated like the layers of a sedimentary rock, and give the appearance of an original indefinite extension laterally and vertically (though it happens that the ore bodies have at the present day a lenticular form through the accident of fragmentation by thrusting).

The Unst chromite was originally identified at outcrop, and its exploitation has followed the empirical course of trailing the lenses in depth. Such conditions of working are precarious when shearing disrupts or squeezes out a band or shifts a band outside the range of visible outcrop. Both the nature and the fragmented form of the Unst rock reveal in a well-proved example the need for a prospecting of occurrences of similar ore deposits elsewhere in the Highlands by other means than surface survey: the few small bodies already discovered are scarcely likely to be the only ones in Shetland, and elsewhere in Scotland, as at Corrycharmaig, small outcrops of chromite ore are but the incidental sign of what might lie hidden at depth or distance.

IV. VEIN MINERALS

(*a*) Mode of Occurrence

Some vein minerals, notably calcite, are the products of deposition or metasomatic replacement by percolating mineralised waters usually descending under gravity or moving as part of the normal circulation of ground-water: occasionally they may be of considerable importance, for instance when the calcite as "Iceland spar" is of optical use.

The majority of vein minerals in Scotland—almost all those of economic value—are not of ground-water origin, however: they are igneous or hydrothermal offshoots from magmatic sources, and most of them have the form of extremely slender dykes and sills. They commonly follow pre-existing fractures, swelling into thick pockets where the structures allow, thinning to the merest threads or pinching out completely where the fissures are tightly packed or sealed. The vein fluids, dregs in the process of magmatic cooling, were injected under enormous pressure, and so long as the conduits were open to them they continued (laterally and upwards) for long distances, sometimes miles, from their primary magmatic reservoir. Although they also cooled as they flowed, their mobility was sustained partly by the regional warmth of the country rock, partly by the fluxing action of "water" and dissolved gases, partly by low freezing-points—some of the minerals of the Leadhills suite are estimated to have crystallised out at a temperature of much less than 200° C.

The actual minerals occurring in a lode therefore reflect the influence of a number of factors—the composition of the source magma, the differentiation undergone before injection of the vein fluids, the availability of open fissures, the speed of flow and rate of cooling, the physical chemistry of the crystallisation process, the continued mobility of the fluid residues at each phase of crystal formation, the replenishment of stocks from depth, and the secondary metasomatism after solidification of the vein. In such circumstances the intersection of a vein by the accidental present land-surface of Scotland (an eroded land-surface of post-Glacial age) inevitably reveals a distribution of vein minerals in neighbouring lodes that appears to be random: veins of lead-zinc are recorded from Strathspey and Ardrishaig; of haematite from Tomintoul, Kishorn and Garleton; of mispickel from Cairnsmore of Fleet; of copper pyrites from Shetland and the Ochils; and of barytes from Arran and Nairn. Periods of mineralisation may also have been recurrent: for instance, some of the Leadhills minerals appear to have been deposited in Caledonian times, some in Hercynian: and mineral suites were usually not identical in successive periods.

The single vein when by chance it follows an open fracture may carry strong concentrations of ore; the Tyndrum fault is the course of a vein tens of feet in width containing rich shoots of lead, zinc and pure quartz; and the Strontian fault similarly carries a thick vein of lead and zinc (and locally a basalt dyke). But if the fracture is not open, or is not flanked by broken walls with cavitous fault breccia, the mineralisation is commonly discontinuous or insignificant. The majority of Scottish records appear to be of modest lodes; and although the occasional vein, insignificant at the surface, might prove rapidly to enlarge and be enriched at depth, the likelihood is that most of those already sampled have been worked out in the sense that returns from further excavation would scarcely repay cost except during times of unusually high metal prices.

There must, however, be a host of veins still undiscovered, many of them under only thin cover of peat or drift and easily accessible. The greater number of these no doubt would give only a small yield, but two or three should prove to be fat and rich. Where a consanguineous association of mineral veins suggests a closer proximity to a primary source, as in the country about Loch Fyne (cut by many fractures, some of them occupied by basaltic dykes, that have yielded small amounts of copper and nickel), the promise of any one vein may be inconsiderable, but the field is obviously one worth exploring as a unit.

(*b*) The Leadhills Suite

A consanguineous association of veins is most clearly revealed in the Leadhills-Wanlockhead field, where the signs of a network of ore bodies are as strong as they are in the northern Pennines. It is clear from the structural pattern of the whole Southern Uplands that a major element of tectonic strain is a system of north-and-south fractures that transect the caledonid strike of the Lower Palaeozoic strata. Repeatedly from Galloway to the Tweed valley the rocks are mineralised notably by lead and zinc in veins following the courses of these fissures, and have for many years been successfully (if intermittently) worked for ore. The Leadhills-Wanlockhead field is merely the richest so far discovered: it illustrates the pattern of structure and of mineralisation very clearly, but in doing so draws attention to similar patterns seen farther west.

A multiplicity of veins around the granite masses especially of Criffel and Cairnsmore of Fleet is an association implying that the granites belong to the same phase of igneous emplacement and intrusion as the veins, and may represent the immediate parental magma from which the mineralising fluids were derived (farther north, a similar association is seen between the Strontian granite and surrounding veins). The granites are now widely exposed, however, only because they have been unroofed, and vein development from them is mainly lateral. The complementary relationship appears at Leadhills, where no granite as yet breaks the surface, but where the ore bodies riddle the rocks much more completely than the lateral shoots in the ground farther west and presumably overlie a granite boss emplaced at no great depth (in the comparable country of the northern Pennines geophysical evidence is accommodated by a granite body at about 5,000 ft. below the present land surface). The economic significance of a genetic connection between surface veins and a deep-seated source lies in the implication of a likely extension of veins with depth.

The Leadhills mines are far from being worked out even at their present levels: their periodic abandonment has arisen partly from intrinsic difficulties (including flooding) in their working, partly from fluctuations in free-market metal prices. An extension of the field into even richer veins might well revivify the industry and restore the main Scottish supplies of lead and zinc. A first demand is for geophysical exploration of the foundation over much of the Southern Uplands, to be followed by drilling to prove what the geophysical evidence suggests—a deep borehole in the Lowther Hills might be no less rewarding than one in the north Pennines.

V. MINERALS IN METAMORPHIC ROCKS

In regional development the nature and occurrence of metamorphic minerals are dependent on the composition of the parent rock and the intensity of the stress changes imposed upon them. Alternations of rock type in a normal sedimentary sequence may thus be reflected in corresponding banded variants of a regional mineral association in derived schists or gneisses. In addition, the more severely altered rocks may lose much or all of their primary characteristics, and at sufficient depths of metamorphic burial become "plastic", "mobilised": they suffer a reconstitution that gives them an internal structure (including a novel mineral assemblage) approximating to, sometimes scarcely distinguishable from, that of an igneous rock. In subsequent exposure they combine the features of initial form and of derived composition in outcrops of sub-parallel metamorphic zones (not necessarily cognate with antecedent stratigraphical zones), and in a graded transition from recognisable sediments through layered schists and banded gneisses to virtually uniform "granites".

"Pure" (monomineralic) rocks undergo the changes with little radical conversion to new mineral species: sandstones become quartzites, limestones become marbles. Mixed rocks like shales, on the other hand, and more especially shales associated with sandstones and limestones, may be converted to phyllites, schists and gneisses; and, being rich particularly in iron and aluminium, are the principal sources of the main Scottish species of economically valuable metamorphic minerals—andalusite, sillimanite, hyanite, staurolite and garnet. The greater mixture of original constituents in the Dalradian rocks tends to make them generally richer, as sources of a varied suite of metamorphic minerals, than either the Lewisian or the Moine.

The minerals of the schists and gneisses are disseminated through a matrix (dominated by such secondary felted minerals as sericite, chlorite, talc and micas which give the rocks a characteristic foliation) that usually forms the bulk of the rock and is usually not of any economic importance. Where weathering disintegrates the rock, the naturally separated minerals, especially if they are appreciably different in grain size and specific gravity, may be sluiced and selectively sorted into rich alluvial concentrates, as they are in the garnet sands of some of the valleys opening into the Great Glen. As a source of industrial minerals (used in ceramics, as abrasives) the placer deposits suffer, however, from the usual deficiencies of shallow depth, limited extent and cramped situation, and cannot compare with rock-in-place for sustained production. The massive unweathered rock, on the other hand, is usually hard: the desired minerals may be extracted only by crushing and sorting—a process not difficult in for instance the garnet-schists, whose garnets are both granular and dense, but not so effective in coarse-grained intimately mixed gneisses, and not at all effective when in some strongly quartzose rocks there is interlocked growth of the metamorphic minerals with the recrystallised quartz grains.

As a general statement it is thus true to say that several species of metamorphic minerals are to be found abundantly in many parts of the Highlands. It is not so true to assume that they are readily got or that they are necessarily worth getting. A full assessment of their potential industrial significance can follow only from an appraisal of their occurrence and their reserves on a comprehensive and organised basis.

Contact metamorphism is much more highly localised. It arises through igneous intrusion, the larger granite masses of both the Highlands and the Southern Uplands being wrapped in well-developed aureoles. Though it may be accompanied by stress effects, it is usually different in kind from dynamic metamorphism, for the minerals of the country rock do not form a completely enclosed system at the time of intrusion—they are both thermally cooked by the hot ascending fluids and chemically corroded by ionic and molecular migration in seepages of the fluids from the main mass of the intrusion. The influence of the migrant ions, in a series of complex reactions depending on the composition of country rock and magmatic fluids, is highly variable: it is dominant near the contact with the intrusion and only allusive at some little distance away, and much care needs therefore to be exercised in sampling the rocks of the aureole, for local composition may not be average. Thus pure limestones amongst the Highland marbles may suffer almost no change in chemical composition in a thermal zone, though their calcite may be recrystallised; and dolomite may only lose some of its CO_2 to be converted into a recrystallised mosaic of calcite and brucite: but when there is infiltration its effects are commonly revealed in veins of silica enrichment marked by green serpentine and scattered crystals of garnet.

Contact metamorphism in its nature is far more restricted than regional metamorphism, and there are not usually to be expected "inexhaustible" supplies of industrially useful aureole rocks. Thus the west Highland marbles are almost completely worked out on Tiree and Iona, and in their more massively uniform beds on Skye (where they display rapid changes in quality). There may yet be outcrops where good marble in large blocks is to be got, but they are likely to be small, with only a short working "life".

A combination of intense regional deformation with infiltration by migrant fluids (presumably of igneous origin) is revealed in the pattern of quartz veining to be seen in the Highlands. The veins riddle the country rocks along joints and bedding planes, and swell out into pods and lenticles along the axes of the innumerable folds. Over vast areas the vein-quartz forms a conspicuous part of the rock, in aggregate quantity that must be enormous. Usually, however, the size of the intercalated veins and lenticles is not great, and the quartz could be got for industrial purposes only by bulk working of the whole rock and by difficult, or at least costly, extraction. The very thick lenticle at Dalwhinnie, at maximum over 80 ft. wide and with a sample purity of 99·7 per cent. silica, and the veins at Tyndrum and in Glen Orchy, are exceptional in their magnitude, and are the only known occurrences where direct large-scale quarrying not involving much sorting is possible: but geographically they suffer from being remote and not easily accessible.

What may be a product of dynamo-thermal metamorphism with some "mobilisation" are the veins of magnetite in Tiree and Iona, and perhaps at Clothister (Shetland) also, which appear to be interlayered with a garnet gneiss and not to be intruded or fissure fillings. They may then have an extension appreciably greater than their present outcrops show.

VI. A MINERALS POLICY

The work of the Geological Survey makes it highly unlikely that there remain to be discovered any large deposits of exceptionally valuable ores or minerals in Scotland comparable with the diamond pipes of South Africa or the copper veins of Montana or the pyrite of Spain; and there is no prospect of a radical change in industrial bias in the foreseeable future arising through the lucky strike of some enterprising prospector. Only the discovery of "new" kinds of minerals (like the uranium ores, of which there is not much sign) for power production would transform established industrial practice. Coal, so long as it does not become too "expensive" in the international market, will remain Scotland's principal mineral product—and, as a source of primary energy, perhaps a more important and permanent basis for evolving industry than could be any other single mineral of only limited application. Similarly, the Midland Valley may be expected to continue to supply the vast bulk of native raw materials.

Nevertheless, the modest resources of a variety of minerals that are known to occur in all three major areas in Scotland are plainly being neglected. Their exploitation would not make Scotland rich, but it would certainly make it richer. They have been neglected for a number of reasons, of which immediate opportunity of getting cheaper supplies elsewhere is one, and the persistence of habit and tradition in industry is another. But amongst the reasons is ignorance—ignorance of the kind and quantity and distribution of each mineral, of its physical and chemical properties, of its actual and potential uses in existing industry, of the means of "improving" it to reach required standards, of the application of novel techniques in its processing and of novel uses to which it may be put, of the social reorganisation needed to work it, generally of its possible place in the national economy.

Such ignorance of the actualities of Scottish economic geology is wasteful and stupid and waits to be remedied. It can best be remedied by a skilled survey comparable in quality with, and complementary to, the work of the Geological Survey. In a few instances, of which coal is an outstanding example, the survey can properly be left to the large industrial or national corporation, which knows its own needs and how best to carry out its own prospecting; but the private industrial company or research organisation wealthy enough to undertake such a task understandably concentrates its efforts in areas where the signs give promise of rich returns, and necessarily orientates them along lines appropriate to its own special interests. In practice, except as an occasional gesture of goodwill, it almost never concerns itself with mineral deposits outside its field.

In present circumstances, the kind of comprehensive survey needed can be provided best under governmental aegis, though functionally there might well be close co-operation with industry in studies of both mineral resources and mineral use. Its first purpose being to collect information, its value is not to be measured in terms of an annual profit-and-loss account, or its justification to reside in any immediate economic advantage expected to follow from it. At worst, even if as it progressed the various mineral deposits should continue for the time being to be as unpromising as many of them now appear to be, even if no discernible improvement in Scottish industry should follow, the survey nevertheless would scarcely need apology (at this stage of social evolution) as the activity of a competent husbandman, skilled and long-sighted in management, who makes an inventory of his possessions. In an exponentially increasing world-wastage of assets, when in due course the compulsion of necessity will drive industry to use whatever minerals are available, it is but prudence and good sense to discover what assets there are and to organise their use accordingly.

Government also is the only likely source of the variety of instruments needed to make such a survey sufficiently comprehensive and adequate in both field and laboratory. The field work would begin where the normal work of the Geological Survey ends: as in the geochemical prospecting of soils and other superficial deposits, to trail minerals to their source or to provide clues to ore bodies hidden from view; in geophysical prospecting by a variety of means, to explore at depth; and in drilling, mostly shallow, sometimes deep, to confirm surface signs or to test inferences of occurrence or quality or quantity. The laboratory work would begin with the determination of the physical and chemical properties of minerals to assess their suitability for industrial use; it would lead on to studies of mineral processing and methods of beneficiation, and to pilot-plant experiments in novel industrial techniques adapted to the natural or the processed mineral. The survey in its earlier stages might do little more than systematically record information and review prospects, but as it developed it should become a direct stimulant to technological progress.

The magnitude of such a many-sided task can be made to look formidable, but in scale it is the sort of task that large industrial (and some national) corporations assume as a normal part of research when their interests are involved, and it is the sort of task explicitly proposed by the Mineral Development Committee in 1949 (and by lesser authorities since) as integral to continued industrial growth. Laboratory provision of the right kind is already available in existing Government establishments, proportionately the cost of the survey would be small, national (including strategic) interests are directly affected, and ignorance needs dispelling.

BIBLIOGRAPHY

The publications of the Geological Survey, of which a full list is given by Dr. G. H. Mitchell in an accompanying paper, are the main storehouse of information on Scottish economic minerals and ores: a very convenient summary is to be found in:

MACGREGOR, M. (1940). Synopsis of the mineral resources of Scotland. *Mem. geol. Surv.: Spec. Rep. Min. Resour. G.B.*, **33**.

Other recent publications providing information on particular kinds or occurrences of economic minerals include:

BURGESS, I. C. (1960). Fossil soils of the Upper Old Red Sandstone of south Ayrshire. *Trans. geol. Soc. Glasg.*, **24**, 138-53.

BUTLER, A. S. *et al.* (1954). Dolomite in Scotland. *Rep. Miner. Resour. Panel Edinb.*

FLETT, W. R., MACGREGOR, M., and ROBERTSON, R. H. S. (1954). Talc in Scotland. *Rep. Miner. Resour. Panel Edinb.*

KNORRING, O. VON, and DEARNLEY, R. (1960). The Lewisian pegmatites of South Harris, Outer Hebrides. *Min. Mag.*, **32**, 366-78.

RIVINGTON, J. B. (1953). Recent chromite exploration in Shetland. *Min. Mag.*, **89**, 329-37.

ROBERTSON, R. H. S., and WHITEHEAD, T. H. (1954). Serpentine and olivine-rock in Scotland. *Rep. Miner. Resour. Panel Edinb.*

TEMPLE, A. K. (1956). The Leadhills-Wanlockhead lead and zinc deposits. *Trans. roy. Soc. Edinb.*, **63**, 86-113.

WHETTON, J. T., and MYERS, J. O. (1950). Geophysical survey of a magnetite deposit in the island of Tiree. *Trans. geol. Soc. Glasg.*, **21**, 237-62.

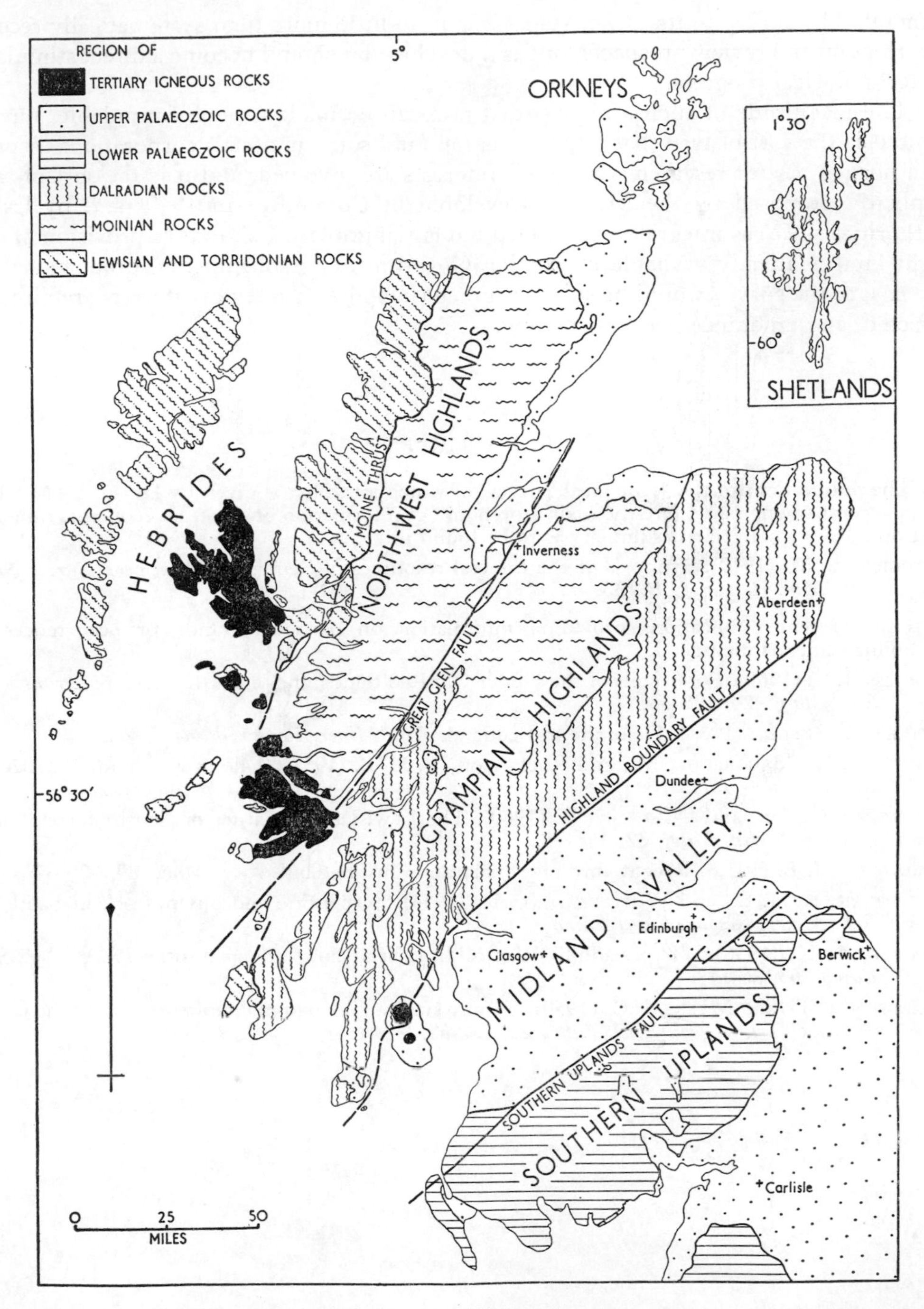

FIG. 1. Outline map, slightly simplified, showing the structural pattern and principal rock types of Scotland. (After the maps of the Geological Survey.)

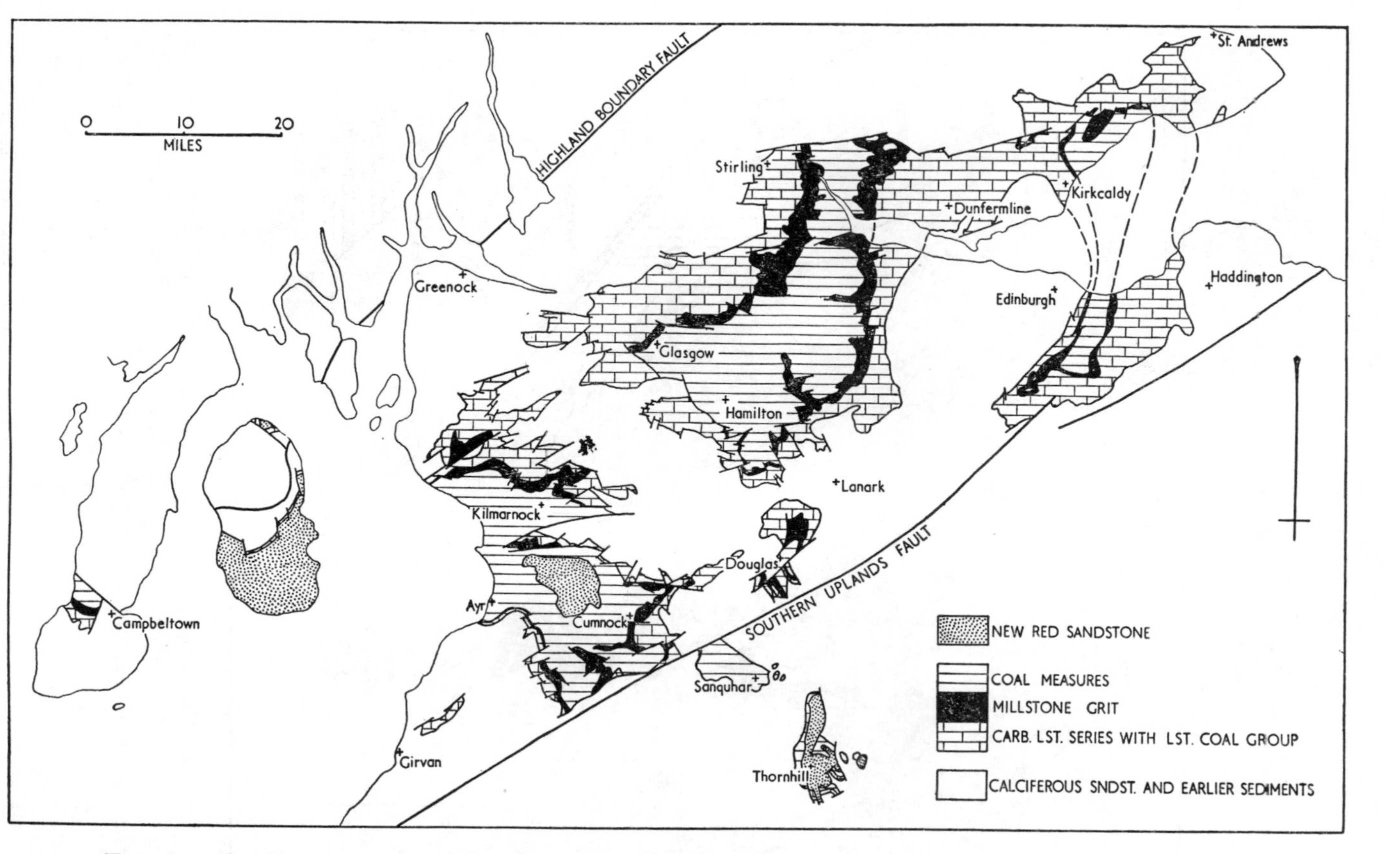

FIG. 2. Outline map of the coalfields of Scotland. (After the maps of the Geological Survey.)

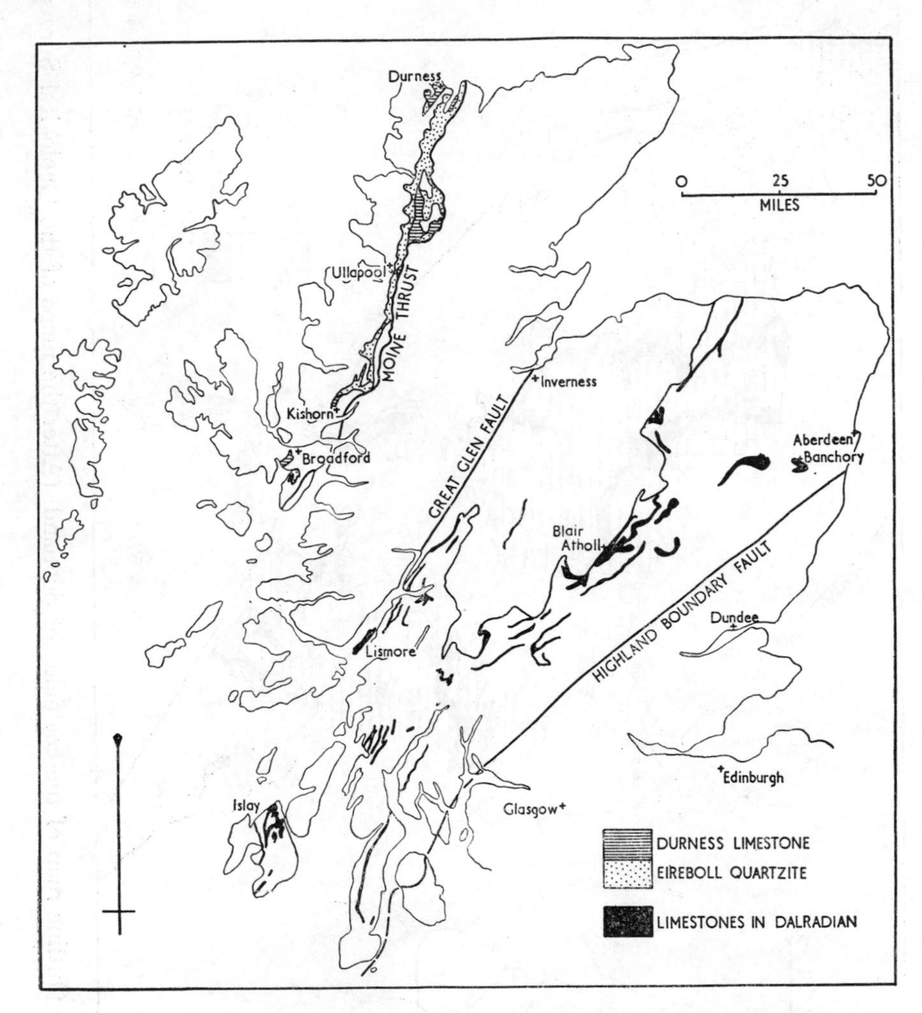

FIG. 3. Outline map, simplified and generalised, showing the distribution of the major outcrops of limestone in the Highlands and of the Eireboll Quartzite. (After the maps of the Geological Survey.)

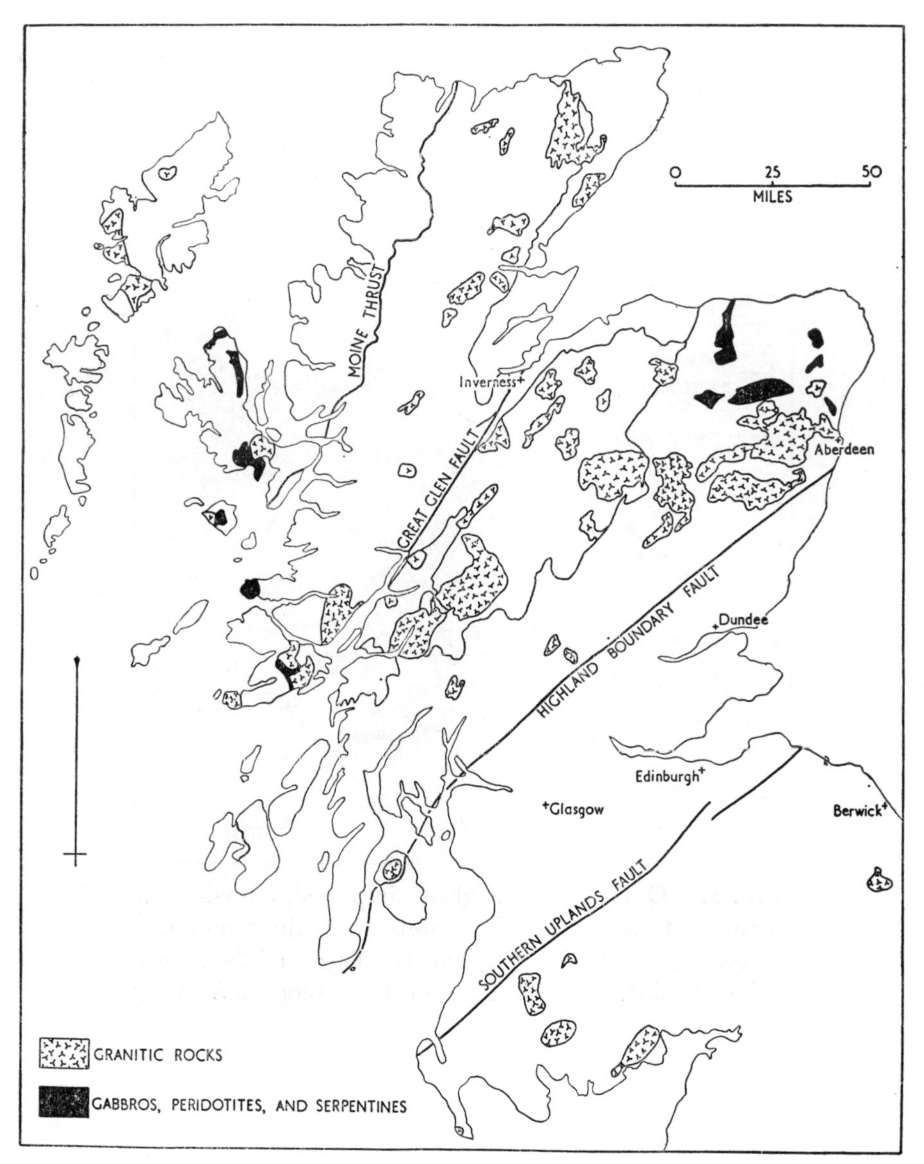

FIG. 4. Outline map showing the larger igneous intrusions in Scotland. (After the maps of the Geological Survey.)

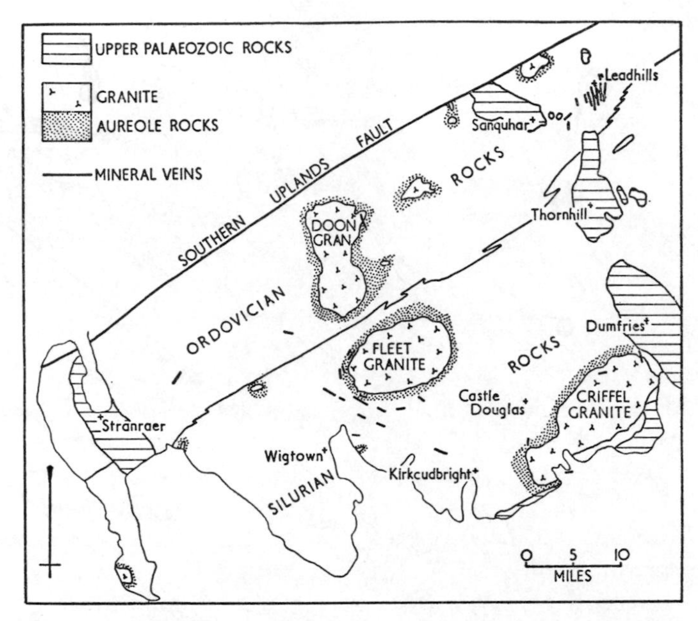

FIG. 5. Outline map, slightly simplified, showing the main granitic igneous intrusions with their aureoles, of the Southern Uplands, and the larger of the known mineral veins. (After the maps of the Geological Survey.)

Survey Methods

P. A. Rankin, D.F.C., B.SC., A.R.S.M., A.M.I.M.M.
Technical Manager, Hunting Surveys Ltd., Elstree

This paper presented in the section of the conference dealing with Mineral Resources, in fact covers surveying of many types of Natural Resources in addition to minerals, as requested by the Committee.

A broad division is made between surveying the atmosphere, water-bodies and land masses.

Under the section on the atmosphere only two aspects, namely meteorology and communications, are dealt with since these seem relevant to the conference discussion. Methods of survey are not discussed, but instead the need for improved meteorological services appropriate to Scotland is stressed together with some suggestions regarding the need for better dissemination of information, mainly local in type.

Surveys of water-bodies can be conveniently divided into those applicable to deep sea, continental shelves and coastal waters, underground and surface water.

Systematic oceanographic surveys could well be commonplace in the next decade. Systematic surveying of the mineral wealth of the continental shelves is possible now. Mining and oil companies are doing it and there is merit in governments performing at least the initial reconnaissance surveying, for instance, to interest privately financed mineral exploration and exploitation.

Detailed surveys for engineering projects such as harbour installations, channel clearance and the laying of pipe-lines and cables make use of recent developments in geophysical and electronic equipment.

Some serious thought should be given to the need to husband and farm our fish food resources. This implies surveying underwater and bottom conditions and the study of the ecology of fish life.

Underground and surface water studies involve topographic, geological, geophysical and vegetation surveying. Many lessons applicable to Scotland can be learnt from such surveys carried out abroad.

Surveys of land masses involve geological, vegetation and topographic methods. Many areas abroad are now surveyed by teams covering all such aspects concurrently.

The speed of topographic surveying for many purposes has been increased by the use of air photographs with no loss of, and sometimes gain in, accuracy. Instead of photographing Scotland in a spasmodic fashion as is done today, time and money could be saved if users co-ordinated their requirements.

Vegetation surveys include ecological studies. It is suggested that much land in Scotland is not being used gainfully, through the lack of a co-ordinated approach to development involving, as a basic requirement, maps showing existing factors on which to base logical development.

Regional geological, geophysical and geochemical methods of survey developed abroad in unexplored areas still apply, with suitable modification, to Scotland. In fact, regional geophysical coverage is being carried out by the Geological Survey.

A reappraisal of Scotland's mineral resources is now appropriate due to the advances in mining and mineral extraction techniques. A review of existing mineralised areas is one way of achieving this. Another way is the regional geochemical prospecting of geological units. There is a great need for concerted action in the field of mineral exploration in Scotland.

SURVEY METHODS

This paper, though given under the general title of "Mineral Resources", in fact will, as called for by the Committee, cover survey methods in the wider field of natural resources.

The paper will outline types of natural resources surveys and mention some examples which may be relevant to Scotland's needs.

The paper is divided into sections dealing with surveying of the atmosphere, water-bodies and land masses.

THE ATMOSPHERE

Only two aspects of atmospheric phenomena are considered relevant to the discussion, namely meteorology and communications.

Meteorology

Meteorological conditions affect our lives in all ways. The science of meteorology suffers from the problems of the major earth sciences; that is, the laboratory is vast, the workers many, and the subject highly complicated.

Survey methods consist of taking measurements of the elements—pressure, wind strength and direction, amounts of cloud, rainfall, etc.—and deducing patterns of existing and future weather therefrom. Measurements are taken at points on the earth's surface and from aircraft (fixed-wing and balloon).

All of us, particularly those perhaps whose work is connected with farming, whilst realising some of the difficulties, could wish for more complete and rapid collection of data, more rapid treatment and thus better and more detailed forecasting. Although perhaps life would be much less interesting, one can easily think of the benefits to mankind if weather prediction were accurate in detail.

The writer is not competent to suggest better methods or even methods of forecasting useful to Scotland. However, one aspect seems clear. As with other earth sciences, there is a need for collection and treatment of far more data, so that complicated weather patterns can be mapped, understood and predicted. Were we to start collecting sufficient information now, however, it would probably need years for patterns to emerge.

The thought is left, therefore: "As weather affects us all and its prediction would assist development, is Scotland doing all it can to obtain data and analyse it quickly and usefully?" and "Where it is possible to control weather (e.g. seeding clouds), should Scotland do anything?"

One particular aspect of meteorology, atmospheric radioactivity, is a topical subject for survey these days. The methods vary with the problem to be studied.

Where the need is to know the variations in general level of radioactivity, say for scientific or public health reasons, aircraft or balloons with counters or filter apparatus can be flown on suitable patterns guided by radio navigation systems.

Counter apparatus, generally scintillation in type, can give continuous records and is more useful from that point of view than the filter type of apparatus which gives the total quantity gathered over certain periods of time (for instance the duration of a flight). However, the filter system allows chemical analysis of the particles captured whereas the scintillation counter gives only total count; the components from the various sources of radioactivity, e.g. cosmic, the earth and man-made fission, not being distinguishable.

Since accidents in reactors, industrial and experimental, can take place, the general public need to have a system of warning and of safeguarding life against their effects. Surveys around reactor sites, with this object in view, use three methods. One consists of having numerous radioactivity monitors recording constantly over a suitable area around the reactor. The stationary monitors record the "normal" variations of radioactivity usually. When an incident occurs, they indicate the areas of contamination so that measures can be taken to isolate them particularly in regard to milk production. An adequate system of this sort needs a great number of monitors and personnel for maintenance.

The second system consists of making periodic surveys along roads using car-borne scintillation counters. The results are recorded in map form so that the normal level and variation of radioactivity is known. When an incident occurs, teams are mobilised for rapid survey and areas of contamination mapped.

The third system uses low-flying aircraft—usually fixed-wing—though helicopters could be used. Here a pattern of flight lines is flown, say at 500 ft. above ground, periodically. When an incident occurs, the aircraft flies the pattern again as rapidly as possible giving information on areas of anomalous radioactivity in a matter of a few hours. The airborne method has the advantage of speed. This is critical when one realises the main effect of an incident is contaminated milk; the production cycle grass to milk being a matter of hours only.

Communications

Although the development of communication methods of all types is necessary for the development of an area, there is one form of communication, that is the transmission and reception of information, which is particularly worthy of attention.

Such is the need for rapid, accurate and clear communication by post, wire, radio and television on a world scale that we can take it as read that everything possible is being done in this field to advance methods and applications at least in a general way, but are we happy that the transference of information using the atmosphere is developed as far as possible for Scotland's needs internally?

It is very interesting to know one can talk easily or send messages (or personnel or equipment for that matter) from Glasgow or Edinburgh to Johannesburg or Accra in a matter of minutes or hours, but what about communication between Glasgow and Edinburgh and the distant parts of Scotland and the islands? Is it worth thinking of a survey of such communication systems in Scotland?

It would be easy enough to collect data on existing communication systems. What would be more laborious and difficult would be collecting data on peoples' and organisations' requirements and planning a system to meet the general need.

One quite important sidelight on this matter is the dissemination of purely local information within and between small isolated communities. The writer, in hospital some years ago in a small Ontario town, realised the value of the local radio station for propagating purely local information. The information transmitted in this way was, in general, accurate, and this helped to suppress "gossip" which bedevils small communities. In addition, and most important, the community spirit was helped. Would this not apply to the islands and remote parts of Scotland where communities are diminishing—young people leaving? One might even think of television rather than radio.

WATER-BODIES

For convenience, this section is divided into sea, near-shore (mainly the continental shelf, say to a depth of 100 fathoms) and deep sea (depths to say 3,000 fathoms and oceanic trenches), and land (surface water and underground water).

Sea Surveys

Some of the techniques used in surveying the sea include underwater photography, air photography, magnetometry, seismic, echo-sounding, radiation detection, and sampling.

Information can be obtained by instruments carried in aircraft (including towed birds), ships (including sledges or devices towed by ships), submarines, torpedoes and bathyscapes.

The Deep Sea

Oceanographic surveys until recently have been undertaken by isolated ship voyages; the ships containing a number of scientists armed with some equipment, including sledges, grabs, etc.

In the United Kingdom pure oceanographic research is carried out on a limited scale at the National Institute of Oceanography at Wormley in Surrey. They possess a research vessel from which they carry out a wide range of investigations, including underwater photography and some interesting work using sideways-facing echo-sounders.

Applied oceanographic research is carried out by the Admiralty Research Establishment. Other research is carried out by the Ministry of Agriculture and Fisheries.

A number of Universities are carrying out oceanographic research. For instance, at Cambridge undersea surveying is being carried out using echo-sounders, proton magnetometers and gravity meters.

However, interest in deep-sea surveying has been stimulated lately for defence reasons, so thought has been given recently to the need for systematic surveying the deeps and methods to do it.

For systematic surveys of the deeps, methods currently used on land can be adapted.

Underwater vehicles can be made to carry magnetometer, gravimeter, seismic equipment, camera and depth-sounders. Such instrumentation can also be carried in towed objects from surface vessels. The recording of data obtained can be effected in the vessel itself (whether it be towed or free) or relayed by wire or other means to the surface ship or shore station.

Guidance problems for free underwater vehicles are a major headache, but it is clear that with this solved it would be possible by this method of survey to obtain measurements of magnetism, gravity, current speeds and direction, salinity and bottom topography, and to take bottom samples and to make seismic measurements into the bottom itself.

Towed or free remote-controlled vehicles have the advantage over submarines and bathyscapes of excluding the need for accommodation, etc., for personnel.

If it is necessary and useful to take photographs of the bottom, this could be done either by causing vehicles to follow the topography of the bottom, thus giving photographs at the same scale or by surveying at a constant depth, providing the water is sufficiently clear and the bottom sufficiently level. The photographic method is handicapped by the turbidity of the water, which allows, in general, photography from a range of 90 ft. maximum, more usually 30 ft. or less.

As far as Scotland is concerned, the surveying and exploration of the deeps is perhaps a development from the surveying and exploration of coastal waters, since one would logically think of developing near-shore waters first. There is some value, however, in thinking of the immense volume of unconsolidated material in the deeps—oozes, etc., which might be gathered for man's use. To map them, undersea techniques are necessary.

NEAR-SHORE AND COASTAL

Here we are dealing with continental shelf areas up to depths of say one hundred fathoms.

Investigations of the continental shelves include undersea oil and mineral deposits, including coal; civil engineering works; location of wrecks and obstructions; placing undersea cables and pipe-lines; location of fishing grounds and fish food and undersea farming.

Not long ago, the area covered by continental shelves was calculated showing its immense area. The paper concerned suggested the mineral resources of the shelves are worth developing.

Oil and Mineral Deposits. One can think immediately of beach sands and oil accumulations and of extending mineral deposits already known on shore.

The beach sands of Africa and India recovered for titanium and iron content; the National Coal Board's work off-shore in Scotland for coal; the Wabana Iron Ore in Newfoundland—all come to mind. Mineral exploration is usually a commercial undertaking in the Western world, so the deposits must be economic (in the commercial sense) to exploit. Governments concerned with the rapid depletion of our mineral resources, however, could well assist in the problem by providing comprehensive surveys of the mineral resources of the continental shelves—a charting of our near-shore undersea mineral resources to interest commerce in exploitation.

Methods of survey for minerals including drilling, undersea geophysics (e.g. magnetic, gravity and seismic), undersea cartography (e.g. depth surveys and bottom topography, bottom photography), current surveys and weather surveys. Most of them, if not all, can be carried out by surface vessels using surface and underwater towed apparatus.

The equipment can be towed by ships following pre-set grids of lines positioned by radio methods such as Decca, Shoran (and variants of them), with data recording on paper charts, punched cards or magnetic tape, and with the final treatment of the data on shore or ship by computer or graphical methods.

The Economist published a paper (about two years ago) on Continental Shelf Mining. One scheme used watertight bubbles on the sea floor with living and working accommodation incorporated. Oil companies are developing offshore drilling methods, and one company is mining sulphur in the Gulf of Mexico. The National Coal Board is, of course, drilling off Scotland. Thus the study of continental shelf areas for mining is going on and continental shelf mining is commercially interesting. Man will probe further in his quest of minerals and survey methods offshore will, therefore, develop.

The first phase, of course, in mineral surveying is the reconnaissance survey. This can be easily and quickly done using aircraft (generally aeroplanes although helicopters and powered balloons might be applicable).

Aircraft can carry magnetometers and gravitimeters and be positioned accurately enough by Decca or the Doppler Navigator system. Such surveys consist of recording the physical quantity required along pre-set flight paths spaced in accordance with the result required, with sufficient cross-traverses to relate profiles one to another and to the datum, taking into account instrumental and periodic drifts of the physical quantity measured.

It is important to remember weather as a major factor in surveying and exploitation of resources offshore. For instance, oil companies have found weather forecasting most important. Expensive offshore drilling equipment can be lost in bad weather, particularly just previous to the drilling structure being firmly seated on the bottom. Yet again, the speed and the economy of surveying can be greatly affected by weather.

Undersea Farming, Fishing Grounds and Fish Food. There has been increased interest in food from the sea. A paper (by Sir Alister Hardy, F.R.S.) in a recent issue of the *New Scientist* discussing the need to farm undersea to provide food for our increasing population (also incidentally suggesting man must become amphibious in order to survive) is worth reading.

Surveys of aquatic vegetation are under way, or conceived, in many parts of the world. In these studies, bottom conditions are mapped; so far by human agency or sporadic photography. It would seem that systematic surveying of this type is necessary, using, for instance, recording depth measures and photography with sampling by grab or humans. Instead of photography we may think of television.

It seems clear that a scientific study of fish grounds and areas of fish food is much needed. It is conceivable that disputes over coastal waters and fishing rights would be a matter of history were comprehensive mapping of fish population and ecology a routine world study. From this leads the thought that perhaps sellable fish could be induced to breed and live in convenient selected areas and then husbanded, as cattle are on land and trout and salmon are in rivers.

Civil Engineering Works. Man needs coastal installations of all sorts. Here we are concerned with detailed surveys of small areas. The civil engineer needs to know depth of water, tidal variations, current speed and direction, bottom conditions and depth to solid rock.

The recent exercise on the Channel Tunnel, under the guidance of consultants from Imperial College, London University, involved surveying of various sorts. More particularly, the investigators were concerned with bedrock, its strength and permeability (in the widest sense). Much drilling was done and much offshore seismic work.

The drilling was followed by core analysis (strength, permeability, density, etc.) and a fascinating, beautifully executed, palaeontological study from which geological structure was worked out.

The seismic method used was that popularly known as "Sparker", a single geophone system using an electric spark or gas exploder. The geophone is towed behind a boat which has the recording and explosive system installed. The ship was positioned on this survey by the Decca Navigator System.

These Sparker surveys show bottom topography and underlying geology to depths of up to a few hundred feet. Thus the engineer gets water depth and sub-bottom information invaluable for siting foundations of breakwaters, sea walls, harbour installations and the like and information for clearing channels and hazards to shipping. As is well known, "sonic" methods of depth sounding are also used in these investigations. Much interesting competitive effort is going on to develop the seismic and sonic methods for engineering application undersea.

In connection with clearing channels for shipping, it is interesting to note the recent use of radioactive markers in tracing the movement of muds, etc., in waterways. A survey of the bottom of the canal, channel, estuary or river concerned is first made using sled-borne scintillation counters. This establishes the "normal" background radioactivity pattern for the area (a similar practice to that used for environmental surveys of reactor sites mentioned earlier in this paper). Radioactive material is then introduced into the mud. Periodic bottom sled-borne radioactivity surveys are then made giving the required information on the movement of mud.

In a recent exercise in the Thames Estuary it was proved by these means that routine dredging operations carried on for many many years are, in fact, useless since mud deposited in "a deep" off the coast is naturally and automatically transported back to the dredging area by currents in a matter of months only. The choice of a better dumping area should not be difficult.

Location of Wrecks and Obstructions. Wrecks may form obstructions to shipping and, therefore, need location prior to clearance, they may also be valuable to recover for themselves or their cargo.

The most topical wreck in Scotland at the moment is the Spanish galleon in Tobermory Bay in which the Duke of Argyll is much interested.

A review of his methods to date is interesting since they are concerned with locating gold in or near the wreck of a wooden ship. No geophysical method can directly detect wood or gold under the sea. Indirect methods had to be used.

The earliest attempts involved divers digging around the supposed position of the wreck in the belief that the bullion would have remained in, or very close to, the wreck. This hypothesis was supported by the recovery of fairly heavy cannon balls made of iron and stone.

Some little while later, Kelvin and Hughes carried out echo-sounding surveys in an attempt to disclose irregularities on or near the sea bottom which might be accumulations of material from the galleon.

Later still an underwater magnetometer survey was worked out but not implemented. This called for the traversing of a very sensitive fluxgate magnetometer on a sled towed by a slowly moving vessel. The spacing of the traverses was decided from a study of the magnetic effect of one cannon ball recovered from the area and the possibility that more than one cannon ball would be found cemented together in pyramidal form, by rust.

The latest attack on the problem is to be made using "a submarine detecting device", the details of which have not been made public.

The detection and location of bullion from a Spanish galleon is not a common requirement, but it will be interesting to note if the Duke of Argyll is successful since his methods may have wider applications in the location and removal of undersea obstructions. In this connection mention should, of course, be made of the use of television as an undersea survey technique in the location of wrecks.

A more common requirement is the locating of iron ships for salvage of itself or cargo. This has been successfully done by magnetic methods, either ship or airborne.

For instance, an iron ship of 8,500 tons carrying a non-magnetic cargo wrecked off Dar-es-Salaam gave a total magnetic field anomaly (peak to peak) of 45 gammas at a height of 500 ft. above the ship. Again a ship of 1,800 tons carrying 200 tons of steel wrecked off Stockholm gave an anomaly of 20 gammas at 500 ft. above the ship.

A common means of positioning traverses run by ship or aircraft in such searches is Decca, since Decca coverage is widespread in coastal waters and salvage economics dictate the wreck be in relatively shallow water, that is, generally, in coastal waters.

Placing Undersea Cables and Pipe-lines. Undersea cables have long been a feature of long-distance telephone systems.

Cable-laying problems and surveys perhaps really fall under the category of "deep sea" since it is the deep-sea troughs and ridges which present the major problems and thus should be charted. Nevertheless, coastal problems exist for cable layers and pipe-lines and are generally laid in shallower waters although the projected pipe-lines connecting North Africa to Europe will pass through some deep areas.

Those laying pipe-lines and cables near shore have to decide whether to lay them on the bottom or suspend them from the surface. In both cases studies of tidal and current movement are necessary. In the former case, the nature of the bottom, its firmness and whether it is being scoured away or built up are important. As mentioned under "mineral deposits", the weather is a most important factor.

Water Resources on Land—Surface and Underground

Surface Water. In Scotland, perhaps the most significant use of surface water industrially in recent years has been its impounding and use for hydro-electricity and reservoirs for urban purposes. Whilst this reduces the resources for tourism and the naturalist, we can assume it brings advantages for the common good.

It is worth dwelling on some aspects of surveying connected with dam and reservoir engineering. The engineer needs to know three things, namely, the topography, the geology and the erosion pattern.

He needs maps in plan and elevation. These have been obtained quickly and accurately by aerial methods abroad. It is assumed the reader is familiar with the basic principle of air photography and the fact that stereoscopic viewing of adjacent air photographs is used to obtain plan and height information. It is perhaps not so widely known that some ground information is needed to produce the more accurate topographic maps, needed for reservoir and dam studies, by aerial means. Simpler forms of topographic maps are at scales of 1:1,000 to 1:10,000 with contours at 5-ft. to 20-ft. intervals, accurate to half the contour interval.

In order to relate together the evidence from photographs to form accurate maps, some network of known height and position is necessary. This is done in a variety of ways.

Height information can be obtained by spirit levelling theodolite or barometrically or electronically (by the Airborne Profile Recorder (APR)).

Scale and position information can be obtained by triangulation or traverse with angles measured by theodolite, and distances either by chaining or, nowadays, electronically by tellurometer or geodimeter.

On a particular dam project in Nigeria recently, the APR was used to give height control to a mean square accuracy of 4 ft. and the tellurometer to give distance to an accuracy of 1 in 50,000. With the APR method we measure depths below an aircraft whose height above sea-level is accurately known instead of measuring heights above sea-level as is done in traditional methods. We work down, not up. Owing to the coverage of topographic mapping already existing in Scotland, and the relatively small areal extent of any reservoir, the use of the APR may not be applicable.

To illustrate survey methods giving erosion and geological information as part of dam and reservoir studies, examples in the Sudan and Pakistan have been chosen.

The study of the Jabel Marra area—an area of mountains of volcanic origin in West Sudan—was designed to answer the problems, simply stated as follows:

1. How much water is available?
2. When and where does it fall?
3. How can it be impounded?
4. How can it be utilised?

The survey involved a team of geologists, ecologist, foresters and hydrologist in a three-phased programme.

Phase one consisted of obtaining air photocover and the stereo study of it together with the preparation of mosaics; phase two was a field season using helicopters for rapid transport of personnel; and phase three was the final analysis and mapping of the data obtained with recommendations for future work.

Because of the short field season and the high cost of helicopter operations, the field planning was very thorough. Hence the pre-field photo-interpretation covered not only natural features such as topography, geology, tree and vegetation cover and soil type, but also—and this applies to all good pre-field photo-interpretations whatever the object of the survey—a study of the best type and use of transport media. Thus camp sites, helicopter landing and pick-up points were sited so that ground and air traverses over important sections and ground studies of selected areas (e.g. dam sites) could be made with the best and most economical use of men and machines.

The catchment area of the proposed reservoir for the Mangla Dam in the northern part of West Pakistan is being very heavily eroded. This will silt up the reservoir in tens of years and ruin the surrounding area for agriculture. A survey, now in the report stage, was made to study this problem, produce land-capability maps and recommend preventative measures. The method of survey consisted of obtaining air photocover for interpretative study. Field work using the air photography was undertaken by a plant ecologist and an engineering geologist.

It has been observed that erosion in this area is partly determined by geology, with lithology and attitude of the sediments intensifying the damage caused by faulty land-use erosion. From the maps the areas of most active erosion can be located and attention directed to preventative measures in those areas as a first priority. Preventative measures include restoring vegetal cover, reducing the intensity of land use and by installing the usual checks to run off such as check dams, terracing, etc.

The Kacchi Plains at Sibi and east of the Baluchistan Plateau have agricultural potentialities if sufficient irrigation water can be impounded and the torrent floods which cause widespread damage can be controlled. A joint engineering soils and agricultural investigation is being undertaken to locate suitable dam sites, design dams, and map the soils of some one million acres of the area for the purpose of delineating the land blocks most suitable for irrigation development. The geological studies include a preliminary photo-interpretation of the existing photography to select potential dam sites followed by field geological investigations with drilling and by the use of the MD1 seismograph.

Apart from the regional use of geology in reservoir studies as shown particularly in the case of the Mangla Dam investigation, specialised geological studies are now commonly undertaken in the choice and design of dams, and indeed other civil engineering studies. These are detailed studies using drill-hole cores and shallow geophysical methods (e.g. seismic and resistivity) as well as detailed geological mapping.

The writer is reminded of an interesting use of photography here. The scene is a proposed dam site in Iraq. The country rock is fissured limestone. The problem is to render the abutments of the dam watertight. The method proposed was grouting by cement. A series of overlapping horizontal photographs were taken along the faces of the abutments. A stereoscopic study of the photographs enabled the mapping of fissures, etc., the estimation of volumes of cement and the design of the drilling pattern to be completed quickly and accurately.

Underground Water. Surveys for underground water usually demand a co-ordinated use of both geological, drilling and geophysical methods. There is, generally, no one geophysical method which is always applicable; the appropriate methods being chosen by what is known of the geology of the area. Hence, in one particular area, the geological structure may be all important and the seismic method may prove applicable. In another area, lithology may be the key and the resistivity or the electromagnetic method might be applicable.

Thought is now being given to the development of a high-frequency electromagnetic system for underground water location.

To show the co-ordinated use of a number of specialised techniques an interesting survey in Pakistan is used as an example.

A ground water and general hydrological investigation in the Porali Basin area of Pakistan is being carried out in conjunction with a soils, agriculture and pasture resources study in order to determine the feasibility of establishing irrigation in this arid part of the country, and to decide what steps should be taken to obtain the best use of and to conserve the grazing resources of the region. The ground water study will be made with the help of geophysical equipment while the soils investigation will be in accordance with the usual technique of field sampling at a prescribed density and using aerial photography to assist in plotting the soil group boundaries.

LAND MASSES

Here a division is made into topographic, vegetation and geological surveys.

Topography

Traditional methods of topographic survey are well known. The writer will, therefore, concentrate on air survey methods and applications.

The principles in the use of aerial photography are presumed to be well known and the fact that in producing topographic maps a combination of ground information and air photography is generally used.

Although all topography survey problems do not as yet warrant the use of air photography, the range of mapping by air photographs is constantly being extended since, more and more, the methods of air survey are being found to be economically, and technically, sensible.

For regional surveys in unmapped countries the advantages of air photographic survey are clear. The vast areas covered by planimetric plots at 1:50,000 in Africa produced by Overseas Geological Surveys, London; Institute Geographique National, Paris; and the Survey Departments of the various territories themselves in Africa and Asia are proof of this. The continual demand for photographic mosaics by mining concerns in regional and detailed exploration is again proof of the usefulness of these methods of producing "first" maps of unknown areas.

It is not perhaps so widely known that maps from air photographs to scales of, for instance, 1:480 (40 ft. to 1 in.) can be produced to ground accuracy greater than 6 in. An example is the mapping for British Railways. The flying height here was 1,500 ft. above ground and the camera had a 6-in. focal length giving a photographic scale of 1:3,000. Premarking (prior to photography) of important railway features enabled the mapping to be done quickly without the delays encountered on such works by traditional methods due to the movement of rolling stock on busy lines.

Mention was made earlier to the use of air photographic techniques in detailed topographic mapping for dam and reservoir investigations. The example sited used three new electronic aids, namely the Doppler Navigator, the Airborne Profile Recorder (APR) and the Tellurometer. The Doppler Navigator was used for navigating the photographic and APR aircraft along pre-set lines and also to give accurate drifts for pressure gradient corrections, using Henry's formula, to give the accurate measurement of heights by the APR.

The science of photogrammetry has developed a great deal since 1946. It is now possible to compute volumes for "cut" and "full" on road or railway alignment surveys using HISPEC, a photographic technique which computes volumes from profile information obtained by photogrammetric measurements based on a skeleton framework of ground control points. The method can also be used to compute volumes of stockpiles or waste tips. Some mines abroad run a yearly, or more frequent, inventory by this means. They find, for instance, that loss due to "erosion" by humans is a factor to account for in, for example, coal stockpiles. Thus amounts measured at the time of stockpiling can be materially in error after say six months or a year.

Air photographic methods of survey depend on obtaining the air photographs themselves. In difficult weather areas such as Scotland this may have caused such methods to have been abandoned in the past. However, advances in the manufacture of film (stability of material, resolving power, speed and spectral sensitivity) and lens design mean that photography obtained by modern cameras and films (or plates) can now be used for an increasing range of purposes and scales of mapping. This means, of course, that modern photography once taken over a particular area will cover more applications than it would have in the past. Hence, were it possible to co-ordinate topographic and various resources mapping projects where air photography would be applicable over say relatively large areas of Scotland, one series of photographs could suffice. Thus the bogey of the time and cost necessary to obtain the essential air photographs would be laid. Instead of aircraft being positioned to obtain cover of isolated small areas, as now is the case, a photography unit could be positioned for say a year to cover all requirements far more cheaply and satisfactorily.

Admitting that the weather problem is far different, there are lessons to be learnt by the way the French, through the Institute Geographique National, are covering vast areas of North Africa with photography at one or two scales. These photographs are used by topographers, geologists, soil scientists, ecologists, agriculturalists, etc., either individually, through French Government Bureaus, through Aid Agencies or through Contractors to survey areas for development. The initial cost of obtaining air photographs being, in effect, shared by many development projects. This sort of co-ordinated initial air surveying could well apply in Scotland.

VEGETATION

Under this broad heading come studies of all land growing vegetation, the soils that support them and the ecological conditions affecting their growth.

An early use of aerial photography was forest inventories. It was found possible in Canada and latterly in Northern Iraq to classify the tree species in forests, map their extent and estimate cordage by photographic interpretation based on sampling on the ground.

Trials with infra-red film have shown its value in such studies.

Since those earlier days, land use studies of large areas warrant the use of air photographs providing very quickly, for instance, inventories of present land use for future planning purposes.

Again, soil surveys of regional type use air photography. Sampling at wide intervals with subsequent or concurrent photographic interpretation provide maps of soil types or their capability. Such a survey in Iraq, in conjunction with drainage studies, produced answers to the size of small-holding a displaced family could farm to obtain a reasonable living together with advice on crop type and rotation methods. Yet again, for instance, the Nyasaland Government wished to know if the Elephant Marsh, if drained, would yield useful arable land. Air photographic interpretation based on bottom samples taken on cut lines under water by special augers showed that a greater portion of the bottom soil was first grade. Infra-red photography was used with success here also.

Whilst the surveys mentioned were of great areal extent, it is thought there may be areas in Scotland which would benefit by surveys of this kind. There may be relatively large areas of land which, when suitably studied, could yield arable or grazing land of good quality after appropriate remedial measures have been taken. The principles of sampling and analysis using air photographs are generally the same as those used by more traditional methods covering small areas, but the organisation of carrying out the survey expeditiously and the techniques developed in the process of carrying them out could well apply to studies of smaller areal extent in Scotland.

It is particularly appropriate to mention in this general context that the problem of the proper use of marginal lands is one of very great moment for Scotland, where it has been estimated that about eighteen million acres fall into this category. The importance of rehabilitating these areas, for the benefit of the local inhabitants and for the national interest, has been stressed in the report of a Natural Resources (Technical) Committee under the Chairmanship of Sir Solly Zuckerman issued in January 1957. It comments unfavourably on the insufficient use and abandonment of much of upland Britain due largely to progressive soil deterioration, and notes especially that practically no attention has been paid to the importance of the proper vegetation management of catchment areas to conserve water supply and prevent flooding.

Improved land use in Scotland will result from afforestation, the improvement of improvable grazing land (estimated at some 750,000 acres) and the better management of the remainder by the adjustment of numbers of stock and deer and better cycles of moor burning so that soil deterioration and erosion are reduced. It is realised that the rate of advance is mainly controlled by local socio-economic factors and by the problem of reconciling the rival claims of forestry and agriculture to marginal hill lands.

Much of Scotland has been surveyed by both the Forestry Commission and the Department of Agriculture for their own purposes; but, in spite of some combined work carried out by both bodies for joint planning, further research and survey are required to determine how far the two interests overlap.

It is suggested that surveys should be made of certain specified areas (which should preferably be catchments) to supply the evidence on which integrated plans for forestry, improved agriculture and wild life management could be prepared.

The objective of such surveys would be to map existing soils and vegetation, including bracken and the different types of heather moor, thus enabling plans to be made for such improvements in land use as the adjustment of stocking of sheep, cattle or deer to the capacity of the land; the need for drainage and the determination of the correct procedures for burning particular moors. They would also draw attention to the need for catchment control and to the extent of recession of earlier agriculture. These surveys would be most useful if they were to be carried out in catchments where stream gauges have already been installed.

Once suitable techniques are established it should prove possible to extend mapping by photo-interpretation to other similar catchments with much reduced field work and consequent lower cost.

This work will be facilitated by the research carried out by the Nature Conservancy, especially the vegetation survey begun in 1953.

Geology

Under this broad heading, surveys using geophysics and geochemistry are included.

For convenience the subject is divided into airborne and ground-borne methods. In general, geological studies certainly of large areas, and very often of small areas, use both airborne and ground-borne techniques as appropriate to the problem nowadays, as will be shown by examples cited here.

Airborne Methods. There are two main types of airborne survey in geological studies, whether they be mineral prospecting, hydrological, engineering or regional in type. The one is photographic, the other geophysical.

Air Photographic. The use of air photography in geological studies is not new in concept. Each year, however, brings some new application.

Air photographs were first used by geologists as an aid, but not an important one, in field mapping. Occasionally, structures or rock masses were seen in photographs and field time saved thereby. The proper use of air photographs as a necessary part in field studies began when governments, mining and oil concerns were faced with vast areas to map. Hence early users of air photographs were oil companies, who found that broad structural patterns in sedimentary areas are reflected in the topography, including the drainage system, and in the vegetation pattern. This is perhaps well shown in desert areas (where dune sand is not present), but perhaps it is not so well known that photography of thick forest areas can reveal structure and lithology also.

The attitude of geologists has changed over the years. Instead of rejecting air photography after a cursory glance because of quality, scale or apparent unsuitability to the problem and area in question, the geologist now strives to analyse and interpret air photography however poor a tool it may at first seem, not rejecting it until he is quite sure he has gained all he can from it.

In general, of course, air photographic interpretation and field studies should be combined. This is best achieved if the interpreter is also the field man. In all but a very few cases the geological studies using air photography with which the writer has been associated have involved the geologists concerned in three stages of work. Firstly, the assembly of known data on the area and the study of air photographs is carried out. Secondly, field work based on the first stage follows. It is, of course, an important point here that in the course of the preliminary pre-field study traverses have been planned to cover important key sections and problem areas in such a way as to make economical use of the geologists field time. Thirdly, collation of field and photographic evidence, laboratory studies, final mapping and reporting takes place.

Three major points of advantage in the methods are shown to be:

(1) the value of team work;
(2) the advantage of relatively short field seasons of concentrated effort supported by the assistance obtainable from discussion with co-workers and others who have been in the area or had similar geological problems facing them;
(3) the ability to produce maps consistent in quality and concept over large areas.

It is this last point which most distinguishes work by this method from that produced by traditional one-man work. The area is considered as a whole all the way through, not as a series of maps which need co-ordination prior to final presentation.

On the whole, these studies have been concerned with large areas with mapping at say a scale of 1:50,000 or smaller.

In recent years, however, air photographic interpretation has also been applied to detailed geological problems. Work in Nigeria in the location of pegmatites is an example. This small area was difficult to traverse, so much so that airborne radioactivity surveys by helicopter were proposed as an indirect method of locating the pegmatites. As a first phase of the work, photographic interpretation was carried out, the pre-field laboratory study being augmented by field traversing (not in this case by the same geologist) to very good effect. Sufficient information was obtained to enable the airborne survey to be cancelled, with great saving in cost.

Another example was a study in Nigeria for the location of buried channels which might be tin-bearing. This study comprised photographic interpretation only. It was successful in locating a number of buried channels (and incidentally revealed some other interesting geomorphological features), thus enabling the concentration of prospecting effort in the most likely places.

Nearer at home, detailed work of this type in England, Wales and Scotland had proved useful to mining companies, particularly in the location of structural patterns (e.g. faults, dykes) which controlled or influenced mineral concentrations.

Airborne Geophysics. Three geophysical methods have been successfully adapted for traversing in aircraft (fixed-wing or helicopter) namely, the magnetic, the electromagnetic and the radiometric. For convenience, instrumentation will be considered first, followed by methods and applications.

The most common magnetometers developed for airborne use are those which measure the total field either by a self-orienting fluxgate system, or, more recently, those using the principles of proton precession or electron deflection. The fluxgate and electron deflection magnetometers measure continuously and give a continuous recorded profile of the variation of total field along the flight path traversed. They do not measure absolute field, but this is no real disadvantage in practice. Of the two types, the fluxgate is more precise, giving accuracies of relative measurement of $\pm\frac{1}{2}$ per cent. with a maximum error of ± 3 gammas. Maps using fluxgate magnetometers with contour intervals as close as $2\frac{1}{2}$ gammas have been produced for special applications although the usual contour interval is 10 gammas.

The proton precession magnetometer measures absolute field, but discontinuously. The measurement of absolute field may well have advantages from an academic point of view, but the discontinuity of the readings has some practical disadvantages.

Another type of airborne magnetometer measures the vertical component only. The impossibility of maintaining its measuring fluxgate sufficiently vertical at all times, however, leads to a poorer accuracy than the total force instruments already mentioned; accuracies of 25 gammas to 50 gammas being all that is possible.

A very recent development is the so-called Rhubidium Vapour magnetometer which measures field gradient variations. The measuring of gradients is said to make surveying during periods of high rates of diurnal variation (e.g. magnetic storms) possible, such conditions precluding accurate surveying by total field measuring equipment.

Fluxgate magnetometers are fairly heavy (200 lb. including recorders) and need aircraft of Anson size (e.g. 8,000 lb. all-up weight) or larger to carry them effectively. Proton precession magnetometers can be made much smaller in size and weight although the present production survey versions (with their recording apparatus) weigh as much as fluxgate instruments.

It is true to say that only the fluxgate and proton precession types of instrument can be classed as survey instruments, i.e. stable enough to produce results with sufficient accuracy to justify contouring of the results obtained.

The electron deflection and vertical component magnetometers are classed as detectors—"anomaly finders". They are not stable enough to allow for presentation of their recordings in contour form. The Rhubidium vapour equipment is the most accurate of all those mentioned, but is really only in the development stage as yet.

Electromagnetometers, except in one case, the AFMAG system, cause an artificially generated and transmitted electric field to pass through the ground and record the variations in ground conductivity by measuring the differences between the transmitted field and the resultant field received on a coil on or in the aircraft.

Thus these systems generally employ aircraft (fixed wing or helicopter) fitted with both transmitting and receiving coils although one uses a transmitter coil lying on the ground, the receiving coil being in the aircraft.

The transmitter or receiver coils may be vertical (e.g. Rio Tinto/Mullard and Newmont), horizontal (Ronka) or rotary (e.g. ABEM) and the component measured may be out-of-phase (Ronka) or both in-phase and out-of-phase (Rio Tinto, ABEM and Newmont). The horizontal out-of-phase type (Ronka) which also uses two frequencies simultaneously, has had great success in finding near surface sulphide ores in Canada; the rotary field (ABEM) system has produced useful results in Scandinavia and West Africa; and the vertical (in-phase and out-of-phase) systems have produced useful results in Canada, East Africa and Cyprus. The horizontal (out-of-phase) system was used in Cornwall and Devon by the United Kingdom Geological Survey and Museum.

The AFMAG system, a relative newcomer, uses fields naturally generated by electrical storms rather than artificial fields generated in coils attached to the aircraft (or on the ground).

No true comparison can be made of the systems as yet as, until recently, no controlled tests have been made. Recently, however, the Director of Overseas Geological Surveys (Tolworth) has caused two areas in East Africa to be flown by the Rio Tinto/Mullard, the ABEM and the AFMAG systems in an attempt to assess their relative merits in African conditions. The result will be interesting, but will apply only to a limited set of geological conditions.

Radiometric. Earlier radiometric instruments employed Geiger-Müller tubes, but for some time now scintillation counters using sodium iodide crystals or plastic phosphors have been the generally accepted instruments for aerial survey use.

The volume and areal extent of the phosphor are important no less than the use of the correct sampling or integration time in the ratemeter. Hence the development, and this equipment has been to larger crystal areas as well as to more stable ratemeters; culminating in the very sensitive three detector instruments developed by the Atomic Energy Research Establishment, Harwell, Berkshire, now generally accepted as the most useful airborne detectors available.

It has been a contention for some time that it should be possible to discriminate between quanta emitted by uranium oxide, thorium oxide and radioactive potassium.

Equipments capable of some discrimination in energy levels have thus been developed. Problems in circuit stability have been encountered and it is unfortunate that interest in uranium prospecting has waned to the extent that development in this direction has virtually ceased.

The distance between the detector and the emitting source has, of course, a great effect on the quantity of particles hitting the detector, the bulk of radioactive particles having small energies and thus not travelling far from their source. It is, therefore, interesting to note that the development of equipment capable of compensating for the varying height of the detector above the source (assumed to be at ground-level) is about to commence in Great Britain, by the same team who perfected a system in which two detectors were used, one in the aircraft and one on a cable 250 ft. below the aircraft.

Type of airborne magnetometers, electromagnetometers and scintillation counters have been mentioned in some detail since, to date, these are the only airborne geophysical instruments of proven use. It is worth mentioning, however, that development of airborne gravity meters is beginning with some high hopes that the formidable instrumentation problems can be solved.

Survey procedures for all the above instruments are basically the same. Aircraft fitted with one or more equipments are flown generally on parallel lines at a spacing and height applicable to the object of the survey.

Thus, commonly, the magnetometer, electromagnetometer and scintillation counter are flown on spacings of one mile down to one-eighth of a mile and heights of 300 ft. to 1,000 ft. above ground where the object of the survey is regional geological mapping or ore prospecting. Where the object of the survey is depth to crystalline basement determination (as in oil prospecting using the magnetometer), spacings from say 30 miles down to 2 kilometres at heights of say 2,000 ft. above mean ground-level may be used. In this latter case, constant altitude above sea-level is maintained, where as in the former case a constant height above ground-level is maintained.

In order to keep a check on, and record, the height of the aircraft, recording radar altimeters are used, and in order to plot the actual track of the aircraft, 35 mm. vertical photography, or radio location systems (e.g. Gee H, Shoran, Loran, Decca and now Doppler) are used. Of all these radio systems, the Doppler is proving the most useful since the equipment is fully contained in the aircraft, no ground stations being necessary.

The information obtained on each traverse is related to a common datum by flying a series of cross-traverses (in the magnetic and sometimes in the electromagnetic method) or re-occupying a specially chosen line or point at frequent intervals (in the radiometric and magnetic methods). Diurnal and instruments drifts are removed and the data transformed by graphical means (or by computer) to values which can be contoured (in the magnetic and sometimes in the radiometric and electromagnetic methods) or presented as diagrammatic profiles (in the electromagnetic and radiometric methods).

By far the most common and useful form of presentation of magnetic results is by contours, whereas the most common and useful form of presentation of radiometric results is by diagrammatic profiles. Although the magnetic results stand by themselves since we are measuring and mapping a natural ambient field, some analysis of the electromagnetic and radiometric records is necessary before a satisfactory presentation is possible. In the radiometric method this treatment consists of choosing background values and amplitude intervals appropriate to the results obtained and the purpose of the survey and applying generalised corrections for height variations of aircraft above ground. In the electromagnetic method, it is usual first to derive empirical relationships between anomalies and their causes either by studying the results of model experiments or, preferably, by flying over known geological conditions. These relationships are then applied to the area of survey.

It is generally true to say that airborne geophysical methods apply to surveys of relatively large areas. National coverage by airborne magnetic and radiometric surveys is now routine in Canada and the United States of America and to a certain extent in Australia, whilst the United Kingdom's Geological Survey and Museum is gradually extending such surveys to cover the whole of the British Isles. Such regional coverage is to be welcomed and urged since it is now generally accepted that such data, on a regional scale, interpreted on the basis of existing geological information gives regional geological information not obtainable by any other means.

It has become increasingly obvious to the writer, as a result of experience of such surveys in other lands, that geology generally, and mineral development in particular, has and would be immensely benefited by a procedure whereby geological provinces are first treated as a whole followed then and only then by more detailed studies of logically selected areas.

Government geological survey departments and mining organisations have generally tackled the problem the other way round. That is they have spent much time and effort on detailed work in small areas gradually and very slowly building up the whole regional picture. This is not a criticism of past work. One has only to study the work of the old Geological Survey of India (when under British Rule) to realise that superb work over vast areas was done (and, no doubt, still is by other national survey departments) using traditional ground methods on a sheet by sheet basis.

The writer is now advocating that, with the availability of proven airborne regional geological tools, very serious consideration should be given to a procedure when large units of area are subjected to aerogeophysical and geological surveying using air methods to produce a framework of geological knowledge into which to fit detailed work. Even though the Geological Survey of Scotland is well advanced, there is great merit in such a procedure since it would provide a regional appreciation of the geology of Scotland as a whole, not only on the surface, but underground also, providing explanations for many of the puzzling phenomena which are having to be tackled individually. It is thus very encouraging to note that the Geological Survey has a programme for complete aeromagnetic coverage of Scotland within the next few years.

Ground-borne Methods (*geological*, *geochemical*, *geophysical*). It has already been mentioned that in many types of geological surveys, from regional and small scale to detailed and large scale, air photographic interpretation techniques have been used successfully principally to work out the general structures and the major rock types and also to plan economic field traversing. Even in very detailed studies, air photographs themselves can act simply as a base map to very good purpose, saving the effort of producing a map by normal survey methods and providing far more detail for location than is normally shown on planimetric maps.

Geological survey techniques are, of course, many and vary with the problem.

To illustrate the aspects of geological survey work particularly relevant to this discussion, we will consider briefly the geological work undertaken by mining companies from the point when a decision to study a particular area is taken to the exploitation of an ore body itself.

The subject is restricted to near-surface metallic ores, sedimentary ores such as coal being excluded.

Most prospecting studies involve geologists from the start nowadays, the first stage being a reconnaissance of the area and a study of any previous work done in the area. The type(s) of investigation to be undertaken is then decided from the geological and topographic evidence available. Thus the first stage may well be a photogeological study with its attendant reconnaissance field work and the preparation photo mosaics. This may be followed by, or run concurrently with, an airborne geophysical survey of the types mentioned earlier. The aim is, of course, to narrow down the target areas for concentrated prospecting work which may be geological (mapping, drilling, pitting, trenching), geochemical or geophysical in type.

The exploration company may well start with a series of pilot surveys using various combinations of methods over, say, known ore occurrences in order to decide the best combination of techniques to use. This presupposes time and money is available to do the pilot work and adequately study the results. More often than not, however, there is great pressure to get on and such logical preliminary work is left out. It is true to say that when metal prices are low, that is the proper time to do exploration. Firstly, because time and personnel are then available, and secondly, so that the mining company concerned has ore reserves available for exploitation when metal prices are right. This sounds good sense, of course, but until better methods of predicting metal consumption and price are available, only the very large mining corporations can afford to take such a long-term view, and most of them do not, in fact, do so.

Let us now assume mineralised areas have been outlined by the regional prospecting methods already mentioned. The next stage is to investigate these areas in detail. If the first indication of say iron-ore was given by the aerial magnetometer, the next stage would be detailed ground magnetic and perhaps gravity surveys over the anomalous areas interpreted as being most likely to contain ore. This could well be followed by drilling.

Yet again, in areas of sulphide mineralisation, target areas might have been found by airborne electromagnetic plus photo and field geology, in which case it would be logical to follow up this preliminary work with ground electromagnetic or possibly self-potential or geochemistry.

There are a variety of electromagnetic and electrical geophysical equipments available. Those electromagnetic equipments designed for fast traversing and shallow penetration are, for instance, the ABEM Electromagnetic Gun and the Ronka Geophysical Mark III and IV, whereas for greater penetration equipments such as the ABEM Turam are used.

Rates of traversing of the order of 1 mile to 2 miles per day per equipment are common on spacings of say 50 ft. or 100 ft. It is interesting to compare this rate of traversing (say 6 to 12 miles per week) with that of airborne electromagnetic traversing namely 1,000 to 3,000 line miles per week, since it illustrates the logic of flying relatively large areas to limit the extent of the slow ground methods of prospecting.

Geochemical prospecting methods are widely used now. More specifically they are of value in exploration for sulphide ores, e.g. copper, lead, zinc, but the range of metals is always being extended. Geochemical prospecting methods detect dispersion patterns of metals in soils, vegetation and stream sediments. It is usually necessary to perform an orientation survey in an area before the plan for geochemical sampling can go forward. This is because so many factors affect the design of the survey, e.g. soil or vegetation cover, stream patterns, topography, superficial cover (e.g. boulder clay), type of ore expected and its condition (e.g. depth of weathering and oxidisation).

In practice, geochemical prospecting surveys involve the collection of samples from specific points on a grid or along streams at previously defined intervals and under certain specified conditions, e.g. at certain levels in the soil profile or at points in streams where fresh sediment exists uncontaminated by spoil from previous workings or vegetable material. These samples are properly and systematically bagged and labelled and transported to a central or local laboratory when delicate colorimetric or spectrographic determinations are made.

Let us now assume that one or more interesting areas have been found sufficiently precisely for drilling, pitting, etc., to take place. Geological control of these operations is usual to make sure adequate information is obtained from drill core samples and pits. Detailed mapping of pits and trenches may be involved. An example of this is the extremely detailed mapping of pit and trench sides carried out by the Junta de Energia Nuclear personnel in the Urgeirica area of Portugal following airborne and ground-borne scintillation counter-traversing which localised the areas of interest in the first place.

From the foregoing work together with attendant mineral and assay laboratory work estimates of tenor of ore and reserves are possible. This information considered together with the problems and methods of mining and mineral dressing, logistics of mining operations as a whole, available market and selling price of the ore, etc., lead to a decision whether the project is viable or not. If it is viable and the mining method is decided, the ore body is opened up and the geologists commence detailed mapping of the workings. Detailed mapping of the workings then continues throughout the life of the mine in conjunction with exploratory drilling underground or surface. In this way, the geology of the ore body is kept constantly under review so that workings can be driven and exploration, for extensions to the body, undertaken logically.

In the process, of course, the mine geologist gathers information regarding the probable origin of the ore and the factors controlling its emplacement. This gives a basis for further exploration not only of extensions to the ore body worked, but also for mineralisation in the general area of the mine.

Whilst the discovery of, for instance, the gold-fields of South Africa and the sulphide ores of Broken Hill, New South Wales, was accidental from outcrop, the continued fortunes of the areas have in large measure, been due to continuous painstaking geological mapping, the basis for logical development. In the Witwatersrand such logical thinking based on such detailed information caused the discovery of a new gold-field a few years ago. Such thinking is now also leading to new thoughts and ideas on the origin of the major metal ore bodies. In fact, the syngeneticists are gaining ground over the epigeneticists and more and more thought and study is being given to sedimentary environments as the source of the major disseminated ore bodies. On the other hand, those mines which have not had adequate geological advice and have not kept adequate geological records, often find themselves with ore bodies with apparently only a few years of life left and no basis for exploratory investigations. Perhaps it can be said that the mines in the United Kingdom are generally in this state. In this connection it is deplorable to note how much effort and money is wasted by mining companies when they discard drill cores. Drill cores are a source of evidence for years to come. The most progressive mines store their cores and other samples and refer to them time and time again when some new idea or evidence needs checking.

This brief account of the search for, appraisal and development of an ore body illustrates the need for continuous geological study, a commodity sadly lacking in many mining areas. It leads to suggestions for action in developing the mineral resources of Scotland. Thus the following general suggestions are made based on experience in other parts of the world:

(*a*) A general review of all the mineralised areas noted by the Geological Survey and others with a view to their re-assessment in the light of modern development and treatment methods. This would take two years or so and should be put in the hands of a carefully chosen mining geologist/engineer. This would not be a very expensive operation. Mining houses might well be interested in such co-operation venture which would give them up-to-date information cheaply. From the Government point of view it could well stimulate fresh mining activity. The scheme has the limit of only reworking old ground, not investigating all potential mineralised areas which is the merit of the next suggestion.

(*b*) A longer more ambitious programme would be the regional geochemical prospecting of the major part of Scotland. This could well show up new mineralisation in areas where nothing is previously known and show up new mineralisation in old mining areas. Although details would have to be worked out, it is suggested that a programme extending over say ten years would be reasonable, using an initial sampling pattern at say ½-mile intervals. A start could be made say in the Southern Uplands or Argyll and, for educational and financial reasons, incorporate university personnel, mainly students. Initial finance could come from Government and various business houses such as mining groups, metal brokers and large chemical combines, e.g. Imperial Chemical Industries Ltd. or Monsanto. Continuing finance could come by the sale of information, say, to the participating business houses themselves or, if they are not interested, to other business houses. The results could eventually become public property.

(*c*) The first two suggestions are concerned with metal ores, e.g. lead, zinc, nickel, copper, chrome, molybdenum, but similar co-operative schemes could apply to industrial minerals and building materials, e.g. felspar, mica, silica, diatomite, talc, sand and gravel.

(*d*) It is suggested that large parts of Scotland need to be studied as geological units by a body of men interested in Scotland's progress who will put to practical use all the evidence accumulated through the years by the Geological Survey, Universities, the Mining Community and individuals and extend that knowledge by concerted effort.

INTRODUCTION TO DISCUSSION

E. P. HUDSON, M.A., F.R.S.E.
Managing Director, Scottish Agricultural Industries Ltd.
Chairman, First Day

Statement by Mr. ELGOOD

I am very sorry to say that the Chairman appointed for the day, the Lord Bilsland, has not been too well and so he has asked me to excuse him today, but he will be Chairman tomorrow in the place of our lamented friend, Sir Cecil Weir. At very short notice, Mr. E. P. Hudson, Managing Director, S.A.I. Ltd., has consented to act as Chairman for the day. Now I would like this noted if you would be so good, and that is that anybody who likes may take part in this discussion; the things that he says will be recorded and after the Symposium will be sent to that gentleman to be edited and returned to go into the proceedings. In the same way, if anybody for some reason or another did not take part in the discussion but felt that they had something to add to it, he may send in a written paper which will also be included in the proceedings. I would now like to call on Mr. Hudson to be the Chairman of the day and to start our proceedings.

Mr. HUDSON

Mr. Elgood, Lord Polwarth, Ladies and Gentlemen: Mr. Elgood has explained to you the circumstances under which I present myself to you at this moment, to act as Chairman, to introduce the first day's papers, instead of merely helping in the proceedings during the first half of the morning session as a Deputy Chairman. I am sure we are all very sorry that Lord Bilsland could not be here, not least myself. But I am glad to know that he will be here tomorrow instead. The purpose of this few moments of introduction to today's work is to remind you, ladies and gentlemen, that today it is the basic resource facts about Scotland with which we are concerned. Now these facts are not only for specialists but obviously of importance to everyone, and particularly to the users of resources at all stages; there are often very many stages in the processes which lead ultimately to manufacturing operations and to consumption of specific products of saleable products, of merchandise, of raw materials for industries and so on. So we are concerned with those resources to make sure that we know what they are and where they are. And I think I am bound myself to add that we are also concerned in another way too. We want to make use of our own resources and we want to make sure what the resource position is before we use other resources. I am in an industry which has to depend for a great many of its raw materials on overseas sources of supply, which is a pity in some ways, although the ship-owning fraternity and harbour authorities might think it would be a pity if everything went one way. We are concerned with what resources we have and also with what resources we have not got, and are concerned not only with raw materials for manufacture but equally importantly with the raw materials for the services which make industry possible, the raw materials for power services, water and such like. Now, these basic resource facts are, as you can see from the list of papers given today, recorded by many different authorities, and the purpose of today's session is to try to look at them all at the same point in time; at this moment of time and to consider where they interlink. This record depends not only on the existence of materials which are so recorded but also on the techniques of measurement, of application, on the economic climate and on the general and the social climate in the broadest sense; so it is bound to be a moving record. We do need today, when we see such a record at this moment in time, how we can make sure that in future moments of time it can equally well be looked at and intelligently appraised. This is not the first attempt to make a record. I suppose that if you go to the Bible and early English history, to the Domesday Book, we can find plenty of examples of early records. In Scotland it is worth remembering the first of the new statistical accounts. I think the First Statistical Account was started in Scotland in 1791, and perhaps it is not insignificant that the foundation of the Royal Society of Edinburgh, in whose rooms we meet for these three days, was 1783. That was a time of a great surge forward of enquiry, of investigation, when men's minds were in a ferment, and I would hope that we could decide that this is similarly a time when our minds should be in ferment and where we should be and are determined to make a surge forward again. There was a reference to the interest of underdeveloped countries in an operation such as we are conducting here. I suppose in a sense, at the time of the First Statistical Account of Scotland, Scotland might have been called at that time an underdeveloped country—I am not quite sure. But we have behind us a long record. Lord Polwarth was talking about the lead-mines. It is 536 years ago that the lead-mines of Scotland were (as it were) "nationalised" at that time by being declared Royal Mines, and the Leadhill mines were opened in 1513. So it is time they were opened again. Even such an industrial enterprise as the mining of coal in Brora in Sutherland—I am reminded of this by what the Lord Provost said about things outside the Central Belt of Scotland—even that is almost 400 years old. We come today to reappraise the whole of the information that is available and try to see how we can use that information to make our resources work harder. I think that during the course of today there is one thing we must devote some time to, over and above seeing how to keep the thing going for the future; that is to see that the facts which we look at today and which we try to correlate today, to see that these facts do become adequately available and accessible, not just to the specialists who are gathered here today but to the whole economic body of Scotland in its separate parts as it may require this information in future. As is nearly always the case, in almost anything you discuss nowadays, good communications, effective communications, must be an important part of our deliberations. The subjects we have before us today are soils, minerals, water, fish, seaweed, wildlife and finally the National Atlas. I have been asked to make one point about fish, and that is that any discussion today on the subject of fish should, in this case, cover the utilisation of fish as well as on its existence and the methods of winning it. The basic facts of fish need to be supplemented here by consideration of its utilisation, because there is going to be nothing on that subject tomorrow, tomorrow being the day for consideration of the utilisation of resources. The work we do today is fundamental and the information we can gather, the way we can see that it is kept up to date, the way we can see it can be communicated to everyone, will have a great bearing on the speed with which people can seize upon the opportunities that may exist or may be created by good knowledge, and one can never tell quite where those opportunities will lie. The Secretary of this Conference reminded me of the American gentleman whose shanty stood on an evil-smelling oily soil, and he went off to the oil-fields to seek his fortune, and when he returned out of luck a few years later he found his shanty was no longer there because oil was being worked on a very large scale underneath. I was reminded of that as an illustration of his point that we never know where the opportunities may arise. But I cannot refrain from adding that I started my own industrial career in a great chemical and fertiliser works in the north of England which was originally set up by the Ministry of Munitions and started as an experimental operation round about 1917 to try and make explosives out of the nitrogen of the air, and it was set up on what seemed a very convenient place for the purpose; it was not until quite a number of years later that what was going to be one of the most important raw materials for the whole of the manufacturing operations of the Billingham factory of I.C.I., namely anhydrite, was right underneath the factory, and that factory operates now with a large mine right in the middle of it, with very substantial mine workings carried on right underneath it to provide one of its basic raw materials. I think that is a remarkable example of a piece of good luck. Today we want to do better than good luck—we want to find how we can improve ourselves by good management.

Now, my Lord, Ladies and Gentlemen, we come to the first session which is concerned with soil and mineral resources, and this is where I turn myself into a Deputy Chairman in charge of this particular session. I think I had better just explain one or two points of procedure which will apply to this session and will also apply to other sessions no doubt, with improvements as we go along. The idea is, of course, that the papers are not to be read, not even the summaries. Not in every case will the authors be present—I think they are this morning, and it would be proper to introduce the authors at the beginning of the session. The procedure of discussion is: a Reporter will attempt to weave a short comment which covers all the papers for the session in the course of five or ten minutes, and after that Papers can be discussed. I hope it will be discussion rather than question and answer. There may be some points of clarification. If they are important, it would be a good thing to be cleared out of the way, but if they are minor points of clarification, perhaps it would be easier not to take up time of the whole meeting but deal with them outside the meeting. The Scottish Council is very anxious that all the words of wisdom that fall should be recorded; for that purpose you are being overheard by a tape recorder and it is intended that those who wish to speak will have a microphone . . . as well as the others present. There is a microphone there, and if anyone catches the eye of the Chairman and wishes to speak, then it will be sent down to him so that what he says can be heard and recorded. As I said, a Reporter will start, and after that it is a free for all, except that certain gentlemen and perhaps ladies have asked if they could say something, and Chairmen of each session will have a list of those names and will call on these people. That being so, I will start, if I may, by asking if the authors of the Papers would care to make a bow and introduce themselves:

First paper—"Soil Survey of Scotland"—Dr. Glentworth.
Next we have Dr. Mitchell on "The Work of the Geological Survey".
Then Professor Neville George—"Economic Minerals in Scotland".
Finally, Mr. Rankin on "Survey Methods".

Now, having performed those introductions we proceed by asking our Reporter to speak on these papers as a group. In the earlier literature you found the name of

Dr. Raistrick down as Reporter—a member of Mr. Elgood's Committee. At short notice his place has been taken by Dr. George Bremner. I have an idea it is nice that he should be here, because I would not be surprised if somewhere on these shelves you didn't find a book by David Bremner under the title *Industries of Scotland their Rise and Progress and Present Position in 1869*, which was an attempt almost one hundred years ago to look at industrial Scotland in the same sort of way as we are looking at resources today.

STATEMENT BY THE REPORTER

J. G. M. Bremner, M.A., B.SC., D.PHIL., F.R.I.C., M.I.CHEM.E., O.ST.J.
Research Director, Scottish Agricultural Industries Ltd.

Mr. Chairman, Ladies and Gentlemen: I have to give a short report to you on four papers. The first one deals with soil and the other three with mineral resources. Now, I cannot help thinking that the Council has been extremely astute in putting soil as the first paper—it may, in fact, be a gentle reminder for us to keep our feet on the ground during the rest of the discussion! As our Chairman said, I have been called on at short notice, but I am extremely fortified by having the authors in front of me who are available to elucidate any points which perhaps I may not put to you in the way they would wish.

The first paper, presented by Dr. Glentworth, entitled "The Soil Survey of Scotland", describes the work done by the Soil Survey of the Macaulay Institute of Aberdeen, and I think I can expect most of you to have a copy with you. It is worth while turning to Figure II given at the end of the paper, which sets out the extent of this Survey. One glance shows that it is the east, the north-east and south-east that have received attention, with a little of the south-west of Scotland, but we see a large blank patch over the rest of Scotland. In fact, Dr. Glentworth has been good enough to estimate for us in this paper what fraction of the total survey work has so far been carried out, and, of course, the figure is less than half. Furthermore, he has calculated that it will take 25 years to complete this Soil Survey. Now, some of you may care to make comment on that.

The other point that Dr. Glentworth makes is the application of soil surveys and soil information to recommendations for fertilisers. This is a subject on which several people here have worked and, in fact, they might like to comment on the status and possibilities of correlating soil properties with both plant and animal nutrition. Dr. Glentworth indicates some of the future possibilities—for example in speeding up, say, methods of sampling and also methods of analysis. There may be physical methods yet to be developed which would in fact speed up the work.

The other three papers deal with mineral resources. One describes the work of the Geological Survey and is presented by Dr. Mitchell, Assistant Director of the Geological Survey in Edinburgh. Another by Professor George, of the University of Glasgow, surveys economic minerals, while in the third Mr. Rankin, Technical Manager of Hunting Surveys Ltd., talks about survey methods. Now, if I could just refer first of all to Dr. Mitchell's paper. He gives us an account of the work that has been done by the Geological Survey of Scotland and indicates by lists the maps and memoirs that have been published, but unfortunately, as he points out, much of this work is not readily available. Dr. Mitchell makes the point that many of these maps and memoirs are now out of print, largely because of destruction by enemy action during the war. A lot of work of his Survey has been an attempt to replace these, and considerable progress has been made.

Professor George in his paper reviews the occurrence of minerals in Scotland and asks us to be careful in our use of the term "economic minerals". He asks us to be sure when we use the terms "economic" and "uneconomic" that we are quite certain we have thought very carefully about it. He writes in a comprehensive way on this aspect and makes specific recommendations. He asks that a skilled survey be made comparable to the work of the Geological Survey of Scotland. He makes the suggestion, which will interest later authors, that finances for this should be provided by the Government. He goes further and suggests that alongside this work a detailed investigation should be made into possible new processes for working up these minerals at present thought "uneconomic", with a view to discovering new processes and thereby founding new industries in Scotland.

Mr. Rankin gives us a most interesting and broadly based account of methods that can be used in carrying out surveys on the atmosphere, over water and over land masses, and perhaps other authors later in the Conference may like to refer to his paper. I think the one that particularly interests us at this juncture is his reference to land masses, and there he stresses the speed achieved by the use of aircraft in such surveys. He is kind enough also to make a suggestion that we ought first to have a reappraisal of all existing geological information, because in the light of developments it may be possible, as Professor Neville George indicated, to utilise these minerals with modern techniques. He proposes a ten-year plan to do "chemical prospecting", and suggests that finance might be met partly by Government and partly by industry.

DISCUSSION

Dr. A. G. MacGregor, *lately Assistant Director (Scotland) in the Geological Survey*

Mr. Chairman, Lord Polwarth, Ladies and Gentlemen: My contribution is concerned mainly with some of the post-war investigations of Scottish minerals, and thus presents basic resource facts not dealt with by Professor George and Mr. Rankin.

From Sutherland to Sky, *dolomite and limestone* have been examined by an industrial firm which claims that its work constitutes a complete investigation of North-West Highland dolomite in relation to iron and steel manufacture[1]. The *iron-ore* resources of Raasay have been reassessed by the same firm.[1] Magnetite in Tiree[2, 3] has been investigated twice with a view to exploitation.[1] The possible extension of occurrences of magnetite in Shetland, tested during the war by magnetic and other methods,[3] has been reinvestigated. *Chromite* deposits once worked in Unst have been re-examined.[4] The abandoned mines and *lead/zinc* veins of Leadhills and Wanlockhead have been subjected to a thorough and prolonged examination, including geophysical and geochemical surveys and diamond drilling.[5] The old mines and lead/zinc veins at Strontian have twice been re-examined, the later investigators using geophysical and geochemical methods.[6] Two Loch Fyne areas, where *nickel* and *copper ores* were known, have been reassessed.[7] *Serpentine* and talc-breunnerite rock near Killin have been sampled and tested by the Geological Survey and, in a special publication,[8] suggestions for beneficiation and industrial uses have been made. Except at Killin, these investigations were undertaken by the metal or mining industries. In no instance has exploitation followed. Mention may be made, however, of diatomite in Skye[9] and of dolomite in Duror,[10] where industrial initiative did lead to exploitation under the current economic conditions.

I suggest that industrialists, both south and north of the Border, should be congratulated on their enterprise and thanked for the expenditure of much money in efforts to assess the economic possibilities of Scottish minerals at present undeveloped. Such assessments will serve as useful guides to the possibilities of exploitation under more favourable economic conditions.

It may not be widely known that information in Geological Survey publications on Scottish rocks of potential economic value (e.g. limestone, dolomite, quartzite, serpentine) is not confined to descriptions of field occurrence and mineralogy. Representative chemical analyses are provided (over 250, of which some 150 are full analyses, in the case of limestone and dolomite), and suggestions made for possible industrial uses and for quarry sites.

A publication entitled *The Future of Non-Ferrous Mining in Great Britain and Ireland* (Institution of Mining and Metallurgy, 1959) contains post-war information on some Scottish minerals; for instance detailed accounts of the Leadhills/Wanlockhead[5] and Strontian[6] investigations and of the active barytes mines of Gasswater and Muirshiels.[11]

Immediately after the war the Mineral Development Committee of the Ministry of Fuel and Power undertook a review of the potentialities of United Kingdom minerals, exclusive of "substances of widespread occurrence" such as coal, oil-shale, limestone, dolomite and quartzite; their report[12] was published in 1949. In their assessment of Scotland they relied largely on their Scottish sub-Committee's reports, based on extensive wartime investigations carried out for the Ministry of Supply by the Geological Survey, in collaboration with mining engineers, economic geologists and representatives of industry. A general assessment of many Scottish minerals, including almost all the vein-minerals, has thus appeared within the last twelve years.

In connection with the proposal for *widespread geochemical prospecting*, I suggest that, if this undertaking located mineral veins at present unknown, very considerable additional sums of "risk capital" would be required, in each case, to prove whether the occurrence had any practical value.

REFERENCES

1. *Glasgow Herald*, 13th April 1959.
2. *Trans. geol. Soc. Glasg.*, **21**, Part ii, 1951.
3. Ministry of Supply Permanent Records of Research and Development: Monograph 20/703, 1952.
4. *Mining Magazine*, 1953.
5. *The Future of Non-Ferrous Mining in Great Britain and Ireland*, London, 1959, p. 49.
6. *Ibid.*, p. 107.

7. *Ibid.*, p. 102.
8. Geol. Survey Wartime Pamphlet No. 9: Supplement No. 1, 1949.
9. *Glasgow Herald*, 30th September 1953.
10. Geology of Ben Nevis and Glencoe. *Mem. geol. Surv.*, 1960, p. 286.
11. *The Future of Non-Ferrous Mining in Great Britain and Ireland*, London, 1959, p. 85.
12. Report of the Mineral Development Committee, Ministry of Fuel and Power, 1949.

Dr. Robert A. Mackay, *Mackay & Schnellmann Ltd., London*

I feel that there is a great deal to be said for Dr. MacGregor's very harrowing tale of woe. But I think that he has ignored the fact that Professor George lays great stress on two things: that minerals must not be looked at in only one context, the context of what we might call the present price—though Professor George uses other words—and the context of present technology. These things are mobile. I want to elaborate what I am saying in writing, but I want to put it briefly now. I had a good deal to do with the Leadhills venture. It is not worked out, it is just uneconomic at the present price of the mineral. When that project was conceived the price of lead was about £160 per ton. When the operation started it was about £70 a ton. The break-even price was somewhere between £90 and £110—I must not give the exact figure. Now, the price has been £160 in the past. Who is going to say that it is not going to be that again, and over a longer period? Or somewhere between? No, Leadhills is not worked out by any means. It is absolutely, totally uneconomic at present prices, but it is not worked out.

The iron ores of Scotland have been mentioned too as completely hopeless. Well, all I can say is that iron ores of at least the stated quality and occurring in what appears to be even smaller quantities are being worked at a profit in Norway today. And that is another point I want to elaborate upon. One has got to consider the context of price and technology, and if these things are changing, things that now look to us completely useless may be important to this country in the future.

Mr. R. White, *Department of Mechanical, Civil and Chemical Engineering, The Royal College of Science and Technology, Glasgow*

This contribution might appear of minor importance in relation to the wide issues which are to be discussed at this Conference, but I think it is essentially practical. It is relevant to the question of gathering *data*, and I am encouraged to make it by a remark of our Reporter this morning when opening the session, when he said that some of the methods of examining soils seemed to him to be haphazard in the least. I am referring to Dr. Glentworth's paper where he mentions two methods of examining the physical properties of soil. One of these, the texture of the soil, is judged by the feel of the moistened soil between the fingers; the second one consists of dropping the soil in the form of a clod and seeing how it breaks up. It does not say, but presumably there is a technique for deciding, from what height it should be dropped and on to what kind of surface. Now, it seems a pity to use methods like these, which I cannot see are directly comparable from observer to observer and soil to soil, when there are available perfectly good techniques used by the civil engineer in the study of soil mechanics. This is referred to later on in the paper when co-operation between the Road Research Laboratory and the agriculturalist is mentioned; the Road Research Laboratory solved a very difficult and intractable problem by going to the agricultural soil specialist and asking something about the soil, thereby discovering that they were dealing with podsols. Now, a great deal of money and time might have been saved if they had asked the specialist first, and I suggest that reciprocal action here might help and that perhaps in the soil survey the physical characteristics of the soil might be dealt with by a simplified method, but by using already existing, well-tried tests, which the engineer has developed simply to overcome the problem of describing soils to different people in different parts of the world in consistent systematic terms. In other branches of soil exploration the civil engineer has to provide the Geological Survey, by law, with the results of underground borings. As so much soil survey is being done currently in connection with road works and other civil engineering structures, similar machinery might be evolved whereby the physical results of such soil examinations might be sent to the Soil Survey, if not by law, then on a voluntary basis. If the Soil Survey then adopted this systematic classification, the results of these surveys could be marked on the maps which they are producing. They might be of assistance to agriculturalists; they certainly would be of assistance to engineers in preliminary reconnaissance—before further soil surveys were attempted. There would be advantage to agriculturalists, because in the work of soil cement stabilisation for road works a great deal has already been learned about the equipment which started as agricultural equipment—ploughs, harrows and so on—and a great deal has been learned of the effect of the physical properties of soils on the design of such machinery. No doubt something similar might help the agricultural plant engineer, and as this data is available on a growing scale—hardly any job of civil engineering is attempted without a soil survey—it seems a pity that this information should not be included on the same basis in the Soil Survey as in the Geological Survey.

Dr. Robert Glentworth, *The Macaulay Institute for Soil Research*

From your remarks it is obvious that you have not read the *Soil Survey Memoirs*, had you done so you would see that mechanical analysis is undertaken on representative profiles. X-ray and differential thermal analytical techniques are also used to find out the amount and kind of clay minerals present. In the field, for obvious reasons, soil texture is judged by the feel of the soil between thumb and finger.

I agree that some of the physical analyses used to assess bearing strength and shear strength which are of interest to civil engineers might be introduced on a routine basis, since Soil Survey Maps are now being found of use not only to agriculturalists but for road-construction, pylon-lines, water mains, etc. The material engineers are normally concerned with is usually below soil depth after the soil has been removed by the bulldozer. It is a matter we must look into.

Mr. P. A. Rankin, *Hunting Surveys Ltd., and Hunting Technical Services Ltd.*

I do not want to say any more about Survey Methods in particular, but something on how these methods might be employed in Scotland.

I think both the Geological Survey and the Soil Survey at, for example, the Macaulay Institute, are without doubt, doing a magnificent job in obtaining basic facts, but we hear that the Soil Survey will take another 25 years, and I am not sure how long the Geological Survey will take, because geology, more than soils, is a subject that is never ending. That is not a reflection on the existing organisations, but what I do suggest is that, alongside this collecting of basic facts, it might be sensible to choose also an area for concentrated study.

I have been associated with a group that has had the job of tackling areas in overseas countries with teams of earth scientists working together. This approach, I think, has great benefit to the work because you have a team of specialists in related fields who are dedicated to one particular area for the duration of the job. In such a way the unit keeps a co-ordinated approach and it is possible to view the area as a whole rather than from separate scientific speciality viewpoints.

I can imagine that one of the problems of this idea is that there are so many interests to consider that finding an area which will be satisfactory to all may be difficult in itself.

One of the points that I mentioned in my paper is that basic material for such an investigation could be aerial photographs. One of the problems with aerial photographs is to obtain cover which is suited to many purposes. This is difficult in the present system in the United Kingdom whereby photographs are taken by, or on behalf of, a number of bodies which are apparently unco-ordinated. What I am pleading for is co-ordination, under the aegis of the Scottish Council, to bring all the interested bodies together to choose an area, or areas, whether they be ones which are appropriate for vegetation survey (in its widest context), or ones which are applicable to mineral survey. Let us get together behind a project or two—limited if you like—but something which is tangible, something that we can cope with in *our* lifetime.

Professor HUGH NICOL, *West of Scotland Agricultural College*

Some alarm and despondency seems to have been incited that the Soil Survey of Scotland might not be completed before 25 years. In any case Dr. Glentworth is young enough not to worry much about what is going to happen to him when he runs out of Scottish soil to survey and map. So I leave him to worry about that. But on the practical point of the apparent slowness of survey I would like to raise a matter which Dr. Glentworth has probably been too tactful to include in his cyclostyled paper, and this is that I believe that the proportion of soil area mapped in Scotland is larger than that of England and Wales. I would like to know whether this is so or not? A few years ago when I was a member of the Soil Survey Research Board much the same anxiety about slowness arose, and I was at that time able to reassure the Chairman of that Board that the position in Scotland was not nearly as bad as it appeared to be, anyhow, as the map published with the paper shows, a very large proportion of the most productive soils of Scotland have already been mapped or are in the process of being mapped. There is not much left to be done if one excepts the wet deserts of, say, the mountainous parts or the outer northern islands.

Taking up the line of Mr. White's policy in Glasgow, I would like to suggest that some more information on the soil mapping could be got by combining the sole physical parameter that is now used in soil determination—namely the pH on which I need not enlarge—with an estimation of conductivity: in other words with a measure of the ionised salts. To use pH alone I have felt for many years is of no use whatsoever by itself in any sphere, whether you are concerned with biochemistry or with boiler water, but if you join that in a function which was elaborated by one of my colleagues at the West of Scotland Agricultural College—if you join pH with what we call pC (the analogous negative logarithm of specific conductivity) a great deal more information comes out and in particular you get a physico-chemical expression which is a characteristic for that soil or sample of soil. I don't mean the whole soil, but Dr. Glentworth will understand "a characteristic of each horizon" (to use a technical term). To use pH on a soil map, or as I have suggested for boiler water or for any other industrial or biological purpose, is like fixing a single point on a chart. If pH is suitably combined with a statement of the electrical conductivity, the resulting expression is a two-point fix—like a statement of both latitude and longitude. Considerable precision of statement about soil property and potentialities can thus be obtained by invoking simple ionic measurements.

Mr. W. Parker, *National Coal Board*

Mr. Chairman: I am not on my feet to say anything at all about the Geological Survey. Dr. Chamberlain, my colleague, who is here, can speak much more expertly and competently on that. I would just like to make one observation on the excellent paper by Professor George which is in front of us. After reviewing the situation, he draws certain conclusions, and I think it is only right to say that I do not agree with these conclusions. He draws the conclusion that, because of the exhaustion of certain minerals—certain coal reserves—we are going to see a repetition of the ghost towns of California in some of the mining villages. Now, I just do not agree with that; I do not believe it, and I think it is right that I should stand up and say so. A further conclusion he draws—he sketches the very true difficulties of coal mining in Scotland, problems of reserves, of the thicker seams becoming exhausted, but he comes to the conclusion that that means the industry in future cannot be viable. Again I do not agree. I think there are other factors which will enable the industry to be economic over these years. Now, sir, if Dr. Chamberlain has anything he would care to add on the Geological Survey side I am sure the Conference would find it of interest.

Dr. J. B. Caldwell, *National Coal Board.*

In his own paper at a later stage Dr. Chamberlain will be dealing with most aspects of the Coal Board's contribution to the survey of natural resources. However, let me say that the Coal Survey branch is at present engaged on a detailed survey of the quality, structure and thickness of all coal-seams in Scotland and will publish this information in map form. This may be regarded as an extension of the work of the Geological Survey, contained in their maps and memoirs, to the special field in which we are interested. I believe mapping of this kind could be followed by others interested in mineral resources, remembering that the mapping of the quality and structure of minerals not laid down in sedimentary form can be a difficult problem. Furthermore, the National Coal Board, being a public monopoly, has nothing to lose by making such information available to a wide public, whereas a private firm may be naturally reticent about publication. Action by a national agency, such as the Geological Survey, might be necessary before such data could be made generally available.

Professor T. Neville George, *Department of Geology, University of Glasgow*

Mr. Chairman, Ladies and Gentlemen: I hope you will not regard what I have to say as anything based on contentious differences with Dr. MacGregor. The remarks he made are, as he said, remarks on fact, and in that I would agree with him that what he has said is indeed true. But the implied interpretation of his remarks is something with which I would not agree. It is true, and perhaps I should have said a bit more about it in my paper, that the Geological Survey and a number of the larger industries have indeed done a quite magnificent piece of work in exploring some of the industries or possible sources of minerals for industry in parts of Scotland. Indeed, if I might speak personally for a moment, it would be to say that I look back with some pride at myself having once been a member of the Geological Survey even though I never found a coal-seam or a piece of galena that was of any value whatsoever. Now, in looking back on these three years I feel that what I did then is the sort of thing I am suggesting might be done in Scotland so far as the economic minerals are concerned. The results to the country in an economic sense from what I did in three years were quite insignificant, I think always will be quite insignificant, but I trust that the country did not think that the salary it paid me was to that degree altogether wasted.

And it is quite true that the dolomite has been examined by the steel industry and the silica rocks too, to some extent, by the steel industry, the magnetite in Tiree, the magnetite in Shetland, and so on. But I would reply, as Dr. Mackay has replied, that these are particular studies made at a particular moment for a particular purpose. That that is a complete answer, however, I simply cannot believe. And what I am saying in effect in my paper, and what we have heard about the National Coal Board, should be applied to all minerals, economic or not at the present time, in Scotland. If I may presume to say so, I think the National Coal Board is doing an absolutely magnificent job of work in the systematic examination and weighing up of the possibilities of the uses of coal in this country.

What I would like to say is that the work of the Geological Survey, for which I have no criticism at all, should be extended in the same way for other minerals than coal, and I am suggesting it should be done in the same sort of way as the Geological Survey itself is carried out, as a national responsibility, the measure of which—put in simple terms —is that of how much profit or loss do we make in any particular year?

On the two particular points mentioned by one of the speakers from the National Coal Board I would only say this. It may not be yet that we have ghost towns quite so bad as those of California, but I think if we build a culture—if we have towns based upon one single kind of industry—then they must inevitably look to a future, we can expect a future, in which those towns will not last for ever on an industry that in its nature is wasting its asset. And the second point I would make: I do not mean to imply that the coal industry would not be economic in the future, but I would remind you of what Lord Polwarth said earlier on. If there is a competing intention to apply different sources of power in industry, it might be that one source of power finds itself at a disadvantage compared with another, and at some time, some point, it might be that coal is too difficult to get or there is too little of it left to compete with other sources of power. It is merely a theoretical possibility, the likelihood of which I do not see, at least in my lifetime.

WRITTEN CONTRIBUTIONS

W. R. FLETT, Esq., B.SC., F.R.S.E., F.G.S.

Few people with an objective approach to the problem of development of Scottish mineral resources would disagree completely with the substance of Dr. MacGregor's contribution to the discussion on the papers by Professor George and Mr. Rankin. But his comments seemed to have no direct relevance to the main thesis, implicit in Professor George's paper, which, while candidly admitting the many adverse factors affecting the exploitation of Scottish minerals, insisted that no possibility, however elusive, of making them commercially acceptable should be ignored.

In some respects Dr. MacGregor's observations could be misleading in so far as some of them as applied to certain minerals could be interpreted as official concurrence in what was by implication the final abandonment of the project. In some cases cited by Dr. MacGregor the decision to suspend operations was not, in fact, contingent on the findings of the investigations to which he refers.

Certain of the investigations to which Dr. MacGregor made special reference appeared to be limited in their context, being concerned mainly with grade, and reserves, of ore as determined by surface examination only. In the case of the dolomite in the North-Western Highlands, apart from the Ullapool area where it is now being worked, only two bore-holes have been sunk throughout the extensive outcrops ranging over approximately 100 miles. The number of surveys listed as re-investigations suggests that there was no finality in the decision to cease work. It has also been recognised by those who have extended their surveys beyond the range of investigations implicit in Dr. MacGregor's summary that there are several additional contributory factors affecting the acceptance or rejection of a mineral by industry. It was clearly Professor George's contention that there was still a very large field for ancillary investigations beyond the limits of primary field surveys, and sustained search for novel methods of utilising the Scottish minerals, regarded as substandard in the light of current industrial requirements, could quite possibly produce encouraging results.

The question of the exploitation of the mineral resources of Scotland is rather reminiscent of Mahomet's problem with the mountain, and it would seem that the solutions to the respective dilemmas are not dissimilar. If industrial specifications could, with increase of tolerance, arising from newly devised techniques as the outcome of unbiassed exploratory research, move close to the natural properties of Scottish minerals, the gap between the field investigations of a mineral deposit and its acceptance by industry could be significantly diminished if not completely closed. A compromise solution to this problem of rapprochement, involving methods of beneficiation of the raw material, would perhaps, reduce the area which research on new techniques might otherwise require to explore.

Perhaps it would be pertinent at this point to refer to Mr. Teodoro Moscoso's advice to the Symposium audience: "If you have no natural resources, use your imagination". Scotland has the advantage over Puerto Rico in possessing mineral resources, possibly substandard, according to established industrial practice, but with imaginative research on new or untried techniques they could possibly become significant factors in the Scottish economy.

Professor NEVILLE GEORGE, *Glasgow University*

Dr. A. G. MacGregor's remarks in their overtones can only be regarded as negative and defeatist. They imply that Scottish minerals are mostly substandard, that field studies already carried out are uniformly unpromising, and that the greater part of the Highlands and the Southern Uplands must be written off as bottomless pits of ill-invested capital. On the facts of geological occurrence Dr. MacGregor writes with the authority of a former Assistant Director of the Geological Survey, but in his implications he is quite unconvincing.

It should scarcely now be necessary to say that former economic surveys, carried out by industry for purposes *ad hoc* in the circumstances of their time, may or may not be relevant to changing needs and changing processes; or to say that a decision at a particular moment not to work a deposit, or to abandon working before a deposit is exhausted, may commonly be made on grounds, economic or political or traditional or even domestic, having only a remote or indirect relation to the geology of the minerals as such. In contradiction to Dr. MacGregor's remarks it is proper to assert that the dolomite belt of the North-Western Highlands has only at a few localities enjoyed a detailed industrial investigation—nowhere a "complete investigation"—and its bulk potentialities are untried; the Raasay iron-ore is there, equally like the English Jurassic ores, to be won if non-geological conditions should be propitious; the Shetland magnetite is still largely unworked; the Unst chromite suffers from a fragmentation by faulting and thrusting and is not easily won, but its reserves are indefinitely large; the whole lead-zinc field of the Southern Uplands, explored only in part, is now dormant not because of any deficiency or exhaustion of the ores but because of tumbling world prices, and the Strontian mines, though not so extensive, suffer from the same ill.

The impression given by Dr. MacGregor's contribution is sadly misleading and a social disservice if it encourages an abandonment of effort or interest, or if it dims possibilities of exploratory surveys, or if it causes industrialists without further ado to turn elsewhere for their raw materials.

Dr. MacGregor's charges of gracelessness come oddly when they allude to a neglect of the work of the Geological Survey, of the Mineral Development Committee, and of enterprising industrialists. My paper explicity began a principal section with "What is known of the distribution of Scottish economic minerals is very largely the result of the activities of the Geological Survey"; and it ended with "The publications of the Geological Survey . . . are the main storehouse of information on Scottish economic minerals and ores". It would be impossible (even for a former member of the Geological Survey) to overstate the immense value of the work done by the Survey in both scientific and economic fields: the Survey is unique of its kind, and a source of national pride: because of its central position in British geology it is an example of institutions in applied science that (as I contend) might be repeated in a bureau of economic geology.

The Mineral Development Committee, far from being overlooked by me, was a main inspiration of the proposal to establish a minerals research centre: in its review of Scottish (as of other British) resources it offered not merely a conspectus of known mineral occurrences but revealed the depths of ignorance that need to be plumped before systematic and rational exploitation is possible, and it provided a major stimulus to the central policy of the Mineral Resources Panel of the Scottish Council.

The Panel repeatedly makes clear in its reports that it would be helpless and its work trivial if it could rely only on its own members and its own resources for its findings: what it is able to accomplish is possible only because of the help of universities and the even more considerable help received from industry in the field and in the laboratory. More generally, it is obvious to the point of being trite that past exploitation of Scottish minerals (partly excepting coal) has been the work of private industrialists, without whose enterprise there would have been no economic development; and a tribute to that enterprise is implicit in every comment on worked minerals in my paper.

A symposium on prospects, however, is scarcely the place for lavish "acknowledgments"; and a brief account of Scottish minerals must take up its thesis at the moment of discussion. What may best improve Scottish economy is not answered by referring to past history alone, or by claiming that little is left to be done. On the contrary, the need for a sustained appraisal of Scottish minerals was acknowledged ten years ago when the Scottish Home Department and the Department of Scientific and Industrial Research conceded the appointment of a Minerals Liaison Officer—an appointment that was not taken up only because of the lack of a suitable candidate. It was indirectly met, so far as it bore on mineral processing and beneficiation, by the establishment of the Warren Spring Laboratory. What is now wanted in Scotland is an extension of the exploratory activities of a Minerals Officer and a more direct utilisation of the facilities of Warren Spring. Administratively the work might be done as an extended activity of the Geological Survey; or under the central direction of the Department of Scientific and industrial Research; or under the combined control of the Department and industry; or (less satisfactorily) by research *ad hoc* sponsored perhaps by the Departments and carried out in appropriate university or other research centres. The design of the instrument is a secondary matter: it waits only on purposive intention.

Dr. R. A. Mackay offers very welcome examples of the sort of approach that, highly successful in other countries, might revitalise Scottish mineral economy and that, activated by a spirited will to work whatever deposits lie to hand, contrasts with a passive pessimism founded on indeterminate past ventures. His criticism of the limitations of "pure" geologists is no doubt apt; and the kind of mineral assessment always needed must go far beyond mere occurrence or geological context. The Geological Survey is in present character primarily a research establishment, inadequate (as it has itself repeatedly declared) in staff and equipment to be orientated directly towards industrial ends: a survey economic in its bias needs specialists who are competent to visualise the whole process of transformation of minerals from their natural state to the finished industrial product.

Professor Stewart similarly emphasises the need for a re-assessment of Scottish resources. His experience in England and America gives added strength to his support of the proposal to institute an economic survey; and his use of the analogy of the Canadian Bureau of Mines provides a powerful example (though doubtless on a very much larger scale) of the sort of instrument that might serve Scotland well. His instances of methods and applications underline the suggestions made in my paper.

R. A. Mackay, Esq.

The problem as I see it is not so much the existence of natural resources as the will to put them to work.

Scotland has fish and Scandinavia competes successfully; there is an abundance of seaweed; so there is in other countries of similar latitude, and the same applies to peat; and, of course, seawater is ubiquitous; there is lead which, as I have elsewhere stated, I think is currently uneconomic; there is iron but it has not, for their particular purposes, suited those who investigated it. Incidentally, Dr. MacGregor, who spoke on this matter of iron on Monday and implied the unlikehood of it being of value, has not in fact actually seen the recent drilling results.

What then is the cure for stagnant natural resources? One can only look to other parts of the world where resources of an average or less than average quality have been put to work and see what has been done and infer from this why it has happened. The answer is usually necessity and planning. Necessity because for some internal reason the country must have the commodities concerned if it is to expand or must develop them in order to obtain other currencies. With necessity goes planning, usually, but not always with Government assistance and advice, if not aid. One may conveniently take some examples.

Israel is currently working phosphate of a grade which is not commercial anywhere else in the world and she is working copper which was written off by outside engineers as far as normal world economics are concerned. Jordan has the same two minerals, the phosphate is of high quality but there were insuperable transport problems which one vigorous planner to a very great extent overcame. Jordan's copper and manganese were completely written off for metallurgical reasons after very considerable conventional research. These same metallurgical difficulties were on the other hand overcome in Israel.

Pakistan is profitably working coal in poor seams of very inferior quality. She may also work non-self-fluxing iron of very low grade.

Norway works molybdenum of a lower grade than anywhere else in the world, and the answer is they have integrated it with other industries. They also work profitably iron mines which are poorer, as far as can be seen on the available information, than those which have been rejected in Scotland.

Ireland works its peat quite extensively. In these latter cases will, ingenuity and planning play a more important role than necessity.

In Nigeria it was officially said that there was inadequate limestone for cement. The efforts of one man who refused to believe this has led to deposits of limestone being discovered which will result in several cement factories.

In Iran there is a small deposit of iron 600 kilometres from the coast which is being worked and sold to Czechoslovakia! The ingenuity of one man in reducing costs and noticing the deposit was singularly low in phosphates and that Czechoslovakia was particularly keen for low phosphate ore led to the working of this deposit. In this latter case and in many others, necessity and planning still entered into the picture in spite of the Government not being concerned, because the individual had the will to put the resources to work and the ingenuity to do it.

It is in general difficult to say how the cure can be put into effect in a country which does not have a planned economy. One instance has been quoted immediately above and another is the way Lord Adam revived Cumberland, again using resources which were not above and possibly a good deal below average quality. The will was here again. In these cases of the individual, inventiveness is usually borne of ingenuity and hard experience.

The speaker does not agree with the suggestion made on Monday that the Geological Surveys should initiate these investigations or plans of this nature. The value of the Surveys in providing basic information at a steady and regular rate cannot be overestimated, but they can be essentially thought of as research organisations regarding the maps as the end product of research. They are not equipped in personnel to go into the main economic and commercial aspects of putting to work the potential resources which they record. Their staff is, moreover, frequently if not usually of men whose experience lies in one country of which they are the specialists and it has not been their business or training to acquire the background information necessary to raw material utilisation study.

The writer is familiar with many examples where they have tried and where absolutely first-class geologists have done more harm than good because they have departed from their speciality into realms into which their experience had not fitted them. Deposits have been underestimated by them and overestimated. Two base metal deposits with which I am familiar around the world have failed because they were over assessed and over capitalised and production can therefore not meet the interest, and bankruptcy was therefore inevitable; on a smaller scale they would have succeeded.

Two more deposits are lying idle because the Governments, on Geological Survey advice, sought help from monopolists in a particular commodity as to whether or how the commodity was viable. The deposits concerned were not of interest to the monopolists for themselves so that their advice, though accurate in point of fact, was so phrased as to discourage the venture.

It must therefore be a special group of geologists working with mining engineers who study how to exploit resources that are known in a country or indeed whether they can be exploited. If a Survey is to be concerned, it should be an almost autonomous department staffed with such men.

I would repeat that nothing I have said detracts from my view on the high basic value of Geological Surveys. Much of my own past experience (and incidentally some of my happiest years) have been when a member of a Survey.

To conclude with a variation of my opening phrase, it is my opinion that unless the quality of resources are much above average, which those of Scotland are not, the will to put them to work is the first thing to be built up. How to foster this will is outside the scope of the writer.

F. H. STEWART, Esq., *Professor of Geology, Edinburgh University*

A very large body of information on rock and mineral resources has been built up by H.M. Geological Survey and the Soil Survey of the Macaulay Institute and is contained in the publications of these institutions and in unpublished records in their offices. This very valuable work is still proceeding, and there will be the need for such fundamental studies. However, the number of workers in these Surveys is far too small to cope with all that is desirable, and our detailed knowledge of potentially valuable materials outside the coalfields is decidedly patchy.

It is clear, I think, that enough is known for us to be able to say that, under present economic conditions with present methods of winning and utilisation, it is unlikely that any *major* discoveries will be made with a more detailed economic survey. The finding of very large potash deposits in Yorkshire in 1938 shows that the days of major discoveries are not over. The possibility is certainly there, but the probability is low. It is however probable that a more thorough survey would bring to light *some* new deposits worth working under present conditions.

I should hesitate to say that, in this sense, the game would be worth the candle, but this is not the important point. The crux of the matter lies in the point, made by Professor George, that methods of winning and of processing are not static. As these progress, some of the unworkable and useless materials of today will become workable and useful. It is, therefore, only common sense that we should make a really detailed inventory of our possessions, so that we may be able to step in at the right time when a new material is wanted.

The main work of H.M. Geological Survey has been and will, I think, always be concerned with fundamental geological mapping and research, together with work of immediate application to working industries such as coal mining. This is of the greatest importance. I believe, however, that it is worth while considering the formation of a second Government body, perhaps roughly equivalent to the Bureau of Mines in Canada, which would be responsible for economic surveys built on the foundation supplied by the Geological Survey. The two bodies would work hand in hand, and the economic body would have to be in close liaison with industry. It would extend the type of work done by the Geological Survey during the wars. It could perhaps be responsible for a systematic geochemical survey of Britain, geophysical surveys accompanied by drilling programmes in districts of potential economic interest, and investigation and mapping of the physical and chemical variation in materials such as limestones, dolomites, silica rocks, serpentines, road and building stones, etc., in greater detail than can be done by the existing body.

I doubt very much whether this would lead to results of much economic importance in a short time, but as a long-term project it could be very valuable.

The written contribution by the Hydrographer of the Navy on pp. 159-60 is also relevant to this discussion.

BASIC RESOURCE FACTS

SURFACE AND UNDERGROUND WATER RESOURCES AND MARINE RESOURCES

Survey of Scottish Water Resources

R. MACLAGAN GORRIE, D.SC.
Convener, River Flow Studies, Royal Scottish Geographical Society, Edinburgh

Water resources are assessed for their share in the locating of old industries and in their effect upon (*a*) the current demands for industrial development, (*b*) the needs of hydro-electric power and (*c*) future developments in industry and agriculture. The damaging effects of floods and nadir flows can be mitigated by reservoir storage. Scotland has little resource in underground water supplies. The special character of Highland streams is indicated by their rainfall-runoff ratios differing radically from those of English rivers. A strong criticism is raised that there are great gaps in our knowledge of mountain rainfall, and that only a small number of Scottish streams are gauged for stream flow; these gaps lead to deficiencies in the published *Surface Water Year Book*. We need more fundamental river behaviour studies.

The loss to Scotland through the removal of Captain W. N. McClean's records of stream flow (1912 to 1940) to the Imperial College, London, is pointed out and their return is called for. The Spey Drainage Report of 1951-54 should be published. There is need for a water map or brochure to be published summarising Scots water resources for issue to enquiring industrialists.

The runoff from peat needs close study in view of the widespread erosion from burnt moorland; this enquiry should be handled as part of a long-term research project to assess forest and moorland influences on river flow specifically for Scottish conditions; this should also cover the contribution of snow to runoff and the erosive effect of frost at high altitudes, as well as the effect of recent changes in land use such as deep sheep-drains and afforestation furrows. Administration and research need a state-supported organisation to deal with Water Survey or Water Resources in all aspects.

1. VALUE OF WATER FOR INDUSTRY

The nations have exploited river water since the dawn of history. The most successful early civilisations have all been based on the great rivers such as the Tigris, Euphrates, Oxus, Indus, Ganges, Nile, and the rivers of China. In Scotland the siting of our early industrial ventures has depended upon pure water for the spinning and weaving of linen and cotton, paper-making, distilling, brewing, and the smelting of iron and aluminium. But a good supply of fresh water is never appreciated until it runs short. It needs the experience of the hardships of life in the drier tropics to evaluate this. Even today it takes a dry summer and a shortage in the capital's water supply to focus the citizens' attention on it. And yet the whole future development of our major industries such as Colville's steel plant, the chemical and petrochemical industries at Grangemouth, the B.M.C. motor plant at Bathgate, and the various atomic power plants such as Dounreay depends upon an adequate water supply. Fresh-water fisheries depend upon suitable beds for spawning.

2. Water as a Source of Power

Water is itself a source of power, and in terms of power production the hydro-electric supply coming from Scottish hill streams is a vital part of the power system, because although the base load can be met by coal-burning and atomic stations, the fluctuating peak load can best be met by hydro-electric stations, and particularly those of the pumped storage type. The North of Scotland Hydro-Electric Board has done a fine job in ensuring a supply to many out-of-the-way communities which would otherwise never have got it, but the task is by no means complete and many of the crofting townships are still without a supply. The demand in Scotland is growing by 5 per cent. per annum, so that new sources of power have to be planned to double the output every decade. The great point in favour of water for power is that it can be used more than once for power production in the mountains before it is released for industrial purposes in the lowlands. In the competition now going on between hydro-electric on the one hand and coal-burning and atomic stations on the other, it is devoutly to be hoped that the electrification of all our Highland communities will be completed and that their continuing needs will be met from the grid whether the hydro-electric programme is completed or not. Power and better transport are the two essentials in any plan to develop our unpopulated moorlands, which are actually the main source of our surface water.

3. Water-table and Underground Supplies

The circulation of water between the clouds and our rivers is known as the "hydrological cycle". This starts with precipitation from the clouds to the earth and follows with the disposal of this moisture by various routes through or over the ground to the rivers and the sea. A varying amount of moisture is taken up *en route* by the transpiration of plants and by evaporation from all sorts of surfaces, including the soil and the water surfaces of lakes, rivers and the sea. The extent to which the rain and snow contribute to the underground reserve depends chiefly on the fate of the runoff after the losses from evaporation plus transpiration have been deducted; part goes down the river direct and part goes into the underground storage but may later emerge as springs. The so-called "water-table" is an inadequate name for a very complex situation, for a great many of the Scottish rock strata are quite impervious and therefore hold no water at all. The underground water supplies are therefore confined to a few aquefers of limited distribution among which are the raised beaches and the old river beds. The Clyde sands pumped for Glasgow and the Tay gravel-beds pumped for Perth city were examples of the early use of this resource. A large body of underground water lies in the flooded and disused coal-pits, but the water from this source is almost invariably foul or poisoned, so it has to be treated before it can be used. Compared with the great and clearly defined water-bearing beds of the London greensands, the chalk and Triassic sandstones, Scotland really has no extensive water-bearing strata. What there is has been described in detail in a series of Geological Survey Wartime Pamphlets in which all recorded well bores throughout the Forth and Clyde basins have been located and analysed for rock strata and water production. This will be dealt with in detail by members of the Survey.

4. Floods and Nadir Flows

The hydrological cycle is a convenient concept for the purpose of assessing the available surface water supplies, but there are many phases between precipitation and the return of the rain-drop to the ocean which prevent us from exploiting any large proportion of this cycle. Some losses are unavoidable, but some are not. Some are due to historic changes in land use, some are even now taking place. By and large, the river regime tends to deteriorate and become more subject to ever higher floods and lower minimal or nadir flows. One might say that floods and the damage they do are the opposite of a resource; they are in fact a liability, but must be included in any tally of the water resource, particularly if the use of rivers for transportation or storage is included. The simplest attempts at canalisation or reservoir storage bring us face to face with the complications of peak floods and the intervening minimal flows.

5. High Dams and Erosion Losses

The economics of high dams for storage depend upon the estimated life of the storage, and this is apt to be adversely affected by soil erosion, a subject on which the average Scot is completely ignorant and unobservant. One could quote instances from practically every country in the world to show that erosion (usually man-made) has exceeded the engineer's assessment of how much space for storage of water will be usurped by erosion debris brought along by the river in flood. In Scotland erosion is less spectacular than it is in the dry tropics, but the Bathymetric Survey of 1904 showed that many of our lochs were silting up. There are three specific phases of erosion which are having a very deleterious effect on our lochs and river beds, and therefore on our water supplies. I refer to:

(*a*) the erosion of sloping hillsides where peat erodes seriously after the moor has been burnt to get rid of old heather and cotton grass;
(*b*) torrent erosion along the gullied banks of steep hill torrents;
(*c*) bank erosion along the flood planes of our major rivers.

(*b*) and (*c*) are definitely on the increase as a result of speeded-up runoff from the sheep walks and afforestation areas where deep ploughing on a downhill alignment of drains or planting furrows tends to throw off storm water much more quickly than in the past. In fact, the whole tendency of modern land use is towards a regime of quicker drainage. One would not wish to put the clock back or interfere with more efficient land usage, so we must be realistic and anticipate that this will inevitably bring flashier floods and more intense droughts between.[1]

6. Knowledge of Rainfall Essential

In analysing the hydrological cycle for local conditions, the first study is of course the rainfall, and we are confronted with considerable gaps in our knowledge of this. This will be dealt with in detail in Cranna's paper on climate. The main gaps in the rain-gauge grid are due to the high hills and have been filled in by drawing isohyets which are lines of equal rainfall. Considering that these are "inspired guesswork" based on the local study of contours and wind currents, they agree astonishingly with discharge observations for many conditions, and their general acceptance is a testimony to the dedicated study of meteorologists such as G. J. Symons and his successors in the compilation and publication of successive annual volumes of *British Rainfall.* The isohyetal conception is, however, an unsatisfactory substitute for real and actual measurements. Take as an example the Perthshire Lyon with a catchment of 62 square miles descending from 3,000 ft. on the very wet Argyll-Perthshire divide. There is one old rain-gauge at Meggernie at 800 ft. a.s.l. and this registers an average of 61 in., but 20 per cent. of the hill-tops are reckoned to be in the 100 to 110 in. isohyet and another 10 per cent. is above 110 in.[2] The isohyets are, however, practically useless for a detailed local study on such a high divide. The Hydro Board now have at least a dozen rain-gauges in this area, some of them approaching 2,000 ft., but none of these readings are yet available to us because the *Surface Water Year Book* up to 1957 is blank for the Lyon rainfall, and *British Rainfall* is still at 1956. The Lyon produces a peak flow per square mile of rather more than double that of any other Scottish catchment of comparable size for which we have any record. When the data are eventually published we should then be in a better position to produce a true rainfall-runoff ratio, though for a realistic unit hydrograph we need rainfall intensities.

7. Gauging Data Criticised

To take another and more important example, the *Surface Water Year Book* shows the Aberdeenshire Dee to be one of the most regularly gauged streams; it was in fact one of those for which Captain McClean produced a continuous flow record in 1934. But there is a mile distance and 15 ft. drop in level between the river section at Woodend and the water-level station at Cairnton, which latter is on a gravel bed, so that errors in the discharge are likely to creep in unless the basic dimensions and the river-bed profile are frequently checked. For rainfall the position for the Dee is even less satisfactory; instead of using the isohyetal data produced by the Meteorological Office for the catchment which starts at 4,300 ft., the figures have been compiled by the city engineer from the 20 rain-gauges maintained in the valley. But out of these, 5 are downstream of the river-gauge while of the rest Ben Breac is a monthly reading, and the highest is Derry Lodge at 1,000 ft. We therefore have still not got a clear picture of the mountain rainfall contribution in this 528 square mile catchment. These instances are quoted to show that making good the deficiencies in the rain-gauge network of Scotland seems to be nobody's business, whereas in England and Wales the River Boards are held responsible for this.

8. Spey-Tay Data Incomplete

For the Spey and the Tay the intermittent borrowing of water from across their common watershed for hydro-electric purposes has gone unrecorded, and again there are not enough rain-gauges. Thus the N.S.H.E. Board cannot produce the withdrawal and runoff data required by the Surface Water Survey for their year book, nor can the Meteorological Office give them enough about rainfall for the Survey to base a firm rainfall-runoff ratio for either of these important rivers. This appears to me to be the weakest point in the *Surface Water Year Book* in its present form; the point I wish to make here is not to criticise any of these organisations, but to appeal for more and better data of rainfall, runoff and catchment characteristics so that we can have some real progress in applying the growing science of hydrology to our local problems.

9. Hydrologic Data Derived

We already possess enough data to show clearly that Scottish rivers have a very different regime from the English ones. The rainfall-runoff ratio for 17 Scottish rivers is:

$$A=\tfrac{7}{8}R-8 \text{ (in inches) (see Figure 2, line A-A)}$$

as compared with Bilham's figure for the Thames basin:

$$A=0{\cdot}57R-6{\cdot}05 \text{ (in inches) (see Figure 2).}$$

From the work of Penman and others on evaporation it seems that in Scotland the average evaporation loss is about 14 in. a year compared with England's average of 18 to 19 in. The variation between the recorded Scottish rivers is shown by the data for 11 rivers plotted in Figure 2, from which it can be seen that they show individual aberrations from the mean of the A-A line which have so far defeated any sort of correlation that I could think of. The indication is that each catchment must be treated as an entity with its own peculiar characteristics. So far we do not have enough data for any one river to justify a detailed hydrological analysis of its behaviour trends comparable with the recently published *River Great Ouse Basin Hydrological Survey*, and so the hydrologists are driven to producing unit hydrographs from highly questionable data.

10. Rainfall-Runoff Ratios

Figure 2 does, however, show that the ratio of rainfall to runoff makes a reasonably consistent pattern for all these highland catchments where the greater altitude, heavier rainfall, and very large areas of hillside peat are the main factors fixing river behaviour. Out of the published records the peak floods in the Shin, Conon, Beauly, Ness, Dee, Lochy, Earn and Kelvin all register between 30 and 70 cu. ft. per second per square mile for catchments varying from 130 to 700 square miles in extent. The Lyon, already mentioned under rainfall, had a flood in December 1949 which produced 185 cu. ft. per second per square mile for a catchment of 62 square miles; this figure is not at all unusual when compared with the data from rivers of a similar size in other countries where there are serious conditions of erosion, but we have not got enough comparative local data to know if it is exceptional for Scotland.

11. Early Developments and Surveys

Historically Scotland made a good start with her assessment of water resource with the admirable Bathymetric Survey by Sir John Murray and Laurence Pullar, 1897 to 1909. This contains much valuable information about our fresh-water lochs and their geological history, the evidences of silting and impermanence, and of their fauna and flora. As a private enterprise it was a bold and magnificent gesture. Then in 1912 Captain W. N. McClean started his river studies. Work was continued intermittently between the wars on the Lochaber Garry, the Moriston, Ness, Lochy and Dee with the publication of 9 short papers between 1925 and 1935. But he failed to get Government assistance and eventually most of his gauging stations were taken over by the N.S.H.E. Board. His records, which should obviously have been kept in Scotland, were offered to various Scottish bodies but were not accepted, and they are now with the Imperial

College, University of London, being used as training material for hydrology students. I suggest this Conference agitates for their return to Scotland.

12. Spey Drainage Survey

Another outstanding example of lost effort is the Spey drainage report which was prepared by a team of technical workers and field staff of the Department of Agriculture for Scotland. This work took up the best part of 4 seasons, 1951 to 1954, in an effort to assess how far the historic reclamation of riverside lands from Laggan downstream to the sea had deteriorated during the 150 years it had been functioning. This report contains amongst other matter a complete summary of all known records, historical and newspaper, on Spey floods—the sort of material which the Royal Scottish Geographical Society's standing committee on River Flow Studies aims at collecting and publishing. In 1956, when working on a reconnaissance of river bank erosion on behalf of Nature Conservancy,[2] this report would have been of the greatest help to me, but I was not allowed access to it; as a tax-payer as well as a research worker I naturally took a poor view of this. I now wish to put forward a firm resolution that this Conference asks for this report and its appendices to be printed.

13. Flood Analyses

A further step in the sequence of flood analyses was taken by the Institution of Civil Engineers who in 1933 published an *Interim Report on Floods in Relation to Reservoir Practice*, with the object of estimating the *probable peak* of a flood. It included an "envelope curve" for all recorded floods on British rivers, including several Scots ones. This report has been revised and brought up to date with fresh records in 1959[3] and is one of the chief tools of the civil engineers, many of whom are engaged in working for the hydro-electric board and for local water authorities in Scotland. It is to be hoped that the next revision of this most valuable work will make a fresh attempt to analyse the differences in behaviour and in output of water between mountain and lowland, catchments.

14. Need for a Water Map

Apart from flood estimation, a need has been greatly felt for a water map or summary of water resources which could be made available to enquiring industrialists. In 1952 the Scottish Council (Development and Industry) technical officers set about the preparation of an index of possible industrial sites and their water status from data already available to them from the Department of Health, but permission to publish was refused. The result is that this has never been printed, so enquiries about industrial water supplies have to be dealt with on the basis of an enquirer first stating his choice of location. This seems to me a quite inadequate way of presenting Scotland's resources to enquirers. A brochure stating what is known about the water situation should have been available at the recent New York British Trade Fair.

15. Suggestion re "Surface Water Year Book"

While on the subject of publication, I would like to make a suggestion about the *Surface Water Year Book*. This has appeared as an annual volume during the last few years after an 8-year back-log had been produced for 1945-53. It is a most valuable production, but in its present form it is expensive for the casual enquirer. I would suggest that the Scottish rivers be made the subject of a separate publication, or that a single sheet or card be put on sale for each individual river with its data brought up to date.

16. Rainfall Intensity Figures Needed

J. E. Nash's experimental use of the unit hydrograph to prognosticate the speed of rise and fall in flood peaks is of value where no other data are available[4] but one would prefer to have a great deal more basic measurements such as rainfall intensity, absorption of rain by the ground, evaporation, transpiration and river discharge during flood stages, before any great reliance could be placed on the unit hydrograph as a means of determining the expected peaks for the 10-year, 100-year and 1,000-year storms. This Conference seems to be an opportunity to draw up a set of objectives so that future work on such matters can be co-ordinated.

17. Gaps in Stream Gauging

A detailed analysis of the river gauging so far published leads one to the following unsatisfactory conclusions:

(*a*) that only a few of our Scottish rivers are adequately gauged, either for rainfall or stream flow;
(*b*) that only the Ness, Spey, Lochy and Dee (all begun by McClean) and the Tay, Melgam and Inzion have any substantial continuity of flow record (see Table I for a check of the records from 1945 onwards);
(*c*) that several of these accepted records are not above suspicion as to their accuracy;
(*d*) that few of the gauging stations are sufficiently often calibrated;
(*e*) that there should be some means of checking the amount actually discharged during high flood peaks (Scottish rivers with notably unstable beds are the Cromdale Avon, the Ruchell in Glenartney, and the Annan).

18. Gauging Technique

The question of an acceptable standard for gauging will be dealt with by Mr. J. K. C. Wilson in his paper. I would here like to pay tribute to the devoted work which he and his small group of workers have put into the pursuit of flood records in the field. We appear now to be within sight of a big development in river gauging through the use of a digital recorder which is being tested intensively in the U.S.A. by the U.S. Geological Survey and by the Wear and Tees River Board in England. The introduction of this type of equipment would make the actual gauging much simpler and cheaper through economy in manual and clerical work, but would entail radical changes in the drill for the handling and storage of records.

19. Research needed on River Regimes

From the many discussions which the River Flow Studies Committee has had, we have come to the conclusion that much more fundamental data should be collected over a long period of river behaviour. It is possible that some of the changes in regime experienced in many of the larger tropical rivers can be replicated here in a modest and

TABLE I

"Surface Water Year Book" Data of Rainfall-Runoff, Recorded Years since 1935

No. in SWYB	River	Catchment in sq. miles	'35-53	'53-4	'54-5	'55-6	'56-7	Total	Remarks
3	Shin	191	3	1	1	1	1	7	Loch Shin included
4	Conon	375	8	1	—	—	—	9	Latter years R incomplete
5	Beauly	328	4	1	1	1	1	8	Loch Mullardoch included
6	Ness	692	8	1	1	1	1	12	Canal abstracted
6	Blaraidh	10	2	1	1	—	—	6	Incomplete
12	Dee	528	8	1	1	1	1	12	Record unsatisfactory
15	(Tay) Newton	6	4	1	1	1	1	8	Grouped in graph Fig. 1
15	(Tay) Melgam	16	4	—	—	1	1	6	Grouped in graph Fig. 1
15	(Tay) Inzion	10	4	—	1	—	1	6	Grouped in graph Fig. 1
16	Earn	232	6	1	—	1	1	9	Incomplete 1954-5
21	(Tweed) Fruid	9	6	1	1	1	1	10	Talla spill since 1952
84	Kelvin	128	2	1	1	1	1	6	Runoff not complete 1948-52
91	Lochy	301	4	1	1	1	1	8	Inaccurate
90	Leven	58	3	1	1	1	1	7	Blackwater Reservoir

Notes: Spey, Tay and Lyon all incomplete.
Nith 4 readings, Irvine 3 readings, Calder 5 readings — omitted.

less spectacular way. J. P. Gunn's research work on the Jhelum and other Punjab rivers has shown that for the same level readings and current recordings the actual discharge could vary considerably owing to the fact that the base level of the stream-bed can be deepened and disturbed temporarily by a high flood. With the changes in river regime being brought about by current changes in land use and by the hydro-electric regimentation of streams and torrents, it is not enough to fix a bench mark for the sill and presume that the cross-section of the stream will remain constant. In the direction of the stream-bed's profile, hill torrents alter their regime radically over a period of years after a sill or barrage has been installed, and these changes extend both upstream and downstream of the obstruction. This is happening in some of the N.S.H.E. Board high catchments where an aqueduct collects water from a number of hill torrents, e.g. in Sloy, Lawers, Almond, Errochty and Livishie.

20. Runoff from Peat

Alongside this purely hydrological research I would press for much more attention to be paid to the effect of changes in land use upon runoff. Out of Scotland's total area of 19 million acres, some 12 million are under peaty moorland classed as "rough grazings" and "deer forest". Most Scottish rivers have 80 to 90 per cent. of their catchments in such land, so changes in land use which affect the runoff will affect river performance. Two trends have already been pointed out, namely the erosion of peat following upon moor burning, and the quicker drainage of hillsides through mechanically dug sheep-drains and planting furrows. All of these must affect the runoff to some extent. There can be no question of putting the clock back by stopping the use of heavy drainage ploughs, so I would only point out now that the erosion of hill peat is an important factor in the current deterioration of the river regimes. If the country continues to ignore these changes it will inevitably suffer for it. One has to face the fact that the river regimes are altering for the worse, but we do not know how much. The effect of frost and thaw on exposed and eroding peat at high altitudes should be under the serious consideration of the Hydro Board, particularly in those high catchments where water is being collected from a series of mountain torrents above 2,000 ft.

21. Forest and Moorland Influences

Linked with these studies of land use is the measurement of evapo-transpiration. This is such a significant factor in water resource surveys that it deserves systematic study, but delay in setting up a research organisation has handicapped the few research workers already on the job. Various schemes for measuring the effects of forest cover on the runoff either as a single factor or as part of a wider forest influences study have been discussed between the Forestry Commission, the water engineers and the forest influences group of the Oxford forestry school. But so far as one can judge, the study of moorland water losses from the acid peat hillsides whose afforestation is peculiarly Scottish and of some importance in land-use decisions, is not being studied in Scotland at all. Some work is being done by Nature Conservancy workers in the Cairngorms[5] and in the Pennines on evaporation from high-level peat, and the Hill Sheep Farming Research Organisation has interested itself along with the Macaulay Soil Research Institute in the water yield from peat. The Scottish Peat Survey deals with the larger blocks of flat bog peat and the utilisation of peat as a raw material. I consider that the present facilities for these few isolated workers is quite inadequate. We must have a fully fashioned Scottish study of forest and moorland influences which will include not only the moderating effects on local climate of isolated shelterbelts, but of the influence on water supply of large afforested blocks all the way up to and beyond the upper altitudinal limits of afforestable land. Even if and when such data are produced for English conditions, they will not be applicable to Scotland because they cannot be realistic for our conditions.

22. Gaps in Scottish Water Administration

Turning now to the administration, England has a long history of local efforts in river management which were focused to some extent by the 1930 Drainage Act and later and more effectively by the River Boards Act of 1948, which provides for a river board for each region or major catchment and authorises the assessment from riparian owners of a cess which can be spent on improvements. Scotland has had nothing parallel to this and there has been no provision for river boards; so far we have only the Rivers (Prevention of Pollution) (Scotland) Act of 1951, which authorises the control of pollution only.

23. Agencies Employed

The agencies gauging streams in Scotland have in the past been the Land Drainage Branch of the D.O.A.S., the North of Scotland Hydro-Electric Board and several of the chief local water authorities. These were joined more recently by the South of Scotland Electricity Board and eight River Purification Boards for the rivers in the industrial belt. These River Purification Boards are authorised to take a full range of gauge readings, but their budgets restrict them to taking only the nadir flows which are their chief yard-stick for regulating pollution dilution, so they are not measuring flood flows. The remaining Scottish rivers not yet under the 1951 Act must also soon be dealt with because the menace of pollution has recently been extended into agricultural areas with the poisonous effects of silage effluent.

24. Future Demands

In attempting to present a picture of the present water use and possible future demands I have had great difficulty. The *Surface Water Year Book*, as already pointed out, deals only with about 16 per cent. of Scotland, and if we exclude the Tay and Spey on the grounds already discussed, the metered catchments are only 9 per cent. of the area. In terms of use the daily consumption of 25 major suppliers according to the *Water Engineers' Handbook* for 1960[6] shows a total of 260 million gallons; out of this the ratio of Domestic to Trade is 160 to 100. But this excludes very large and important private water supplies organised by industrialists. Domestic consumption per head is going up fairly steadily as our national standard of living improves; 12 of the Scottish suppliers report an average use per head of 80 gallons a day, the highest being Inverkeithing with 104. Trade consumption, on the other hand, is not going up steadily but in a series of bounds whenever any large new plant is established. The heaviest users are paper-makers, steel works and other heavy industries, chemicals and atomic power stations. New demands for single enterprises for 5 million gallons a day are now fairly common along the Forth-Clyde industrial belt, whose water-bearing strata for pumping are already fairly fully tapped, so further industrial developments must depend upon the location of ample reservoir sites from which the water can be piped to the factory. This clearly indicates the tapping of our Highland streams before they have emerged on to their lowland flood planes—in fact the taking over of free-flowing water as soon as the hydro-electric engineers have finished with it. Future demands must also be expected from the farmers; over much of England, particularly in the south-east, the value of supplementary spray irrigation for farm and vegetable crops is already being exploited, and it will not be long before the farmers in the Lothians, the lower Tweed, Fife and the Carse of Gowrie, Strathmore and the north-east start staking a claim on local streams for this purpose. A recent paper by M. E. Castle and D. Reid of the Hannah Dairy Research Institute read at the International Grassland Conference, 1960,[7] showed the value of irrigation in improving grass yields.

25. State-supported Organisation Needed

All these points emphasise the need for some better river organisation which could deal with each catchment as a complete land and water unit, and look after the interests in it for both administration and research. There are many known objections to copying the English River Boards Act, which is in any case not applicable to present Scottish conditions of land-holding and balance between private and Government ownership, so I would suggest that this Conference presses for better and separate legislation. In this connection I would urge a close study of the Danish unofficial body Hedeselskap, which has been built up over the last century and now handles hydrological work and land drainage schemes and shelterbelt planting for the whole of Denmark. It receives considerable sums from Government in grants and subsidies which it administers although it is not a Government department. I believe we could get a great deal of work done cheaply and effectively in Scotland on a similar basis, and I suggest for serious consideration that the River Flow Studies Committee of the R.S.G.S. already forms a suitable nucleus on which such an organisation could be built up.[8] The opinion of most of my colleagues in this committee is, however, that only a government body or a state-supported organisation with considerable resources and staff could handle this. Even if the case for purely Government control is accepted, it will need the support and guidance of a strong unofficial backing such as this committee has already marshalled.

26. River Basin Assessment

A recent discussion between Mr. L. B. Leopold, Chief Hydraulic Engineer of the U.S. Geological Survey, and our River Studies Committee has shown conclusively that owing to the lack of basic data Scotland is not at the moment in a position to make use of the new hydrological approach to river basin assessment of W. B. Langbein, because this depends upon the analysis and correlation of known data under a number of different heads such as rainfall, rainfall intensity, runoff, sunshine, soil moisture storage, evaporation, river gauging, pollution, irrigation and water utilisation in all its forms. The objective is a long-term working plan which will ensure the correlation of the various elements, often competitive in their exploitation of the land and water resources of each river basin. Every effort should be made to remedy the gaps in our local knowledge which have now been discussed. The case I am now presenting for more basic data and a sound control of development is by no means new, and in closing I would like to quote from Sir Alexander Gibb who tried twenty-five years ago to have this same case presented. At the World Power Conference at Washington in 1936 he made a strong plea for the handling of water under all its headings of drainage, domestic supply, fisheries, hydro-electric power and irrigation as a national asset and under national control. In another address in Britain the same year he said:

"The Government has now partially accepted the recommendation to initiate a water resources survey. Undoubtedly the results should be valuable but it seems unlikely that its scope will be as wide as it should be; or that it will be such as to provide an adequate basis for the foundation of a definite water policy. The survey seems to be directed almost exclusively to water supply; and even in this restricted field the whole ground is not being covered. A hydro-geological survey is an essential part of any present study of water resources."

These words were written twenty-five years ago[9] by one of the best civil engineers this country has produced. The need for implementing his proposals is even more pressing today because so little of what he recommended has been done in the interval.[10] A national Water Survey or Water Resources organisation is more than ever essential if Scotland is to be removed from the list of undeveloped countries.

I wish to acknowledge the assistance given to me by several members of the River Flow Studies Committee of the R.S.G.S. in preparing this paper.

REFERENCES

1. GORRIE, R. M. (1958). Soil erosion in Scotland and as a world problem. *Trans. roy. Highl. Agric. Soc. Scot.*
2. GORRIE, R. M. River-bank erosion. Typescript deposited with Nature Conservancy 1956.
3. Interim report on floods in relation to reservoir practice. *Proc. Instn. civ. Engrs.*, **5**, Feb. 1960.
4. NASH, J. E. Unit Hydrograph study with particular reference to British catchments. Cyclostyled by Hydraulic Res. Station, Wallingford.
5. GREEN, F. H. W. Cairngorms Weather Survey. *Weather*, **10**, 2 Feb. 1955, and *Nature* (ref. No. 8 below).
6. *Water Engineers' Handbook*, 1960. Published Colliery Guardian Co., 30 Furnival St., London, E.C.4.
7. CASTLE, M. E., and REID, D. (Hannah Dairy Res. Inst.). *Proc. Internat. Grassland Conf.* 1960.
8. Water resources and water needs in Scotland; report on symposium, Glasgow, 1958, British Association. *Nature*, **82**, 1193-1195, Nov. 1958.
9. HARRISON, G. *Alexander Gibb*, a biography. Bles, 1950.
10. ALLARD, W., GLASPOOLE, J., and WOLF, P. O. Rainfall and Runoff sub-committee: Recent developments in Hydraulics. *Min. Proc. Instn. civ. Engrs.*, **4**, 1033-1049, Dec. 1955.

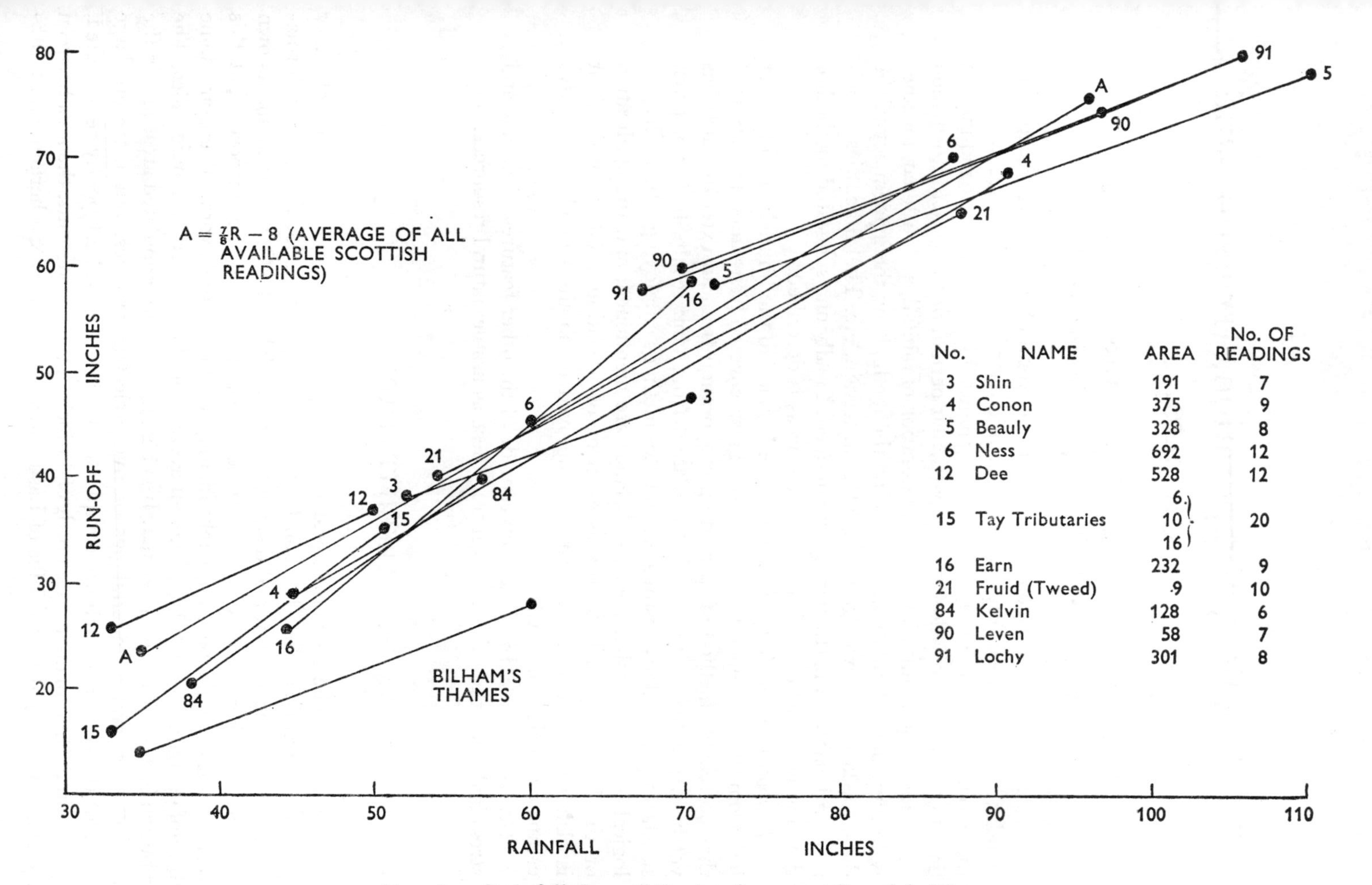

FIG. 1. Rainfall-Runoff Ratios for some Scottish Rivers

Precipitation, Evaporation, Irrigation and Climate

R. CRANNA, M.A., B.SC., and R. W. GLOYNE, B.SC., PH.D.
Principal Scientific Officers, Meteorological Office, Edinburgh

Precipitation. The shortcomings of the network of observing stations in Scotland are discussed, especially the erratic distribution, the infrequency of measurements and the lack of recording gauges. The methods of handling the data to provide information for any particular period, or to extract information on averages, variability, intensity and duration of rainfall, are outlined, together with some of the limitations imposed on the methods by the inadequacy of the data, the lack of knowledge of the effect of terrain, etc. The difficulties associated with snow, in particular, are mentioned. Finally one suggested method of defining water deficit and water surplus areas is described.

Evaporation and Irrigation. Reference is made to the limited data on water loss from standard open tanks and from grass-covered lysimeters. It is stressed that no reliable method of measuring evaporation from an extensive area has yet been produced, and that extrapolation from tank results have not given satisfactory quantitative estimates. Indirect methods employing either a hydrological or an atmospheric energy balance are mentioned, and the application of the latter approach to the assessment of irrigation need is outlined: it is claimed that this method can be employed to obtain a good quantitative estimate of irrigation need.

General Climate. Brief mention is made of the other features of climate and stress laid upon the value of regarding these as usable natural resources.

PRECIPITATION

RAINFALL

Basic Network. The Meteorological Office depends very largely on the voluntary co-operation of public bodies, local authorities and private individuals for the information it receives on the amount and distribution of rainfall. The Office maintains its own network of observing stations, mainly on airfields, for forecasting purposes, but this network by itself would be completely inadequate for rainfall work. There are some 1,250 rainfall stations in Scotland,[1] i.e. an average of about 1 per 24 square miles. The distribution is, however, very irregular. It is best in the more populated areas and in the vicinity of major water undertakings or hydro-electric schemes, but there are large stretches of the country which are completely ungauged or at best poorly represented, e.g. the central Grampians to the north of Pitlochry, the Cairngorms, the area between Ardgour and Glen Quoich, the hills of Easter Ross, and eastern Sutherland and Caithness. About one-third of the gauges are read at infrequent intervals. Some of these are read every week or fortnight, but the great majority are read only once per month; this applies particularly to the gauges in the remote hill areas, and in such places all detail is lost.

The study of the intensity and duration of rainfall, and the measurement of the amounts which fall in less than 24 hours, depends almost entirely on the records of automatic recording gauges. The network of such gauges in Scotland is very poor. There are about 45 recorders only, and the records of many of them are not fully analysed by the authorities who maintain them; in most cases reports of the duration of rain and total daily amounts only are received by the Meteorological Office and no information is supplied about hourly amounts, maximum falls in given periods, or the times for given amounts to fall. Moreover, practically all of the recorders are situated near the coast or on low ground. It would be possible to count on the fingers of one hand the number of recorders in the hills north of the Highland line, and all of these are at moderate elevations in the bottom of glens.

From the information available it is possible to make reasonable estimates of the annual[2] or monthly areal rainfall in any given year or month for areas where there is at least an outline network of gauges. Such estimates are normally done by drawing isohyets, and in the more densely gauged areas probably have a standard error of about 3 or 4 per cent. This may increase to about 10 per cent. in areas which are thinly gauged but are still considered worth attempting.[3] Some areas, e.g. the Cairngorms, are so lacking in gauges that estimation is not considered justified. The demand for estimations of areal rainfall for such purposes as the *Surface Water Year Book* has grown to such an extent that the possibility of programming an electronic digital computer to produce objective estimates is being examined.

More detailed estimates for shorter periods, e.g. for a particular storm in a fairly large catchment, are more difficult; it depends on the amount of detailed information available, and no useful generalisation can be made.

Hitherto all data from the stations have been processed by hand, but it is hoped that by within a few years the data will be recorded on punch cards or tapes. Once a reasonable backlog has been accumulated this will make for much greater speed and flexibility in answering enquiries.

Averages. Until 1958 the standard period to which rainfall averages were related was the 35-year period 1881-1915.[4, 5] A changeover is now being made to the new period 1916-50.[6] It should be emphasised that, as a guide to the future, the new period has no particular advantage as far as is known; the next 35 years may resemble the period 1881-1915 more closely than they do 1916-50. The change is being made because it was becoming increasingly difficult to maintain valid links with the earlier period. It will also be possible to take advantage of the advances which have been made in the technique of rainfall measurement, the experience which has accrued in the interval, the greater mass of material available and the results of an intensive programme of inspection visits which has been undertaken in recent years.

Annual and monthly averages for long-term stations can be calculated directly. The annual averages can be used to construct maps for each year showing the percentage of average rainfall in each area for that particular year. These in turn can be used to determine, with a known degree of precision, estimated long-period averages for stations with shorter records. The technique can be applied to a record covering one or two years only, but the standard error naturally increases as the period shortens. Maps showing the percentage distribution of the total annual rainfall between the different months can also be drawn, based on the long-term stations, and these maps can be used to split up the estimated annual averages for short-term stations into monthly values. Finally, using all available long-term and estimated averages, isohyetal maps can be drawn showing the distribution of the annual average rainfall over the country. As this involves interpolation between stations and extrapolation to higher levels, there is still a considerable subjective element in this stage. Attempts are being made to introduce more obejctive methods.

The daily values of a selection of long-term stations have already been transferred to punch cards and, if necessary, daily averages or averages for periods of less than a month could be readily extracted. From the records it is also possible to produce averages and frequency distributions of such things as the number of rain days (·01 in.), wet days (·04 in.), etc. To a limited extent the punched cards have already been used in these ways.

Reliability. Looking at rainfall as a resource, the aspect which is probably of most interest is its reliability, i.e. the highest and, particularly, the lowest total falls which are ever likely to be encountered in any period of consecutive months or years; possibly also the frequency with which the amounts fall within certain limits. This subject has been studied by Glasspoole[7] and others,[8] and working from the basic isohyetal maps it is possible to give very reasonable estimates of these figures for any place or area.

Intensities. For the purposes of culvert and sewerage design it is necessary to know the maximum intensities over a given period which are likely to be encountered at a place or over a catchment. There the estimates are on less firm ground. From a study of the results of recording gauge records, Bilham produced a formula giving the expectancy of a given amount of rain in a given time at a certain place.[9] It is uncertain, however, how far this formula needs to be modified for hilly terrain, and it does not give any indication of the area covered by a rainfall of a certain intensity. The Meteorological Office is investigating this latter aspect at a site near Cardington as representative of level ground, and arrangements are in hand to extend the investigation to broken country (in the Cotswolds).

The previous paragraph deals with the probability of short-period rainfalls of given intensities. Information for any particular storm depends on the record from a representative recorder. As the network of recorders is so open it is unlikely that such a record will be available, but in the present context this aspect is scarcely relevant.

Duration. The duration of rainfall is a factor which affects many outdoor human activities. Information on duration depends on recording rain-gauges and is therefore scanty. One fact which emerges, however, is that the overall rate of rainfall over a considerable period (of the order of a year or more) is fairly constant throughout the country. If, therefore, the average annual rainfall is known, a good estimate can be made of the average duration of rain of all intensities. It is not known how far this can be applied in really rugged country.

For many purposes it is the duration of rainfall above a certain intensity which is important, and the estimation of this presents greater difficulties. McConalogue[10] and Thomson[11] have tackled it from different aspects, McConalogue dealing with the actual duration and Thomson with the number of clock hours in which a given amount of rain fell, regardless of the duration within that hour. Both have produced formulae which can be used with the usual reservation that it is not known what happens in the hills. McConalogue's examination in particular was restricted to coastal stations.

This problem can be taken further, e.g. the number of occasions on which x consecutive hours have a rainfall of y inches, but the matter is too complex to deal with here.

Snowfall

Quantitatively the measurement of snowfall is one of the greatest remaining problems under the heading of precipitation (hail can be damaging and economically important, but outbreaks in Scotland are relatively mild and so spasmodic that they do not lend themselves to statistical treatment).

Snow, with its low terminal velocity and liability to drift, presents three main problems:

(i) the choice of a site which will be representative;
(ii) when such a site is found, catching a representative sample of the snow that falls;
(iii) measuring and recording the caught snow.

It can be said quite briefly that no really satisfactory solution to these problems has yet been found, either in this country or in others where it is much more important. The matter is naturally receiving a good deal of attention.

The practice in this country for the purposes of measurement is to treat snow as a form of rainfall, and to measure its water content in terms of the equivalent inches of rain. The normal rain-gauge network is used, the snow in the gauge being melted and measured as rainfall. For the reasons mentioned in the previous paragraph there is a good deal of uncertainty in this method, particularly in the case of monthly hill gauges, and considerable estimation and adjustment of the records is required each year to give a coherent picture. These adjustments are based on known relationships between gauges during snow-free periods, but there is obviously an element of conjecture involved.

In recent years the Meteorological Office has taken over from the British Glaciological Society the organisation of the Snow Survey of Great Britain. This is maintained by a network of voluntary observers in the neighbourhood of the main hill ranges. Observations are made daily of how far down the hillsides the snow cover extends. No depths are given except at station level.

The network of climatological stations, both official and voluntary (about 140 in Scotland), have for many years recorded the number of days with snow falling and the number of days with snow covering more than half the ground,[12] but it is only recently that the total depth has been systematically recorded. Still more recently the fresh depth of snow since the previous morning has been measured at voluntary climatological stations. Manley[13] and others[14] have studied the results and have evolved empirical formulae to try to extend the application of the available information. The main lack at present is information on the depth of snow, but data are being accumulated and the matter is being studied.

General. There are so many aspects of precipitation which may be of interest, and so many forms in which enquiries may be framed, that no attempt will be made to provide specific information here. For a broad picture the type of treatment used recently by Gregory[8] may suffice. He defined three types of area:

(i) those areas receiving less than 30 in. of rain at least 3 years in 10;
(ii) those areas receiving more than 50 in. of rain at least 7 years in 10;
(iii) the intermediate areas.

He suggested that areas of type (i) are bound to experience water deficits at fairly regular intervals, while areas of type (ii) can be exploited for their water surplus. In Scotland an eastern coastal strip, varying in width but averaging something like 20 miles, is considered to be type (i). The greater part of the Western and Central Highlands, and the western half of the Southern Uplands are classed as type (ii).

EVAPORATION

Of the other phases of the hydrological cycle, evaporation is one in which the Meteorological Office, along with other bodies (e.g. research institutes, University departments) takes considerable interest.

General Problems

As regards the quantitative evaluation of water loss to the atmosphere, it can be briefly stated that:

(1) As yet no really satisfactory method has been developed whereby the water loss from an *extensive* area can be directly or indirectly measured: this is true with respect to open water surfaces, but even more so with respect to natural ground surfaces.[15]

A method of measuring the net upward flux of water vapour from *limited* areas with a homogeneous cover of ordinary agricultural crops, e.g. grass, cereals, has been developed,[16, 17, 18] but it is essentially a research tool, needing extensive and precise instrumentation.

(2) Methods of estimating the loss of water by evaporation may be divided into:

(*a*) those in which evaporation is the unknown quantity in a water budget consisting of rainfall, percolation, runoff, and storage changes;

(*b*) those in which it is the unknown quantity in an atmospheric energy balance-sheet, with adjustments, where necessary, to allow for differences in the movement of water from a free water surface, and that from a soil or vegetated surface;

(*c*) empirical relationship between weather factors and water losses from tanks, and lysimeters of various dimensions; again, as with 2 (*b*), with some attention to soil and plant characteristics.

Studies under 2 (*a*) have been mainly pursued by water engineers, those under 2 (*b*) and 2 (*c*) by meteorologists, plant physiologists and the like. The latter methods have been extended in order to develop a rational policy for irrigation.

These matters are considered in more detail, with special reference to conditions in Scotland, in the following paragraphs.

Direct Measurement of Water Loss

From Open Water Surfaces. For some decades[19] observation of the changes in level of water in a standard tank have been used as a measure of evaporation from an open water surface. Such tanks are usually 6 ft. square, containing some 450 gallons of water and having a rim 3 in. (sometimes 6 in.) above the surface of the surrounding ground.

For Scotland the following records are available:

Period	*Place and Authority*
1907-1953	Talla Water, Peeblesshire. Edinburgh Water Department.
1908-1914 1922-1930	Edinburgh. Edinburgh University.
1930-1945	Glencorse Filter, Midlothian. Edinburgh Water Department.
1936-1950	Amlaird Filters. Burgh of Kilmarnock.
1903-1909*	Falkirk. D. Ronald, Esq.

In connection with the activities of the International Geophysical Year, measurements of water loss have been made at the Meteorological Office Observatories:

Eskdalemuir (Dumfriesshire) . .	Since October 1957
Lerwick (Shetlands) . . .	Since March 1958

In these cases a standard US tank is used,[15] i.e. a 4 ft. diameter circular pan with upper rim some 18 in. from the ground: the pan is about 10 in. in depth, and stands above the surface of the ground so that the water surface is about 15 in. above ground-level.

From Bare Soil or Vegetated Surfaces. Percolation gauges or lysimeters[19] attempt to simulate loss from actual bare soil, or vegetated surfaces, by exposing to the atmosphere an undisturbed core of soil isolated from the surrounds by impermeable vertical walls and having an impermeable base at a sufficient depth below the surface (viz. 20 in. below a bare soil surface and 20 in. below the deepest roots of a turfed surface) for it to be assumed that the base does not interfere with the natural movement and exchange of water. Drainage from the base of the core is measured.

The only long-period records for Scotland are those from three pasture-covered gauges of 40 in. depth each of $\frac{1}{1000}$ acre in area, maintained at Craibstone, Aberdeen, from 1921 to 1946.

A short record 1905-09 from a grass-covered lysimeter at Falkirk is also available.

Recently the Nature Conservancy[20, 21] has experimented with a type of lysimeter in which measures are taken to ensure that, within the root-range, there is sufficient soil moisture to allow the turf-covered surface to transpire at the rate equal to that required by the ambient atmospheric "stress". The amount of water so removed is termed the "potential (evapo-) transpiration". Thus, as with the open water surface, and in contrast to the Craibstone and most other lysimeters, the amount of water removed is almost entirely a function of atmospheric conditions; with the conventional lysimeter, percolation and drain gauges, on the other hand, the actual water loss in dry periods is limited by the amount of water available for removal at the surface. The extreme case of the difference between the operation of the two types is exemplified

* Loss from small floating tank 8 in. diameter with rim 2 in. above surrounding water-level.

by the desert, where the evaporative potential is very high but where there is no water near enough to the surface to be removed, and hence no water loss.

As mentioned, it has not been found possible to estimate satisfactorily the water loss from extensive surfaces—especially in an area of rugged topography and rapid change of surface conditions (from bare rock to densely vegetated bogs, as in Scotland).

These strictures, however, do not necessarily invalidate the use of evaporimeters, or other such devices, as diagnostic tools in biological and other studies—we merely state that it does not seem valid to regard data from such devices as giving a representative and quantitative estimate of water loss in general.

Estimation of Water Loss

From Rainfall/Runoff/Storage Data. These methods are almost exclusively the province of the hydraulic engineer. Dr. Gorrie has already mentioned certain runoff/rainfall relationships, and all that is required in this note is the reminder that with respect to total precipitation there are certain geographical deficiencies in the gauging network, and serious deficiencies in the measurement of snowfall and of precipitation intensity. The river gauging side, including the accuracy of the measurements, is being dealt with in another paper.

Atmospheric Energy Balance. This method, linked with the name of Dr. Penman of Rothamsted,[22, 23] has been extensively used, and has been further elaborated and exploited in connection with irrigation.

Over large areas of East Anglia, South-East England and similar areas of gentle relief, where the typical ground cover is one of permanent and deep-rooted turf, it has been found possible to estimate annual water loss from certain catchments to better than 10 per cent. of that independently obtained from catchment data, changes in well-levels, etc.

In much of hilly Scotland, where the rock surface is bare or covered only by a thin soil layer with a variable vegetative cover, such a satisfactory result is unlikely in general, and the departures of the actual conditions from those postulated in the basic theory may be serious. For example, how does one treat, on the one hand, light falls which evaporate *in situ* from rock surfaces, and, on the other, heavy falls most of which runs rapidly from steep rocky slopes into deep swiftly moving streams? One of the basic concepts of the method—that of a layer of soil in which the moisture reaches field capacity regularly during the winter—cannot apply, nor has the postulate of a uniform green sward with a root system with ready access to water as wide a validity as is the case in England.

Fundamentally, Penman determines a "potential evapo-transpiration" and his estimates of the average annual evaporation for Scotland vary from about 16 in. in the south to 14 in. or so in the extreme north. Such checks as he was able to obtain suggest that these estimates in the northern half of the mainland may be overestimated by 1 or 2 in. or more.

In spite of possible criticisms, however, it is true to add that in the typically arable and horticultural areas of Scotland the physiography is not dissimilar to that of much of England, and there is no reason to suppose that the application of the Penman approach to irrigation planning—so successful in England—will not be equally successful in the appropriate parts of Scotland.

Other Empirical Approaches. Many are adaptations or developments of Thornthwaite's work[24] in the U.S.A. These have been considered, e.g. by Green,[20, 21] and briefly seem to offer no advantages over the cautious extrapolation of direct measurements or the use of methods of estimation outlined above.

IRRIGATION POSSIBILITIES IN SCOTLAND

A realistic estimate of the amount of water likely to be required per acre for a particular crop depends upon:

(1) estimates of the rainfall and potential transpiration;
(2) decision as to the deficit of soil moisture below field capacity which a given crop can stand without suffering growth check: this implies in practice a decision as to how long a given deficit may be tolerated by the plant, and hence be allowed to affect it;
(3) reasonable assumption as to the capacity of the irrigation equipment to deal with the peak loads required of it.

The data listed under (1), covering April-September inclusive (i.e. the months when biologically significant deficits of rainfall below that needed by the plant are most likely to arise), are available for Scotland. These data are certainly accurate enough for practical purposes in those areas where irrigation may be of importance, viz. much of Scotland south of the Forth-Clyde gap except the inland hill masses, and including many areas in Ayrshire and southwards and then eastward along the coastal strip to the Solway Firth; east of a line Stirling to Aberdeen, and the Moray Firth area.

The points mentioned in (2) will be immediately appreciated when it is realised that less water will be needed if it is judged sufficient to ensure a particular net balance of soil water at the end of (say) a two-monthly period than if the same level of soil moisture is to be ensured at the ends of successive shorter periods (e.g. fortnights) within the two months.

The effects on irrigation need, of the amount of the permitted deficit, and of the frequency with which the water balance is struck and irrigation need assessed, may be illustrated by the following figures for two places in South-West England.[25]

(1) (*a*) Number of years in 20 when some irrigation needed to supplement "seasonal" (April-September) rainfall in order to avoid a soil deficit of more than 3 in.:

Porton (nr. Salisbury, Wilts.)	14 years in 20
Exmouth (Devon)	10 years in 20

(From Calculation of Irrigation Need, *Tech. Bull. M.A.F.F.*, No. 4.)

(*b*) As (*a*), but ensuring that a 3 in. deficit does not arise at the end of any fortnight within the six months[26]:

Porton	18 years in 20
Exmouth	18 years in 20

The result of postulating certain deficits is illustrated below.[26]

(2) Number of years in 20 when irrigation need at least as much as indicated, assuming stated permissible deficits—fortnightly balance.

Irrigation Need (in.) .		0			2			4			6	
Permissible Deficit (in.)	1	2	3	1	2	3	1	2	3	1	2	3
Porton . . .	20	20	18	18	17	16	17	14	13	10	7	5
Exmouth . . .	20	19	18	18	16	14	15	13	7	7	4	3

Thus on 3 years out of 20 irrigation of at least 6 in. will be required at Exmouth, if a deficit of 3 in. or more is to be avoided, on the basis of a fortnightly assessment.

The above facts are presented merely to illustrate how it is now possible to give some reasonable quantitative estimate—on an actuarial basis—of the possible extent of irrigation water needed.

As regards a particular season or year and for the areas likely to be concerned, current advice on irrigation need (on a monthly, in some cases on a fortnightly basis) can be supplied by the Meteorological Office in Edinburgh. For such advice, a measurement or satisfactory estimate of current sunshine in the area of the particular site is required, together with knowledge as to the actual rainfall (as rainfall is so variable in time and space this requirement reduces to a direct observation of rainfall at a site representative of the farm or holding).

OTHER ASPECTS OF CLIMATE

The fact that consideration of the water-balance in Scotland has also involved aspects of the atmospheric environment other than precipitation justifies brief consideration of other features of Scotland's climate as a natural resource.[27]

The relatively high winter temperatures of the western coastal areas and islands (similar to those of west Wales) indicate a possible area for horticultural expansion, although the stronger winds experienced (a climatic asset from the point of view of the wind-generation of power) may need to be mitigated by shelter hedges, intercropping or other techniques. Outside the dense industrial belt these same winds maintain a relatively unpolluted atmosphere and this alone or in conjunction with the prolonged summer daylight may well be advantageous for certain enterprises.

For space heating, and for air-conditioning generally, the climate may for some types of enterprise present advantages over conditions farther south, e.g. lower extreme dew points for dehumidifying. In winter there is practically no temperature difference between London, Edinburgh and Lerwick. In summer the average daily mean temperature in the North of Scotland is some 5° F. to 7° F. cooler than in the South of England.

As regards communications generally, the relative infrequency of fog assists all forms—notably aviation—whilst the winter hazards due to snow, on the lower ground and in the southern half of the country at least, are probably overestimated in the public mind as compared with much of England.

Although our knowledge of the climate of Scotland is far from complete—particularly in the more remote areas—it is most unlikely that the Meteorological Office will be found unable to offer any assistance in the task of weighing up, with respect to any particular enterprise, the assets and liabilities of the natural environment of Scotland as compared with any other region.

In general, the Meteorological Office charges for services particularised for special needs. The charges are based on the time spent and the grade of the staff appropriate to the work.

REFERENCES

1. Meteorological Office. *Brit. Rainf.*, Ann. Vols., General Table. London: H.M.S.O.
2. Min. of Housing and Local Govt. and Scottish Office. *Surf. Wat. Yearb. G.B.*, Ann. Vols. London: H.M.S.O.
3. BLEASDALE, A. (1957). *Met. Mag., Lond.*, **86**, 207.
4. Meteorological Office. Book of Normals of Met. Elements, Sect. V. London: H.M.S.O.
5. Ordnance Survey (1949). Map. Rainfall Annual Average, 1881-1915. London: Ordnance Survey.
6. Meteorological Office. *Averages of Rainfall for Gt. Britain and N. Ireland, 1916-1950.* London: H.M.S.O.
7. GLASSPOOLE, J. (1955). *Quart. J. R. met. Soc. Lond.*, **81**, 268. (Gives earlier references.)
8. GREGORY, S. *Weather, Lond.*, **14**, 227. (Gives earlier references.)
9. BILHAM, E. G. (1935). *Brit. Rainf.*, p. 262. London.
10. MCCONALOGUE, D. J. (1935). *Met. Mag., Lond.*, **82**, 304.
11. THOMSON, A. B. (1954). *Met. Mag., Lond.*, **83**, 293.
12. Meteorological Office. *Mon. Weath. Rep.*, Ann. Vols. London: H.M.S.O.
13. MANBY, G. (1952). *Climate and the British Scene*, p. 197. London: Collins. (Gives earlier references.)
14. BONACINA, L. C. W. (1955). *Brit. Rainf.*, p. 219. London. (Gives earlier references.)
15. World Met. Organisation (1958). *Tech. Note W.M.O. Secretariat*, Geneva, No. 21.
16. PASQUILL, F. (1949). *Quart. J. R. met. Soc. Lond.*, **75**, 239.
17. PASQUILL, F. (1950). *Quart. J. R. met. Soc. Lond.*, **76**, 287.
18. RIDER, N. E. (1954). *Quart. J. R. met. Soc. Lond.*, **80**, 198.
19. Meteorological Office. *Brit. Rainf.*, Ann. Vols. from 1903. London: H.M.S.O.
20. GREEN, F. H. W. (1959). *Quart. J. R. Soc. Lond.*, **85**, 152.
21. GREEN, F. H. W. (1956). *J. Instn. Wat. Engrs. Lond.*, **10** (5), 411.
22. PENMAN, H. L. (1948). *Proc. roy. Soc.*, A **193**, 120.
23. PENMAN, H. L. (1950). *Quart. J. R. met. Soc. Lond.*, **76**, 372.
24. THORNTHWAITE, C. W. (1948). Geogr. Rev., **38**, 286.
25. Min. Agr. Fish. & Food (1954). *Tech. Bull. M.A.F.F.*, No. 4. London: H.M.S.O.
26. HOGG, W. H. (1956). *Mimeo.*, Met. Office. London.
27. Meteorological Office. Climatological Atlas. London: H.M.S.O.

The Measurement of Surface Water Flow in Scotland

J. K. C. Wilson, M.I.C.E., A.M.I.STRUCT.E., A.R.I.C.S., A.M.I.W.E.
Department of Agriculture for Scotland, Edinburgh

The paper discusses the measurement of surface water flow generally and the present lack throughout Scotland of factual information concerning surface water discharges. A short account is given of surface water measurements which have been made and of work presently in hand describing briefly the current activities of the principal authorities which engage in flow measurement together with the arrangements for publication of the resulting data. The necessity for expansion of the present flow-measuring arrangements to a properly organised systematic survey is emphasised and a suggestion made as to the coverage which might be necessary to provide an adequate assessment of water resources and other discharge information. Reference is made to the present standard of flow-measuring technique and to the forthcoming publication of British and International Standards relating to flow measurement. The bibliography includes reference to all known accounts of flow measurement or of discharge statistics relating to Scotland.

As a natural resource water may be considered to be one of the most commonly used raw materials of our civilisation, one of the great sources of power in nature and a widely spread medium for the support of fish life, for navigation, for the dilution and conveyance of wastes and for human recreation. Regarded as such, water is part of the wealth of a country. Conversely, too much water in the wrong place at the wrong time is liability instead of an assest.

Water is a natural commodity, but unlike land or mineral deposits it is not static. It is constantly changing both in form and in place. In form it passes through four phases in what has come to be known as the Hydrologic Cycle, viz. (1) Vapour, (2) Precipitation (rain, snow, dew, etc.), (3) Runoff, by surface or underground flow, and (4) Sea water. While water has value for one purpose or another in each phase of the cycle, this paper is concerned with surface runoff which is part of the third phase of the cycle. In this third phase water, which reaches the surface of the ground by precipitation, starts on a journey across that surface which terminates at the sea. In the course of the journey which commences as sheet flow over the surface or as interflow in the immediately accessible upper layers of the soil, flow quickly becomes concentrated in small runnels or channels which coalesce to form ever larger streams and ultimately rivers. At all stages in the journey surface flow suffers depletion from losses to underground flow (percolation) and by the direct passage of a part of the surface flow back to the vapour phase of the cycle (evapo-transpiration). In later stages surface flow may be augmented by the return of a proportion from underground to surface flow.

In a country such as Scotland which is adequately or abundantly provided with water, water as a commodity is only of value when it is present in the required quantity and quality in the required place, and in order to assess its value it is necessary to be able to state the quantities which are or can be made available at all times at a selected site as well as to give an assurance that the water will possess the qualities which are desirable. The direct way to obtain this information is by measurement and testing of the flows in the watercourse at or near the site at which it is to be used. Looking again at the obverse of the coin, when excess water is present, flow measurement is the direct means of determining the amount of the excess.

The measurement of large quantities of flowing water is not a simple matter. From early times measurements have been made directly or inferentially with greater or less degrees of accuracy in the case of small quantities, but it is only within the last fifty years or so that techniques have been developed which permit measurements of large quantities to be made with an acceptable standard of accuracy. Methods currently in use include (1) the direct measurements of the cross-sectional area of the stream together with the determination of the mean velocity of flow by the use of current meters, floats or other devices; (2) the assessment of the volume of water passing through a reach of channel in unit time from measurements of the dilution of chemical or radioactive substances added to the flow; and (3) the indirect measurement of the flow by determining the head required to force the stream over a weir or through a flume of predetermined form and dimensions for which the required coefficients have been ascertained by full-scale or model experiments.

Since the flow in a stream or river is a constantly changing quantity which may vary between wide extremes, single spot measurements of the discharge are seldom sufficient to afford the information desired and it is usually necessary to have continuous recording of the discharge over a period at least long enough to establish a reliable mean value and the amount by which the discharge may vary from that mean. This may involve the continuous measurement of flow over a number of years. The continuous measurement of flow is accomplished in the case of the first two methods of measurement mentioned above by establishing a relationship between water-level and discharge at the point of observation and by recording the water-levels there continuously or at close intervals of time. In the case of the third method of measurement, similar recordings are required of the head lost through the structure. For some purposes it is desirable to have concurrent records of temperature and chemical composition.

With the exception of a few rivers for which flow records of some duration are available, there is in Scotland generally insufficient data to permit the assessment of water resources to be made on a factual basis. Estimates of total annual runoff may be made from rainfall data, but having regard to the inadequacy of rain-gauge coverage on high land and in sparsely populated areas and to the lack of positive knowledge of losses or of rainfall-runoff relationships such estimates can only be regarded as approximations. Estimates of runoff made on this basis are inadequate for many purposes since they cannot take account of day-to-day fluctuations in discharge. It is characteristic of Scottish rivers that there are wide variations between "average daily discharge" and maximum and minimum discharges. The ratio of low to average to ordinary flood discharge is commonly in the region of 1 to 10 to 100 for lowland rivers, but there may be wide departures from this ratio on individual streams, particularly in upland areas.

An extreme case shows ratios of 1 to 300 to 8,000. The real relationship for any stream can only be established by systematic measurement and recording of flows. Similarly, the factual data concerning flood discharges which is required in connection with schemes of flood protection or for the determination of suitable waterways for bridges or culverts is usually lacking, as is also data concerning the level of medium flow at which underdrainage systems may suitably evacuate and for design purposes it becomes necessary to substitute estimates based on rainfall data and/or experience. Fortunately, in some ways, few urban areas in Scotland are affected by flooding. Nevertheless there are substantial areas of agricultural or potentially agricultural land which are affected by flooding or by inadequate drainage facilities and in respect of which such information is required.

In Scotland large flows are most commonly measured by the current meter method (1, above), small or medium flows by measuring structures (3, above). The method of dilutions is particularly suitable for the measurement of mountain torrents and should have a considerable field of application in Scotland, but so far it has only been used experimentally on account of the cumbersome apparatus which its use entails and the specialised technique involved.

In general it may be said that the application of modern methods of measurement to the systematic observation of river flows commenced in Scotland only after the end of the 1939-45 War. It is known that C. H. Roberts, City Engineer of Aberdeen, used both current meter and dilution methods to measure the flow of the River Dee (Aberdeenshire) before 1919, but we have no detailed record of the technique employed or of the measurements made. Captain W. N. McClean commenced current meter measurements on the River Garry (Inverness-shire) in 1912. His work was interrupted by the 1914-18 War and he did not publish any records until 1927. During the following fifteen years he measured and published flow records of several rivers in the Great Glen area and established flow-measuring stations on the River Spey at Aberlour, on the River Ness at Ness Castle Farm, and on the River Dee (Aberdeenshire) at Woodend which are still in operation. Dundee Corporation set up measuring weirs on streams feeding the city water supplies in 1927. In the late 1930s the Department of Agriculture for Scotland commenced to establish flow-measuring stations on a number of rivers in connection with land drainage works, but the work was interrupted by the 1939-45 War before these had been calibrated. This work was not resumed until after the war, at which time the North of Scotland Hydro-Electric Board also entered the field. In the early 1950s River Purification Boards which have power to engage in flow measurement began to be set up. So far none of the latter bodies has made any significant contribution to the work.

In Scotland there is no single authority or group of authorities charged with the duty of measuring and recording stream flows. As matters stand, a number of bodies engage in flow measurement in pursuit of their particular interests, which tend to confine their activities to circumscribed areas, to limited reaches of the rivers and to restricted aspects of flow. Similarly there is no authority responsible for co-ordinating the activities of these various bodies, for securing that measuring stations are sited in situations which will provide the most widely useful data or for publishing the records. In practice, the overlapping of measuring stations is generally avoided by fairly close collaboration between the authorities operating in the same area, and the authorities send most of their records for publication in the *Surface Water Year Book of Great Britain*, which is prepared for publication by the Surface Water Survey section of the Ministry of Housing and Local Government and published under the joint authority of that Ministry and the Scottish Office.

The brief notes in the following paragraphs describe the activities of the principal authorities in Scotland which engage in flow measurement. The number of flow-measuring stations credited there to each authority is the number contributed to the latest edition of the *Surface Water Year Book* (1957-58). Most of these bodies have other stations which are in course of construction or calibration and will be put forward for publication once this work has been accomplished. There are in addition a few more stations which are not likely to be given for publication owing to their anticipated short life or to doubts regarding their accuracy. Scattered throughout the country there are a large number of staff gauges which have not been calibrated and so provide intermittent records of water-level only. Some of these are kept by the above-mentioned authorities and others by burgh or county officials, by private estates, by fishing associations and by industrial establishments. Occasionally these records can be of interest, but it is essential that care should be exercised in making use of them as they may be badly sited, inaccurately graduated or subject to unrecorded changes of datum or of "control".

A census covering nearly all gauging points in Scotland was made on behalf of the Scottish Council by R. J. Mutter in 1959.

The North of Scotland Hydro-Electric Board operate in the area north of a line joining the Firth of Clyde to the Firth of Tay. In this area the Board have set up and and no doubt will continue to set up flow-measuring stations on streams which they have developed or propose to develop for power production. The purpose is to check the potential yield of the catchment and variation of flow before undertaking a scheme of hydro-electric development or, after a scheme is in operation, to provide records of downstream flows in connection with the release of compensation water. These flow-measuring stations are generally in the upper reaches of streams and some are short lived owing to the ultimate diversion of the water or flooding of the station site. The stations which are for the post part current meter stations are established, calibrated and operated by the various consulting engineers engaged by the Board for the design of their several schemes.

The Board supply for publication records from permanent stations and from some of the temporary stations which are expected to last for a significant period. Records from seven stations were reported in the last issue of the *Surface Water Year Book.*

The Board have stated that in areas which have been developed for the production of power information concerning runoff may be deduced from their records of power generated. The records available usually include particulars concerning storage, spillage and compensation flow.

The South of Scotland Electricity Board operate hydro-electric stations in the Clyde Valley and in Galloway. It is understood that arrangements have been made recently whereby records of flow in the River Dee (Kirkcudbrightshire) are to be supplied by the Board for publication in future issues of the *Surface Water Year Book.*

The North British Aluminium Co. Ltd. develops hydro-electric power from an extensive drainage area in Lochaber. The water used for power generation is measured in venturi meters and records are kept of stored water, compensation flows and spillage. Details of average discharge are supplied through the Department of Health for Scotland for publication in the *Surface Water Year Book.*

The Department of Agriculture and Fisheries for Scotland operates flow-measuring stations on a number of rivers throughout the country to obtain information concerning normal and extreme discharges in connection with existing and prospective schemes of land drainage or flood protection for agricultural land. These flow-measuring stations are situated on upper, middle and lower reaches and are all open river stations calibrated by current meter. The stations are constructed, calibrated and operated by the engineering staff of the Department. The records from a few of the stations are continuous from the late 1930s, but most have been established within the last ten years. The number of stations operated is being gradually increased with the object of securing that at some time in the future data will be available wherever it may be required in connection with land improvement schemes. So far as it is possible, having regard to the immediate purpose for which they are required, stations are situated so that they will fit into a national network of flow measurement when that is established. Data from Department stations are made available to River Purification Boards, Local Water Supply Authorities, Consulting Engineers, etc., when requested.

At the present date 50 stations have been constructed and are in operation, of which 26 are now fully calibrated and the remainder are in course of calibration. Records are furnished to the Surface Water Survey for publication as soon as each station is working satisfactorily and the calibration proved. Sixteen records were contributed to the latest issue of the *Surface Water Year Book* (1957-58).

Several of the Local Water Supply Authorities in the Country maintain flow-measuring stations in connection with existing or proposed impounding or abstraction works. These are generally located in the headwater reaches of streams and consist of weirs or flumes calibrated by formula. In some cases the principal object of the installation is the measurement of compensation water and calibration is not extended to upper extreme discharges. Some other Local Water Supply Authorities keep records of storage and overspill at impounding reservoirs from which are deduced the average amounts of runoff from the relative drainage areas.

The River Purification Boards which cover the country south of the Caledonian Canal are authorised by the Act of Parliament under which they were set up to make measurements of stream discharge within their areas. Most of these authorities which have only been in existence for a few years have set up some staff gauges and made measurements of flow at low levels of discharge, but it is only recently that one or two of these bodies have taken steps towards the establishment of full flow-measuring stations.

The Department of Health for Scotland, as the central department responsible for public water supply and for river purification, collects from the local authorities described above the records of their measurements and forwards suitable records to the Surface Water Survey for publication. Currently, records are contributed only from Water Supply Authorities and from the Lochaber Power Area. These comprise eight flow measurement records and data from six reservoired areas.

All who are concerned with the measurement of stream flows, whether actively engaged in flow measurements or as users of the resulting data, are sensible of the need for a properly co-ordinated systematic survey of river flows carried out to recognised standards. Scotland is now one of the very few countries in the world where such a survey has not yet been organised. This is probably due (1) to the comparative abundance of water resources in the country as a whole and (2) to the fact that in the river valleys generally, floodable bottom lands are usually free from urban development. However, in the more heavily populated industrial districts local resources of water are becoming ever more heavily strained under the burden of increasing demands made by the expansion of population and of industry, so that the full development of these local resources and their allocation is becoming a matter of serious public interest. The augmentation of local supplies from the resources of neighbouring areas has already been started and it should be assured that such fringe resources are allocated and developed to serve the general public interest in the most economical way. This cannot be done properly without the accurate knowledge of the extent of these resources which can only be obtained by their systematic measurement. This expansion of population and industry also creates problems relating to the disposal of wastes from urban areas and industrial concerns as effluents into rivers and streams. For the solution of these problems accurate knowledge of river flows is equally essential. The ever-increasing absorption of agricultural land for urban and industrial development is making it necessary to undertake the improvement of the sheltered and fertile bottom lands which, though often of small extent themselves, are essential adjuncts to many times their own area of hill land. Many of these bottom lands at present suffer from periodic flooding and from lack of full drainage facilities, and the first step towards their full and more efficient use should be the improvement of the arterial drainage channels, which can only be done economically if the discharges which these channels must carry can be assessed on the basis of systematic measurements and records.

This situation and the necessity for systematic flow measurement and recording is known to the central government departments concerned, and in fact consideration is being given to the desirability of establishing a national water survey, to the density of coverage which would be necessary, to the most practical and economical means of achieving such a coverage within a reasonable period of time and to the amount and source of the necessary financial provision. It is not possible for the writer to anticipate the decisions which may be reached.

After having given the matter a considerable amount of study, the writer would suggest that such a National Water Survey might comprise between 200 and 250 first-class flow-measuring stations. These should be so distributed throughout the country that a fair assessment of total water resources could be reached. A proportion of the stations might be operated indefinitely, but others might be retained only for such a period as would establish the main characteristics of the stream and permit a correlation to be made with the nearest permanent station. Thus the apparatus and effort employed would become available for another site. The erection of such a network could not be achieved overnight and might take ten years to establish.

It could not be expected that a survey of the type envisaged would provide direct information at every point at which local data could be required. It would, however, serve as a base against which fairly reliable estimates of local conditions could be made or with which local *ad hoc* stations could be correlated.

In considering the possibility of a national water survey being organised it is essential that all concerned should appreciate that such a survey would not be effective unless all measurements are made to similar high standards of accuracy, so as to be strictly comparable throughout. The techniques of measuring flow in open channels are now sufficiently established to permit the preparation of British and International Codes of Practice in regard to their use and it is expected that the British Codes dealing with current meter and dilution measurements will be published by the British Standard Institution in the course of the next twelve months. It is likely that these Codes will prescribe fairly high standards of accuracy and will set forth the procedures necessary to achieve these standards. It is hoped that all who engage in flow measurement in Scotland will adhere to the recommendations made so that the fullest use may be made of all records available to assess the water resources of our country.

BIBLIOGRAPHY

LESLIE, A. (1882-83). The Edinburgh Waterworks. *Min. Proc. Instn. civ. Engrs.*, **74**, Pt. IV.

McCLEAN, W. N. (1927). Rainfall and flow-off, River Garry, Inverness-shire, *Trans. Instn. Wat. Engrs.*, December.

—— Practical river flow measurement and its place in Inland Water Survey as exemplified on the Ness (Scotland) Basin. *Trans. Instn. Wat. Engrs.*, **38**, 1933.

—— Records of discharge of rivers Ness, Garry (Inverness-shire), Moriston, Spey and Dee (Aberdeenshire for various periods between 1929 and 1941. Pamphlets and graphical records published by *River Flow Records* 1937 to 1941.

MACDONALD, R. H. (1952). Relation between daily rainfall and flow of the River Shin. *Min. Proc. Instn. civ. Engrs.*, **1**, April.

Ministry of Housing and Local Government and Scottish Office. *Surface Water Year Book of Great Britain*, from 1935 onwards. H.M.S.O.

MUTTER, R. J. (1959). *Directory of Hydrometric Stations in Scotland* (not complete). Report to S.C.D.I. (Typescript, limited circulation).

REID, W. C. (1912-13). The Yield of Various catchment areas in Scotland. *Min. Proc. Instn. civ. Engrs.*, **194**, Pt. IV.

ROBERTS, C. H. (1919). An investigation into the flow of the River Dee (Aberdeenshire). *Trans. Instn., Wat. Engrs.*, **24**.

TAIT, W. A. D. (1906-07). Talla water supply of Edinburgh and District Water Board. *Min. Proc. Instn. civ. Engrs.*, **167**, Pt. I.

Various River Purification Boards. "Annual Reports" from 1955 onwards.

WOLF, P. O. (1952). Forecasts and records of floods in Glen Cannich. *J. Instn. Wat. Engrs.*, **6**.

Amounts and Distribution of Underground Water in Scotland*

J. R. Earp, M.Sc., Ph.D., and R. A. Eden, B.Sc.
Geological Survey of Great Britain, Edinburgh

The bulk of the rocks of the Highlands and Southern Uplands are impervious, and underground water supplies are only available in relatively small areas. Much of the Midland Valley is, however, occupied by semi-pervious rocks from which supplies can often be obtained. These include rocks of New Red Sandstone, Carboniferous and Old Red Sandstone age. Some water is also pumped from unconsolidated surface deposits. Calculations of likely yields from the solid rocks are difficult because of their structural complexity, because the precise positions of fissures in which water moves cannot be readily located, and because of a varying surface layer of impervious boulder clay. There are, however, areas where moderate underground supplies could probably be obtained from aquifers which are as yet but little developed. The Geological Survey publishes maps which show the surface geology, and from these the water potential of particular sites can be assessed; it also publishes pamphlets which summarise the results from most existing wells and boreholes.

Since 1946 the Survey has been the appropriate authority to which details of new sinkings for water 50 ft. or more deep must be notified and the fund of information available to help in siting new sinkings is therefore continually growing.

INTRODUCTION

The availability of underground water is directly dependent on the type of rock formations underlying a particular site and its study is essentially a branch of Geology. We propose here to consider first the relevant geological facts and then to touch on the administrative aspects of ground-water work in Scotland.

For water-bearing purposes rocks may be broadly classified into three types—pervious, semi-pervious and impervious. Scotland has only a few pervious rocks because the bulk of the solid rocks in the Highlands and Islands and Southern Uplands are impervious, and in these areas underground supplies are small. The most important of the present and potential sources of ground-water supply are to be found in semi-pervious rocks, the main outcrops of which are in the Midland Valley. Elsewhere, as a rule, reliable water supplies from bores can only be expected where relatively small areas of pervious or semi-pervious rocks occur.

The principal water-yielding rocks are beds of fissured sandstone and grit of the

* Reproduced with the permission of the Director, Geological Survey of Great Britain.

solid rock formations, but superficial deposits of sand and gravel are also locally valuable as sources of supply. In practice, ground-water is obtained, in areas where the geological structure and surface conditions are favourable, mainly from the Old Red Sandstone, Carboniferous and New Red Sandstone formations in that order of importance, although when pumping for mine drainage is taken into consideration the Carboniferous may be the most important aquifer. The surface distribution of these formations is shown in fair detail for almost all of Scotland on official maps published by the Geological Survey of Great Britain. Two categories of rocks are delineated on these maps: (*a*) the superficial deposits including peat, alluvium, sand gravel and Boulder Clay; (*b*) the solid rocks which comprise the uppermost layers of the earth's crust. These maps also show data about another factor which is of major significance in attempting to assess the underground water potential in particular areas, i.e. the complex folding and faulting of most of the rocks of Scotland. The widespread mantle of mainly impervious Boulder Clay which partially seals off the outcrops of the pervious beds is a further important consideration. All these factors make the prediction of hydro-geological conditions extremely difficult in many areas. It is, for example, almost impossible to calculate theoretically what percentage of the rainfall can percolate into the ground and enter an aquifer. Moreover, in semi-pervious rocks of the type commonly found in Scotland most of the underground water movement is through fissures rather than through the pores of the rock. It is rarely possible to predict the precise position of such fissures, but the yield which a borehole produces will depend in very large measure on the nature of the fissures which it happens to cut. For this reason adjacent boreholes often give quite different yields.

PRINCIPAL AQUIFERS

The main water-bearing formations, in downward geological sequence are:

Unconsolidated Surface Deposits

Surface deposits vary greatly in character from stiff clays, which yield no water, to highly permeable sands and gravels, which yield freely. Their thickness, too, is variable, normally ranging from a few feet to over a hundred feet and exceptionally reaching several hundred feet in a buried channel. Permeable superficial deposits assume some importance as aquifers where they overlie impermeable rocks, although individual yields may not be high. The variation in importance is emphasised as each of the types of drift is examined.

Recent blown sand affords the best yields where it is thick and widespread and fills basins on impervious deposits. Peat is useful in holding up rain water which later drains to streams, thus delaying direct runoff, but it is not a source of ground-water supplies. Although peat can store large volumes of water, such water is not readily given up to wells. Alluvial silts and clays, although saturated with water, do not readily give it up, but where river deposits consist of sand and gravel, considerable quantities of water may be obtained from shallow wells, e.g. industrial supplies ranging from 2,000 to 50,000 gallons per hour are obtained from river gravels at Selkirk and Galashiels, in Selkirkshire, and at Hawick, Roxburghshire.

Where the deposits of the Late Glacial and Post-Glacial Raised Beaches consist mainly of sand and gravel, or contain intercalated beds of sand and gravel, they form an important local source of water for domestic and farm use. Under favourable conditions, useful industrial supplies are obtained, e.g. yields up to 24,000 g.p.h. have been pumped from shallow wells at Arbroath in Angus. The Raised Beach clays, such as the brick clays, and the "carse clays" of the Clyde, Forth and Tay estuaries, are valueless for water supply, but large supplies may be obtained locally where they are underlain by water-yielding sand and gravel, as, for instance, at Newburgh on the Tay Estuary, where two adjacent boreholes 160 and 147½ ft. in depth give a total of 30,000 g.p.h.

The moundy spreads of sand and gravel of glacial origin such as those of the Tay basin, Strathmore and North Fife, and also the fluvioglacial sand and gravel terraces that are extensively developed in many of the main valleys, provide abundant supplies which have been, and in some cases still are, of considerable importance both for domestic and industrial use. At Aberdeen a yield of 10,000 g.p.h. was obtained from a borehole 150 ft. deep which pierced 30 ft. of gravel resting on granite. At Forfar, industrial supplies up to 18,000 g.p.h. are obtained from wells which are probably in very large measure fed from a spread of waterlogged sand and gravel. Where the sand and gravel is underlain by Boulder Clay or other impervious rocks, perched water-table conditions give rise to springs near the base of the sand and gravel; locally such springs give adequate supplies for small towns, as, for example, Lasswade and Bonnyrigg in Midlothian.

Boulder Clay is mainly impervious and yields very little water, although it may contain or overlie sandy or gravelly deposits from which small supplies can be obtained.

All the drift sources of water supply are liable to pollution, especially in built-up and farming areas. Many of them are also notoriously unreliable in that they are liable to dry up during periods of drought.

THE NEW RED SANDSTONE

The New Red Sandstone is a water-bearing formation, but it crops out over only a limited area and, owing to the small number of wells sunk into it, little is known about its water-yielding capacity.

In the Dumfries area there is a basin of these rocks from which yields of a few hundred to 54,000 g.p.h. have been obtained in bores ranging in depth from 50 to 700 ft. In some cases, e.g. in the lower parts of the basin, water is under sufficient hydrostatic pressure to overflow at the surface when tapped by bores. Similar rocks occur also between Loch Ryan and Luce Bay, but despite their disposition in a basin similar to that at Dumfries, the only deep bore sunk in them failed to strike water, possibly owing to the prevalence of conglomerate or breccia, or to a cover of clay on the outcrop preventing percolation. At Annan on the Solway Firth 700 to 800 g.p.h. were obtained with a temporary hardness of 114 and a permanent hardness of 125 parts per million. A 188-ft. bore into sandstones at Mauchline overflowed at the rate of 1,440 g.p.h., and a neighbouring bore is similar. There may well be a considerable area of water-bearing strata in the central part of the Mauchline basin. These rocks occur elsewhere in a number of other small basins, but little information is available about their water yields. In England large spreads of New Red Sandstone provide an important source of water.

CARBONIFEROUS

Carboniferous rocks are confined almost entirely to the Midland Valley. The Upper (Barren) Coal Measures at the top of the system rarely yield large supplies, although borings in them at Dalkeith provide water suitable for brewing as well as for domestic use. The numerous thick sandstones in Ayrshire are used as sources of water for industrial purposes, e.g. 2,000 g.p.h. have been obtained at Catrine. In the Lothians, a combined shaft and bore at Dalkeith yielded 4,000 g.p.h. of hard water.

Considerable quantities of water are pumped to drain mines in the Productive Coal Measures, but water from these mines is liable to be hard and mineralised. In the Lothians most of the water is derived from the higher beds. An industrial bore favourably situated in the higher beds, at Inveresk in Midlothian, produced 60,000 g.p.h.—one of the highest yields recorded in Scotland—with a temporary hardness of 330 and a permanent hardness of 200 parts per million. Some of the Lothian mines have to be pumped at the rate of 12,000 to 66,000 g.p.h. to facilitate working, and in the past a number of mines have been closed owing to the high cost of pumping. In the Wishaw-Cleland district the abandoned mines are flooded and water has risen to its former level. An exception to the normal fairly good yield of the Productive Coal Measures is evident in the area immediately to the south of the Ochil Hills in Clackmannanshire, where, despite the synclinal structure and the occurrence of numerous sandstones, they yield negligible supplies.

The Passage Group, formerly called Millstone Grit, lying beneath the Coal Measures, as a rule yields large supplies of good-quality water, except where a narrow outcrop restricts the replenishment area. At Windygates, Fife, an industrial supply of 28,000 g.p.h. has been obtained from a bore cutting 479 ft. of Passage Group beneath 16 ft. of superficial deposits, and at Roslin, in Midlothian, a bore produced 6,420 g.p.h. The Passage Group is particularly important as an aquifer on the flanks of the syncline of Clackmannan and Airth. The southern part of the western limb has not been drilled to any great extent, but, north of the River Forth at Alloa, Cambus and Tullibody, supplies of 1,000 to 15,000 g.p.h. of good-quality water have been obtained. The eastern flank of the syncline has been explored only at its southern end. The water is of medium hardness, most of which is temporary.

Next in downward sequence the many thick standstones of the Upper Limestone Group yield water; for instance 12,000 g.p.h. have been pumped from Lady Victoria shaft at Newbattle, Midlothian, and 3,000 to 7,000 g.p.h. from bores at Alloa and Cambus, in Clackmannanshire. In Ayrshire yields are poorer than in other districts. The most persistent aquifer is the Bishopbriggs Sandstone overlying the Index Limestone (equivalent to the Joppa Sandstone of the Lothians), near the base of the Upper Limestone Group. The water from this group is rather hard, the hardness being mainly temporary with little or no calcium sulphate.

The Limestone Coal Group, between the Upper and Lower Limestone groups, is not to be recommended as a source of ground-water, as the water, particularly in mining areas, is frequently mineralised, hard and somewhat acidic. In Stirlingshire and the Lothians considerable quantities of water have to be pumped from collieries. In the latter area, the water is derived mainly from four thick sandstones; these appear to be supplied mainly by percolation of water from the surface by way of faults and joints in the overlying strata, for inflow into the mines varies with rainfall. Inflow from the sandstones is said to be somewhat greater in the vicinity of dolerite dykes.

Varying quantities are obtained from the Lower Limestone Group, e.g. poor yields of ferruginous water were obtained from a bore sunk at Linlithgow to a depth of nearly 500 ft. in the group, which included about 30 ft. of igneous rock. Overflowing water has been obtained from bores less than 250 ft. deep in the western limb of the Cousland and D'Arcy anticline east of Dalkcith, Midlothian.

The Calciferous Sandstone Measures, at the base of the Carboniferous, yield water varying in quantity and quality according to the district and the part of the formation concerned, e.g. Crail Burgh Council in Fife pumped 4,000 g.p.h. from a bore in this series; in East Lothian a bore 425 ft. deep produced in 1905 an artesian flow of 10,000 g.p.h. of potable water, but by 1931 the flow had declined to 2,100 g.p.h. In the Lothians, water is generally found in the thick belt of sandstones at the top of the Calciferous Sandstone Measures, confined by the overlying impervious Lower Limestone Group. Supplies are obtained locally from volcanic rocks in these Measures, e.g. about 2,500 g.p.h. have been obtained in Edinburgh. In the district west of Queensferry and Mid-Calder, 32 million gallons per week have been raised from the oil-shale mines. Traces of Petroleum have been reported from several springs, for example from "St. Bernard's Well" on the east bank of Water of Leith, Edinburgh. In areas other than the Lothians the Calciferous Sandstone Measures are locally important as a source of rural supplies. The Cementstone Group at their base consists mainly of impervious beds and yields from wells or boreholes rarely exceed 1,000 g.p.h. In Edinburgh, however, industrial supplies ranging from 4,000 to 8,700 g.p.h. are obtained from deep wells, from some of which collection tunnels have been driven; small industrial supplies are also obtained from the lavas and tuffs which immediately overlie the Cementstone Group.

Old Red Sandstone

The Upper Old Red Sandstone is found largely in the Southern Uplands and Midland Valley. It is one of the best aquifers of the Lothians with yields ranging up to 13,000 g.p.h. The water is free from organic impurities and is particularly suitable for brewing on account of its chemical character. Before 1676 this formation was the source of water supply to Edinburgh. Outside the Lothians it is locally important as a source of rural water supply. It is worthy of particular note that the resources in many areas have not yet been explored.

In Ross and Cromarty, along the south-eastern slope of Millbuie Moor in the neighbourhood of Delmaduthy and Auchterflow, several strong springs issue from the Millbuie Sandstone Group of the Middle Old Red Sandstone. These are sources of supply for Rosemarkie, Avoch and Rosehaugh, north of Inverness.

Lower Old Red Sandstone sediments form a valuable source of ground-water for domestic and industrial use in Central Scotland, in areas west of Dundee and Stonehaven and in Aberdeen. The most important aquifers are the thick sandstones which, along with conglomerate, shale and marl, occur above and below a series of largely impervious volcanic rock. The conglomerates have been found in general to be unproductive, and little or no water comes from the shales. The marls are probably to a large extent impervious but where well-jointed may yield useful supplies. Yields of 3,000 to 5,000 g.p.h. are common in the Old Red Sandstone and up to 16,000 g.p.h.

have been recorded in the Strathmore Basin and in the Dundee area. At Stracathro in Angus two bores 25 yds. apart tapped artesian water in well-jointed marl at depths of 150 and 170 ft. respectively, and on pumping yielded 15,600 and 5,100 g.p.h. A small part of the Edinburgh supply is derived from springs issuing from the lavas of the Pentland Hills. The water from the Old Red Sandstone is locally highly mineralised and is generally hard to very hard in character, e.g. at Dunblane, Perthshire, the permanent hardness is 612 and the temporary hardness 228 parts per million.

Old Palaeozoic Sedimentary Rocks and Igneous and Metamorphic Rocks

The older sedimentary and the metamorphic rocks are mainly impervious, and although little information is available about their water-yielding capacity, it is likely to be poor as a rule. These rocks yield only small supplies from water percolating through joints and fissures. Boring under these conditions is highly speculative. Spring supplies are, however, of local importance, as for instance in Arran, where powerful springs issue from granite.

HYDROGEOLOGICAL PROSPECTS

In attempting to sum up prospects it is easier to indicate areas where underground supplies are unlikely than to point to areas where good yields can be expected with confidence. Local conditions such as folding and faulting of the strata and the width of the effective outcrop of the aquifer are of paramount importance so that generalisation is difficult.

The best indication of areas of reasonably good water potential is to be obtained, however, by examination of a map showing the outcrops of the various geological formations, at the same time bearing in mind the considerations detailed above. A supply can be hoped for in much of the ground covered by the outcrop of the New Red Sandstone, Carboniferous and Old Red Sandstone and most of the aquifers in these formations are probably as yet not fully exploited.

There are certain areas where it appears that prospects are on the whole favourable, but which are as yet little used:

New Red Sandstone Outcrops

Conditions somewhat similar to those in the Dumfries basin, where good results have been obtained, occur in the centre of the Mauchline basin, at Lochmaben, Thornhill and in the district from Annan to the Border.

Passage Group Outcrops

1. An area surrounding the Midlothian Coal Measures, comprising a narrow belt of country stretching from near Portobello through Lasswade to three miles south-west of Penicuik, and another similar belt from east of Musselburgh to Carrington.

2. The eastern flank of the Central Coalfield-Clackmannan syncline where the Passage Group crops out from Dollar in the north through Kincardine, Polmont and Whitburn to Carluke in the south. The formation becomes thinner southward and hence of decreasing importance as an aquifer. Along this belt the Passage Group is virtually untapped, but yields of up to 15,000 g.p.h. have been obtained from the western flank of the syncline.

3. East Fife, where the formation crops out in a north-south tract between Markinch and Kirkcaldy and in an anticlinal area extending south-westwards from Kennoway. In this area the Passage Group is up to 1,000 ft. thick. It yields 26,500 g.p.h. from one 500-ft. 15-in. bore on the north-south tract, and 12,500 g.p.h. from a 500-ft. 20-in. bore in the anticlinal area.

OLD RED SANDSTONE OUTCROPS

1. A wide tract extending from Alexandria and Dumbarton north-eastwards through Doune, Perth, Dundee and Forfar to Stonehaven. The sedimentary rocks are locally intercalated with lavas, particularly in Angus. Yields of up to 16,000 g.p.h. have been recorded mainly from the sediments.

2. A similar tract starting at the northern end of the Pentland Hills and extending along the southern flank of the Midland Valley to Girvan, but broken up into isolated areas mainly because of the presence of overlying Carboniferous rocks, and interbedded volcanic rocks in the lower part of the system.

3. A narrow belt from Loch Leven, Fife, through Cupar to Leuchars. A recent 6-in. bore, sunk 120-ft., obtained 12,000 g.p.h.

4. An irregular area stretching southwards from Dunbar to the Border. Recent bores have shown results varying from no yield to a few thousand gallons per hour.

5. A strip along the south side of the Moray Firth between Inverness and Buckie.

ADMINISTRATIVE ASPECTS

Because of the close relationship between the geology of an area and its underground water supplies, the Geological Survey of Great Britain has been, since its inception over 100 years ago, very much concerned with underground water. This interest resulted in the production of a series of publications on this subject and was formalised when in 1935 an Inland Water Survey Committee, appointed by the then Minister of Health for England and the Secretary of State for Scotland, reported that as regards underground water: "The work of examining and securing the amplification of the information on this subject could best be done by the Geological Survey, who have on their staff persons with the necessary knowledge and experience."

During the last war, when the Department of Health for Scotland was charged with the task of organising emergency water supplies in Scotland, the Geological Survey was able to assist the Department by the provision of lists of wells in and around Scottish towns and cities, compiled from its already considerable records. In order to augment those records and bring them up to date, the areas in question were visited and owners of wells and drilling contractors were circularised for further data relating to the wells of which the Geological Survey had knowledge and for information about others not then known. In this way it was possible to prepare site maps of all important wells and water bores, and much relevant data regarding their depth, diameter, yield and quality of water was obtained.

In order that the Geological Survey's water records might be more readily available, a beginning was made during the war to bring together the essential data (including statistics of water pumped at working collieries) in a series of mimeographed Wartime Pamphlets. Eight of these, covering almost the whole of the southern half of the country (south of an E.-W. line through Aberdeen) have now been issued and are available to the public.

In 1946 the Water (Scotland) Act gave to the Secretary of State for Scotland a general responsibility for co-ordinating and conserving supplies of water in Scotland. Under the provisions of this Act all new sinkings for water, if over 50 ft. in depth, are notified to the Geological Survey, the officers of which have access to information relevant to the sinking. This makes possible a fairly complete hydrogeological assessment of each newly explored site. Section 3 of the Water (Scotland) Act also empowers the Secretary of State to make regulations requiring periodical returns as to quantity and quality of water abstracted from underground sources, but regulations have not yet been made to implement the Section.

Such periodical returns are in fact required in England, where they provide data for detailed assessment of the underground water resources in the major aquifers, on which to base measures for the controlled exploitation of the aquifers and in particular to attempt to prevent over-pumping.

It should be stressed, however, that there are fundamental differences between the extent of aquifers in the two countries and it is perhaps on this account that the legal requirements differ at present. In England there are very large areas of pervious rocks with simple geological structure and often slight cover of impervious clays, and in these areas underground water can be dealt with on a statistical basis. These conditions do not obtain in Scotland and it is unlikely that Scottish underground supplies will be in general as amenable to statistical treatment as those of much of England. The study and conservation of water underground is, however, unquestionably facilitated by the collection of systematic records over a long period. Although the present use of ground-water resources in Scotland is relatively small, it is clear that these resources are limited and should therefore be developed with as much skill as is practicable, bearing in mind the somewhat difficult geological conditions. Unrestricted development in England led in the past to local lowering of the water-level with consequent drying up of streams and some wells, and to the seeping of saline water into areas of heavy pumping near the coast.

An important part of the work of the Geological Survey in Scotland is the tendering of advice on problems of underground water supply. In recent years an average of about fifty enquiries a year have been dealt with, the quantities involved ranged from quite small amounts for domestic purposes to yields of over a million gallons a day for industrial concerns. To answer these enquiries accurate six-inch geological maps are essential, no matter what other records are available, though clearly the more numerous and detailed those records are, the better can be assessed the prospects in any given area.

Chemicals from the Sea

W. C. GILPIN, PH.D., A.R.C.S., F.I.CERAM.
Technical Director, Steetley Organization Research Department, Worksop

Many elements can be extracted from sea water, but in Britain only magnesia and bromine are produced in large quantities.

Chemical plants for producing either magnesia or bromine must be positioned with care. Sea water of high salinity, not diluted by the fresh-water discharge from rivers, should be available and local tidal conditions should be such that spent sea water will not be readily re-cycled through the plant. For magnesia production large reserves of good-quality limestone or dolomite must be readily at hand together with adequate supplies of solid or liquid fuel. As bromine is used principally in the manufacture of ethylene dibromide a bromine plant will only be operated with commercial success if ethylene is being produced on a large scale near-by.

Potassium and sodium salts can be made from the sea, but they are likely to be more expensive than the similar materials obtained from the working of natural land deposits.

Gypsum can be produced from the spent sea water of a magnesia plant at a competitive price, but its commercial exploitation may be difficult.

Although it is possible to extract copper from sea water, the copper is present in such small amounts that much technical development will be necessary before a commercially profitable process can be evolved.

There are many important elements in sea water and their concentrations as determined by Goldschmidt[1] are given in the table below.

Salt recovery is probably the oldest commercial activity connected with the sea, solar evaporation being a technique that has been practised for centuries. It is only within the last hundred years, however, that the sea has been used as a source of materials other than salt. Those chemicals obtainable directly from the sea and without the aid of solar evaporation are of the most interest to us, and these are magnesium hydroxide, calcium sulphate, potassium salts, sodium salts, bromine and copper. At present only magnesium hydroxide and bromine are produced commercially, the rest can be obtained more easily from sources other than the sea. First, then, we shall consider the established processes for extracting magnesium hydroxide and bromine from sea water and later we shall discuss the technical possibilities of the manufacture of other materials from the sea.

MAGNESIUM HYDROXIDE

There are $4\frac{1}{2}$ lb. of magnesium chloride and 2 lb. of magnesium sulphate in every 100 gallons of sea water, and when sea water is treated with either a high calcium or

Constituents of Sea Water

Element		%	Weight per million galls. (tons)	Current commercial value per ton
Oxygen	Chiefly as water	85·89	3834	
Hydrogen		10·80	482	
Chlorine		1·93	86·2	As sodium chloride, £1 to £1, 10s.
Sodium		1·07	47·8	
Magnesium		$1{\cdot}3 \times 10^{-1}$	5·80	As magnesium oxide refractory and caustic grades, £13 to £20
Sulphur		$8{\cdot}8 \times 10^{-2}$	3·93	As gypsum (calcium sulphate), £1, 5s. to £5, 10s.
Calcium		$4{\cdot}2 \times 10^{-2}$	1·87	
Potassium		$3{\cdot}7 \times 10^{-2}$	1·65	As potassium sulphate, fertiliser grade, £19
Bromine		$6{\cdot}6 \times 10^{-3}$	$2{\cdot}9 \times 10^{-1}$	£280
Carbon		$2{\cdot}0 \times 10^{-3}$	$8{\cdot}9 \times 10^{-2}$	
Strontium		$1{\cdot}0 \times 10^{-3}$	$4{\cdot}5 \times 10^{-2}$	
Boron		$1{\cdot}0 \times 10^{-3}$	$4{\cdot}5 \times 10^{-2}$	
Silica		$1{\cdot}0 \times 10^{-4}$	$4{\cdot}5 \times 10^{-3}$	
Fluorine		$1{\cdot}0 \times 10^{-4}$	$4{\cdot}5 \times 10^{-3}$	
Rubidium		$2{\cdot}0 \times 10^{-5}$	$9{\cdot}0 \times 10^{-4}$	
Lithium		$7{\cdot}0 \times 10^{-6}$	$3{\cdot}0 \times 10^{-4}$	
Zinc		$7{\cdot}0 \times 10^{-6}$	$3{\cdot}0 \times 10^{-4}$	
Phosphorus		$6{\cdot}0 \times 10^{-6}$	$3{\cdot}0 \times 10^{-4}$	
Iodine		$5{\cdot}0 \times 10^{-6}$	$2{\cdot}0 \times 10^{-4}$	
Arsenic		$2{\cdot}0 \times 10^{-6}$	$9{\cdot}0 \times 10^{-5}$	
Copper		$1{\cdot}0 \times 10^{-6}$	$5{\cdot}0 \times 10^{-5}$	£250
Caesium		$2{\cdot}0 \times 10^{-7}$	$9{\cdot}0 \times 10^{-6}$	
Silver		$3{\cdot}0 \times 10^{-8}$	$1{\cdot}0 \times 10^{-6}$	
Gold		$1{\cdot}0 \times 10^{-9}$	$5{\cdot}0 \times 10^{-8}$	

dolomitic lime a fine precipitate of magnesium hydroxide is produced and the calcium passes into solution. The reaction is summarised by the following equation:

$$CaO.MgO + MgCl_2.MgSO_4 + 2H_2O = Mg(OH)_2 + CaCl_2.CaSO_4.$$

In 1937 the first pilot plant in the world was set up by the Steetley Co. at Hartlepool to produce dead-burned magnesite from the sea. A year later a plant capable of producing 10,000 tons per annum was completed at Hartlepool, and this same plant has been expanded until it now produces 150,000 tons of magnesite per annum and is consequently the biggest of its kind in the world. The flow sheet for the sea water magnesia process is shown in Fig. 1.

Dolomite, quarried some 15 miles from Hartlepool at Coxhoe and Thrislington, is crushed, graded and burned in rotary kilns to form calcined dolomite or dolime. Hopper-bottomed railway wagons are used to transport the dolime to Hartlepool, where it is slaked to a fine dry powder with fresh water, made into a slurry with sea water and then classified to remove coarse impurities.

Sea water is drawn by centrifugal pumps into large storage tanks which ensure the steady flow of water to the process at all stages of the tide. From the storage tanks the water flows to pretreatment tanks, where it is dosed with a small part of hydrated dolime to remove calcium bicarbonate hardness by precipitating it as calcium carbonate. Treated sea water is then pumped to agitated reaction vessels in which it is mixed with the main bulk of classified hydrated dolime slurry. Magnesium hydroxide is precipitated and the dilute suspension is allowed to settle in large-diameter shallow tanks equipped with rake mechanisms. Settled magnesium hydroxide is drawn to the centre well by the rakes and is pumped out as a sludge, having the consistency of cream. After washing with sea water this sludge is filtered by rotary vacuum disc filters to give a filter cake containing 50 per cent. solids by weight. Rotary kilns, fired by pulverised coal, are used to burn the magnesium hydroxide filter cake at a temperature of over 1,600° C. to give a refractory magnesia known as dead burned magnesite. Magnesite from this Hartlepool plant is used for making magnesite and chrome magnesite refractory bricks for the steel industry. It is also used in granular form for the maintenance of steel furnace hearths and a substantial tonnage is exported.

A sea water magnesia plant is best situated where the local sea water has little or no dilution from rivers and where the in-shore currents run parallel to the shore so that spent sea water which has had the magnesia extracted from it will not be recirculated into the plant. Large local supplies of quarried dolime or limestone are obviously necessary and fuel for kiln firing must be readily available. Impurities, when well dispersed in the dolomite, should not exceed 1½ per cent. by weight if an acceptable magnesite is to be made.

Bromine

In the early 1920s the discovery of anti-knock petrol enormously increased the demand for bromine so that the annual production has risen from 1,250 tons per annum in 1914 to about 100,000 tons per annum today, of which the greater part is taken from the sea.

Bromine is at present made by a process first used commercially in 1934 and developed jointly by the Dow Chemical Company and the Ethyl Corporation.[2] In this country the process was operated during the war at Hayle in Cornwall by Imperial Chemical Industries Limited, working under licence from the Associated Ethyl Corporation. At present the Associated Ethyl Corporation are operating a plant at Amlwch on the Anglesey coast. A flow sheet for the process is given in Fig. 2.

Sea water is taken into settling ponds and then pumped into the plant through rubber-lined pipes where sulphuric acid from the end of the process, supplemented by fresh dilute sulphuric acid, is mixed with it to reduce its pH to 3·5. After the acid, chlorine is added to the sea water and the bromine, which is liberated in the reaction

$$2NaBr + Cl_2 \longrightarrow 2NaCl + Br_2,$$

is blown out with air in wood-packed towers. The moist bromine-laden air is mixed with sulphur dioxide and drawn through falling water and a circulating solution of bromine and hydrobromic acid when the following reaction takes place:

$$Br_2 + SO_2 + 2H_2O \longrightarrow 2HBr + H_2SO_4.$$

When the bromine-hydrobromic acid solution has been made sufficiently strong by recirculation it is reacted with chlorine and the free bromine vapour is steamed out of solution and collected as a liquid. A small quantity of hydrochloric acid is present in the residual acid solution which is pumped to the beginning of the process to reduce the pH of the incoming sea water. Over 90 per cent. of the available bromine is extracted in this type of plant which must handle 3·85 million gallons of sea water for every ton of bromine that is produced, and must acidify this sea water to within a narrow range of pH.

Considerable care needs to be exercised when selecting a site for a bromine plant for there are huge quantities of spent sea water to dispose of, and if this inadvertently becomes mixed with fresh incoming sea water the output of the plant will be seriously reduced, firstly by the lowering of the bromine content of the water and secondly by an associated reduction in efficiency of extraction. Fresh-water dilution from rivers will have a similar effect to that produced by spent sea water dilution and dilution caused by other industrial water may cause a loss of chlorine. The main outlet for bromine is at present the manufacture of ethylene dibromide, and so a readily available source of ethylene is essential for the successful operation of a sea water bromine plant.

A survey of the inshore waters round the coast of Great Britain for bromine content, salinity, chlorine demand and the amount of acid required to reduce the pH to 3·5 was carried out by Haslam and Gibson.[3] The results show that the ratio between salinity and bromine content is fairly constant except where fresh-water dilution is excessive. Water of the highest salinity is to be found off the Cornish coast, the salinity decreasing in the Irish Sea and from Fishguard northwards and then increasing along the west coast of Scotland. It is also fairly high along the east coast of Scotland away from the river estuaries. A map showing sample positions, salinities and bromine contents off the coast of Scotland is given in Fig. 3.

POTASSIUM

There is one ton of potassium in every 590,000 gallons of sea water, but its recovery is complicated by the presence of about twenty-eight times as much sodium. For this reason ion-exchange processes are not applicable since sodium is absorbed along with potassium and no separation can be achieved. A reagent which will selectively precipitate potassium is dipicrylamine which gives an orange-red compound in slightly alkaline solution. It was first proposed by Polucktoo[4] as an analytical reagent for the detection of potassium and has since been applied to its recovery from sea water. This process is the subject of a patent taken out by the Norsk Hydro Elektrisk Company, British Patent 22025, and a flow sheet is given in Fig. 4.

A soluble salt of dipicrylamine, preferably the calcium salt although magnesium sodium or lithium salts may also be used, is added to the sea water in amounts slightly less than the equivalent of the potassium content. Insoluble potassium dipicrylaminate is precipitated, settled, filtered, washed and then treated with an acid such as sulphuric, nitric, hydrochloric, acetic or carbonic acid to produce a soluble salt. Dipicrylamine liberated during the acid treatment is filtered from the potassium salt solution and then treated with milk of lime to produce a solution of calcium dipicrylaminate, for reaction with further sea water. A 70 per cent. recovery has been claimed for this process.

Dipicrylamine is prepared by nitrating diphenylamine and is, consequently, an expensive compound, and so the completeness of its recovery is important for the successful operation of the process. Part of the dipicrylamine added to the sea water does not react with potassium and remains in the filtrate after the removal of the potassium dipicrylaminate.

In the Norsk Hydro Elektrisk Company's process dipicrylamine is recovered from this source by acidifying the spent sea water to a pH of 3·5. The dipicrylamine is precipitated and filtered, the amount of acid required for this purpose is equivalent approximately to 1,000 lb. of sulphuric acid per ton of potassium extracted. This acid is not recoverable, but it might be possible to use the effluent from the potassium process for bromine recovery without further acidification.

It is unlikely that any sea water process could compete with a mining and fractional crystallisation process based on reasonably high potassium salt deposits such as sylvite, sylvanite, carnallite or polyalite. In England about 400,000,000 tons of potassium chloride have been estimated to be present in the potash deposits of lower Eskdale, and so the extraction of potassium from sea water is unlikely to be a commercially profitable enterprise.

Sodium Salts

Several processes have been considered for the production of sodium salts from sea water using ion-exchange reactions. Sodium nitrate has been produced on a pilot scale at Heroya in Norway by the Norsk Hydro Elektrisk Company Limited. A granular bed of exchange material is converted to the sodium state by allowing sea water to percolate through it. The reaction is summarised in the following equation:

$$R_2Ca + 2NaCl \text{ (sea water)} \longrightarrow 2RNa + CaCl_2,$$

where R is often a phenolic group. When the reaction is complete the sea water is shut off and the ion-exchange bed flushed out with fresh water and then treated with a solution of calcium nitrate. Calcium ions exchange with sodium ions on the bed to give a dilute solution of sodium nitrate:

$$2RNa + Ca(NO_3)_2 \longrightarrow R_2Ca + 2NaNO_3$$

which is evaporated and the salt crystallised out.

Similar processes for the preparation of sodium sulphate and sodium carbonate or bicarbonate are described in British Patents 553,114 and 535,854. Although the plant required for recovering sodium salts by ion exchange is simple large quantities of fresh water are likely to be needed for the flushing operation, that is about the same as the volume of sea water used. Either a solution of an acid or a salt may be used to regenerate the ion-exchange bed, but unless such materials are available as waste products at a very low cost, as is the case at the Norsk Hydro Elektrisk Company's works, regeneration is likely to be an expensive operation. Finally, solutions of sodium salts produced by ion exchange are usually fairly dilute, for example, if either 2 normal acid or a 10 to 15 per cent. salt solution is used for regeneration then a 10 to 15 per cent. solution of sodium salt is finally obtained and the recovery of the product from such solutions will be costly.

When compared, then, with the standard methods of making sodium salts from saturated brines or rock salt, ion-exchange processes are likely to be much more expensive.

Gypsum ($CaSO_4 . 2H_2O$)

If more than 70 per cent. of the total magnesium hydroxide obtainable from sea water is precipitated with calcium hydroxide, then the sea water becomes supersaturated with gypsum.

When all the magnesium ions have been removed from the sea water the supersaturation of the gypsum reaches ·95 grams per thousand grams of water, and it can be crystallised out by agitation in the presence of seed crystals. A flow diagram for a continuous extraction process using spent sea water from a sea water magnesia plant is given in Fig. 5. In order to obtain the maximum output of gypsum it is essential that the sea water magnesia plant should feed the gypsum plant with spent sea water free from magnesium ions so as to maintain the maximum degree of supersaturation in the crystallisers.

About 50 per cent. of the available gypsum can be extracted in such a plant, and the sea water product is comparable to the best natural material and can be manufactured at competitive prices.

Copper

In order to produce 1 ton of copper from the sea, 224,000,000,000 gallons of sea water need to be treated; at present the total volume of water pumped every year in the sea water magnesia works at Hartlepool would supply about half a ton of copper.

Ion-exchange devices have been reported[5] which can extract copper present at a concentration of ·32 parts per million from water containing concentrations of salt nearly equal to that in sea water, using 1 M. hydrochloric acid, the copper can be recovered from the exchangers at a concentration of 44 parts per million. Copper is recovered from plating wastes, and cupromonium wastes produced in the rayon industry, by ion-exchange processes. However, these wastes usually contain at least 120 parts per million of copper and the regenerant effluent from which the copper is precipitated is two to three hundred times more concentrated than this.[6]

Although it is possible to extract copper from the sea, enormous quantities of sea water would need to be handled to maintain even a moderate output of copper, and clearly much technical development will be necessary before such a process can become commercially profitable.

Concluding Remarks

Although many materials can be extracted from the sea, few can be sold. Magnesia and bromine are the only chemicals being manufactured on a large scalc from raw sea water. Gypsum can be produced at competitive prices from sea water if magnesium hydroxide is extracted beforehand, but the market is small and uncertain. Potassium and sodium salts made from the sea are likely to be more costly than those derived from natural deposits. Profitable extraction of copper from raw sea water must await further technical developments.

REFERENCES

1. *Fortschr. Min., Kryst. Petrog.*, 1933, Vol. 17, p. 112.
2. *Chem. metall. Engng.*, 1939, **46**, 771.
3. Haslam, J., and Gibson, R. O. (1950). *The Analyst*, July, p. 357.
4. Polucktoo (1934). *Michrochemic.*, **14**, p. 265.
5. Pennington, L. D., and Williams, M. B. (1959). *Industr. Engng. Chem.*, June, p. 759.
6. Beaton and Furness (1941). *Industr. Engng. Chem.*, **33**, 1500.

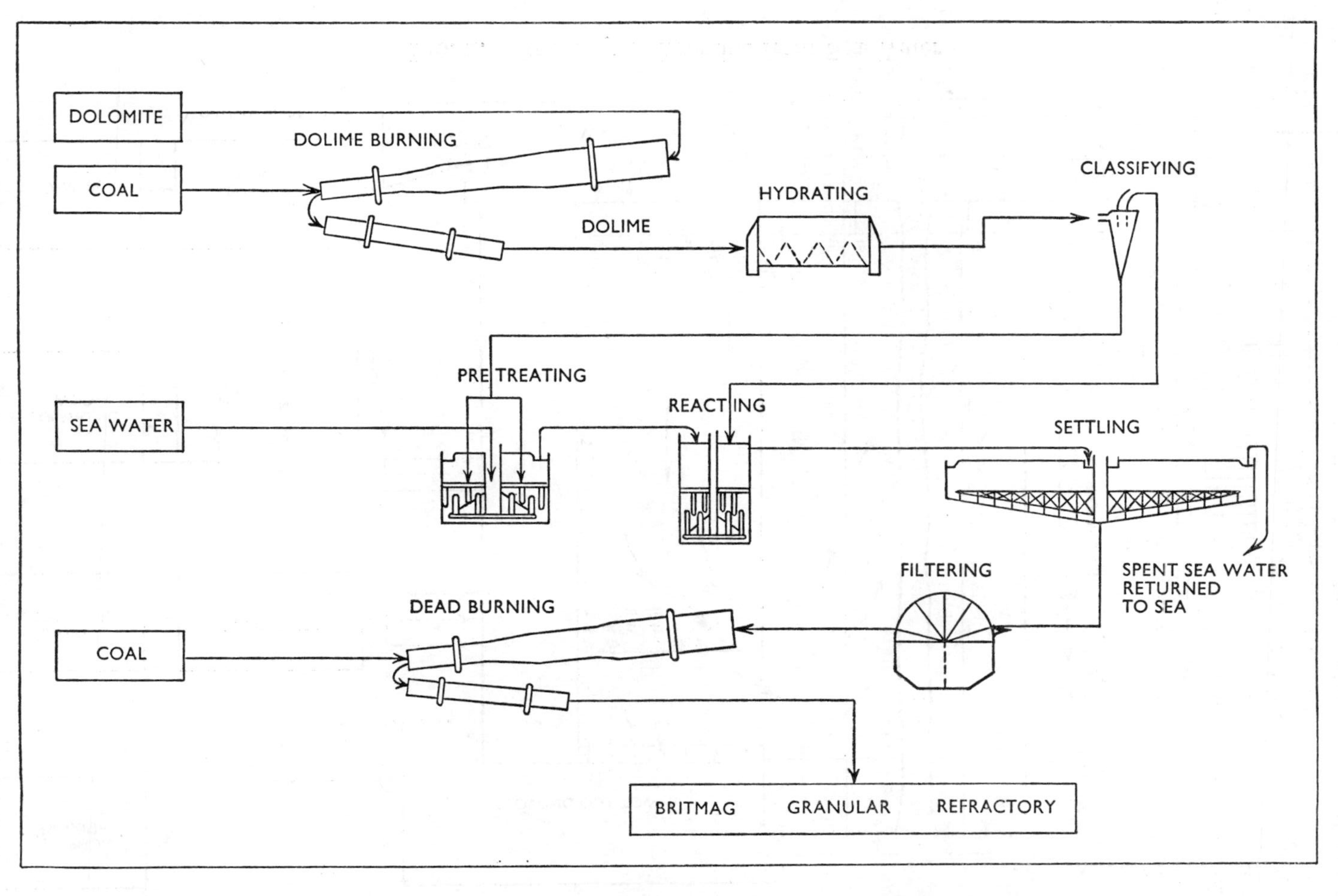

FIG. 1. Recovery of Magnesia from Sea Water

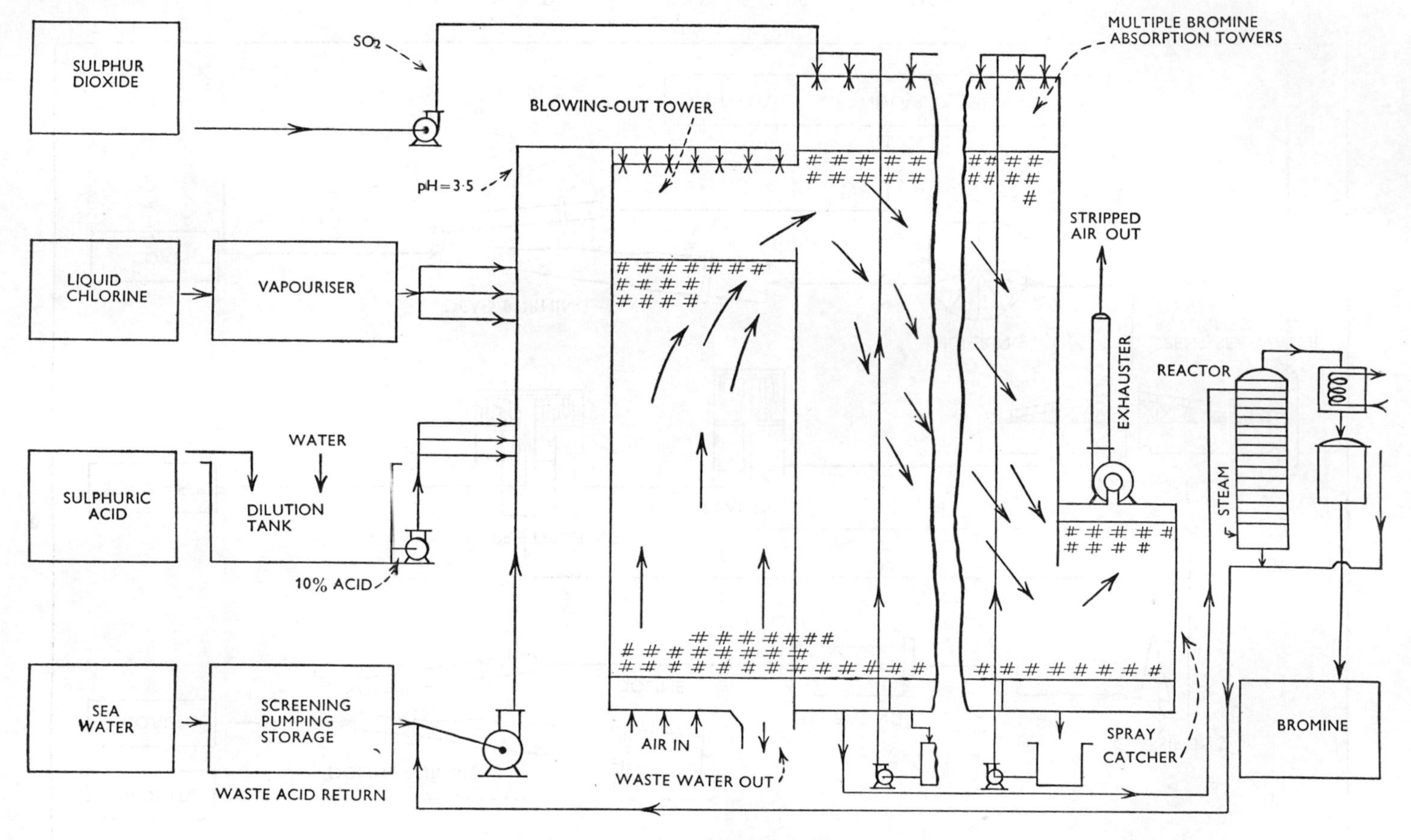

FIG. 2. Recovery of Bromine from Sea Water

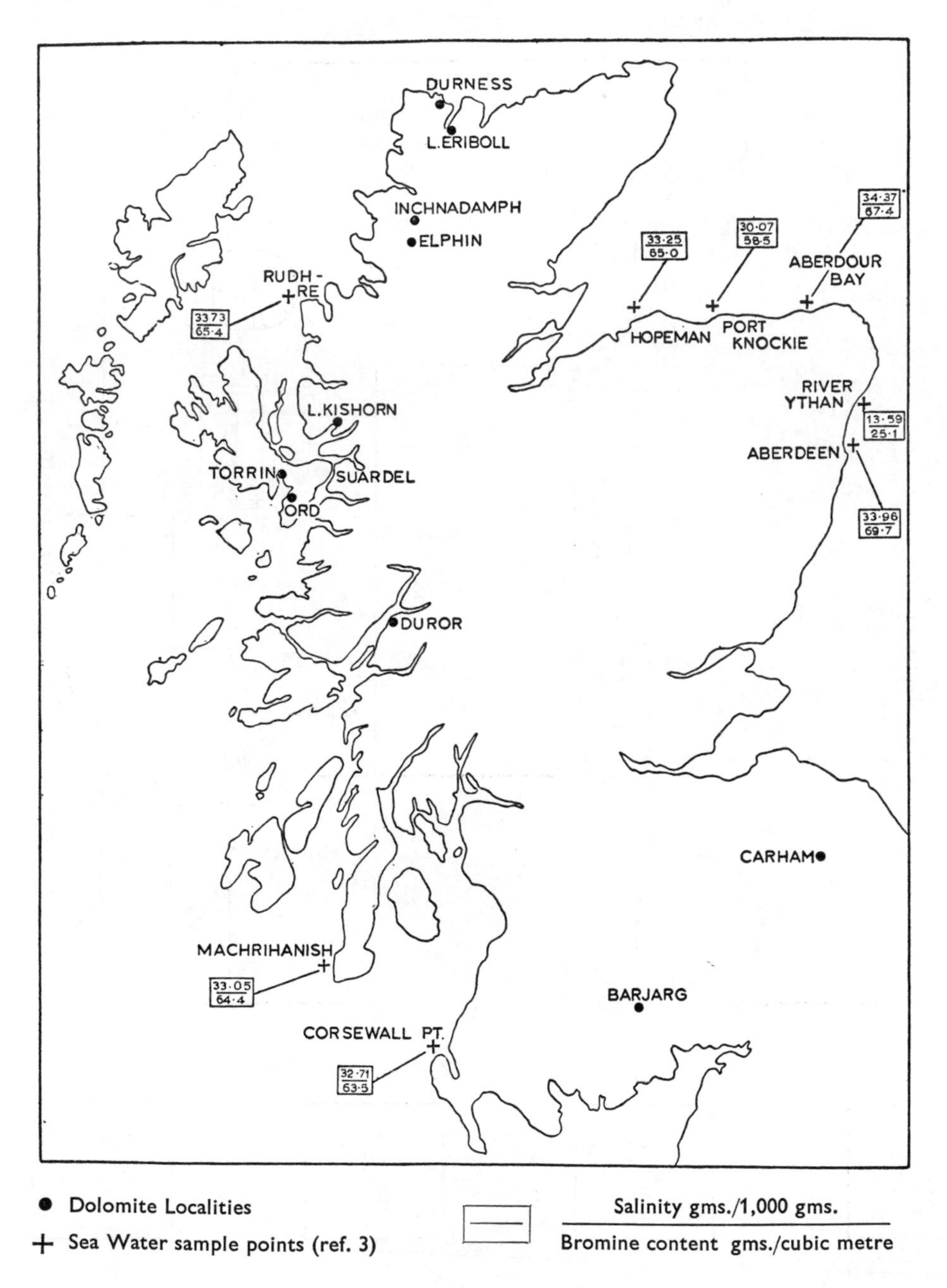

FIG. 3. Salinities and Bromine Contents of Scottish Sea Water

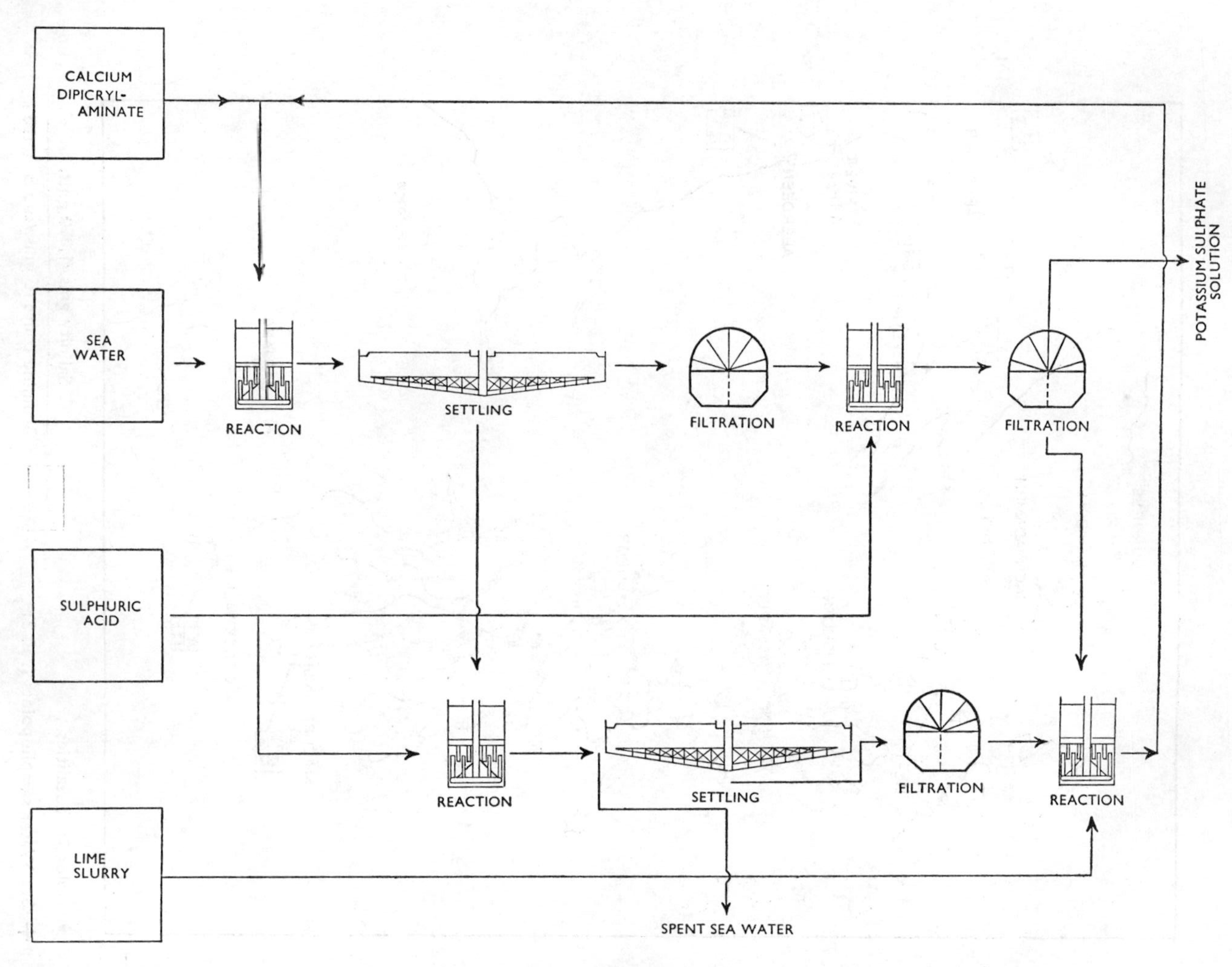

Fig. 4. Recovery of Potassium from Sea Water

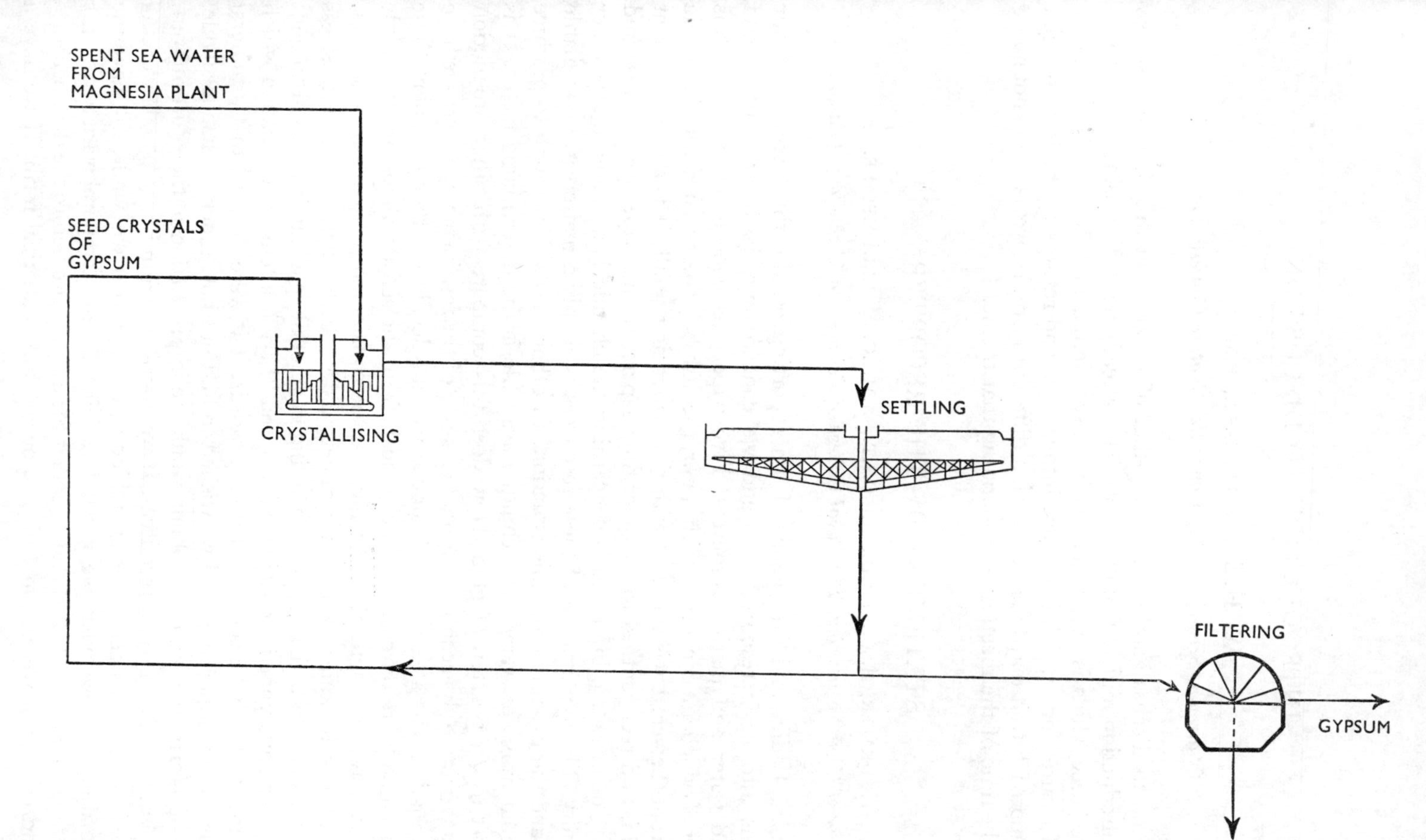

FIG. 5. Recovery of Gypsum from Sea Water

INTRODUCTION TO DISCUSSION

W. H. PEARSALL, D.SC., F.R.S.
Chairman, Scientific Policy Committee, Nature Conservancy

We now go on to discuss another resource—that of water—and this, if I may say so by way of introduction, differs from those we have already been discussing—minerals—in being a resource which is in fact *not* continuously diminishing. It is one of the cyclic resources of nature—one which goes back into the sea and returns in the form of rain. Hence our approach to it may take a somewhat different form. However, I am not going to take up the time of the meeting in elaborating that theme.

STATEMENT BY THE REPORTER

W. FRAZER, B.SC., PH.D., A.R.C.S.T., A.M.I.C.E., A.M.I.MECH.E.
Professor of Civil Engineering, The Royal College of Science and Technology, Glasgow

Mr. Chairman, Ladies and Gentlemen: I am reporting on the third section of our investigations into basic resource facts and we concern ourselves with surface and underground water and marine resources. Five papers have been presented on this subject, four of which are concerned with water, the fifth being concerned with inorganic chemicals from the sea. I wish to deal with this paper first of all. It is a paper of great interest and is in direct contrast to the other four papers. In this paper we are presented with accurate quantitative information concerning the chemicals available in sea water of high salinity. The exploitation of these resources is simply a matter of the available techniques and the existing economic situation. In other words, if we wish to produce copper or gold from sea water the technique available is the determining factor. It is going to cost us £*x* per ton of gold. How does this compare with other production methods? Is it going to be economic or not? It is one of the few instances where we have all the information and at a moment's notice we can decide whether to exploit these resources or not. The resources, too, in chemicals from the sea are almost inexhaustible within any conceivable length of time which can be considered in surveying resources.

When we come to water we find a complete difference, and I would like to stress this difference. The fact is that as well as varying in amount spacially it varies in amount with time. I think everyone is conscious of this, that there is a temporal variation which we do not find with other resources. In other words, if it were decided that a mineral resource was now of importance and we wished to find out how much we had available, the amount of information we could obtain would be in proportion to the effort put out. Now this is not the case in water resources. If we double the number of people working on the assessment of water resources or trebled it, by next year we would still have the same information because what we must determine is this temporal variation. This involves stations being established and operated for many years before the data becomes of value, and even then we can only give resources in a statistical form. If we have a collection of data concerning water resources, the answer we can offer those wishing to exploit such a resource is as follows: "The chances of flow of such a magnitude (and by 'flow' I mean either a low flow, a flood, mean daily or mean yearly flow) occurring next year are 1 in *y*." We talk about 100-year floods and 25-year floods, when what we mean is the chance of a flood of that magnitude occurring next year is 1 in 100 and the chance of it occurring the year after that is slightly more because of the fact that extreme values tend to accumulate. What this really means is that no amount of effort can yield results in a short time interval. A great deal can be done, and is being done, by comparison methods, as, for instance, comparing ungauged catchments with gauged catchments, but here errors can be very gross.

Now, I have used the word "Stations" concerning points where we measure water resources, and it must not be thought that these stations refer only to quantitative measurements of rainfall and river flow, or to evapo-transpiration. In addition to those, before we can establish the pattern of Scotland's water resources, and before we can assess the effects of utilisation which are so important, we must consider the whole hydrological and hydraulic environment and try to obtain as much knowledge as we can on the temporal and spacial distribution of such factors as the amount of dissolved material (the amount of dissolved oxygen in particular which is so important for the support of biological life); the amount of suspended material which relates to erosion; the temperature, because we can use our water as a resource for cooling water, and that is dependent on the temperature. You are no doubt aware of the effects or the alleged effects of hydro-electric schemes on fish. The fact of the matter is that I do not consider we know enough about the biological life in our rivers to assess the effect of utilisation accurately. Coupled to this, and again forming part of the hydraulic environment, is the whole question of erosion, both of the bed and in the catchment area.

Now, the four papers which we are presented with this morning set out to examine how, in fact, this work is being carried out in Scotland, and to my mind they present rather a sad story. All the authors are extremely active in this field, and without exception they stress the paucity of our knowledge in this important subject. This is no new revelation. It has been commented on and many recommendations have been made to Government on the subject certainly over the last 25 years, and even before that. It is not possible to deal with all the points in the papers and, of course, I wish to leave as much time as possible for discussion. I would just like to point out one or two things. In Dr. Gorrie's paper, which is a general survey of the resources, he draws attention generally to the gaps which exist in river gauging and in rainfall data. In this connection I would like to point out that a number of gauging stations are being operated to a very high standard of accuracy indeed, whose sole function is the recording of compensation water against the evil day when account may have to be made to the Court of Session. They contribute very little to our knowledge of the flow. Dr. Gorrie, as the other authors do, stresses the need for a central organisation to deal with water resources in all aspects.

Mr. Cranna from the Meteorological Office covers a very wide range, dealing with evaporation, precipitation, irrigation and climate. He draws attention to the shortcomings of the rain gauge network in Scotland, pointing out that most stations are located at lower altitudes, which may cast a little doubt on Dr. Gorrie's rainfall runoff formula. There is a statement in his paper regarding isohyetal maps. Some areas, for example the Cairngorms, are so lacking in gauges that estimation is not considered justified. Next door you will find a map of the average isohyetals in Scotland and this raises the whole question of maps. People tend to believe maps. Once a thing is in print and is presented they tend to believe it and from the available information it seems to me that we should have a nice white area in the middle of our rainfall map of Scotland with the legend "Here be kelpies" or something like that. I do not want to raise the question of the National Atlas, but it does mean this map being published and being used, and here we have doubt being cast on the actual values. These things are all right as long as we know them. So long as people who are using it are conscious of it. Mr. Cranna also raises the question of irrigation and the importance of the estimation of the water balance in this field and the importance of work being done in this area.

Mr. Wilson, in discussing the problems of stream gauging networks, points out its deficiencies, and estimates that about an additional 200 to 250 first-class stations are required in Scotland, which will take 10 years to establish. I am not sure whether that is at the present rate or whether it allows for the speeding up of the work. He points out that these 250 stations would only give a base from which we can work. In other words, these are the long-term stations, where in 20 to 25 years' time we would hope to obtain accurate results. In addition to that, *ad hoc* stations for particular purposes would need to be placed in other catchments and correlated with our base stations. The period of operation of these *ad hoc* stations would, of course, be much shorter.

In Dr. Earp's and Mr. Eden's papers the paucity of information is implied and the need for further work is stressed. They point out the interesting fact that Section 3 in the Water (Scotland) Act also empowers the Secretary of State (I am quoting from p. 1811) to make regulations requiring periodic returns as to the quantity and quality of water abstracted from underground sources. But regulations have not yet been made to implement this section. In other words, the powers are there but they have not yet been implemented. There is a heartening note struck, if I may refer to Mr. Wilson's paper, that this is actively being considered by Government in regard to the desirability of establishing a national water survey. They are considering the density of coverage which would be necessary and the most practical and economic way of achieving such a coverage. This strikes a heartening note in an otherwise pretty sad story.

To summarise the papers, then, they show us that as far as the basic resource facts in water are concerned, there is a paucity of information. We require a lot more stations of all descriptions and here may I pay tribute to the good work which is being carried out by the recently established River Pollution Boards. I have seen several of their reports and they are doing an extremely good job, especially on the other data which I mentioned—dissolved material, suspended material, etc.—which is in many cases just as important as actual quantity. I must stress that all who work in this field are keenly aware of these shortcomings, and what is being done with the available staff and money at their command is excellent work of a very high standard.

DISCUSSION

Mr. J. P. Gunn

Mr. Chairman, Ladies and Gentlemen: We have got one of our most precious resources in water, which is drawn from rivers. It is a great temptation to think that a river is always the same, when in fact it is not; the same natural forces that led to the river forming its present bed are still in action. There are complex relations connecting the discharge of a river, its slope, its cross-sectional shape and the bed material. If any one of these factors is altered, then the river promptly adapts itself to the new conditions. It is, therefore, reasonable to study not only the water in a river but the movement of the bed. Dr. Gorrie has emphasised the effect of more rapid drainage on the low-lying land along the river banks in the valleys. Changes in the regime of rivers are difficult to detect, continued readings of stick gauges will eventually give you some results, but Mr. Wilson has referred in his paper to the gaps that occur in these records, and of just how little use they are. It is true that an example to the contrary—a study of gauges on the Indus system of rivers showed the effect of opening each successive canal as it occurred, but the gauges available were very satisfactory and were mostly of 30 to 60 years in duration. The speediest way to trace the regime changes in a river requires observation of discharges as well as gauges. If you plot each year the readings of a gauge for selected discharges, say a high discharge, a medium one and a low one, you begin to get, in 5 or 6 years, some idea of the trend of the river flow. Dr. Gorrie's plottings of rainfall against runoff show no constant relations, but there are three groups, 5, 90, 91; 4, 6, 21; and 15, 16, 84 which seem worth investigation. In addition to Dr. Gorrie's remarks about the *Surface Water Year Book*, I would add that the standard form of reporting discharges could be modified to make the data more useful for general research purposes by adding columns showing plus or minus pondage and plus or minus transfers, so that the account would refer to a geographical catchment. His remarks about drainage from peat, and increase of runoff due to drainage, are the only references I could find in the papers about this important engineering activity. As there is something like 200,000 acres of land in Scotland capable of being agriculturally improved by drainage, could Mr. Wilson be asked to give a sketch of the reclamation carried out to date and the outlook for the rest of the reclaimable area? In his paper Mr. Wilson has given full details of the development of flow measurements in Scotland, and has put forward suggestions and a number of statements which his experience and local knowledge lead him to consider adequate. It may help to explain the details implied by the proposals if I make reference to the similar discharge observing organisation of which I was in charge for a few years in the Punjab. May I say I can confirm all Mr. Wilson said about gaps in discharge and gauge-reading observations. This organisation was set up by order of the Government of India in 1920 in the Provinces of Sind and the Punjab to observe discharges with the ultimate object of studying the use made of the flow in the Indus and its tributaries. Its duties consisted in observing daily discharges with current meters at points along the rivers where there were no other officials of the Irrigation Branch who could take the discharges. In addition to these they also got records of observed discharges from another 15 headworks sent in by local engineers. To keep all these observations going a small workshop for maintaining the fifty-odd meters, and a tank for rating them after repair, was required, and Sind had a similar set-up. Now, besides these routine observations the organisation was often asked for advice by local officials and also rated the large-size meters in the canals. The clerical staff prepared a water account from the observations showing gains or losses and withdrawals in the various reaches of the rivers and each year that was compared with the account prepared by Sind. It may be remarked that over a period of years these were the data on which it was possible to draw up a treaty, that has just been done, between India and Pakistan regarding the use and distribution of the waters of that system. Now, I hope that this will make it clear why I support Mr. Wilson's suggestion that only a Government organisation can get the continuity and the control over it necessary to give a working knowledge of the water resources.

Mr. HYWEL JONES, *South of Scotland Electricity Board*

Professor Frazer, and Dr. Gorrie in his paper, have referred to the need for more information, and I thought it might be useful if I told you something of what the South of Scotland Electricity Board is doing in the Galloway area. We are trying to find a relation between afforestation and water supplies and doing this in conjunction with the Forestry Commission and in close co-operation with members of the Forestry Research Station. An investigation into the effects of afforestation on available water resources is now proceeding.

Soon after the Galloway Water Power Company commenced operations in the early 1930s the Forestry Commission started work on a major programme in the south-west Scotland area. In recent years it has become evident that some change is taking place in the general conditions of water draining into the supply scheme. This has been attributed to the steady increase in the reafforestation schemes and to the growing maturity of many of the earlier plantings. Investigation was begun in 1958 and the South of Scotland Board agreed to allocate the sum of £4,000 towards the installation of equipment to measure the flow of water over a long period in an area where further development by the Forestry Commission is now starting. There was some delay initially because of changes of personnel in the Forestry Research, but progress has been resumed. The installation of the measuring equipment on the Pullaugh Burn in the Grannoch area is nearing completion. This is a long-term project and it is the expressed opinion of experts that positive results cannot be expected for about 10 or 12 years.

I have a note here about the work we are doing to kill blight and help the fishing, but I think that is more appropriate to this afternoon, so if you agree I will pass it on to the Secretary.

In addition, at the request of the Department of Inland Waterways, the flow of water in the Galloway Dee at Glenlochar Barrage was measured in 1959. This was compared with measurements taken 25 years ago and the data supplied to the Department. Subsequently the Department enquired if the Board were agreeable to extend this type of survey, and this the Board has agreed to do. I should strike a note of caution, however. In 1959 we had the measuring devices at the Glenlochar Barrage recallibrated. It is of no use callibrating and expecting the callibration to remain the same over many years, so when we compare the present-day readings with the early ones, there will be some inaccuracy which I think I should mention.

Councillor BRUCE RUSSELL, *Lothians River Purification Board*

I raise the point of the abstraction of water for agricultural and irrigation purposes. The River Inspectors Association of Scotland was so perturbed about this that they have brought the matter to the notice of the Scottish River Purification Advisory

Committee. One report said that the growing abstractions may seriously deplete the natural flow of many rivers and streams. The chief of these abstractions is for irrigation, which are increasing apace. Spray irrigation requires large quantities of water. A typical arrangement is for the equivalent of 1 in. of rain to be applied to land every 10 days. Hence if a farmer is irrigating 100 acres he will use approximately 230,000 gallons of water per day. In very few cases is sufficient water available from a public supply for irrigation and it is usually obtained by direct abstraction from streams. It must be strongly emphasised that, in the case of abstractions for irrigation, no water is returned to the water course; I suppose that is because it is spread over such a large area, and, of course, water is not abstracted in a large quantity except in times of drought and when you get drought you get a tremendously heavy evaporation of water. Consequently such of it that does return to the river is practically negligible. Of course, spray irrigation is of undoubted value to agriculture, and there is no desire to restrict its use unnecessarily, but unless some measure of control is exercised a serious situation could arise, as has already arisen in some parts of Eastern England. The Lothians River Purification Board, of which I happen to be the Chairman, made a very quick survey recently on this matter and we found out that firms supplying irrigation equipment are actively engaged throughout Scotland. It is anticipated that saturation point will be reached in 5 years' time. £25,000 worth of equipment has been sold in East Lothian alone this year. During the period 1955-65 it is anticipated that in East Lothian alone sufficient equipment will have been sold to irrigate 30 million gallons of river water per day. A note on that—that the gauge dry weather flow of the River Tyne at Prestonmills during the period September 1959 to date has been shown to be 20 million gallons per day. Another point arises. Any local authority which uses water for its general water supply has by law to provide compensation water to streams and catchment areas. The point arises, what is the use of providing compensation water which is only going to be extracted and which is going to be used, perhaps unnecessarily, over wide areas and leaving our already depleted rivers practically dry? What effect that is going to have on fish life I hesitate to say, and also on the conditions of the river beds. I think this is a matter which calls for urgent action, and we in Scotland here, and now I am speaking on behalf of the River Boards Association of Scotland, would like to see legislation brought in to give us some measure of control over the abstraction of river water for irrigation purposes.

Dr. Gorrie, *Convener, River Flow Studies Committee* (*R.S.G.S.*)

I would like to emphasise that in terms of air photo cover Scotland is still lamentably deficient. The Health Department has, in fact, a complete cover of air photos, but many of these were taken in mist, and they were all taken with antiquated equipment. Air photography has definitely advanced since these photos were taken. I have just been working on the Soil Erosion Survey of the Mangla Dam in Pakistan, and the quality of the air photos we have been using for this particular survey is incredibly good when compared with what York Buildings can produce; it just is not in the same age. I would like to recommend that arrangements be made for re-photographing the whole of Scotland from the air.

I don't think I need elaborate the points which everyone seems to be fully agreed upon, namely that we are not getting enough data either for the rivers or the rainfall;

but I would like to put in a word for the voluntary organisation of which I am Convener, The River Flow Study Committee, which the Royal Scottish Geographical Society very sportingly said they would back. They are able to help us to have meetings, but that is the extent of their financial help, and we have no money whatever to undertake the projects and enquiries which we would very much like to start. We tried to get money from various sources, including D.S.I.R., but failed to do so, and we are still without any visible means of support for doing all these jobs which we would like to tackle.

I was particularly pleased to learn recently about the South of Scotland Electricity Board's undertaking to measure forest influences. I feel myself that this is an important phase of river research work. With this should also be taken the question of peat and what peat represents as a basic resource for producing our water. Peat bogs are like sponges. Well, sponges are all right in their way, but if you want water out of a sponge you have to squeeze it. You cannot squeeze a peat bog; you have got to wait till the weather does that for you. Hillside peat is not really covered adequately by any of the peat surveys, but it is in a place by itself as contributing something like 90 per cent. of Scotland's water supply. Anything which provides as big a proportion of our water should surely be examined thoroughly and we should find out how much a sponge it is. This function is interfered with by erosion which commonly occurs on the peat of the sloping hillsides where fires have exposed the peat. Since the sheep became the only stock, fires have become more numerous. The shepherds cannot control them, and you get big conflagrations in land that has deteriorated so far that it is just a mass of cotton grass which burns like a furnace. You have to walk across that burnt land after rain just to realise what is happening in Scotland. I am not talking about flat bogs, but about hillside peat. I think from the biological angle it is essential that we should find the basic facts and functions of our large peat resources.

Mr. CRANNA, *Meteorological Office, Edinburgh*

First of all, a short comment on Professor Frazer's abodes of the kelpie and the abominable snowman. The position as far as a long-term average isohyetal map is concerned is not quite as bad as it sounds. We do not like to venture into estimating the areal rainfall in certain areas for an individual month or an individual year, as is required for the *Surface Water Year Book*, but we do know that there are certain relationships between rainfall and altitude which do operate over a reasonably long period. It is conjectural a little bit, perhaps, but at least we have some idea, and so it is not quite a blank on the map when taken over a period of 35 years. It may not be strictly true, but I would be surprised if it is very far out.

One other thing: I would like to elaborate on the last section of my paper and to say a few words on the help that the Meteorological Office can give in furthering the aims of this Committee. It so happens that we were called upon to contribute a paper in the section dealing with water resources, but climate and weather are themes which run right through this Symposium, and climate and weather are our particular territory. There still seems to be an idea that the Meteorological Office is an organisation which produces a few forecasts for the B.B.C. and spends the rest of its time pre-occupied with aviation. That is very far from being the truth. It so happens that we are a branch of the Air Ministry, but that is purely a matter of administrative convenience. The Meteorological Office is, in fact, a state organisation, and it is the policy of our Director General—his very emphatic policy—that we should do all we can to help anyone who has got a weather problem of any kind. And, in fact, there are very few aspects of human activity that are not affected in one way or another by the weather. On the forecasting side, we now have automatic weather telephone forecasting services in Edinburgh and Glasgow where you can dial a number and get a forecast. A weather centre has been set up in Glasgow whose main function it is to provide forecast advice for the general public, for contractors, civil engineers and caterers—in fact, for anyone who wants it. In the front of any telephone directory you will find numbers that anyone can ring up at any time—motorists, yachtsmen, farmers—and get a forecast. There is no charge for this service, apart, of course, from the price of the phone call. But the point I would like to make is that forecasting is only one side of the picture. For planning purposes we still cannot give you a long-range forecast, but we can put things on an actuarial basis for you. We have collected a lot of records of past weather, we have acquired a certain amount of know-how and we can tell you how many times in so many years something is likely to occur. So whether you are interested in horticulture in the Hebrides or the temperature effects on an arch dam somewhere in a highland glen, or the wind stresses on high blocks of flats, or where to site a factory to get certain conditions, or temperature and humidity conditions for air conditioning—the variety of enquiries we get is really endless and we can usually contribute something. Actually, the planning aspect of meteorology is the job of our people in the Meteorological Office here in Edinburgh. As I said before, it is our Director General's policy that we should be a real public service and we are only too pleased to help with any of these problems.

Mr. Kinloch, *Town and Country Planning Association*

I just want to speak about one thing—the metal about which I think the Scottish Council know all the necessary points except where to get the money to utilise it—magnesium. They have supplied me during the past 10 years with a great deal of information. In the 1940s Britain discovered that we were not making magnesium metal in this country, and we spent millions in subsidising a town in Texas to manufacture magnesium by the Dow process. By all the information I have got from the Scottish Council and wherever else I could get it, I think there is a more suitable place than Texas, for everything seems to be at hand here. Up at Durness you have the tide running along the coast, a very speedy tide carrying away all the effluents. You have got the necessary substance—5 million tons in every cubic mile of the Atlantic—inexhaustible. You have got dolomite to extract it. (The Americans used shells.) You have electricity there. You have a site for a town. People say to me—who would go there? If they place the town near Durness at Balnakiel it is a delightful site with sandy beaches for bathing both to the north and to the west. Its June rainfall is considerably lower than that of Paris, and its winter temperature (January temperature) is higher than that of London. You have everything there. America has given great sums to build up the industry. It can only be done by Government aid. America's output of magnesium is 90 per cent. nationally controlled. It looks like socialism, but they call it defence policy. The rest is subsidised. America considers it worth while to bring magnesite 1,200 miles from one side and peat 1,000 miles from another, and up there at Durness you have got all that is necessary together. I believe also there is a process of the quartzite production which would be cheaper. The only point is to get electricity cheap enough. When I began working for this in 1925 nobody would listen to me. I began working for hydro-electricity in 1903. After 40 years we got it. I hope it will not be 40 years until we get magnesium in the Highlands.

Mr. P. JOHNSON-MARSHALL, *International Centre for Regional Planning and Development*

I wonder if I may ask a question which I think should be addressed to Mr. Wilson. It concerns urban expansion and surface water runoff, and is particularly interesting to us, who are just starting the new course on civic design and town planning at the University here. This urban expansion is now going on, in very large areas around our major cities, particularly, for instance, on the higher ground. I would like to know what research is being carried out on surface water runoff with regard to the different kinds of urban development, such as, for instance, if you have a high block of flats surrounded by a green area, one has a certain amount of percolation and a certain amount of runoff. If you have speculative estate development you have a good deal more hard surface with maybe a more rapid runoff and I just wondered whether studies are being undertaken, and if so, what are they in terms of resource surveys which could lead us to a closer analysis of what are the most desirable forms of urban expansion which are being undertaken at the moment? Could I ask Mr. Wilson this question?

Mr. J. K. C. WILSON, *Department of Agriculture and Fisheries for Scotland*

I would like first of all to deal with the note in Dr. Gorrie's paper where he complained that the River Spey Survey was not made available to him. In fact, the Report on the Survey was completed at the end of 1954. It was regarded initially as confidential until the Ministers had an opportunity of considering it, and in the middle of 1957 it was decided that it was impossible to publish the Report because of its sheer size. It consisted of 28 pages of report, 31 pages of appendices, 21 charts, diagrams and coloured plates—foolscap size, 22 coloured plates of twice foolscap size, and an Ordnance Survey map of the Spey valley. To prepare and make available 50 copies would have cost at least £20 a copy, and nobody saw any demand arising for even 50 copies. In fact, a copy of the Report was sent to the Department's Area Office at Inverness, and the following were advised that it was available:

The Convention of Royal Burghs,
The Spey District Board,
The District Council's Association,
The Town Clerk of Grantown-on-Spey, and
Inverness County Council.

The Report is still in Inverness, and our information is that there have been eight requests to see it. A copy was also in the hands of Kingussie Burgh Council from February to October 1958. I think actually that Dr. Gorrie's request to see it came within the period in which it was regarded as confidential and consequently it was held up for that.

Now to deal with some of the matters raised by speakers. I would like first of all to deal with the point raised by Professor Frazer, who mentioned that the results of a Water Survey could only be given in statistical form. That, of course, is very true. The other speakers have referred to the length of time over which it would be necessary to work before significant results could be deduced. I have just recently received a publication from the United States Geological Survey in which they deal with this matter, and they found as a result of statistical analysis the length of record necessary to allow estimation within 25 per cent. of the probable value of a flood of any given period of recurrence—frequency, chance, or percentage chance—if you would care to call it. To be within 25 per cent. of the correct value 95 per cent. of the time, it requires 12 years of record to assess the mean annual flood which is taken as the flood with the period of recurrence of 2·33 years, 80 years of record for the flood having a period of recurrence of 10 years, and 48 years for a 100-year flood. These periods are reduced somewhat if you are prepared to consider 25 per cent. correct 80 per cent. of the time. If you want to be within 10 per cent. of the correct value for the mean annual flood, you need 40 years of record to get 95 per cent. confidence, or 25 years of record to get 80 per cent. confidence. For a 10-year flood you need 90 years of record and 38 years of record respectively, and for 100-year flood 115 and 100. I do not know how firm these figures are, but I know that the Americans made a very comprehensive statistical analysis of the chances of occurrence of this random data and that is their result. The other point raised by Professor Frazer was the number of 250 stations to which I referred in my paper, and to my estimate of 10 years as the necessary period of time to put these stations in operation. This is an accelerated rate of installation. The whole question of setting up a survey is bound up with the question of staffing. There are very few people in the country who are trained in the technique of river flow measurement, and any survey set up in Scotland would in my opinion have to be a central survey if for no other reason than for the necessity to get uniform results—any such central organisation would largely have to train staff. It is no use training staff that you are going to discharge half-way through the job, and you have got to balance the intake of staff with the construction of stations and maintenance of stations. It would be possible to produce quite a good balanced programme for the construction of about 200 stations (we have some 50 stations at present in operation which could be incorporated into a survey) over a period of 10 years.

In answer to Mr. Johnson-Marshall, I would just say that so far as I know there is no research being made into changes of runoff values. A lot of research is being done in England into the runoff from urban areas, but I have no details of that at present, and so far as I know there is nothing being done in Scotland.

Mr. Robinson, *Water Research Association*

First a question to Dr. Gorrie. There appears to be some evidence that soil erosion is the cause of excessive algal growths in lochs. Has this been or could this be investigated?

Secondly, to Mr. Cranna. There seems no vertical component for air movement allowed for in the Penman formula. In an energy balance approach the first manifestation of a different effect of, say, a woodland, might be a lowering of temperature, leading to turbulence in the air. I understand that those who fly light aeroplanes find turbulence over woodlands. Would Mr. Cranna expand on his reservations on the Penman formula?

Dr. ALBERT PARKER, *formerly Director, Fuel Research*

I was deeply interested over a long period in records of river flows as for some years I was Assistant Director and then Director of Water Pollution Research in the D.S.I.R. We were then, and still are, badly in need of reliable records of the flows of rivers and their changes over periods of years. The opinion is often expressed that the measurements should be taken and the records kept by the Government. Such a method would, in my view, be unnecessarily expensive. It seems to me that the organisation should be somewhat on the lines of the Rainfall Organisation of the Meteorological Office, or by the kind of procedure by which the D.S.I.R. collects records of air pollution from local authorities, industrialists and other organisations who together operate several thousand instruments in different parts of the country. There is required a small but enthusiastic staff at the centre to advise on how to make the measurements, to persuade river authorities and others with local interests to take the readings and to send them to the central office for collection, correlation and publication. The appropriate Department for such a system would be the D.S.I.R., which does not have any bias as a user interest and whose Geological Survey is already concerned with underground water resources.

I was also interested in the paper on magnesium from sea water, because I was associated with the introduction of synthetic resins for ion exchange. It was hoped to be able economically to use the resins for the extraction of valuable materials from sea water. However, the precipitation process, as operated by the Steetley Co., is still the most economic for the extraction of magnesia; but some day there may be discovered resins or other materials or methods whereby more of value can economically be derived from sea water.

Dr. J. R. EARP, *Geological Survey of Great Britain*

I will be very brief because really the discussion has turned neither on the amounts nor distribution of underground water, so I think all I should say in amplification of our paper is to bring to the attention of members the existence of the Geological Survey, and that we have, since our inception, taken considerable interest in underground water. We have, I suppose, an unrivalled collection of records of wells, boreholes, shafts and so on, and we are available to interpret and distribute this information to anyone who is interested. I think that is all I should say.

K. W. PEARCE, Esq., *Steetley Magnesite Co. Ltd.*

I would like to make some remarks about magnesium metal.

Magnesium metal has, I think, an unpleasant taste in the mouths of many industrialists because a lot of magnesium is wanted in wartime and large plants are erected to satisfy these demands. When peace comes, the need for magnesium diminishes suddenly and the industrialists are left with a lot of redundant plant on their hands.

To manufacture magnesium economically, you should have plenty of cheap electricity available, and this is the case in Norway, where there is one of the biggest electrolytic plants in Europe making magnesium metal. I believe that most of the magnesium produced in Norway is sent to Volkswagen and used in the light-alloy cylinder blocks of their motor cars, so if you can persuade any big motor car manufacturer in this country to start making light-alloy cylinder blocks, the demand for magnesium metal will be increased.

About ion exchange, at Steetley we are interested in this process because we believe that eventually ion exchange may provide a better method for extracting magnesia from sea water than our present precipitation techniques.

Copper was mentioned in the paper, and although it can be extracted from sea water prodigious quantities of water need to be handled, pumping costs alone are likely to be £100 to £120 per ton of copper.

Because the main outlet for bromine is the lead scavenging compound ethylene dibromide, bromine manufacture will only be worth while if there are plentiful supplies of ethylene to hand.

In conclusion, then at present you can manufacture economically two things from sea water—bromine and magnesia. Although other valuable materials are present in the sea they can usually be obtained from alternative cheaper sources.

Professor Pearsall

I must draw this discussion to an end. We have dealt with assessment and I would emphasise two points before we leave the subject. One is the very long-term nature of assessment. We shall not do this in a moment, and there we have, I think, Dr. Parker's very valuable suggestion as to the method of approach to that problem. The other thing that stands out I think from these papers is that water is one of the things for which there are multi-purpose needs. It is no good just talking about water: the quality of water is quite important; we do not want the same quality for potable water as we should require for cooling water. And so our assessment of the problem might well be coloured by that fact. Then, of course, lastly, we have the fact that all water users tend to want water when it is most scarce, and this suggests that every method of drainage, for example land-drainage, should be somewhere associated with water storage so that the water is still available at the right season. Those are the three points which strike me in this discussion.

WRITTEN CONTRIBUTIONS

South of Scotland Electricity Board

Research and Experiment in Galloway Scheme of Recent or Current Origin

1. *Afforestation and Water Supplies*

In conjunction with the Forestry Commission and with the close co-operation of members of the Forestry Research Station, an investigation into the effect of afforestation on available water resources is proceeding.

Soon after the Galloway Power Company commenced operation in the early 1930s the Forestry Commission started work on the major programme in the South West Scotland area. In recent years it has become evident that some change is taking place in the general condition of water resources. This has been attributed to the steady growth in the reforestation schemes and to the growing maturity of many of the earlier plantings.

Investigation was begun in 1958 and the South of Scotland Board agreed to allocate the sum of £4,000 towards the installation of equipment to measure the flow of water over a long period in an area where further development by the Forestry Commission is taking place. After some delay caused by change in personnel in the Forestry Research Department progress has been resumed. The installation of the measuring equipment on the Pullaugh Burn in the Grannoch area is nearing completion.

This is a long-term project and it is the expressed opinion of experts in the Forestry Research Station that positive results cannot be expected for about 10 or 12 years.

2. *Improvement of Salmon Fisheries*

Steps towards the improvement of the salmon fisheries in the South West area are in progress. This will entail modifications to the fish passes at Tongland, Carsfad and Earlstoun. The proto-type modification has already been made at Tongland with considerable success. In conjunction with this the reservoirs are being cleared of coarse fish and pike killing has been carried out during the past year. It is hoped that restocking of the reservoirs with brown trout will be carried out in the near future. This work is being done in conjunction with the local Angling Associations and in consultation with the Department of Agriculture and Fisheries for Scotland.

3. *Measurement of Water Resources*

At the request of the Department of Inland Waterways, the flow of water in the Galloway Dee at Glenlochar Barrage was measured in 1959. This was compared with measurements taken 25 years ago and the data supplied to the Department. Subsequently the Department enquired if the Board were agreeable to extending this type of survey, and the Board have indicated a desire to co-operate.

J. H. SPENCER, *River Inspector, Clyde River Purification Board*

Firstly I would refer to the statement in para. 23 of Dr. Gorrie's paper that River Purification Boards are "taking only the nadir flows . . . so they are not measuring flood flows".

Mr. A. Gerard Boulton, Engineer-in-Charge, Surface Water Survey, stated in a paper to the Association of River Inspectors of Scotland in September 1958: "From the point of view of river pollution, it might at first be thought that only the dry weather flows are of interest, but a little reflection will show that, if the effects of water supply schemes or industrial uses are to be studied, it is necessary for all ranges of flow to be continuously recorded. Only then does it become possible to build up a duration curve, to ascertain the modal or average discharge and to be sure of recording the extreme values, both upper and lower. If the water resources are to be conserved in the best interests of all concened, information of this sort is indispensible."

That statement embodies the principles and policy on which my own River Purification Board, is acting and so far as I know, it applies equally to my colleagues.

In Mr. Wilson's paper (p. 122) somewhat slighting reference is made as follows: "In the early 1950s River Purification Boards . . . began to be set up. So far none . . . have made any significant contribution to the work."

The oldest River Purification Board was formed less than six years ago and the latest was only set up within the last 12 months. River gauging is one permissive function in a mass of duties the Boards have to fulfil. It speaks well, therefore, that some of the older Boards have already quite a network of gauging stations and that others have acquired apparatus and staff for the purpose. In view of the experience of the Department of Agriculture and particularly of their own difficulties and tardiness in erecting and calibrating gauging stations, it ill becomes them to criticise later entrants to the field.

On the question of how and by whom river gauging should be carried out, I would suggest that each river basin is a natural complete unit. Each River Purification Board is already dealing in a number of ways with such a catchment area (or a parallel cluster of them) and is consequently the rational clearing house for the collection and dissemination of river information. This could then be co-ordinated and centralised over a wider area by some such body as the Surface Water Survey. This would not preclude the Department of Agriculture from continuing and extending the gauging work it has begun, but all the indications are that they will leave untouched quite sizeable waters which have little or no agricultural interest. The River Boards hope to fill such gaps, and all, working harmoniously together, can gradually complete a picture of our water resources.

One other point to which I would draw attention is the legislative parochialism in the application of Parliamentary enactments to Scotland in the sphere of pollution prevention and river work generally. Very few such Acts of Parliament have applied to the whole of Britain and there is often a considerable time-lag before equivalent laws are specially made for Scotland. There are still no Scottish Land Drainage Acts. Drainage of trade premises is only just beginning to be considered for Scotland, nearly a quarter of a century after the English Act. The most recent example is that the Clean Rivers (Estuaries and Tidal Waters) Act, 1960, only applies to England and Wales, despite efforts to include Scotland, whose foreshores are just as liable to be fouled by pollution. Some odd consequences can occur in the Borders, where different legislation applies to opposite banks of the Tweed and Solway. Perhaps the Scottish Council might assist in getting Britain treated as a legal whole in such matters.

The Hydrographer of the Navy

HYDROGRAPHIC SURVEY IN SCOTLAND SINCE THE END OF THE SECOND WORLD WAR

1. The Hydrographer of the Navy has employed one survey ship continually, and two occasionally, in Scottish waters since the end of the Second World War. Most of the survey work has been planned for one of the following two reasons:

(i) To improve and extend the accurate sounding cover of the approaches to the coasts and ports of Scotland.

(ii) To modernise the existing charts of Scottish waters by echo sounding and by incorporating the modern topographical surveys.

2. The need for the work undertaken under the terms of (i) above is indisputable. General knowledge of the ocean floor and that of the continental shelf is most desirable and accurate bottom topography is of value to Fisheries Research, Geophysical Investigation and the like, apart from the needs of submarine navigation for military and, possibly in the future, commercial purposes. The increasing use of electronic fixing aids has improved the accuracy of offshore surveys as well as reducing the time taken to carry out such surveys.

3. In the field of inshore surveys, 1 (ii) above, the Hydrographer has been working to implement his normal and continuous policy of improving existing charts. Additionally, he works to the demands of Commerce when such demands are supported by a responsible National Authority.

4. A number of surveys of ports and approaches such as Aberdeen, Peterhead and Fraserburgh on the east and the Clyde in the west have been completed. In the course of such surveys, as indeed in all surveys, all wrecks and obstructions have been located and fixed, their least depth being obtained by echo sounder or by sweeping. It can be assumed that any area of survey undertaken by the Hydrographer is meticulously and accurately completed and that it provides the necessary data for compiling a chart or charts on an appropriate scale. It should, however, be appreciated that when the working is planned from within the Department, it is designed to produce charts for navigation. Hydrographer also makes surveys all over the world for specific development projects and these are usually on a far more detailed basis than would be justified for normal chart production. Such surveys are sometimes carried out in co-operation with some other firm such as an oil prospecting or a photogrammetric mapping organisation.

5. Hydrographer was interested to note, in a paper presented by Mr. Rankin of Hunting Surveys, a reference to oceanographic and inshore surveys. There is undoubtedly a great deal of room for closer co-operation between a Commonwealth Hydrographic Authority such as the Hydrographic Department and firms such as Mr. Rankin's in problems of common interest to users. What must, however, be realised is that Hydrographer has so much routine work to do to maintain the existing series of charts and publications that he is not likely to be looking for new projects. He must rely on approaches from interested parties to set special investigations going.

BASIC RESOURCE FACTS

FISH AND WILDLIFE

Scottish Freshwater Fish

K. A. PYEFINCH, M.A., F.R.S.E.
Department of Agriculture and Fisheries for Scotland
Freshwater Fisheries Laboratory, Pitlochry

Of the thirty species of freshwater fish in Scotland, only salmon, sea trout and brown trout are of prime importance. Statistical information on their abundance is limited, but estimates based on the information available show that their value as a source of food is severely limited and, though improvements should be practicable, these would not be likely to alter their status as a food supply radically. All three fish are, however, of considerable value as a recreational asset and their indirect economic value is therefore important.

Eels, pike and perch are the most important coarse fish. Eels are common and could form the basis of a useful, if modest, fishery, but this possibility has never been thoroughly exploited. Pike are dangerous predators and should be eliminated or rigidly controlled in waters where salmonid fisheries are important, but the dangers of perch in salmonid waters are much less certain.

It is not easy to present a full survey of Scottish freshwater fish resources, because there is so little detailed information upon which to base any comments. About thirty species of freshwater fish have been recorded from Scottish waters, and of these there are only two species (the Atlantic salmon, *Salmo salar*, and sea trout and brown trout, *Salmo trutta*) which are of prime importance, though there are others (e.g. eels, pike, perch, grayling, char and powan) which are of interest for one reason or another and which are either widely distributed or common in particular areas. Even for the two most important species, details of catches are only available for salmon and sea trout from 1952 onwards so that here the statistical picture is by no means as complete as it could be. Much of the material in this paper must, therefore, be speculative and, since speculation on some of the less important species would be particularly unprofitable, it is proposed to restrict discussion to the more important species, particularly salmon, sea trout, brown trout, eels, pike and perch.

SALMON AND SEA TROUT

Although salmon and sea trout are distinct species, it is convenient to deal with them together because they are linked together in official returns. This arises because they are fish of similar habit, spending the major part of their period of growth at sea and returning to fresh water to spawn, and also because they are caught by similar methods, namely various types of fixed engine (chiefly on the coast), sweep netting and rod and line.

Economically, salmon and sea trout are the most important Scottish freshwater fish. The official returns[1] over the period 1952-59 give an indication of the size of the catch and its value (see Table I).

TABLE I

Year	*Catch* (tons)	*Value* (£)
1952	1,631	1,005,000
1953	1,457	1,019,800
1954	1,644	1,013,000
1955	1,595	1,071,840
1956	1,369	997,000
1957	1,601	866,678
1958	1,705	1,001,420
1959	1,663*	1,303,792*

* Provisional figures.

Before returns under the Salmon and Freshwater Fisheries (Protection) (Scotland) Act, 1951, first became available in 1952, an estimate of the catch was made using the returns made by the railway companies showing the weight of salmon they dispatched from their various stations throughout the country. As the railway companies have continued to make these returns since 1952, it has been possible to compare them directly with the statutory returns and to calculate a rough correction factor. Using this factor, the returns earlier than 1952 can be compared with those after that date and the results indicate that, at least for the purpose of the present survey, the catches shown in the Table above can be considered to be representative and that the annual catch of salmon and sea trout has, with six exceptions, been between 1,000 and 2,000 tons for the past 30 years.

The railway returns merely gave an overall estimate of the catch and did not indicate how much of the fish was caught by different methods. Since 1952, further details have been available and an analysis of the annual catches is given in Table II.

TABLE II

Year	*Rod and Line* (tons)	*Net and Coble* (tons)	*Fixed Engines* (tons)
1952	205	700	726
1953	233	595	665
1954	282	741	621
1955	240	674	681
1956	279	547	543
1957	322	671	608
1958	327	698	680
1959	233*	826*	604*
Totals	2,121	5,452	5,128
Average	265	682	642

* Provisional figures.

Thus, the average rod and line catch over the period 1952-59 accounts for about one-sixth of the total catch, the remainder being divided fairly evenly between catches by net and coble and those from fixed engines.

Most of the salmon catch comes from the east coast since all the most important Scottish salmon rivers (the Tweed, the Tay, the North Esk, the Dee and the Spey) run into the North Sea and the greatest intensity of coastal netting is found on the east coast, particularly from Montrose northwards to the Moray Firth. As an indication of the importance of the main salmon rivers, the catches from their fishery districts account, on average, for over 50 per cent. of the total catch per annum from 1952 onwards.

The economic valuc of the salmon and sea trout catches is much enhanced by the high market price of these fish, particularly salmon. Thus, comparing the catches given above with those of marine fish, the cash value of the salmon and sea trout catch in 1959 was about one-eleventh of the cash value of marine wet fish landings[2] but the weight of salmon and sea trout landed was only about one-twohundredth of the weight of wet fish. Expressed in another way, the weight of salmon and sea trout caught in Scottish waters could only make a very modest contribution to the country's food supply. The average catch of salmon over the period 1952-58 (inclusive) was roughly 3,115,200 lb. per annum; taking the population of Scotland at its estimated level in 1958 (5,169,000) the salmon caught would provide a little over ½ lb. of fish per head per annum. The contribution of sea trout to the nation's diet would be even more modest, since the average annual catch of sea trout over the 1952-58 period was only about one-tenth of the salmon catch (the figure for sea trout being about 398,100 lb.).

Though it would be reasonable to suggest that the catches of salmon could be improved, it must be admitted that our present knowledge of salmon management is too scanty to allow any assessment to be made of the extent to which improvement might be made. The relationship between catch and stock is not yet known and the spawning stock required to maintain an adequate catch is also an unknown quantity—in short, we do not know that we are using our present salmon stocks to their best advantage. Despite these problems, it should be practicable to find ways of increasing present stocks, because it is known that losses are heavy during the initial period in fresh water. For example, mortality between hatching and the end of the first summer of the young fish's life may be as high as 90 per cent. It should be possible to reduce this mortality and so increase the number of seaward migrants and, subsequently, the stock returning to our coasts and rivers, though it should be remembered that mortality in the sea is also high. Recent developments in Sweden, where (because of extensive hydro-electric developments) an attempt is being made, with success, to maintain salmon stocks virtually without rivers by establishing a series of salmon-rearing stations throughout the country, give some indication of what can be done. Similar developments in Scotland would undoubtedly be affected by the fact that so many of our salmon fisheries (both net and rod) are in private hands, but there are encouraging signs that thoughtful anglers and netsmen are beginning to realise the value of a sound policy of management.

It is perhaps worth mentioning a further point in connection with salmon and sea trout catches. These migratory fish first spend some two or three years in fresh water, then migrate to the sea, where they grow rapidly (the salmon smolt migrating in May one year weighing an ounce or so may return during June or July of the following year weighing, perhaps, four or five pounds) and then return to our fresh waters. At a time when restrictions on offshore marine fishing are evidently increasing, methods of increasing the catch of fish which feed at sea but come inshore to be caught are worth more than passing consideration. This habit is not limited, of course, to Atlantic salmon and sea trout; Pacific salmon behave in the same way, and attempts are being made to acclimatise some species of Pacific salmon elsewhere, notably in Russia.[3]

Though, in this paper, stress has been laid on the size and value of the salmon catch, mention should also be made of other aspects of salmon fisheries. Men directly employed in the commercial salmon fishing industry number about 1,600 to 1,700.[1] This is a minimal figure, as it should be increased by those employed in ancillary trades, and particularly by the considerable numbers employed as gillies and water bailiffs. The recreational value of salmon and sea trout fishing, though not easy to estimate as a national resource, is nevertheless considerable and should certainly be included in any assessment of the value and potentialities of these fisheries.

Brown Trout

Brown trout are widely distributed and are found in a wide variety of streams and lochs all over the country. They are probably the commonest freshwater fish, but it is very difficult to assess their status as a natural resource because of the absence (with a few notable exceptions) of published records of catches.

It is not easy even to estimate the annual catch of brown trout, but some idea of its magnitude can be gained from the limited information available. For example, the catches from Loch Leven, perhaps the most famous of Scotland's trout lochs, have averaged, over the period 1902-51, 7·5 lb. per acre. The area of Scotland's lochs and streams is not easy to compute, but the total area of the lochs surveyed by the Bathymetrical Survey[4] is 340 square miles or 217,600 acres. If the average catch for Loch Leven is applied to all the lochs surveyed by the Bathymetrical Survey, the annual catch is 1,632,000 lb. (or about 730 tons). This can only be regarded as the roughest of assessments, as two major assumptions have been made in producing it—namely that the annual catch from Loch Leven is representative (whereas in fact it is probably well above the national average) and that the total area used is a reasonably accurate figure (whereas it is manifestly too low, as the Bathymetrical Survey did not cover all the Scottish lochs and covered none of the streams). The correction that should be made for each of these opposing errors is unknown, but it seems unlikely that, even if reasonably accurate corrections could be applied, the annual catch quoted above would be substantially increased.

An annual catch of 730 tons represents about one-third of a pound of trout per head of population—an even more meagre addition to the nation's food supply than that provided by salmon. Although this situation could be improved, experiments carried out at Pitlochry over the past eight years indicate that the improvement, though significant, is not spectacular. For example, the addition of mineral fertilisers such as superphosphate to the waters of lochs of moderate or low productivity may double the weight of trout of a given age,[5] so that this treatment would not increase the catch to a figure which would make brown trout a significant item of diet. It could, however, improve the value of a loch as a sporting asset.

Fishing for brown trout is a popular recreation and the number of brown trout anglers has increased rapidly over the last ten or fifteen years. This increase would seem likely to continue because of the increase in the amount of leisure and the increased mobility of the population generally. The recreational aspect of this natural resource is thus important, but the increase in the numbers of trout anglers has brought its own problems, notably that of the damage caused by the activities of groups of anglers who are anxious to catch as many fish as possible and who are not always scrupulous about the methods they use. Many angling clubs and associations are anxious to improve their fishings (though, it should be noted, this "improvement" is more often an adjustment of the population structure to provide larger numbers of "takeable" fish than an increase in productivity), but are discouraged from doing so because the result of their efforts may only be that their waters attract the attentions of the fishing (or poaching) gangs. Even if stricter legislation were introduced it is difficult to see how stricter laws could be enforced without a considerable increase in the number of bailiffs and, under present arrangements, money is not available for this increase. In this connection, however, reference should be made to the arrangements made recently by the Scottish Tourist Board, which make it possible for angling clubs and other associations of anglers to obtain financial help for improving their fishings provided they comply with certain conditions, in particular, that the fishings are beneficial to the tourist industry and that the associations are willing to make their fishings available for the payment of a reasonable fee.

Eels

Though eels seem plentiful enough in Scotland, a full-scale commercial fishery has never developed. The reason for this seems to be that there are fears, if eel fisheries were established, that they would interfere with salmon fisheries but, as Menzies[6] points out, these fears are quite groundless. In Ireland, flourishing eel fisheries are maintained in conjunction with salmon fisheries and there is no obvious reason why the same situation should not obtain in Scotland. The effect of eels on a salmon fishery has long been a matter for dispute, some maintaining that eels are dangerous predators, whereas others consider their deleterious effects to be much less, but as nobody has yet suggested that eels are of benefit to a salmon fishery no harm could result from their removal. Apart from their use as food locally, eels could find a ready market in the south as considerable quantities of eels are imported from Ireland and from the Continent.

In the absence of any organised fishery, no estimate can be made of the quantity of eels which could be caught in Scotland. Menzies[6] records that one fisherman took 1,180 lb. of eels during 17 days in May 1917. As an indication of the order of catch that might be available from Scottish waters, the weight of eels caught in Eire over the period 1948-52 averaged about 250,000 lb.[7]

Pike and Perch

Both perch and pike are common Scottish freshwater fish, but their potentialities as natural resources cannot be assessed because both are regarded as disadvantageous to the more important salmon and trout fisheries. Pike are certainly dangerous predators and can do a great deal of harm unless they are rigidly controlled, but the harmful effects of perch are less well defined. Perch exist in some numbers in many trout lochs, but their effect on a trout fishery, either directly as predators on young trout, or indirectly as competitors for the same food supply, is not accurately known.

REFERENCES

1. Report on the Fisheries of Scotland, 1954, 1955, 1956, 1957, 1958, 1959. Edinburgh: H.M.S.O. (1955-1960).
2. Scottish Sea Fisheries Statistical Tables, 1959. Edinburgh: H.M.S.O. (1960).
3. Nikolsky, G. V., and Koshin, N. I. (1959). Some peculiarities of salmon biology which are important in their reproduction. *Rapp. Cons. Explor. Mer*, **148**, 66-68.
4. Murray, J., and Pullar, L. (1910). *Bathymetrical Survey of the Scottish Fresh-Water Lochs*, Vol. I. Edinburgh.
5. Pyefinch, K. A. (1960). *Trout in Scotland.* Edinburgh.
6. Menzies, W. J. M. (1948). The common eel and its capture. *Fisheries, Scotland, Salmon Fish.*, 1948, No. 1.
7. Department of Agriculture, Eire, Fisheries Branch. Report on the Sea and Inland Fisheries, 1949, 1951, 1952. Dublin: Stationery Office (1950-53).

Scottish Inshore Fishery Resources

C. E. LUCAS, C.M.G., D.SC., F.R.S.E., B. B. RAE, M.A., B.SC., PH.D., and
H. J. THOMAS, B.SC., PH.D.

Department of Agriculture and Fisheries for Scotland, Marine Laboratory, Aberdeen

In this review the term "inshore" is used in a wider sense than usual to include all fisheries involving an absence from port, by the vessels concerned, of anything up to two days.

Truly inshore fisheries for crabs, lobsters, periwinkles, mussels, etc., are considered in some detail. The steady increase in the yearly catches and value of shellfish landed in Scotland is demonstrated and reference is made to resources which could possibly be more heavily exploited.

Scottish pelagic and demersal fisheries are considered in brief. A Table giving average yearly landings and values for the period 1953-59 is used to illustrate the relative abundance and importance of the various species caught off the Scottish coast. The importance of a keen demand and of economic prices on the market is emphasised. The possibility of increasing the catches of certain less traditional species is discussed.

The North Sea with its adjacent waters is one of the world's richest fishing grounds. Not only is the area prolific in fish, and not only has it borne very intensive fishing during the last 40 years, but it is also characterised by a variety of commercially important species such as are not found together on many comparable grounds. Scotland is therefore conveniently placed for the exploitation of these stocks.

The term "inshore" is rather loosely used. Strictly speaking, it should perhaps be restricted to fisheries within the three-mile limit, prominent among which are the various shellfish fisheries (lobsters, crabs, prawns, shrimps, mussels, etc.), with some herring fishing and some small- and hand-line fishing and such seining as is permitted by bye-law inside that limit.* But for many purposes this is too restrictive a term, as is instanced by the "inshore" herring fishing and seining which cannot properly be differentiated from the remainder of those important fisheries conducted mainly within 50 or 60 miles from the coast. It is characteristic, too, that the seine-net fishery cannot easily be differentiated from the trawl fishery which extends roughly over the same areas, outside the three-mile limit, to distances much farther from the Scottish coast. This paper therefore will review first the truly inshore shellfish fisheries and then try to set the other, somewhat indeterminate, "inshore" fisheries in relation to the remainder of Scotland's fisheries. Ideally, for this purpose, a boundary would be drawn roughly dependent on the distance from land at which the inshore vessels operate, reckoning among them only those vessels which are absent from port normally no more than two days at a time. This definition would include most of the herring fishing vessels and seiners and most trawlers up to

* In addition, there are the coastal fisheries for salmon, which will be discussed in another Paper by K. A. Pyefinch.

100 to 110 ft. in length. Official statistics are not collected upon this "inshore" basis, however, except for shellfish. The Scottish statistics for the North Sea and the west coast must therefore be used, recognising that on the west coast the fishery is almost entirely "inshore" while the North Sea fishery is principally conducted in the north-western North Sea.

Table I attempts to set these fisheries in perspective for the period 1953-59, relative to Scottish fisheries as a whole, which extend normally to Faroe and Iceland. For example, nearly six million hundredweights of marine fish (other than shellfish, Table II)

TABLE I

Average Yearly Landings and Values of Fish landed in Scotland by British Vessels, 1953-1959 *inclusive*

Species	Average landings (cwt.) (all areas, all methods)	Average value at first sale	Average price per cwt.	Average landings (cwt.) (all methods)	
				North Sea	West Coast of Scotland
		£	s. d.		
Herring	2,206,285	2,068,952	18 9	1,159,677	1,044,059
Haddock	1,346,565	3,554,643	52 10	873,768	315,471
Cod	795,449	2,239,235	56 4	447,869	126,674
Whiting	728,149	1,475,211	40 6	591,962	120,600
Skate	109,771	272,835	49 8	69,724	27,113
Plaice	104,780	608,082	116 1	85,918	15,636
Sprats	90,126	39,138	8 8	89,519	606
Saithe	88,182	108,926	24 8	41,552	25,875
Lemon Sole	57,610	468,200	162 6	41,981	4,984
Ling	56,411	89,184	31 7	24,873	6,486
Mackerel	50,163	55,408	22 1	28,706	21,373
*Dogfish	49,523	56,977	23 0	26,554	21,198
Hake	49,295	348,243	141 4	19,494	29,569
Monks	46,931	90,869	38 8	36,720	2,433
Halibut	34,967	367,785	210 5	5,304	1,388
Witches	24,586	90,597	73 8	19,568	4,582
Torsk	24,049	36,375	30 3	3,028	429
Megrim	20,467	68,383	66 10	13,575	6,499
Dabs	18,182	46,777	51 6	13,708	2,526
Turbot	12,480	81,062	129 11	12,009	454
Catfish	6,292	10,553	33 6	3,430	31
*Lythe	5,114	8,741	34 2	1,846	3,232
Conger eel	3,919	6,263	32 0	469	3,088
Gurnard	1,506	1,523	20 2	888	591
Flounder	1,335	1,612	24 1	368	940
Redfish	1,152	1,423	24 8	16	1
Brill	208	1,302	125 2	164	43
*Porbeagle	139	825	118 8	85	4
Sparling	37	225	121 7	37	—
Livers, roes, etc.	83,320	122,256	29 4	45,924	13,686
Total landings	6,016,993	12,321,605	41 0	3,658,646	1,799,571

* No record 1953.

were landed in Scotland by British vessels in 1958, of which over five million (90 per cent.) came from the North Sea and western grounds. Of the North Sea and west coast fish, nearly 70 per cent. were white fish, taken by seine net (35 per cent.), trawl (29 per cent.) and lines (3 per cent.), while 33 per cent. were herring taken by drift and ring nets. Taking the rough definition of "inshore" given above, some 70 to 80 per cent. of the total Scottish catch of fish from the North Sea and west coast was produced by the inshore fisheries.

The value of white fish at first sale in 1958 was about £12 million, of herring about £2 million and, for comparison, shellfish about £$\frac{2}{3}$ million. Some 9,000 fishermen are fully employed in these fisheries and 2,500 are in part-time employment, largely in local handline and shellfish fisheries. The vessels employed include some 1,750 under 30 ft., mainly motor, and over 1,250 larger motor vessels. More than 100 trawlers are engaged at one time or another in "inshore" waters.

Despite the fortunate distribution of marine resources around the Scottish coasts, it must not be assumed that all the stocks are constantly available in similar quantities. They vary from time to time and from place to place for a number of reasons, dependent on (1) water conditions such as temperature, salinity, depth and the nature of the sea bed; (2) the habits of the fish: for example, their concentration in different areas for spawning or for feeding; (3) considerable fluctuations in annual recruitment to the stocks, resulting in periods of relative abundance or scarcity which may be reflected particularly in the inshore catches; (4) longer-term variations arising from environmental causes; and (5) the varying fishing intensity. Circumstances farther afield, moreover, from fishing intensity to brood fluctuations, may affect the proportions of the stock available inshore.

SHELLFISH

Fishing for shellfish is essentially an inshore occupation, and only in the case of squids do any appreciable quantities come from well offshore.

General

The value of shellfish landed in Scotland is increasing, and for this reason reference is made to 1959 when landings first realised over £808,500 at first sale. The approximate figures for the various species in 1959 were: lobsters, £373,000; Norway lobsters, £267,000; crabs, £100,000; squids, £35,000; periwinkles, £13,000; shrimps, £12,000; scallops, £4,000; mussels, £3,500; and cockles, £1,000.

Comparable values for 1953-59, given in Table II, indicate the steady increase in yield and value. The importance of the fishery, however, cannot be judged solely on these values. It is largely a "small man's" industry and consequently its effects are widely spread. It is particularly important in crofting counties where shellfish frequently contribute a considerable proportion of the income, and in consequence the pursuit is closely involved in the current social problems confronting these communities. Most shellfish are readily saleable only in the live state, and this introduces special problems, especially in areas remote from markets with the consequential tendency to high transit losses. Such difficulties are most acute in warm weather and, for certain species, largely determine both the areas and seasons of fishing. An additional factor is the preoccupation of many fishermen on the west coast with crofting pursuits during spring and autumn. Shellfish catching, in general, is not a whole-time occupation; it is frequently combined

TABLE II

The Weights (cwt.) and Values (£) of Shellfish landed in Scotland, overall and by species, for the Years 1953-59 inclusive

		1953	1954	1955	1956	1957	1958	1959
Lobster	cwt.	13,540	12,633	14,147	14,643	15,529	13,858	16,116
	£	173,373	179,800	205,291	231,175	266,431	330,370	372,618
Norway Lobster	cwt.	9,446	11,331	21,341	20,819	27,028	22,518	45,579
	£	32,116	52,426	102,582	98,903	128,532	124,835	267,225
Crab	cwt.	36,009	37,539	37,386	40,353	39,401	41,272	35,888
	£	78,376	104,190	98,725	108,543	101,844	111,958	99,837
Squid	cwt.	892	2,061	8,084	9,413	15,028	17,889	15,945
	£	795	2,481	15,668	22,269	38,312	48,920	35,065
Periwinkle	cwt.	18,181	12,727	15,819	14,279	13,550	11,836	9,389
	£	27,860	15,970	20,102	18,996	17,844	15,348	12,657
Shrimp	cwt.	1,241	1,697	2,849	1,520	1,940	3,430	2,410
	£	4,960	6,720	9,492	6,080	9,700	17,150	12,050
Scallop	cwt.	1,911	2,272	2,315	4,352	3,315	2,847	1,123
	£	6,698	8,317	7,817	15,362	12,148	10,754	4,280
Mussel	cwt.	22,780	15,917	18,473	15,345	17,311	12,510	9,453
	£	6,619	6,139	7,404	6,494	6,865	5,106	3,574
Cockle	cwt.	599	1,008	1,200	2,140	2,173	2,053	1,360
	£	390	864	701	1,337	1,510	1,877	1,262
Oyster	cwt.	—	17	—	—	—	—	—
	£	—	456	1	—	—	—	—
Total	£	331,187	377,363	467,783	509,159	583,186	666,318	808,568

with other fishing, crofting or regular employment ashore. Partly on this account it is subject to wide variations in effort, depending on the relative attractiveness of other activities.

LOBSTERS AND CRABS

Creel fishing, for lobsters and crabs, is undertaken all round our coast, providing employment to over 300 full-time fishermen and part-time to over 1,000. A variety of craft is used, from the small rowing boat worked by one man, perhaps retired from more active employment at sea, to 55-ft. diesel-engined vessels with winches and a crew of 5 or even 6 active men. The two main factors regulating the fisheries are weather and transport problems. Transport difficulties are particularly acute in the case of crabs, with the result that the location of crab fishing is dependent more on local selling outlets than on the occurrence of fishable stocks. For this reason crab fishing has been mainly confined to the east and north coasts. Elsewhere, the crabs, taken with lobsters, are frequently discarded.

Landings of lobsters are heaviest in summer when the market price is low. At this season also, transit mortalities are heaviest. Nevertheless, buying organisations with improved transport methods and facilities have overcome this difficulty, at least in part, so that in Orkney and at certain places on the west coast, for instance Oban, operations of merchants have enabled fishing to be carried on in summer, which is impossible in areas where the industry is less highly organised. Alternatively, to overcome the disadvantages of summer marketing with low price and high transit loss, lobsters may be kept in ponds or other storage installations, the stock being accumulated in the summer for distribution to the winter markets. Storage installations enable merchants to regulate their supplies of lobsters to the market and also to accumulate favourable consigning or selling quantities. Such methods have increased considerably since the war and in the last few years have enabled development of a considerable export trade to Holland and France.

Crabs are not normally stored. In recent years crab processing plants have operated at Thurso, Tweedmouth, Boddam and Inverbervie. These now take most of the catch. The development has resulted in increased activity in existing crab fisheries, especially where the factories are located. These processing plants also handle lobsters and, by providing a floor to the summer price, have recently helped to sustain lobster fishing at this season. At the processing plants the fish are cooked and the meat extracted and frozen or canned. The creel fishing industry at the present time is both active and optimistic.

Norway Lobsters

Norway lobsters (or *Nephrops*, often referred to as prawns) occur widely on muddy bottoms at depths of 20 to 150 fathoms. They have regularly been taken by trawl and seine-net boats, incidentally to the catch of white fish. Since 1950, however, when landings totalled about 3,000 cwt. and sold at an average price of 37s. per cwt., a great increase in the market for this species has occurred with the result that both landings and price have forged ahead to reach levels of 42,579 and 126s. respectively in 1959. They are still caught incidentally to white fish, although boats may make some hauls specifically for them on the "prawn" grounds. In addition, a number of boats now work primarily for Norway lobsters when these are abundant and special gear for this fishing has been developed. They are caught at all seasons. Landings are sold on the pier and buyers dispatch mainly to processing plants where the cooked tail is extracted and frozen for sale in Britain and abroad. The demand for this species continues to grow and the supply is inadequate.

Shrimps

A small but flourishing grey shrimp fishery exists in the Solway, based on Annan. Shallow-draught motor boats are used for beam trawling on the sandy bottom, out to 2 fathoms, as far west as Wigtown Bay. Shrimping is prosecuted from April to December, the crews switching to other fishing in the off-season. The catch, having been sieved to separate unwanted sizes, both large and small, is cooked at sea, then "picked", prepared and packed in local "factories". The packed cartons are bought by local merchants, who freeze a proportion so that supplies are spread out over all months. A new development in 1959-60 is the fishery in this same area for pink shrimps. There exists a considerable unsatisfied demand for this species. A programme investigating the distribution and potential for commercial exploitation elsewhere around Scotland and in particular off Berwickshire and in the Firth of Forth has been initiated.

Squid

Traditionally, squids have been used by Scottish boats as a line-fishing bait, but now the main outlet is the export market. From July to the end of the year, squids are caught along with white fish by local trawlers and seiners. They are bought on the market by merchants, then packed in 7-lb. boxes and frozen prior to export. Squids of good quality sell at about £3 per cwt., and at this price supply often falls short of demand.

Periwinkles

Periwinkles, known locally as whelks or buckies, are gathered to some extent on most parts of the Scottish coast. Pickers work about two hours either side of low water, especially at spring tides, at all seasons but to a less extent during the summer. The periwinkles are dispatched in sacks to inland markets, mainly Billingsgate, and are exported to France.

Scallops

Scallops (clams) are mainly exploited in the Firth of Clyde. The fishery is of comparatively recent origin, being initiated by Irish vessels in 1936-37, since when local craft have been engaged. Fishing is confined to the period October to April, being suspended in the summer on account of the high transit mortalities and low market price. The scallops are brought into one of the Clyde ports, adjacent to the grounds, packed in sacks and consigned by the fishermen to inland markets, chiefly Billingsgate.

Mussels

Gathering of mussels as bait for line-fishing was an industry of some importance in the early part of this century. It has fallen off with the decrease in lining, which, nevertheless, still takes the main part of the landings. Because of this, the fishery is centred mainly on the east coast, where line-fishing is mainly undertaken. For the most part mussels are hand-picked at around low tide, although dredging for mussels is undertaken on certain beds. The fishery is pursued at all seasons. A proportion of the landings from the Firths of Forth and Clyde are sold for human consumption, mainly in Edinburgh and Glasgow.

Cockles

Cockles are gathered at North Bay, Barra, generally between November and March. The amount of fishing undertaken by the crofters varies considerably according to the availability of more attractive employment, and landings have decreased progressively since 1946.

Oysters

A number of oyster beds were formerly exploited in Scottish waters, but most are now barren. A native stock of oysters still exists in inner Loch Ryan, and commercial dredging was undertaken until recently, the oysters being sold in Glasgow. With Government encouragement efforts are being made by the Millport Laboratory of the Scottish Marine Biological Association towards resuscitating this fishery.

Development

As with all other industries, development or recession is tied to profitability. Landings of Norway lobsters, crabs and squids have all increased in the last few years, stimulated by improved market prices. At present there is no serious risk of overfishing shellfish. In certain cases, for instance lobsters on the west coast, the reverse may well apply. In this instance development would appear to lie in the adoption of larger vessels, manned by whole-time fishermen undertaking cruises of several days' duration. However, whilst this could lead to fuller exploitation of the lobsters it is alien to the traditional organisation of societies of the area. Fishing has been stimulated by the development of an export trade and this could be multiplied if more attention were given to the requirements of customers abroad particularly in regard to size. So it is, or could be, with other species. For example, with a larger market for frozen or canned meat the crab fishing could be developed. Some of the recently developed grounds could supply more prawns. There appears to be a market for all shrimps, particularly "pink" shrimps, that can be landed. In each instance, and particularly for the less valuable shellfish, a Scottish outlet would be very helpful. Several kinds of shellfish could yield more than they do. It is one of the industry's major handicaps that shellfish, which are abundant around our shores and are esteemed elsewhere, are so neglected by our own people.

FISH

About thirty species of marine fish are differentiated in Scottish statistics, but the bulk of the catch is made up of a few species, principally herring, haddock, whiting, cod, plaice, skate and lemon sole (Table I). Details are published in the Annual Reports and Sea Fisheries Statistical Tables of the Department of Agriculture and Fisheries for Scotland (formerly the Scottish Home Department).

Herring Fisheries

Traditionally, Scottish fishermen are herring fishermen. However, since reaching its peak in the years prior to the 1914-18 War, the Scottish herring fishery has declined, mainly as a result of the loss of foreign markets for cured fish. This decline is clearly illustrated by reference to the following records. In 1913 nearly 5 million cwt. of herring were landed in Scotland by British vessels in a total landing of all kinds of 7·8 million cwt., while nearly 2½ million were landed by Scottish fishermen in England. In 1958 herring formed only 1·6 million cwt. in a total landing of 5·8 million cwt., while only 229,000 cwt. were landed by Scots in England. Thus from 61 per cent. of the total Scottish catch in 1913 herring landings fell to 28 per cent. in 1958. The main factor in this decline has, of course, been the falling demand and the consequent diversion of effort away from herring fishing.

Another striking change from earlier conditions is the lengthening season for herring fishing on the west coast, extending over the greater part of the year. The herring fishery is subject to large annual fluctuations in yield, resulting from variations in recruitment of young fish to the fisheries.

A recent feature of the Scottish herring fishery has been the development since the war of the dual-purpose vessel, readily converted from herring fishing to white fishing and vice versa.

Demersal Fisheries

The development of the dual-purpose vessel has also been a feature of the growth of seining by Scottish fishermen, since the method was first taken from the Danes as anchor seining in the early 'twenties and rapidly developed as the Scottish technique of fly-dragging immediately before, during and since the war. So rapid has been this development that, quite apart from the major share taken by such vessels in the herring fishing, in the last year or two their landings of white fish have almost rivalled those made by Scottish trawlers. That the fishery is still in a state of active development is witnessed by the recent skilful adaptations by the fishermen of wing nets for seining and trawling. While the principal port for trawling is Aberdeen, seine netting is also carried on there and at all the smaller Scottish fishing ports. For a detailed account of developments in inshore white-fish fisheries over the past forty years readers are referred to Dr. A. Ritchie's report "The Scottish Seine Net Fishery, 1921-1957" in the Department's Marine Research Series.

As to disposal, the fish landed in Scotland, particularly from inshore waters, have a high reputation for their quality and normally provide few disposal problems. Probably the major proportion is exported by rail and road to England, where the demand is sufficient to leave relatively little for export abroad, usually as processed fish.

Next in importance to the herring as regards quantity is the haddock. In 1958 1·4 million cwt. of this fish were landed from the North Sea and western grounds thus providing 27 per cent. of the total catch of all kinds and 40 per cent. of the white-fish catch. This is more than twice the quantity of haddock caught in 1913 and clearly indicates the swing in Scottish fisheries from the pelagic herring fishery to the demersal fishery for white fish. From being under-fished in the first decade of the present century, the haddock stocks are now over-fished, despite the conservational measures being employed. The haddock is by far the most abundant commercial demersal fish in Scottish waters and by weight provides about twice the catch of any other single species. Like the herring it is subject to seasonal movements and to brood fluctuations which from time to time have a marked effect on stocks and consequently also on the catches.

In addition to haddock, Scottish inshore demersal fisheries are mainly dependent on six other species: cod, whiting, plaice, lemon sole, skate and hake. Of these, the moderately priced cod and cheaper whiting each amounted to about half of the haddock catch in 1958, and together these three gadoids provided rather more than 80 per cent. of the "inshore" Scottish catch of white fish. Among the higher-priced varieties, the plaice is the most abundant species in Scottish waters, and is also the most typically "inshore" fish, providing just over 100,000 cwt. (less than 2 per cent. of the white-fish total) yearly. It is also landed in greater quantities now than in 1913 (43,650 cwt.). This is associated partly with the fairly recent development of the seine-net fishery which is mainly carried on in coastal waters frequented by this species, and partly with the regulative measures in force on sections of the Scottish coast which have as one of their purposes the conservation of immature plaice stocks.

Despite the relatively small quantity of plaice landed, this species and others such as the lemon sole (41,000 cwt. in 1958) and hake (38,000 cwt.) are of greater importance economically than their totals would suggest. All three are amongst the six highest-priced varieties on the Scottish market and each fetches from two to three times as much per cwt. as cod and haddock. Of the remaining species, dogfish, skate and saithe contribute appreciably to the inshore landings, but their overall value is, even combined with plaice, far less than that of any of the first four species. To illustrate the relationship of bulk and value more fully, the average quantities, values and price per cwt. of individual species of fish landed in Scotland from 1953 to 1959 are given in Fig. 1.

POTENTIALITIES

Even though Scotland's herring fisheries have diminished, catches of some of the white fish and shellfish have increased appreciably and the resource, as it has been tapped since the war, is a valuable one. It is natural, however, to consider whether it is capable of further development and there is no doubt that this is so. It cannot be stressed too strongly, however, that no such development is likely in the absence of an encouraging market for the fishermen, and an economic rate of transport to the main centres of distribution.

Possible "inshore" developments may be considered under four headings:

(*a*) As already indicated, Scotland has a rich inshore fauna and several shellfish are at present increasing steadily in our landings. Given the demand, and with rational fishing, further development should be possible.

(*b*) There is little doubt that, with a satisfactory demand and a reasonably cheap means of satisfying it, greater quantities of fish such as herring, whiting, hake, saithe, sprat, mackerel, tunny, dogfish and shark could be taken in most years. The problems are indicated by the fact that tunny, for example, for which there is a major demand in some parts of the world, are never landed in Scotland. Every summer shoals of tunny move quickly northwards along the west coast of Scotland into the North Sea (Fladen Ground), where they are fished by Scandinavian and German fishermen, but somehow the incentive to meet the world's demand for this fish has not been felt by the Scottish fishermen. For rather different reasons, saithe, which is regarded as a major resource by Germany, for example, plays only an unimportant part in the Scottish catch; the market, at an economic price, is limited. There is an increasing interest in dogfish which seems likely to continue. In recent years a major fishery for whiting has developed, but it fetches relatively low prices, although, if the demand were greater, the available stocks could probably support heavier fishing. Mackerel and sharks are almost neglected, while much more hake is caught off Scotland by English than by Scottish vessels.

This brings us to the herring, on which so much has been said in recent years. Whatever may be the position about the stocks in the southern North Sea, and although the composition of the Scottish stocks has changed appreciably in recent years, some large catches have been taken in "Scottish waters" since the war, as recently as 1958, by fishermen of Scotland and of other countries. In particular, Continental countries are showing how, in some fisheries, good catches are to be taken by trawl, some even being landed in Aberdeen, and the possibilities off the east coast (Fladen Ground) and west coast (from Donegal to Shetland) deserve investigation. Of most years it can fairly be said that the yield has been restricted by the market and by the number of boats going to the herring fishing rather than by the available stocks. In other words, although it would not have been possible to fulfil all kinds of market demands, in almost every year it would have been possible to supply more herring from "Scottish stocks" if the market had been attractive.

There are also good shoals of sprats off Scottish shores, truly inshore, and the possibility of finding suitable markets for this species, and of exploiting its stocks, deserves investigation.

(*c*) Of the stocks of other major species, any increase in yield must depend on further conservation. The depletion of the stocks of haddock, cod, plaice, etc., in the North Sea since the 1914-18 War is a sad and familiar story, and there is no doubt that greater yields could have been obtained more economically (i.e. at a lower cost per man) if suitable and sufficient conservation regulations could have been introduced and enforced in time. For some years now we have had international mesh regulation under the Permanent Commission of the Fisheries Convention of 1946, and there is no doubt that it has improved the position, or at least prevented it from deteriorating further. It is not easy, however, to regulate mesh sizes to suit several stocks of fish being caught by several countries, with two or three gears, in the same area. The different fish require different kinds of regulations if they are to provide their optimum yields, while the various nations have their different interests. An attempt to meet these requirements under a more flexible North-East Atlantic Fisheries Convention is now being made, and meanwhile the important thing is that each of those stocks would produce greater yields, and/or more economic yields if agreement could be reached to operate this Convention effectively.

(*d*) Reference has been made, however, to the need for a public demand before the catches of any fish can profitably be increased, and for an economic means of meeting that demand. It is on the second of these points that perhaps Scotland has suffered most, particularly because of its distance from many of the principal markets. Brave attempts are being made to solve these problems. Indeed, the bulk of Scotland's white fish and shellfish is sent south of the border while some of her fish goes as far away as Australia and periodically "plane loads" of shellfish are dispatched to the Continent. In no instance, however, can demands from new markets, whether home or distant, be met without a means of transporting the fish economically in good condition to those markets. Valuable research is being done at the Torry Research Station, Aberdeen, on the problems of retaining the prime quality of fish—at sea, on the market and during transport—although more needs to be done in applying the knowledge already available. In some instances, however, this may add to the costs of transport and much more needs to be done to reduce those so that more distant markets can be satisfied economically.

These points are particularly important when considering the possibility of increasing Scotland's fishing, whether inshore or offshore, by including species which have not been traditional. A good example is provided by *Sebastes*, the redfish, soldier or Norway haddock. Although this is certainly not available to Scottish inshore fishermen, great supplies are available within the traditional range of Scottish fisheries. Major redfish fisheries have been developed in recent years by German, Icelandic and Norwegian fishermen, but Scotland does not or cannot participate. Of this and some other fish, including inshore fish, it is said that although Scottish fishermen are much nearer to these grounds than English fishermen, for example, they would not be able to sell them at a profitable price, allowing for the costs of transport from the Scottish quays. Somehow, this kind of problem has to be met, and it will perhaps only be met when Scotland provides sufficient processing plants for the much smaller bulk of a finished product to be carried to the south, east and west at an economic price, although it would be a useful start if home (Scottish) consumption of the various species could be raised. This applies equally to some of the inshore potential as well as to the offshore.

BIBLIOGRAPHY

Report on the Fisheries of Scotland (Annual). Edinburgh: H.M.S.O.

Scottish Sea Fisheries Statistical Tables (Annual). Edinburgh: H.M.S.O.

Scottish Home Department (1952). *Practical Hints for Lobster Fishermen.* Pp. 16. Edinburgh: H.M.S.O.

THOMAS, H. J. (1957). *Lobster Storage.* Pp. 20. Edinburgh: H.M.S.O.

Readers are also referred to scientific papers on various subjects by members of the staff of the Marine Laboratory, published in the Marine Research Series by H.M.S.O., and to more popular articles in the biannual Scottish Fisheries Bulletin which is issued free of charge to fishermen.

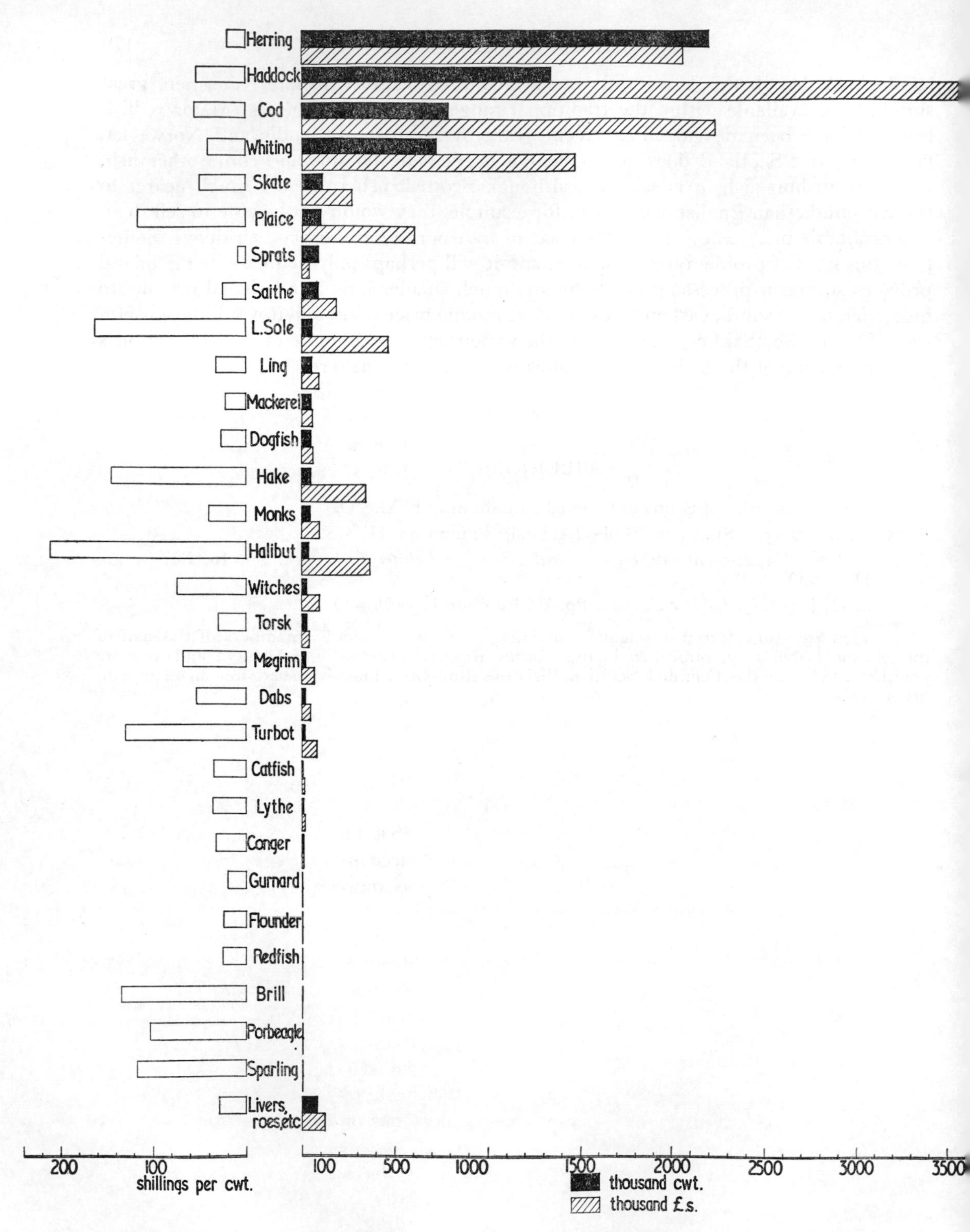

FIG. 1. Average Yearly Landings, Value and Price per cwt. of Fish landed in Scotland by British Vessels, 1953-59

Scottish Seaweed Resources

E. Booth, A.M.C.T., F.R.I.C.
Principal Scientific Officer, Institute of Seaweed Research, Inveresk

It is well known that a seaweed industry once flourished in Scotland and that it declined from about 1880 and finally died in the 1930s. The revival of the industry is less well known, but the alginate and the seaweed meal industries are post-war developments based on seaweed which together have nine factories in Scotland.

The extension of this industry is dependent upon knowledge of our seaweed resources and also on the harvesting and conservation of these resources. In post-war years, the Institute of Seaweed Research has estimated that there are 4 million tons of harvestable sub-littoral seaweeds in Scottish inshore waters and had studied the growth of several areas over a period of years. This work suggests 1 million tons per annum could be harvested. A harvesting vessel has been designed and operated and several schemes for the utilisation of this seaweed have been evolved. It has also been shown that 180,000 tons of littoral brown seaweeds grow at an average crop density of 30 tons per acre on 540 miles of our coast and it is considered possible that twice this figure may better represent the harvestable crop. It has been further shown that the crop can, under suitable conditions, recover from cutting in two years, but a four-year cycle is considered a safer harvesting period. On this basis 45,000 to 90,000 tons per annum could be harvested. The market for these brown seaweeds is expanding and imports in 1959 amounted to £66,600.

A wartime survey of the red seaweeds showed that these were not particularly plentiful in Scotland, but it did suggest that Tiree might support a small industry. It is felt, however, that this could be no more than a part-time venture for a small group of crofters.

In considering seaweed as a raw material, account has been taken of the known and potential markets for seaweed, and extensive use has been made of the data compiled by the Institute of Seaweed Research, formerly the Scottish Seaweed Research Association, and by a wartime study of the red algae.[1] The Scottish seaweed industry is rather more than 200 years old and has been based largely on the islands of North and South Uist and the Orkneys. Technical developments have been responsible both for the decline and revival of the industry and today the country has one large and three small firms processing seaweed.

Whilst there are very many varieties of seaweed, only the red and the brown have any commercial value. The red seaweeds which are available from the Scottish shores have a market value of £70 to £100 per ton (air-dry) according to quality and the brown seaweeds, when dried, sell at £20 to £22 per ton, but Irish seaweed is available at prices as low as £16 per ton f.o.b. Galway. Imports of red seaweeds in 1959 were valued at

£49,644 and imports of brown seaweeds in the same year were valued at £66,654. The availability of these two classes of seaweed and the uses to which they are put are so dissimilar that it is convenient to study them separately.

RED SEAWEEDS

(a) *Porphyra umbilicalis.* This seaweed, also known as laverweed, is considered a delicacy in South Wales, and a market survey[2] has shown that about 100 tons is sent annually to Swansea from Stranraer and about 10 tons from Dunbar. This seaweed is fairly common on our shores, but no quantitative survey has ever been made. The need to send the freshly collected material direct to Swansea, usually by passenger train, imposes a severe limit on the areas where deposits of this seaweed can be exploited and only minor developments in this trade can be envisaged.

(b) *Carragheen.* This name is applied to two seaweeds, *Chondrus crispus* and *Gigartina stellata*, which are often found growing together and which are usually mixed indiscriminately in commercial supplies. They are very similar in many respects; *G. stellata* is more commonly found on the Scottish coast, but not in large quantities in any particular area. Nevertheless, a collection was organised during the last war (*loc. cit*) and an average of 21 tons per annum was collected in the years 1943-45; the report (p. 14)[2] makes particular mention of Tiree, which was not surveyed quantitatively, as a potential site for future development "... with the return of peace-time conditions, a harvest might

TABLE I

Availability of Carragheen on the Scottish Coast

Location	Quantity Available (tons)	Remarks
Dunbar—North Berwick	12	
Mull of Kintyre—Oban	11	
Mull of Kintyre—east coast	44	About 7 tons in 1½ miles at best location
Loch Long, Gairloch, Loch Goil	25	
Cowal area	2	
Wemyss Bay—Ardrossan	5	
Wrights Island—Burrow Head	15	
Inchmarnoch	5	
Great Cumbrae	30	
Wee Cumbrae	7	
Arran	18	
Bute	39	
Islay	18	
Jura	2	
Colonsay and Oronsay	10	
Raasay, Flodday and S. Rona	16	
Skye	146	
Tiree	(say) 150	Survey reports no figure but claims Tiree to have better supply than elsewhere
Total	555	

profitably be taken on Tiree, which has the richest yields of any of this group of islands". The only other locations which appear to hold promise of development are Skye, with the nearby islands of Raasay, Flodday and South Rona, Bute, and a small stretch of the Kintyre coast about 6 miles south of Campbeltown Bay. In these areas there is sufficient seaweed of this type to support a small venture. The harvesting period (August-September), however, conflicts with such seasonal crofting activities as crop harvest, peat cutting and tourism. The main locations where this seaweed is available are given in Table I. From this it is evident that no large-scale collection of this type of seaweed is feasible, but it would be possible for crofter-collectors to earn a modest income in a few areas.

BROWN SEAWEEDS

The brown seaweeds may be conveniently divided into those which grow between the high and low-water marks (littoral) and those growing below the low-water mark (sub-littoral); storm-cast sub-littoral seaweeds also merit consideration. The littoral and storm-cast sub-littoral seaweeds are obviously easier to collect than sub-littoral, and until the supply of the more readily available types is fully utilised there will be little demand for the sub-littoral seaweeds. The Institute of Seaweed Research has, however, designed and operated a harvester[3] for these sub-littoral seaweeds and all the design data is available even though the demand for such harvesting has not yet been made.

It is convenient to consider the resources of these different types of brown seaweed separately.

(a) *Cast Seaweeds.* Each year, about May-June, the sub-littoral laminarias produce a new frond (leaf) and shed that of the previous year; these fronds are washed ashore in huge quantities. No survey of this so-called "May cast" has ever been made and, so far, it has proved impossible to utilise it. The total quantity available is large, but it is difficult to dry and soon decomposes if left on the beach.

Winter storms dislodge the sub-littoral laminarias from the sea-bed and cast the seaweed on the beach. Usually the frond (leaf) and sometimes the holdfast (root-like appendage) is removed from the plant by the wave-action and the stipe is cast on the beach—this type of cast is commonly called "tangle". It may be cast during the storm or in the period of heavy swell which normally follows bad weather; under these conditions it is normally cast high up the beach, where it will remain until it is carried away by a subsequent storm.

TABLE II

Quantities of Cast "Tangle" observed on Certain Beaches

Location	No. of Beaches	1945-1946 Total weight (tons)	1946-1947 Total weight (tons)
Lewis	4	24,000	1,600
North Uist	11	15,500	37,400
Tiree	9	62,600	11,500
Sanday	1	2,300	13,100
Total	25	104,600	63,600

A study of 25 typical beaches,[4] each 1 to 3 miles long, over 2 consecutive years (Table II) revealed that most of these casts stayed on the beach for a week or more and decomposition starts at the bottom after 1 to 2 weeks. About two-thirds of the casts exceeded 500 tons and the largest observed was one of 23,000 tons. Tangle is usually carted from the beach, heaped over stones and allowed to air-dry; 15 to 20 tons of this air-dried tangle per man may be produced in the winter months, but the average individual collection is much less than this. Since the cast is dependent upon the weather, it is impossible to predict where and when the tangle will arrive, which makes planned utilisation difficult. Nevertheless, about 2,000 tons of air-dried tangle is collected annually by one firm and the demand is increasing.

(b) *Sub-littoral Seaweeds.* From the low-water mark to a depth of 10 fathoms, the laminarias grow in profusion on suitable rocky bottoms; *Laminaria cloustoni* forms the large bulk of this crop of seaweed. The Scottish coast-line, including the islands, has been estimated at 5,300 miles and the area of sea-bed between the low-water mark and 10 fathoms approximates 2 million acres. Extensive surveys of this sub-littoral zone have been carried out by the Institute of Seaweed Research[5]; an area of 71,000 acres has been shown to support the growth of over 1 million tons of seaweed (Table III).

TABLE III

Survey of Sub-littoral Seaweed

Location	Area Sampled (Acres)	Seaweed (1,000 tons)	Tons/Acre
Bay of Firth	3,050	45	14·7
Scapa Flow	800	14	17·5
Sanday Sound	8,350	127	15·2
Lopness Bay	4,800	127	26·4
Newark Bay	3,600	85	23·5
Westray	3,840	91	23·7
Rapness Sound	2,470	49	19·8
Car Ness	219	4	18·3
Sanday	1,168	25	21·3
Work Head—Deer Sound	688	16	21·6
Shapinsay	1,524	48	31·4
Holme Sound	1,300	20	15·4
Orkney total	31,809	651	20·5
Dunbar	3,400	50	14·7
North Berwick	424	7	16·5
Arran	4,600	187	40·6
Elie	1,300	22	16·9
Luce Bay	2,570	25	9·7
Girvan	4,192	44	10·5
Campbeltown	1,100	12	10·9
Macduff	2,875	25	8·7
Girvan	1,881	23	12·2
Kyleakin	3,690	26	7·0
Kintyre	1,369	21	15·3
Little Loch Broom	900	4	4·4
Loch Ewe	5,577	17	3·0
Guinard Bay	5,250	32	6·1
Total Survey	70,937	1,146	16·2

By using aerial photography and physical survey methods, the total crop of sub-littoral seaweed is considered to be about 10 million tons, of which 40 per cent. is believed to be in areas which could be harvested with a suitable vessel. (The harvesting vessel[3] proved that these seaweeds could be mechanically harvested at what is believed to be an economic cost.)

Naturally this crop of seaweed is subject to gale damage, but repeated surveys over the same area suggest regular regrowth and, of course, the long history of the seaweed industry confirms the view that the supply is virtually indestructible. Very little use has yet been made of this standing crop, but any major expansion of the seaweed industry must be dependent upon this untapped source of supply.

(c) *Littoral Seaweeds.* Where a suitable rocky sub-stratum occurs the area between the high- and low-water marks support the growth of seaweed. This, together with cast seaweed, has supported the Scottish seaweed industry for the past 300 years and is still a source of manure for the crofters and, in the last 10 years, has been used commercially by the alginate and seaweed meal industries.

The physical difficulty of exploring in detail the entire Scottish coast-line forced the Institute of Seaweed Research to restrict its survey of littoral seaweeds[6] to those areas where the growth exceeded 100 tons per mile. A more detailed survey would probably reveal substantially more littoral seaweed, and it must be stressed that the arbitary figure of 100 tons per mile does not represent the minimum figure for economic harvesting. This survey showed (Table IV) that 540 miles (*c.* 10 per cent.) of the coast supported

TABLE IV

Survey of Littoral Brown Seaweeds where growth exceeds 100 *Tons/Mile*

Area	Total Seaweed (tons)	Survey Details		Seaweed Density (tons/acre)
		Miles	Acres	
Mainland W. and N.W.	8,540	57	356	24
Orkney Islands	38,774	199	1,813	21
Inner Hebrides	8,263	60	278	30
Outer Hebrides	125,136	244	3,500	36
Total	180,713	560	5,947	30
Typical Area rich in littoral brown seaweed:				
Loch Sumart	812	6	23·7	34
Loch Long	1,206	6·4	44·4	27
Loch Torridon	777	5	26·3	30
Mull	2,507	2·5	15·7	16
Skye	5,443	41·1	177·4	30
Orkney Mainland	16,370	97	781	21
Westray	3,590	18	166	21
Sanday	7,089	21·5	303	23
Loch Roag, Lewis	4,950	27	134	37
Loch Seaforth, Lewis	2,100	18·5	78·4	27
Islands of Sound of Harris	18,770	24	1360	14
Loch Maddy, North Uist	39,840	30	480	83
Loch Boisdale, South Uist	11,800	20	261	45

180,000 tons of littoral seaweed growing at this high density (average 30 tons per acre) and it is quite possible that the total available littoral seaweed is double this amount.

The seaweed *Ascophyllum nodosum* formed 62 per cent. of the total surveyed and separate trials have shown that this seaweed can be harvested in alternate years and will then yield 25 tons per acre if carefully harvested; harvesting every third or fourth year should conserve the crop against improper harvesting.

REFERENCES

1. NEWTON, L. (1949). *A Study of certain British Seaweeds and their Utilisation in the Preparation of Agar*. H.M.S.O.
2. HAMPSON, M. A. (1957). *Laverbread Industry in South Wales and the Laverweed.* H.M.S.O.
3. JACKSON, P. (1957). Harvesting machinery for brown sub-littoral seaweeds. *Engineer, Lond.*, **203**, 400, 439.
4. Scottish Seaweed Research Association, Annual Reports, 1946, 17; 1947, 14.
5. WALKER, F. T. (1954). *J. Cons. int. Explor. Mer*, **20**, 160.
6. WALKER, F. T. (1947). A seaweed survey of Scotland. *Proc. Linn. Soc. Lond.*, **90**.

Wildlife as a Natural Resource in Scotland

DAVID JENKINS, D.PHIL, M.A., M.R.C.V.S., and ADAM WATSON, PH.D., B.SC.
Nature Conservancy Unit of Grouse and Moorland Ecology, Natural History Department, University of Aberdeen

Most of the surface of Scotland is high land on which the main wildlife populations are red grouse, mountain hares and red deer. On the cultivated low ground there are partridges, pheasants, brown hares and rabbits. Other potential resources are ptarmigan, capercaillie, blackgame and roe deer.

The financial value of wildlife as a resource is inseparable from its amenity and aesthetic value. Sportsmen and tourists alike profit from the range of wildlife found in Scotland and from the places of natural beauty in which these creatures are found. Agricultural practices associated with shooting are responsible for much of the present character of rural Britain.

The sporting rental of good grouse moors is an important part of the finances of a hill estate, sometimes more important than the farming rents, but such estates none the less seldom do more than pay their way. Money accruing through the shooting is channelled via the rates to the Exchequer, and additional sums contribute in several different ways to the local economy. A very rough estimate of the value of grouse killed in Scotland would be £¼ to £½ million per annum.

Immense numbers of waterfowl winter in Scotland and are an important resource through their amenity and aesthetic values.

Red deer live on remote hill land that often cannot be used for any other profitable purpose. There are now too many deer and they are beginning to be a nuisance to farmers. By Continental and American standards the Scottish harvest is rather small and the annual crop might be increased. Its present value is about £126,000; if the crop was increased the nuisance problem would be lessened and the resource would be more efficiently exploited.

INTRODUCTION

The value of wildlife as a resource may be reckoned in terms of (*a*) its aesthetic or amenity value and (*b*) employment and the local and national economy. The aesthetic value of wildlife is recognised in Britain, and the tourist industry is increasingly conscious of it, though by no means as much as abroad. It is impossible to put a value on aesthetics, involving the sight of wild animals and the preservation of the open spaces where they live, or to evaluate the relaxation provided by shooting and walking over the moors, but these are very important in our modern community. Shooting is not confined to wealthy magnates, since grouse, hares and other wildlife are shot on many small estates by professional people, farmers, landowners and increasingly by workers from the towns. Their shooting is an integral part of their holiday amenities. Moreover, immense numbers of people enjoy simply walking on the hills or stopping to look at the wide views typical of moorland scenery, and more and more do so every year. In an industrial society this is undoubtedly valuable in terms of health alone. If the moors were all covered with blocks of impenetrable timber (as over much of Scandinavia), these amenity values would suffer.

GROUSE AND MOUNTAIN HARES

Most of the surface of Scotland is high land with relatively poor soils. Most of this hill ground is covered by heather moor with some rough grass, and the main resources of this type of country include its wildlife, principally red grouse and mountain hares. Ptarmigan on the higher mountains are a potential resource that remains largely unexploited.

The financial value of moorland wildlife involves two aspects: (*a*) sporting rents for landowners and (*b*) wildlife as a useful cash crop. The rateable value of hill land is often high and many large estates meet their rates through letting their shooting. The cash value of wildlife is realised chiefly by the lessees of shootings and by farmers and others who either sell their grouse and hares to game-dealers or use the meat as food for themselves or their livestock.

A high proportion of landowners in Scotland depend on shooting rents to maintain their estates, but exact figures are not available. However, in 1911 the total rental from all grouse shootings in Scotland was estimated at £1 million, which would be equivalent to considerably more today. As an example, an estate occupying 100,000 acres of typical hill ground in east Scotland lets grouse shootings for £14,000 annually. This compares with a total rent of £6,700 from the numerous hill farms on the same area, and it is therefore clear that the shootings play a major part in the economy of this area.

The landowners' costs in connection with the shootings amount to just about the total shooting rents received. If rates are taken into account, few if any estates make a profit out of letting their shootings. Thus the total rental received is paid immediately into the local and national economy. On the area mentioned above, the landowner pays wages to a staff of 20 gamekeepers and others employed in connection with the shootings, and he maintains a large number of houses, shooting-lodges, game-larders, fences, paths, roads and bridges as well as vehicles. In addition he employs local people seasonally each year. Hence the grouse shootings in Scotland channel very large sums into public funds and employ many people, sometimes a high proportion of small communities. The money is especially important for the finance of poorer counties that lack much industry or intensive agriculture, when shooting becomes an important industry in its own right. There is little doubt that withdrawal of the shooting industry from many places without an adequate substitute—and forestry to be adequate would often need very heavy subsidy from the state—would cause severe depopulation locally.

The shooting tenant's expenses during the shooting season are also considerable. They include wages for gillies and beaters (often university students in need of exercise and pocket money), hire of ponies, motor transport and living expenses, and the employment of indoor staff at the lodges as well as the outdoor staff on the hills. These and other expenses may cost the tenant as much as the rent he pays the landowner. Again this all adds to the national economy, particularly when foreign exchange is brought in and when one considers that without shooting all this money might be spent on recreation abroad. Apart from the local shops and tourist industry, shooting game has other effects on the economy, notably in a specialist section of journalism, in the clothing industry, and among gunsmiths and cartridge makers. Game is important enough for I.C.I. to finance a special game research station; and scientific problems arising from game interest the universities and the Nature Conservancy.

The shooting tenant sells the grouse, usually for between 5s. and 9s. per bird. Only in a very good year with big bags will he manage to pay off his rent with the sale of grouse, and he may never do so if the rent, as sometimes, is reckoned in terms of so much (up to £1) per grouse killed in the bag. On the typical large estate mentioned above, the rent stays the same no matter what the bag is in any particular year, and the tenant usually takes the head-keeper's advice about when shooting should stop; 20,000 grouse might be shot on the whole estate in a very good year, but perhaps only one-tenth of this or less in a very poor year. On larger areas the differences tend to be smaller. For example, in the county of Angus where 50,000 grouse are shot in a good year, as many as 15,000 are killed in a poor year. In 1911 the average annual bag for Scotland was estimated at about 1¾ million birds, and though the total might not be as great today, this figure does give a rough idea of the production of grouse moors, and also of the revenue received by game-dealers who are part of the poultry industry. A very rough estimate of the value of grouse actually killed would be £¼ to £½ million per annum.

In addition, many mountain hares are taken from grouse moors. Some are killed during the grouse season by visiting sportsmen, but very large numbers are taken by more casual shooting and by snaring, mainly by farmers, shepherds and keepers. Hare numbers fluctuate greatly from year to year, and the highest bag recorded in one survey was one hare to about two acres on a moor in north-east Scotland. The average bag over 30 to 40 years from six different moors was about one hare per ten acres, but bags were much smaller in the south and west. Nevertheless, the numbers killed are very large and these are minimum figures, since they include only those that were sold. Many others are used for human consumption locally as well as for feeding dogs or poultry or for baiting traps. The game-dealer's price varies, but is usually about 1s. 6d. per hare, and a shepherd killing thousands of hares during a winter is usefully augmenting his income. Most hares that are sold are eventually used as dog food, but increasing numbers are being exported to Germany.

GAME FROM LOW GROUND

The chief kinds are partridges, pheasants, brown hares and rabbits. Roe deer, blackgame and capercaillie are other potential resources that have not yet been appreciated in Britain. On the European mainland they are widely regarded as important wildlife crops that can be harvested from the natural countryside (and the revenue from gun licences abroad is generally used to improve conditions for these natural resources). Partridges, pheasants and brown hares are most common in farmlands and may be regarded as by-products of an agricultural system. Numbers of wild partridges have decreased latterly in association with modern methods of intensive farming, but wild pheasants have shown widespread increases. This has been partly associated with artificial propagation, but truly wild pheasants now occur in the absence of artificial rearing on many game preserves.

Since the game is often associated with agriculture or forestry, it is usually difficult to assess the rateable value of lowland sporting ground, and though the sport may be taxed indirectly its chief importance lies in its values as an amenity for sportsmen, in producing a food delicacy, and in the extra employment that game preservation provides for gamekeepers and others. Large sums are channelled into the Exchequer through similar routes to those mentioned for grouse, plus an industry based on the breeding, feeding, housing, training and showing of dogs. Revenue from gun licences should not be forgotten, and far more sporting licences are held by people who shoot over low ground than by those who shoot moorland game.

No figures are available for the total numbers of low ground game taken in Scotland, but in Angus approximately 10,000 pheasants and 15,000 partridges are sold annually. Most pheasants are sold to the dealers at prices varying from about 5s. to 15s. each and most partridges for 5s. to 10s. Employment is provided for one keeper to 2,000 to 5,000 acres of low ground game preserve. Another aspect of game preservation is the maintenance of hedges and coverts that would otherwise be grubbed out by modern farmers. The character of much of lowland Britain is largely due to the interest in game preservation shown by many nineteenth-century landowners; they instilled a tradition into rural practices that is in danger of being lost with the break-up of so many large estates.

Brown hares are widespread and very numerous; they are usually regarded as vermin and no effort has been made to utilise the important meat resource they could provide. Many more brown hares than mountain hares pass through the hands of most game-dealers; though there is slightly more hill ground than low ground in Angus, almost twice as many brown hares are sold (about 10,000 annually) as mountain hares, and the price is generally about 4s. 6d. per hare. Most hares are eventually used as dog food or fertiliser or are exported to Germany, where their value as human food is better appreciated than here. Hares, like venison, are a wildlife resource that has yet to be properly exploited in Scotland.

Though they are properly regarded as a scourge to agriculture, rabbits have been an important wildlife resource on low ground and sometimes on the lower hills. In Angus, an average of about 20,000 rabbits per week were sold to game-dealers up till 1955; now, several years after the first outbreak of myxomatosis, the number is still as high as about 2,000 per week, and dealers pay several shillings per rabbit. Rabbits give sport to very large numbers of people who can shoot only in their spare time. In addition many are poached, along with some brown hares and lowland game-birds.

Wood-pigeons, an economic pest, are very common in many agricultural counties of Scotland, and have increased greatly with the rise in farming and forestry. In many places few are shot, but large numbers are taken where a more serious effort is made, for example on small estates near the towns and on areas with intensive agriculture. One typical small agricultural estate of about 5,000 acres in Aberdeenshire shoots 1,000 pigeons annually. In addition, farmers on the estate shoot large numbers.

WATERFOWL

Immense numbers of wildfowl spend the winter in Scotland, coming mostly from countries farther north. Wild geese, ducks and shore birds are shot by a small but widespread fraternity of hardy sportsmen, and are also enjoyed by an ever-growing number of bird-watchers. Undoubtedly they are an important resource through their amenity and aesthetic values.

RED DEER

As a rule red deer live in the more remote hill land that cannot, except occasionally through forestry or as summer grazings,* be used for any other profitable purpose. Red deer are thus a means of exploiting much of Scotland's wilderness hinterland, and the total area of deer forests in Scotland was reported by the Maconochie Committee in 1954 to be about 3,200,000 acres. This large area is probably now reduced to about 2,800,000 acres (Department of Agriculture figures 1957), but in recent years red deer have to an ever-increasing extent been marauding in, and also colonising, the hill ground of sheep and other farms, and visiting cultivated land. Thus these animals which, properly managed, would constitute a valuable resource on ground of little use for any other purpose, are now becoming a considerable nuisance over a great part of their range. A Government commission has been appointed to study and control this nuisance. The problem, in brief, is probably largely due to overstocking and underexploitation along with changes in land use; land formerly available to deer for winter grazing is now unavailable or grazed by domestic stock. Also the widespread reseeding of moorland and of former hill pastures now attracts wandering deer, retaining them on ground they would not otherwise have occupied.

The problem of deer and deer-forest management is basically one of correctly exploiting a natural resource. In the whole country there are probably between 155,000 (Nature Conservancy estimate, 1960) and 180,000 to 190,000 red deer (Darling, 1955, West Highland Survey; Whitehead, 1959, *Field*), and of these about 15,000 (Whitehead, 1960, *The Deer Stalking Grounds of Great Britain and Ireland*), say about 10 per cent., are harvested annually. In addition, many deer have been killed by poachers and many marauding deer are now killed each winter on grouse moors and sheep farms. However, the crop as a whole is rather small and there is little doubt that it could be greatly increased without much affecting the size of the breeding stock. Cropping is not at present preventing deer from increasing and extending their range, and the only real check is that imposed by cold winters when many red deer starve to death in the snow and few calves are born in the following summer. If there were fewer deer, there might be more food for them and possibly landowners could afford to provide food supplements.

A more reasonable annual harvest might be of the order of 15 to 20 per cent., comparable to the annual kill of 17 per cent. of red deer in Denmark (Westerskov, 1951, *Journal of Wildlife Management*), or even higher. Despite an annual kill of 25 per cent.,

* The trouble with grazing domestic stock in the hills in the summer is that sheep, and especially cattle, often spend much time in the readily accessible low-lying haughs and bogs, eating bare the winter food of the deer. Thus there is little food on the low ground for deer when the high hills are covered with snow. Putting sheep and cattle to the hills for the summer may thus aggravate the deer problem. In these circumstances the landowner has to decide not only which is the more profitable use of the grazings but also what alternative winter food the deer should have if sheep and cattle spend the summer in the hills, i.e. he should regard the deer as a semi-domestic stock and prepare a definite management policy for them.

a studied population of the Rocky Mountain wapiti (an animal very like the red deer) in Washington State maintains its breeding numbers (Mitchell and Lauckhart, 1948, *Trans.* 13 *N. Amer. Wildl. Conf.*). The optimum harvest must differ from place to place and this aspect is now being studied by scientists of the Nature Conservancy and by the Red Deer Commission. None the less it seems clear that the annual kill of red deer in Scotland is low. A great part of the crop that could be harvested is going to waste because the animals often die from starvation in a most pitiful and painful state, or are killed by farmers (sometimes with shotguns) when the meat is past its prime and is useless for human consumption. Proper annual control measures would limit this inhumane wastage.

In some places deer numbers should be drastically reduced, particularly where it seems to be the rule for them to stay on low hills and cultivated ground off the deer-forest proper. In such places, where deer are common, as many as one-third to one-half of the present deer population might be killed; such culling might be beneficial to the remaining stock and might result in more successful reproduction (more hinds conceiving and more and stronger calves being born) and in larger and stronger animals.

The chief value of deer as a resource is at present as any amenity for tourism and sport. Very large numbers of people enjoy seeing deer though few may realise how abundant they are in the Highlands. It is and will remain a pleasure for hunters to stalk and kill them, and this is one of the most skilful and arduous sports in Britain. However, deer forests, like grouse moors, seldom do more than pay their way, and they are often a liability. The game-dealer's price for a stag is now about £10, and for a hind about £6, 10s. 0d. Using Whitehead's (1960) figures, about 7,800 stags and about 7,400 hinds are killed on average each year, a potential national income of about £126,000 (though many carcases are eaten locally). Bearing in mind the total deer population, this is a small figure, and less than that yielded by grouse moors, but under present methods of deer-forest management it might be difficult greatly to increase it. One factor limiting the number of deer killed is usually manpower, and, faced with the autumn and winter climate in highland Scotland (when the hills are often covered in mist, rain or blizzards), and with other commitments such as grouse and pheasant shooting, each stalker often kills as many beasts as he reasonably can. The harvest could be increased given more hill roads and tracks, mechanised transport and adequate labour both for the actual killing and for removing the carcases from the hill. These items all need money, and though revenue might be increased by letting the hill more often for shooting (possibly for the hinds as well as for the stags), this could not be expected to increase the harvest.

More money might come through selling more venison, but it would be necessary to popularise this meat. A demand might be created for it, as has been done recently for other commodities. It is surprising that nearly all the venison from Scottish hills is at present sold in Germany. Scottish hill-folk enjoy deer-meat, indeed it is often their staple winter meat and good venison is very palatable, but there is practically no sale for venison in the towns. This is remarkable since the wholesale price of venison is rather low, 1s. 5d. per lb. in November 1960, and one would think that a better price could be obtained through efficient advertising.

A better demand and a better price are not in themselves the whole answer. When meat was rationed in the 1940s, the price of venison was much higher than it is today; yet no more deer were killed to satisfy the demand. There is a considerable latent resistance in many stalkers and proprietors to the idea that they do in fact have too many deer; they are reluctant to believe that their ground is overstocked and they are tempted to place their faith in such palliatives as deer fences and attempts to drive colonising deer back to the forests. If a scientific management policy could be accepted, and if there were an improved demand and sale for venison, the landowner would find it profitable to organise the killing and sale of more deer. In addition, the resource would be more efficiently harvested, work would be provided for countrymen and money brought to the hills, crops would be saved from damage and the deer would be more humanely managed. Here is a case for co-operation between biologists, landowners and experts in advertisement and marketing; between them these people could surely show how this wildlife resource should be exploited most efficiently.

INTRODUCTION TO DISCUSSION

F. Fraser Darling, D.SC., PH.D., N.D.A., LL.D., F.R.S.E.
The Conservation Foundation, New York

Mr. Chairman, Ladies and Gentlemen: Somebody said to me how wild do you have to look to be a wildlifer. It is perhaps not the best word, "wildlife", for these animate natural resources with which we are dealing this afternoon. In speaking of natural resources I could not help but notice Lord Polwarth's remarks early this morning thinking in terms of minerals and so on and then he mentioned the fact that wildlife came in too. Of course, anybody who is a biologist tends to think of natural resources perhaps too heavily in terms of the animate ones—the renewable natural resources. When they are animate and renewable, then we begin to think in terms of constructive dynamic conservation of them. In Scotland we have so much what might be called wild land which has been combed over a great deal in the last 2,000 years, but nevertheless on that wild land there is much that is most interesting and economically, as well as scientifically, valuable in the wildlife. The seas around Scotland and the beaches of Scotland, the littoral, are also such an immense part of our special topography and position in the northern seas—the extremely rich fisheries around our coast and for hundreds of years they have been a great part of our life. But it is only within the last 100 years and particularly almost within the last ten that very intensive research has been put into these animate natural resources of both sea and land. The old Fishery Board, of which a past President of this Society, Sir Darcy Thomson, was a naturalist and adviser nearly 80 years ago, started much of this active scientific fisheries research. The research in Scotland has been extremely fruitful; with the national laboratory at Aberdeen and the Marine Biological Association's Laboratory at Millport. The work on fisheries has been intense and protracted. But on the wildlife of the land itself we have a very much shorter history. The grouse enquiry of 1905, between then and 1910, was the beginning, and a very fine beginning it was. One can look at those volumes now of the Grouse Enquiry and not be ashamed of it in the light of what has gone since, and within the last three years the Nature Conservancy and Aberdeen University have joined in carrying through a protracted research on the red grouse in the Highlands and Southern Uplands. I would like to emphasise the research effort which has grown up within the last ten years: nature conservancy itself is only eleven years old and its record in research in Scotland I think is a creditable one. There is one other point: so many of the contributors to this afternoon are my colleagues and friends through half a lifetime, and in particular I would mention the Freshwater Fisheries Laboratory at Pitlochry. I had the privilege of being a member of the Supervisory Committee for ten years since its inception in 1948. We owe that Laboratory and that activity entirely to Mr. Tom Johnston. It was his vision and forethought and interest which made that possible. During these ten years this much-neglected aspect of Scotland's economy—her freshwater fishing—the brown trout—has come along at a quite extraordinary rate and I am so glad that we have Mr. Pyefinch, the Director of that Laboratory, who has written one of the papers this afternoon, and he will be contributing in the discussion I hope. May we ask the contributors to stand up as they did this morning so that the audience shall know them?

Dr. Lucas . . . Aberdeen.

Mr. Pyefinch . . . Pitlochry.

Mr. Booth . . .

Dr. Watson and Dr. Jenkins, Grouse research, Aberdeen University.

Thank you. And I have a small list of those who wish to take part in the discussion here, but I hope that there will be many more who have not yet passed up their names. I have been asked to mention that the cards would be appreciated if they could be returned to the Secretary. Could I ask the Reporter to make summary?

STATEMENT BY THE REPORTER

V. C. WYNNE-EDWARDS, M.A., F.R.C.S., F.R.S.E.

Regius Professor of Natural History, University of Aberdeen

Mr. Chairman, Ladies and Gentlemen: As the Chairman has said, we are dealing this afternoon with renewable natural resources, and in this field we have become very much interested in questions of sustained productivity. I think some of you may be unfamiliar with this kind of resource, and I might mention that we often distinguish primary productivity, which is the conversion of various nutrient substances, carbon dioxide, etc., into plant tissues, and secondary productivity—the conversion of plant materials into living animal tissues. As far as Scotland is concerned, primary productivity of wild renewable resources has of course greatly diminished as agriculture has advanced. In many countries the forest products from naturally renewed forests are of very great importance, but that is no longer so in Scotland, where for most of the vegetable products we require we now depend on agriculture or sylviculture. We are rich still in secondary products, namely wildlife and, especially, fisheries.

Of the papers we have this afternoon, one on seaweeds deals with primary products. Seaweeds to a small extent are used directly for food and to a much larger extent they are processed in the alginate and seaweed meal industries. Seaweeds, of course, grow as far as we are concerned in this country attached to the sub-stratum either on the shore between tide-marks or in shallow water; they depend on a sufficiency of light for photosynthesis. They are therefore confined to a comparatively narrow zone, but we are told in this paper that the coast of Scotland is estimated at 5,300 miles, and if you take the area between low-water mark and 10 fathoms, which is the richest region for the production of seaweeds, it amounts to one-tenth of land area of the whole of Scotland and the isles. This is a very considerable area, and it makes one suspect that this resource might be capable of extensive development. The average standing crop is about 5 tons per acre and the price about £20 per ton. Much credit must be given to the Seaweed Research

Association for the survey they have made of the seaweed resources of Scotland and the work they have done in developing a harvesting machine. This may be a resource that is only partially exploited at present and needs further enterprise for its development.

The other papers deal with secondary production—animal resources used almost entirely for food—but we should not forget that behind these lies the production of the pasture or whatever else it is that provides the primary food. There is a very interesting paper by Mr. Pyefinch on freshwater fisheries; salmon and sea trout are treated together because commercially they are caught and recorded together. The production of salmon in Scotland does not contribute very much to the actual food consumed by the population, but it is a very valuable resource. Salmon is our most valuable fish, pound for pound; in price it fetches about four times as much as halibut at first sale and about fifteen times as much as cod. The salmon and sea trout fisheries of Scotland produce an income exceeding £1 million per annum and employ a large number of persons. One of the points to notice in Mr. Pyefinch's paper is that we still have insufficient knowledge on which to base the planned development and use of the salmon fisheries. We do not know whether the present catch can be greatly increased without causing depletion, but this kind of information is being actively sought at the present time. Salmon and trout also have a great sporting value and we should bear in mind the large amount of trout and salmon caught which do not find their way into the official statistics. Another point of interest is Mr. Pyefinch's reference to the possibility of artificially increasing the yield of fresh waters by the use of fertilisers. The Research Laboratory at Pitlochry have made experiments, and the best that can be hoped for through fertilisation of Scottish lochs seems to be an increase of the standing crop to about double: that is about the limit which it appears possible to achieve.

The largest paper of the four is the one by Dr. Lucas, Dr. Rae and Dr. Thomas on the Inshore Sea Fisheries. This is, of course, one of the greatest traditional sources of wealth in Scotland, something which has been exploited for a long time. The total value at first sale of the products of the sea, coming from the north-western part of the North Sea and the western fishing grounds which lie within a two-day trip from a Scottish port, is of the order of £15 million per annum. The authors have subdivided this into (i) shellfish, the revenue from which is about £800,000, (ii) herring—about £2 million, and (iii) white fish—about £12 million. Of shellfish, about half the value comes from lobsters. One of the interesting points here is the change in popular demand and the immensely rapid rise of the market for *Nephrops*, the Norway lobster. You will find that the landings were double in 1959 what they were in 1958, and that the industry has only come into being in the last five years. This reflects the rise in demand for scampi or clayfish, and we have here a product formerly shovelled back into the water which is now the object of a special fishery. Somewhat the same on a smaller scale applies to squid. There is at present a rapidly developing market, mainly abroad, though we may see more of squid in this country in years to come.

Exploitation of these resources depends very much upon the popular demand and on the development of markets. For lack of markets or lack of demand the shellfish resources are underdeveloped at the present time just as are the seaweeds, and the same is possibly true of the herring. The herring may possibly be overexploited in the southern part of the North Sea, but it does not appear to be so yet as far as Scottish landings are concerned. On the other hand there are some resources which are known to be overfished, especially the haddock. I would like to draw your attention to the fact that fishery biologists understand the principles of management of their resources exceedingly well at the present time, and they are perhaps ahead of anyone else at having discovered just what can be taken from the sea without dipping into the capital, without diminishing the stock. The difficulty arises from producing practical means of giving effect to the restrictions which must be imposed. Exploitation also depends to some extent upon tradition developed among those who go after these resources. In this paper the authors notice that for instance tuna is something for which other people come to Scottish waters to fish, though we do not participate ourselves; and there are similar underdeveloped resources such as mackerel, sharks and sprats.

The last of the four papers deals with the terrestrial animal wildlife resources, by Dr. Jenkins and Dr. Watson, who were introduced to you. I think one of the important features of their papers is the production, I believe for the first time, of valuations and market prices for some of our game resources. The yields of game can be artificially increased by various forms of management, and this very often means management of the habitat and takes us back to questions of primary production—of getting best vegetable yield out of the soil. The importance of moor game to Scotland is very great. I believe that 70 per cent. of the surface of Scotland is covered by moors or still higher land in the hills, so that such moorland creatures as red grouse, mountain hares and red deer are of considerable importance to us. In some parts of the Highland area deer are more numerous than sheep, and individually they are rather larger. In this case, therefore, there is something more than a sporting resource, something which is of sizeable proportions as far as food is concerned. One of the things we most need here is to encourage a market for venison. If the present price of venison could be doubled, there would be a much bigger use made of this resource than at present. Deer as a resource are underexploited, and at the same time they are increasing and in some parts of the country becoming a major pest to agriculture. Again, as with the salmon, we do not yet know enough about their bionomics to lay down scientific plans for their management. The Nature Conservancy, however, have got an active research programme on red deer going at the present time; and within the last year we have had established in Scotland a Red Deer Commission, to deal with the agricultural problem and with matters concerning the management and conservation of the red deer.

It would be right to draw attention to the fact that Scotland is very rich in these animal and sporting resources. I remember taking an eminent Canadian wildlife scientist up above Ballochbuie on the slopes of Lochnagar on a December afternoon some years ago. It was very still; and within an hour or two we had seen roe deer, red deer, capercaillie, black grouse, packs of red grouse and many white hares, and we could hear the ptarmigan croaking in the corrie high above us. He looked around and said, "I have never seen such a wealth of wildlife in one place in all my life". We should indeed value this as a great resource.

There appear to be three things that we need to watch in further development of our wildlife resources. In some cases we require more research to tell us how to manage them, and how to take the maximum crop without depleting the stock. In other cases, as with the deer, we need to build up or create new popular demands for the consumption of their products; and lastly there are some cases where we must take measures to relieve the pressure on resources which we know are already being overexploited.

DISCUSSION

Mr. E. M. Nicholson, *Nature Conservancy, London*

I suspect there are quite a number of people here who regard the wildlife resources (*a*) as absolutely minimal scale, (*b*) as of practically no relevance to the general question of natural resources. I will not deal with any of the specialist questions but will try and address myself to the question of what there is in common between the problem of wildlife resources and the problems we were talking about this morning. I think that running through this morning's discussion was a sense of the lack of knowledge and above all lack of measurements of the problems. In the wildlife field, in the broader sense, we are attempting to measure productivity, we are attempting to measure things which are of great importance for resources, through as you may think by unconventional media. It may for instance be unnecessary to measure the climate through rain gauges and thermometers: it mày be possible to measure it through indicator species of plants. There are plants and animals which are highly sensitive to humidity and to all factors which we are interested in. There is a record written on the ground which will tell us, for instance, the annual duration of frost and what the rainfalls are. If we could only get the knowledge to read that record it might enable us to cut very considerably these periods of 25 or 40 years' observation in order to get a reliable picture. Indeed, members of our Conservancy staff have been lost to the Hunting Aerial Survey who needed our ecologists to interpret what they were getting by aerial photographs. So this is a possible technique of measurement which can be very important and can be very time-saving and money-saving when we want to know about resources.

Now another aspect of the measurement problem is the great difficulty and the intense irritation and waste of time there is every time land use conflict has to be reconciled between say an industrial or agricultural project or a road project, and considerations of scientific value, amenity, tourism and recreation and so on. Now we have the possibility through biological measurement and the measurement of soils and water, of getting data which can be translated into material for solving these matters rationally.

You can look at this from three angles. You can look at it on the trusteeship angle: in the very long term, is the soil being improved or deteriorated by the use you are making of it? Is that river regime deteriorating to a danger point, and so on? In fact, long-term trusteeship requires equally long-term programmes of observation, which the Nature Conservancy are setting up, although rather gradually and very belatedly. Then there is the biological dividend. For instance, south of the Border experimental plots on Forestry Commission land have been created on a scheme which was proposed by the Zuckerman Committee on Forestry, Agriculture and Marginal Land to measure the productivity of the given area of poor land under (*a*) conifers, (*b*) hardwoods and (*c*) sheep. We are measuring the productivity under those different forms of land use on a long term and thus you can work out the biological dividend. Although Professor Wynne-Edwards mentioned that there is an attempt to quantify the economic return from wildlife, that is still very crude and primitive. I do want to plead for a development here of resource economics, and not only in relation to wildlife; that is a very unimportant part of it. In America, I had the privilege of attending a seminar at Harvard. They have this technique of resource economics which they are applying to these problems of water-shed control, and they are getting long-term comparisons on what will be the economic and social effects of certain investments of capital. We do that on an absolutely hit-or-miss basis. The whole basis of our forestry programme in this country, for example, will just not bear scientific examination at all. It may be that the figures the Forestry Commission are working on are the right answers, but if so it is entirely by accident. There is absolutely no economic justification for those figures as against other figures, and that is the trouble. We stagger about and spend very large sums of money without any basis in resource economics. Now, the Americans have developed these cost benefit studies and so on, which enable one to quantify the relationship between conventional economics in agriculture and industry and those which we regard as pretty well immeasurable such as recreation. You can, for instance, measure how much comes out of a steel works. You can also measure a particular group of Highland glens in foreign exchange, bearing in mind that the total foreign exchange earned by the tourist industry just about equals that earned by the steel industry, and you can pinpoint to some extent where that foreign exchange comes from. Yet when it comes to a land-use problem you have a project, for putting something in that glen which might destroy its tourist value, taken on a basis that the loss is entirely in amenity and immeasurable. It does seem to me that this business of going round with the Fiery Cross and getting out the claymore as a way of settling these disputes between amenity and such considerations and things like power stations schemes is equivalent to what went on before 1745. There must be and there could be a more reasonable and civilised way of measuring these things, and I would appeal to Scottish Universities in the course of this great expansion which is going ahead to try to fill some of these gaps in resource economics. No University in the whole of Great Britain has a school of higher studies in land use at the moment. No University has higher studies of this water problem we were discussing. The Universities are simply not there on most of these problems. There is a chance which may not recur again in this huge expansion which is going ahead at such a breathless pace. I do hope that the Scottish Universities will be there at the time and not come along ten years later complaining that Scotland is not getting a fair share because we are all most anxious that the Scottish Universities should be in the forefront and there are huge opportunities now in this way.

Finally, reference was made this morning to grants. I would like to say that as far as the Nature Conservancy are concerned, consideration is being given to the problem of these natural resources questions. If there are scientific investigations which it would be proper for the Nature Conservancy to consider backing I do hope that any of you who are interested will get in touch with the Nature Conservancy. There are many grounds on which it may prove impossible to provide money, but lack of enthusiasm for getting something done in Scotland will not be one of them.

Professor Frazer, *Royal College of Science and Technology, Glasgow*

As a member of the College in Scotland which is not quite a University for some unknown and obscure reason, I would just like to point out that for the last five years we have been running a course called "Environmental Control Engineering and Resource Utilisation" where the broad multipurpose outlook is taught. We try to put across the picture that there is no single solution to the problem of a Highland glen. What is wanted is for everyone to get together and decide what is the best method of maximising the resources of an area, whether it be tourism, ranching, forestry, hydro-power or a combination of the lot.

I may say too that the Nature Conservancy have changed their tune in the last few years. Not so long ago, within the last five years, I had a student who wished to study soil erosion, and the Forestry Commission were very willing to co-operate. Could they give some money to support him? The answer I got was that the Nature Conservancy did not think the erosion came within their terms of reference, but I am glad to hear now that things have changed.

Professor HUGH NICOL, *West of Scotland Agricultural College*

May I say Mr. Nicholson's remarks were most gratifying to me, not so much personally but because at a meeting which I attended in these rooms some months ago there was a discussion on the Scottish freshwater lochs and a long history of passing the buck on observation at work and about defraying the costs. During the discussion and in private afterwards it appeared that the situation as regards financing proposed research on vegetation in the Scottish freshwater lochs is now precisely what it was in 1890. If this is true, here is an opportunity for those interested in vegetation of freshwater lochs who took part in the previous Symposium of the Royal Society to contact Mr. Nicholson—or rather the Nature Conservancy—at once! My own interest in this was that I thought something could be done on the trace element chemistry of the vegetation. I am not a biologist actually, but I did point out that Scotland has better facilities than any other country in the world for spectrographic investigation of any agricultural land-use problem. We have equipment throughout Scotland. We could with a small grant employ one or two extra people; we would need some money for transport as well. Until now it has been "no dice"; but the prospect seems much brighter for the investigation of vegetation of the Scottish lochs.

Dr. FRASER DARLING

It seems to me that one of the values of this session will be some linking up of otherwise separate compartments. What you were saying, sir, on the vegetation of the fresh water was rather a marginal subject because the fresh water—anything below the surface of the water—falls within the purview of the freshwater laboratory at Pitlochry and perhaps as a kind of border line now between terrestrial resources and the water. I wonder if Professor Yonge of Glasgow, who was the Chairman of the Supervisory Committee of the Pitlochry Laboratory for eleven years before it was established as it is now, would care to speak on the development of the research?

Professor C. M. YONGE, *Department of Zoology, Glasgow University*

Following Professor Nicol's remarks, it would be quite possible, either from Pitlochry or from the Field Station of Glasgow University on Loch Lomond, to investigate the flora and the contained trace elements for the fresh waters of Scotland. We did, as the Chairman said, have a very profitable time during the initial ten years of the establishment, due to the initial impetus of Mr. Tom Johnston, of the laboratory at Pitlochry, in beginning to understand the freshwater resources of Scotland, and when our terms of reference expired wc were able to hand over to what is now the Department of Agriculture and Fisheries for Scotland a Freshwater Fisheries Laboratory which is well equipped both in terms of staff and apparatus.

I would like to make some mention of the sea, where my major interests lie. Among the things that have not been mentioned in the reports which I have read is the possibility of resuscitating our oyster fisheries. There was a time when the oyster production from the Firth of Forth alone was several times greater than the entire production in Great Britain at the present moment. The edible oyster would now appear to be completely extinct in the Firth of Forth. It must be a classic and wonderful case of overfishing, utter and complete obliteration of a formerly incredibly abundant animal. The report by Dr. Lucas notes that we have a surviving oyster bed in Loch Ryan. From Millport we have taken this over with the financial aid of the Development Commission and are hoping to resuscitate the fishery. It would be my long-term hope that in the course of time we can bring the oyster back to its former haunts around the coasts of Scotland. It did live there; why should it not live there again? There is no question that if you can produce oysters, you can sell them. The greater problem is to get people to eat things which are there in abundance and which they do not like; they do not fancy the Norway haddock, a red fish which is much eaten in Norway. I remember working in Norway 20 years ago and there it was pointed out to me as the finest fish in the sea. That fish is present in enormous quantities in the North Sea and the Atlantic. It could be caught and retailed in Scotland. But there, of course, you are up against the problem of educating your public, and that is a matter beyond the scope of the fisheries biologist.

Professor PEARSALL

I did not intend to speak on this subject, but while I was having lunch I was asked certain questions which suggested to me that at some stage in these proceedings we should ask "What are our resources?" We have so far spoken in terms of oysters and some trout and all sorts of things. I wonder at what stage—I think later on tomorrow—we come to the question of amenities and the values of civilised man puts on the things which arouse pleasure in him, interest and knowledge. I am sure you have plenty of ideas on the subject. I wish that somebody had found the time to express them.

Dr. FRASER DARLING

In the morning session after 11 o'clock, where we speak of wildlife and recreation, there are two papers—one utilisation and the other outdoor recreation potential. These are just the opposite ends of the pole in a way, and somehow tomorrow we will have to come to some reconciliation between these two subjects, and I think possibly that what you bring up, Professor Pearsall, might be discussed at greater length in that session tomorrow. I think now that we should speak about seaweed. Nobody has mentioned it yet. As I was reading Mr. Booth's paper on seaweed it struck me that there has been a very big change-over in use. He mentions the age of the Scottish seaweed industry, going back into the early parts of the last century and earlier still, through the Napoleonic wars, back into the eighteenth century, but what he did not emphasise which struck me, was the completely different industry that it was then and now. Alginate was never heard of in those days. Then it was kelp, the salts from the seaweed when it was burnt, which were of use for defence purposes and so on; but now the kelp industry is completely dead and we are dealing with the production of an organic salt. In that change-over it also made me think of the attitudes of people. One of the difficulties in getting seaweed collection going in the Highlands was the racial memory of the kelp days. It was considered in the Highlands to be the lowest ebb you could reach and the kelp industry was linked almost with depression and starvation, when gathering kelp was just a way of keeping body and soul together. It was felt as a shameful thing. Those days are over. This new alginate industry is entirely, as it were, respectable, and could be very attractive as a way of using one's spare time in the Highlands. There was this difficulty in getting over the human attitude of mind; an entirely different thing, kelp and alginate, and I think that fact of change-over is a thing that we are much concerned with in this Conference. The whole resource field is dynamic. What is a resource today? It may be something entirely different that we want from it tomorrow and it needs sociological accommodation, which can be quite difficult to bring about.

Mr. BOOTH, *Institute of Seaweed Research*

There is of course, as Dr. Fraser Darling says, no doubt that the seaweed industry, and in fact every other human activity, is dynamic. Even the alginate industry as it is today is not based on the same scheme of operation as it was when formed twenty years ago. A firm was originally formed to make an alginate film in 1934. After the war they changed over to selling alginate for a multitudinous range of purposes. In the last two or three years, certainly within the last five years, the market for alginate has altered completely and at least a third of the alginate produced is sold for surfacing paper or for thickening a certain type of dye stuff. So that there we have a typical example of the way in which industrial demand changes, and of course there is the need for the operating firm to change their techniques both in manufacture and selling according to how the market changes. In other respects, too, the seaweed industry has changed considerably in the last few years. There has been a market developed within the last nine years for seaweed meal as an additive to animal feeding-stuffs and in the same period a separate market has been developed for seaweed as a fertiliser, and in particular there has been great growth in the development of a liquid seaweed extract as a fertiliser. Both the fertiliser field and feeding-stuffs were virtually unthought of ten years ago, so that we have every reason to think that the whole industry is still in a state of change but very much removed from what it was in the days of kelp burning. There is a further feeling in my mind that the chemical extraction of mannitol from seaweed which, a few years ago, was virtually damned by the industrial manufacture of mannitol—a by-product in the manufacture of sorbitol. I believe there is evidence pointing towards the extraction of mannitol from seaweed in the future. I am not optimistic about it at this minute, but the demand for mannitol is outstepping the demand for sorbitol, and since sorbitol is a main industrial product and mannitol is a by-product there are firms today considering the manufacture of mannitol to keep up with the sales of that product. Dr. Darling also mentioned the resistance of the collectors, how they felt that seaweed collecting was degrading. They also feel, in parts, that it is a woman's work. It has been traditional, particularly where the crofters used it for manure. It has been the custom for the crofter to cut the seaweed and for the womenfolk to carry it up the beach in creels, so that in parts of the country where seaweed is still used as a manure there is a resistance of the men to doing what they think is women's work. But I must say I think that by and large there has been progressively more co-operation from the collectors, and today most of them are paid on a piece-work basis and I think I am right when I say that all the collecting firms get all the material they require.

Mr. CADZOW, *Scottish Agricultural Organisation Society*

I would like to say something now which has to do with Dr. Booth's most interesting paper on our seaweed resources. I do so because my Society has been interested in the development of a seaweed industry in its modern form, especially since the formation of the original Scottish Seaweed Research Association, now the Institute for Seaweed Research and with which Mr. Booth is so closely connected. I am speaking of post-war developments rather than the seaweed industry of bygone days, which I agree with Mr. Booth was looked upon as only for the poorest of the poor. Before people took to do with seaweed they were destitute—down and out—and it was the last resort, sometimes to find something to eat because there are edible seaweeds, but usually to try and earn a penny or two to keep body and soul together. But fortunately it is no longer a woman's job. The post-war developments and the modern industry, despite the changes of recent years, have shown that seaweed harvesting today has a very considerable influence on the economy of a widely spread number of Scottish islands. It is practically an island industry and a job for the men who are the tractor drivers. You find it on North and South Uist, Benbecula, Grimsay, and perhaps to a lesser extent in Lewis. But then go farther north: it is a developing industry in the Orkneys, already on a considerable scale, and you will have noticed from Mr. Booth's paper he brings out the point that given conservation—that is, regular harvesting in rotation, just as with land crops, then you have what is nearly an inexhaustible resource which today is very much underused. I say that knowing perfectly well that the uses for the chemicals which can be extracted from seaweed have first to be in demand before we will see it really utilised to the full, but extended utilisation and development could be of tremendous benefit to our crofting areas. I can speak from practical knowledge of one island community consisting of not more than 140 people which today has an annual income of £5,000 from the harvesting of seaweed. If we could see a natural resource of our Scottish shores utilised to that extent by other crofting communities then I do think that that industry would be bringing untold benefit to a very hard-up section of our community.

May I ask Dr. H. D. Slack to speak? Dr. Slack has been very largely responsible on Professor Yonge's staff for the remarkable survey of one Scottish loch: the largest in Scotland in area—Loch Lomond. His own and his colleagues' biological studies are, I am sure, very well known, although not so widely outside the biological field.

Dr. H. D. SLACK, *Department of Zoology, Glasgow University*

Mr. Pyefinch has dealt ably in his paper with the major fisheries of Scotland in fresh water, and what I would like to do is to add a little, the minor fisheries, which I think are worth bringing to your notice. First of all, in Loch Lomond we have the white fish (in the freshwater connotation) *Coregonus clupeaides*, which is an abundant fish. This, the powan, is sometimes called the freshwater herring although it is not related to the herring and only occurs in Loch Lomond and Loch Eck. Powan formed an economic fishery during both world wars, but only then. Professor Yonge has just said that we have to educate the people into the utilisation of an unfamiliar product, and I do feel that there is a local possibility there of utilising white fish. The second point, at the risk of rousing the ire or incurring the ridicule of all the Scots, the non-salmonid fisheries of Scotland, Mr. Pyefinch has referred to three of them—pike, perch and eels—but there are several species which, though they cannot claim any economic food value, may be considered from the point of view of amenities and sport, and especially if our Lowland rivers are eventually freed as far as possible from pollution. If they are, and they will not be freed entirely for there will be an increased amount of mineral salts in the lower reaches, making them more suitable waters for non-salmonid fishes. We have for example chubb in the River Annan, bream at Lochmaben, roach at least as far north as Loch Lomond and although these are not considered as important angling species in Scotland as yet, they are considerably appreciated in England and might be attractive to English visiting anglers. Again, a fish that I do not think has been mentioned, the grayling, widely distributed in Scottish rivers. One might even consider that a borderline species between game and the so-called coarse fishing.

Dr. LUCAS, *Marine Laboratory of the Department of Agriculture and Fisheries for Scotland*

Well, sir, I rather thought that my colleagues and I in a sense had done just this in an attempt to cover very briefly, because of the large number of papers coming into this meeting, the nearer water fisheries in which Scotsmen are interested. We were glad to have the opportunity to do that because fish has traditionally played a very important part in the history of Scotland and its economy. I merely wish to say now that although those nearer water fisheries do cover the bulk of the Scottish fishing interest, they form by no means the whole of it. Although I hope that Scotland will gain even more in the future from those nearer water fisheries, by a mixture of international conservation and modification of eating traditions, so that fish which we do not use at present can be used. I hopc in addition that Scotland will be able to take its share in the considerable development which I feel sure is going to come from the seas and oceans in the future, both in terms of the fisheries and indeed several other things among their vast potential.

I wonder if it would now be in order to say something I might have said this morning if it were not for the considerable competition to speak on the interesting subjects which were then raised. If Mr. Rankin would permit me, I would attempt to make a correction or at least to put something a little more into perspective. In referring to the oceanographic investigation going on, he did say, after mentioning one or two Institutes, that there is also oceanographic research proceeding in the Ministry of Agriculture, Fisheries and Food. But of course it is also proceeding not only in our own Department of Agriculture and Fisheries for Scotland, but very much so in the Marine Laboratory of the Scottish Marine Biological Association at Millport and indeed in its sister laboratory in Edinburgh, which I might claim is conducting the largest marine survey, to be run regularly by standard methods over a number of years, in the world. Admittedly that is limited to the subject of plankton, but since that is the basis of life in the sea I think it may be said that Edinburgh itself is taking a very real share in oceanographic and marine research.

Mr. N. S. Main, *Glen and Henderson, Linlithgow*

Later on I shall put forward a paper on various points, and it is partly in view of that that there is one point I would like to make in regard to this fishery question. My idea about the publication of these Natural Resources is that it is to be for the benefit of the future industrialists of Scotland and also the rising generation. We have heard a lot about the rising generation leaving Scotland—the best of them—and I am quite convinced that one of the prime motives that takes them away is their feeling that Scotland is rather played out, and that there are far better opportunities in other countries. I think accordingly it is very important that when we put forward a survey of the resources of Scotland we should point out where Scotland's resources are better than those of other countries. Not out of any feeling of pride, but simply as a statement of fact. Now, I do not think I have seen mentioned in the papers on fisheries any comparison of the value of the fisheries in Scotland compared with the value of fisheries in England. It is one point only that I want to make, but I would like to repeat it when it comes to agriculture and some other things. It is a theme which I feel should be at the back of our minds, and in so far as we can show the resources of Scotland are better than the resources of England, we should put this forward. Where our resources are worse than England's I do not see any reason why we should not state this. We want a frank case. I think we have quite a good case, but we want to state it.

Mr. R. H. S. Robertson, *Director, Resource Use Ltd.*

I would like to make the contrast between the growth of the alginate industry in the last twenty years, where people took a fascinating material from which you can get all kinds of weird, sticky stuffs and worked on the thing with the view "What on *earth* can we make of this stuff, or these materials?" They, frankly, were acting by foresight. They were looking forward. They were working in the strength of ignorance. You must start off in that way in resource development. You must be humble and find out. But in the depressing list of industries which did not come about, which Dr. McGregor gave, everyone of those was a firm having an established raw material coming to it, looking backwards over its shoulder and saying, "Can we get dolomite, limestone, iron ore or so on in Scotland?" and finding they could not. This is really looking backwards, and I should have thought that in this day and age people should stop this particular method of approach: it leads nowhere, except to the expenditure of a great deal of time and money and the most fearful disappointment.

Mr. T. Moscoso, *Puerto Rico*

With your kind permission I would like to talk about something I know very little about: fish and wildlife. I literally drooled when I heard about the wonderful fish resources you have in Scotland. In Puerto Rico we have very little commercial fishing, almost none. If you look at a map of the Atlantic Ocean you will see the reason why. Just a few miles off shore from Puerto Rico is the deepest spot in the Atlantic. As a matter of fact I know that you men of science will recall that that spot was surveyed for the possible drilling of the Mo Hole, because the ocean was so deep in that particular area. That means, of course, that having no banks we have very little commercial fishing. We do have some very good game fish and we are utilising this to the utmost in developing our tourist industry. However, since we did not have the commercial fish, we tried to bring the fish to our shores. We did it in the following manner. Through aggressive promotion, such as Lord Polwarth usually gets done here to bring industry to Scotland, we have managed to bring the three largest U.S. canners of tuna to Puerto Rico. So now the tuna clippers are bringing in fish at the rate of 90 tons per day, and by the time the third cannery is open, at the rate of 120 tons per day. That has provided us with an industry which will give a total value of products of 30 million dollars annually. I wanted to mention this point to show that if you try, sometimes the lack of resources can be converted into a useful asset, because at least it sharpens your imagination.

F. L. Nugent, Esq., *MacFisheries Ltd.*, *Aberdeen*

Although Dr. Lucas has stated in his paper that he is not unduly worried about prawns being overfished, I am afraid that I must disagree with him in as much that when these prawns were first being caught on a commercial basis some eight years ago the catch was mainly of large-sized fish. Currently, we appear to be getting a considerably higher proportion of small fish and I do hope that this is not an indication of the future with large catches of small-sized prawns, as commercially they do not compare with the imported prawn.

On the question of haddock, I have discussed this problem with Dr. Lucas last year and may say that we are very worried. This variety of fish happens to be the most important of my Company's production and sales that we handle. This year we noticed landings have decreased further against the preceding year, and I would put the question as to whether we would not be wise in considering the action that has been taken in other countries, such as Iceland, and the prospects that in the Faroes, Greenland and Norway they will also extend their limits. I believe that we must seriously consider the recommendation of extending our own. I appreciate that many people in the industry will disagree with me in this matter, but I feel that they should look at the marketing side of the fish trade and here they will find that more and more fish is being imported into Britain from these countries and the biggest selling gimmick that they have (and there is no other word for it) is that it is line caught, fresh line caught. I have seen this fish myself both in Iceland and on the display counters in this country and it is really a wonderful quality, well handled, very clean and all of good proportions. In our own Scottish fishing now we are getting a very high proportion of small-sized fish. Fortunately we have been able to develop a good market for it in this country, particularly in the case of the Golden Cutlet from Aberdeen, but would we not be wiser to have another look at our coastline and not be too worried about the effects on the deep-water ports in Britain and their trawlers? After all, the fish in Scotland is for eating and that from Hull and Grimsby is for selling.

With regard to the paper on dog-fishing, I would like to add a further point. Approximately 3,000 tons of skinned dogfish is imported into Britain annually from Norway, yet the fish is caught off the Shetland coast. My firm have had several attempts to try and develop this fishing in Scotland and in the Shetlands, but have never found the fishermen very keen. Recently I have endeavoured to get further interest in this variety, as the belly-flap of the fish is sought after in Germany, but the belly-flap only represents about 5 per cent. of the total weight of the fish and the edible body about 32 per cent. You will see we have many problems, particularly with marketing and also in convincing the fishermen to catch the correct type of fish in the same manner as the Norwegians. Much has been achieved in the last few years in getting co-operation with the fishermen, but I would suggest that they find seine netting somewhat less arduous than line-fishing for Dogs.

I should like to make one reference also to herring processing. In this part of the industry we have seen quite a reduction in the number of people actually processing herring in the form of kippers and other methods, but at the same time there has been a tremendous development in the use of freezing equipment by one or two firms and there is every indication that this will continue in helping to redevelop home market sales for the consumption of kippers. Recently we have experienced some restrictions caused by management problems within the fleet. We hope the fishermen will tackle this in a sensible and enlightened manner.

The last item on which I should speak is not really concerned with any of today's papers but is on the question of management, and I note a very similar problem has been mentioned before in connection with the seaweed industry. There generally appears to be in Britain a strong stigma attached to anyone who announces that he works in the fish trade, and I find many people, including the educationalist, who rate the fish trade of a very low social status. Because of this, we are finding it very hard to get young men of ability to come into our industry as Trainee Managers and help us develop for the future. We have got to get away from the old ideas of the industry and get new approaches and with it new thinking. Mr. T. Moscoso has mentioned what has been achieved in Puerto Rico with new ideas and the vigour of youth, and we are going to need this to help us. I would ask all to carry with them the thought that the fish industry has an old and traditional background, yet offers a wonderful future full of advantages for young men who want excitement in life and their work, for it is most exciting to try and forecast and plan just how much fish you will have today, or tomorrow, or next year from a source that is still largely controlled by Nature. There is full opportunity to allow one's initiative I almost said to run riot, but it is not quite that, but certainly for full development, for there is so much scope and so much work still to be done and we are so short of good management material both for production and for selling, and remember unless you can sell, production is of no avail.

Mr. Cadzow

I want to speak also on the shellfish paper and in particular on the lobster fishing industry which provides another example of the benefits that the development of such an industry can be to the crofting communities. It has been brought out in the joint paper on the inshore fishing industry that shellfishing is a small-man industry—that applies to all inshore fishing—and is practised throughout the crofter counties. The shellfish industry is certainly within the reach of even the single man because one man with a boat can go out after lobsters and crabs and it is of tremendous importance in the economics of these areas.

Let me quote from figures from one of our Societies which has about 150 active accounts in its books—lobster fishermen all of them. I do not know how many men are represented in all, because there may be from one to four men to a boat. The average income of these 150 accounts during the past year has been £330, and that of course is by no means their total income because they may have been selling Norway lobsters, crabs and probably lobsters to other markets. I extracted the earnings of ten individuals whom I knew; their average was £287 from lobsters alone. Amongst larger vessels I took three again known to myself each with a crew of three, where after deducting the boat's share of the income these men themselves averaged over £1,000 a year from lobsters alone. All referred to are genuine crofters and doing an excellent job of work on their crofts. These are both industries—seaweed and inshore shellfishing—which could be tremendously developed, and as Dr. Lucas brought out regarding lobsters it is very probable that if the average size of lobsters, in other words the average age of the lobsters, caught round our West coasts was reduced the income would go up because it is the smallest size of lobsters which are in greatest demand and earn highest prices on the Continent.

Dr. Fraser Darling

In just finishing the discussion I was very much interested in the remarks from our friend of the fish marketing; again these human attitudes, and in the course of this Conference we are going to have to deal with the limitations, the curious canalisation of human behaviour and the possibility of change before Scotland's resources can be fully utilised on a conservation basis. I was thinking as a matter of fact during this discussion about line-caught fish. I reckon myself as a bit of a connoisseur of fish; I eat whenever I have the chance, which is all too rare, I am afraid, line-caught fish fresh from the Forth and from the Moray Firth. We have too little of this, and when you remember our young days when the fishwife used to bring absolutely fresh fish to the door, we may reflect that in some industries when you get mass production you eventually find a small but none the less thriving industry for the best product. This could be so with line-caught fish, or is line fishing almost out nowadays as a profitable end of one's labour? These are the things we would like to know more about on a resource basis, and I feel that that magnificent race of women, the Newhaven fishwives, should come out in their full finery and do something about this in the towns of Scotland and further south.

WRITTEN CONTRIBUTIONS

C. E. Lucas, *Department of Agriculture and Fisheries for Scotland*

In reply to the very interesting points raised by Mr. Nugent (Messrs. MacFisheries of Aberdeen), I should like to begin with his reference to the recent scarcity of haddock.

Although we have still a lot to learn, we know the biology of this fish perhaps the best of all. It is still overfished in the North Sea, although the measures taken under the 1946 Convention have abated somewhat the strain exerted on the stocks. To this extent, with more stringent regulation, it could be more abundant than it is. On the other hand, this is not the prime reason for the recent scarcity, which is undoubtedly due to the succession of two extremely bad year-classes produced in 1956 and 1957, following a series of unusually good ones. While the production of an average year-class in 1958 has helped to lessen the effects of the bad ones, we are now short of the 3- and 4-year-old fish, while any improvement depends on the success of the 1959 year-class, about which we are not yet quite certain.

This brings me to Mr. Nugent's question about the size of Norway prawns, and here I must make it clear that the rapid development of this fishery, since its possibilities were realised by the fishermen, means that we are by no means so well informed about its biology, behaviour, etc. We can only say that there is as yet no reason to suppose that stocks, even in the Firth of Forth, are being overfished. The larger proportion of smaller sizes now being produced appears to be partly due to the effects of poor year-classes a little earlier. Fortunately some control is being exerted by the relatively low price offered for the smaller sizes.

The limits problem is of course tied up with very wide international issues of a political and legal character on which I would not comment. One cannot but agree, however, with Mr. Nugent's opinion on the high quality of most line-caught fish. Fortunately lining of one sort or another is still a feature of Scottish fishing and it is to be hoped that the merits of its product will continue to be recognised in the market.

This brings me to the point raised by Mr. Main. In brief, the answer to his question about the relative value of English and Scottish fisheries is shown by the comparison between the value of the total quantity of fish landed in Scotland (about £15 million) with the total landed in the U.K. (about £50 million). In relation to her population, therefore, Scotland makes a greater contribution to U.K. fish supplies than does England, and the prime quality of most Scottish fish is well recognised in markets south of the border. As I inferred in my paper, Scotland's fishing potential is limited mainly by the demands of the market and the provision of an economic means of satisfying it. In fishing, therefore, Scotland can set her aims high, if she will also give her attention to the latter problems in terms of (1) improving local demands, (2) improving facilities for processing and transport and (3) thereby competing effectively in the more distant markets.

Professor V. C. Wynne-Edwards, *University of Aberdeen*

Fish and wildlife are renewable natural resources. It is desirable to manage their exploitation so as to give the maximum sustainable yield. Some of these resources are known to be overexploited—for instance, the fishing for haddock, which would give greater yields if the fishing pressure could be reduced; others are utilised far below their known potential—such as seaweeds and several other kinds of marine fish. In several cases (salmon and red deer were mentioned) we still lack all the basic information needed in order to estimate the maximum crop that could safely be taken.

Further development depends, according to circumstances, either on gaining more scientific information or on finding practical means of preventing overexploitation, or—in yet other cases—on developing popular demand for resources at present untapped and unappreciated. (The need for enterprise in development was particularly well brought out by Mr. T. Moscoso, of Puerto Rico, speaking from the floor.)

BASIC RESOURCE FACTS

NATIONAL ATLAS

The Cartographic Representation of Resources in an Atlas of Scotland

Professor RONALD MILLER, M.A., PH.D.
Department of Geography, University of Glasgow

Resource questions can be answered well on maps, particularly when the question is "where", and is of a compound nature. In addition, relationships appear on maps at a glance, and can be better appreciated there than through index systems.

Government responsibility for the atlas map class, however, has never been acknowledged. True, we have a small but valuable set of maps on a scale of 1/625,000 showing certain topics like population, administrative boundaries, farming types, etc. These, though not bound together, are sometimes referred to as a National Atlas, but they serve only to emphasise our lack of a national atlas. We require within one convenient pair of covers maps of natural features like geology, land form, soils, climate, vegetation, etc.: of economic features like forests, farms, road and rail capacity, gas, electricity, water sewage, land and property values and taxation rates, etc., and a whole host of social features involving for example population (another census is due next year and will yield a multitude of maps), employment, housing and other such distributions which are not normally mapped except for *ad hoc* purposes by planning offices.

Co-operation between those interested in resource survey and use, geographers, and the various Government departments is required to put right the deficiency in documenting Scotland in atlas form.

A national Atlas of Scotland will be of great service in developing her potentialities.

We are all more or less map-minded. Some of us, however, restrict our use of maps to showing where places are. True, this is the primary use of maps, but we are throwing away a powerful tool, especially if our interest is the study of Scotland's resources, if we do not advance further into the cartographic field than this.

I take it that it would not be an undue simplification of the purpose of the Resources Survey to say that the object is to marshall the relevant information in such a way that we can ask ourselves "what has Scotland to offer that can be developed for the service of man?" or even more bluntly, as the business man enquiring from outside is liable to do, "Have you got so-and-so and this-and-this and where is it and how do I get at it?" He may be thinking of labour, weather, a mineral or one of many other things, but almost certainly the query will have two characteristics:

1. It is very likely to contain the word "where": that is to say, space and position are involved: no tables, no card index can give the answer to "where" so fully as a map.
2. It is likely to be a compound query involving variables which are not normally

linked and which, therefore, are not normally the business of the same bureau, much less the same tables or card index. An enquirer may be seeking abundant soft water supplies and female labour; or limestone, electricity and rail transport; or sunshine and light soils.

Such questions are very well answered in maps: in fact, the necessary generalisation and simplification on the map may bring out features which the sheer weight of information in tables or on cards may mask. This is not, of course, to say that tables and card indexes are not necessary when just such massive detail is indispensable. Moreover, two or more distributions can be shown on the same map, and very often when this is done relationships appear—this is what makes geographical studies so exciting—that could not possibly emerge unless the *space* relations of the data were allowed to emerge, i.e. they are plotted on a map. Such cartographic techniques can be as revealing as looking down from a mountain-top on a maze of paths and clearings in which one has been confused.

We have all seen Scotland depicted as a whole on one sheet of paper, if only in a school atlas. This type of map is on a small scale—only a millionth part or less of the real thing. We can call maps of this or smaller scales, atlas maps. They usually show only the broad distribution of high and low ground, major rivers and the larger settlements. They may or may not include roads and railways, but generally speaking little more is shown. Their small scale, enabling all of Scotland to be seen at once, is however their virtue, and wherever we are seeking broad patterns we would use such scales. The broad climatic regions of Scotland, the areas with different types of agriculture, the main roads and railways, the electricity grid and the like would all appear on the small scale.

Another type of map which most of us know is the Ordnance Survey one-inch or Bartholomew's half-inch. Here only an arbitrary slab of Scotland is shown, as much as the available paper will take at scales larger than 1 in a million but not much bigger than 1 to 10,000: in fact, we might take the (relatively) new Ordnance Map at 1 to 25,000 as being the limit. Here, of course, very much more detail is possible. Instead of the broad distribution of high and low ground, the contours and other aids to the representation of relief allow us to depict the *form* of the ground and instead of showing settlements down to say villages, we can show every building. Such maps (they are generally called topographic maps, though they do much more than merely show topography) clearly have their own function, arising out of this ability to show more detail, particularly as to the *form* of the ground. An industrialist interested in say forestry waste, the electricity grid and access to tide-water would use the "atlas" map to indicate suitable areas and then turn to topographic maps to choose promising sites which he would then examine on the ground.

The maps on the largest scales of all—generally called plans—also have their function, though they do not concern us so much here. They can, of course, show great detail, including even individual lamp-posts and letter-boxes in the street. They are often consulted in matters of legal boundaries and are thus styled "cadastral" plans. They thus would not normally be involved in resource mapping except in the last stages of laying out an installation. They would not normally be used to study topography except in such engineering problems as calculating the volume of water that a given valley would hold if dammed to a certain height.

Three classes of maps have been mentioned. These differ not only in function but in provenance. The two latter classes, the topographic map and cadastral plan, have long been recognised as a Government responsibility, and the Ordnance Survey caters for us in what will be a most efficient way once the current new developments enable them to overhaul the backlog of the war years.

Government responsibility for the atlas map class, however, has never been acknowledged. True, we have a small but valuable set of maps on a scale of 1/625,000 showing certain topics like population, administrative boundaries, farming types, etc. These, though not bound together, are sometimes referred to as a National Atlas, but they serve only to emphasise our lack of a national atlas. We require within one convenient pair of covers maps of natural features like geology, land form, soils, climate, vegetation, etc.; of economic features like forests, farms, road and rail capacity, gas, electricity, water sewage, land and property values and taxation rates, etc., and a whole host of social features involving for example population (another census is due next year and will yield a multitude of maps), employment, housing and other such distributions which are not normally mapped except for *ad hoc* purposes by planning offices.

We geographers have often felt the lack of such an atlas, especially as other countries, one after the other, have been producing them of recent years. It was, I think, the appearance within a short time of each other recently of Atlases of British Columbia and of Northern-Eastern France that shamed me into action. I suggested to my geographical colleagues in the Scottish Universities and in the Royal Scottish Geographical Society that it was time that this deficiency in the documentation of Scotland was made good. We started our consideration of the many problems involved about the same time as the Resources Survey was first mooted. We think we are doing in our vernacular—the map—precisely what you are seeking in perhaps a more specifically economic sphere, and I personally at least trust that we may be able to co-operate to our mutual benefit. We geographers are only too conscious of the enormity of the task of preparing such an atlas of Scotland, but many of us think it is a worthy effort and one that must be undertaken soon. Some of the raw material lies ready to hand in various Government offices and we have always enjoyed the most willing assistance from them all in the past. We think that St. Andrew's House should actively help with the project and we would be glad to link hands with them in this matter for we have always enjoyed our contacts with them in the past. We geographers, if I may say so, have the know-how where maps are concerned: Scotland has in Bartholomew's a firm of map-makers who are second to none in this world, and I am glad to say they are co-operating with us: the Resources Survey would seem to be the biggest single customer for maps: I trust that between us all we may be able to produce something that is not only due to Scotland but will be of great service in developing her potentialities.

INTRODUCTION TO DISCUSSION

F. Fraser Darling, D.SC., PH.D., N.D.A., LL.D., F.R.S.E.
The Conservation Foundation, New York

We have half an hour left to discuss the Scottish National Atlas. In some ways I believe this is a controversial subject, although for the life of me I cannot see why it should be. Somebody said this morning, I think it was Professor Frazer, that we expect maps to tell the truth and we believe them. Equally I think all of us feel that whenever we are being told anything about a country or resources we say "Let's see a map", and if we can see a map the whole thing is clear. If not, it is mere conjecture as it were, and in the technique of map making, which has developed enormously in the last twenty years and even in the last ten years, I think that it is a very right and proper subject for discussion at a resource conference. Resources as a whole can be demonstrated by mapping techniques. Most of us—I suppose I should speak for myself—are a little bit dull in thinking about maps. Now, Professor Miller and Mr. John Keates, and Professor Watson is here from Edinburgh too—we have a good body of talent who can really tell us something about the representation of data cartographically, and within Edinburgh I think we should always remember that we have a very great cartographical institute and that there is practically no problem of the production of maps which could not be tackled here in Scotland and in Edinburgh. May I call on Mr. John Keates to lead the discussion on Professor Miller's paper?

DISCUSSION

Mr. Keates, *Glasgow University*

I hope that you have all seen Professor Miller's short account of the ideas behind a National Atlas of Scotland. This is a question of great concern to people who are concerned with such a Symposium as this. The analysis and appraisal of the resources of a country depends upon relating all the various factors concerned in such a way that they can be studied in relation to each other. In fact, they all have one common denominator, they are distributed in space; and it is precisely this element which a series of related maps would attempt to show. If, for example, one is concerned with establishing a new industry or with examining a particular market, one would ask quite a number of specific questions; where people are, what the transport facilities are in the immediate area, how various resources can be brought together. These and many more detailed questions can to a certain extent be solved by examining properly produced maps.

From this point of view we have quite a number of good examples of what has been done in many other countries. About seventeen countries in the world, large and small, have already produced their own National Atlases; some, such as Finland, have gone as far now as three different editions. Something like ten or eleven more are in course of production. One can say that they have one factor in common, that is that they are specifically designed to meet the needs of a particular country. I feel that quite a lot of misapprehension often exists about the use of maps, especially maps which are largely designed to show the distribution of statistical information. I think that from this point of view one should take into account the needs of the non-cartographer and the non-geographer, and that the information which is contained in a particular map can often be well supplemented by additional text material, and by dealing specifically with particular areas by means of larger scale maps or by means of diagrams. This type of atlas, which has been discussed in general terms, is clearly something that people concerned with developing resources in Scotland should have as a tool. We have the basic question of how we can achieve the construction of a series of maps which can be used by a large variety of different people and can be employed profitably for solving practical questions. This I think leads us to one or two points straight away. We obviously need to consider these maps strictly from the point of view of problems of great contemporary importance in Scotland, and therefore both private industry and Governmental and educational organisations would all need to be concerned, to some extent, with both the planning and the designing of the type of product they would need. On the other hand we have to achieve some form of practical production, and as many national atlas organisations have shown, I think this does depend on having a fairly limited number of people actually dealing with the immediate progress of the work. As our Deputy Chairman has said, there is no shortage of skill or production capacity in Scotland. What we need basically is to accept a particular target, to come to agreement about the sort of things we want, and then as far as possible to steer straight for what may be a limited objective but one that can be practically realised. There are at the moment a number of maps or projects for maps which in some ways do relate to this particular question. We have a small series of maps produced on the 10-mile scale by various Government departments with the Ministry of Town and Country Planning. These like other projects suffer from one or two disadvantages even though they have a great deal of basic information in them. The trouble is that they are concerned with the very general statement of main principles, they are not examining specific Scottish questions from a Scottish angle, and it is quite clear that the more specific you can be in this the more use such an atlas would be to Scottish business and to Scottish industry. Clearly an atlas designed to cover the whole of Great Britain is limited both in terms of scale and content through dealing with subjects of general importance. Whereas, as it must be clearly seen from this Symposium, there are many particular Scottish problems which require their own treatment. We also have a private project by Oxford University Press for an atlas of Britain of which I have seen some of the initial sheets and which is clearly going to be a fine and useful publication. Even so, I do not think we can assume from this that the needs for an atlas for Scotland will be met in all detail, and this major work could well be used in combination with a much more specific work for the needs of Scotland itself. I feel that there are a variety of subjects which ought to be dealt with, but we should think of these as detailed applications of knowledge to be shown on maps and not in general terms of geology and climate and so on. We want to find out what are the basic types of information we need and seek to construct maps which are designed to help people to solve problems related to them. The only experience I have directly in the production of national atlases is from the Atlas of Sweden, and there we have a good example of how maps and text can be combined to produce an attractive and very useful tool, and one which I happen to know is widely used both in private industry and in education. This is, in fact, a private venture, and I think gives some clue that from an economic point of view there is a fairly wide if rather uneven market for the maps which such an atlas should contain. This particular atlas is produced in loose-leaf form, a section of maps and texts for each particular subject, and this has the great advantage that, first of all, it can be issued sheet by sheet as prepared, and secondly that the requirements for individual maps can be directly related to the particular demand for such maps. Clearly some maps in such a large-scale production would have a much greater market or field of use than other more detailed ones. In this way we could combine the demand for particular maps in certain Government departments or industries with the amount that we printed, and eventually could build up stage by stage what would be a complete survey of all the different types of resources and an analysis of all the main questions which are involved in dealing with problems of resources and development in Scotland.

Professor WATSON, *Department of Geography, Edinburgh University*

I think it would be best for me to augment Professor Miller's paper simply by referring to my own experience in national atlases and how they are organised and how they are used. For many years I was chairman of the committee that produced the national atlas of Canada which came out three years ago after some ten years of organisational meetings, map compilation, drawing and reproduction. We found that we very much needed the support of groups of business men and of educators. Indeed, it was the meeting of these groups, and the case they put forward, which persuaded the Government finally to put out money in producing that atlas. So I do think it is very appropriate, sir, that the case for the National Atlas of Scotland should be made to a group such as this—a group who are interested in resources, who are anxious to make use of these and have a sense of responsibility for the development of Scotland.

Professor Miller's paper has already indicated how very useful maps can be, and I can assure you that in the case of the Canadian National Atlas its use has been very widespread indeed not only in planning the development of underdeveloped parts of Canada in planning roads and railways, the placement of hydro-electric plants and the expansion of agriculture in the north, but also in planning for the growth of the settled areas in the south. You are due to have a paper tomorrow on the competition between land uses. This is a very real problem in cities and in the surrounds of cities. There is competition between industrial and agricultural and recreational uses of land in the immediate perimeter of cities. Maps on the land use in cities, on land use in the immediate vicinities of cities, on the migration of the population between cities and the flow of traffic into cities, on the spheres of urban influence, the competition between cities, and so on, could all be of tremendous value for business men and town planners, regional planners and Government ministries.

I would think the Scottish Council could help a great deal if it were favourably disposed to the idea of an atlas. In the first place it could itself support the project and indicate what it would like out of an atlas. In the second place it might encourage the Committee already set up under Dr. Allan of the R.S.G.S. by asking—"What are your needs, what are your problems, how could these be met?" We believe from discussions with various members of Government departments that these departments themselves would be very interested to make available material to be published in map form. I am also convinced that business in Scotland could offer a good deal of information. In Canada, I obtained a great deal of information from the Canadian Pacific Railway and from many of the large hydro-electric power companies and development companies in the country, who had been filing away reports, drawings and surveys, but who had not made all this available to the general public. In Scotland, I am sure there must be a lot of this material in business files. Could it not be made available to the public? In any event, I wish to assure the Council that an atlas would help us all in our work, whether we are Government administrators, town and regional planners, business men or educators.

Mr. Butler, *Department of Health for Scotland*

I did not come here prepared to speak, though I threw the cat among the pigeons today. It was at my suggestion that Professor Miller was invited to give this paper. Because I have been so long associated with this mapping business, I thought it was time that some fresh mind was brought to bear upon it. My mapping work in Scotland started during the war years when I came on the staff of Professor Matthew, who has just arrived here amongst us and who had the responsibility in the Department of Health for organising background information for town and country planning in Scotland. It fell to me to gather in as much information on natural resources and other subjects as possible at that time and to present it in map form. The idea of the published planning maps sprang out of the National Atlas Committee of the British Association for the Advancement of Science which was formed before the war. During the war Lord Reith was given a special remit to organise the types of research and survey which would be needed for post-war reconstruction, and it was largely through two members of his Committee, Dr. Stamp and Dr. Eva Taylor, that the National Atlas project was handed over to the then Ministry of Works and Planning (which later became the Ministry of Housing and Local Government) and the Department of Health for Scotland. But our work in preparing these maps virtually ceased about ten years ago. We had a long list of maps in mind, but with increasing restrictions on Government expenditure the mapping side of town and country planning was unfortunately slowly and gradually curtailed, so that the series of maps as they stand are mostly out of date, except perhaps for the latest version of the 1951 population density map, which will be published very shortly. I was hoping that the Atlas Committee that has been set up by the R.S.G.S. under Dr. Allan's chairmanship would help us to reassess and review the programme of maps which we started long ago. Perhaps we might revert to the original intention that reduced in scale these maps should ultimately form the basis of a national atlas. An ex-colleague of mine, Professor O'Dell (I do not know whether he is present today—I was hoping he would be), I believe gave advance notice that he would speak not exactly against but that he would be critical of the paper that Professor Miller has produced. I think what he really intended was to point out all the difficulties of producing a Scottish National Atlas rather than be opposed to it. I think he holds the idea that a supplement to the Clarendon Press Atlas should be attempted rather than an entirely new Scottish National Atlas. Probably that point has to be thrashed out. There is certainly need for co-ordination between the ideas sponsored in the first place by the B.A. Committee and subsequently by the planning departments and then by the Clarendon Press and now by the R.S.G.S., to avoid unnecessary duplication. I think probably Professor O'Dell would agree with me that there should be further discussion on this to see how it can be done. I am very sorry that Bartholomew's are not represented here today, because I have heard them discussed as a possible sponsor in this scheme, but this idea would probably be brought to them by Professor Miller, because I believe Bartholomew's are on the R.S.G.S. Committee.

Professor MILLER, *Department of Geography, Glasgow University*

After Professor Watson's advocacy there remains little for me to say on this point. I was very gratified that the Scottish Council invited me to give a short paper. I made it as short as I could in the hope that you might read it, being short, but I cannot help feeling that one is talking to the converted. I have been here since 9 a.m. this morning; I have looked at maps next door; I have heard maps mentioned; I have heard the word "plotting", I have heard the word "survey" used over and over again. Clearly in everyone's mind is the cartographic representation of the kind of thing we have been speaking about today. The problem really is how to go about it. It is very pleasant indeed to hear Mr. Butler say, as I hoped he would, that the Government is waiting to co-operate with a body willing to take some initiative in this matter. We in the Scottish Universities use the Royal Scottish Geographical Society as neutral ground and we think that, being an old-standing body, it is a very suitable one to bring together the variety of interests in Scotland who simply must have an atlas. I do not think this is the place where we should decide what maps we want, what shape of page and so on. Bartholomew's have been mentioned, and so have the Clarendon Press. I mentioned the word "Bartholomew" twice I think in my paper; first, because everyone knows their half-inch map; secondly, to make the point that we did, in fact, appreciate the difficulties of printing maps—a very expensive exercise—and that we did not quite have our heads in the air. We asked Bartholomew's as a commercial firm to consider the possibilities and tell us whether we were talking nonsense in hoping to have a National Atlas. Bartholomew's said, "You are not talking nonsense. It will be difficult and it will be expensive; it will not be an easy job." But this is the kind of job Scotsmen thrive on, these difficulties. It would, I think, sir, be, if we can bring this off, a very useful forum in which all the other interests represented here and tomorrow and Wednesday could exchange their findings. I am not clear what the Scottish Council has in mind for the future. Presumably the activity of the various interests represented here is going to be stimulated and each of us hopes that he will know what the other is doing in the next few years. It seems to me that almost all of the activities represented here have an aspect in which the question "where?" comes in. They are all, I think, likely to want a map or maps and it could be that some kind of atlas—call it National or otherwise, as you please—an atlas centring these activities would serve a very useful purpose. I have forgotten who said early on this morning that one thing that Scotland needs in connection with young people going overseas is a feeling of "nationhood", and here I should say in our schools a great many of the plates in a national atlas would be of first-class importance. I think it was Mr. Keates who mentioned the idea of a loose-leaf atlas. We do not think that everyone would want all the maps. There might be a selection for schools, a selection for Government, and selection for businessmen and so on, but this is not a very complicated matter if you use the loose-leaf form. We could, in fact, I think, form a very useful addition to our national culture. We in the Universities talked about this first in February and then transferred our discussions to the R.S.G.S. in order to bring in a wider circle, and it was in June, I think, that Mr. Robertson kindly asked me to lunch and we spoke about this. I would hope that this idea may move forward one stage yet and perhaps be linked with the assembly of interests we have here this afternoon.

Mr. D. P. Bickmore, *Clarendon Press*

Mr. Chairman, My Lord, Ladies and Gentlemen: I am speaking at the end of a long day and the end of a long line and from a place called Oxford which I am aware is a long way from Edinburgh. But I would like to emphasise that the work which we in the University Press hope to publish next year, the Atlas of Britain, is, I hope, only a beginning of these cartographic investigations which have been talked about this afternoon. I hope that the labours with which we have been involved over the last six years—and when I say "we" I embrace in this term distinguished contributors such as Professor Pearsall, British Railways, many of the Ministries and a whole host of eminent academic authorities, Dr. Penman on the water balance situation, and many others—this atlas that we have been trying to produce will in fact be available, we hope, next year, and I hope that it may be possible to build a series of reliable atlases of the whole of Britain extending the information that we have tried to collect. The only thing that I do want to emphasise is the great lack of information or statistics about many of the things that one would like to map. It is admirable to talk about making a map showing the flow of traffic on the railways, but it is an extremely difficult thing to do, and the statistics for this are not available. It is an extremely dangerous thing to do to invent statistics or to rig up some kind of map in that context. The same thing applies to problems, I suspect, even the problems of rainfall which were mentioned this morning. There are very large areas in the Highlands where the rainfall statistics are scarce to say the least, and the question of how this information should be treated cartographically requires very careful thought. In our case we have avoided the old technique of showing isohyets and have plotted only observed scientific information rather than the imaginery or imaginative lines which go round them sometimes. I hope that in the work that has been done in producing a map which is to be published—1/1,000,000 scale of superficial deposits in the whole of the country's superficial geology—that we have been able to fill in an extremely important cartographic factor, that is, the illustration of differing degrees of reliability. Unless one can take into cognisance the fact that the information one is trying to deal with on any extensive area varies greatly from place to place, one is liable to produce misleading and relatively unacademic information.

Mr. P. D. McGovern, *International Centre for Regional Planning and Development*

I think for the record it is desirable that a few words should be said about the atlas of resources recently produced in British Columbia, which Professor Miller mentions in his paper. There are two points of interest, one being that work was started on the atlas at the same time as the Atlas of Canada was being produced. The two atlases are complementary in the same way as I think an Atlas of Scotland could be complementary to the Atlas of Britain. And secondly, the atlas of resources of British Columbia was the outcome, as some of you know, of an annual resources conference very similar to this meeting. For the past twelve years there has been such a meeting in British Columbia, and from some points of view one of its greatest achievements has been the production of this atlas, the combined product of the Universities, the Government departments and business. Finally, I note there is a copy of this atlas on one of the tables in the main hall, and I hope some of you will now have a look at it and think of something on the same lines for Scotland.

WRITTEN CONTRIBUTIONS

Professor A. C. O'Dell, *Department of Geography, University of Aberdeen*

The Proposed National Atlas of Scotland

1. Although there are doubtless many theoretical arguments for a National Atlas of Scotland, the practical problems seem to fall into the following heads:

(*a*) How is the project related to the O.S. 10 Mile Series and the O.U.P. Atlas of Britain?

(*b*) Is there sufficient new material or demand to justify such an expensive and time-consuming project?

(*c*) Can, in fact, some of the suggested maps be constructed with available data *or* within a reasonable period of time?

(*d*) How can the work be done?

(*e*) What are the costs likely to be and how can these be financed?

2. The O.U.P. intend publishing in 1961 a major Atlas of Britain covering the United Kingdom and Northern Ireland. This work started in 1954. The atlas will have about 200 pages of large format showing the United Kingdom on scales of 1 : 1 mile and 1 : 2 miles, and will sell at about £20. Even with considerable outside help and the considerable resources of O.U.P.'s Cartographic Department it has thus taken seven years to complete. O.U.P. feel they must now publish or further delay will make many distribution maps dated and less attractive to potential buyers.

3. A small buying public (largely restricted to libraries and like bodies) can be envisaged for a volume costing £20. The original idea was for the volume to cost about £10. Inflation and rising costs have clearly taken a toll. How do we cater for this eventuality, remembering that the publisher sees only about 2s. 3d. of the retail price? The peculiar circumstances of O.U.P.'s commercial organisation put them in a stronger position than other publishers to publish unremunerative projects. O.U.P. reckon library purchase averages 700 copies.

4. An atlas of this kind can never hope to "break even" on real costs. The Canadian National Atlas was sold at $25 and got a $25 subsidy per copy: its real cost was thus $50. Costs may be considered to be:

(a) *Collection and compilation of maps.* There is a theoretical possibility that free labour may be forthcoming—but from where? The overworked teaching staffs of University Departments of Geography? Government Departments? Are there any research funds for this? There is a limited pool of people with sufficient knowledge and experience, but this pool cannot be increased without substantial changes in establishment.

(b) *Drawing, proving and editorial work.* Are there sufficient people in Scotland to do this work? For instance, are there sufficient cartographic draughtsmen with the requisite skill for this type of work?

(c) *Plate-making and printing.* Plate-making costs remain the same irrespective of the size of the edition, but some economy could be made in printing if large runs were possible.

Even without costs of printing, paper, binding and distribution, O.U.P. have been involved in spending £50,000. Where does the equivalent money for a Scottish atlas come from? R.S.G.S.? Treasury? Carnegie Trust? Industrial concerns?

5. A project of this kind requires very carefully controlled relations between compilation, production and editorial aspects. How do we achieve this? To produce a coherent atlas of multi-coloured maps is a much more complicated process than to produce small black and white book illustrations—it is highly desirable that compilers and editors should be aware of what can and cannot be done within given cost limits and defined reproductive processes. Because these branches were divorced and inadequately co-ordinated, a recently published national atlas nearly came to nothing. The proposed pre-war atlas came to grief not only because it could not enlist adequate financial guarantees, but also because a division of work to sub-committees led to "too many cooks spoiling the broth". The present committee organisation of the proposed atlas contains inherent dangers through inadequate knowledge of and control over the production side. Can we be sure that by using committees we shall get the balance required to produce a full-scale atlas? Do we have any idea how many people are genuinely interested in the project and will abandon all other commitments to devote the large amount of time required to the work?

6. Can geographers obtain the data to compile many of the maps? Easy access to unpublished statistical material is essential. The industrial maps in the forthcoming Atlas of Britain took a whole-time compiler two years to prepare ready for checking by civil servants and trade organisations. The railway flow map took two years to produce. Only 25 per cent. of the outside assistance in the Atlas of Britain has been given by geographers, which includes virtually no compilation work. Many of the most important physical maps cannot be produced without adequate field work. Mere compilation from topographical maps serves no scientific basis. How can such work be done in a period short enough to fit in with reasonable dates? Moreover, will the academic prestige of individual geographers be enhanced to the same degree as if they continued research in their own present fields?

7. This project clearly overlaps both the O.S. "National Atlas" series and the Atlas of Britain. In these two projects there is already inevitable duplication in such maps as geology, relief, etc. Does anyone want the labour of triplication? Will people who buy the O.U.P. atlas also buy an Atlas of Scotland which duplicates a great deal of the material? A possible solution lies in an idea of a volume of Scotland supplementary to

the Atlas of Britain. Perhaps the volume might contain maps not already in existing publications and include maps of regional extent, e.g. population distribution in the Central Lowlands, types of rural settlement, hydro-electric power, etc. The contents cannot, however, be properly settled until the Atlas of Britain is published. There is also the possibility of a more commercially attractive small atlas (of two-colour maps) restricted content (e.g. Mediaeval Scotland). There may be a good market for a small general "popular" students' atlas showing the main geographical features of Scotland. A further possibility might be an atlas restricted to the planning problems of the Central Lowlands.

Contents of Atlas of Britain—A Summary

	General Map, Relief, Slope.
16 pages	Maps of solid and drift geology.
6 pages	Maps of coastal features and tides, also deposits on continental shelf, salinity and temperature.
10 pages	Climatic maps of temperature, rainfall, sunshine and length of day, fog, snow, vapour pressure, mean wind speed, cumulative degree days under and over 60° F.
4 pages	Water supply, including annual evaporation and river flow, underground water and aquifers.
14 pages	Soils, vegetation, botanical distributions and forestry, showing types of trees and woodland.
14 pages	Regional maps at 1 : 1 mile showing relief, solid geology, superficial deposits and land use.
25 pages	Agricultural distributions and fishing. Include land use, agricultural labour, holdings, fertilisers, markets, milk production, slaughterhouses, and distributions of individual crops and animals.
7 pages	Fuel and power, including coal mining and distribution, oil, gas and electricity and atomic power.
6 pages	Iron and steel making, including mining of raw materials, rolling, plating, wire-drawing, etc.
25 pages	Distributions of individual industries and mining, including textiles, distilling, engineering, wood working, paper and clothing.
17 pages	Regional maps at 1 : 1 mile showing employment, specialisation and fuel consumption.
8 pages	Population distribution and changes, age groups, mobility of labour, housing conditions, shops, etc.
6 pages	Administrative divisions of local government and ecclesiastical authorities, national parks, nature reserves, etc.
12 pages	Transport, including railway, road and canal flows, trade.
14 pages	Regional maps 1 : 1 mile of population and transport, showing roads, railway, canal and air traffic movement.
13 pages	General maps at 1 : ½ mile scale.
	Gazetteer. Loose overlay maps.

D. P. Bickmore

THE MAPPING OF NATURAL RESOURCES OF SCOTLAND

1. In 1954 the absence of any British National Atlas lead a small group in Oxford and Cambridge to initiate plans for the Atlas of Britain which the Clarendon Press hopes to publish in 1961. A list of the topics involved in this collection of maps (mostly at 1 : 2 miles and 1 : 1 mile) is shown on p. 224.

2. The chief limiting factor in preparing these maps has not been time, technics or money, but the shortcomings of available surveys and statistics. It is these limitations that have in the main decided the scope as well as the scale of the maps: to map the available material at any larger scale than their detail warrants would simply mean more pages and more expense.

3. Professor Miller's paper draws attention to some of the features which it would be desirable to map in a National Atlas of Scotland. One of the topics he mentions is "Railways", and I would like to use this topic as an illustration. We have already discovered—as he will discover if he presses his enquiries—that the British Transport Commission simply have not got information on the flow of passengers and of freight analysed and subdivided in a form suitable for the detailed maps we had envisaged. At length, however, they have prepared for us, *ad hoc*, a train-density map based on the probable expectation of the situation by Traffic Controllers in the various regions of British Railways. We believe that we can show the details of this information at 1 : 1 mile scale. Several general points arise from this:

(*a*) It seems unlikely that the British Transport Commission will be able to produce the more scientific and analytical statistics on which to base a more detailed map for many years.

(*b*) Even the relatively approximate train-density information that we are now mapping ought to be reviewed in the same terms ten or fifteen years hence to show the pattern of change. (An important function of the map is as a series of X-ray recordings to show the patient's progress over a critical time.)

(*c*) Equivalent traffic flow maps on the same scale are equally desirable for roads, canals, coastwise shipping and domestic air-routes: we are attempting to cover all these aspects of transportation in so far as we have been able to assemble the statistical facts relating to them (e.g. 1955 Road Census), even though these facts are generally not on a directly comparable basis.

(*d*) The transportation pattern that does exist makes sense when studied for Britain as a whole: I am not sure whether it does make sense if studied from the point of view of Scotland alone.

4. As with the problems of transportation, so with those of industry, farming, forestry, water resources, climate and many other topics. Everywhere there is the same difficulty of assembling facts in mappable (or mapworthy) terms and in making maps in such a way that valid comparisons can be made between map and map—the main purpose of such an atlas.

5. The more attention that can be directed to recording more of the facts that will be wanted, the more effective can be their cartographic presentation if—as with transport

—maps are the best way of presenting them. But one will never reach Utopia, for the facts that one will want to know tomorrow are often not the facts one has thought of collecting today. One has to devise means of mapping information that varies in its reliability and of making this variability in source material as immediately clear as in any other scientific statement. In this kind of mapping the illustration of variations in reliability must not come second to aesthetic considerations.

6. In planning the exciting "Nova Scotia" that your Symposium envisages, you, sir, would obviously be wise to grasp the proffered Scottish cartographic resources of capital, research and technology. But if in the work that the Cartographic Department of the Clarendon Press has done over the last six years for the Atlas of Britain we have material or statistics whose further investigation might be of interest to the Scottish Council, we shall naturally be happy to place them at your disposal. Should you wish to enlarge on any of the subjects we have dealt with, it would seem that co-operation (e.g. over definitions, sources, etc.) would be of material help to the geographers or economists, to the planners or administrators, and ultimately to the historians concerned with this field of knowledge.

Professor J. Wreford Watson, *Department of Geography, Edinburgh University*

Atlas of Scotland

(Given in a letter to Dr. Douglas Allan)

In reflecting upon the proposals for an Atlas of Scotland put forward to the Scottish Council Symposium on natural resources, and also to the Royal Scottish Geographical Society, I should like to make the following comments:

1. I should very much like to see the publication of such an atlas and believe that it would be of considerable value for Universities and high schools, for business, and for Government.

2. However, I feel strongly that this should be a scholarly atlas, representing all the main features of Scotland, its history, culture and life, and not merely an atlas of convenience centred on natural resources, economic activity, and population—i.e. built around topical interests or problems.

3. I also feel strongly that it should not duplicate the Scottish section of the new Atlas of Britain which Mr. Bickmore is about to bring out on behalf of the Oxford University Press. According to the minutes of the first meeting of the R.S.G.S. Atlas Committee, we had agreed to bring out an atlas on the basic scale of 1 : 1 mile, with maps for special areas on larger scales. Mr. Bickmore has already mapped the fundamental aspects of the physical, economic and social geography of Scotland at the scale of 1 : 1 mile.

We are left with the choice of *either* bringing all this material out again at a larger scale *or* of supplementing what has been done.

The former alternative could scarcely be warranted (*a*) because it would make the atlas too large, (*b*) it would raise the costs appreciably, (*c*) much of the material could hardly be published on a larger scale.

4. The second alternative should, then, be our choice, viz.—to supplement the O.U.P. Atlas of Great Britain. This could be done through some arrangement with the

O.U.P. by which we could use all their general maps of Scotland at 1 : 1 mile, together with their regional maps of the Central Valley of Scotland.

5. The supplementation would involve (*a*) other general maps, particularly on the historical, cultural and social geography of Scotland, at a scale of 1 : 1 mile, along with (*b*) a series of special regional maps, at as large a scale as would be feasible, of the more populous parts of Clyde, Forth, Tay and Dee.

I should like to see an atlas containing:

The growth of the idea of Scotland in maps from Ptolemy to the O.S.
The historical geography within Scotland of
 (*a*) the settlement;
 (*b*) the internal boundaries;
 (*c*) the agricultural and industrial revolution
  from the earliest times relevant to these themes to the present.
A special section on the historical geography of Scottish cities (in which, after all, most of Scotland resides).
A survey of the natural features and resources of Scotland.
The economic geography of Scotland.
The social geography of Scotland.
The cultural geography of Scotland.
The geology, geomorphology, climate, drainage, soils (where possible), mining and industry, communication, other economic activities, economic ratios and trends, settlements, urban morphology, inter-urban relations, population and population behaviour of the Greater Glasgow, Greater Edinburgh, Greater Dundee and Greater Aberdeen areas.

6. I would wish to see the effort made match the project and urge the concept of an atlas where the results of real research and scholarship could be shown by first-rate cartographic techniques. This would, of course, involve us in a considerable cost—I believe the rough estimate of £80,000 to £100,000 was mentioned—but the cost would be worth it, if we brought out a work worthy of Scotland.

7. If this were accepted, we should plan on a research and compilation programme of about seven years, and a reproduction programme of an additional one to two years. The Atlas of Canada, of which I was the first editor, took eight years to compile and publish, even although we had in addition to the services of the Geographical Branch the full co-operation of geography students working for three and a half months every summer for six summers. The O.U.P. Atlas of Britain has already taken about five years and will probably need another two years before completion.

8. The R.S.G.S. should actively sponsor this atlas (*a*) by making an annual grant to it, sufficient to cover all the expenses of a lively Atlas Committee (who would meet two or three times a year), (*b*) by helping to guarantee the publication of the atlas, (*c*) by using its influence with the Scottish Office, the Scottish Council, and other bodies to persuade them to share in the costs of publication, (*d*) by approaching the Oxford University Press and/or Edinburgh cartographic houses to secure commercial backing for the main part of the undertaking and (*e*) by offering its services to create that liaison between University Geography Departments, and Government Offices through which alone the atlas could be effectively produced.

SECOND DAY

UTILISATION OF RESOURCES

PROGRAMME

Introduction

UTILISATION OF RESOURCES
The Rt. Hon. LORD BILSLAND, K.T., *Chairman, Second Day*

Deputy Chairman

M. A. M. DICKIE, O.B.E., D.S.M., M.A., B.SC., N.D.A.
Late Chief Lands Officer, Department of Agriculture for Scotland

INTRODUCTION

THE RT. HON. LORD BILSLAND, K.T.
Chairman, Second Day

My Lords, Ladies and Gentlemen: Thank you very much for your kind welcome. . . . I think our thoughts this morning must be of the deep regret with which we have heard of the death of Sir Cecil M. Weir, who was to have been Chairman today. He was one of the most outstanding men in Scotland of his generation, and his notable public services covered a wide field. . .

I am very glad indeed of the opportunity to preside at this most interesting meeting. At yesterday's meeting we discussed the resources we possess, the basic resource facts; today we are concerned with the utilisation of resources and the complex relationship between resources. The complex of interwoven resources involves the main subjects before us today, Agriculture, Forestry, Wildlife, Recreation, Water, Energy, Minerals and Biological Resources. These are the resources from which industries are made and grown and are further developed and become interconnected. We have many papers to cover today and therefore I suggest discussions be confined to matters which cover the boundaries between the different resource usages. Thus we will not, for instance, discuss forestry as such, but rather forestry and the soil, forestry and water and forestry and sheep—in short, in this example, a facet of land use. In every development of resources, whether in agriculture or general industry, there is need for power to mechanise production; without this power we should all be manual workers of very low productivity. It is perhaps important to note that the amounts spent on energy in Great Britain by industrial and domestic consumers is more than 10 per cent. of the total national income excluding the tax on oils. Although there is only one paper on mineral resources and one on biological resources at the end of a large number of afternoon papers, I feel that these papers should be given rather more time for discussion than would be indicated by their small paper representation. I sympathise with the task of Dr. Parker, who will be in the Chair to take that part of the meeting. I would like to put to you the thought that while we are in this session concerned with Natural Resources, the development and utilisation of these resources depends upon the application of our minds to making the plant which, one way or another, will turn these resources into saleable products. Scotland, by tradition, manufactures plant for developing her own and overseas resources. I feel sure, therefore, that a meeting of this kind might well be attended by people who make the plant, because the closer these people are to the thinking of those more intimately concerned with primary resources, the more readily will they anticipate future requirements, and the more able will they be to lead in their trades. Finally, please do not hesitate to send in a written contribution to the discussion should you wish to do so after today. We will try to arrange that points forthcoming in this way will be answered and recorded in the subsequent publication of the Symposium proceedings. I now call upon the Deputy Chairman, Mr. Dickie.

UTILISATION OF RESOURCES

MULTIPLE AND AGRICULTURAL LAND USE

Conflicts in Land Use

G. P. WIBBERLEY, B.SC.AGRIC., PH.D., M.SC., F.R.S.A.
Department of Agricultural Economics, Wye College, Ashford

In all societies there are conflicts between individuals and between groups about how the land of the community should be used. These conflicts arise mainly through differences in the situation of particular pieces of land. In most developed societies the movement of land to its best use is not necessarily secured by letting it go to the use for which the highest market price is offered. If the highest market price is the determinant of the land use pattern, then certain undesirable movements can and do take place.

Housing and amenities can disappear from the centres of cities. On hill land afforestation and users of water can afford to pay a higher price for them than can unsubsidised agriculture. Parts of the country may come to contain scattered residences over a wide area leading to the partial merging of town and country; in cases of this kind, if amenity and architectural standards deteriorate, such areas can easily become problems of rural blight.

The simplest way of not using market price as a determinant of the land use pattern is to put the land in the possession of one individual or organisation. However, while many of the land use patterns decided by individuals emphasise extensive land use of high amenity, the decline of personal fortunes can lead to descendants becoming conscious of market values of land and finding it necessary to take advantage of them by complete or partial sale.

Committees, on the other hand, may not be able to initiate change of any magnitude and, in essence, the town and country land planning organisation of this country has been primarily of a permissive character.

Increasing private mobility is leading to a greater search for quiet places and away from people. If this need can be handled sympathetically, the gulf between the isolated rural area and the crowded city can be turned into a mutually beneficial two-way partnership.

In all societies, irrespective of their particular position on the ladder of general economic and social development, there are conflicts between individuals and between groups as to how the land of the community should be used. The conflict is not related to any fixed proportion between land and people, though many people speak as if this was so. This is because the conflicts arise mainly through differences in the situation of particular pieces of land. Certainly there are differences between pieces of land in their basic suitability for different uses. Differences in topography, soil and micro-climate, for example, circumscribe the agricultural and forestal use of land. But for most other uses, such as residential, industrial, communications and commercial, most pieces of land can be used for such purposes with a greater or lesser degree of adaptation. Anyone who doubts the flexibility of land use that is possible and practical should note, for example, the kind of sites being used for urban development in the mining valleys of South Wales or on the outskirts of Bergen in Norway.

Conflicts in land use, therefore, occur because of differences in the natural aptitude of land for different purposes, but they are mainly related to differences in situation. Isolation in relation to a piece of land has been greatly altered and improved by modern developments in both transport and communications—the train, bus, car and aeroplane enabling people to get to and from places more quickly and easily and the letter, telephone, radio and television enabling people to get over a feeling of isolation by keeping in touch with the main stream of events. Though these developments have cut down, in absolute terms, the isolation of any one place, they have left undisturbed the relative position of one piece of land as against another. Wasteful though human beings may be of time, as judged by profitable or productive use of it, they have become increasingly conscious of relative differences in its use, particularly in regard to time of travelling from one place to another. Therefore, though every situation has improved in its general accessibility, society has become even more selective in the emphasis placed on the relative situation of each piece of land.

The importance of each piece of land is shown by the price it can command in the open market if a free market in land is allowed to operate. The sharpening of relative differences in the value of pieces of land as sites thus shows itself in a widening of land values as between good and less good situations. The strong rise in land values in Great Britain, especially over the past year, has shown this widening even though increases have occurred all over the country—in rural areas as well as in town.

It is accepted in most developed societies, however, that the movement of land to its best use in the community is not necessarily secured by letting the land go to the use for which the highest market price is offered. If the highest market price is the determinant of the land use pattern, then certain undesirable movements can and do take place. Certain uses, thought important to considerable sections of society, are squeezed out from certain areas because the market price they command is relatively low. Housing, except in the form of tall flats, is squeezed out of the centres of towns, together with open spaces of all kinds. Town parks, central housing, sports grounds, children's playing-fields—all these will disappear from the centres of cities if market price for land is allowed to operate freely and uncensored. On the fringes of towns and throughout the accessible lowland, especially along lines of communication, the erection of houses, in estates or singly, will always take over agricultural land, no matter the intensity and efficiency of its practice, if the decision is left to price alone. On hill land in many places afforestation and water authorities can afford to pay a higher price for land than can an unsubsidised agriculture.

The use of market price to determine the land use pattern of a country also leads to inequality and unfairness of treatment as between individuals and groups. Individuals holding land may benefit substantially from rises in land values caused entirely by the activity of other individuals or the community in general. A man owning a farm at a value of, say, £150 an acre may find, because of a general increase in economic productivity or rising standards of living, that his land is wanted for the erection of new houses. As soon as this demand for new land for housing becomes effective in terms of market price, the farmer will find that his land has sharply increased in value—even up to a hundred-fold. The huge surplus he has gained has, in many cases, been due to no effort—

mental or physical—of his own. The rise in value has in fact been created by the rest of the community but, because changes in values are allowed to accrue to the holder of the particular piece of land at this particular point in our history, the owning farmer receives all the gain. (It is simple to state the basic social inequality giving rise to ideas of "compensation and betterment". All of us know how badly this problem has been handled in most parts of the world.)

A final difficulty, arising from the undisputed influence of market price on the pattern of land values, results from the long-term nature of some of the important changes in land uses in modern society. Changing agricultural land to housing, for example, commits the land to the new use for a long period of time—measured at least in centuries. Even afforestation is thought of in a rotation period of some 50 to 70 years. In urban uses, with the exception of maintenance and adaptation costs, most of the capital expenditure is incurred at the beginning of the period of such use. Yet the previous use of this urban land, which is normally agriculture, is a use which uses capital and other resources and gives a product on a continuous basis rather than once and for all. The comparison of these different uses—especially of their worthwhileness—leads us into difficult problems of time preference—which has been discussed at length elsewhere.[1]

Of course, the simplest way of not using market price as a determinant of the land use pattern is to put the land into the possession of one individual or organisation. We have had many cases in the past of one individual owning large areas of land and using it according to his own dictates and independent of the price any portion of his land would fetch in the market if offered for sale. Many of the land use patterns decided by these individuals are visible today and many are admired because of their insistence on a master plan in design and the emphasis on extensive land uses of high amenity. The estates and parkland of parts of England and France and parts of towns like Bath, Cheltenham, London and Paris are examples of such privately controlled land uses.

But the work and design of such individuals has often been vitiated through the passage of time because a decline in personal fortunes has made such persons and their descendants conscious of market values of land and finding it necessary to take advantage of them by complete or partial sale. This is one development arising from death duties on personal estates which we have to accept whether we agree or disagree with the principles underlying such taxation.

As soon as a committee, be it local or national, attempts to make decisions controlling or guiding the land use pattern, then a different situation is involved. In a democracy where the consent of the governed must be constantly watched and where justice must be done and be seen to be done, control of land uses is bound to be of a permissive character only. It will have to persuade and guide change to the area and land where it is most wanted, but it will not be able to initiate change of any magnitude. (This is a fair statement in relation to recent actions of the British Government as to new industrial location. Expansion in the steel and motor car industries was initiated by private companies—the guidance of this expansion to geographical areas different from those to which it would otherwise have gone has been the action of the Government and inducements of a political and economic nature have been heavily used in the persuasion of the private companies concerned.)

In essence, the town and country land planning organisation of this country has been primarily of a permissive character. It is questionable, however, as to whether permission, but little initiation, is a suitable way of handling the increasing tempo of change in the use of landscape and townscape.

A few of the major and immediate conflicts in land use which are with us in Great Britain at the present time can be emphasised. One arises from the seeming release of the town and city from most of the physical conditions which prevented their continuous growth and spread in the past. The mobility of power, through the gas and electricity grids and the use of petroleum products, has broken the association of most secondary industries with a fixed location. The development of private and public mobility, with cleaner and more sanitary living and working arrangements, has enabled housing and industry to be more effectively associated in space and time, with few disadvantages to either. Looking at things dispassionately and trying to forget any personal value judgments about the right kind of place in which to live and work, we may well be seeing the end of the conventional city form and the beginning of a new, more personally satisfying form of community living which is in the form of a matrix of road, rail and air communications in which are embedded interconnected areas of industry, shopping and residential uses.

But if the city assumes this amorphous form then the definite physical line between town and country, which has helped land allocation in the past and which produces aesthetically attractive contrasts, will also lapse. Separate living-boxes scattered throughout a suburbanised but farmed countryside could well result. The residential areas of those parts of each country which are receiving the greatest spur in general physical development—such as the south and south-east of England—may well become a green archipelago—scattered residences over a wide area of green field, copse and woodland. Where this has already happened on a large scale, as in some parts of Canada and the United States, the merging of town and country is, visually, not very satisfying and individuals living in such areas stress their regret at the lack of contrast. If amenity and architectural standards deteriorate, such areas can easily become difficult problems of rural blight, such as was the case before the 1939-45 War with Billericay in Essex and Peacehaven in Sussex.

This changed nature of urban growth, together with its increased tempo in selected parts of all countries, means a greater area of lowland agriculture moving over into long-term urban uses. Earlier estimates of land use change, with which I have been intimately connected,[2] are now too small and probably inaccurate in their geographical incidence. The food replacement problems caused by this have been discussed in full elsewhere[3] and these should not change in their nature even though they do in degree.

But two problems arise from the changed nature of such development. The first is the intermixing of uses which is occurring. This is having a tremendous effect on land values. With private residential development becoming dominant again, as it was between the wars, and the full market price being allowed to accrue to the holder of land, the effect of increased demand has been to sharply increase prices offered for land sold with vacant possession. It is understandable that prices paid for farms near to growing towns and in favourable areas should be well above the levels at which men can make reasonable incomes from *bona fide* farming activities. It is more difficult to understand why high prices should also be paid for farms in fairly remote areas, where an alternative use other than farming is very unlikely. It is well known that inflationary forces do affect land values in general. In addition, the sale from a farm of only a few acres for non-farming uses can, because of the high prices realised, make it economic to handle the rest of the farm as an agricultural unit even though the rewards from farming would not cover the total capital cost of the farm.

The solution of this problem is related to more realistic allocations of land for non-agricultural development in the town maps of areas highly esteemed by industry and private residence. It is also part of the problem of compensation and betterment which most countries have failed to handle in a fair and workable manner. It is the failure to handle it that gives strength to those who look favourably on nationalisation of the land. One immediate danger in the situation is that inflated agricultural values of land will be taken as a proper part of the costs of food production in this country and so be woven in as a permanent part of the cost increases allowed at the annual February agricultural price reviews.

The changing pattern of living is also accentuating the differences between the thickly populated, congested but thriving conurbations and the 'problem' rural areas which appear, more and more, to be close to or past the margin of acceptable living. These problem areas, like Central Wales and parts of northern Scotland, are losing their absolute isolation, but their relative isolation is growing. With a combination of poor soils and climates, difficult topography and thin and scattered populations with a heavy concentration of older males allergic to change, such areas are notoriously resistant to marked social and economic improvement.

Perhaps our attitudes towards such areas have been too circumscribed in the past. We have thought about and measured our actions too much in terms of rural depopulation—of maintaining or even increasing the numbers of people living permanently in such areas. But so much of our system of communications is now nationwide. The television set and radio gives the same programme to the isolated cottage as it does to the busy town café. The private car, jeep, lorry—even aeroplane in some places—gives access to the city from any part of the British countryside and, what is most important, the knowledge that such mobility is possible. Isolation to individuals is, after all, a state of mind. This is why Government help to such areas designed to improve mobility and communications is all important so that the few people which the isolated rural areas need to operate them can be full members of this twentieth century in much of their day-to-day lives.

These isolated and thinly populated areas have an increasingly important part to play as reception areas for tourists from the large centres of population. Increasing private mobility, through the motor car, is leading to a greater search for quiet places off the beaten track and away from people. If this need can be handled sympathetically and yet canalised, especially by the National Park Authority, then the gulf between the isolated rural area and the crowded city can be turned into a mutually beneficial two-way partnership.

REFERENCES

1. WIBBERLEY, G. P. (1960). *Agriculture and Urban Growth*, p. 208. Michael Joseph Ltd.
2. BEST, R. H. *The Major Land Uses of Great Britain*. Studies in Land Use, No. 4. Department of Agricultural Economics, Wye College, University of London.
3. *Agriculture and Urban Growth*, especially Chapters 6, 7, 8 and 9.

Agriculture in Scotland

W. O. KINGHORN, B.SC.

Technical Development Officer, Department of Agriculture and Fisheries for Scotland, Edinburgh

Scotland's agriculture is highly diversified with livestock predominant and forming the link between different types. The production potential consists of a large number of comparatively small production units. The main regional types are arable-livestock, dairying, cropping and livestock rearing. Annual agricultural output is currently valued at £168 million, four-fifths of which is livestock products. The production of milk, beef, potatoes, mutton, eggs and pig meat in that order make up £131 million of the total output. Raspberry growing, the seed potato trade and pedigree livestock breeding are small but important specialist forms of production. About half of all Scotland's farms are tenanted and half are owner-occupied. The proportion of farms owner-occupied is slowly but steadily increasing. The present full-time labour force is 68,000 workers and the number is falling by about 2 per cent. p.a. Mechanisation and redeployment and increased efficiency of the force is making good the loss. The industry is stabilised by a complex system of state support, including guaranteed prices and markets, and schemes of assistance and improvement. Since the war production has risen to 60 per cent. above the pre-war level and the emphasis is now on quality and efficiency. The industry is highly organised and is supported and aided in its task by a large variety of organisations, private and official. The heavy capital cost of modern equipment and techniques is encouraging the development of specialised production possibly in a smaller number of larger units.

NATURE, EXTENT AND OUTPUT

Scotland is divided fairly sharply between mountains and moorland, which cover about two-thirds of the total area, and undulating lowland areas hemmed in between the hills and the sea. By British standards climatic conditions are harsh in the Highlands, with rainfall usually in excess of 50 in. and frequently 80 in. near the west coast. Cool summers are followed by comparatively mild winters, for snow does not usually lie long below 2,000 ft. While a fair proportion of the land lies above 1,000 ft., the hill areas are everywhere dissected by glens or by sea lochs and this allows most of the land to be worked as part of farms which have their buildings and in-bye land at no great altitude. At the same time, soils which frequently barely cover great areas of resistant rock, stripped and smoothed by glaciation, generally support herbage of low nutritional value, while in the glens the areas of land productive enough to provide adequate winter keep for the stock which can be grazed on the hills during the summer are extremely restricted.

Some 3,000,000 acres of the Grampians and Northern Highlands (nearly one-quarter of all the mountain and moorland in Scotland) are given over to deer forests, some of which are grazed by sheep, though perhaps half of their total area is too rough or poor to be grazed by farm stock.

At the other end of the scale are the districts around the Tay, Forth and Tweed where rainfall below 35 in., good deep soils and a fair amount of sunshine are associated with some of the best arable land in Britain. The western half of the central valley of Scotland experiences a milder, damper climate less suited to the production of sale crops but well able to produce the grass and fodder crops needed by the dairying industry focused on the densely populated Clyde Valley.

The low, rolling plateaux of Aberdeenshire and Banffshire, together with Orkney and areas of Caithness, are also largely under the plough, but rather poorer soils, a harsher climate and distance from markets restrict the production of sale crops. The Southern Uplands share some of the characteristics of the Highlands, but the hills and the rainfall are lower, rocky outcrops are rare, and the natural vegetation is usually much more nutritious.

TABLE I

Basic Statistics of Acreage and Livestock—June 1959

(Thousands)

	SCOTLAND	Highland	North-east	East and South-east	South-west
Total Agricultural Acreage	16,841	7,814	2,334	3,664	3,029
Rough Grazings	12,481	7,399	1,128	2,174	1,780
Crops and Grass	4,359	415	1,206	1,489	1,249
Permanent Grass	1,010	150	96	295	469
Rotation Grass	1,803	147	589	551	516
Tillage	1,546	117	521	644	264
Barley and Wheat	313	11	77	203	22
Oats	720	61	301	207	151
Potatoes	150	11	29	87	23
Cattle	1,892	190	531	467	704
Dairy Cows	353	25	45	58	225
Beef Cows	246	52	83	79	32
Sheep	8,384	2,364	1,054	2,794	2,172
Pigs	428	15	122	173	118
Poultry	9,044	546	4,221	1,907	2,370
No. of full-time farms	30·5	3·0	10·1	8·1	9·3
No. of part-time farms	24·0	13·7	5·6	2·2	2·5

In spite of this diversity of conditions, livestock is almost everywhere the foundation of farming and often forms the connecting-link between various types of farm. On the hill sheep farms, which account for much of the land in the Highlands, what cultivated land there is frequently fails to provide all the winter feed required by the summer stock of sheep and cattle, and the younger breeding stock must be sent to winter pasture on more favoured farms, usually near the east coast. The hill farms cannot normally feed their lambs to slaughter weights: nor is the rather better land of the upland rearing farms, which occur in a fringe all round the Highlands, sufficiently productive to fatten the cattle they breed and rear, and they must be sold at eighteen months or two years to more arable farms in the south and east.

In the north-east the extensive arable acreage is mainly in roots, oats and young leys, needed to support the rearing and feeding of beef cattle, and in the south-west the limited cropping programme is directed to maintaining the dairy herd. Even on the arable farms of the east and south, where income derives mainly from the sale of potatoes, barley, oats, wheat and sugar beet, batches of store cattle (often from Ireland) retained for fattening play their part in maintaining soil fertility.

Scottish farming is also diversified by a number of specialised forms of production. Market gardens occupy some of the best land in the Lothians. The bulk of the British raspberry crop is grown in Strathmore, while tomatoes grown under glass are important in the middle Clyde Valley. The narrow, sheltered raised beaches along the coast of Ayrshire and Wigtownshire produce a substantial tonnage of early potatoes. The specialised raising of seed potatoes of guaranteed purity is a major enterprise, especially in Perthshire and Angus, and upwards of a quarter of a million tons are sent to English farms every year. The rearing of pedigree stock is carried on by relatively few farmers, but exports of Aberdeen Angus and Shorthorns from the north-east, Ayrshire and Galloways from the south-west, and Blackfaces and Cheviots from various parts of Scotland go all over the world.

Over nine-tenths of Scotland's farming activity is carried on by the 30,000 or so full-time farms, which may be grouped as follows:

10,000 livestock with arable farms—typical of the north-east;
9,000 dairy farms—mainly in the south-west;
5,000 hill sheep and upland rearing farms—in the Highlands and the Southern Uplands;
4,000 cropping farms—mainly in the east and south-east;
2,000 horticultural, poultry and pig farms—nearly all in the central valley.

During the last few years the agricultural output of Scotland has been valued at around £168 million per year, of which about two-fifths have represented sales of fat and store stock, another two-fifths livestock products (mainly milk) and only one-fifth crops, including fruit and vegetables. Some of the main items are given in Table II.

TABLE II

Value of Principal Items of Agricultural Output, 1958-59

(£ million)

Item	£ million	Item	£ million
Fatstock:		Milk and Milk Products	39·5
Cattle and Calves	32·0	Eggs	14·4
Sheep and Lambs	15·7	Wool	4·6
Pigs	12·3		
Poultry	3·1	Crops:	
		Potatoes	17·5
		Oats	3·4
Store Stock*:		Barley	2·5
Cattle and Calves	2·4	Wheat	1·0
Sheep and Lambs	2·4	Fruit and Vegetables	4·9

* The values shown for store stock relate only to stores sent to England and Wales—they do not include sales from one Scottish farm to another.

Table III shows what a small proportion of crop production enters into output—i.e. is sold for human and industrial use—the bulk of it being fed to stock on the farms.

TABLE III

Production and Output of Principal Crops in 1958-59

(Thousand Tons)

	Production	Output		Production	Output
Oats	724	129	Sugar Beet	175	175
Barley	279	90	Turnips and Swedes	4,746	—
Wheat	115	34	Hay	816	2
Potatoes	1,002	463*	Grass Silage	411	—

* Ware potatoes only.

THE RESOURCES OF THE INDUSTRY

The foregoing section has given us a picture of the nature, extent and output of Scotland's agriculture today. When we consider that net output of the industry is now 60 per cent. above pre-war, it is evident that the basic resources of Scotland's agriculture have not only been made good use of but indeed have been improved upon and supplemented to evolve modern agricultural practice.

The modern resources of Scottish agriculture include both those which represent the harnessing and the controlled development of basic natural resources such as soil and those which have been introduced to the land to aid its exploitation such as modern machinery, systems of agricultural tenure and credit facilities.

The soil is the farmer's major capital asset. The story of its development to a fruitful agricultural medium was in earlier times a long and unpredictable one tracing the accumulation of soil fertility from centuries of agricultural practice. Now of course the picture is transformed and by the widespread and scientific use of fertilisers and land drainage methods the fertility of the basic soil can be improved and sustained. For Scotland this has proved of great benefit and in a country where over 12 of a total of 19 million acres is given over to rough grazing, and when there is a continuing loss of fertile land to urban development, the reclamation of agricultural land from natural moorland is important. In recent times in Scotland the successful work of reclamation of land from heather moor, often boulder-strewn, carried out in Orkney is a good example of the kind of work which on a national scale has given us the fertile farm lands of Scotland.

The development of native livestock breeds, particularly beef and dairy cattle and hill and lowland sheep, and of plant varieties is a further example of particular importance to Scotland of the way in which basic resources have been utilised and improved upon.

But it is the introduction of capital resources in the broad sense other than the basic natural resources which has laid the foundation of modern agriculture. An early development was the division of the land into estates, farms and fields along with the evolution of the various types of agricultural tenure which is fundamental. In Scotland, the latter part of the eighteenth century saw the resurgence of agriculture with a revolution in land management and methods. This was the period of the enclosures, the abolition of the wasteful runrig system and the beginning of security of tenure for the tenant farmer. These changes did not however come overnight, nor did they develop uniformly over the country. They continued to evolve throughout the nineteenth century and, with the break up of many great estates and the gradual increase in owner-occupation, throughout the twentieth century also.

Existing side by side with this historical development which emerged gradually under a combination of economic, social and political pressures there is the largely Government-operated system of land settlement, a planned exercise under the Small Landholders (Scotland) Acts, 1911-1931, which gave birth to "smallholdings" with their own peculiar brand of agricultural tenure. In more recent years the tendency has been to concentrate on increasing the efficiency of existing holdings rather than to create new ones.

Outwith this picture altogether are, of course, the Highlands and Islands, untouched by the agrarian revolution and experiencing instead the demoralising effects of the clearances and large-scale depopulation. The problems of this area are specialised and not solely agricultural; the development of the crofting counties is largely the story of Government intervention from the Crofters Holdings (Scotland) Act, 1886, to the Crofters (Scotland) Act, 1955, under which was established the Crofters Commission with the functions of "reorganising, developing and regulating crofting in the crofting counties of Scotland, of promoting the interests of crofters there and of keeping under review matters relating to crofting".

Leaving aside the special tenures pertaining to smallholdings and to crofts, the present position in Scotland is that about 40 per cent. of all farms are owner-occupied, 50 per cent. rented and the balance partly owned and partly rented. Since the war there has been a marked tendency for sitting tenants to buy their farms, and currently some 500 farms each year become owner-occupied.

The long leases of former years have become much less common, and indeed only a quarter of full-time tenanted farms are now held under a lease; year to year tenancy obtains on nearly 60 per cent., while the remaining farms are held on tacit relocation. But tenant farmers are assured of a reasonable security of tenure under post-war legislation.

Since before the war the rent of the typical tenanted farm has increased by about 50 per cent. The current average rent of hill sheep upland rearing and non-intensive livestock-with-arable farms is around £185 per annum, about £220 for dairy farms and about £300 for cropping farms.

One of the current economic problems of the farming industry is its greatly increased capital requirements. Modern techniques involving greater mechanisation, increased livestock production with greater outlay on breeding and other classes of stock and greater use of fertilisers, better seed mixtures and so on, demand development capital of a size often reaching and even at times surpassing the land capital, which is, of course, required also by the increasing numbers of owner-occupiers. Indeed, today it can be said that the farmer is a true capitalist and on many modern farms the capital investment per worker exceeds the capital investment per worker in industry. To give some indication of the figures, on a good-class arable or dairy farm it will cost up to £50 per acre to stock, equip and work. If the cost of purchasing the land is added, figures of over

£100 per acre would not be exceptional; thus an outlay of £25,000 to £30,000 might well be required to purchase and equip a moderate-sized arable farm of 200 acres.

Obviously in this situation the traditional need of farmers for credit facilities is greatly increased. Heavy death duties and the rarity of the joint stock company in the industry narrows the field in the hunt for liquid resources. The traditional overdraft from the bank and merchant credit meet the problem of financing the day-to-day running in the period leading up to the harvest or the sales. Long-term agricultural credit is however a specialised matter. In Scotland, in addition to the facilities offered by the banks and the Agricultural Credit Corporation, improvement grants are however available from the Lands Improvement Company and from the Scottish Agricultural Securities Corporation Limited. The Government has further recognised the difficulty and gives encouragement through various grants for long-term improvements.

When we look at the fixed equipment of the countryside, the collective equipment essential to modern farming such as roads and railways, water and electricity, it is again the size of the capital investment which strikes us, and the increased realisation of the necessity to appeal to resources outside farming, namely central and local government and the private investor. Clearly the farm is a much less self-sufficient unit than it used to be; the industry has become economically (and indeed socially) interlocked with the nation as a whole.

HUMAN RESOURCES

No picture of the natural resources of agriculture would be complete without a mention of its human resources—the Scottish farmer and farm worker. The traditional image of the Scottish farmer is probably of a shrewd, canny, independent man, skilled in husbandry and with a good eye for a beast. Nowadays, however, while these traditional skills and qualities are still necessary, the farmer has to acquire some additional ones. He must, for instance, be something of a technician, a businessman, a scientist, an economist and an accountant. The "lad o' pairts" has a different significance nowadays.

Despite the farmer's sturdy independence, however, he is not averse to co-operating with his fellows. The vast majority of Scottish farmers belong to the National Farmers' Union of Scotland, which represents their interests in discussions with the Government, or with organisations such as the Scottish Landowners' Federation or the Farm Servants' Section of the Transport and General Workers' Union—the major trade union operating among the 68,000 full-time agricultural workers employed on Scottish farms.

Scottish farm workers have their minimum wage rates regulated by law. The Scottish Agricultural Wages Board, which performs this function, consists of representatives of employers and workers, together with independent members appointed by the Secretary of State. Different rates are fixed for all the various categories of workers—ploughmen, stockmen, dairymen, etc. The modern trend is towards greater numbers of specialist workers, but recently there has been a steady decline in the total amount of labour employed; since the war the number of men in the force has fallen each year by about 2 per cent. That this decrease in numbers has been accompanied by increased output reflects both the skill of the individual worker and the increase in mechanisation, which shows no sign of slowing up. For example, during the three years from 1956 to 1959 the number of combined harvester threshers had increased by 1,500 (80 per cent.), pick-up hay and straw balers by 2,700 (135 per cent.) and tractors by 5,800 (11 per cent.). How far the labour force can fall without endangering the level of farm output is a moot question, but the evidence on the whole would seem to be that increased mechanisation and efficiency can still offset declining numbers. The industry's realisation of the need for expert training and efficiency is shown by its sponsoring of a farm apprenticeship scheme and by the interest presently being shown in farm management including the application of work-study techniques to farming.

The Scottish farmer makes full use of the advisory services provided free of charge by the three agricultural colleges in Scotland. The advisers bring to the farm the results of work at the research institutes and carry back to the scientist the farmer's experience and his problems. In the field of research the farmer is well served by Scottish institutes of world reputation dealing with such widely varied subjects as soils, plant breeding, animal nutrition and diseases, dairying, horticulture and agricultural machinery. The colleges and institutes are self-governing bodies but are financed by the Exchequer.

ORGANISATIONS OF THE INDUSTRY

The agricultural industry is served by a wide variety of non-Government organisations on various levels. For example, for various individual commodities there are producer marketing boards constituted under the Agricultural Marketing Act. Their powers range from full trading powers to buy and sell the whole of the home-produced product to fairly limited regulatory powers. The only purely Scottish boards are the three Scottish Milk Marketing Boards which have been in operation for almost 30 years. Other Boards—for potatoes, eggs, wool and tomatoes and cucumber—operate on a G.B. or U.K. basis.

Other types of organisations include farming co-operative societies (initiated by the Scottish Agricultural Organisation Society Ltd., which promotes agricultural co-operation in various fields), trade associations and breed societies. On a less official level there are many agricultural societies, each enlivening its district with its winter discussion meetings and with its summer show of stock and produce. The Scottish Women's Rural Institutes and the Scottish Association of Young Farmers' Clubs are also important threads in the intricate pattern of rural life.

ANCILLARY INDUSTRIES AND SERVICES

A very big part is played in modern agriculture by the industries serving it; just how big can be gauged from the fact that Scottish agriculture's total bill for fertilisers, feeding-stuffs, machinery and seeds is now around £80 million. These services, however, are for the most part provided by regional or even national undertakings based mainly in urban centres, and the traditional rural industries have had to readjust themselves to modern conditions. Instead of primarily serving agriculture they have had to find new outlets for their services; for example, the village smithy is probably nowadays an engineering workshop and garage, or the smith may be producing wrought-ironwork for a predominantly urban market. Instruction and advice on this and other rural crafts, such as weaving and boatbuilding, are given by the Scottish Country Industries Development Trust. The Trust also gives financial assistance towards the erection, reconstruction and equipment of rural workshops.

THE IMPACT OF VARIOUS GOVERNMENTAL ACTIVITIES ON AGRICULTURE

Over the last few decades the Government has played an increasingly active role in agricultural developments particularly during and since the 1939-45 War. The foundation, however, of the present-day Government policy of assistance to the industry to make effective use of its resources by means of various schemes of improvement and financial assistance together with the provision of guaranteed prices and assured markets is found in post-war legislation, including particularly the Agriculture Act, 1947, which speaks of the promotion and maintenance of "a stable and efficient agricultural industry capable of producing such part of the nation's food and other agricultural produce as in the national interest it is desirable to produce in the U.K.".

Since 1951, as world supplies of food and Britain's own agricultural production and trading position improved, the wartime and immediate post-war policy of control has been relaxed and the Government have gradually restored to private businesses both the import of food and domestic trading in food. Since that time stress has been laid on more economic home production of food of the kinds and qualities required by the market rather than on indiscriminate expansion of production. More economic production demands greater efficiency, and to help the farmer meet this demand the Government have introduced, during the last decade, various schemes of financial assistance designed to enable him to improve his land, buildings and equipment.

CURRENT TECHNOLOGICAL ADVANCES AND POSSIBLE FUTURE TRENDS

So much for an outline of the present shape and state of Scottish agriculture. What can we see of the future? It could be said that forecasting the future of an industry with the chequered past of agriculture is hardly an exact science. But we can still do a little better than that earlier farmer who could only "guess and fear". The system of Government guarantees gives the industry a degree of stability that it has never before enjoyed, and it is reasonable to forecast that this overall stability will continue and that the resultant progress and development of the past twenty years will continue into the next. At any rate it is only on such an assumption that any sketch of the industry's future can be drawn.

Organisationally the industry will probably remain such as it is at present—a large number of small production units. The variability of Scottish farming conditions and the traditional independence of the Scottish farmer will together ensure for a long time to come a generous mixture of farms of various sizes and types. The trend towards owner-occupancy will probably continue. There will however be a distinct movement towards streamlining and rationalisation of production. It is likely that the present policy emphasis on quality and lower production costs will continue and possibly intensify, giving rise to production methods of the broiler chicken type where a single commodity is concentrated and intensified in a comparatively small number of units. The product is standardised and the production costs are lowered. There are signs of a similar development in beef production and to some extent in sheep. The dairy industry could follow the same trend.

Similar developments will be seen in the case of crops. Mechanisation has long passed the stage of merely replacing the horse. It now replaces human manual labour and is being developed more and more to carry out entirely new processes. We are probably on the threshold of automation in the industry—not perhaps the universal adoption of the radio-controlled tractor, but the introduction of such highly practical devices as the mechanical feeding of fodder to cattle by automatic conveyer belt direct from the silo and operated by pre-set mechanism.

Developments such as these with their heavy capital investment tend to favour the larger unit. There will follow some redistribution of production between farm and farm resulting in the larger and better farms taking on the types of production more suited to full mechanisation and leaving to the smaller units the products which require a greater amount of human care and attention.

Technologically the field for development is of course unlimited; precise detailed forecasting is impossible. Wartime agriculture demonstrated both the possibilities and the problems of modern farming, and a major post-war development was the re-organisation of the agricultural research organisation to cope with the new situation. The new research institutes have now been established and are settling in to their tasks. Within the next twenty years the results from this reorganised research service and from the greatly increased commercial facilities for research will provide farming with the basis for many new techniques, mechanical, chemical and biological.

This sketch of the future can perhaps be concluded by instancing a few of the more noticeable broad trends in agricultural research and technology such as the modern comprehensive approach to research whereby a single practical farming problem is analysed and interpreted into a series of scientific questions and possibilities and a comprehensive attack made. Another outstanding development is the post-war realisation that grass, our commonest natural plant, is also our most valuable farm crop. A vast new effort is now being directed to devise techniques to enable this crop to be used to its full potential. Of particular interest to Scotland is a trend to devise methods of agricultural production which are as far as possible independent of natural conditions such as weather. Into this category come such techniques as barn hay drying, irrigation and indoor animal production. Over all the research programme can be seen an increasing emphasis on the biological sciences, seeking to understand the vital processes of plants and animals so that, better understood, they may be turned to man's greater advantage. Such developments as the use of antibiotics and oestrogens, the introduction of systemic insecticides and the discovery of a method of induced twinning in cattle are without doubt only the beginning of a long series of biological discoveries awaiting just around the corner.

Agriculture and its Possibilities

EAST and SOUTH-EAST SCOTLAND

J. D. NUTT, B.A., N.D.A.

Advisory Economist, The Edinburgh and East of Scotland College of Agriculture, Edinburgh

(One of three Scottish Regional papers, the others being "West of Scotland" (p. 262) and "North Scotland" (p. 276).)

The agriculture of south and south-east Scotland shows a wide range of farm types associated with differences in soil conditions, elevation, topography and rainfall; economic conditions have also had their effects on the evolution, layout and tenure of farm holdings and in modifying the use to which land is put.

An examination of the changes which have taken place in land use over the last twenty years shows that, apart from the loss of a relatively small proportion of the total area to non-agricultural usage, there has been little change in the broad pattern. Rough grazing as a proportion of the total acreage has shown no change though there were modifications in the proportions of the other major sections—permanent grass, rotational grass and tillage—but not to such an extent as would constitute a radical change in the overall picture. The really significant changes have taken place within the arable section, both as regards the distribution between tillage and rotational grass and the importance of individual tillage crops. These changes have been accompanied by changes in livestock numbers which, overall, are now much in excess of pre-war numbers.

Intensification of land use is demonstrated by heavier manuring and heavier crop yields as well as by the increased stock-carrying capacity, and net output is now more than half as much again as in 1939.

Other changes in the structure of the farm economy, such as modification in the sizes of farm units and the increase in the number of owner-occupiers, have taken place. The most spectacular feature, however, has been the adjustments in the labour-power situation to comply with the present-day economic and technical conditions.

A consideration of the differences between average and high outputs from farms of different types has suggested that, together with the potential arising from future improvements in technology, an overall increase in output of upwards of 25 per cent. should be possible.

The title of this paper poses the problem of what to deal with first, but if the whole picture is to be brought into perspective, it is necessary to describe first of all what sort of agriculture is found in this area, secondly what changes have taken place to bring agriculture into its present form, and thirdly to hazard some estimation of the potential of the industry in the area.

To describe the agriculture of south and south-east Scotland adequately it is necessary to devote some space to the natural conditions which, very largely, determine the use to which land is put. The conditions met with in this area are as varied as can be found in any part of the United Kingdom, with the possible exception of the limestone uplands and black fens met with south of the Border. These varying conditions reflect the differences in soil, elevation and climate which render particular forms of land use possible or impossible and account for the almost bewildering changes in farming types and methods from district to district and even from farm to farm. It must be remembered, too, that other factors come into the picture—the way in which farm units have been evolved to give their present economic structures in terms of size, layout and capital facilities; the terms on which land is held, either by ownership or by tenure; the social and economic conditions which affect the labour situation at any time and place. All these influence the uses to which agricultural land is put and are the more general or background factors which need only be referred to briefly. They are, of course, quite important when consideration is given to the potential use of land.

The basic natural condition is the soil type. As far as this area of Scotland is concerned, most of it has been covered with glacial deposits to varying depths and the underlying strata have little significance for the surface soil except where the glacial deposits are thin or absent. Even the hill ground which takes up much of the area has been affected in this way. But this is not to say that there is any uniformity in the type of soil throughout the area as the whole range from heavy clay to light sand is met with from district to district. Indeed, soils of extremely different characteristics can be found in close proximity and under similar conditions of climate and/or elevation. The vagaries of nature have left the Scottish farmer to mould an infinite range of soil conditions and have thus contributed to the differences in farming types and methods found throughout the area.

The basic geological formations have their greatest influence on land use where they have given rise to the ranges of hills which comprise so large a part of this area of Scotland. The names of the Cheviot Hills, Ettrick Forest, Tweedsmuir and the Moorfoot, Lammermuir and Pentland Hills south of the Forth and, to the north, the Ochil, Cleish, Lomond and Sidlaw Hills and lastly, but by no means least, the Grampians, in themselves evoke mental pictures of hill and upland farms where sheep and a few cattle obtain a by no means easy living.

Generally speaking, elevation and topography and the associated climate and rainfall will determine the types of farming which would originate from the soil types. The south-east of Scotland enjoys an equable climate free (except for such occasions as the winter of 1947 and the summer of 1959) from extreme conditions during either winter or summer. But this is not to say that the climatic conditions can be relied upon at any period of the year or in any particular district. Like everything else connected with agriculture it is easy to generalise and then be faced with exceptions in every direction. There is, however, a rather marked variation in the average rainfall experienced in this area. The eastern seaboard has a relatively light average precipitation of between 25 in. and 30 in. per annum which is increased towards the west and at the higher elevations to between 40 in. and 60 in. per annum. Differences of this order entail appreciable differences in the use to which land can be put. In the higher rainfall districts more emphasis is placed on grass and livestock husbandry and less on tillage crops which are much more dependent on annual cultivations and on the absence of rain at harvest time.

Economic and social factors have also played their part in the development of land use. The fact that there are only two sizeable conurbations, Edinburgh (population 467,410) and Dundee (population 180,166), has meant that much of the farm production in the area is, ultimately, for export if only as far as Glasgow, though the importance of these two towns and the smaller ones such as Perth, Dunfermline, Hawick and Galashiels as markets for agricultural products should not be ignored. Even so, it may be argued that this importance is diminishing and that the market for agricultural (and horticultural) produce is nation wide rather than local and that such centres do not offer much in the way of protected markets for local producers. This aspect of reduced economic isolation has probably had its effects on the labour situation on farms. Vastly improved methods of communication for people as well as commodities have brought the competition of industry and urban life closer to the farm gate. The reductions in the numbers of full-time and casual workers is a significant reflection of this; equally so are the enormous strides which have been taken in farm mechanisation over the last 30 to 40 years.

CHANGES IN LAND USE

The main concern of this paper is with the use to which land is being put and how that use is operated. From this point of view physical data are likely to be more informative than any measurements in terms of monetary values, though these are ultimately significant both to the nation and the individual, and a discussion on land use should be based primarily on the extent of the changes which have taken place in cropping, types of livestock and the inputs of labour, power and raw materials—where these can be measured or indicated. These are the features which illustrate the use of farm land and which would be expected to alter or be modified in response to external pressures in so far as the basic conditions of soil, climate, etc., would allow. This latter point is of the utmost importance in an area where so much of the land is at high elevations and is subject to conditions which preclude anything but pastoral agriculture. In many districts agriculture is restricted to sheep farming only. Thus economic changes, even drastic ones, are unlikely to produce quick or radical changes in the use of such land though the methods employed may be adjusted.

At the other extreme, where soil and other conditions permit of a wide range of alternatives, the way is open to changes in both types and methods of farming. But even so the built-in rigidities of personal preference, experience, labour, capital investment, size of farm, etc., all offer opposition to radical changes in type of farming, though here methods are likely to prove much more responsive to external pressures.

The broad picture of land use in this area can be established by consideration of the distribution of the total acreage under four main headings—rough grazing, permanent grass, rotational grass and tillage.

The official statistics indicate an area of round about three and a half million acres of land in agricultural use which is being continuously encroached upon for urban, industrial social and communication developments and, to a limited extent, for forestry. However, this loss of land to other uses has only amounted to less than 1 per cent. of the total area since 1945. This loss has, however, fallen very largely on the better arable land adjacent to urban centres and represents a loss of over 52,000 acres, or nearly 4½

TABLE I

*Land Utilisation—South-east Scotland,** 1939, 1945, 1958

	Total Acreage	Percentage Distribution			
		Rough Grazing	Permanent Grass	Rotational Grass	Tillage
	'000 acres	%	%	%	%
1939	3,521	56·7	15·0	12·1	16·2
1945	3,528	57·5	9·0	11·0	22·5
1958	3,499	57·5	10·5	13·5	18·5

* For this table the whole of Perthshire has been included in the south-east area though only the eastern part comes within the ambit of the East of Scotland College.

per cent. of the total arable land. The really interesting point arising from these figures is the very restricted extent to which the broad picture of land use was affected during this period. In round figures the proportion of rough grazing remained unaltered at 57 per cent. of the total acreage under crops and grass. The suggestion is that the natural conditions relating to this type of land are such as to completely inhibit any major modification in its use, even in response to wartime requirements for maximum food production. Where the cropping (and rough grazing must be regarded as a crop in the context of land use) has remained unaltered, the inference is that production would remain similar in type and quantity, or with only slow change in quantity. It is when attention is focused on the other sections of cropping that the responses to changing economic and political environment become more noticeable. Ploughing-out during the war entailed considerable inroads into the acreage of permanent grass, its percentage of the total fell from 15·0 to 9·0 per cent.; this was equivalent to a reduction of some 40 per cent. in the acreage of permanent grass itself and represented a transfer of some 213,000 acres to other forms of usage. Similarly there was a reduction of approximately 38,500 acres in the acreage under rotational grass; this represented about 9 per cent. of the 1939 acreage but was not more than 1 per cent. of the total agricultural land. The restricted nature of this transfer must be accepted as indicating the importance of rotational grass in the cropping systems practised in this area—a form of resistance to change which emanates from an established system of arable farming at a relatively high level of crop husbandry.

The converse of these changes is to be seen in the increased acreage of tillage crops in 1945. These had been increased from 16·2 per cent. to 22·5 per cent. of the total acreage. The tillage acreage itself increased by 39 per cent. between 1939 and 1945.

Since 1945 the broad picture has reverted to a position somewhere about midway between pre-war and the immediately post-war positions, with rather more emphasis on intensive grassland usage as represented by rotational grass. There has been some reversion to permanent grass and the temptation is to ascribe this to the laying down to permanent grass of land which should never have been ploughed out or which it is difficult to continue under an arable rotation. The overall position of the arable sector in 1958 was that the acreage had been reduced from 33·5 per cent. in 1945 to 32·0 per cent. in 1958. It is difficult to suggest that a change of this order represents any significant

TABLE II

Farm Types in South-east Scotland, 1947*

A. *Numbers, Size and Cropping Distribution of Major Farm Types*

	Hill Sheep	Stock Rearing	Rearing and Feeding	Cropping	Dairy	All Farms
Number of Farms . .	538	953	1319	3088	1255	—
Average acreage per farm .	2704	391	466	211	192	—
Distribution of Crops	%	%	%	%	%	%
Rough Grazing . .	96·5	64·5	32·5	6·0	12·5	57·5
Permanent Grass . .	2·5	12·5	16·5	9·5	25·0	9·0
Rotational Grass . .	·5	10·5	24·0	24·5	24·5	12·5
Tillage . . .	·5	12·5	27·0	60·0	38·0	21·0
	100·0	100·0	100·0	100·0	100·0	100·0
Proportion of Total Area .	42·5	11·0	18·0	19·0	7·0 }	
,, ,, ,, ,, .	Dairy with Hill Sheep (41 Farms)				2·0 }	100·0
,, ,, ,, ,, .	Other Types (Specialised, 651 Farms)				·5 }	

B. *Livestock Numbers per Farm and per* 100 *Acres*

Type of Farm	Dairy Cattle Per farm	Dairy Cattle Per 100 acres	Beef Cattle Per farm	Beef Cattle Per 100 acres	Breeding Sheep Per farm	Breeding Sheep Per 100 acres	Other Sheep Per farm	Other Sheep Per 100 acres	Pigs Per farm	Pigs Per 100 acres	Poultry Per farm	Poultry Per 700 acres
Hill Sheep	7	—	23	1	990	37	441	16	1	—	82	3
Stock Rearing	15	4	24	6	151	39	109	28	3	1	135	35
Rearing and Feeding	8	2	55	12	232	50	233	50	6	1	140	30
Cropping	5	2	28	13	29	14	35	17	8	4	115	54
Dairy	56	29	3	1	25	13	29	15	3	1	107	56

* Adapted from data in *Types of Farming in Scotland.*

divergence from the pattern established by the requirements for maximum output during the war and post-war years and continued by the pricing system of subsequent years. One of the basic principles of this system is to induce modifications in methods aiming at higher efficiency rather than imposing drastic changes in types of farming—although changes in type of farming are not necessarily outwith the objects of the system.

FARMING TYPES

Farming types in the area have been classified using the nature of the farm output as the primary basis[1] and while there must be an obvious correlation between the nature of the farm output and the soil and other natural conditions under which farms operate, there can be no sharp demarcation between areas of farm types. Conditions merge and change and so do farming types, and even where the type of farming is broadly the same, there may be significant differences between farms. For example, a hill sheep farm capable of carrying a Cheviot flock is not the same as a "black hill" farm restricted to the Blackface breed, though both would be classified in the same general group. Where conditions allow greater latitude in cropping and livestock policies, the problems of realistic classification are multiplied. For general purposes the classification into a limited number of major "types" is adequate for this discussion of land use. The figures in Tables I and II give the salient facts concerning the numbers, average size and distribution of cropping and livestock in these types. The location of the types follows, in general terms, the physical features of the area but becoming more intermingled as conditions, including economic, allow greater choice to the individual farmer.

Taken together, the two Tables show the principal differences between the major farm types. The extensive hill sheep farms with a relatively simple economy, mainly sheep with some cattle, have a low level of land usage in terms of stock carried per 100 acres. The variations then proceed on expanding lines via changes in the relative importance of categories of livestock and of crops grown until on the cropping and the dairy farms land usage is at a high level. In the former case the emphasis is more on crops for sale; in the latter on crops, both tillage and grass, for feeding.

The distribution of cropping in 1958 shown in Table I corresponds very closely with that of 1945 and, indeed, with that of 1939, and it is a fair assumption that, were the farms in this area reclassified on the same basis at the present time, it would show no significant change in the broad pattern of land use.

The changes in land use which have taken place since 1939 are more a question of objectives and methods rather than any alteration in the basic pattern. The proportion of rough grazing has remained unaltered, a small proportion has been added back to permanent grass, but the arable land, at 32 per cent. of the total, is slightly higher than the pre-war total of 28 per cent. The inference is that it has not been easy to modify the overall pattern of land use though there have been marked variations within this. For example, although the arable land only increased from 28 per cent. to 33·5 per cent. of the total after five years of war, tillage crops increased from 16 per cent. to 22·5 per cent. of the total agricultural land. This meant an increase of more than one-third in the area available for cash cropping. Since 1945 economic and political conditions have been such as to maintain and even develop the post-war pattern rather than produce a swing back to the pre-war situation. This view is substantiated by consideration of the details of the changes in acreages of crops and numbers of livestock on farms in this area which are given in Tables III and V.

TABLE III

Cropping Changes, South-east Scotland—Principal Crops as Percentage of Total Arable

	1939	1945	1958
	%	%	%
Wheat	6·5	6·5	5·5
Barley	5·0	10·5	12·0
Oats	23·0	24·5	19·0
Potatoes	7·5	10·0	7·5
Sugar Beet	·5	1·0	1·5
Turnips	11·0	10·0	7·5
Rotational Grass	43·0	33·0	42·5

By 1945 the three principal grain crops occupied an increased share of the extended arable acreage; barley showed the greatest individual increase. Potatoes, too, had increased and the small acreage of sugar beet had doubled its share. Turnips had been reduced slightly in importance, but the greatest reduction was in the case of rotational grass.

Thirteen years of post-war conditions have produced changes in emphasis on particular crops. Interest in wheat has declined slightly and there has been a marked decline in the importance of the oat crop; against these the barley crop has become of greater importance. The potato crop has been trimmed to its pre-war status in terms of acreage, but sugar beet has flourished up to the limit of processing capacity. The decline in the turnip crop has continued, while the rotational grasses are back to the 1939 level. To repeat—there have been changes in emphasis within the pattern of land use rather than radical overall changes.

A factor which must be considered at this point is the extent to which intensity of land use may have changed. This can be illustrated in two ways, by considering the yields of the various crops and by considering the numbers of livestock which are now being carried on farms in this area. It is common knowledge that crop yields are now heavier than was the case prior to the war, though official statistics do not provide all-round conclusive evidence of this. Averages of the county yields for the principal crops for the ten-year periods 1934-43 and 1948-57 are given in Table IV.

TABLE IV

Average (10-year) Crop Yields

	1934-43	1948-57	Change
	cwt.	cwt.	%
Wheat	22·4	24·3	+8·5
Barley	20·6	24·4	+18·5
Oats	17·5	20·0	+14·0
Hay	37·4	36·4	−2·5
	Tons	Tons	
Potatoes	7·5	8·1	+8·0
Turnips	18·0	19·3	+7·0

In view of the fact that the above figures represent averages of 10 years it is possible that current yields are actually higher than those for 1948-57, and it is difficult to accept the suggestion that yields of hay per acre are now lower than pre-war. It must be accepted in general terms that intensity of land use has shown a very considerable increase over the last 25 years.

The numbers of livestock carried in this area provide additional evidence. The figures in Table V show how stock numbers have fluctuated along with the changes in the acreages of cropping.

TABLE V

Indices of Livestock Numbers in South-east Scotland

	1939 Number ('000s)	1939 Index No.	1945 Index No.	1958 Index No.
Dairy and Breeding Cattle	97	100	118	159
Total Cattle	313	100	106	141
Breeding Sheep	724	100	82	91
Other Sheep	1,062	100	81	93
Breeding Pigs	12	100	76	229
Total Pigs	90	100	81	216
Total Poultry	1,763	100	79	102

With the exception of dairy cattle there were considerable reductions in the numbers of livestock carried on farms in this area during the wartime period. Priority was given to crop sales off the farm and there is no doubt that the restrictions imposed on agriculture in every way inhibited the development of intensification in the usual economic sense. In the context of these restrictions farmers in the area did a remarkable job of work. Since 1945, and particularly after the era of direct control came to an end and development and intensification could proceed, the upsurge in livestock numbers, associated with maintaining a high level of crop husbandry, speaks for itself. To the actual increases in numbers must be added the continued improvements which are taking place in the breeding and nutritional aspects of both livestock and crop husbandry.

The present situation may be summarised by quoting estimates of the volume of output from Scottish farms and making the not unwarranted assumption that farmers in the south-east have contributed at least as much as their contemporaries elsewhere.

Indices of the value of the net output of Scottish Agriculture at constant prices[2]

Pre-war, 100. 1943-44, 136. 1957-58, 158

In so far as it is possible to reduce a comparison of the total volume of produce going off Scottish farms to the confines of a single concept, they are now producing well over half as much again as was the case prior to the war.

An increase such as this cannot, of course, be achieved without some modifications in the factors of production which are part and parcel of the farming scene. Imports of feeding stuffs, seeds and store cattle are allowed for in the foregoing calculation of net output and the increase shown must be mainly attributed to the quantities of other inputs and the ways in which they have been used—in so far as these can be measured or dissociated from the overriding importance of the management factor. Pre-eminent amongst these other inputs are labour and power, and considerable changes have taken place in these.

Table VI shows the numbers of the various categories of workers in south-east Scotland for the three years chosen for comparative purposes.

TABLE VI

Numbers of Workers in South-east Scotland

	1939	1945	1958
Regular Workers:			
Male, over 21	20,840	21,379	20,240
Male, under 21	5,509	5,142	3,092
Male, Total	26,349	26,521	24,151*
Female, Total	3,433	5,828	4,073*
Casual Workers:			
Male	2,885	4,847	2,230
Female	2,407	3,503	2,135
Total Workers	35,074	40,699	32,589

* Including "Part-time" regular workers.

The expansion of production up to 1945 under conditions which precluded any great modification of methods through further mechanisation (with the notable exception of the rapid increase in the use of tractors, both privately owned and in the hands of private and official contracting agencies) and at a time when much of the labour available could not have been of first-class quality, e.g. P.O.W. and Women's Land Army, meant that, numerically, the labour force had to be increased substantially. This was particularly the case with male casual and with both regular and casual female workers. The present position is that a still higher level of production has been achieved on the basis of reduced numbers of all categories of workers with one exception—regular male workers over 21 years of age. Significant changes have been the reduced numbers of young men in regular employment, the much fewer women in regular work on farms and the sharp drop in casual workers of all types. There appears to be the necessity for a hard core of experienced, regular workers but these now have a highly developed array of tools at their disposal which enables them not only to cope with the share of the work which previously fell to them, but also to absorb a considerable part of the work previously done by the casual employee.

The developments which have taken place in mechanisation since the war can be illustrated by reference to the numbers of some of the principal power units and machines used on Scottish farms. Numbers alone cannot measure the significance of mechanisation—evolution has meant increased efficiency in all aspects of mechanisation. Again the official figures for Scotland may be taken as a guide to what has happened in the south-east area.

TABLE VII

Mechanisation on Scottish Farms

	1942 No.	1958 No.
Working Horses	100,000	12,000
Tractors—Tracklaying	329	2,290
Wheeled	12,589	54,339
Combined Seed-Fert. Drills	701	5,828
Binders	28,400	26,915
Combine Harvesters	52	3,365
Sugar Beet Harvesters	—	339
Potato Harvesters	—	122
Pick-up Balers	—	4,658
Grain Driers	—	1,104
Milking Machines	5,648	12,294

The dramatic changes in the numbers of horses and tractors and the equally dramatic development of all types of harvesting machinery reflect the alterations which have taken place in the labour-power situation. In addition, there have been immense strides in the use of electric power for a wide range of operations and much, too, has been done to reorganise building layout and in the construction of new types of buildings to enhance labour efficiency. The face, if not the pattern, of farming has changed indeed!

One other factor which is important in relation to intensity of farming is the general level of manuring, and some indication of the extent to which applications of artificial manures have been increased in recent years is provided by a recent report issued by the Fertiliser Manufacturers' Association, Limited.[3] The report refers to usage of artificial manures in the United Kingdom but there is no reason to think that farmers in the south-east of Scotland have not participated to the same extent as farmers elsewhere in the increased use of manures. The relevant paragraphs of the report may be quoted:

> ". . . potash fertilisers have risen from an estimated 40,000 tons K_2O in 1938 to approximately 350,000 tons K_2O in 1957-58."
>
> "The 315,000 tons of nitrogen consumed in U.K. in 1957-58 compare with the 1938-39 delivery figure of just over 50,000 tons, whilst total P_2O_5 usage has increased at a slower pace, from 195,000 tons in 1938-39 to 345,000 tons in 1945-46 largely as a result of a trebling of superphosphate production. In 1957-58 386,000 tons P_2O_5 were consumed."

In short, the present day usage of artificial fertilisers has shown the following increases compared with pre-war:

Nitrogen by	530 per cent.
Phosphate by	98 per cent.
Potash by	775 per cent.

It is common knowledge that applications of lime have increased by leaps and bounds, and to this must be added an increase in the available dung consequent upon heavier crop production and increased numbers of livestock.

There is one further aspect related to land usage and its potentialities and that is the number and size of agricultural units in the south-east of Scotland and the extent to which these units are operated by tenants or owner-occupiers. It has been said that the face of farming has changed but that the overall pattern has not been modified to any great extent. What of the basic structure, the size and tenure of farms? Table VIII gives the numbers of farms in selected size groups at 1945 and 1958.

TABLE VIII

Numbers of Farms in South-east Scotland

Farm Size acres	1945 No.	1958 No.	Change %
1-15	4,908	3,641	−26
15-30	1,129	803	−29
30-100	3,083	2,460	−20
100-300	3,680	3,447	−6
Over 300	1,279	1,405	+10
Total	14,079	11,756	−17

The figures suggest that in this area of Scotland more than one-quarter of the holdings up to 30 acres in size have been absorbed into larger units since 1945 or the land has been lost to agriculture; of the medium-sized farms one-fifth no longer exist as separate units. Farms of between 100 and 300 acres have shown a relatively slight reduction in numbers while the larger farms have shown an increase of one-tenth in number. The changed economic and technical environment of farming in this area does appear to have brought about an appreciable change in the size distribution of farms. This should be conducive to the more efficient application of modern farm technology, but the real extent of these changes and the factors which have contributed to them call for more detailed investigation than is possible in this brief survey.

Changes have also taken place in the numbers of farms in the hands of owner-occupiers which have increased considerably during the years since 1945. In that year slightly more than one-quarter of the holdings were owner-occupied; by 1958 the proportion had risen to over 45 per cent. As far as the different size groups are concerned, the rate of increase of owner-occupiers was substantially the same, indicating that the change in status had been widespread. In so far as owner-occupancy is likely to provide encouragement for high farming, this movement should be welcomed. On the other hand, it may well be that owner-occupancy, which could result in a shortage of working capital, might lead to low farming. This is another aspect of farming which requires further investigation.

POTENTIALITIES OF FARMING

This survey of the agricultural environment, farming conditions and structure and the changes which have taken place in the south-east of Scotland may be summarised as follows. This is an area which includes a wide range of farming types consequent upon very variable conditions of soil, elevation, topography, climate and, to some extent, economic situation. As with farms in any part of the United Kingdom, farms in this area have been subjected to pressures, direct and indirect, which have brought about relatively little change in the overall pattern of rough grazings, permanent grass, rotational grass and tillage. In the sphere of general organisation there have been changes in numbers and sizes of farms and in the numbers of owner-occupiers. There is at least a tendency to conform with the requirements of modern technology which call for the economies of scale in farming as in other industries; there has been an appreciable move towards bringing the property in land as well as its operation under single control.

There have been changes of emphasis within the broad pattern in both livestock and cropping policies on farms in the area and these have been accompanied by the incorporation of new ideas and practices into the economy of farming. With these and with the changes in inputs of labour and power, with building extensions and improvements and with all the modifications in cultural practices it is not too much to claim that farming in this area is on a substantially higher plane than either before or after the war.

All this poses the more speculative problem of the potentialities of land use in this area. An historical survey, complex enough when it is necessary to follow widely differing but interdependent trends, is relatively easy. There is at least some factual information. Looking ahead entails consideration of all the imponderables—the general economic and political situation in the years to come, the further development of mechanisation and agricultural technology generally and the extent to which optimum use can be made of such developments in the existing structure of farm sizes and tenure, the capacity of the land to respond still further to intensive usage and (of supreme importance) the capacity of farmers generally to make full use of all the opportunities which may be offered to them. There are no facts to even suggest the answers, but, in the main, the problem is one of building up increased output in relation to a fixed or even dwindling area of farm land.

In the context of the potentialities of land use any consideration of the economic environment is beside the point—an improvement of the economic situation as it affected farmers could stimulate further production, a worsening would, ultimately, lead to a reduction. Thus potentialities have no reality unless the assumption is made that economic conditions remain favourable. It goes without saying that there will be progress in every aspect of technology, the difficulty will be in making the optimum use of such developments in the absence of flexibility in the structure of the industry, but at least there will be some measure of improvement in farming methods and hence a greater potential.

There remain the two basic factors—the capacity of the land and the capacity of the farmers; as far as the latter is concerned it is only possible to express an opinion. As the arts of husbandry become more and more impregnated with the knowledge of the scientists there is no reason to believe that farmers generally will do other than they have done in the past—incorporate the new knowledge into current practice.

The capacity of the land to produce more may be gauged to some extent by the differences in output which exist at present between farms of similar types and working under similar conditions. Economic data collected from farms in this area show such differences of output which are usually, but not invariably, associated with differences in profit. On the assumption that high profit (the final expression of good management) and high output go together, the differences between the outputs of high-profit farms and those of farms of average profitability should indicate the minimum scope of the potential which exists under present conditions. The following figures show such comparisons for the 1958-59 cropping year:

TABLE IX

Output per Acre of South-east Scotland Farms, 1958-59

Type of Farm	Average Farms	High-profit Farms	Potential
	£	£	%
Upland Farms (extensive rough grazing)	4·8	6·4	+33
Upland Farms (moderate rough grazing)	10·9	13·0	+19
Livestock Farms (sheep important)	21·9	17·7	−16
Livestock Farms (mixed cattle and sheep)	24·0	30·7	+28
Arable Farms with Livestock	26·1	29·3	+13
Dairy Farms with cash crops	59·9	68·1	+14
Dairy Farms cash crops unimportant	43·1	47·5	+10

Figures such as these may be criticised as an oversimplification of the situation, but in every category but one high output and high profit have gone together. In other words, land use has been pushed to higher levels within the ambit of prevailing economic conditions and it is at least feasible to suggest that the average run of farms could also realise a much higher output. In the case of specialised livestock farms such as the dairy farms in the above Table, it is possible that high output is a function of purchased feed rather than of the land potential, but with most types of farms high output is largely obtained from the labour, machinery, seeds, manures and management applied to the land and realised either as direct crop sales or via the medium of livestock. In terms of ordinary common sense there appears to be a substantial part of the potential output of farm land which is not being realised at the present time. If the possible future increase in potential is added to this, there is an almost unavoidable temptation to plump for a figure of 20 per cent. to 25 per cent. increase in output as the measure of the potential which could be realised through the more effective use of the agricultural land in the south-east of Scotland.

REFERENCES

1. *Types of Farming in Scotland.* D.O.A.S., 1952.
2. *Scottish Agricultural Economics*, Vol. IX, D.O.A.S., 1958.
3. Fertiliser Report and Statistics, 1959.

Agriculture and its Possibilities

WEST OF SCOTLAND

J. A. Gilchrist, B.SC., N.D.A., N.D.D.
The West of Scotland Agricultural College, Glasgow

[One of three Scottish Regional papers, the others being "East and South East Scotland" (p. 249) and "North Scotland" (p. 276).]

Province of West of Scotland Agricultural College

Livestock farming, rather than cash-crop farming, is the essential feature of south-west Scotland. Overall, the agriculture is built round the dairy cow, the hill or upland ewe and, of recent years, the hill cow. Beef production is relatively unimportant. The main variations are the early potato growing of the south coastal areas, the seed and "ware" potato growing of western Perthshire and the horticulture of Clydeside.

Within the province lies the Clyde conurbation with a population of around two million people: the largest food market in Scotland. Milk supplies come almost wholly from local production. For all other foods, supplies from other parts of Scotland, from south of the Border and from overseas, play an important part. As elsewhere, urban food consumption habits are moving into new patterns.

Marked changes in the key types of farming in the immediate future are unlikely. The trends in production for the staple commodities will depend mainly on political and economic decisions regarding the place of U.K. agriculture and its branches in the national economy. At farm level, the possibilities to be examined are the technical and organisational factors which will lower production costs.

THE FARMING AND THE FARMS

(The Appendix contains some statistics for the province)

Land Utilisation

The College province is made up of 11 counties plus the western part of Perthshire. (The Agricultural Statistics for Scotland are issued as county totals, and as a break-up of Perthshire is not possible from the published data, most of the statistics given exclude West Perth.)

The total farming land ("Crops and Grass" plus "Rough Grazing") for the 11 counties is about 4¾ million acres. (Bringing in West Perth makes the province not far short of one-third of Scotland.) Of this, some 3⅓ million acres are classed as Rough Grazings, and about 1⅓ million acres as Crops and Grass (i.e. the low-ground farming area and the improved foothill land). Of the Crops and Grass area, in 1958 rather less than ¾ million acres were Arable Land (i.e. Tillage and Temporary Grass) and about ⅔ million acres were Permanent Grass. Over the 11 counties, grassland and grazings (on the low ground, on the foothills, and on the rough grazing lands) made up 94 per cent. of the area. From another viewpoint, about 21 per cent. of the Crops and Grass area is under the plough. These proportions suggest that livestock farming is far more important than cash cropping. In fact, the province grows only about 9 per cent. of the wheat, 7 per cent. of the barley and 14 to 15 per cent. of the maincrop potatoes in Scotland. Overall, the land under the plough—with the exception of the potato acreage and a little wheat—is almost wholly for stock feed, with oats and turnips the two most important crops. On the mown grassland areas, the hay crop is, as yet, by far and away more important than the grass silage crop.

On the livestock side, the province carries slightly over 40 per cent. of the cattle and almost 40 per cent. of the breeding ewes of Scotland, also about 25 per cent. of the breeding sows, adult fowls and turkeys. On the rough grazings, the hill ewe is the keystone of the farming, but there has been some increase in the production of beef calves from cows on hill farms. Elsewhere the greater part of the low ground fodder crops and grazings go towards the production of milk and replacement (or surplus) dairy stock. (We carry slightly over two-thirds of the dairy cows in Scotland and three-quarters of the replacement dairy stock.) Low-ground or park ewes (as distinct from hill ewes) also contribute to the livestock output.

Our share of the horticultural output of Scotland includes (by acreage) one-quarter of the strawberries, more than half of the black-currants and gooseberries, somewhat less than two-thirds of the orchard area and more than two-thirds of the area under glass.

Relative Importance of the Types of Farm

Information supplied by the Department of Agriculture for Scotland (from their 1956 Classification of Farms) illustrates, in another way, the relative importance of the farming types. The College province (including West Perth) contained 11,098 "full-time farms", plus 3,752 "part-time" farms. Dealing only with "full-time" farms, 6,327 were Dairy Farms, 1,354 were Upland Rearing Farms and 1,013 were Hill Sheep Farms. Adding 348 "intensive" Pig and/or Poultry Farms these types together make up 81 per cent. of "full-time" farms. In addition, 1,042 farms were classed as Livestock with Arable Farms and only 390 as Cropping Farms.

Farming Regions

The farming type regions are as follows:

Hill Sheep or Upland Stock-Rearing. (i) Most of Argyll; Upland and hill parts of Bute, North Dumbarton, North Stirling and North-west Perth. (ii) The central belt from Dumbarton to beyond Gleneagles, with "green" hills more common. (iii) The Southern Uplands, which make up a large part of the land area in Lanark, Dumfries and Ayr and extend into Renfrew, Kirkcudbright and Wigtown.

Cash Cropping (linked mainly with non-dairy farming). Lowground West Perth; parts of Stirling and Clackmannan; Clyde Valley "terrace" area of Renfrew; Solway district of Dumfries.

Dairying. Lowground Bute and Dunbarton; parts of Stirling and Clackmannan; the lowground and foothill areas of all other counties.

Small Livestock. A glance at the "small livestock" position is necessary. The great bulk of the eggs produced come from farm-flocks, generally in the 100 to 300 bird range and, today, housed mainly in laying cages or on "deep litter". In addition there are the specialist flocks on smallholdings or on small areas of land. Overall, pig-meat production, especially the "fattening" side, tends to be concentrated on a small number of farms (or holdings) in relatively large units, rather than widespread in small lots.

Horticulture. The main commercial development is on Clydeside, beginning slightly up-river from Hamilton and stretching to Lanark. There is also some production in Renfrewshire and in the vicinity of Ayr.

Within these broad outlines, there is little detail to add. Stirling (on the "heavy" carse land) produces Timothy grass seed for sale, and North Ayrshire produces some ryegrass seed for sale. In West Perth seed potatoes are important, while coastal Ayrshire (and to a lesser extent, coastal Wigtownshire) produce early potatoes.

FARM ORGANISATION AND MANAGEMENT

Size of Unit

Judged by the size of cow herds, dairy farms in the whole central belt—from Dumbarton round to Ayr and in North Dumfries—lie in the 30 to 40 cow herd group. For the West Highland area, the average cow herd is rather smaller. In Wigtown and Kirkcudbright there are a considerable number of large herds of 75 cows and over.

In the hill sheep-farming areas, there is a wide range of size, from say 250 ewes to 1,000 to 1,500 or more, or say 750 acres to 5,000 acres. Generally, the upland stock-rearing farms are smaller, say 300 to 700 acres. The more specialist cropping farms are usually around or over 200 acres, but some of the farms which combine livestock (and small livestock) with potato growing lie in the 100 to 175 acre size group.

Labour

On a large proportion of the farms, the farmer combines the duties of management with an active part in the day-to-day work. Also, male family labour is everywhere important.

The number of regular hired workers on farms continues to decline, with, as far as field work is concerned, mechanisation as one of the causes.

Salaried management is relatively uncommon. Profit-sharing is virtually absent, but some farms pay incentive bonuses to dairy labour.

Capital and Tenure

It is not possible to deal fully with the many aspects of ownership capital and tenancy capital, including the increasing capital requirements as mechanisation spreads. As regards tenure, there has been an increase in the number of owner-occupiers. The sale value of farms is higher than at any time since the war and borrowing on mortgage is common. Bank overdraft borrowing for tenancy capital is probably higher than ever before, while hire-purchase, particularly for tractors and motor vehicles, is now common. On the fixed capital aspect, the assistance given by the State, as grants under the Livestock Rearing Act, Farm Improvement Schemes, the recent Small Farmer Scheme and Horticultural Scheme, has to be noted.

Mechanisation has brought large and continuing capital outlays. Although the investment in our province in grain-handling equipment is considerably less than in the east, tractors, dung-spreading equipment, more modern milking equipment and hay balers are common while, at present, forage-harvesters are increasing quickly. Milk-tanks for bulk handling are the latest innovation with the number of bulk-tanks installed, or applied for, now close to 600.

THE PRODUCTS

The Dairy Farm

Measured by value of the output and by the resources employed in production, milk easily takes first place as the main product. The production of milk has, as elsewhere, increased. The 11 counties sold (for the fresh milk or manufacturing markets) about 103 million gallons in 1938-39; in 1948-49 this had risen to about 120 million gallons; last year (1959-60) the figure was 161¾ million gallons. Of the milk sold off farms in the province now, slightly more than half goes direct to the fresh-milk market and slightly less than half to manufacture—cheese, condensed milk, butter, fresh-cream, etc.

The marketing side is organised by the Scottish Milk Marketing Board. Of the total milk handled (administratively and/or physically) by the Board, the College province contributes about 80 per cent.

The overall pattern of seasonality of production is that the largest quantities are available in the March to September period, with the height of the grass season—May and June—usually the peak months. It is during the spring and summer months that manufacture is most active. The milk manufactured in 1958-59 (over the whole S.M.M.B. area) was converted as follows:

Cheese (including farm cheese)	32·6 million gallons
Condensed milks	23·2 million gallons
Butter	18·7 million gallons
Cream	2·3 million gallons
Full Cream Milk Powder	·3 million gallons
	77·1 million gallons

In brief, the S.M.M.B.'s pricing arrangements, as they affect the numerically most important "wholesaling" farms, mean the pooling of receipts from fresh and manufacturing milk, the addition of the subsidy to bring the per gallon return, over the year, up to the guaranteed price (on a standard quantity), and the deduction of a haulage rate. In this connection the important points are (i) that the fresh milk market gives the highest per gallon return, (ii) that the manufacturing markets give lower prices per gallon and (iii) the standard quantity, i.e. the guaranteed price is not paid on unlimited gallonages. Thus, unless fresh consumption and total farm production increase "in step", increasing milk production (or low cheese and butter prices) lead to a lower per gallon price to the producer.

Keeping in mind the reputation of the Ayrshire cow and also that many farms rear more than the needed number of replacements, there has been a considerable export trade, into England, of milk stock. A more recent development, partly due to A.I. facilities provided by the S.M.M.B., is the production of beef-type calves from dairy herds by crossing with Shorthorn, Galloway, Friesian or Hereford. These cross calves may be sold a few days after birth or carried, on the producing farm, until sale at various stages—store or fat. Part, if not most, of this new development is due to the subsidy on beef-type calves.

The Hill Farms and Upland Stock-rearing Farms

The most clear-cut type is where the stock carried, with the exception of a few milking-type "house cows", is wholly sheep. Generally, except for a fringe part of Dumfriesshire, the ewe stocks are of the Blackface breed, bred pure to give Blackface lambs. Cropping may be absent or limited to some hay-making. As the ratio of beef-type cows to ewes rises, the hill farm becomes more "mixed", and generally more cropping—to provide "winter keep"—is done, although here again, especially in the deep glens, hay (and/or grass silage) may be the only source of home fodder. On farms with more low ground, oats, hay (or silage) and turnips (or silage) may be grown. On the true "hill farm", fodder available generally goes to cows, with calves being sold off, at about 6 months old, in the autumn. The upland stock-rearing farm is smaller, crops more, carries a closer ratio of cattle to sheep and may often have enough fodder to carry calves over a winter into the stirk stage for sale in the spring, or in the autumn at about 18 months old.

Of the total ewes in the 11 counties, hill ewes (attracting subsidy) make up about 72 per cent. of total ewes, leaving 28 per cent. as park ewes.

The contribution of this farming group to national food and raw material supplies is partly direct and partly at second hand. Depending on locality, quality of grazing, etc., varying proportions of the lambs are sold fat for immediate slaughter, but, overall, most of them (and most of the cattle) are sold store for fattening elsewhere. Surplus ewe lambs and the better draft ewes are sold to the lower uplands or low ground to give replacement breeding stocks. Wool from the Blackface flocks is almost wholly for coarser manufactures, e.g. the carpet trade.

Wool, marketed through the British Wool Marketing Board, carries a guaranteed price. There is no direct subsidy assistance for store sheep, but store prices are, of course, influenced by the supported mutton and lamb prices. A hill-sheep subsidy is paid following years of unusually low farm "net income". On the hill-cattle side, a subsidy is paid on cows carried mainly on rough land and a calf subsidy on beef-type calves. Again, store cattle prices are influenced by the supported fat cattle prices.

Pig Meat

As elsewhere, the three types of organisation are found—breeding to sell as weaners or stores; buying weaners or stores to fatten; combining breeding and fattening. Some of the traditional factors localising pig husbandry have disappeared and often the presence or absence of the pig enterprise follows personal inclination.

For Scotland generally, the proportion of pigs going to the bacon market is higher than for England and Wales. Fresh pork consumption is greater than before the war, although it is unlikely that the rise in pork consumption has been as high here as south of the Border. Fat pig prices are supported.

Eggs and Poultry Meat

The 11 county statistics for "total fowls" (an index, compared with 100 in 1939, of 101 in 1958 and 103 in 1959) suggest, if the increase in broiler birds is kept in mind, that the total egg production flock is little larger than pre-war, although there are variations between counties. But, with increased yield per bird, the total output must be higher. Although there are some large- and medium-scale broiler enterprises, the total development is probably less than in some other parts of Scotland.

The turkey flock has risen (index of 162 in 1958 and 224 in 1959 compared with 100 in 1939).

Egg prices are supported, but not poultry meat.

Beef

This product has been referred to partly under beef production from cattle on the hill farm and partly under dairy beef. These (plus the cast stock from the dairy herds) are the main sources of store beef cattle or fat cattle in the province. Although Irish stores are imported through West of Scotland ports and some remain in the province for finishing, the majority, after sale, go further east. The practice of farms buying beef-type calves (often Friesian bullock calves) is increasing and some of these calves are brought up from England. Generally the amount of beef production from single-suckled calves on low-ground farms is small. It is most commonly linked with pedigree breeding.

Two figures regarding beef production are of interest. Over the whole province the number of cows qualifying for the hill-cow subsidy has risen from about 25,500 in 1951 to about 46,500 in 1959. Also, in the province in 1959, some 92,000 calves qualified for the calf subsidy compared with 50,000 in 1955.

Fat cattle prices are supported.

Crops

The importance of the "Ayrshire" early potato to the trade during the high summer months is well known. On the "seed" side, West Perth produces important quantities, some for export to England, while there is some development of seed growing in Dumfries. There is a large import of maincrop "ware" into the province from eastern Scotland. The Potato Marketing Board has all Britain as its fields of operation.

Little wheat is grown (the "millable" type is likely to be used for the biscuit trade). Some of the barley grown is fed direct, on the farm, to pigs.

The Carse of Stirling, a hay-exporting area, has a place in filling the fodder requirements of some of the hill farms.

The cereal prices are supported.

Horticulture

In the Clyde Valley area most types of vegetables are grown (generally on a "holding" scale rather than on a "farm" scale), but there must be a considerable import into the province from eastern Scotland and from England. In the past, for the glass area, the tomato crop was all important, but for various reasons some diversification has taken, and is taking place, e.g. lettuce, chrysanthemums and bulb flowers. Strawberry growing, because of disease, has had a chequered history, but the crop—as a dessert fruit or for jam—is still important. Flower bulb growing in some of the Argyllshire islands is now in post-experiment stage.

Horticultural products are not subject to price support.

THE TECHNICAL AND MANAGEMENT BACKGROUND

With regard to possibilities, it is necessary to look at the background. Since 1914, agriculture in the U.K. has been subject to constant change, with the periods from the mid-1920s to 1939 and again from 1945 to date especially notable. The decade before the 1939-45 War saw the adoption into agricultural practice of the results of some of the earlier research and investigations—animal nutrition, animal health, plant breeding, fertiliser use, etc. Mechanisation—mainly the use of tractors and cultivation machinery—was broadening down from the larger units. During and since the 1939-45 War, the rate of change has accelerated, with mechanisation in field and steading, better crop and grass varieties, better control of animal and plant diseases and fairly stable guaranteed or support prices, production grants, capital grants, etc., all playing a part. Crop yields are higher, with oats showing the lowest rate of increase among the cereal crops. Most vegetable crops and tomatoes are giving higher yields. This increased production of both farm and market garden crops is associated partly with increased use of fertilisers and better disease and weed control. Grassland husbandry over Britain as a whole has markedly improved since 1939. Dairy cattle yields have risen, as have egg yields. Overall, the agriculture of 1960 is giving markedly higher gross output, and in some cases higher net output, per acre or per man, than in 1939.

On the management and organisational sides the average level of thinking is also higher than it was, due partly to the spur of rising wage rates. As the older men move out a mechanically minded generation moves in, most of whom have had the benefits of membership of the Young Farmers' Clubs, and many of whom are not unacquainted with the "efficiency standards" of the farm economist—gross and net output per acre and per man; profit per acre; profit per layer, etc.

It is not possible for me to say how highly one would rate the south-west on each and all of these points, but the farmers of the area have not been passive. The important point is that possibilities can only be considered in relation not to a static industry but to one which is alive and on the whole intensely interested in modern developments, some of which entail some shift of emphasis from the production to the marketing side.

INDUSTRIAL AND SOCIAL BACKGROUND

Within the Clyde conurbation lies Scotland's main market; at least two million people. No statistics are available as to total food consumption within this area and the other towns and villages of the province, nor on the proportions of consumption which are met from within the province, or from other parts of the U.K., or from Commonwealth and foreign countries overseas. Except for fresh milk and early potatoes, however, food imports into the province must play a large part in providing the bill of fare. The contributions from other parts of Scotland are impossible to assess, but must include considerable quantities of north-country eggs and turkey meat, maincrop potatoes and vegetables from the east and south-east, and beef, mutton and lamb from these areas.

Danish bacon, Danish and New Zealand butter, New Zealand and Continental cheese, New Zealand lamb, Argentine beef, bread from imported wheats, all play an important part.

Within and beyond the province are the changes in *total* food demand and in the *types* of food demand in this modern world. U.K. population today is higher by several millions than in 1939, and official forecasts suggest an increase of 4½ millions by the end of 25 years. Land is being lost to non-agricultural uses. Together these suggest a greater total demand and a smaller farming area in the U.K.

The post-war record of fuller employment, rising family incomes and changing food habits (due to travel, desire for "convenience" or "preferred" foods, an ageing population, etc.) have already changed the picture. For example, butchers speak of the modern housewives' disinclination to buy fatty meat. If continued, these factors are expected to change the pattern even more. Those who have studied the subject suggest a declining per head consumption of wheat, grain and potatoes, butter and margarine (considered together) and increasing consumption of fruit and vegetables (especially processed), beef, veal and lamb, poultry, eggs and (possibly) cream.

Looking even beyond that are the "imponderables" of the world food situation, with the twin problems of enabling total food production to keep pace with rising numbers and to raise the food intake of many millions of people. Not all opinions are pessimistic, e.g. to quote F.A.O. (1955), "technically the horizons of food production are still distant and perhaps more distant than they have ever been". In this connection, recent statements suggest that attention ought to be paid to increased output from the "underdeveloped" countries rather than the transfer of the surplus from the Western world.

POSSIBILITIES FOR THE PROVINCE

Thinking of "possibilities", it is necessary to clear some ground in relation to policy on agricultural pricing and on the place which food and raw materials produced in the U.K. are to play in relation to total supplies. The decisions at the annual price-review relate mainly to U.K. as a whole, and the Marketing Boards for Eggs, Potatoes, Wool and Tomatoes (and Cucumbers) operate over the whole country. For milk, although the Scottish Milk Marketing Board does determine the seasonality of milk pricing, the guaranteed price (subject to the standard quantity) is the same as for other parts of Britain. So, overall, it is a case of considering the possibilities within the British price framework and within the political decisions as to ". . . such part of the nation's food and other agricultural produce as in the national interest it is desirable to produce in the U.K. . . ." (Agriculture Act, 1947).

In the light of that clause and the operative words ". . . such part . . ." the present is a most difficult time for looking at the future. The already high rate of supplies for some commodities, the future of the U.K. in Europe, inter-Commonwealth relations and the annual subsidy bill to Agriculture, taken together, make up some of the pieces of a formidable jig-saw pattern, with others still to be fitted in. Considering the individual farmer in relation to the generally rising standard of living, the small unit is less happily placed today, especially when handicapped by inferior land or lack of capital. In what used to be regarded as the "blue chips" of the small-farming world—eggs, pigs, milk, small fruit and some vegetables—modern developments and, of late, narrowing profit margins mean that the bigger unit (often with more capital and often better technical knowledge) can handle these enterprises efficiently and on a large scale. For less intensive units (e.g. the upland rearing farm or the non-dairying low-ground farm), sheer lack of "acres" may be the limiting factor. Broadly, the requirements of modern farming need higher output—from intensification or from more acres. Or, on the marketing side, improved bargaining power and better marketing techniques.

The speed of modern transport, the refrigeration facilities and the scientific techniques now available mean that some of the local "comparative advantages" arising from proximity to market (or raw materials) no longer operate as strongly as once they did. Transport costs still matter, but with supplies at a high level no area now has a monopoly in its own consuming zone. Leaving aside those products for which much of the south-west would operate at maximum economic disadvantage, other imports from other parts of Scotland—eggs, broiler meat, turkey-meat, bacon and pork—illustrate this point. The very fact of their availability at competitive prices discourages any great extensions within the province. For such items, the extension of local production depends on one factor only—the skill of the individual producer plus, in these intensive days, the adequacy of his capital.

The group in which the province has no natural comparative advantage can be extended to include most cash crops and even some horticultural produce, i.e. where soil, rainfall, sunshine hours and temperature play a part. Examples are bread grain and coarse grain, maincrop potatoes and, operating through greater heating expense, some glasshouse produce. For these, the only comparative advantages lie in transport costs, or timing of production, or freshness, or quality, with the last two depending, to some extent, on discriminating buyers. To a large degree these are partly possibilities for the individual rather than for the province as a whole, although, for the previous group and for this, anything which places local produce more attractively and temptingly before the consumer (preferably under a brand designation) can play its part.

I am not competent to deal with the possibilities of grass-seed production in Stirling and North Ayr. The latter, declining in the 1930s, increased in acreage during the war, but has again declined somewhat. There is competition from oversea alternatives as constituents of grass-seed mixtures.

That leads us to considering dairy produce, lamb (and wool) and beef. Consideration of the first two brings us "slap up against" the future as regards Europe and the Commonwealth, especially New Zealand, and against that phrase ". . . such part of the nation's food and other agricultural produce . . ."! Consideration of the beef position brings in the future trend of Argentine beef supplies to the U.K. and complex problems of meat consumption, i.e. the extent to which beef, lamb and fresh pig meats are substitutes, any or all, for each. This whole group brings up the question of present per capita consumption (and the possibilities) of the produce of the dairy cow, the beef cow and the ewe.

Previous sections of this paper contain much "spelling it out", but it seemed necessary to stress the importance of external factors on the agriculture of the province. Also that, apart from wool, the final demand point is on the tables of an urban consuming public whose tastes are changing and whose demand for food, especially in the lower-income groups, may take little account of the country of origin. While the practical skill, the technical knowledge and the machines for a further increase in output are there on the farms, the determining factors are the size of the outlets, the level of prices and the political decisions which will affect both.

"Possibilities" as such are of two types:

(i) In relation to national needs, i.e. production of more food either to replace imports, or to meet the food needs of a rise in population, or to reduce food imports so that greater quantities of industrial raw materials may be imported.

(ii) In relation to the individual farm, so that standards of living on the farms may be maintained or increased.

On the national side, it is not possible to foresee future policy nor to follow through all its implications for this province, but on the only view that can be taken at present the immediate future for the south-west does not seem to hold a prospect of increased cereal, maincrop potato or sugar beet cash cropping nor of greatly increased egg-production, pig-meat or poultry-meat production, although individual producers may expand output of some of these lines. Similarly, on the horticultural side, it seems true to say that the staple crops will increase slowly, if at all. For dairy produce the most remunerative outlet is the fresh-milk trade and advertising may bring some demand increase there, though probably not enough to absorb a very marked upward swing in the total milk production of the province. Increasing surplus over fresh-milk requirements can only find an outlet through the cream trade or the manufacturing outlets. Any replacement of imports of dairy produce by U.K. production will depend on inter-European politics. As regards mutton and lamb, possibilities of increased output have been, and to some extent still are, available, but while imports remain at present levels we may be near an equilibrium point in supply at present price levels. Official policy in recent years has favoured an expansion in beef production, with the longer term outlook for increased U.K. output varying from optimism to pessimism according to forecasts of future Argentine supplies. Taking it that the U.K. has to fill, and go on filling, a substantial gap here, the province will be affected mainly through three types of beef enterprise—the production of store cattle from the hills and uplands; the supply of beef-type cattle bred out of dairy cows and the supply of store or fat cattle from purchased beef-type calves.

If the foregoing is substantially sound, the concern for the immediate future is mainly with the efficiency of the technical and economic processes of production in the types of farming already common in the province. The immediate need is to maintain present outlets in the food markets, without undue subsidy increases, and to be able to gain and hold the increased markets that rising population will eventually provide. In short—price and quality! That other national aspect, that of saving animal feed imports by increased utilisation of home-grown produce, is too large for discussion here, but at least as far as milk is concerned many farms are now achieving a higher level of "self-sufficiency".

"Possibilities" in the light of the individual farm and its financial returns is also too large for adequate discussion here. Realising the possibilities of certain individual farms (say by increasing production to gain greater efficiency) may ultimately result in diminishing the possibilities for others, by reduced prices (e.g. of milk, eggs. broiler-meat and pigs), lower profit levels and "forcing-out" the marginal producers. In an industry made up of so many small units, even production quotas will not lead to a completely static position.

Elaborating on the many technical ways by which an improved farm performance may be obtained—better health and lower mortality in livestock, higher crop and livestock yields, better food conversion rates—is unnecessary. Given adequate working capital, capital for efficient stock-housing, efficient and interested hired or family labour, very high performances are within the reach of many. To these must be added the possibilities lying within the province of the "farm economist"—the extent to which hard thinking on the organisational problems of individual farms—including budgeting, costings, work study—can point the way towards more intensive or less intensive methods cost reductions and the maintenance of a skilled, productive and well-paid labour force on the farms.

APPENDIX

Table I

The Farming Area, 1958

(Figures are acres)

	West College Province (excluding West Perth)	Scotland	College Province as % of Scotland
(i) Arable Land	705,208	3,145,864	22·4
(ii) Permanent Grass	667,766	1,230,383	54·3
(iii) Crops and Grass (i)+(ii)	1,372,974	4,376,247	31·4
(iv) Rough Grazings	3,355,243	11,033,661	30·4
Total ((iii)+(iv))	4,728,217	15,409,908	30·7

Table II

Tillage and Grassland, 1959 (*excluding West Perth*)

(Figures are acres)

	Acreages	As % of Arable Land	As % of Crops and Grass	As % of Farming Land
Total Crops and Fallow	287,781	34·0	21·1	6·1
+Total Temporary Grassland	557,635	66·0	41·0	11·8
=Total Arable Land	845,416	100·0	62·1	17·9
+Total Permanent Grassland	516,040	—	37·9	11·0
=Total Crops and Grass	1,361,456	—	100·0	28·9
+Total Rough Grazings*	3,355,243	—	—	71·1
=Total Farming Land	4,716,699	—	—	100·0

* 1958 acreage of rough grazings.

TABLE III

Grain Crops and Potatoes, 1959

(Figures are acres)

	West College Province (excluding West Perth)	Scotland	College Province as % of Scotland
Wheat	7,202	84,415	8·5
Barley	15,742	228,465	6·9
Oats	165,139	720,352	22·9
Potatoes (1st early)	7,180	21,018	34·2
Potatoes (Others)	17,763	128,501	13·8
Sugar Beet	57	15,948	·4

TABLE IV

Livestock, 1959

(Figures are head of stock)

	West College Province (excluding West Perth)	Scotland	College Province as % of Scotland
Cattle:			
Dairy cows	238,236	352,713	67·5
Other dairy cattle	299,065	401,087	74·6
Beef cows	48,355	245,729	19·7
Other beef cattle	194,431	892,882	21·8
Total Cattle	780,087	1,892,411	41·2
Sheep: Breeding Ewes	1,297,233	3,457,721	37·5
Pigs: Breeding Sows	11,774	46,123	25.5
Poultry:			
Fowls—6 months and over	1,134,929	4,239,911	26·8
Fowls—Under 6 months	1,292,593	4,540,109	28·5
Ducks	21,283	74,051	28·7
Geese	3,542	19,015	18·6
Turkeys	45,415	170,455	26·6

TABLE V

Horticulture, 1958

(Figures are acres: Glasshouses in sq. ft.)

	West College Province (excluding West Perth)	Scotland	College Province as % of Scotland
Vegetables	1,608	11,495	14·0
Strawberries	381	1,531	24·9
Raspberries	129	8,040	1·6
Black-Currants and Gooseberries	231	412	56·1
Other kinds and mixed	179	513	34·9
Orchards	656	1,043	62·9
Glasshouses	9,450,005	13,328,699	70·9

Table VI

Trend in Numbers of Agricultural Workers

West College Province (excluding West Perth)

(1939=100)

	Regular Male Workers (including part-time)	Regular Female Workers (including part-time)	Casual Workers
1959	88	90	74
1958	88	98	75
1957	90	102	72
1956	92	108	70
1955	96	109	71
1954	99	113	89
1953	95	91	119
1952	99	102	128
1951	104	105	119
1950	105	109	118
1949	106	112	122
1948	104	112	134
1947	101	116	117
1946	100	117	107
1939	100	100	100
Actual numbers:			
1959	20,327	4,835	3,807
1939	22,988	5,384	5,118

Table VII

Some Machinery Types

West College Province (excluding West Perth)

	1942	1946	1950	1954	1959
Tractors (all types)	3,319	5,444	8,993	11,796	15,833
Combine Harvesters	10	16	17	89	603
Pick-up Balers	*	41	26	280	1,999
Grain Driers (all types)	*	5	6	23	171

* Classifications not comparable.

TABLE VIII

Some Crop Acreages and Livestock Numbers

West College Province (excluding West Perth)

(1939=100)

	June 1958	June 1959
Crops and Fallow	105	102
Temporary Grass	111	*
Permanent Grass	81	*
Oats	98	94
Turnips and Swedes	99	94
Temporary Grass for Mowing	132	*
Permanent Grass for Mowing	66	*
Dairy Cattle: Cows	117	115
Others	118	116
Beef Cattle: Cows	263	296
Others	179	203
Breeding Ewes	98	102
Breeding Sows	143	111
Total Fowls	101	103
Total Turkeys	162	224

* Figures for 1959 not fully comparable.

Of the grassland acreage mowed in 1958, the following shows the relative importance of hay and grass silage:

	In 1,000 acres	
	Hay	Silage
West Highland counties	23·9	2·7
West Central and Clyde Valley	111·4	14·1
Galloway and Dumfries	69·0	9·1

TABLE IX

*The Contribution from Home Agriculture to the Food Supplies of the United Kingdom**

	Average 1934-38	1958 Provisional
	%	%
Wheat and Flour	12	19
Butter	9	8
Sugar (as refined)	18	18
Carcase Meat and Offal	51	65
Bacon and Ham	32	42
Cheese	24	45
Eggs in shell	71	99
Potatoes	94	84

* Source: *The State of British Agriculture*, 1959-60 (A.E.R.I.).

Agriculture and its Possibilities

NORTH SCOTLAND

G. G. HAYES, B.SC.(ECON.), N.D.A.

The North of Scotland College of Agriculture, Aberdeen

[One of three Scottish Regional papers, the others being "West of Scotland" (p. 249) and "East and South East Scotland" (p. 262).]

This paper deals with the agriculture of that part of Scotland which, for advisory purposes, is under the jurisdiction of the North of Scotland College of Agriculture. Part 1 describes the structure of the agriculture of this area with particular reference to the years 1939 and 1958. Part 2 discusses certain weaknesses apparent in the present structure, while Part 3 suggests ways in which these weaknesses may be overcome.

Certain facts emerge clearly from this analysis. The average size of farm is too small to permit the development of permanently viable units, except those which are highly specialised and intensively operated. It is suggested that normal economic forces should be permitted to bring about the desirable amalgamation of holdings, unhampered by Government intervention.

The social income of agriculture is spread over too many persons, thus reducing the income per head. An amalgamation of holdings will go some way towards correcting this. More important still, a reduction in the number of agricultural workers should not be regarded as undesirable. The maintenance of a rural population should depend more on encouraging industry to go into the country, rather than restricting the flow of workers out of agriculture.

Finally, great importance is attached to education. Despite the drawback of its being a long-term policy, it is undoubtedly the key to a prosperous and progressive agricultural community.

INTRODUCTION

Any worthwhile consideration of the possible development of agriculture in the north of Scotland cannot be undertaken without reference to past performances. Further, such developments as appear to be worthy of consideration should be examined within the general economic framework of the country as a whole. It is upon these two facts that this paper is based. The general format will therefore be:

(*a*) a brief consideration of the structure of agriculture in the relatively immediate past and as it is at present;

(*b*) the productivity of farming in this area;

(*c*) weaknesses of the present system;

(*d*) correction of these weaknesses.

This paper will deal specifically with the area of Scotland covered by the North of Scotland College of Agriculture (see Table I). All Tables are given in the Appendix to this report.

THE STRUCTURE OF AGRICULTURE

A broad picture of the cropping and stocking of this area is given in Tables II and IV, where certain statistics for 1939 and 1958 are given for the 11 counties. In the interpretation of these figures it is important to realise the limitation of statistics on a county basis. This is particularly the case with rough grazings. In the county of Aberdeen, for example, the rough grazing is concentrated in certain areas. Parts of the county will show a very high percentage of this grazing while other areas will have very low percentages. This limitation is, however, insuperable when reliance has to be placed on published statistics.

In the analysis which follows, the North College area is divided into two parts, depending on the percentage of rough grazing. The areas may be designated "Highland" and "Lowland" and consist of the following counties:

Highland		*Lowland*	
Nairn	Sutherland	Kincardine	Moray
Inverness	Caithness	Aberdeen	Orkney
Ross and Cromarty	Shetland	Banff	

It would seem desirable to consider the agricultural statistics of a year before the last war, a year which illustrates the impact of this war on the agricultural structure, and the most recent year for which statistics are available. The years selected are thus 1939, 1944 and 1958.

CROPPING

Some very considerable movements in cropping took place in both areas between 1939 and 1958. A brief description of the changes in each area follows.

From 1939 to 1958 the Highland area appears to have lost some 26,000 acres of crops and grass. The tillage area, after an increase of 16,000 acres in 1944, fell by 35,000 acres to 142,600 acres. The wheat area increased two and a half times in 1944, and finished in 1958 by being twice the area recorded for 1939. Barley shows little change between the beginning and the end of the period, but practically doubled in 1944. There appears to have been a fairly sharp falling off in the acreage of oats after a small initial rise in 1944. Potatoes rose by 50 per cent. in 1944 but then declined to a 1958 figure below the 1939 level. The acreage under roots and forage crops generally remained unchanged, while the area devoted to other crops fell by 50 per cent.

Much of the increase in the arable acreage which took place during the war years was obtained at the expense of the temporary grass area. The acreage mown fell, but the biggest drop appeared in the grazing area. Recovery has been considerable since 1944, particularly in the temporary grass area.

A reduction in the acreages of crops and grass has also taken place in the Lowland area, but to a much smaller extent, being only 5,000 acres. The tillage area has actually increased. The acreage devoted to wheat is roughly four times that recorded in 1939. Barley shows a substantial rise, but the oats acreage is only slightly greater. Potatoes are 50 per cent. higher. These increases have taken place at the expense of roots and other crops. The temporary grass area has increased by nearly 20,000 acres. It is in the area of permanent grass that a substantial fall has occurred. The decline is no less than 43,000 acres, some of which is now under cropping, and some under temporary grass.

Stocking

Changes in livestock numbers have been considerable. Dealing first with the Highland area, cattle numbers were approximately 25 per cent. higher in 1958 than they were in 1939. All classes of cattle showed increases, but if it is possible to judge from the number of heifers in calf, the rate of increase has dropped sharply. In this series of three years, 1944 is the only year in which it is possible to distinguish between dairy and beef cattle. Dairy cows accounted for 68 per cent. of total cows, and dairy heifers in calf approximately the same percentage of their appropriate class. Too much importance should not be placed on this division. Many so-called dairy cows are in fact beef producers, but since they are milked and a certain proportion of this milk sold to the Milk Marketing Board, they are classed by the farmer as dairy cows.

Sheep, in total, exhibited little change over the period, and appear to have suffered only slightly during the war years. This is due to the fact that a large part of the Highland area, consisting as it does of rough grazing, was unaffected by the national need for more cropping. Hence, since most of the sheep are in hill flocks, they were unaffected by this cropping policy.

Pigs dropped significantly during the war period, due to the universal shortage of feeding stuffs. A very rapid recovery took place when food supplies once more became available, with the result that the 1958 figure is 70 per cent. higher than that of 1939. Poultry, on the other hand, although subject to the same external influence, showed little significant change.

The rate of increase of cattle has been slightly higher in the Lowland area than that indicated for the Highland region. This is very marked with cows and heifers in calf, the 1958 census return for the former being 39 per cent. above the 1939 level, and for the latter no less than 65 per cent. Again, it is difficult to distinguish between dairy and beef cattle. The 1944 census suggests that 60 per cent. of the cows and an equal percentage of the heifers in calf are dairy cattle, but the division should be accepted with caution.

Sheep fell off very sharply by 1944, due to the requirements of the national cropping policy. By 1958, however, they had recovered almost to their 1939 level. In this respect the trend of events in sheep has been very different from that recorded for the Highland area. There is, further, some indication that sheep numbers will continue to expand.

Pigs fell back very sharply in 1944 for the reason already indicated. Recovery, as a consequence of improved food supplies, has been remarkable, the 1958 figure being more than twice that of 1939. A very similar course of events may be recorded for poultry.

Other Statistics

The number of holdings in the area, together with their average size, is given in Table V. These figures should be read with caution. They are averages, and possess in a marked degree the inherent weakness of averages. They give no indication of the range of sizes—an important factor. Neither is it possible to obtain the range of sizes from the published agricultural statistics, since in the appropriate Tables in those statistics rough grazing is omitted. In many areas, and in particular in the Highland area, the amount of rough grazing plays a vital part in the farm economy. Very many viable units consist of a small acreage of crops and grass, and a large area of hill, thus giving an entirely erroneous impression of size of unit.

An index of the measure of the social prosperity of an area is said to be the number of workers employed. The validity of this assumption is open to serious doubt. Certainly the economic prosperity of an agricultural region is not related to the number of men employed, since there are machines to do the work previously done by man. Table VI indicates the total number of agricultural workers in each area at 4th June of each year. The most noticeable feature is the very sharp reduction in the number employed in 1958 as compared with 1939 or 1944. In the Highland area the 1958 number was only 61 per cent. of that for 1939, while for the Lowland area the corresponding figure was 81 per cent. It is highly significant that this drop in numbers is not associated with a corresponding fall in either cropping or stocking. Based on figures of man-labour requirements given in the *Scottish Farm Management Handbook*, the work content of the farms is as follows:

1. *Highland Area:*		2. *Lowland Area:*	
1939	31,300,000 hours	1939	50,300,000 hours
1958	30,500,000 hours	1958	66,800,000 hours

In other words, in the Highland area a fall of 39 per cent. in the number of persons employed has been associated with a drop of 3 per cent. in the work required. In the Lowland area the corresponding figures are a drop of 19 per cent. in the number of workers, and an increase of 15 per cent. in the amount of work. This has taken place despite a significant shortening of the working week. Mechanisation has played an important role in this change.

1. *Highland Area:*	1950	1959	2. *Lowland Area:*	1950	1959
Tractors	2,524	5,033	Tractors	9,919	16,129
Combine Harvesters	14	154	Combine Harvesters	44	495
Forage Harvesters	17	36	Forage Harvesters	24	154

Finally, an additional point to examine is the change—if any—which has taken place in the yields of crops in these two areas over the past twenty years.

	Average 1948-57	1939	1944	1958
1. *Highland Area:*				
Wheat (cwt. per acre)	21·3	23·1	20·5	23·7
Barley do.	17·3	15·3	15·4	20·4
Oats do.	14·1	13·6	12·8	16·3
Potatoes (tons per acre)	6·3	5·8	5·1	5·1
Roots do.	15·2	15·1	14·7	17·4
Silage (cwt. per acre)	—	—	—	63·4
Hay do.	21·3	19·8	19·2	22·8
2. *Lowland Area:*				
Wheat (cwt. per acre)	23·5	21·1	18·3	22·8
Barley do.	19·8	17·6	16·1	20·8
Oats do.	17·0	15·9	14·6	17·5
Potatoes (tons per acre)	6·6	7·4	5·4	5·2
Roots do.	16·2	14·9	15·1	16·6
Silage (cwt. per acre)	—	—	—	115·5
Hay do.	30·9	30·5	31·5	34·3

It is doubtful if any of these figures indicate an improvement in productivity, except possibly the hay figures for the Lowland area. The variations are due much more to the vagaries of the weather rather than to any long-term changes in productivity. This means that changes in total production are due more to variations in acreages grown rather than changes in yield per acre. These crop yield figures must, however, be read with caution. They are unweighted averages of estimates, and are very much subject to the normal human errors inherent in crop yield estimations.

WEAKNESSES IN THE PRESENT SYSTEM

Having considered in some detail the structure of agriculture in the north of Scotland, the next step is to examine the weaknesses in the present system, and to go on from there to a discussion of the possible development of the area. This section, therefore, will be devoted to an examination of certain weaknesses inherent in the present agricultural organisation.

The first point which arises relates to the size of the farm. As indicated in Table V, the average size is small, particularly if the acreage of crops and grass only is considered. This is unrealistic in the Highland area, where the acreage of rough grazing plays such an important part in the farm economy. It is, unfortunately, impossible from published statistics to determine a frequency distribution of farm sizes. This is only possible for the acreages of crops and grass, since the analysis excludes rough grazing. It is doubtful, therefore, if the size group analysis given, for example, in Table 38 of the 1958 Agricultural Statistics has any real value.

In order to arrive at some estimate of the importance of farm size, an analysis has been made of farm accounts made available by farmers to the Economics Department of the North of Scotland College of Agriculture. For this purpose, a successful farm is taken to be one which produces a profit at least equal to an agricultural worker's wage of £550 per annum plus interest at 5 per cent. on the capital invested in the farm. The object of this exercise is to determine what proportion of the farmers concerned would be better off financially by leaving the farm, investing the capital so obtained in some gilt-edged securities, and working for another farmer. The results are given in Table VII.

The figures given in Table VII may be summarised below:

Percentage of "Unsuccessful" Farms in each type group

Feeding Farms	51
Rearing Farms	68
Dairy Farms	50
Upland Rearing Farms	40
Hill Sheep Farms	70
Overall Average	56

These figures mean, in effect, that more than half the 326 farmers in the sample would be better off financially by working for some other person rather than themselves. It cannot be too strongly emphasised, however, that many of these farmers realise the position, but prefer the non-monetary rewards they obtain by being their own masters.

The figures given above refer solely to the year 1958-59 involving the disposal of the 1958 crop. The picture for the two years preceding this period is slightly more favourable in that a somewhat smaller percentage of farmers (50 per cent.) may be regarded as "unsuccessful". Nevertheless, the distribution of such farms according to acreage conforms remarkably well with the details given in Table VII of the Appendix.

An interesting feature of Table VII is the extraordinarily high percentage of farmers in the dairy farms group, size up to 100 acres, who must be regarded as unsuccessful. This is a type of farming which is normally regarded as admirably suited to small farm conditions, but according to Table VII the farmer with fewer than 100 acres has not got a particularly good chance of being successful. This in part is due to the high capital investment on these small dairy farms. Another factor of some importance is the detailed farming system followed by these relatively small farms. They tend to adopt a cropping and livestock policy much more suited to the larger farm. In other words, there is a marked tendency for them to "ape" the larger farmer instead of adopting an organisation specifically designed to meet the needs of the small farm.

Size of farm is of very considerable importance in determining the profit level of individual farms, and hence the income of individual farmers. But a close examination of many farm accounts clearly indicates that in all types of farming and in all sizes of units the one factor of overriding importance is the managerial ability of the farmer. It is possible to state quite categorically that, no matter how productive a farm may be, or how productive the livestock on that farm, without a high level of managerial ability the farmer cannot reach the desired level of income. Little can be done to correct a condition of low managerial ability, but it is the field in which sound advice and guidance will reap the greatest reward.

A second factor in the agricultural situation is the economic inertia of the farmer in this and in all other areas. The comments which follow are based on observations only, since it is impossible to prove the case statistically without reference to individual farmers' cropping programmes. Certain classes of farmers tend to retain a cropping structure for an indefinite period and to remain uninfluenced by price changes. An outstanding example of this is the almost inviolate nature of the six-course rotation in the north of Scotland. On very many farms a rotation consisting of oats, roots (including potatoes), oats (or barley) and three years' grass has been in operation for generations. The only differences in the acreages of various crops has been due to varying sizes of fields, and certainly not to any deliberate planning. Even if a third-year ley is in very good condition it is broken up, simply because not to do so would disturb the even tenor of a six-course rotation. It is extremely doubtful if, in this area, the subsidy paid for ploughing grassland has had any marked effect on the acreage ploughed.

Changes in cropping have taken place. The violent ones of the war period were more the result of Executive Committee activity than any other factor. The post-war period saw a gradual settling down. Now changes in cropping obviously still take place, but they are more due to variations on the farms of really progressive farmers than to changes on all farms.

The age factor probably enters here. To adopt a flexible attitude towards cropping implies thought processes to which, by and large, the older generation of farmers are unaccustomed. Indeed, to be fair to them it must be stated that they have had no training in this type of managerial approach. The younger generation of farmers is getting this training through various channels, particularly the Agricultural College and Advisory service. The future farmer should be much more flexible in his approach.

This economic inertia may also be applied to the livestock policy on many farms. Indeed, a lack of flexibility in cropping policies is almost certain to lead to a similar managerial deficiency in the stocking side of the farm organisation. A common saying in farming is that farmers grow roots to feed cattle to produce dung to grow roots to feed cattle. . . . Like all such sayings, it is not wholly true, yet there is some measure of truth in it. Far too many farmers purchase expensive store cattle in the autumn in order to eat the turnips grown for them. A moment's reflection would have shown them that the prices paid for store cattle of recent years was incapable, in many instances, of returning a profit when these cattle were sold fat. The farmer might well have been better placed financially if he had grown no roots and had no cattle to feed during the winter. To do so would, however, have meant a considerable disturbance to the accepted organisation. Economic inertia operates very strongly to prevent this change. Again it must be emphasised that the younger generation of farmers is, by and large, much more receptive to changing ideas—much more responsive to economic pressures.

An important point of weakness in the existing agricultural organisation is connected with milk production. Too much milk is being produced in this area, and too much of it is being produced on farms which are not ideally suited for this purpose. The actual disposal figures are given in Table VIII. In considering these figures, it is important to realise that the difference between the price received for "liquid" milk and "manufacturing" milk is considerable. The greater the proportion of "manufacturing" milk, the lower is the price paid to the farmer. He gets an average price for his milk—the average of the receipts from "liquid" and "manufacturing" sales. Farmers entered dairy farming primarily because such a system held out greater prospects of profit than any other. Much capital has been sunk in dairy cows, equipment and buildings. Hence, even with a recession in profitability in this particular type of farming, farmers are unwilling to change to a potentially more profitable system because of the almost certain loss involved in the realisation of their dairy capital. There is, in addition, the added attraction of a regular cheque each month. Observation shows that there are many areas, particularly upland districts, where farmers are producing milk when they ought to be breeding and rearing cattle and sheep. The two reasons mentioned above prevent this desirable change. The only factor which would bring this about is a very sharp reduction in the price of milk—a change which is impossible under existing legislation.

Certain commonly accepted measures of efficiency include such things as fertiliser use, livestock carry and labour use. Crop production, including grass, is closely associated with the use of fertilisers. Livestock carry depends to some degree on crop production and also capital investment in stock and buildings. Man labour use is to some degree a reflection of the organising ability of the farmer himself.

Information on fertiliser usage may be obtained from the various reports on the "Survey of Fertiliser Practice in Scotland". The details given in Table IX are extracted from the reports so far issued by the North of Scotland College of Agriculture in conjunction with the Agricultural Research Council Unit of Statistics, University of Aberdeen. These reports are difficult to summarise, but a few of the salient points are given in Table IX, which shows the percentage of certain crop groups which received artificial manures, and the average dressings. By way of comparison, figures for the United Kingdom are also included. This comparison is particularly interesting.

	Average Rate per Acre—cwt.		
	N	P_2O_5	K_2O
1. *Highland Area* (all tillage):			
Caithness (North-east) . . .	0·14	0·75	0·37
Inverness (Upper Speyside) . .	0·28	0·53	0·31
Ross and Cromarty (Black Isle) . .	0·33	0·73	0·41
2. *Lowland Area* (all tillage):			
Aberdeenshire (Huntly) . . .	0·28	0·76	0·36
Aberdeenshire (Ellon) . . .	0·29	0·79	0·40
Aberdeenshire (New Deer) . .	0·26	0·93	0·48
3. *United Kingdom:*			
Arable Land	0·33	0·44	0·35

Taking the tillage area and assuming it to be equivalent to the United Kingdom arable area, it is apparent that in the application of nitrogen only the Black Isle is up to average. In both phosphate and potash the average applications are above or well above the United Kingdom.

Considering the application of nitrogen further, the heaviest dressings could be expected in the group "Temporary grass—mown". The percentage using nitrogen on their mowing grass is surprisingly small—as low as 44 per cent. in Orkney (West Mainland) and 48 per cent. in Aberdeenshire (New Deer). The highest was 88 per cent. in Inverness-shire (Upper Speyside) and 80 per cent. in the Huntly district of Aberdeenshire. The average dressing ranged from just under 1 cwt. sulphate of ammonia to just over 1¾ cwt.

All levels of manuring for all crop groups is well below the generally recommended rate. In practical terms this simply means that the potential level of productivity is substantially greater than that at present achieved. It is difficult to estimate the potential productivity of the land in the North College area. Nevertheless, it does seem that with the adequate application of the correct fertilisers output could increase by not less than 25 per cent.

A second factor of importance is the density of the livestock carry in the two areas. To arrive at this figure two calculations are necessary:

1. All livestock are converted into their cow-equivalent numbers by the use of recognised conversion factors.
2. All rough grazings are converted into their equivalent rotation grass figures. For this purpose, eight acres of such grazings in the Highland area are considered as equivalent to one acre of rotation grass. In the Lowland area the appropriate conversion factor is four. These rates are open to criticism, as indeed is the whole process, but they are considered fitting and desirable in the context of the report.

The final figures then obtained are as follows:

1. *Highland Area:*
   1939 28 cow units per 100 adjusted acres.
   1958 31 cow units per 100 adjusted acres.
2. *Lowland Area:*
   1939 37 cow units per 100 adjusted acres.
   1958 44 cow units per 100 adjusted acres.

A lower level of livestock carry could reasonably well be expected from the Highland area. Nevertheless, the above figures do suggest that, in that area, some substantial improvement is possible. Whether such an increase is desirable is problematic. Much of the western part of the Highland area is relatively isolated, with expensive and difficult transport facilities. Except in very favourable areas it is difficult to see how the western part can hope to compete with the eastern side, or, more so, with the Lowland area. Some alternative form of land use would appear to be worthy of consideration.

The livestock carried in the Lowland area may be compared with that indicated by an examination of accounts submitted to the Economics Department of the North of Scotland College of Agriculture. From these records, the livestock carry ranges from about 50 cow units per 100 acres up to 55 or more. It would appear, therefore, that an improvement of the order of perhaps 20 per cent. is possible. This potential increase agrees reasonably well with the suggested increase in crop productivity already noted.

The labour force on farms consists of the hired worker and the farmer together with members of his family. It is very difficult to formulate a reliable estimate of the amount of work performed by the farmer and his family, yet it is essential if a true assessment of the labour force is to be made. In the Highland area the labour supply is taken to be the number of agricultural workers as returned at 4th June 1958, together with family labour equal to one-half the number of farms. This gives a total force equivalent to 18,745 men to undertake work equal to 27·1 million hours, or 1,427 hours per man. In the Lowland area the same process is employed except that family labour is taken to equal three-quarters of the number of farms. The total force thus numbers 30,858 men to perform 54·5 million hours of work, equal to 1,758 hours per man. These hours per man may be compared with a standard figure of 2,400 per annum. It is apparent that there is, in both areas, a substantial over-supply of agricultural workers, leading to the division of the social income of agriculture over a larger number of persons than is really necessary. The imperfections of the calculation are readily apparent, but it does serve to indicate a weakness in the existing organisation.

CORRECTING THE WEAKNESSES

Attention has been directed towards a consideration of the existing standard of farming in the north of Scotland. This was followed by a discussion of certain weaknesses inherent in the present system. The final stage of the report is to examine the desirability of correcting these weaknesses and the manner in which such correction can be effected.

In order to clarify the discussion, the points which emerge from the immediately preceding section may be listed below.

1. The size of individual holdings is, in many cases, far too small to enable the farmer and his family to enjoy a reasonable standard of living.
2. Close observation of farmers, farms, and farm accounts suggests that there exists a high degree of economic inertia in the agricultural community. Such inertia prevents the farmer taking advantage of changes in the economic climate under which he operates, makes him unwilling to change, and thus leads to an income level below that which could be obtained in the industry.

3. Too much milk is being produced in this area, and too much of it is being produced on farms which are not ideally suited for this purpose.
4. There appears to be considerable scope for increased fertiliser usage. Such a step could lead to higher production of crops, a higher livestock carry, and hence a higher output from the farm. This higher output should lead to an increased level of profitability with a consequent increase in the standard of living of the farming community.
5. The general level of livestock carry has been noted, and compared with certain available averages. There is some indication that, in the Lowland area in particular, a substantial improvement is possible.
6. Finally, a calculation is made to determine the work content of the available labour force. This would appear to be above that which is really necessary, leading to a reward for manual labour below that which could be obtained.

The first point relates to the relationship between size of farm and profitability. It is evident from Table VII that on the low ground farms the chances are 7 to 10 against a small farmer being "successful" in the sense in which it is used in this report. Indeed, it is not until the 200-acre mark is reached that there are really good prospects. Except under exceptional conditions, particularly of management, the non-specialised Lowland farm of under 100 acres has little chance of being successful. Their condition can only be improved by the employment either of special and permanent grants or by a price structure too high for any Government to contemplate. It is doubtful if the community would gain by the continued injection of grants to farmers operating units of this size. Such grants would have to be permanent, since it is doubtful if a temporary scheme of assistance would lead to a permanent improvement of sufficient magnitude.

What, then, should be done? It is evident that farmers operate small farms through a combination of desire and necessity. Lack of capital is the commonest "necessity". It is equally evident that if men wish to operate a small farm, knowing full well that they would reap a higher financial reward by investing their money elsewhere and working for someone else, then they should be allowed to do so. A freedom-loving democracy will not tolerate any compulsion of this order. It follows from this that the compulsory amalgamation of holdings should not take place if it involves the eviction of a farmer and his family. On economic grounds the amalgamation of holdings should take place, in order to develop units of not less than 150 acres. This amalgamation should result from the unhampered operation of economic forces. If this be accepted, it must follow that the Government should not introduce schemes designed to keep these small farms viable.

Similar arguments can be made in connection with upland and hill farms. Here, however, the unit size must be considerably greater simply because of the lower level of productivity per acre. The greater the proportion of rough grazing, the larger must the farm be. Similarly, the lower the inherent productivity of the rough grazing the larger the farm must be.

In the foregoing analysis the social implications have not been forgotten. Yet certain facts must be faced. It is a common characteristic of an agricultural economy which is becoming increasingly mechanised that the number of employees steadily drops. A progressive agriculture means, amongst other things, a fall in the number of men employed. This is an inevitable move, and it is an impossible task, except by deliberate interference with individual liberty, to stem the flow of men from agriculture into industry. Only when an industry can go into the countryside will the rural population be maintained.

A second point to bear in mind is that the younger generation will not, broadly speaking, tolerate the relative isolation of the lives led by their fathers and grandfathers. This is particularly noticeable in certain areas of most counties. A desire for a higher level of social activities is bound to encourage the movement of the rural population towards towns and cities. This move is in accord with the beliefs of an economist, and will take place despite the wishes of the Government or of sociologists. It is part of the economic force which is bringing about—slowly perhaps—the amalgamation of holdings.

In the second point reference is made to the widespread existence of economic inertia. Broadly speaking, farmers are slow to change, and respond equally slowly to price movements. This characteristic is an inevitable consequence of the long-term nature of agricultural production. Yet, under modern economic conditions, a flexible mind is an important characteristic of profitability. To overcome this inertia, the managerial ability of the farmer must be raised.

Very many farmers are highly skilled technically but very deficient in managerial skill. To them, it is sufficient to produce a good crop, or plenty of milk and so forth. Whether it pays to do so appears to be a secondary consideration. This economic inefficiency can only be overcome by education, particularly in the practice of farm organisation and management. Much greater importance should be attached to the teaching of this subject than has been the case in the past.

Certain changes in the pattern of agricultural production appear to be desirable. Milk has been instanced, while reference has also been made to the livestock carry. Price incentives can be used, but changes in the price level will have to be greater than those permissable under Government's long-term guarantees. The supply of milk is greater than that economically justifiable, but the price reduction necessary to stem the flow of milk will have to be much greater than that which is at present possible. With the current high price of store cattle, there is every inducement to farmers to increase their breeding herds. The Hill Cattle Subsidy is very valuable in this connection, and has done much to increase the number of hill cows. There is some justification for widening the classification of farms eligible for such a subsidy. Alternatively, the price of fat cattle could be increased to encourage the breeding of more store cattle, but here again the price change will have to be more substantial than the Government would perhaps be prepared to contemplate.

Reference has been made to the existence of certain weaknesses in the agricultural economy of the north of Scotland. Their permanent cure is a long-term project. It can only be brought about by a vigorous and expanding programme of education and advisory work amongst the agricultural population. Subsidies and grants, while valuable in themselves, are but poor substitutes and can, by their very nature, effect only temporary alleviation.

APPENDIX

TABLE I

Counties Covered by the North of Scotland College of Agriculture

Kincardine	Moray	Ross and Cromarty	Orkney
Aberdeen	Nairn	Sutherland	Shetland
Banff	Inverness	Caithness	

TABLE II

Acreage of Tillage, Grass, Rough Grazing

County	Crops	Temporary Grass	Permanent Grass	Total Crops and Grass	Rough Grazing	Total Area	Rough Grazing as % of Total Area
(*a*) 1939							
Kincardine	54,036	48,321	12,950	115,307	65,168	180,475	36
Aberdeen	261,850	297,025	58,709	617,584	247,520	865,104	29
Banff	66,188	71,860	17,406	155,454	97,226	252,680	38
Moray	43,982	39,672	10,820	94,474	91,978	186,452	49
Nairn	11,350	10,796	2,768	24,914	50,918	75,832	67
Inverness	46,059	33,434	63,123	142,616	1,734,755	1,877,371	92
Ross	54,582	49,702	31,164	135,448	1,145,998	1,281,446	89
Sutherland	8,920	9,940	11,005	29,865	1,006,418	1,036,283	97
Caithness	30,757	44,848	25,262	100,867	317,158	418,025	76
Orkney	40,922	48,043	20,265	109,230	71,028	180,258	39
Shetland	9,546	2,411	16,958	28,915	316,689	345,604	92
Total	628,192	656,052	270,430	1,554,674	5,144,856	6,699,530	77
(*b*) 1958							
Kincardine	59,829	48,334	9,183	117,346	59,273	176,619	34
Aberdeen	277,675	312,749	23,887	614,311	272,447	886,758	31
Banff	70,163	68,475	15,791	154,429	109,634	264,063	42
Moray	45,747	38,694	7,189	91,630	99,029	190,659	52
Nairn	11,481	11,113	2,032	24,626	51,689	76,315	68
Inverness	37,210	36,456	61,339	135,005	1,985,859	2,120,864	94
Ross	50,226	50,680	32,203	133,109	1,369,978	1,503,087	91
Sutherland	7,637	10,010	11,760	29,407	1,033,812	1,063,219	97
Caithness	30,537	39,900	23,519	93,956	293,928	387,884	76
Orkney	35,153	55,784	18,419	109,356	71,178	180,534	39
Shetland	5,555	3,014	12,265	20,834	311,611	332,445	94
Total	631,213	675,209	217,587	1,524,009	5,658,438	7,182,447	79

TABLE III

Cropping Changes

	Highland Area			Lowland Area		
	1939	1944	1958	1939	1944	1958
Wheat	1,281	3,237	2,472	3,984	8,502	15,192
Barley	10,994	19,433	11,245	36,023	87,591	55,743
Oats	90,859	96,841	78,518	280,227	340,264	284,799
Potatoes	12,241	18,731	10,672	16,793	44,609	25,846
Roots and Forage Crops	33,348	33,776	33,679	125,728	123,318	102,077
Other Crops	12,491	5,780	6,060	4,223	13,667	4,910
Total Crops	161,214	177,798	142,646	466,978	617,951	488,567
Temporary Grass:						
Mown	41,609	36,191	45,255	95,631	70,866	107,530
Grazed	109,522	90,848	105,918	409,290	320,682	416,506
Permanent Grass:						
Mown	22,626	20,229	17,881	5,081	3,874	2,041
Grazed	127,654	111,891	125,238	115,069	63,886	72,428
Total Acreage	462,625	436,957	436,938	1,092,049	1,077,259	1,087,072

TABLE IV

Stocking Changes

	Highland Area			Lowland Area		
	1939	1944	1958	1939	1944	1958
Bulls	1,475	1,889	2,709	2,782	4,243	4,490
Cows	49,976	50,785	62,875	76,334	80,161	105,660
Heifers in calf	3,497	5,203	5,435	8,151	10,960	13,542
Cattle under 1 year	32,079	32,042	47,359	77,442	72,268	115,354
Cattle 1-2 years	22,199	31,421	29,485	109,548	103,873	141,759
Cattle over 2 years	7,598	11,245	8,759	64,912	77,840	78,761
Total	116,824	132,585	156,622	339,169	349,345	459,566
Rams	20,847	22,528	27,337	9,429	8,345	9,675
Ewes	662,984	713,742	746,838	310,915	178,861	263,605
Sheep under 1 year	597,135	560,812	588,075	403,745	216,963	353,217
Sheep over 1 year	230,972	321,247	322,949	75,172	74,844	96,337
Total	1,511,938	1,618,329	1,685,199	799,261	479,013	722,834
Boars	172	137	231	596	425	1,145
Sows and Gilts	1,453	846	2,487	7,356	3,796	16,098
Other pigs	10,006	6,274	17,838	48,284	23,007	117,827
Total	11,631	7,257	20,556	56,236	27,228	135,070
Poultry	647,382	643,424	671,984	2,855,695	2,144,734	4,097,955
Horses	20,070	16,820	3,867	41,813	33,938	3,557

TABLE V

Average Size of Holding, 1958

County	No. of Farms	Total Acres: Crops and Grass	Total Acres: Rough Grazing	Total	Average Size—acres: Crops and Grass	Average Size—acres: Rough Grazing	Average Size—acres: Total
1. *Highland Area:*							
Caithness	2,244	93,956	293,928	387,884	42	131	173
Inverness	6,877	135,005	1,985,859	2,120,864	20	289	309
Nairn	293	24,626	51,689	76,315	84	176	260
Ross and Cromarty	7,223	133,109	1,369,978	1,503,087	18	190	208
Sutherland	2,227	29,407	1,033,812	1,063,219	13	464	477
Shetland	3,256	20,834	311,611	332,445	6	96	102
Total	22,120	436,937	5,046,877	5,483,814	—	—	—
Average	—	—	—	—	20	228	248
2. *Lowland Area:*							
Aberdeen	8,647	614,311	272,447	886,758	71	32	103
Banff	2,280	154,429	109,634	264,063	68	48	116
Kincardine	1,306	117,346	59,273	176,619	90	45	135
Moray	1,172	91,630	99,029	190,659	78	85	163
Orkney	2,845	109,356	71,178	180,534	38	25	63
Total	16,250	1,087,072	611,561	1,698,633	—	—	—
Average	—	—	—	—	67	38	105

Note—The number of farms given in the 1958 Agricultural Statistics excludes holdings consisting entirely of mountain and heath land. The published figures have been adjusted to include these holdings, using the 1944 census returns.

TABLE VI

Number of Agricultural Workers

	1939	1944	1958	1958 as % of 1939
1. *Highland Area:*				
Caithness	1,880	2,011	1,248	66
Inverness	3,460	4,508	2,397	69
Nairn	509	504	402	79
Ross and Cromarty	3,976	4,423	2,243	56
Sutherland	911	1,077	513	56
Shetland	1,863	2,504	882	47
Total	12,599	15,027	7,685	61
2. *Lowland Area:*				
Aberdeen	12,738	13,898	10,330	81
Banff	3,079	4,049	2,547	83
Kincardine	2,431	2,910	2,239	92
Moray	2,089	2,226	1,922	92
Orkney	2,633	2,790	1,634	62
Total	22,970	25,873	18,672	81

Table VII

Percentage of "Unsuccessful" Farmers, 1958-59

Size of Farm (acres)	Feeding	Rearing	Dairy	All
	Type of Farm			
Up to 100	63	73	85	70
101-150	61	65	44	60
151-200	47	71	83	61
201-250	25	25	50	30
251-300	14	—	14	13
Over 300	33	67	11	39
All Sizes	51	68	50	56

Size of Farm (acres)	Upland Rearing	Hill Sheep
Up to 250	20	—
251-500	75	—
501-750	—	—
751-1000	—	100
1001-1500	—	100
1501-2000	100	100
2001-2500	—	—
2501-5000	—	67
5001-7500	—	67
7501-10,000	—	—
Over 10,000	—	57
All Sizes	40	70

Note—A successful farm is one which produces a profit at least equal to an agricultural worker's wage of £550 per annum plus interest at 5 per cent. on the capital invested in the farm.

Table VIII

Disposal of Milk

(Million Gallons)

	Total Sales	Sold for Liquid Consumption	Sold for Manufacturing
1. *Aberdeen Board Area:*			
1957-58	21·3	10·5	10·8
1958-59	21·0	10·4	10·6
1959-60	22·1	10·5	11·6
2. *Inverness Board Area:*			
1957-58	9·0	5·5	3·5
1958-59	8·9	5·5	3·4
1959-60	9·4	5·7	3·7

Liquid Milk as a Percentage of Total Production

	1957-58	1958-59	1959-60
Aberdeen Board	49	50	48
Inverness Board	61	62	61

TABLE IX

Application of Fertilisers

Area	% Acreage Receiving				Average Rate per Acre—cwt.			
	N	P_2O_5	K_2O	CaO	N	P_2O_5	K_2O	CaO
1. HIGHLAND								
(a) *All Cereals*								
Caithness (North-east)	48	82	53	7	0·10	0·61	0·27	40·3
Inverness (Upper Speyside)	97	98	97	5	0·24	0·45	0·26	—
Ross and Cromarty (Black Isle)	69	77	77	9	0·20	0·43	0·24	20·0
(b) *All Roots*								
Caithness (North-east)	97	100	91	11	0·20	1·11	0·55	43·9
Inverness (Upper Speyside)	97	99	99	10	0·35	0·72	0·41	14·0
Ross and Cromarty (Black Isle)	100	100	100	9	0·51	1·19	0·69	18·0
(c) *All Tillage*								
Caithness (North-east)	60	87	62	8	0·14	0·75	0·37	41·5
Inverness (Upper Speyside)	97	98	98	7	0·28	0·53	0·31	18·0
Ross and Cromarty (Black Isle)	79	84	84	9	0·33	0·73	0·41	18·0
(d) *Temporary Grass—Grazed*								
Caithness (North-east)	17	22	16	7	0·14	0·55	0·31	30·4
Inverness (Upper Speyside)	36	31	28	9	0·24	0·43	0·24	18·0
Ross and Cromarty (Black Isle)	23	23	22	15	0·32	0·42	0·40	14·0
(e) *Temporary Grass—Mown*								
Caithness (North-east)	63	68	57	19	0·19	0·62	0·37	37·2
Inverness (Upper Speyside)	88	89	85	45	0·31	0·51	0·33	22·0
Ross and Cromarty (Black Isle)	78	80	77	16	0·33	0·46	0·37	20·0
2. LOWLAND								
(a) *All Cereals*								
Aberdeenshire:								
Huntly	73	96	90	11	0·26	0·61	0·31	16·2
Ellon	79	91	83	15	0·26	0·57	0·33	16·0
New Deer	74	94	87	20	0·24	0·65	0·30	16·0
Orkney (West Mainland)	41	87	49	17	0·16	0·80	0·23	27·4
(b) *All Roots*								
Aberdeenshire:								
Huntly	98	100	98	7	0·32	1·19	0·50	17·3
Ellon	95	100	94	13	0·34	1·36	0·56	17·4
New Deer	98	100	100	7	0·32	1·50	0·51	—
Orkney (West Mainland)	76	100	78	18	0·23	1·19	0·34	27·6
(c) *All Tillage*								
Aberdeenshire:								
Huntly	79	97	92	10	0·28	0·76	0·36	16·4
Ellon	83	93	86	14	0·29	0·79	0·40	16·3
New Deer	81	95	91	16	0·26	0·93	0·48	16·0
Orkney (West Mainland)	47	89	54	17	0·18	0·88	0·26	27·6

Table IX—*continued*

Application of Fertilisers

Area	% Acreage Receiving				Average Rate per Acre—cwt.			
	N	P_2O_5	K_2O	CaO	N	P_2O_5	K_2O	CaO
(d) *Temporary Grass—Grazed*								
Aberdeenshire:								
Huntly	25	27	17	14	0·29	0·83	0·33	18·2
Ellon	24	23	17	12	0·29	0·77	0·35	20·3
New Deer	23	23	22	18	0·28	0·48	0·31	16·0
Orkney (West Mainland)	12	21	10	5	0·24	0·85	0·31	27·2
(e) *Temporary Grass—Mown*								
Aberdeenshire:								
Huntly	80	76	63	16	0·29	0·58	0·29	18·0
Ellon	56	63	51	14	0·33	0·98	0·39	16·8
New Deer	48	55	52	30	0·36	0·58	0·33	16·0
Orkney (West Mainland)	44	49	29	7	0·27	0·62	0·25	—
3. United Kingdom								
Arable Land	—	—	—	—	0·33	0·44	0·35	—
Agricultural Land	—	—	—	—	0·12	0·16	0·13	—

0·2 cwt. N = 1 cwt. Sulphate of Ammonia.
0·2 cwt. P_2O_5 = 1 cwt. Superphosphate.
0·6 cwt. K_2O = 1 cwt. Muriate of Potash.

Horticulture in Scotland

T. Swarbrick, M.Sc., Ph.D.
Director, The Scottish Horticultural Research Institute, Dundee

By comparison with agriculture, horticulture is much more highly capitalised, employs much more labour and produces much more per unit area of land employed. There is no shortage of land suitable for horticultural expansion in Scotland, but production is at present in balance with demands.

Scots as a people do not eat the range and amount of fruit or vegetables as do their English counterparts, and further expansion must be linked to an increased intake by the food processing industry.

Ample practical and scientific information is available through the three Scottish Agricultural Colleges and through the Research Station to enable growers to begin on sound lines.

INTRODUCTION

In order to discuss the contribution which horticultural industry can make to an expanding Scottish economy, it is necessary to state clearly that horticulture must be treated as an industry in its own right and not as a part of "agriculture". The main reason for this differentiation is the way in which the two industries use the land at their disposal. By comparison with agriculture, horticulture is much more highly capitalised, employs much more labour and produces much more produce per unit area of land employed. In its most extreme case this may be illustrated by the glasshouse section of the industry. It costs upwards of £20,000 to build equipment and bring into use an acre of heated glasshouse, built on land which for agricultural uses would at most not be worth more than £200 per acre. Such an acre of glass would find regular employment for 5 to 6 men and produce 40 to 50 tons of tomatoes plus a crop of flowers and a partial crop of lettuce to a total value of £8,000 to £10,000 or more. In effect, the productive capacity of one acre of heated glass is comparable with that of the average 40 to 60 acre farm. The intensive vegetable grower—such as those to be found in the Lothians and the Clyde Valley—frequently turns off upwards of £400 to £500 worth of produce per acre per year. By comparison, one acre of wheat would be worth £30 to £40, an acre of sugar beet £80 to £90 and an acre of ware potatoes £90 to £100. The important point is that, so far as the employment of capital and labour is concerned, a 5-acre horticultural holding is comparable to a 60 to 80 acre farm.

It must be admitted that as things are at present there is no prospect of the economic expansion of horticulture in Scotland. The present distribution pattern of the horticultural industry in Scotland was determined half a century ago when things were very different from what they are today. For example, 90 per cent. of the Scottish glasshouse industry is centred on the Clyde Valley and was developed there because it was within easy distance of Scotland's industrial belt and because coal could be had at under £1 per ton. Today, of course, the man at the pithead has little or no advantage over the man 20 or even 50 miles away because both have to pay a "standard" price. In these days of fast modern transport there is little or no virtue in the Clyde Valley as a site for a glasshouse industry *when cheap coal is not available*. Indeed, in some respects the valley is a poor site for glasshouses. If, in the future, glasshouse heating must depend upon *standardised* charges for coal, gas, oil or electricity, the siting of glasshouse development will be determined by factors other than the price of fuel, and the development of this part of the horticultural industry will certainly not be in the Clyde Valley.

It is also well known that the main vegetable-producing areas in Scotland are the Clyde Valley and the Lothians. Both these areas developed during the period before the modern food-processing industries and when this highly perishable commodity went to market in horse-drawn vehicles. It must be clearly pointed out that today the modern housewife uses large quantities of canned and frozen fruit and vegetables and the fresh fruit and vegetables must always compete with the canned or frozen product. Fifty years ago when the horticultural industry was developing along with the developing industrialisation of Scotland, there was no such conflict. It was fresh fruit and vegetables bought on a day-to-day basis, or nothing. It should also be noted that despite the large and intensive production of a wide range of vegetables in the two main market-garden areas of Scotland, there is not a single sizeable canning or freezing plant in these areas.

Which brings us to the remarkable fact of the concentration of the Scottish food-processing factories in the Dundee-Arbroath-Montrose-Blairgowrie area. These factories of course rely upon raspberries and peas as their main raw materials, and in addition process fruit both U.K. grown and imported, beetroot, sprouts, beans and sometimes fish. In fact, they process anything which can be bought at a sufficiently attractive price to enable them to sell the product to the public and make a profit.

The main points brought out in this preamble—and which must be kept clearly in mind in considering the possibility of expanding horticultural production as a contributor to an expanded Scottish economy—are as follows:

1. Horticulture is a highly specialised industry, employing large amounts of capital and labour, and produces large quantities of food from small areas of land.
2. The present pattern and location of horticultural production in Scotland was determined over 50 years ago, that is *before* the days of fast motor traffic, refrigeration and large-scale food-processing factories, and standardised charges for coal, gas, oil and electricity.
3. While there is a known, steady demand for fresh produce, the processed foods—canned, frozen and dehydrated—now dominate the trade.

LAND USAGE

There is no shortage of land suitable for horticultural expansion in Scotland. While land which could be used for an expansion of horticulture is at present used by agriculture, the loss to our agricultural production, if horticultural production in Scotland were doubled or trebled, would be insignificant, and there would, of course, be a substantial nett gain since the land would produce two or three times as much food per acre as it does now. It is of course true that the horticulturalist is very particular as to site and type of land. But without going into detail there are thousands of acres of land in the Lothians, in Stirlingshire, Perthshire, Angus, Fife, Aberdeenshire, Kincardineshire and the Black Isle and the Borders at present in agriculture which are potentially good horticultural sites. Such land is not currently used for horticulture because it is too far from a "market". Market in this sense means any large and consistent buyer of a reasonable range of horticultural products.

The importance of a local "market" as a stimulus to local production may be illustrated by the following experience. In mid-summer 1959 a well-known canning company with a large fish cannery at Fraserburgh but with fruit and vegetables canneries in England came to see me to discuss the possibilities of adding fruit and vegetables to their line at Fraserburgh. They wanted for autumn 1959 upwards of 500 tons of carrots. The nearest commercial source of carrots in Scotland was the Perthshire-Angus area, where they are grown in quantity for the local canners. But carrots for canners are normally grown on contract and it was very difficult to get even 200 tons. Research in progress at Mylnefield showed that provided the growers used the right varieties and adopted proved growing methods, there was no reason why carrots and peas could not be grown quite successfully in the Fraserburgh area, and the company was encouraged to try. To cut a long story short, this firm succeeded in 1960 in getting grown for them upwards of 300 acres of peas and upwards of 50 acres of carrots by farmers who had previously never grown these crops. The important point about this development is that both the peas and carrots were completely new crops to the area and have given the growers a far better return (profit) per acre and employed more labour and capital than the crops they were growing.

Suitable land is available in several districts as a basis for a large expansion of horticultural production in Scotland and its diversion to horticulture would have no measurable effect on agricultural production in Scotland.

TECHNICAL ADVICE AND SERVICE

The three Scottish Agricultural Colleges maintain a horticultural advisory service. At present the available manpower is concentrated in areas where there is already sufficient horticulture to warrant the expenditure, but the service covers the whole of Scotland and practical advice, including soil analysis, etc., is available to anyone who wishes it.

The Scottish Horticultural Research Institute is the Horticultural Research Centre for Scotland. Much of the work now in progress aims at providing information on which a soundly based expansion can be based. There are departments of Virology, Pomology, Mycology, Vegetables, Plant Pathology, Genetics and Physiology. A vigorous programme of plant breeding in raspberries, strawberries, black currants and vegetables is under way. The Institute's staff embraces a wide field of knowledge and experience which is at the disposal of all sections of the industry.

PROSPECTS FOR EXPANSION AND DEVELOPMENT

It has been shown that large areas of land now used for agriculture are quite suitable for development to horticulture. It is also known that the colleges maintain an adequate advisory service and that this is backed up by the work of the several Scottish Research Centres, particularly the Scottish Horticultural Research Institute and the Macaulay Institute for Soil Science. Obviously these factors in themselves are not sufficient grounds upon which to base an expansion, although without them expansion of the industry would at best be hazardous in the extreme for newcomers into this specialised field of production.

It must be clearly stated that in general horticultural production is static in Scotland because it is already in balance with existing demands. It is regrettable, but nevertheless true, that the Scots as a people do not eat anything like the range or amount of fruit and vegetables as do their English counterparts. This is not the time or place to make a detailed analysis of the reasons for this regrettable state of affairs, but it must be admitted that in general the English housewife can buy her fruit and vegetables very much—and I mean very much—cheaper than she can in Scotland. One has only to walk the shopping areas of say Birmingham on one afternoon and do the same in Edinburgh or Glasgow the following morning to see this difference. After ten years' residence in Scotland I am still appalled by the way in which *fresh* vegetables are regarded as semi-luxuries by the average weekly wage earner in Scotland. How far this is due to the general high price of vegetables or to the extremely conservative habit it is impossible to say. What is indisputable is the fact that if the Scots as a nation ate the same quantity of fruit and vegetables as their English counterparts, horticultural production in Scotland would have to be stepped up very considerably indeed.

By contrast with the price of fresh fruit and vegetables, which vary from day to day and as between England and Scotland, the prices of the canned goods are very much the same all over the U.K. The processors—probably because they cannot use the excuse of perishability—have standardised their prices, not only over the country as a whole but over the year as a whole. The processor also knows the ceiling price beyond which buying stops. This in its turn has an effect upon the price which the processor is willing to pay the grower, which in practice is often fixed by contract, often before the crop is sown. For example, a processor will contract for carrots at say £10 a ton and peas at £45, delivered to his factory. Growers must decide whether they can earn a profit at these prices. Unfortunately the price of fruit for processing is often fixed by hard bargaining just before picking crop begins. This latter unfortunately leads to wide fluctuations in the price from year to year.

Unless the Scottish public can be persuaded to buy more fresh fruit and vegetables either from the small greengrocer on the corner or the large multiple chain or self-service store the Scottish horticultural grower must face a static or even a declining demand for the range of goods he produces on an all-the-year-round basis. In my view the *small* grower can only hope to survive, let alone expand in Scotland if he produces a speciality line that the public will buy at a price that allows him to employ the labour and the high capital charges that he must inevitably face. The present trend—and this will certainly increase—is for *large-scale* production of a smaller range of fruit and vegetables under conditions where management skill and the high capitalisation involved in the purchase and operation of the specialised machines used in production, washing and packing can be recovered by quantity production. This trend is seen in the way in which the larger processing firms are going into the production side. The largest single canning and freezing firm operating in Scotland is now by far the largest single grower in Scotland.

They operate 5 to 8 large farms and in addition purchase large quantities of fruit, peas and vegetables from other growers. But this makes those firms no longer dependent upon individual growers with whom they have to negotiate prices for the basic intake for their factories, and this makes them very firm negotiators, since the price they are willing to pay is related to that at which they can themselves produce on a large scale. Other canning companies are following although as yet there are some who rely entirely upon supplies purchased from individual growers.

The point I wish to make is that any further expansion in horticultural production in Scotland must be clearly and definitely linked to an increased intake of the products of horticulture by the food-processing industry.

Experience over the last thirty years shows that the processing companies have placed their factories in these areas where there was already an established pattern of production, e.g. in the Worcester, Wisbech, Cambridgeshire, Kent, West Lancashire, and Perth-Angus areas. In all these areas there is extensive production of a range of fruit and vegetables sufficient to ensure a six to seven months' processing season based on local production. In no case to my knowledge has any firm put up a factory in a *potentially* productive area, but this is precisely what we must have in Scotland if we are to expand horticultural production, which means getting production going in new areas.

In Scotland the factories have gone mainly into Perth-Angus. These factories are based essentially on raspberries and peas and strawberries from local production with various fruit and vegetables brought in in quantity at other seasons. In Scotland the main potential development areas are (*a*) the Carse of Stirling, (*b*) the Black Isle, (*c*) the Dumfries area.

In the last two decades it has become established practice to attract new industries into areas of high unemployment by both direct and indirect support from public funds. The industrial estates where factory space is built and leased on very generous terms is a case in point. My contention is that the whole of Scotland north of Dundee is under-employed and that there is not much more that can be done to increase agricultural employment. But reasonable sized processing factories making a range of products would employ people both in producing the raw material and in its processing. I visualise that these factories would process meat, poultry and near the coast also fish, etc.

All this of course presupposes that the factories could find a market for their produce. This is something which must be faced elsewhere in another connection.

CONCLUSIONS

1. There is no lack of suitable land on which to base an expanded horticultural production in Scotland. Large areas of suitable land occur in the Black Isle and on the Moray Firth area.

2. Ample practical and scientific information is available through the College Advisory staffs and the Research Stations to enable growers near to this industry to begin on sound lines.

3. The present horticultural production in Scotland is in uneasy balance with existing demands by both the fresh (domestic) and the processing industries, and only if an increased demand can be created would it be possible to expand horticultural production on sound economic lines.

INTRODUCTION TO DISCUSSION

M. A. M. Dickie, O.B.E., D.S.M., M.A., B.SC., N.D.A.
Late Chief Lands Officer, Department of Agriculture for Scotland

I want to suggest a slight alteration in the order in which we shall deal with the large numbers of papers which come into the session during which I am acting as Deputy Chairman. I intend first to consider the purely agricultural and horticultural uses and follow that with the conflicts in land use, which dovetails better into what, I think, may prove to be an interesting discussion—the conflict of land use between forestry and agriculture. [A few words on procedure.] I should perhaps at this stage introduce the speakers whose papers we are going to consider first: Dr. G. P. Wibberley of the Department of Agricultural Economics, Wye College, University of London; Mr. W. O. Kinghorn, Technical Development Officer, Department of Agriculture and Fisheries for Scotland; Mr. J. D. Nutt, Advisory Economist, The Edinburgh and East of Scotland College of Agriculture, Edinburgh; Mr. J. A. Gilchrist, Senior Economist, The West of Scotland Agricultural College, Glasgow; Mr. G. G. Hayes, Agricultural Economist, The North of Scotland College of Agriculture, Aberdeen; and Dr. T. Swarbrick, Director, The Scottish Horticultural Research Institute. I now call on Dr. Stewart to report on the papers.

STATEMENT BY THE REPORTER

A. B. Stewart, M.A., B.SC., PH.D., F.R.I.C., F.R.S.E.
Director, The Macaulay Institute for Soil Research

Those of you who have done your homework will, I am sure, agree that it is impossible in a brief report to do full justice to the wealth of information and of carefully considered views contained in the six papers before us this session. You will appreciate, therefore, that all I will attempt to do is to scratch the surface of the fields which the individual authors have so ably cultivated. Although the discussion, as the Chairman indicated, will come to Dr. Wibberley's paper last in this particular series, I think from the point of view of reporting we will take it as being in the order in which the papers are published. We are, of course, all familiar with the fact that disagreements or conflicts on land use do quite regularly arise. I need remind you only of the worthy arguments that take place occasionally between foresters and farmers, between industry and amenity, and so on. In his paper Dr. Wibberley stresses that conflicts in land use arise mainly through differences in the situation of particular pieces of land. Topography, soil conditions and micro-climate are factors of decisive importance to agriculture and to forestry, but for such other uses as residential, industrial, commercial and amenity purposes or for communications, land quality as such is much less important. Broadly, the importance of each piece of land is reflected in the price it commands in the open market, but Dr.

Wibberley points out that, if the highest market price is the determinant of the land use pattern, certain undesirable movements can and do take place. This leads him to thought-provoking consideration of the question of the private or the public control of land uses; he shows how committees and public bodies can do much by persuasion towards guiding land use pattern but underlines that the Town and Country Land Planning Organisation in this country is primarily permissive rather than initiative. It is not always easy to initiate changes in land use, but increasing private mobility is undoubtedly helping to bridge the gulf between the more or less isolated rural area and the crowded city. There are many points that could be stressed further in Dr. Wibberley's paper, but I think these will emerge in discussion later on.

The four papers by Messrs. Kinghorn, Nutt, Gilchrist and Hayes give excellently comprehensive national and regional pictures of the immediate past, the present and the likely future of agriculture in Scotland. Nationally, agricultural land use is determined largely by the fact that mountains and moorlands occupy about two-thirds of the total area, leaving for more intensive agricultural systems undulating lowland areas hemmed in between the hills and the sea. Broadly, as we all know, rainfall increases from east to west and, over the years, farming systems have been developed to suit climatic and soil conditions, elevation, topography and other factors. Regionally, the main farming types which are dealt with in detail, from both the technical and the economic viewpoints, are arable-livestock, dairying, cropping and livestock rearing, with emphasis on cropping in the east and south-east, on dairying in the south-west and on rearing or feeding in the north-east and north. Overall agricultural production is now about 60 per cent. above pre-war level and annual agricultural output is currently estimated at £168 million, 80 per cent. of which comprises livestock products. It is emphasised that despite a wide diversity of soil and climatic conditions, livestock is almost everywhere the foundation of farming, whether it be the dairy cow, the fattening bullock, the hill cow, the pig or the hill or upland ewe. Raspberry growing, the seed potato trade and pedigree livestock breeding are small but important specialist forms of production. About half of all the farms in Scotland are tenanted and the remainder owner-occupied. It is pointed out that the proportion of the latter is slowly but steadily increasing. Over 90 per cent. of Scotland's farming activity is carried out in some 30,000 farms inclusive of about 2,000 horticultural, poultry and pig farms. Of the latter, a high proportion are in the central valley. The present full-time labour force is some 68,000 workers, a number which is steadily falling due to mechanisation, redeployment and increased efficiency. These are but a selection of the facts and figures given in the papers before you.

A point stressed by all four authors is that one of the current economic problems of the farming industry is its greatly increased capital requirements, and Mr. Kinghorn makes the important point that it is the introduction of capital resources in the broad sense, rather than the basic natural resources themselves, which has laid the foundation of modern agriculture. The farming industry is highly organised and is supported and aided in its task by ancillary industries and by a large variety of organisations, both private and official. Among various developments to which Mr. Kinghorn draws special attention are the post-war realisation that grass, our commonest natural plant, is also one of the most valuable farm crops. It is mentioned that the agricultural industry in Scotland is well served both by enlightened trade organisations and by State-sponsored research and development. Mr. Kinghorn instances the modern comprehensive approach to research whereby a single practical farming problem can be analysed and interpreted into a series of scientific questions and possibilities, and a comprehensive attack made, both through the background work of a chain of research organisations and intensively and directly through the excellent advisory or extension services provided by the three Colleges of Agriculture in the country.

Among other points of importance in the regional picture of agriculture in Scotland I mention the following: Mr. Nutt examines for the east and south-east the changes which have taken place in land use over the past 20 years and shows that, apart from the loss of a certain proportion to non-agricultural usage, there has been little change in the broad pattern of agriculture in the area. The really significant changes have taken place within the arable section both as regards the distribution between tillage and rotation crops and the importance of individual tillage crops. Heavier manuring and other technical developments have led to high crop yields, increased stock-carrying capacity and intensification of land use. Mr. Nutt estimates that nett output in the south-east of Scotland is now more than half as much again as in 1939. From consideration of the differences between average and high outputs from farms of different types and of the potential arising from future improvements and technology, he concludes that an overall increase in output of 20 to 25 per cent. is still possible through the more effective use of the agricultural land in the south-east of Scotland.

Mr. Gilchrist draws attention to the fact that, within the area served by the West of Scotland Agricultural College, lies the Clyde conurbation with a population of around two million people, constituting by far the largest food market in Scotland. Milk supplies come almost wholly from local production. To meet the demand for other foods, supplies come from other parts of Scotland, from south of the Border and from overseas, and he stresses the importance of the fact that urban food consumption habits are moving into new patterns. He sees little likelihood of changes in the key types of farming in the immediate future. As in other regions, the trends in production for the staple commodities depend mainly on political and economic decision at Governmental level, whilst at farm level the important factors to be examined are technical and organisational means of lowering production costs. Mr. Gilchrist also deals in detail with the wide diversity of farming types occurring in the West College area, with special reference to hill sheep or upland stock rearing, cash cropping, especially potatoes, in the low ground areas, dairying, small livestock and horticulture, the latter particularly in the Clyde Valley. The already high rate of supplies for some commodities, the future of the U.K. in Europe, inter-Commonwealth relations and the annual subsidy bill to agriculture are all pieces of what Mr. Gilchrist describes as a formidable agricultural jigsaw pattern with many other pieces still to be fitted in. He has analysed carefully the factors involved in improving farm performance, which he considers will hinge on the efficiency of the technical and economic processes of production in the types of farming already common to the province.

In discussing agriculture in the north of Scotland, Mr. Hayes gives a comprehensive picture of the structure of agriculture in the area, and draws attention to some of the weaknesses of the present system and suggests how these might be corrected. In particular, he distinguishes between the problems of the highland as distinct from the lowland areas. Size of farm is shown to be a factor of major importance in the determination of profit level and Mr. Hayes expresses the view that, particularly in the north and north-west, the average size of farm is too small to permit the development of permanently viable units, except those which are highly specialised and intensively operated. He shows, for instance, that many of the farmers in the area would be better off financially by leaving the farm, investing the capital obtained and working for another farmer. Mr. Hayes emphasises very strongly, however, that many of these farmers fully realise the position but prefer the freedom and the non-monetary rewards which they obtain by being their own masters. Mr. Hayes also suggests that although there is an abundance of technical skill there is a certain degree of economic inertia in the agricultural community. He sees scope for increased fertiliser usage and for improvements in the general level of livestock carry, and expresses the view that too much milk is being produced in the north area, particularly on farms which are not ideally suited for the purpose. He draws attention to the importance of further education which, although necessarily a long-term policy, is, in his view, the key to a prosperous and progressive agricultural community. He also expresses the view that a reduction in the number of agricultural workers need not be regarded as undesirable and that the maintenance of a rural population should depend more on encouraging industry to go into the country rather than restricting the flow of workers out of agriculture.

In his paper on horticulture in Scotland Dr. Swarbrick deals exhaustively with the contribution which this industry can make to an expanding Scottish economy. Compared to agriculture, horticulture is much more highly capitalised, employs much more labour and produces more per unit of land employed. Dr. Swarbrick points out that the present distribution pattern of the horticultural industry in Scotland was determined half a century ago when things were very different from what they are today. Now that cheap coal, for instance, is no longer available, Dr. Swarbrick sees no virtue in confining the industry to its traditional home in the Clyde Valley and stresses that there is no shortage of land suitable for horticultural expansion in Scotland. He goes on to point out that Scots as a people do not consume the range or amount of fruit and vegetables consumed by their English counterparts and considers that further horticultural expansion must be linked to an increased intake by the food-processing industry. While there is a known, steady demand for fresh produce, the processed foods, canned, frozen and dehydrated, now dominate the trade and make it necessary to look afresh at the horticultural industry. Dr. Swarbrick draws special attention to the horticultural potentialities of such land as occurs in the Black Isle and Moray Firth areas, and stresses that ample practical and scientific information is available through the three Scottish Colleges of Agriculture and his own Scottish Horticultural Research Institute. That is, in brief, some of the points covered by the various speakers. Dr. Swarbrick has stressed the importance of the food-processing industries. Perhaps in the course of discussion there will be an opportunity for him to say something about the non-food aspects of horticulture, such as bulb-growing.

DISCUSSION

Mr. W. B. Swan, *National Farmers' Union of Scotland*

My Lords, Ladies and Gentlemen: I am very grateful to have the opportunity of opening this discussion on behalf of the National Farmers' Union of Scotland.

The matter to which I would like to refer to specifically this morning is the question of the development of rural and upland areas. Mr. Kinghorn in his paper mentioned that about two-thirds of the area in Scotland is upland and rough grazing and I think that this is a matter to which we have got to give very great attention. It is interesting to recall that some three years ago a Committee under the Chairmanship of Sir Solly Zuckerman was appointed to discuss the natural resources of the country and made this report: "We need to remind ourselves that a nation as dependent as is the United Kingdom on imports can ill afford to neglect the possible savings that might be obtained by the exploitation of the whole of its land resources. On the grounds of the problem of the balance of payments we conclude that it would be imprudent to allow the wastage of our marginal land and the decline in its fertility to continue unchecked, as though it were a necessary and inevitable process."

I think that this report highlights the importance of our upland and rough grazings, and in the early part of the war the Government themselves recognised the importance of production in these areas by introducing a special type of scheme known as the Marginal Agricultural Production Scheme. The aim of this scheme was to try to increase the production in the uplands of the country. This scheme was operated by the A.E.C.s and money was paid on the basis of work done. Farmers had to submit receipted accounts for seeds, manures, cultivations carried out, and so on, and the scheme was extremely popular because farmers felt that the money was going where it was required and the job had to be completed before payment was made.

Since the war the situation has changed considerably. The emphasis has become more on winter keep, on producing better grass, and the A.E.C. have modified their assistance to meet these requirements.

In this country today we only produce about 33 per cent. of the mutton required and some 67 per cent. of the beef required, and we can see the vital need of an adequate reservoir for the production of cattle and sheep in our hills, and the cattle and sheep which are produced in the hill land are without doubt the best-quality cattle and sheep in the country and produce the best beef, lamb and mutton.

Here is what Dr. Stewart himself says: "Nor should it be forgotten that the production of more winter keep for stock for all such land would in itself do much to accelerate the cycle of improvement in hill land grazings. The provision of more winter keep means that there would be more stock to act as mowing machines and manure barrows and hence be incidental improving agents on our hills." These words emphasise the importance of cattle and sheep on our hills, and this can best be obtained by the special type of assistance known as the Marginal Agricultural Production Scheme.

This type of assistance has valuable social effects too because, as we know, it is difficult to sustain the economy of our remote areas, and I think it is generally recognised that special assistance will be required if we are to maintain the population in our farms and in the remote areas of our counties, and the more prosperous these areas can become the better will be their purchasing power, which will have its effect on the economy and the more urban areas also.

The Marginal Agricultural Production Scheme has recognised very widely the special difficulties of the remote areas, particularly the Highlands and Islands. So you can imagine, sir, the feelings of alarm and despondency which were felt throughout the country when, some two years ago, the Government intimated a decision that they were planning to cancel the assistance provided under the Marginal Production Assistance

Scheme. The Scheme cost some £1¼ million at that time, which is a comparatively small figure when we consider the total assistance given to agricultural support, and many people just could not understand the reason for the decision.

The position today is that the scheme is being operated on a very seriously reduced basis, probably about half what it was two years ago, and this has happened in spite of extensive protests by farmers and landowners, particularly through their organisations—the Farmers' Union and the Scottish Landowners' Federation—up and down the whole length and breadth of the country, and it was remarkable that when discussions were taking place on this matter every farmer, every landowner seemed to support the need for this special type of assistance whether they themselves were going to gain financially or not.

We hope very much that there will be a change of heart on the part of the Government in this matter, and for the sake of the future of this very important aspect of our agricultural production we hope that the Government can be persuaded to realise the merit of adequate assistance to farmers in these areas and will in the future ensure that this assistance is provided.

Sir Robert Urquhart, *Crofters Commission*

My Lords, Ladies and Gentlemen: A quick word of thanks, Mr. Deputy Chairman, but a sincere one from the Crofters Commission to the Scottish Council for the invitation to be present here and for this magnificent material so well and effectively presented. As you know we have been given by Act of Parliament a mandate which by no means is easy to fulfil; one which indeed we may not succeed in fulfilling. It is not that we have lack of information; there is masses of it, but much of it is biased, much of it out of date, and so we are the more grateful to have this up-to-date and expert exposé of so many facts. But with that ray of appreciation, a word, I'm sorry, of regret. We have over 20,000 registered crofts, and the land involved must be over 200,000 acres of reputed arable and something over one million acres of grazing land. So it was with regret, sir, that when the agenda for the admirable and well-inspired Conference reached us that we searched in vain for the word "crofting" anywhere in it. Now we have no objection in the world to scepticism about crofting or about our task. We even excuse cynicism, for the Highlands have known much failure and much defeat. But the land that I mention is a significant resource, and we would very much like the guidance of a body like this as to how we might attempt to deal with it. We will willingly discuss with you. Crofting is dead in many areas and in others it is resolutely committing suicide, because some crofters are showing that same awkwardness which Dr. Fraser Darling mentioned in his Highland Survey, that awkwardness which is their reaction to any attempt at change and betterment. But I do ask you to mark this; that after 80 years of steady run-down we have, as a Commission, found the unity and courage to face facts which have been consistently ducked, among them the one that Lord Napier, with great foresight, pronounced a long time ago in the debate on the 1886 Act, namely, that the sentimental gesture of conferring security of tenure on entirely uneconomic units was a costly mistake, no kindness at all in the long run. We have pointed out that the crofters themselves have recognised this long ago with a great deal more insight than some people in authority have shown. There has developed over many years widespread sub-letting, putting the land into the hands of people who are able and willing to use it. Now, what we would like to do is to get such land legally into the hands of the sub-tenant, who at present has no security whatsoever, when the tenant himself does not want to use it, when in fact he has retired from crofting. We emphasise that the retired crofter would nevertheless be secure in his home, which is after all what he really wants and needs, and that he should have compensation as usual for any improvements to land which he surrenders. The Commission would welcome the independent views of a body such as this on their proposals.

Mr. David Lowe, *Musselburgh*

Mr. Chairman, My Lords, Ladies and Gentlemen: Anything I say must come now surely as an anticlimax. When agriculture suffers from paralysis, I am sure that crofting and the crofters will revitalise it and indeed fertilise it. To turn to horticulture, Dr. Swarbrick has presented a most important paper in his usual forthright manner. He states his views—while growers would, I am sure, be very glad indeed to see people in Scotland eat fruit and vegetables on the same scale, the same ratio, as they do south of the Border, I do not think anything we do today will affect their culinary habits. I think it would be better if we tried to push our Scots oats and our liquid output over south of the Border and thus help our agriculture. He says in his paper more than once that there is room in Scotland for more canning factories, but I disagree entirely with that. In fact, much of the present output is sold south of the Border. The reason for factories initially being established in Scotland was because of our one unique product for canning—the raspberry. These raspberries we grow very well indeed. Although they only occupy a few weeks of the factories' production, it was the basis of their location and the ancillaries, that is the growing of peas and other vegetables for canning as well as the canning of strawberries, which do quite well in Perth and Angus. The work of the Fruit Trials Committee in Scotland over the years has shown, through repeated experiments, that the reason raspberries are grown best in the Carse of Gowrie is that the climate suits them. You will find, if you investigate, why spring cabbages are grown in the Lothians and not nearer the main market in Glasgow and the west; this can be traced back to the foresight or, if you like, the experience of our forefathers. The reason they are grown in the east is that the excessive rainfall in the west just does not suit them.

I think myself that thc cost of transport will limit any great expansion in canning. I must also take issue on one point he makes when he says that canned and frozen fruit and vegetables now dominate the trade. This is, of course, not true. People still eat much more of the fresh fruit and vegetables in this country than they do from cans. But I do not want to join issue with Dr. Swarbrick on all the things he said because I cannot agree with some of them. I would like, with your permission, to say a word or two on something which occurred yesterday—Bruce Russell talking about water usage. This is very important to horticulture. I could not get an opportunity to talk yesterday, but perhaps the most forthright statement made in the forenoon was this one by Councillor Bruce Russell to the effect that we urgently needed legislation to control the use of water from our streams and rivers, and he mentioned particularly the Tyne, and the facts as he had ascertained them which meant that the Tyne might be pumped dry. From that point of view, of course, it might be that he is quite right and we do need legislation, but what I immediately thought of was that if this was left on record as the only expression of opinion here on water usage for irrigation it must be misleading, although one must take care that sufficient water is left in the rivers. If we want to look at Scotland's resources with a view to their best use, surely this one, water, with its great potential, must be used to the best advantage, and we would do well to turn our minds to this problem and of course to find a solution, an obvious one being more storage of water in our hills. We know how only last year the situation was drastic in the City of Edinburgh, with water rationing, and how industry had to spend a lot of capital to cut down their consumption of water by re-usage, and so on. We in horticulture especially, and I am quite sure to a great extent also in agriculture, can use more water. If irrigation is going to get us better crops, then I would maintain that this is sufficient reason for exploiting this resource to the full. In some specialist branches of horticulture—for the last 30 years I have used 8 to 10 inches of water every year. Now this pays me, and this is the sort of thing that the Press might make a headline from, as it would be true to say that what I sell is largely water. You might think it would be a wrong thing, therefore, to apply more. On the other hand, unless vegetables and most fruits are so grown that there is always sufficient water, they are not worth eating. The addition of water is, I think, both economically sound and I think from your point of view, sir, something which should be encouraged. We know the tremendous increase in production we can have by judicious application of two or three inches of water to, say, early potatoes. This, of course, is done on quite a large scale in many counties of England and in some parts of Scotland today. We also know how it is sometimes economic to apply two or three inches of water to grass in the east of the country. Therefore I would say that there is an urgent problem to see how water can be stored in our hills so that it can be available to be used as a tool for agriculture.

Professor HUGH NICOL, *West of Scotland Agricultural College*

Mr. Chairman, My Lords, Ladies and Gentlemen: I think something might be said for a recent small development which should interest this Council, namely the establishment of bulb growing in the Southern Hebrides. This is on machar land which is suitable normally only for rough grazing, and it arose through the initiative of Mr. J. B. R. Anderson, a Horticultural Adviser in Lanarkshire. This man got his ideas taken up and began trials himself, mainly in Tiree; and, with the College's help, he aroused the active interest of the Department of Agriculture and other bodies. The project was taken over by the recently retired Director of County Work. The present state is that a limited company, non-profitmaking, has been formed, so that the thing may be said to be established. I admit that the scope for its extension and adoption is limited. It involves quite new problems of technique, storage and marketing—and there it is. It is a thing which has been taken up quite readily by the crofters, although it is a completely new crop. It has been quite a little success. But apart from a few paragraphs in the Press while the scheme was in its inception, and relating to its early history so to speak, the Scottish Press has, as far as I am aware, taken no interest in it. This moves me to remark that, in general, the Scottish Press shows little interest in what the Scottish Colleges are doing, or indeed in the doings of any other research institution, with the exception of social surveys and some aspects of heavy engineering. I understand that in the States the Press is always on the doorstep of scientific institutions and pressing the inmates to reveal their unfinished thoughts, as it were. Our more sober Press seems to go to the opposite extreme—I will leave it at that. There is established a small but very promising industry producing good-quality bulbs, fit for export. It offers a promising return to the crofter, who does the work mainly himself. The only collective account that I know in print was published last year in the West College's *Former Student's Club Journal.*

LORD BILSLAND

I think that so far this morning we have had an interesting and useful morning. I am sorry I have to leave you to keep another engagement. Before leaving I should like, as President of the Scottish Council, to pay a very sincere tribute of appreciation and admiration to Mr. Elgood and his Committee and all staff concerned for the magnificent way in which this Symposium has been organised and presented. I feel sure it will be of the greatest benefit, and I know that Mr. Elgood and his colleagues intend to follow it up very closely and to get the fullest value out of all the discussion contributions made so authoritatively by people so well qualified to discuss the subjects of which they are masters.

DEPUTY CHAIRMAN

I would like now to call on Mr. Robert Grieve.

MR. ROBERT GRIEVE, *Department of Health for Scotland*

I see around me in this particular session so many people that I know are bound up with forestry, agriculture or wildlife conservation that the remarks I have to make seem to be perhaps excessively on the urban side. But I am speaking, of course, to Dr. Wibberley's paper on multiple land use. Dr. Wibberley has fairly expressed, I think, in general terms the problem of balance in the use of land, the price mechanism against community needs. This is a stock dilemma in Western civilisation countries. It is one of the greatest problems to work out the balance between these two things—what the community needs, and on the other hand what freedom should be given to the entrepreneurs. I do not propose to comment on that in any great detail, but I am going to talk about the point he made about aptitude of land for certain purposes; I should like to make the point that an equally important thing is the attitude of people to what use the land should be put. I think, to give an example, of a place like Holland. An attitude of mind—and mark you, it is nothing more than an attitude of mind—can, in a sense, force Government (as in the original Zuider Zee reclamations) to make big land use changes, because public opinion considers it necessary.

During these three days a great number of papers will have been presented to us by various specialists in various fields; in a sense I suppose this is the first really big attempt to sum up the resources of this country of ours. I myself was asked to give a paper on Town and Country Planning because it was considered, I think, by the organisers of this Conference that Town and Country Planning had already produced a very great deal of survey information. The Planning Acts, as they apply to local authorities, are designed to require them to produce comprehensive surveys as part of this development plan.

The Acts (and those Acts which are related to them—like the New Town Act and the Town Development Act) which regulate the process of planning are beginning to have an observable effect on the face of this country, and they are also having a hidden effect in the sense that the development plans of the local authorities have been progressively covering the country with expressions of developing policy as to the use of land. After the war a number of great regional plans were produced, one of which in particular, the Clyde Valley Plan, has had a profound effect in regional policy-making. All these plans are having the effect, as Dr. Wibberley intimated, of distorting the "natural" pattern which would have developed but for the town planning movement; whether for good or ill is a matter which exercises people's attention now and again—I think for good. And whatever one may think about the whole process it is a fact that the great majority of Scotland is now covered by development plans, by expressions of land use policy. The whole central belt of Scotland is covered and many rural areas, although the operations of the planning system are not perhaps designed to operate there to the same extent as they are in urban areas; the process is really designed to arbitrate in competition in land use, whereas often the rural problem is to induce competition in land use. Now, it would be too much to say that these existing surveys—because it is essential in these plans to produce a survey first—are almost a new Domesday Book for Scotland; but, together with this Symposium and, I hope, others like it, it may well be the beginning of a process which will cover Scotland with an almost complete statement of its resources. Already there is a very great amount of survey material in these development plans, and some of the material of this Symposium overlaps it substantially. What I want to say now—and certainly something like it must be said at the end of the Symposium—is that a very eminent Scot, Sir Patrick Geddes, who set up the Outlook Tower on Castle Hill, produced the famous triad, "Place, Work, Folk"; a means of expressing the necessity for co-ordinating the policies which should condition the development of a country. He preached the need for integrating these three concepts by a process of thought, of administration and Government, and he summed this up in another phrase, "Survey, Analysis, Plan". By the end of tomorrow you will have had three days of discussion and presentation of information; and a great mass of material. May I say, Gentlemen, that as a planner with a long experience I have always found it very much easier to do a survey of a resource than to produce a statement of policy as to how it should be used or used in relation to other resources. This great mass of information will lie on a table somewhere; some of it may even remain in our minds. But, by and large, it will be a great mass of very nearly indigestible material in the communal stomach of the Symposium. What is to be done with it? I am merely suggesting that it must follow the pattern of survey, analysis, plan. The next step, that is, the next step after being quite sure that one has everything that is really necessary in the way of facts about resources, is to analyse it; but not to analyse it in any narrow way, in any "Secretariat of Land Use" sense, but in some total manner, so that sense in the widest sense emerges from it. At the moment, the only legislative arrangements designed to do this sort of thing are our Town and Country Planning legislation. It is certainly not for me to say that these enactments constitute the only possible machinery for putting all this kind of material together, analysing it and crystallising it. I simply say to you that there must be some kind of machinery—official, unofficial—which can digest material of this sort and put it to useful purposes in an orderly, coherent manner. In other words, it must be used for some kind of plan, and there can be many kinds of plans. I should like merely to finish up by saying that Dr. Wibberley's paper has pointed in a very general way to the basic dilemma with which a relatively highly developed country is faced. It is the dilemma which has produced planning and survey for planning; but I should like to repeat that, as in so much early Town and Country Planning work, the danger lies in letting survey dominate synthesis, plan and action.

WRITTEN CONTRIBUTIONS

Scottish Peat and Land Development Association

Reclamation of Marginal and Sub-marginal Land Survey, 1959-60

Introduction

For a number of years the problem of the marginal and sub-marginal land in Scotland has occupied the attention of the Scottish Peat and Land Development Association and, during the past two years, attempts have been made to assess the extent of the problem, the potentialities of the land concerned and the economic aspects of reclamation work. The extent of the problem is roughly measured by the fact that in 1958 some 11 million acres were returned as rough grazing, equivalent to 73·5 per cent. of the total area of crops and grass in Scotland. The official statistics, however, give no guide to the extent to which this vast area is capable of improvement. To even the most superficial observer there are considerable areas which simply could not be tackled by the cultural methods available to the occupiers of rough grazings. The nature of the terrain, accessibility and labour all present problems which are far from easily solved—to say nothing of the problems of providing adequate capital to undertake improvements on any extensive scale.

During the summer of 1959 an attempt was made to collate the available information relating to a restricted area in the neighbourhood of Newton Stewart. This study could do little more than outline the problem in very general terms; the available statistics and reports on the area did not provide adequate data to study the area with any degree of precision as regards soil types, herbage types, drainage, layout of farms and all the other factors associated with land use. Following this it was decided to take steps to ascertain what factors were involved in cases where land reclamation had been undertaken. Since it was apparent that to continue further work on studying the overall extent of the problem would involve a considerable expenditure of time, money and trained personnel, it was hoped that something useful might materialise from a more restricted study which might demonstrate the potentialities of reclamation.

To this end members of the Association were invited to submit details of the work which they themselves had carried out on their holdings. Survey forms were circulated and a total of thirty-two replies were received. Before trying to collate the data provided by this survey one or two general comments may not be out of place. To some extent the present survey suffers from the same weaknesses as the official statistics and the wider reports studied previously. This is not to criticise those members who co-operated in the survey; these weaknesses are inevitable where views and even factual data are given by different people who place their own construction on the questions asked and give information in ways which are open to varied interpretation. Another and very substantial difficulty arises from two facts. First, it is often a matter of years before the full benefits of the actual cultivations, drainage, manurial applications and reseeding become evident; secondly, it is not easy to give precise information on the extent or cost of such operations after a lapse of, often, many years. It was not unexpected, therefore, to find that much of the information provided for the survey was given in very general or descriptive terms. All the information given in this form had to be translated into more concrete terms of quantities and costs. This has meant that a certain amount of estimation and interpolation has been done. On the other hand, care has been taken when making any estimates to avoid cost reduction or to put too high values on estimates of the increased production resulting from reclamation work.

One further point must be borne in mind, reclamation work is almost without exception carried out by farmers endowed with a high degree of management, progressive in their outlook and in a position and willing to make the necessary capital outlay, even though this aspect of the situation is very considerably mitigated by the various grants and subsidies available in connection with this sort of enterprise. Thus it should not be taken as axiomatic that expenditure on reclamation work will, of itself, bring in a given return, or indeed any return. Good management is essential to the success of such work, and how much of the returns should be attributed to the work itself or to the management of land and stock subsequently is one of the imponderables which make the study of agriculture so fascinating and, at the same time, so frustrating. The final answer is never quite clear cut.

General Conditions

To ennumerate all the conditions under which reclamation work has been carried out would almost entail a detailed exposition of each of the 32 records sent in for study. There seems no limit to the range of conditions under which reclamation has been carried out. Work has been done on land at about sea-level and up to as high an elevation as 1,200 ft. Some areas are in exposed conditions, others are sheltered or lying to the sun. Soil types vary from gravel and shale to heavy clay, and peat may or may not be the predominant characteristic. One case quotes 10 ft. of peat; another quotes bracken 4 to 5 ft. in height. In some areas drainage has been a problem; in other areas the natural drainage is adequate. The indigenous herbage is equally variable in type. The intriguing question which cannot be avoided at this stage is: What are the reasons for land being in the condition it is in? Basically, the reason must be economic—the question being whether it has been worth while to carry out development work on land which the improvers have now shown can be brought into a much higher state of productivity. In this connection it may be equally pertinent to speculate not only on the conditions which inhibited development in the past or which have promoted some development in the present, but also on the conditions which may obtain in the future when dependence on extended production of livestock may be a cardinal feature of domestic food policy. In this context the present survey does at least give some indication of the potential productivity and the economies of reclamation work.

It is apparent from the survey records that each piece of reclamation work has been approached on very individualistic lines. The only common feature has been the recognition that basic applications of lime and/or slag were necessary to correct the chronic acidity of soils which have been neglected for long periods of time. Apart from this, individual conditions have shown marked variations, and, quite possibly, individual views as to how to overcome these difficulties have shown equal variations. In some cases there has been what might be described as the massive approach by means of deep, single-furrow ploughing followed by necessary cultural operations to ensure a suitable seed bed; at the other extreme there is a case of no more than applying slag and switching the type of grazing stock from sheep to cattle. In all cases there must have been the balancing of such factors as the necessary cultivations, manuring, type of seed mixture, drainage and even fencing against not only the objective aimed at but the time over which the improvement should take place and the capital available. Against this background any general uniformity of method could not be expected. Neither was direct reseeding to grass the uniform practice; in some cases one or more crops of rape were grown and fed off before attempting to establish an improved sward. In some cases reclaimed land was absorbed in the normal rotation of the arable land. In short, management has been a crucial factor in determining how improvement should be carried out.

Costs of Reclamation

From what has been said already concerning the methods employed to carry out reclamation work it will be realised that costs will differ widely from case to case. In view of the limited number of cases it would have been entirely misleading to try and group all or any together with the object of arriving at some commonly used method or average costs. Such concepts would be largely meaningless. In many cases, too, the information was not sufficiently detailed to avoid some degree of estimation. This was particularly the case where fencing and/or drainage was concerned. In such cases, possibly involving work over a long period of time, it could not be expected that the improver could supply full details of labour and cost. It has, however, been possible in a number of cases to arrive at a reasonable measure of the costs involved in the actual operations associated with reclamation after allowing for grants under such schemes as ploughing, M.A.P. or under the Livestock Rearing Acts. The available information on net costs can be summarised by saying that the average net cost for 22 cases worked out at £18, 3s. 6d. per acre. But this figure has very little significance in view of the wide range in the costs of individual reclamation work. The highest net cost was £43 per acre in a case which involved blasting out tree roots as well as extensive cultivations. The next highest cost was £31 per acre involving deep ploughing and extensive cultivations, and this may perhaps be taken as an indication of the upper limit of net costs under more usual conditions. The lowest net cost was £7, 5s. per acre, involving no more than the application of lime and slag and seeding with a reasonably good seeds mixture.

Some indication of the general run of costs under varying conditions is given by roughly grouping the costs in relation to the intensity of the work carried out. This has been done under three broad headings:

(*a*) Work involving heavy cultivations, plus liming and/or slagging and sowing out.
(*b*) Work involving moderate cultivations, plus liming and/or slagging and sowing out.
(*c*) Work involving a minimum or no cultivations, plus liming and/or slagging and sowing out.

The average net costs per acre were: (*a*) £31, 2s. 0d.; (*b*) £17, 5s. 6d.; (*c*) £13, 7s. 6d.

These figures are only the best estimates which can be made based on the available data in the survey, and those aspects of the work, particularly drainage and fencing operations, for which detailed information is lacking in most cases, would add appreciably to these costs.

The Value of Reclamation

The main question in any activity involving the use of economic resources is simply whether any particular course of action is likely to be worth while in terms of increased income. In this connection the survey was designed to obtain information on the extent of the increased productivity of the improved land. It was not surprising that it was even more difficult to obtain anything in the way of precise measures of the value of improvements. It is not usual for ordinary farm operations to be carried out on the same lines as detailed experimental work which would take full records of all resources used and make precise measurements of productivity both before and after. The replies to this section of the questionnaire were, in the main, couched in either qualitative terms or in very broad estimates of the increased productivity, such as an estimate of the increased stock-carrying capacity in terms of either sheep or cattle, or both. In spite of the difficulty of trying to bring such assessments down to an £ s. d. basis so as to compare the results with the costs, it was evident that, in the majority of cases, improvement had been well worth while and the improver could look back on his work with considerable satisfaction from a business point of view. He would also have the additional pride and satisfaction which every good farmer feels when he can look round at a piece of work well done.

Going back to the estimates of cost, it has been suggested that these are somewhat on the low side if all the capital expenditure entailed could have been properly assessed. To some extent the estimates of the increase in productivity must also be regarded with some scepticism as the method of translating improvement expressed in terms of stock-carrying capacity into £ s. d. has been done on a very empirical basis. The results of converting the stated increases in productivity may be summarised by saying that the average difference between "before" and "after" was in the order of £13 per acre. This, of course, is not a measure of the profitability, but could be better described as the increase in gross product consequent upon the improvements. A whole range of "working" costs would be entailed in connection with this increase in gross product. But it is, perhaps, not stretching things too far to suggest that by increasing the turnover of the farm in this way more efficient use can be made of the overhead elements in farm costs and there should be some measure of profit to reward the improver's efforts.

Figures have already been given suggesting what the costs per acre might be at heavy, moderate and minimum levels of operating cost. The figures for increased production can be grouped to correspond with these as follows:

Costs and Increased Production per Acre

	Heavy Cultivations, etc.			Moderate Cultivations, etc.			Minimum Cultivations, etc.			All Cases		
	£	s.	d.	£	s.	d.	£	s.	d.	£	s.	d.
Costs	31	2	0	17	4	6	13	7	6	18	3	6
Increased Production	17	0	0	16	6	6	8	14	0	13	6	0

Figures such as these must be considered with caution, but even so they suggest quite strongly that these improvements have been worth while. There are various factors to consider, such as:

1. The nature of the survey has precluded anything but crude estimates being worked out.
2. There is the time lag between initiating improvement and the time when production at the higher level is established—this involves a cost which is extremely difficult to assess.
3. The increased productivity will involve further costs, perhaps, even re-improvement from time to time, if the higher level of production is to be maintained. There is no data available on this point.
4. On the other side of the picture there must be an appreciable increase in the capital value of improved land.

Taking all these factors into account, there can be little doubt that, so far as this survey can be taken as illustrating the potentialities of marginal (or sub-marginal) land, the results can be well worth while under present conditions. It may be foolhardy to speculate on the future, but emphasis is being placed on livestock, and almost without exception these improvements have resulted in greater outputs of livestock of which cattle have been a notable feature.

In conclusion it may be stated that this survey cannot be more than a pilot study of the factors associated with land reclamation. It has produced some interesting and valuable suggestions regarding the levels of costs and returns, but even in this context has done no more than touch on the fringe of the problem. The previous attempt to collate the existing material embodied in generalised statistics and reports indicated the need for specific work aimed at clarifying the real position concerning the extent, nature and potentialities of reclaimable land. The present survey has brought together a fund of valuable information on the factors associated with reclamation work, but the data suffers from lack of the necessary precision in terms of cost and production. This is not said with any intent to criticise those members of the Association who obviously gave much of their time and thought and who deserve the thanks of the Association for their co-operation; it is simply due to the fact that no two people will answer a written questionnaire in quite the same way. Furthermore, such answers often require access to recorded data which is often not available and the descriptive or qualitative information is all that can be given.

National Farmers' Union of Scotland

Marketing

The N.F.U. of Scotland supports Mr. Balfour's advocacy of co-operative marketing by producers as a means of achieving economies in the distribution of farm produce, in the purchase of farm requisites and the promotion of uniformly graded and attractively presented agricultural produce.

Less than justice, however, is done to what has already been achieved and what is at present being done along these lines.

The turnover of farm co-operative societies in Scotland increased from £102,835 in 1908 to £34,600,000 in 1958. In the same period membership of co-operatives increased from 2,732 to 46,000. The industry is alive to the need to carry this process further, but it is by no means certain that the pattern of Dutch and Danish co-operatives is necessarily the most appropriate for Scottish conditions. This whole matter is at present under active review jointly by the N.F.U. of Scotland and the Scottish Agricultural Organisation Society following a national conference held in Edinburgh on the subject in the summer of 1960.

Mr. Balfour cites the report of Produce Studies Ltd. as a good example of planning as the basis of improved marketing. This is not the only survey which the Scottish N.F.U., together with the N.F.U. of England and Wales, have sponsored, and it is appropriate to mention here that the same research unit is at present completing for the Unions a comprehensive survey of the whole field of meat marketing.

On the question of marketing boards, it is misleading to suggest, as Mr. Balfour's paper does, that the Government is practically the only buyer of wool, eggs, milk and sugar beet. Marketing Boards exist for a number of commodities, and although they are statutory bodies, they are in effect co-operative organisations, having been brought into existence under an enabling act by the votes of producers concerned. Indeed, provision is made for them to be disbanded by a vote of producers if sufficient numbers are dissatisfied with them. Their sphere of operations are defined by statute and are under the control of a board elected democratically by producers on a regional basis. The functions of boards are too complex to examine here in detail, but they range from sales promotion, research and education, to administering the guarantee schemes on behalf of the Government. In the case of meat, while no statutory board exists, the Fatstock Marketing Corporation offers a further example of producer co-operation on the national scale. The existing marketing boards and the F.M.C. were established on the initiative of the Farmers' Unions.

On the question of imports, farming is of course always affected by Government policy as to the desirable level of output from the home industry and trading relations with other countries. The whole question is complex and the situation varies from commodity to commodity. It is sufficient here to note that output from farms is now nearly 70 per cent. above the pre-war level, and to take the case of eggs, this country is now virtually self-sufficient, with imports satisfying only marginal demands. Scotland itself is a substantial exporter of farm produce, to the tune of £36 million a year to England alone.

So far as farming is concerned, tourism is another aspect of marketing, and the Union is alive to the opportunities which exist in this field. Scotland has a reputation for high-quality food, and many of our exports are based on this reputation. Much remains to be done to build on this in our own country and the Union is co-operating closely with the Tourist Board, and more recently with the hotel industry, in order to enhance the reputation and presentation of home-grown food in hotels and restaurants.

National Farmers' Union of Scotland

The Marginal Agricultural Production Scheme

The Union regard as essential the maintenance of cropping on marginal land in order to ensure a satisfactory level of livestock production. Such cropping can only be ensured by a proper level of manuring, liming and cultivation, and this level has only been maintained because of grants available through the Marginal Agricultural Production Scheme. This Scheme provides grants for certain prescribed operations carried out on marginal land, and the result of the grant-aided operations is that better grass is grown and winter keep produced which, in turn, enables the holding to carry a higher level of livestock.

Without M.A.P. grants much land would revert because many farmers could not afford to pay the total costs of keeping their marginal land in production and, as a result, stock production would be reduced. A reservoir of store stock for fattening on the lower ground is needed because, apart from any other reason, fatstock is one branch of agriculture where further production is still sought by the Government in the national interest.

Reversion of cultivated land would affect not only farmers but would be damaging to the general economy of the areas involved, which of course depend to a great extent on agriculture. There would be less demand for farmers' requisites, including fertilisers, machinery and services, and local traders would suffer from the fall in the purchasing power of the community. Labour forces would be reduced, and this in areas such as the Highlands and Islands and other outlying areas where underemployment is already a serious problem.

The economic and social aspects of farming on marginal land were considered by the Natural Resources (Technical) Committee under the Chairmanship of Sir Solly Zuckerman. In their report of 1957 it is stated "we need to remind ourselves that a nation as dependent as is the United Kingdom on imports can ill afford to neglect the possible savings that might be obtained by the exploitation of the whole of its land resources. On the general grounds of the problem of the balance of payments we . . . conclude that it would be imprudent to allow the wastage of our marginal land and the decline in its fertility to continue unchecked as though it was a necessary and inevitable process. It is essential that investment in farming on marginal land should be considered in relation to the overall role which these areas play or should play in our national life."

The value of the M.A.P. Scheme must be measured not only in terms of economics but also in terms of social good, and consideration will show that the value of the Scheme to Scotland is far above the modest cost to the country of about £1¼ million for Scotland as a whole when the Scheme was in full operation and before the current scaling down was embarked upon.

The Union is convinced that the Marginal Agricultural Production Scheme has been one of the most effective and economical of the production grants. During the period 1945 to 1960 the number of beef-breeding cows in Scotland increased from 107,000 to 305,760 and the Scheme has undoubtedly played a major part in making this increase possible. It has proved itself flexible and able to meet changing circumstances and it has contributed substantially to a solution of Scotland's special problem of the marginal and outlying areas.

R. GLENTWORTH, B.S.A.(MANITOBA), PH.D., *The Macaulay Institute for Soil Research*
(Extract from a letter to Mr. Elgood.)

In response to the request that second thoughts should be submitted to you on the fuller utilisation of Scotland's natural resources I wish to comment on the use and improvement of land above the arable which is sometimes subject to the controversy as to its suitability for either forestry or grazing. This subject was discussed by Mr. Swan of the National Farmers' Union and by the Duke of Buccleuch.

Certain areas of uncultivated land at present in rough grazing are capable of being ploughed and put down to good grassland. The Soil Survey of Scotland is probably better able than any other body, in the first instance, to assess the suitability of this land for possible ploughing and seeding to grass. Its suitability depends on a number of factors, such as the inherent nature of the rock material, the depth and texture of the subsoil, the natural drainage class of the soil, slope and freedom from large boulders, etc. It would be possible in the course of the systematic soil survey to make a map plotting this land. I would not say that we could do this for the whole of Scotland without special briefing to do so, but we could gather data for specified areas. We fully realise that economics and other considerations enter into the actual decision to plough and seed to grass. All we might be concerned with is in plotting the location of improvable land and in possibly arriving at some estimate of its extent in a given area.

A second comment, which is much less positive and which may be premature, is a suggestion that agricultural economists might consider soil type as a possible basis for plotting agricultural statistics data. We are now in a position to supply soil maps for sizeable areas in north-east, south-east and south-west Scotland, and it is our intention to bring this to the notice of those concerned in the three college areas.

JAMES MACAULAY, M.B.E., F.R.I.C.S., M.T.P.I., M.INST.R.A., *Chairman, Scottish Council for National Parks*

MULTIPLE LAND USE PLANNING

The numerous papers and discussions of the three days' Symposium high-pointed the wealth of potential resources of the country and emphasised the fact that all without exception require to be exploited to be effective. The basic purpose of the Symposium is to lead to wise economic and social exploitation, a long-term aim, an essential result.

Great Britain, Holland, most European countries and the U.S.A. are experiencing diminution of available land for fresh development purposes and being forced to consider competing claims for the several uses desired. Such has been the case in regard to an area in one of our larger towns where a food-processing and supply firm desired to add a factory to meet extending demands. The local authority favour housing development and schools—which latter have extensive acreage standards—while a third department of public service is involved. Compensation to the food firm, if required to move, is of the order approximately of £5 to £10 millions. Compromise of some kind is indicated. That is one of many urban examples of the difficulties of land use planning which may involve the replanning of a very much larger area.

In the urban scene there is discussion as to the use of super and elevated or multiple roads, as in Los Angeles and San Francisco.

But multiple use was implied in discussion at the Symposium in rural areas. It took the form of the proposal by Dr. Hunter in the paper by W. J. Eggeling (p. 363)—and I quote—"Together, cattle, sheep and manures can regenerate our hill pastures, which puts in a much simplified nutshell the feeling of conservationists the world over that the most efficient form of land use is multiple use."

Other examples of multiple uses can be stated which in the aggregate are noteworthy. The crofter, fisherman, seaweed harvester, etc., is now also being encouraged to help in accommodating the tourist—sightseer, motorist, caravanner, etc.—and in a few cases has complied by expanding his facilities and activities.

National Parks for Scotland

"A National Park is a tract of country of natural beauty and of scientific, cultural or historic interest affording by reason of its character, opportunities for open-air recreation, and accessible to all under such arrangements that its distinctive qualities remain unimpaired."

The case of establishing National Parks in Scotland may be taken as agreed on the lines of numerous Reports made by the Scottish Council for National Parks over the years since 1931 (Cmd. 3851) and subsequently supported by the Lord Justice Scott Committee in 1942 (Cmd. 6378), the White Paper on The Control of Land Use in 1944 (Cmd. 6537), the Report by the Scottish Council for National Parks in 1945 (Cmd. 6631) and the Scottish National Parks Committee Report in 1947 (Cmd. 7235) approved by the Secretary of State and Parliament.

Not only so but the suggested areas suitable as National Parks, the criteria for their selection were therein set forth, together with the purpose of National Parks, the National Parks Authority Planning Management, Designation of Areas and Establishment of National Parks, Nature Conservation, Staff, Finance and Conclusions, etc.

Eight areas of the country were selected, viz.:

	sq. miles
1. Loch Lomond, Trossachs	320
2. Cairngorms	180
3. Ben Nevis, Glencoe, Black Mount	610
4. Glen Affric	260
5. Loch Torridon, Loch Maree, Little Loch Broom	500
6. Moidart, Morar, Knoydart	410
7. Ben Lawers, Glen Lyon, Schiehallion	140
8. St. Mary's Loch	180
Total	2,600

These Reports were framed after careful consideration of evidence received from the many organisations in Great Britain as scheduled therein, but also from the national parks in countries throughout the world. Such parks are enjoyed in most foreign countries, including those behind the iron curtain, and in the British Commonwealth—28 in Canada, 7 in New Zealand, 5 in Africa, 40 in Australia, also 187 in U.S.A., 19 in Japan, 21 in Germany and others in Holland, Poland, Slovakia, Turkey, Belgium, Spain and U.S.S.R., apart from those in England and Wales.

The importance of National Parks to all countries has been realised recently as of world significance. The International Union for the Conservation of Nature and Natural Resources recommended the United Nations to establish a list of National Parks and equivalent Reserves, together with recommendations for maintaining this list on the current basis and for its distribution.

The need of legislation for National Parks in Scotland is urgent and evident. The areas designated are open to vandalism under present conditions and damage is taking place in many ways especially in the Loch Lomond area. Likewise the Cairngorms are subject to unco-ordinated developments which are in great need of proper planning.

The establishment of national parks in Scotland, properly developed, would attract tourists from home and abroad, prove economic natural resources and promote the health, education and culture of the public.

R. Maclagan Gorrie

Land Drainage

There is practically no reference in any of the agriculture papers to land drainage. I wish therefore to bring the attention of the meeting to the Duncan Report of 1950, in which it was reported that 140,000 acres in Scotland needed drainage, and to ask that the Resources Committee follow up by asking for an analysis of the position today.

In my paper on "Soil Erosion" in Scotland in the *Transactions of the Royal Highland and Agricultural Society*, 1958, I noted: "The findings of the Drainage Committee, Scotland, 1950, were worse than misleading; under 'areas of land still requiring large-scale drainage as reported by the engineers of the Department of Agriculture', the figures of 32,700 acres for Perthshire and 22,400 for Stirling are probably reasonably correct, but for the seven crofting counties (Argyll, Caithness, Inverness, Orkney, Shetland, Ross and Cromarty, and Sutherland) the acreage 'reclaimable' is given as 39,104 acres out of a total of 9½ million acres—obviously a quite ludicrous figure."

Presuming that the 140,000 acres was potential arable and therefore below 500 ft. in altitude, various changes must have taken place—M.A.P. reclamations of possibly 20,000 acres; Forestry Commission acquisition and planting. But this residual area out of the 140,000 acres is presumably all below 500 ft., and therefore forms the lower fringe of the very much greater acreage of rough grazings which lie between 500 and 1,500 ft. whose total runs into some millions of acres of potential stock-raising land.

W. O. Kinghorn, B.SC., *Department of Agriculture for Scotland*

Use of Water

Several references have been made to irrigation, all of them referring to its application in a very dry year. It has been suggested by one speaker that irrigation might be treated on an insurance basis. From these references the impression may have been made that irrigation is carried out mainly, or even exclusively, in very dry seasons and at very dry periods in any season.

In actual fact there is a sound scientific basis for irrigating crops even in seasons of normal total rainfall or where no obvious period of drought occurs during the season. In the case of high-value farm crops it may be economic to apply water, often in relatively small quantities, at any time throughout the growing season when the soil water content falls to a certain degree below capacity even for a short period. It is likely, therefore, that in agriculture there will be a growing demand for irrigation as a normal husbandry operation in the case of such crops as potatoes, sugar beet and raspberries.

It should not be assumed, therefore, that irrigation will compete with other demands for water at times of acute water scarcity only. For these reasons it would probably be wrong to treat all irrigation on an insurance basis. In fact, there is likely to be a considerable normal annual demand for water for irrigation. Very dry seasons like 1959 may highlight the advantages of irrigation as a crop saver. They also tend to exaggerate the amount of water required and divert our attention from that very important other aspect of irrigation, i.e. the "topping up" of soil water in seasons of relative water plenty. We should not allow an odd dry season to dominate our thinking on irrigation and its water demands.

Dr. T. Swarbrick

Horticulture in Scotland

Dr. Swarbrick has spoken of the processing of horticultural produce and has said that the most important outlet is to the food-processing industry. This statement has been challenged by Mr. Lowe, who implied that food processing in Scotland is limited by the transport required for the finished material. I think therefore that I should not let this Conference go by without mentioning that at Aberdeen we have developed a new process for the development of food which we call accelerated freeze-drying. This is not the time or place to go into the technicalities of the process, but I may mention that our research station was set up ten years ago as a defence measure "to study ways of producing compact stable foods for defence purposes". May I emphasise that these foods are compact and lightweight: foods of this type place far less demand upon transport than either their fresh counterparts or their preserved products in any other form. The Government feel that a successful conclusion has now been reached and the research station will close very shortly.

We believe that this A.F.D. process, as we call it, is capable of becoming a sizeable industry with all that is implied in outlets for horticultural and agricultural produce, including meat and fish (especially scampi), and in employment of labour. That we are not alone in thinking this is shown by the fact that a number of industrial firms are taking up the process. Armours of Chicago have installed machinery; the Irish Sugar Company and Liebig's Extract of Meat Company are putting up factories in Ireland. In England, Batchelors have announced their intention of spending £$\frac{1}{2}$ to £1 million on dehydration, including A.F.D.; the Chairman of Batchelors recently said that he thought the 1960s would be the decade of dehydration just as the 1950s were the decade of quick freezing; the Director of the British Food Manufacturing Industries Research Association said he thought that A.F.D. would prove to be the greatest advance in food technology in the past decade.

But where does Scotland stand in this? Hardly anywhere at present. One English firm has a small experimental unit in Aberdeen, primarily as a selling agency for plant manufactured in a foreign country. And I believe that an engineering works in Glasgow is manufacturing vacuum equipment for an English company which has undertaken the manufacture of accelerated freeze-drying equipment. Apart from this, we in Scotland are losing a first-class research station employing about 120 people, and no food manufacturer in Scotland has shown any inclination to take up the process. Now I know the Scottish Council (Development and Industry) has tried hard to interest industrialists here, but no tangible result has been forthcoming; probably they felt the costs were too marginal. Also there is the problem of vested interests. A few months ago a journal in the frozen food trade published an article about A.F.D., but finished by saying, in effect, "we do not expect our readers to take up this process: why should we compete against ourselves?"

I'm afraid this is not a very constructive injection into the discussions, but it does, sadly I think, illustrate one example of a missed opportunity. "A prophet is not without honour . . ."

J. P. GUNN, Esq., M.A., B.SC., M.I.C.E., M.CONS.E.

Irrigation can benefit almost all crops when the moisture content of the soil is low, and in particular it can aid germination, help a transplanted crop and lead to an earlier harvest. These benefits are such that irrigation will continue to attract attention and grow in importance.

The meteorological approach to irrigation is more concerned with the state of the plant and the total amount of water desirable than with the crop variation or requirements at the various stages of growth.

My experience in India of the varying keenness of demand with the stage of the crop led me to enquire how far corresponding changes in crop requirements occurred in this country.

The Bulletins of the Ministry of Agriculture, Fisheries and Food on the subject of irrigation deal much more with the growth of the plant than with the harvest, or the differences from plant to plant, but the National Vegetable Research Station gave me references to papers by their staff reporting on many experiments. In one of these experiments it was shown that a crop of turnips, from which irrigation was withheld in the second growth stage, produced a greater yield than a uniformly irrigated control crop. From which it can be seen that the uniform application of irrigation will not produce the best crop, and the pumping capacity and authorised withdrawal must be based on the peak demand.

Basing the sanction on the peak withdrawal will have the advantage that the irrigator can work out the size of pumps and length and size of piping required for the area he proposes to irrigate.

As the number of irrigators increases in a district it will probably be necessary to form a local association to which sanction for a bulk withdrawal can be given, and which will distribute the supplies to its members and report the withdrawal to the central authority.

Though the demand for irrigation water is in general small, withdrawals approved in one watershed in 1959-60 for spray irrigation were just under a million gallons a day, or sufficient for a town of about 20,000 inhabitants.

Irrigation is necessarily associated with drainage and subsoil water level, so it will be necessary to set up an organisation to measure the discharge of rivers at various points, collect the discharge data from pumps and other water users and record inflows, keep a record of well depths and prepare a water account by reaches for the river, so that natural gains may be kept under scrutiny.

In fact, irrigation will become one more of the industries that depend on the rivers, and the allotment of supplies will require a body with the duty of ascertaining all inflows to the main stream and withdrawals from it and regulating the shares to be given to each applicant. It might be an advantage to initiate a preliminary study of the areas where irrigation could be contemplated as a guide to the magnitude of the withdrawals that might be expected in the various watersheds.

Professor A. C. O'Dell and Colleagues, *Department of Geography, University of Aberdeen*

Notes on Land Reclamation Possibilities in Scotland

Introduction

Land reclamation conforms well with modern ideas of conservation and improvement of the resource potential. It recaptures the spirit, vigour and foresight of the great improvers who with little mechanical knowledge or scientific basis embarked on the reclamation of tidal marsh and upland on which so much of our modern agriculture is based. We require an internal colonisation on the same scale as that of the Agricultural Revolution which would be preceded by detailed surveys of the land which might be brought into more valuable use. It is time that we assessed the waste-land potential of our lowland areas. The spirit of reclamation shown by the Danes and the Dutch is well worth emulating.

Land reclamation could well be considered under three headings:

(*a*) Recovery of land wasted by previous use.
(*b*) Foreshore reclamation.
(*c*) Marginal and hill land reclamation.

There should also be considered reclamation by up-grading of land use, e.g. by conversion of pasture lands to arable.

(a) *Recovery of Land wasted by Previous Use*

Industrial destruction has been serious in the Central Lowlands, e.g. by subsidence destroying field drainage, by piling of spoil from mines, furnaces and ovens, and by pollution. Some improvement schemes could have a double effect (e.g. filling in the "hungry thirties" of part of Polmont quarry with bing waste). The shale and coal bings could be used for embankments along the foreshores of the Forth and clear land at the same time as it was being used to reclaim. Tree planting of coal bings proved successful at Ferniegair near Hamilton. The spent shale heaps are more intractable, but experiments of scattering seed of lupin (which can grow with the minimum of soil) might lead the way to soil formation and so to reclamation.

(b) *Foreshore Reclamation*

The demand for land by many competing interests has been the subject of much discussion in Scotland in recent years. Land required for industrial and urban development is frequently situated in the fertile, less humid, eastern lowland areas. Multipurpose land use can only occur between agriculture, forestry and recreation. To compensate for land lost to agriculture it is desirable to consider if more can be created.

The late Professor A. G. Ogilvie demonstrated (Land Reclamation in Scotland, *Scottish Geographical Magazine*, Vol. 61, No. 3, Dec. 1945, pp. 77-84) that it would be physically possible to reclaim over 400,000 acres from the foreshore:

East coast . .	18,585 acres
North coast . .	1,365 acres
West coast . .	5,197 acres
Irish Sea coast .	15,355 acres
	40,502 acres or 63·3 sq. miles.

The bulk of the reclaimable tidal lands are along the shores of the Moray Firth and the Solway Firth; the task of reclamation should be easier on the east with its smaller tidal ranges.

Such land offers the following advantages:

Agriculture

(*a*) It is possible to accelerate the natural processes which promote the development of salt marsh which builds up the foreshore above the reach of tidal waters (cf. the use of *Spartina* in Southampton Water).

(*b*) Since it is at sea-level there are none of the special climatic problems inherent in the reclamation of land from the hills.

(*c*) The flat land is uniform in quality.

Industry

(*d*) The tide water location offers possibilities of water transport (e.g. Grangemouth).

(*e*) Unlimited cooling water is available.

(*f*) Much of the reclaimable land is situated in districts with good communications and reasonably accessible public utilities.

It should be possible to reconcile reclamation with rights of navigation and the needs of recreation and amenity. The use of tidal models (cf. that of the Tay at Dundee) would ensure that dykes and sluices were situated in positions which did not cause embarrassing siltation or scour problems elsewhere. Reclamation is economically debatable for a short-term viewpoint and for agricultural purposes would need national help, justified by long-term objectives.

(c) *Marginal and Hill Land Reclamation*

Two main categories of land must first be distinguished, viz. marginal land and hill land. At a recent conference of the Association of British Agriculture, Dr. Hunter of the Hill Farming Research Organisation estimated that, in Scotland, not more than 1 million acres of hill land could be classified as marginal (i.e. improvable), which leaves approximately 9 million acres of true hill land.

Present knowledge of soil science indicates the general possibilities of improvement of marginal land, by drainage and the application of artificial fertilisers. Experiments carried out by Crompton and Hunter in the Northern Pennines have shown remarkable improvements of upland pastures quickly brought about by use of artificial fertiliser.

Research is still required on economical ways of establishing on marginal lands a better balance between soils, vegetation and micro-organisms.

Hill land soils in Scotland can be divided into two groups, viz. peaty soils, and thin or skeletal soils with little or no peat. Both types are basically poor and have a low stock-carrying potential. Long-period research is required to see if the vegetation can be improved. Experiments with chemical treatment of bracken, so that the carrying capacity of many rough grazings may be increased, have been encouraging.

On peaty soils surface reseeding without ploughing can rapidly improve grazings. Such hill land is often part of the hill grazings of crofting townships and the crofters may lack capital or initiative or may be physically incapable of either carrying out the improvement or of properly stocking the extra grazing thus gained. By digging a thick cover of peat for use as a source of power, underlying soils may become available. Afforestation can be attempted on land previously thought too wet. Work carried out along these lines at, respectively, Altnabrae and Fort Augustus, could well be extended.

Thin skeletal soils usually occur on steep rocky slopes and are often at high altitude. Yet even there thin soils show a striking and rapid response to artificial fertilisers, and pilot studies of aerial fertilising and seeding should be carried out. Proper utilisation of such pastures would require the correct choice or development of the livestock breeds able to thrive in this environment. After solving the technical problems of hill land reclamation there remain severe economic and social difficulties. Such lands must remain with extensive, rather than intensive, utilisation, with sparse settlements and rudimentary (but expensive) transport links.

In conclusion there could well be a district by district assessment of what is desirable and reasonable for future land use of Scotland weighing the physical and economic factors against the national needs. Such a task cannot be lightly undertaken since not only would more field studies be required by the implications of, for example, afforestation versus farming; improving land drainage would also have to be first assessed.

The Crofters Commission

Crofting

No survey of Scottish resources can be considered complete without taking crofting into account.

There are over 20,000 agricultural units held on crofting tenure within the seven crofting counties. They comprise some 200,000 acres of land classed as arable, the quality of which is often poor, and approximately 1,356,000 acres of rough grazings of varying quality and a great deal of it sheep sick.

Many of the crofts are still held by absentees, even more are sublet on unsatisfactory conditions, and not a few stand derelict. Only a minority of tenants are deriving a full economic return from the working of their crofts.

It is the task of the Crofters Commission to remedy this state of affairs so far and as quickly as their powers enable them to do so. They have the matter in hand and the prospects are steadily improving of their being able, by reorganisation and by persuading the crofters, with the indispensable help of the Colleges of Agriculture, to adopt modern methods of husbandry. It is now possible to regenerate the grazings and to grow grass and clover on a considerable proportion of peaty soil hitherto unimprovable. Where the initial hesitation and conservatism of the crofters have been overcome, the livestock, particularly cattle, are increasing in numbers and improving in quality.

It has long been realised that agriculture alone will not maintain a sufficient population, under modern conditions, nor yield modern standards of living, unless partnered with other activities. This applies even in fertile areas and it has been a weakness of the administration of the Highlands and Islands for many years that efforts to find partner-activities have been half-hearted or misguided or have failed for perfectly good economic reasons.

It is easier now, and becoming even easier as time passes, to provide the necessary partners for agriculture, even in the Highlands. The classic example is weaving in the Outer Hebrides; like any other industry it faces various dangers and depends upon a continuing demand for its product. Given imaginative advertising and enterprising marketing abroad, it should have as good a prospect as any other United Kingdom industry of maintaining and even increasing consumer demand. Given a measure of enterprise on the part of the Lewis men themselves, and a helping hand from outside, garments, e.g. sports coats and men's caps, could be made up in Lewis and further employment provided and profits earned in the island. In the other islands and on the mainland, weaving is slowly developing and there should be no fear of not finding a market. Tartans are still produced in the south in great quantities; even so, they could be produced in the Highlands, and Mackenzie tartan, for instance, guaranteed produced by Mackenzies in the Mackenzie country, would have an irresistible appeal abroad. What appears to be needed are a few American advertising experts, people who understand how to exploit the romantic urges of the great and wealthy American public.

The few small weavers in the West Highlands who cater for tourists are able only to satisfy a minute fraction of the potential demand for cloth home-woven to the buyer's specification.

Again, it is easier now to find industries to partner agriculture, thanks to modern processing. The fishing industry is capable of an extensive revival and the marketing difficulties are greatly eased by deep freezing and canning. Moreover, it is becoming possible to fly cargoes of, for example, live lobsters to markets in Germany and France where there is a public willing to spend more on food of prime quality than we do in Britain.

The bugbear of communications and heavy freight charges serves still to damn the prospects of developing even light industries in the Highlands. But we are at a point where various new breeds of vehicles are in course of development, e.g. aircraft, economical to operate and yet requiring virtually no runways; and now the hovercraft, if its promise is fulfilled, will prove to be the answer to the Highlandman's prayer, because it will be capable of operating where there are no roads, where the ground is marshy, and over water.

Finally, tourism has come forward as a promising partner for agriculture. True, it often becomes the predominating partner where the agricultural value of a given croft is small. But no one need object to that if, in the result, the crofter enjoys a better and happier living. In the wake of tourism, various little industries will follow, sooner or later.

The Crofters Commission repeat, therefore, that no conspectus of Scotland's economic conditions or prospects can be complete without taking crofting into account.

Nor can it be useful unless it examines all the facts imaginatively and without prejudice. For anyone who takes the trouble to look ahead, rather than backwards or at best at things as they are at this moment, the outlook for the Highlands and Islands is definitely brightening, thanks to the possibility, indeed certainty, that a considerable volume of light industry could be developed to partner agriculture and provide the necessary supplement to what agriculture can offer in the way of income. Progress will be slow because people in the Highlands have little experience of industrial processes or business methods. It will be less slow and the more rewarding for Scotland's economy if businessmen and entrepreneurs outside the Highlands have the foresight and the public spirit to lend a helping hand.

At sundry times pronouncements are made about industry for the Highlands, making great play of the fact that it is not economic to plant factories in underdeveloped areas. This should be accepted as basic common sense. While the planting of small factories would be welcomed, that can only be done in the Highlands within narrow limits for lack of labour. New industries will have to grow from small beginnings and expand as they build up their staffs with young people who would otherwise be moving south for employment.

UTILISATION OF RESOURCES

LAND USE—FORESTRY

Forestry in Scotland—
A Review of the Current Situation

A. WATT, B.A.(FOR.)
Director of Forestry for Scotland, Forestry Commission, Edinburgh

The area under managed tree crops is some 920,000 acres, of which three-fifths is under direct Forestry Commission control. Of the remaining area classified as woodland, about 220,000 acres is likely to come under managed tree crops in the foreseeable future, giving a total of 1,170,000 acres. Within the next eight years the forest area will be expanded to the extent of 200,000 acres on hill land.

The type of forest crops is predominantly coniferous, and, with the exception of Scots Pine, the trees are exotic.

The role of the forests is primarily commercial: secondary purposes, such as recreational (National Forest Parks), sporting, agricultural shelter, conservation (fauna and flora), land settlement and protection aspects are more or less important locally.

The contribution of home timber to the country's needs is substantial in the case of the requirements calling for smaller sized timber (e.g. coal-mines and particle board), but presently small in the case of timber for constructional purposes, due to the dearth of stands of sawmill size timber, consequent on exploitation during the two great wars.

On the social aspect forestry can provide more jobs on a given area of land than pastoral farming. While afforestation usually involves some clearance of stock, forestry employment can benefit rural communities by providing a source of seasonal labour and by enabling a greater proportion of the youths in the community to take up employment locally.

AREA UNDER FOREST

At the present time the area of land under managed tree crops is close on 920,000 acres, of which some 560,000 acres are directly under the Forestry Commission and the balance of 360,000 acres are in private and other ownership. On private estates there is in addition almost 400,000 acres of land, classified as woodland at the Census of Woodlands in 1947-49, which is unstocked and for which plans for restocking are not, so far as is known, in hand. However, of this 400,000 acres 5 per cent. is reckoned to have gone to other uses; 28 per cent. is thought to be in important agricultural use (e.g. wintering), and 17 per cent. is believed to be too remote or inaccessible or of such poor quality as to justify exclusion from the forest potential. The balance of some 200,000 acres consists partly of amenity and small woods and partly of areas which might well come under managed forest in due course: possibly half, i.e. 100,000 acres, can be included in the realistic forest potential. In addition, some 70,000 acres of old woodland on private estates is planned for replanting, and the Forestry Commission hold just under 50,000 acres of felled woodland which will soon be replanted.

It is of interest to note that the Census of Woodlands 1947-49 recorded the stocked and unstocked woodland area of Great Britain at slightly under 3,450,000 acres, which is less than 6½ per cent. of the land surface of the country. Scotland accounted for 37 per cent. as against England 54 per cent. and Wales 9 per cent.

Apart from the land carrying managed tree crops and the old bare woodland included in the forest area (i.e. a total of some 1,140,000 acres, just on 6 per cent. of the land area of Scotland) there is a fairly steady annual addition to the managed forest area from land not classified as woodland. The main agent in this is the Forestry Commission, who, from previous and current land acquisitions, are planting some 20,000 acres each year of hill land most of which has been used for some form of pastoral farming.

As this paper is intended to be largely factual, it would be inappropriate to speculate on the future. However, the present plan is for the Commission to plant some 250,000 acres over the next eight years, and of this programme probably close on 200,000 acres will be new forest land. The rate of the Forestry Commission's planting is affected by the rate, extent and location of acquisitions of plantable land. There are other factors, such as the need for planning programmes to ensure stability of employment and to secure economic working. The suitability of the upland areas of Scotland for large-scale afforestation is variable. In general, the proportion of plantable land to total area is higher in the Southern Uplands and the upland areas of central Scotland. The proportion is lower in the Western Highlands and decreases rapidly in the far north and west where low soil fertility and exposure are limiting factors. Although pastoral land has been and is being planted by some landowners, the extent of such planting is relatively small and is unlikely to affect the position substantially.

TYPE OF FOREST

There is little natural forest of commercial value or importance left in this country. There are limited areas of natural or semi-natural hardwood and softwood, but with the exception of some of the Scots Pine areas—mainly in Perthshire, Inverness-shire and Aberdeenshire—their interest is historical and botanical.

For practical purposes the Hardwoods (or Broad-leaved trees) may be ignored: both their extent and their commercial value has diminished rapidly. Except for specialist purposes, such as veneering and to a limited extent boat-building, the requirements of the traditional markets for Hardwoods, for example the furniture industry, are being increasingly met by wood fibre and particle board: the change over from timber to steel in railway wagon construction is a further example. High-quality Hardwoods will always command a market, and Broad-leaved tree species have a part in the maintenance of site fertility and in the amenity role of forests. High-quality Hardwood sites are limited, and are mainly found in the eastern and south-eastern regions of Scotland. The Softwoods (or Coniferous trees) comprise the bulk of the managed crops, and with the notable exception of the Scots Pine, the main species are exotics from the European continent (e.g. Norway Spruce and European Larch) and from the Pacific coast of North America (e.g. Sitka Spruce and Douglas Fir).

ROLE OF THE FOREST

There are several roles which a forest can play either nationally or regionally. The most important role is its commercial use: that is its contribution to the timber needs of the country. The protective use of forest is of relatively minor importance—there are no regions where communities and communications require protection from, for instance, avalanches—although there are places (e.g. Culbin) where forest is used to control or to prevent erosion. Trees can and do serve a useful function in providing protection and shelter in the more highly developed agricultural areas, but the use of trees in this way is seldom, if ever, on a "forest" scale. The recreational use of forests is not extensively developed in Scotland, except through the formation of National Forest Parks. These parks, which are comprised of land largely under the control of the Forestry Commission, are more concerned with providing facilities for the walker, the hiker, the botanist and those interested in natural history on land not required or unsuitable for forestry. An example is the Glenmore National Forest Park, where out of some 12,500 acres about one-quarter is under tree crop and the balance is high-lying ground (Cairngorm Mountains). There are four National Forest Parks in Scotland—Argyll (Cowal), Glenmore, Glen Trool and Queen Elizabeth (Loch Ard-Loch Achray-Loch Lomond area). Camping and, where practicable, caravanning facilities are provided. While the establishment of National Forest Parks is the responsibility of the Forestry Commission—with the exception of part of the Argyll Park belonging to Glasgow Corporation all the Forest Park areas are on land under the control of the Forestry Commission—advice on development and the provision of facilities is sought from an Advisory Committee on which various bodies concerned with country pursuits are represented.

Visual amenity is becoming of increasing importance, as greater numbers of the population have the means and the opportunity of seeing the countryside.

To some extent on Forestry Commission areas, and to a much greater extent on private woodlands the sporting value of woods as cover and shelter for game is a consideration. So, too, is the protection afforded to the natural fauna, some species of which have been assisted in their survival by the upsurge of planting over recent years.

The shelter afforded to agriculture by woods and forests is locally important, and mainly in the upland pastoral areas.

The provision of employment and opportunities for settlement in rural areas are probably the greatest contribution that forests make to the social structure and well-being of the country.

DISCUSSION

Before discussing forestry's contribution to the country, it is appropriate to mention that research has played and continues to play an important part in the development of techniques of large-scale afforestation. Forest research will be a continuing and an expanding need, particularly in the silviculture, management and utilisation of the increasing areas of exotic Softwoods. Nor has the need for trained men been neglected: the Forestry Departments of Edinburgh and Aberdeen Universities, and the Forestry Commission's Training Schools for Foresters are important to Scotland's forestry enterprise.

There are two aspects of forestry which call for more than passing reference: these are the commercial contribution to the country's needs and the provision of useful employment in rural areas.

The current level of home timber production is probably something of the order of 23 to 24 million cubic feet of roundwood, of which about 10 per cent. is Hardwoods and the remainder Softwoods. There is no means of estimating accurately the country's requirements of timber and timber products, but it is known that over 90 per cent. of the Scottish coal-mines' needs of timber for propping and shorting are met from home production—there is a small export of mining timber to the north and midlands of England: in the sawn Softwood and allied categories, appreciably less than 10 per cent. of the needs are met from home production due to the shortage of middle-aged and older stands of trees following on the heavy exploitation in the two wars. It was estimated at the time of the 1947-49 Woodland Census that some 233,000 acres of woodland, most of it cut during the 1914-18 War, had not been restocked. A further 170,000 acres were cut between 1939 and 1947. Only the passage of time will improve the position.

The social contribution of forestry is not spectacular by urban industrial standards. The Forestry Commission employ directly some 4,200 forest workers. It is difficult to obtain reliable figures for other forestry employment, but private estates and the timber trade (merchants and contractors) probably account for about 2,000 employees each. Looked at from a location point of view, this amount of employment is important as the bulk of the managed woodlands are in areas of low population density. Indeed, in the crofting counties special efforts have been made by the Forestry Commission to initiate and expand afforestation schemes as aids to crofting communities, even though this has involved accepting some land of most doubtful forestry quality and above normal costs of working. In the case of large afforestation schemes the change-over in the employment situation from pastoral farming to forestry is quite striking. A one man herding of 500 ewes can give steady employment to five or six men if the land is devoted to forestry.

The impact of the large post-war afforestation programmes—mainly by the Forestry Commission—has led to a considerable increase in the provision of housing for workers: in some cases (e.g. Forest of Ae and Loch Aweside) virtually new communities have been established. However, the susbtantial turn-over of labour recruited in the urban industrial areas has shown clearly the weakness of trying to establish a new and exclusively forestry community, and the merit of adding to existing rural communities, even if this means transporting workers daily.

One point of more than passing importance is the age-class structure. The provision of more opportunities for employment in rural areas gives a chance of retaining a greater number of youths and younger men whose retention is essential to the maintenance of a viable community.

The advantage of forestry as a means of providing rural employment is generally recognised. There are additional advantages. In some areas forest labour is available to help out on farms at sheep handlings and at hay and harvest time. Seasonal help, too, may be available to local hotels, particularly those catering for tourists, from the wives and families of forest workers. There are, too, the indirect benefits to local trade.

It would be inappropriate to avoid entirely some reference to the competing claims for land. With the object of assisting planned afforestation the Forestry Commission in conjunction with the Department of Agriculture for Scotland have, during the past few years, undertaken Rural Development Surveys. These Surveys have covered large parts of the Highlands. While it cannot be claimed that the Surveys have led to a substantial increase in the amount of plantable land acquired for afforestation, much useful information has been collected about the practicability of integrating forestry with agriculture. Few afforestation schemes do not involve the clearance of some stock, but most schemes are on land where, for one reason or another, the pastoral farming economy is marginal.

BIBLIOGRAPHY

Report No. 1 on Census of Woodlands 1947-49. H.M.S.O., 1951.
Census of Woodlands 1947-49, Summary Report. H.M.S.O., 1951.
Annual Reports of the Forestry Commissioners (Various). H.M.S.O.

The Place of Forestry in Scotland's National Economy

Professor MARK L. ANDERSON, M.C., M.A., D.SC., F.R.S.E.
Department of Forestry, University of Edinburgh

The main topics of this paper are:

1. Scotland's original forest cover.
2. Broad forest types and their distribution.
3. Relation of the types to climate, soil and vegetation.
4. History of the exploitation and virtual elimination of the forest and part played in this by other land uses and industry.
5. Effect upon other land uses of this destruction.
6. The national forest policy should have two major obectives, namely, replacement of some forest cover to benefit agriculture and the general commonweal, and replacement of forest cover to produce timber, etc., i.e. a protective and productive aim.
7. These objectives to be realised in two phases, namely,
   (*a*) a phase of reforestation and afforestation, which is normally uneconomic; and
   (*b*) a final phase of managed forestry with a permanent forest cover producing a sustained yield of utilisable produce, or certain protective and other benefits, in perpetuity.
8. Such a forest should be "economic" even if the rate of production is low.
9. The major problem is to strike a balance between that long-term technique which aims at reconstituting a healthy forest cover which will be permanent on a healthy soil, and that short-term technique which aims at production of the most possible per unit of area, without regard to the conservation of the fertility of the site and the future of the forest.
10. The great variety of geology and site in Scotland means that there must be a variety of forest cover and a complicated technique.
11. Difficulty of choice of species and of creating the right kind of stand composition and structure to achieve the long-term objective, that is, in respect of the proportion of the exploitable size and age, the proportion of age-classes and the method of combining them.

INTRODUCTION

A national forest policy, like any other national economic policy concerned with the natural wealth of a country, must aim at making the fullest use of its existing or potential forest resources, which in a country like Scotland, whose original forests have been devastated, include land suitable for reforestation, but not more useful under some other land use.

The guiding principle should be to ensure that these resources are contributing to the general welfare of the community to the greatest possible extent with the least expenditure of energy. Today it is generally accepted that a national policy on any human activity involves some Government intervention in order to ensure that the interests of private individuals are subordinated to those of the country as a whole. It is all the more necessary, therefore, that the national policy on forestry should be clearly stated and fully understood. To this end it is important to appreciate one fundamental point, namely that the forest in its highest form is not a creation of man but a product of nature. In these days man strives to create forests of various forms, but he cannot ignore the natural forest and the effect which it has had on his own development and on his environment.

SCOTLAND'S ORIGINAL FOREST COVER

There is no reason to doubt the generally accepted view that Scotland was originally, except for the high hills and bare rock masses, covered with a woody vegetation in one form or another. Environmental conditions over Scotland offer an immense variety for so small a country. It has a very varied geology and has been subjected to intense glaciation. Hence its topography and its soils are very varied. It is a mountainous country and thus has a wide range of altitude. It has a very varied climate, both in respect of temperature and of precipitations. It is on the whole a wind-swept country, so that its vegetation is exposed to varying, often strong, wind forces, which may, however, be greatly mitigated by the configuration of the land—a very important point in relation to its forests. Speaking generally, the Scottish climate—apart from exposure —is favourable to tree growth, and because of the high proportion of primitive and mineralogically rich rocks and of rich glacial deposits it is specially favourable for the growth of rather exacting tree species.

BROAD FOREST TYPES AND THEIR DISTRIBUTION IN RELATION TO ENVIRONMENT

The almost complete annihilation of the primeval forests and woody growth of Scotland over the centuries makes it somewhat difficult to determine with any certainty what was the distribution of the original forest cover. It can, however, be adduced with some degree of accuracy from what is now known of the ecology of various forest types and on the evidence obtained from tree remains in peat and other deposits. Because of the generally favourable temperature at lower elevations and of the prevalence of minerally rich soils, by far the greater area of the primeval forest was composed of leaf-tree species, and especially of a mixture of oak, ash, elm and alder on the moist sites of the low-lying areas almost all round the coast and extending up along the valleys. On the drier deposits it is probable that there was less ash and elm but more birch along with the oak. On the lower and middle slopes of all the hill ranges over basic igneous and rich secondary rocks there existed above the oak-ash-elm zone an important leaf-tree zone consisting of birch, alder, aspen, rowan and especially hazel, with smaller proportions of other minor leaf-tree species and an occasional oak. Finally, above that there was probably a zone of pure birch and willow, becoming very short and scrubby and open on the hill-tops. As for the Scots pine, it must not be presumed, because of its rather unfortunate name, that it was the most widespread, or even at all a widespread tree. It was confined as the main tree to the valley bottoms of districts in which granite, gneiss and the more siliceous rocks prevail, but always mixed with a high proportion of birch, aspen, alder and juniper. In the region of the Central and Western Highlands with its typical morainic landscape the pine occupied the tops and sides of the morainic mounds, while the hollows carried birch and alder. Over granite and gneissose rocks, at least in the drier east, the pine may have grown nearly pure almost up to the limit of tree growth. It was probably a scattered constituent of the lowland oak-birch forests.

Just where this timber line lay is very difficult to say, but it must have varied considerably, rising high in the centre of the country and lying at a greater altitude in the east than in the west. There are considerable areas of bare rock at all elevations in the heavily glaciated north-west and west on which it is certain that no tree grew.

HISTORY OF THE EXPLOITATION OF SCOTLAND'S PRIMEVAL FORESTS

Before the New Stone Age—roughly between 4000 and 2000 B.C.—man the hunter and fisher made but little impact on the forest. The New Stone Men of that time were farmers, who lived by a form of shifting cultivation, growing barley in the forest clearings. They were equipped with tools and began to make inroads into the lighter forest cover, where the trees were easy to cut or to ring-bark. They cut into the oak-birch forests on the lighter deposits of the lowlands around the coast. The light birch-aspen stands of the far north and around the Moray Firth were also easily conquered. Even the lapse of thirteen centuries of Neolithic civilisation left the main masses of Scotland's forests very slightly reduced, however.

The Age of Bronze, which lasted for sixteen centuries from about 1900 to 250 B.C. or longer, was much more fateful for the forests, for two reasons. First, the farmer was much more efficiently equipped with cutting tools and could use them to expand his grazing grounds. Secondly, more or less fixed farming communities were established, for which larger pastures were needed, and to protect his flocks forest clearances were made to keep wild animals away. It was then that the first heavy attacks were made upon the birch, aspen and rowan forests lying above the mixed oak-ash-elm zone, especially into those forests growing over rich rocks where the removal of the tree-cover resulted in a strong growth of good pasture grasses, as in the Southern Uplands and the central hill ranges. There the higher forest cover must have been gradually opened out and gradually converted to grassland. On the other hand, the pine forest, if it is opened out, seldom changes to grassland but retains a cover of heath and other woody shrubs; hence the persistence of natural pinewoods even today on areas over less fertile rocks.

While Bronze Age Man was little able to cope with the dense, moist oak-ash woods of the fertile lowlands, there is little doubt that the timber line became greatly depressed over base-rich rocks as a result of the use of the high-altitude forest for pastoral purposes. It is not necessary to postulate a change of climate to account for this.

The advent of the Iron Age and the period of Roman occupation up to A.D. 446 certainly resulted in further heavy cutting of the higher and middle forest zones, more especially in the south. The advent of the Anglo-Saxons in the south-east and south resulted in the first serious clearance of the dense oak-ash forests on the heavier soils of the Lowlands, which were converted in time into our finest arable farms.

The Feudal period from 1097 to 1400 saw continued forest clearance all over the country. During this period the main use of the surviving forest was to provide food in the form of venison and game, and clothing in the form of hides and furs. The forest also provided timber which, indeed, had become scarce in the vicinity of the rising villages and towns. With the destruction of wolves, grazing became more and more popular and the preservation of deer and trees gave way, even in the Royal forests, which were very efficiently organised, to rearing of cattle, horses and sheep. The forests were then regarded as valuable economic possessions. Amongst the earliest large-scale sheep farmers were the monks of the many new monasteries, which were mostly established in the surviving fringes of the mixed oak-ash forest in many of the Scottish valleys, and not least in Tweeddale.

During the twelfth and thirteenth centuries, considerable amounts of wood fuel were used for salt-making on the carses and estuaries of eastern Scotland, where the forests were heavily cut for this industry, which finally went over to coal as fuel.

The period of the Stuart dynasty from 1400 to 1707 was remarkable for the rapid rise of sheep farming in the south of Scotland, attended by a continued decrease in the high-lying forest area. The effect of the intensive grazing on the forest was disastrous. Clearance of low-lying forest for farming also continued. During the seventeenth century southern eyes turned to the leaf-tree forests of the west and to the pinewoods of the north. Vast areas of the former were cut for iron-smelting purposes, but, in the absence of satisfactory management, it was only a question of time before much of the woodland disappeared. The valuable pinewoods of Inverness-shire and Ross-shire were brutally devastated in the early nineteenth century while those of Perthshire and Argyll-shire suffered a similar fate. Immense tracts of birchwood were similarly disposed of.

During the eighteenth century the disappearance of the leaf-tree and high-lying birch forests in the Highlands was speeded up when sheep farming spread northwards. As the natural forests went, they were converted into sheep-walks, a procedure which effectively prevented their regeneration.

The late seventeenth century saw the first wave of tree planting in Scotland, by which time the scarcity of timber was taken seriously. There had already been imports from the Scandinavian and Baltic countries since the fourteenth century. This planting was confined to parks and enclosures around the residences of landowners. The trees used were mainly leaf-trees, especially beech, sycamore, elm and ash. These grew well on the fertile soils upon which they were usually planted and later made valuable contributions to the national needs of the eighteenth and nineteenth centuries. A second and remarkable wave of tree planting occurred from about 1750 to 1850, during which time at least 500,000 acres were planted by private enterprise in Scotland alone. The plantations were normally of quite a large size, but more often in the form of belts planted for ornament and shelter. Nevertheless, several very considerable forests were artificially created, some of which were successful, but others not. The main species were still leaf-trees but usually grown with Scots pine as a nurse. Larch was very popular in the early nineteenth century, but injudicious choice of site led to serious losses. Nor could the pine grown on sites too rich for it produce timber that could compete with the ever-increasing supply of high-class coniferous timbers from northern Europe and

Canada, not to mention the best of tropical and sub-tropical timbers from all over the globe.

During the latter half of the nineteenth century, Scottish forestry was in the doldrums and it took two world wars to rouse the country to take some action to make good the mistakes of the past. A somewhat narrow national policy of action was adopted in 1919 when the Forestry Commission was established, namely the formation of a reserve of timber in the country to meet the requirements of timber in the event of an emergency arising. The result has been the acquisition and planting with trees of a considerable area of land in Scotland in the past forty years which will be described by others. This will in time restore the position which was so seriously affected by the heavy fellings in Scotland's woodlands during the war periods. It may be observed, however, that by far the greater proportion of tree species now being planted consist of introduced conifers, especially spruces. A good deal of pine is still used in the north and north-east but very seldom are leaf-trees used. Much of the planting is in fact experimental and it is probably wrong to ignore entirely the experience of the past; time will tell.

EFFECT OF DESTRUCTION OF THE FORESTS UPON OTHER LAND USES

The protective function of the forest is of the highest importance, but this fact has not been sufficiently appreciated in Scotland because our original forests have been removed for such a long time. Their conservation for purely protective purposes was never considered. The forest has a protective influence through its influence upon the climate, especially at high elevations and in districts exposed to persistent strong winds. The use of shelterbelts has for long been appreciated in Scotland and was brought to a high state of efficiency. Recently there has been less enthusiasm for such belts, but there are signs of a renewed interest on the part of the farming community. There seems to be no reason to doubt that the retention of portions of the original natural forest-cover at high elevations would have increased the productivity of the high pastures. Such cover so modifies the climate as to improve the living conditions for a variety of organisms including domestic animals, the herbage which they consume and for the trees themselves.

The disadvantage of the devastation of the forest becomes more serious when the conserving effect of the forest upon the soil is considered. This effect is of special importance at high elevations and in districts with rocks of a poor or only moderately rich content of easily soluble mineral matter. The protective influence of a forest cover against mechanical erosion is often stressed, but the much more insidious degradation which goes on under a covering of heather and other heath plants is now becoming better understood and appreciated. Due mainly to the action of humic acids produced by the decomposition of such a vegetation, a steady removal of the soluble mineral elements and the finer fractions of the top soil to lower elevations goes on. A cover of leaf-trees, however low, prevents the invasion of this form of vegetation, at least over moderately fertile rocks, and maintains a growth of grasses which not only have a food value but tend to conserve the soil fertility. Thus a forest cover of trees or bushes, however short, under whose canopy grasses and herbs are maintained, can be of great value in association with upland grazings.

THE PRINCIPLE OF SUSTENTION

In all industries it is important that the supply of raw materials, labour, production and income should be sustained, but in no industry is the principle of sustention so important as in forestry. Before a sustained production or a sustained yield can be achieved, a certain amount and structure of the growing stock in the forest have to be built up. Before any forest can furnish equal annual yields, which are in fact composed of parts of the growing stock, and normally its oldest or mature trees, it has to be constituted in such a way that a succession of trees ranging from maturity down to one year are present in the forest. In the natural forest as a rule this succession is assured and, under sound management one does not need to wait for a more or less long time before the required graded structure is built up. In the creation of a new forest from scratch, by reforestation or afforestation, the position is very different. No major sustained yield can be obtained until the work has gone on for many years—for anything from 50 to 150 years. As an investment, therefore, afforestation has no attraction and it is very exceptional for it to "pay". It is therefore now generally accepted that the State should shoulder the main burden of repairing its past errors of allowing the country's natural forests to be destroyed and of assisting private growers by subsidies to build up new forests, suitably constructed.

OBJECTIVES OF THE NATIONAL FOREST POLICY

The national forest policy should have two major objectives, namely (i) the replacement of some forest cover of a suitable type to benefit agriculture and the general commonweal and (ii) the replacement of forest cover to produce timber and other commodities. There should thus be a protective aim, to realise which will require the use of leaf-trees mainly, and a productive aim, in achieving which most reliance will be placed on coniferous trees.

The complete realisation of both these objectives cannot be achieved quickly. The task must be planned and accomplished in two phases, namely (*a*) a phase of reforestation or afforestation, during which the fully graded growing-stock is built up, which is normally an uneconomic undertaking, and (*b*) a final phase of managed forestry with a permanent forest cover producing a sustained yield of utilisable produce, or sustained benefit of some kind, i.e. certain protective or amenity benefits, in perpetuity.

Once this second phase has been achieved and the cost of its achievement has been "written off", the forest should be "economic" even when the rate of its production may be quite low, from the fact that income derived from it each year should more than offset the annual running costs.

TECHNICAL DIFFICULTIES IN THE WAY OF SECURING THE DESIRED OBJECTIVES

The major problem in implementing such a policy is how to strike a balance between that long-term technique which aims at reconstituting a healthy forest cover, which will be permanent on a healthy soil, and that short-term technique which aims at the production of the most possible per unit of area as quickly as possible, without regard to the conservation, or improvement, of the fertility and productivity of the site and the conservation of the forest.

The very great variety of topography, geology and climate in Scotland means that there must be a variety of forest cover and that there must be a varied and often a complicated technique. For the various sites and objectives the problem of choice of species is a difficult one. The creation of the right kind of stand composition by species and of the right structure in order to achieve the long-term objective is a difficult task. The correct exploitable size and age has to be determined for each site and forest-type, so that steps can be taken to build up the proper number of age-classes and to decide how they can best be related to one another on the ground.

It is true to say that foresters in Scotland have excelled in the first phase of reforestation in the past. They have been successfully planting trees for some centuries, but they have never yet succeeded in building up a true managed forest. There are several reasons for this. First of all, there was no attempt, if we except the natural leaf-tree areas which were managed for producing tan-bark, to conserve and manage the natural forests. In the second place the very considerable plantations which were formed from time to time were never so planned as to produce the required graded structure of forest. Thirdly, a series of wars more or less compelled owners to destroy what plantations they had formed, and lastly, successive Governments not only neglected to foster forestry but actually put many obstacles in the way of those who might in the end have done much to remedy past mistakes. Too much lip service has been paid hitherto to the application of the principle of sustention. Even the present planting programmes run counter to that principle, and it is futile to preach about the many and important industries which might be fed on the produce of the forest without ensuring that such produce will be constantly forthcoming and of a quality capable of competing with imported forest produce.

THE FINANCIAL ASPECT

The financing of afforestation or reforestation operations is not easy to justify by any orthodox argument. It can, however, be amply justified when it is regarded as a task of reparation or restitution. On the past Scotland's inhabitants and rulers, in their immediate interest, have deliberately and heedlessly exploited and destroyed her original forests. These interests have been the provision of food and apparel; of arable land and pasture for flocks and herds; of fuel for domestic use and for the maintenance of salt-making and iron-smelting—of materials for a mining industry, a ship-building industry, a leather-making industry and to service a navy and furnish military stores, as well as to meet a multitude of minor requirements. All this has been done with no attempt to arrange for the conservation and proper management of those areas of forest that were better suited to furnish forest produce or supply shelter than for any other purpose. In other words, Scotland's living forest capital—her gift from nature—has been converted into other forms of wealth, which have been applied to the furtherance of Scotland's progress towards her present standard of civilisation. If her former rulers had been sufficiently informed and wise enough, with the foresight to determine and set aside those areas of original forest now gone, which ought to have been conserved as forest, and which we are now trying to replace, we would not now be faced with the costly task of reforesting old forest areas, in some of which the soils have very seriously deteriorated often to the extent of being impossible of restoration.

It is reasonable that forestry should receive back from the common pool of capital and resources, built up to such a great extent at the expense of the country's former forest capital, sufficient means to finance the restoration of a great part at least of the former, or an equivalent, forest, without being expected to guarantee any interest or financial return in the ordinary way on the resources employed. There is no other way by which reforestation of the extensive, poorly productive areas can be undertaken, or by which the satisfactory rehabilitation of the so-called poorer marginal lands can be achieved or a satisfactory integration of forestry with farming assured.

Future Trends in Scottish Forestry

JAMES MACDONALD, C.B.E., B.SC., F.R.S.E.
Deputy Director General, Forestry Commission, Edinburgh

The future of forestry is difficult to forecast because of changing uses of wood.

Where wood is supplied for processing by industry uniformity of material is increasingly required. This can force the planting of one particular species, although the forester would have pleasure in clothing individual sites with the most appropriate tree crop.

The areas and proportion of species in Forestry Commission plantations are given in the paper. The Commission does not normally acquire land suitable for broad-leaved species.

One of the problems lies in securing continuous supplies of produce of different sizes. This difficulty will be corrected over a period with a rapid increase in the larger girths towards 1980.

A probable pattern of utilisation will be a large pulp mill, a small number of board mills and a greater number of large modern saw mills.

Planting trees on "unplantable" high peat land, and also where there is soil poverty, is under investigation at the Macaulay Institute.

There is room for co-operative research between the forestry and the agricultural authorities. Many of the mutual difficulties are due to lack of exact knowledge.

If we are to practice successfully any form of integration of forestry and hill farming, we must know far more precisely than we do now what are the effects of a large plantation on the land adjoining it and how those effects are modified by differences in silvicultural practice. At the same time, we must consider how the methods used in pastoral management affect the adjoining plantations. If the agricultural experts could work out, for example, a system of management for hill grazings which did not involve the use of fire they would have taken a very great step towards making possible a really close integration of forestry and farming in our upland districts.

If we are to succeed in making our land as productive as possible, there is no need for a new organisation to achieve it, since it could be dealt with by existing organisations working to an agreed plan.

The effect of land uses on the supply of water is another problem, and one to which forestry has a certain background of experience and could contribute to joint research.

Any consideration of the future trend of development in forestry must inevitably be coloured by an element of speculation, for no author writing on the subject can avoid introducing his own estimates of the nature and size of the changes which may take place. Many of the changes can be foreseen, but others, such as technological developments affecting the use of wood, coming unexpectedly may materially alter the prospects. This paper, therefore, is to a large extent an expression of my own views. Forestry in Scotland is not a new thing although many people seem to think that it is something which has sprung up in recent years. It has actually a long history behind it. What is new, however, is the creation within the last forty years of extensive areas of new plantations by the State, working through the Forestry Commission, and it is this relatively new development by which we now have large forest properties under the control of a single organisation which has completely altered the picture of Scottish forestry. It has also affected the prospects of the timber-using industries which can now see before them the possibility of regular supplies of raw material and of the other growers of timber who have already found new wood-using industries established and new markets for their produce opened.

Since the main purpose of forestry is to provide raw material for industry it is necessary to look first at our forests in relation to industrial demands and possible industrial developments. It is true that what we grow is dictated in the end by soil and climate, but we have many sites on which there is a choice of species for planting, and whether we use this one or that one may be decided by marketing possibilities. Further, the markets which we have to supply to some extent may decide for us how we are to grow our trees and how long we should keep them standing. Conditions in Scotland make it possible to grow with some success a wide range of coniferous trees and a smaller number of broad-leaved species, and the forester can derive the greatest pleasure from clothing each individual site with what he knows or believes to be the appropriate crop. But there are some disadvantages in this when it comes to market what has been grown. It is much easier, for example, for the sawmiller to deal with long runs of one particular species than it is to handle a mixture of species which require different schedules for seasoning and which may create problems in selling. Manufacturers of chipboard are taking mixed conifers into their plants, but Lynam[1] has pointed out that the question of mixing timbers in their manufacturing process depends to a considerable extent on the acidity of the individual timbers, for the degree of acidity affects the setting of the resin adhesive required to glue the wood chips together and that the manufacturer must be careful to maintain compatibility if he decided to mix the timbers. He went on to say that the manufacturing process became easier if timber species did not change. It is clear that many industries, of which chipboard is an example, would prefer more uniformity of material than they obtain at present. Whether they will get it will depend on price essentially, but nevertheless pressures of this kind, long applied, will have an effect on the thinking of foresters and we thus expect a trend towards less diversification in the species used for planting.

Our species in Scotland are primarily coniferous, that is, the species grown for timber production in what we call high forest. The Census of Woodlands[2] carried out by the Forestry Commission in 1947, which covered all the woodlands and plantations five acres in extent and greater, showed that in Scotland 74 per cent. of them were coniferous and 21 per cent. broad-leaved. Of individual species, Scots pine was the most important, covering 36 per cent. of the area, followed by the two spruces, Norway and Sitka, with 27 per cent., the two larches, European and Japanese, with 12 per cent., beech with 9 and oak with 8 per cent. Since then, much has happened for there have been large new planting programmes as well as heavy losses from gales such as that of 1953, but it is certain that the changes in the last dozen years have resulted in a large increase in the area under conifers. This is a trend which looks like continuing. We have no more recent complete record than that of 1947, so it is impossible to study the changes in detail, but figures for Forestry Commission plantations which are available show how the present situation compares with that in 1947.

TABLE I

Species	1947		1959	
	Area	Percentage	Area	Percentage
Scots pine	46,111	23	119,941	23
Pinus contorta	1,870	1	34,767	7
Corsican pine	3,210	1½	7,729	1
European larch	13,179	6½	18,903	4
Japanese larch	7,844	4	47,575	9
Norway spruce	41,562	21	77,674	15
Sitka spruce	71,054	36	185,743	35
Douglas fir	5,734	3	13,027	2
Other conifers	4,486	2	7,262	2
Broad-leaved	3,909	2	7,233	2

Perhaps the most striking difference between the figures for 1959 and those for 1947 are those which relate to *Pinus contorta,* which has risen from the small extent of 1,870 acres to the substantial area of 34,767 acres. This is due to increased planting on peats of the more difficult type on which Sitka spruce had been tried and found disappointing. *Pinus contorta,* on the other hand, establishes itself without too much difficulty and promises now to be the staple species for first crops on these troublesome sites. Another species which has been extensively used during the period under review is the Japanese larch, which is well adapted for acting as a pioneer in the afforestation of moorland in which capacity it serves a most useful purpose. Although in the pole stage it is readily saleable, we do not yet know how its timber will be received when mature. Like the European species it may have only limited uses. Much of it may indeed be removed while still in early middle life and replaced by other species. Sitka spruce retains the first place and together with Norway spruce occupies half the planted area. The pines occupy 30 per cent. Other conifers, the larches, Douglas fir, the silver firs, hemlock and western red cedar all play a subsidiary part.

The area under broad-leaved species is small, but the Commission normally does not acquire much land which is suitable for them. They have, however, a part to play in Scottish forestry.

Production from forests and plantations comes in several ways. It comes from thinning operations from feelings of mature timber at the end of a rotation, as a result of accidental causes such as gales and from special fellings which may have to be made for purposes of forest management.

Thinnings, from which most of our current production is being derived are of great importance for it is known that about half the total yield of a managed crop is obtained in this way. The removal by thinning of trees in order to promote the growth of the crop and to concentrate the increment on the best stems is a process which continues at intervals throughout the life of a stand of timber; the earliest thinnings are small poles which can be used for pitwood, pulpwood, fencing, etc., but during the later stages the stems removed become progressively larger and in the last few thinnings may give timber almost all of which is large enough for sawing.

Production from final fellings will depend to some extent on the length of the rotations used in our forests, and it is only recently that serious thought has been given by foresters in Scotland to this subject. The choice depends not only on species and site but also on the type of market which is being served and the return which is being earned on the capital invested.

There is no doubt that in all our calculations we shall have to allow for the timber which will have to be put in the market as a result of wind-blow, and any plan of management in Scotland must make provision for losses and damage from wind. We seem to have, twice or thrice in every century, a gale of extreme severity which works havoc in woodlands and plantations, but all the time, year by year, there are losses which frequently amount in the aggregate to large volumes of timber. A small grower can be completely crippled by severe wind-blow; large growers with a range of plantations are better able to adjust their operations.

One of the problems which faces a really large grower of timber like the Forestry Commission lies in securing continuous supplies of produce of different sizes. This can be done only if the forests contain a reasonable distribution of age-classes of tree, from the youngest to the oldest. Since in many of our forests much of the planting was completed in a short space of years it is becoming necessary to start adjusting the age-classes by felling some of the crops prematurely and replanting the sites. Continued, this will in time give a series of age-classes from which material of different sizes can be drawn and which will provide continuity by ensuring that when one part of the forest is ripe for final felling, another part is available of the right age and size to take its place. This operation will provide supplies of timber on a "once-only" basis.

Table II gives estimates of the production from Forestry Commission plantations at different periods up to 1980. There are as yet no similar figures for privately owned forests and woodlands.

These figures allow for a certain amount of felling, but do not make any allowance for wind-blow or for systematic felling to adjust age-classes. It will be noted that the totals increase from period to period and that in the later years the volume of the larger sized materials rises sharply.

The timber trade in Scotland has been working under the handicap since the war of having inadequate supplies of timber of sawmill size for conversion in the conventional way, and these supplies were further diminished by the loss of trees in the great gale of 1953. This is a situation which will correct itself, slowly in those districts where the rate of tree growth is slow, more rapidly where trees grow at a faster rate. Eventually there ought to be supplies sufficient to maintain a larger sawing industry in home-grown timber than we have today. But home-grown timber will have to make its way in a strongly competitive world in which it will have to face not only imported timber but alternative materials, and this means that not only will it have to keep its costs of conversion down but also see that the faults commonly attributed to home-produced timber, lack of seasoning, lack of grading and inaccurate sawing are avoided. These are complaints made generally all over Great Britain, but it can now be said that in Scotland the sawing is of a high standard of accuracy. This points to larger installations than many of those to which we have long been accustomed, with seasoning kilns and probably also with plants for preservative treatment of the timber and workshops for lamination of timber and other forms of preparation. If to this the operators can bring regular supplies of uniform logs there is no reason why they should not compete successfully with their rivals and also offer a reasonable price for the raw material. It is unlikely however, that the timber trade will embark on extensive re-equipment until they can be reasonably sure of supplies of logs.

TABLE II

Forestry Commission—Forecast of Production in Scotland: Coniferous Timber

Figures in millions of Hoppus feet
(1 Hoppus foot = 1·273 cubic foot)

Year	Conservancy	Breast-height Quarter Girth (inches)			
		2½-6	6¼-9	Over 9	Total
1965	West	1·6	0·6	0·2	2·4
	East	1·6	0·9	0·1	2·6
	South	1·3	0·4	0·1	1·8
	North	1·2	0·8	0·4	2·4
	Total	5·7	2·7	0·8	9·2
1970	West	2·0	1·1	0·5	3·6
	East	1·8	1·3	0·2	3·3
	South	2·5	0·8	0·1	3·4
	North	1·4	1·0	0·5	2·9
	Total	7·7	4·2	1·3	13·2
1975	West	3·0	1·6	0·6	5·2
	East	2·5	2·1	0·5	5·1
	South	4·8	1·5	0·3	6·6
	North	1·9	1·5	1·3	4·7
	Total	12·2	6·7	2·7	21·6
1980	West	4·2	2·4	0·8	7·4
	East	3·2	3·2	1·1	7·5
	South	6·8	3·1	1·2	11·1
	North	2·8	2·2	2·2	7·2
	Total	17·0	10·9	5·3	33·2

The other important traditional market for home-grown timber has been the mines, but here demand is not likely to increase. The Watson Committee,[3] speaking of mining timber in Great Britain as a whole, said, "The overall position, so far as softwood mining timber is concerned, is one of decreasing total demand; but with home sources currently supplying only one-third of that demand it is clear that there will be room for many years to come for an increasing intake of home-grown softwoods, provided that they can compete in price and quality and carry the same service as the imported article and that economic arrangements can be made for transport from distant areas. It is necessary, however, to draw attention to the facts that the market in Scotland is now being almost fully supplied from Scottish woodlands and that it may not be economic to transport to English coalfields." The problem of cost of transport is critical. Already there is enough material of the required sizes virtually to meet the needs of the Scottish coalfields and to provide quantities of pulpwood, some of which is exported to England. It is difficult to believe that the most important English coalfields can be supplied from Scotland in normal times at a profit to the supplier. Indeed, within Scotland itself as supplies increase there will be a tendency to supply the coalfields with material from districts near at hand and to leave the more distant timber to be dealt with by other markets. What other markets are there? We already have some pointers. A few years ago there was established at Annan a chipboard factory working on home-grown timber and using material which is mainly of a type that would be suitable for mining purposes. Recently, another mill, which is now about to go into production, has been set up in Inverness. In addition, a proposal to erect a pulp mill on our western coast is now under active discussion. It is not known for certain how large this mill would be, but it is already clear that its size would be such that it could not be wholly supplied with home-grown timber. Frankel[1] has stated definitely that the promoters "could not see any hope of building a small mill in Scotland" and it would follow that if the project were pursued on this basis, a good part of the raw material would have to be imported. How long it would be necessary to import would depend on the increase in available supplies in Scotland and on the price offered. If, however, a large mill like this were established here, it would leave little room for another. So far as we can see, therefore, a probable pattern of utilisation in the future would be a large pulp mill, a small number of board mills, a greater number of large modern sawmills, all drawing on a large part of the supplies. We would need also a considerable number of smaller mills and there would be round mining timber and the like often combined in the forest with other operations.

If this should prove to be the pattern, it will pose certain problems for the operators in the forests and woodlands. They will be supplying plants in the creation of which large amounts of capital have been sunk and which therefore must have delivery of supplies in such a way that operations are never held up for lack of raw material. This may not be easy in some parts of our country. Then there is the problem of transport from the forest to the processing plant. Although we do not know what developments may take place with helicopters and hovercraft as means of transport, we are reasonably safe in assuming that the bulk of the timber will be moved by road, and this raises the question of the suitability of our existing road system to carry the traffic which will arise, bearing in mind that many of our large forest areas are served by secondary roads with bridges of limited capacity. It is probable that most of our produce in the form of pitwood and pulpwood is now being carried in loads of seven to ten tons although fifteen-ton loads can sometimes be seen. Experience in Sweden has shown that for road transport of pulpwood something like fifteen tons is the minimum economic load and they would prefer to make it twenty tons by attaching a trailer. Unless we can get loads like this over our roads there will be little profit in the operations.

Will it be possible in future to extend our forest areas by putting under trees some of the land which we now regard as unplantable and which generally has a low utilisation value for other purposes? Broadly, there are two types of land in this category, land which is high-lying and exposed and land such as the poorest *Trichophorum* peats in the north-west where to soil poverty severe exposure is added to make the conditions even more difficult. In fixing the upper limits of their plantations, Scottish foresters have not as a rule played too much for safety, but they are all aware that if they could carry their plantations higher they would be performing a most useful service. At the present time, various experimental plantations are being formed well above the upper levels of our forests in order to discover what chances there are of bringing in some more of this high land. The probability is that not much effective timber-producing ground will be discovered above our existing planting limits. On the poorer peats such as those in the north-west of Scotland we have reached the stage when we can establish crops of *Pinus contorta* with phosphate and with intensive drainage. We do not yet know whether we shall be able to keep them growing. The whole subject of tree growth on what we currently regard as "unplantable" peat is under investigation at the Macaulay Institute, where they are studying the nutrient status of the young trees and also the effect on the peat of the tree growth. There is much land like this in a district which needs some new industry and much therefore depends on the result of these researches.

Another possibility of increasing production from plantations is still in the early stages of discussion and experiment. That is the application of fertilisers to growing crops. We do not know whether the responses, if any, will be great enough to justify the cost of the manures and their application. But this at least offers interesting possibilities not only of obtaining higher yields but also of correcting deficiencies and disorders.

One may also expect improvements in yield through the use of specially selected or specially bred planting stock. Work on tree breeding is still in an early stage in forestry, but it is gathering momentum and should begin to give results which can be applied in practice in the not too distant future.

Forestry impinges inevitably on other forms of land use. Its effect may be almost imperceptible in districts where it has long been part of the rural economy; it may be immediately evident where forestry comes in as a new method of utilising the land, for example in upland grazing regions. This has often given rise to acrimonious dispute. In a paper recently presented to the British Association, the Director of the Grassland Research Institute, Dr. William Davies,[4] had this to say: "There has been much heated discussion as to the place of the forester on the hills of Wales and Scotland. There is clearly a place for both forest and grassland, and I for one would be very happy to see the steep escarpments and the boulder-strewn lands under forest. Surely it seems sensible to plan in such a way that forest, grass and livestock farming in the hills shall be integrated and to do so with a view to make the most of our countryside and of its land potential. To achieve a sensible and practical plan of development demands co-operative research between those interested in forestry and in grassland improvement. Unfortunately during the past quarter-century these various interests have shown little evidence of co-operative development—the attitude of both sides has savoured too much of 'dog and manger' and this has got us nowhere. For the sake of the hills and perhaps for the sake of British agriculture as a whole I sincerely hope that the present attitudes will change and that this will lead to a better appreciation of hill potentials which will surely be developed as a consequence." On this I would comment first that it is not clear why the nimble foresters should be confined to the steep slopes and the lands strewn with boulders while the presumably stiff-jointed sheep and shepherds should have the run of the smooth and gentle slopes. Secondly, this passage does less than justice to the officers of the Department of Agriculture and the Forestry Commission who have the task of agreeing the allocation of land for planting either on individual blocks of land or on a wider scale, as was done in the surveys of Strathoykell and other districts which have been carried out since the war. And, after all, we have got somewhere, for we have greatly increased the area under forest without reducing appreciably the numbers of livestock on the hills. Nevertheless, in his demand for co-operative research between the forestry and the agricultural authorities, Dr. Davies will have the agreement of most of us. Many of the difficulties we have are due, simply, to our lack of exact knowledge.

If we are to practise successfully any form of integration of forestry and hill farming, we must know far more precisely than we do now what are the effects of a large plantation on the land adjoining it and how those effects are modified by differences in silvicultural practice. At the same time, we must consider how the methods used in pastoral management affect the adjoining plantations. If the agricultural experts could work out, for example, a system of management for hill grazings which did not involve the use of fire, they would have taken a very great step towards making possible a really close integration of forestry and farming in our upland districts. Reference was made earlier to the substantial areas of woodland which are used to give overhead shelter to grazing animals at certain seasons of the year, and a recent paper by Michael[5] has given some indications of the benefits to sheep stocks from this kind of protection. It appears certain that this form of shelter is really necessary in many places, but what will happen when it has all disappeared? I ask this question because most of the woods in our upland districts which are used for shelter are, in fact, disappearing slowly but steadily. Because of grazing and burning, there is no regeneration, and as the woodland opens out there is a progressive deterioration in the surface conditions of the soil which would make it more and more difficult for the trees to establish themselves again, even if they had the chance. The intensity of the shelter provided by the tree cover might also be of importance. This is a field in which the special knowledge of the forester might be enlisted in the service of agriculture.

The practice of opening forests, the prime purpose of which is the production of timber, to domestic animals for grazing, is known all over the world, and if it can be carried out without damage to the forest and without injury to the livestock it has something to commend it. It is a practice not unknown in Scotland and recently the Forestry Commission has made a few small trials in its plantations. These have not proceeded very far and have as yet not promised very much though possibly the plantations into which the animals were admitted were rather young. Things may be different with taller plantations of species which do not throw a heavy shade, under which a reasonably good herbage can develop. From the forester's point of view, the danger is not from browsing, because plantations in which this could take place would not be thrown open; he would be more concerned with loss of nutrients taken away in the animals, with their effect on the soil by treading and in other ways and with damage to the surface tree-roots. It would thus be necessary to investigate these matters before any progress could be made and at the same time agricultural research would have to busy itself with the other aspects of the problem. It may well prove that the form of multiple use would not work, but the attempt to find out is well worth while.

These examples have been given in order to bring out the need for combined work by agricultural and forest research in those sections of their respective fields which come into touch with each other most closely. This is a development which ought to come quickly if we are to succeed in our aim of making our land as productive as possible. There is no necessity at all to set up any new organisation to achieve it; it could be dealt with quite satisfactorily by existing organisations working to an agreed plan.

There has been a revival of interest lately in the effects of forests on stream flow and runoff, a subject on which important studies have been made by forest research workers in several countries, notably Switzerland, the Union of South Africa and the United States. This is only part of a wider problem, that of the effect of all kinds of land use on the supply of water. Forestry is still a minor user of land in our catchment areas, taking the country as a whole, but it has a certain background of experience in the sort of investigation which this problem demands and is in a position to contribute to a joint research into this subject if it should be decided to proceed with it and if the necessary funds are made available.

REFERENCES

1. The development of pulp and particle board industries and their effect on forest management. Report of Discussion. Society of Foresters of Great Britain, 1960.
2. Census of Woodlands 1947-1949. Forestry Commission, 1952.
3. Report of the Committee on Marketing of Woodland Produce. Forestry Commission, 1956.
4. DAVIES, WILLIAM (1960). Pastoral systems in relation to world food supplies. *The Advancement of Science*, September.
5. MICHAEL, D. T. (1960). Aspects of shelter in relation to the grazing animal. *Scottish Forestry*, **14**, 3.

STATEMENT BY REPORTER

Mr. A. H. H. Ross

Lately Director of Forestry for Scotland

Mr. Chairman, Your Grace, My Lords, Ladies and Gentlemen: Time presses and I do not want to take it up with any preliminary remarks except to say that I have only been able in this report to deal with a small number of the subjects which are dealt with in these three papers on forestry. I think I ought to start with some basic information. In his paper Mr. Watt has given us important facts of which I will deal with only a few of the more salient. The present woodland area of Scotland, both stocked and unstocked, is a little over one million acres, and that is just about 6 per cent. of the land area of Scotland. Of the existing area of managed forests three-fifths are under the direct control of the Forestry Commission and two-fifths in private and other ownership. During the next eight years it is planned to afforest 200,000 acres of hill land. Current home timber production in Scotland, both private and Forestry Commission, is of the order of 23 million cubic feet of round wood. The Forestry Commission in Scotland employ 4,200 people, private estates probably about 2,000 and timber merchants and contractors also about 2,000, a total of somewhere around 8,000 people. Mr. Watt in his paper observes that, compared with industrial urban standards, this is not a very striking figure, but nevertheless it is a good social contribution when you take account of the fact that most woodland is located in areas of low population density. Going on to discuss the role of forestry, Mr. Watt makes the point that at present by far the most important use of forestry is the commercial one. It is true, of course, that trees do serve other uses, as for instance providing locally important shelter, and, of course, there are some notable examples of forests providing protection from erosion, as, for example, at Culbin. Professor Anderson stresses the importance of the protective function of the forest through its influence on climate at high elevations and in very exposed districts. He says that if only a part of original forest covering in Scotland had been retained there would have been little reason to doubt an increase in the productivity of the high pastures. We have heard something about conflicts of land use, and yesterday Mr. Nicholson had some candid comments, delivered, I think, in a kindly manner, about the Forestry Commission's afforestation policy. I do not want to say anything about that myself, but I suggest that today we do not think so much about conflict—it always takes more than one to make a conflict—we should think more about co-operation by all concerned in the best interests of the people of this country. Mr. Macdonald, referring in his paper to the inevitable competition which occurs between forestry and other forms of land use, particularly agriculture, discusses the subject of integration of forestry and hill farming. He makes the point that more might have been done on this question of integration of forestry and agriculture but for the lack of exact knowledge. He thinks that we must consider how pastoral farming affects adjoining plantations, and vice versa. He goes on to say that if agricultural experts could work out a system of hill grazing management which did not involve the use of fire, they would have gone a long way towards achieving a really close integration of forestry and farming, especially in our upland districts. With this statement I think there will be a wholehearted agreement by those of us who know what an anxious time the muir-burning season is on the one hand for the forester who is responsible for the safety of plantations adjoining hill grazings and on the other hand for the sheep farmer who lives in dread of a crippling claim for damages if his fire gets out of control. Mr. Macdonald urges the early need for combined work, both agricultural and forestry research combining in all such matters. Professor Anderson in his paper deals with the subject of a National Forest Policy. "The National Forest Policy", he says, "should have two major objectives, namely (i) the replacement of some forest cover of a suitable type to benefit agriculture and the general commonweal, and (ii) the replacement of a forest cover to produce timber and other commodities. There should thus be a protective aim, to realise which will require the use of leaf-trees mainly, and a productive aim, in achieving which most reliance will be placed on coniferous trees." He explains that these objects can only be achieved in two phases. One a phase of formation of the growing stock, which would normally take a long time and be not financially profitable, and secondly a final phase, when you have a managed forest with a permanent cover and a sustained yield in perpetuity and that final phase would normally be economic. He emphasises very strongly this matter of sustention or sustained yield. Mr. Macdonald also deals with the matter of sustained yield and the long-term adjustments which it is necessary to make to more or less even-aged forests in order to secure a reasonable distribution of age-classes without which sustained yield cannot be achieved. Professor Anderson goes on to discuss the technical difficulties caused by the very great variety of topography, geology and climate in Scotland, particularly in regard to choice of species. The same point is dealt with by Mr. Macdonald, who says that since the main purpose of forestry is to provide raw material for industry it is necessary to look first at our forests in relation to industrial demands and possible industrial developments. What we grow is dictated in the end by soil and climate, but on many sites there is a choice of more than one species for planting and the actual choice may be decided by marketing possibilities. He gives information on future probable yield from Forestry Commission plantations in Scotland—figures for private woods are not yet available—which indicate happier times ahead for the Scottish home timber trade, who are at the moment hard put to it to find logs of sawmill size. He suggests that the probable pattern of future utilisation for Scotland would be one large pulp mill, a small number of board mills, a greater number of modern large sawmills and a considerable number of small mills. I have referred to only a few of the subjects covered by the three papers, but they provide pointers for consideration and discussion and I should like to suggest the following two points which among others merit close attention. The first is that it seems clear that Scotland is, by and large, a good place for growing trees and it also looks as if eventually there will be ample demand for home-grown timber, provided the price and quality can compete with imported. To what extent, then, is it desirable in the national interest to increase the forest area of Scotland, bearing in mind other interests which are in competition for afforestable land? Secondly (arising out of the first point), if the recommendations for the greater use of forestry in its protective role and for the application of the principle of integration of forestry and agriculture are to be followed up, what action is required? What investigations, both economic and technical, should be carried out, and by whom?

DISCUSSION

THE DUKE OF BUCCLEUCH, *Scottish Landowners' Federation*

Mr. Chairman and Gentlemen: I think you asked me, Mr. Chairman, to speak rather on the conflicts of land use between agriculture and forestry; and in succession to my forebears, as one who endeavours to assist the development and equipment of land for farming and to plant with trees land not suited to farming, I thank you for your invitation to do so. I would say very little about the conflict in regard to the use of the best agricultural land beyond saying that landowners can ask local authorities to take as little of the best land as possible until the last moment, and to use first as much as they can of the land they already have. We realise that good land must continue to go for buildings and factories and roads.

I would like to refer rather more to the use of our uplands, and as one who is equally divided between farming and forestry I must declare an interest in the land but also some experience in its management; and I am able to speak quite impartially as between farming and forestry. It seems to me, after examination of the very excellent analyses and description of farming in Scotland, and keeping in mind our objectives for the better use of our natural resources, that it is right to give more attention to the use of our uplands. I would like to support very strongly the remarks made earlier this morning by Major Swan and to supplement them with a few words. With the loss of good agricultural land for other purposes it is even more desirable to maintain our acreage for farming and to make more use of our best uplands and what are sometimes described as marginal lands. Grants such as those for hill farming, cattle rearing on hills and the marginal agricultural provisions, to which he referred, have been most helpful. It is very important to make the better parts of the Scottish uplands economically productive and permanently productive, and this is being gradually achieved and can still be done on a larger scale. The marginal agricultural provisions are particularly valuable and adapted for this. They are very much suited to Scottish conditions and helpful in a much larger part of Scotland than south of the Border, and I do submit that it would be unwise to reduce, at any rate too quickly and by too much, the help provided in this way. We know that better housing, electricity and modern conveniences are needed to keep Scottish families in the countryside, and it is also important to make and keep productive, and economically so, as much of the land as possible. I believe that Scottish farmers, and I know that those in the south of Scotland, feel strongly that this is a Scottish and agricultural question deserving support. And I believe that a combination of farmer, proprietor and State in the provision of capital and management can steadily continue the improvement of those lands.

I would like to turn now rather more to forestry, and I agree with Mr. Ross that there should be less conflict and a more complementary outlook between the two. I am sure that anyone with knowledge of the land and soil, motoring along any of our roads and valleys in Scotland, will see constantly areas of land, small acreages and bigger ones, which are more suited for trees, for plantations or for forests than for farming, and which can be planted without any injury to farming; and I believe many of you, in many of our valleys where the slopes of the hills are steep, will be noticing the amount of erosion on our hillsides which I feel has increased quite a lot in recent years. There is only one thing to do for that, which is planting, and although it may not be the sort of land which the Forestry Commission would choose, they are the only people who can help to keep that land for some use.

I would like to support those who urge an increase of forestry in Scotland and the claim, as I think Mr. Ross stated, that there are good reasons for it. Though forestry in Britain is coming into its own more than ever before with the gradual increase in planting since the war, the acreage under timber is still very, very small compared to most European countries, and the rate of increase is not very rapid. There is in Scotland much land suitable for growing good timber in small and large acreages which can be made available for forestry without conflicting at all seriously with farming. I do find very often shepherds and farmers, in conversation, view with suspicion and dislike the encouragement of forestry, but I do feel that they realise that the two can be complementary and that a great deal more can be done. While the Forestry Commission have done very good work in Scotland, to which we can pay tribute, there is also the responsibility of those in private forestry, with rather better land, to do the best that we can in providing Scotland with species suited to that land, and which will also make Scotland more beautiful.

I do maintain that it is to the economic advantage of Scotland as a whole, and to the United Kingdom, both to have a much larger supply of timber available in this country and to assist our nation in problems of balance of payments which seem to become more difficult, rather than easier.

Major S. F. Macdonald Lockhart

Mr. Chairman, Your Grace, Ladies and Gentlemen: I will try and be brief. I would like to speak on integration of forestry and agriculture. Integration schemes have been carried out for many, many years by private estates—private landowners—but now, as we have seen in the papers, the nature of the national estate is changing and we are getting more owner-occupiers and a smaller area of privately owned estates and some very large publicly owned estates. I think in the rural area of Scotland there are a great many people who are convinced that integration of forestry and agriculture is a good thing, but the convictions may be very different there, but it is difficult to find a scientific support for them. It is difficult to get advice or help on how integration should be carried out. Landowners in the past have carried out their schemes by the light of nature, quite a good light, but nowadays we would like something more exact. I know that research is being done by foresters and agriculturalists on this subject, but I believe there is a tremendous amount of knowledge in the country on the subject if it could be collected without waiting for specific research projects to be completed. Briefly, my plea is that we can have some solid information on this subject, and may I perhaps be bold enough to suggest that integration is needed in the universities, in colleges and in the Government Departments.

Professor H. M. Steven, *Department of Forestry, Aberdeen University*

My views on this question follow closely those of the last two speakers. When I read the papers, I was struck by the fact that so many people, not only foresters but others, considered, as indeed many committees have done, that forestry has to play a distinctive role in the development of the uplands regions of Scotland. Some people have said what a pity it was that we lost so many of our forests in the past. Well, we cannot do anything about that. Some have advocated new forests, and I would suggest to this Committee, when they sit down to prepare their recommendations, that there is substantial evidence that there should be a further increase in the area devoted to forestry. So that is the first point I would like to make. The second point is this: that there may be a certain amount of conflict because, if the forest area is to increase, then some other user will have less land and it will, of course, be pastoral agriculture. For many years I have felt that what is wanted is not to decrease the production of pastoral agriculture, if more land is taken for forestry from agriculture, but to do everything possible to encourage better and more intensive use of rough grazings, and I would like, as a forester, to support Major Swan, although perhaps my conclusion or deduction from what he advocated may not be quite the same as his. When every effort has been made to make the land at present used for pastoral agriculture more productive, it will be possible to release more land for forestry while maintaining agricultural production from these upland areas. I think that that is really the answer to this particular problem, because I am sure that both in terms of money, and for the welfare of the people of Scotland, you will get more benefit from doing this than the development of either one or the other. The other point I would just like to make is this: that I am rather surprised that there is no contribution from the Hill Farming Research Organisation, because if more is to be done on these pastoral areas, obviously the results of research which is going on, and which I am sure will be very fruitful, should be brought to the notice of the Committee. The next point I would like to make is this: such an eminent authority as Mr. James MacDonald has said that there is a serious lack of exact knowledge about allocation of land. This is true, but I would agree with the Duke of Buccleuch and Mr. Lockhart that there is a great deal of knowledge about this among practical people. Science has got to make its contribution, but if it is to be well done I think you want to go right down, because there are cases in the north of Scotland where once the so-called experts stood aside the real solution was made. You all know how many shrewd people there are in the countryside of Scotland, and their contribution should not be overlooked. Finally, I would suggest that this problem, important as science and practical knowledge are, is really a human and sociological one. It is a case of persuading the present user of land to vary its use. It is not an easy thing to do, but I think that this should not be overlooked. Do not forget the people who will be affected by any change in land use.

Professor G. P. WIBBERLEY, *Department of Agricultural Economics, Wye College, University of London*

I have one thing to say, and I will say it as quickly as I can. I will probably begin quietly but become stronger as I go on, because I presume that, as an Englishman, I was not invited here unless I had something to say which could be without fear or favour and, shall we say, would have no regional bias. Because I realised that the agricultural and pastoral picture of Scotland would be dealt with extremely well by the lecturers who followed me, I therefore took the opportunity of writing a short, but rather philosophical, paper.

In that paper I hinted at the problem of *time preference*. In other words, all of us in our private lives are dominated very much by market values; we decide things according to the salary we have; we decide in farming according to the prices we can get; we decide things in our estate management very much according to land values; but when we leave our private lives and come into social groups, particularly into a group like this, we immediately forget our private motivations and begin to talk as if market values were not really important, and that time preferences were not related to the life of an individual but could be for longer periods. When I hear people talk about the conservation of natural resources, they often appear to have forgotten that in their private lives they judge things in terms of between fifteen and twenty years of purchase of annual increments. This is true in particular of farming. In discussions of the conservation of natural resources some people appear to suggest that there should be a time preference of almost infinity, as if there is one particular use (usually the use they are keen on) which should have preference over all others.

We should be absolutely clear on this. If in all our private actions we accept that everything is relative, then we must accept that the best use of land is essentially a relative problem particularly in a highly developed country like Great Britain. In addition, as soon as we leave market rates of discount and argue for a preferential use of land, we get into this difficult problem of time preference. I have argued elsewhere in print for lower "social" rates of discount in relation to agricultural values of land when rural sites are being considered for permanent changes in land use and given factual information to support this argument. Because in these days we are asking the general community to subsidise things in many ways, we badly need cost-benefit types of studies in problems of conservation. In deciding one use as against another there are certain aspects on both sides which are measurable and other aspects which are intangible or subjective and not measurable. We must try to measure as much as we can on both sides because here is this large arena of intangible things to consider which cannot be measured.

This is why it worries me when I hear agriculture/forestry arguments being discussed in a vague way. There is a case where a cost-benefit analysis is very important, and all the factual evidence I can see suggests that forestry can put up a stronger case than agriculture, particularly a subsidised agriculture—for the use of the uplands, though agriculture can put up a better case than forestry for use of the lowlands. There has been quite a lot of work done on this problem, but some of it is unpublished; some of us have perhaps been luckier than others to see it. It is awfully important to have these sort of measurements, because, unless we do, so many of our discussions on conservation will remain ephemeral, will not get us anywhere, because we are asking society to make judgments different from the type of judgments individuals make in their own private lives. If we ask the community to do this we must put up a really good, logical case. Therefore, I would plead for a little more scientific thought and practice in our discussion, the type of scientific thought which comes from both the natural sciences and the social sciences.

WRITTEN CONTRIBUTIONS

National Farmers' Union of Scotland

FORESTRY

There is no doubt that forestry activities in Scotland are a matter of the greatest concern to Scottish agriculture. This is apparent from the fact that of the total land acquired by the Forestry Commission to date—amounting to over 2,000,000 acres—more than half is situated in Scotland. In 1959, 19,939 acres of plantable land were acquired in Scotland compared with 11,052 acres in England and 7,819 acres in Wales. Of the 19,939 acres of plantable land acquired in Scotland, over 16,000 acres consisted of bare land and clearly a large proportion of this must have been land which was previously used for agricultural production.

The Union has always admitted that there is a place for forestry alongside agriculture in the rural economy of Scotland, and it recognises the benefits which can flow from proper co-ordination of the two interests in the shape of the reviving of declining communities in certain isolated areas and the provision of shelter. The value of home timber production from the import-saving point of view is appreciated, but, on the other hand, forestry in this country has been allowed to develop in a comparatively haphazard fashion dependent on the land which happened to be offered to the Forestry Commission rather than upon a rational plan. There is no doubt that land has been acquired for planting which should not be so used while there is available for the purpose land which is of less agricultural value.

The Forestry Commission acquire land by voluntary sale, but once the ownership of land has been acquired the dispossession of tenants to provide areas for planting has frequently involved compulsory eviction. In many cases the wintering ground has been planted on hill sheep farms with the result that the stock-carrying capacity of the land remaining to the tenant has been greatly reduced.

The Union believes that if the farming community could be convinced that the Forestry Commission's activities were being directed towards the most suitable land on the basis of properly devised surveys, then there would be a prospect of achieving the desirable level of co-operation between farmers and the Commission. This could lead to the offering of land for the planting of shelter belts of reasonable size, and in particular districts these shelter belts could together provide an acreage such that they would form an economic unit from the Commission's point of view, particularly if they could be worked as adjuncts to existing forests in the district. In addition, it is submitted that the possibility of any real conflict between farming and forestry could be avoided for a very long time ahead if the forestry programme were concentrated on land which is not carrying stock, old deer forests, old woodland, bracken-infested land, shelter belts and so on.

Private planting of woodlands cannot, of course, be ignored in the Scottish economy, but its relationship to agriculture is rather different. The owner of an estate who is interested in forestry is usually also interested in agriculture, and this factor tends to ensure that a properly co-ordinated programme of agriculture and forestry is devised.

B. G. McLellan, F.R.I.C., M.I.CHEM.E., F.R.S.E.

The Production of Basket Willows in Scotland

As has been emphasised by many of the speakers at the Natural Resources Symposium, here in Scotland we must look to the soil and the sea for many of our resources. How this is being done is chronicled in the papers dealing with agriculture, forestry, horticulture, seaweed, etc. These represent, in the main, large-scale operations amply supported by legislation and scientific effort. Particularly in the West Highlands, a considerable proportion of farming land is rough and uncultivated and is devoted to cattle and hill sheep. Some of this might be brought into use for the growing of crops, which could be worked in with the farmers' normal routine, to yield an economic, profit-producing return. One such crop might be basket willows and for the past four or five years I have been making a study of this possibility. As far as I have been able to ascertain, there is no systematic growing of willows for basket making in Scotland, Craft Centres and similar activities obtain the bulk of their supplies from Somerset and the south. The chief users in Scotland, namely the Blind Institutions in the four large cities, import all their requirements from England, mainly Somerset, and from abroad.

In Somerset, the growing and processing of willows is a self-contained industry and is not combined with agriculture or horticulture. It is on a large scale and so can afford the tools and plant necessary. In Scotland it might well with advantage be linked with agriculture, so as to make use of cultivators and other farm implements during the development period.

The first step was to ascertain whether suitable willows can be grown and become an economic crop. The project was opened up with the Scottish Council, who arranged that the idea should be discussed with the Conservator for Scotland of the Forestry Commission. This I did in Edinburgh in 1955. As an outcome, arrangements were made with the Forestry Officer in this area (Mid Argyll) to prepare an experimental plot and to make trial plantings. A suitable site of some 670 square yards was chosen at one of the Forestry's nurseries near Tarbert, Loch Fyne. The ground was cleaned and cultivated and samples of the soil sent to the Macaulay Institute for analysis and report; the plot was then treated in accordance with their instructions. The trial ground was enclosed by a 6-ft. fence to exclude deer. In April 1957, plantings were made of about 120 stools of each of four varieties of Viminalis willows supplied by the Forestry Commission. Hoeing, to control weeds, was carried out in June and July. The first cutting was made in January 1958. Three of the varieties had grown well, two particularly so, the fourth not so well. Samples of the willows were sent to two basket makers and to a nearby craft centre, and from these, satisfactory reports were received. About this time I established contacts with the Scottish Country Industries Development Trust; the Rural Industries Bureau in London and also with Mr. Stott, the Willow Officer at Long Ashton; from these, and others, I have had a great deal of advice and help. The second crop, cut in the spring of 1959, was considerably heavier than that of the previous year and was sent to the Craft Centre at Carradale to be used for making "Skye" baskets. The 1960 crop, amounting to some 4 cwt., was sent to the Royal Glasgow Asylum for the Blind for trial and report. The crop due to be cut in the spring of 1961 appears to be even heavier.

Willows are sold to the users in a number of forms and are made up into bundles of different length rods. If the bark is not removed and the crop is sold more or less as it is cut, it is called "brown" or "green". "White" willows are produced by "peeling", which involves removing the outer bark from the wood, and this is done by hand using an implement termed a "brake", or, if large quantities are involved, say from over 5 acres, by a machine employing a similar principle. The production of "buff" willows which are in demand in Scotland, is effected by boiling, a process in which the tannins of the bark impart the desired buff colour to the wood.

I now have sufficient data on which to formulate a scheme to draw up a cost estimate and so to assess what might be the profit per acre of land planted. It has been authoritatively stated that the return from willow growing is lower per acre than from horticulture but well above that from agriculture. A cost statement based on actual data obtained from Somerset was made by Mr. Stott in 1954 and this is being used to prepare a suitable site in Scotland.

The capital required must take into account the fact that there is no profitable return from the first two years, but if a start is made on a relatively small scale, say one or two, or even five acres, initial capital costs can be kept down to a minimum and mechanisation put off until profits begin to accrue. The life of a plantation is some 18 productive years, and the yield should be 6 to 8 tons per acre, all of which can be sold as "brown" or "white" in Scotland, and, moreover, have the competitive advantage of considerably lower transport costs.

Certain other types of willow are of value on account of the fact that not only do they yield rods suitable for fine basket work, but also because the bark is valuable as a source of salicin. Experimental plantings of these have been grown and assays of the salicin content have been made, but it is too early to predict the final outcome.

UTILISATION OF RESOURCES

WILDLIFE AND RECREATION

Utilisation of the Wildlife Resource

W. J. EGGELING, B.SC., PH.D., F.R.S.E.
Conservation Officer, Nature Conservancy, Edinburgh

Those concerned with wildlife must study habitats and be knowledgeable on geology, soil, water and climate, and with the wise use by man of all renewable natural resources.

Man has been responsible in Scotland, or elsewhere, with deterioration of biological production systems. As a result, the overall production in much of it is now of the type characterised elsewhere as semi-desert.

One of our tasks must be to reconstitute original efficient biological systems and also meet the present-day requirements of man. This means the multi-cultural use of land to give diversified yield of plants and animals, and also human needs in farming, forestry, nature conservation and amenity.

Is not the solution to preserving both the game and its habitat to be found in regarding the animals as a valuable natural resource, as a source of food? This would not mean the vast bags of grouse of past decades, but rather a mixed take-off involving deer and grouse as sustained yields with other products too. Thus would be avoided run-down of the land and habitats associated with monoculture.

In addition, while the Tourist Board has shown what can be done in building a profitable national industry by popularising a semi-desert, an appreciable and growing number of visitors are coming especially to get acquainted with our wildlife resource on far wider terms. In 1960 20,000 visitors were attracted to observe in hides a single pair of ospreys.

There are limits to the number of tourists that can be taken to wild areas without sterilising Nature Reserves and such places. Nevertheless, love of nature and the outdoors must depend for its full development in the perpetuation of the resource in which this love has its roots.

Each and every plant and animal is dependent for its existence on its environment. To understand the whys and wherefores of their behaviour and requirements, and of fluctuations in their numbers, and to learn how to manage and control their populations—which is a basic requirement of conservation—one must study also their habitats. This means that geology, soil, water and climate all come into the picture, and it must be emphasised that soil and water conservation are just as much an essential of nature conservation as are studies directed at, say, finding out how to control pest populations of animals affecting the farmer or the forester, or how to manage aggregations of seals which are proved to be threatening fisheries, or at ascertaining the extent to which the toxic sprays now being used to protect agricultural crops and control roadside weeds are having enduring and harmful side-effects greatly reducing their overall efficiency. For example, are these sprays perhaps in certain cases endangering populations of animals and plants other than those against which they are specifically directed, amongst them birds which are on balance useful to the farmer, and bees and other useful insect pollinators?

When we read of the dust bowls of America, the threat of the encroaching Sahara, or the extinction by man of some formerly widespread species, we must not delude ourselves into thinking: "That sort of thing can't happen here." It has happened here, in Scotland. Man, and largely man alone, assisted by his grazing animals and his terribly lethal tool, fire, has bared the once tree-clad Highlands of their covering, exposed them to the erosive action of wind and rain, frost and thaw, and thus cleared them of their topsoil. The result was summed up by Professor W. H. Pearsall, in a symposium dealing with *Land Utilization and Conservation in the Scottish Highlands*, held in Glasgow last year, when he said that the whole of the Highland zone may be considered to represent a series of biological production systems which are badly deteriorated, and that the overall production in much of it is now of the type characterised elsewhere as semi-desert. This is a damning indictment of the use we have made of our heritage, but there is indeed clear evidence that the changes in the vegetational succession which have been brought about by man, for instance the changes from forest to moorland, and from moorland to heath, have involved a great diminution in the size of the standing crops of vegetation. Similarly, "formerly larger species of animals, and larger and more numerous individuals of existing species, occupied sites which are now almost unoccupied areas of moorland or heath. Many archaeological sites of former human occupations are now in a condition which is quite unattractive to man. Thus sites which were once the seat of arable cultivation or intensive pasturage are now covered by infertile forms of heath or by *Nardus* grassland. Their soils often show evidence of degeneration to infertile or podsolic states which could not have been characteristic of their original condition."[1]

In his assessment of the steps which must be taken to stabilise the present position and attempt to improve it, Professor Pearsall stressed that we must not neglect to study carefully the original natural systems of the Highlands. He pointed out that in the course of their creation ages of evolution had produced what were the most stable and most efficient biological systems possible in this often severe environment and that when these natural systems were destroyed biological systems of inferior efficiency and lower productivity inevitably replaced them. One of our tasks must therefore be to attempt to re-create or reconstitute the original systems and find out in what direction their especial virtues lie. By so doing we may be able to devise productive systems not only capable of producing the essential properties but also of meeting the present-day requirements of man. It is exactly this that the Nature Conservancy are hoping to do on some of the recently acquired National Reserves in Scotland, for instance on the island of Rhum. This work is still, however, in an embryonic stage and little more has yet been done than to make a start in assessing the problem in the particular study areas that are involved.

One of the most valuable contributions to the Glasgow symposium was a paper by Dr. R. F. Hunter of the Hill Farming Research Organisation, dealing with conservation and grazing. In this he considered the proposition that quite apart from the effects caused by the now almost universal accompanying muirburn there is direct connection between sheep farming and the degradation of Highland vegetation, and he summed up by saying that, whilst the two did, in a sense, go hand in hand, "to say that sheep are a degenerative factor on hill pastures is only a half truth, it is the lack of cattle which is degenerative".[2] Dr. Hunter's conclusion that "together, cattle, sheep and manures can regenerate our hill pastures" puts in a much simplified nutshell the feeling of conservationists the world over that the most efficient form of land use is multiple use. By this is meant not only the multicultural use of land to give a diversified yield of plants and animals as opposed to monocultures of, for instance, sheep or a single species of tree, but also the usage of one and the same extent of ground for a wide range of human needs including farming, forestry, nature conservation, amenity, recreation, sport, tourist requirements, etc. It is a point of view to which more and more people here in Britain are being forced by pressure of circumstance—by the intense and growing competition between private and public bodies and individuals for a claim in the increasingly limited amount of land that is available to meet a multitude of needs.

Does it not make sense to suggest that just as no arable farmer would think of growing the same agriculture crop year after year on the same ground so there must to some degree be the same sort of hazard in monocultural forestry or in the single-species farming of animals? Stock and milk farming on the one hand and arable farming on the other have tended to give way to mixed farming as the most efficient agricultural land usage compatable with sustained fertility. Mixed use has here been shown to be efficient use, and if one studies the position obtaining in those few places in the globe where man has not, as yet, upset too grossly the natural systems it will be seen that mixed cropping is there the rule. In such situations, for instance, in parts of the tropics and sub-tropics, there are seen to be the herb, grass, shrub and tree growth—each reflecting perceptible differences in rock, soil, water supply and micro-climate, and in the effects of biotic influences, and each with its peculiar associate assemblages of large and small animals living together in perfect equilibrium and making the fullest use of that particular environment. From the ingredients of such a situation we must not exclude man and the strains of animals that he himself has evolved; he and they are equally a part of nature. It is this sort of multiplicity of habitat and use that we must seek to perpetuate and copy, albeit in a modified and more ordered arrangement and with man taking a much bigger part.

Let us turn to a situation close at hand, involving the sport of shooting. An article which appeared in a country periodical a few years back described a Highland estate which included sea-loch foreshore, low ground, a few small woods, bracken lands, and bog and hill, with patches of arable farmland and a stretch of moorland grazing and heather. Here was an area where game birds and game animals, and wildlife generally, were plentiful. In the post-war years, "The bracken was cut and got under control. Land was drained and many more crops grown. Sour land was limed and treated with basic slag. Heather was burned and sheep properly dipped, with the result that the hills were clean and tick-free. Ground and winged vermin were dealt with and the same game stock was encouraged and fostered.

"As a result of all this", the account goes on, "we should now, after ten years, have a good game stock. In fact, we have no game at all."

That briefly is the story. What is the lesson? Are we to believe that good farming should have provided good sport with it? Do the two things go hand in hand, in modern conditions?

If we are to aim at multiple yields, there must be multiple use management. If game as well as farm yields are wanted, some of the ground must be managed primarily for that particular purpose. The overall financial yield from the land may not necessarily be any lower, for the marginal and waste ground will be producing good rough shooting with an assessable sporting value, and a value which can be increased quite out of proportion to the effort involved by the provision of occasional marshy sogs, small patches of scrub or woodland shelter, perhaps a small flighting pond and, above all, cover for ground-nesting birds. This is where the ledges and hedge-bottom growths come in, and the ditch-side vegetation, for it is here that many of the pheasants, partridges and wild duck will breed. A little predator control there may have to be, but it is surprising how often ground-nesting birds will get safely away—even from the now almost ubiquitous hooded or carrion crow—where there is reasonably thick ground cover.

I suggest, therefore, that good farming and good sporting returns do not as a logical consequence go hand in hand. For multi-purpose yields, be they farm produce and sport, farm produce and timber, forestry and sport, or all three, there must be multi-purpose management: and the more varied the crops, and the more diverse the management, the higher will be the overall biological yield and the greater the possibility that this will be maintained without deterioration of fertility. Concentrate on one type of yield and you cannot, as of right, expect the others. If you have varying ages and heights of heather on the hill you can be sure of at least a basic stock of grouse. Burn the whole of the hill, slag it or lime it, and you may be able to increase your sheep stock for a time, but your grouse stock will dwindle and vanish. Get rid of all the bracken, and there is more ground for stock but less shelter and probably fewer roe; clear out the hedge bottoms and "bring under control" the "waste" ground, and there may be no more patridges; drain every wet spot in every rushy field, and there will be no more snipe.

While they are still with us, can we not perpetuate, within reason, the natural habitats? Allow some scenic diversifications, preserve at least a modicum of the character of the countryside, and we will be surprised at the dividend it will pay. One thing, especially, we are in danger of forgetting, the necessity of woody shelter both for crops and stock. We have lost much more of this in the last fifty years than we can afford, and more still is being lost annually as hedgerows and field-side strips are felled without replacement. It is here that the concept of "farm forestry" and small "wood-lots" come in, a field in which we can learn a great deal from other countries.

These are but thoughts to ponder on. Multiple use may well be the key to the entire range of conservation—of the soil, the climate, and the environment in general, and so to the balanced production of all renewable natural resources. And it may well be the answer too, and the only answer, to the preservation of those numerous populations of plants and animals whose existence is being threatened all over the world by man and his multifarious activities.

Conservation is only another name for wise use or intelligent husbandry. Forest conservation implies the rational management of woods to ensure a sustained out-turn of produce without rundown of the site, the yield being measured in the case of production forests in the output of timber and firewood, and in the case of protection forests in the indirect benefits of protection of the soil, safeguarding of catchments and water supplies, preservation of local climates and provision of shelter, the value of which it is almost impossible to assess in terms of cash. The essential thing in all this is active management directed to a specific end. In the wider field of nature conservation, which brings in animals as well as plants, the same rules apply and the ultimate aim is identical: the same and sound management of a natural and renewable but easily destroyed resource.

Much has been written in recent years about the threatened extinction of the unique herds of plain animals in East Africa. With the great and continuing increase in the human population, and the inevitable accompanying extension of agricultural practices into wild land, the game animals are being restricted to smaller and smaller areas and their populations decimated. The position has now been reached when they can be found in numbers only in a few relatively tiny pockets, and even here, in Game Reserves or National Parks, they are threatened. What is the future of such areas and of the animals they seek to preserve? What, I wonder, is happening now in one of the most important of them all in the Belgian Congo? As I said at the Glasgow symposium to which I have referred already, the African is a materialist and few that I have met have been able to see much sense in Game Reserves and Parks. They look at the animals and see only so much good meat going to waste. But need it go to waste? Is not the solution to preserving both game and its habitat to be found in regarding the animals as a valuable natural resource, a resource not necessarily to be shut up in reserves, just to be looked at or to serve as an attraction for tourists, but one which can be utilised as a valuable source of food? To think, in fact, in terms of the farming of wild animals, of managing them to produce a sustained yield of meat with a potential take-off far greater than would be possible with introduced strains of domestic animals, subject as these are to so many hazards and diseases to which the native wild herds are adjusted or immune.

Is all this so remote from Scotland? We have, in this country, a native stock of wild red deer fully adapted to the Highland conditions in which they live, but is the future even of these fully assured, and are we managing these wild red deer and their habitat in the best interests of both the animal and ourselves? The African looks at the plain antelopes and thinks of them only as so much good red meat going to waste: do we not do much the same but in terms of land? So much potential grazing, used only by deer. Is not the long-term answer perhaps to be found in realising that both the game herds of Africa and the red deer of Scotland produce valuable protein, in regarding wildlife in many of its forms as a hitherto not fully utilised productive resource, in managing game and its habitat to yield, like the forests, an annual increment, producing food (and thus money) in perpetuity, and so ensuring at one and the same time the continued existence of the whole wildlife complex involved?[3] If this is in any sense a possibility, even only in so far as it concerns our own red deer, there is plenty to think about. Why, for instance, is venison so highly regarded on the Continent, commanding a high price on the market, but not here? How, to make a start, can we correct that position? Powerful is the medium of advertisement! The Tourist Board has shown what can be done to build up a vastly profitable national industry by popularising a semi-desert. Create the demand, ensure a steady flow of the desired product—in this case Highland venison—and the battle would be largely won. But it will not be easy. On the one hand it implies a great deal of marketing research, the adoption of up-to-date marketing techniques and the provision of cold-storage facilities, on the other a new approach to red deer management.

Others here have studied this problem and are more qualified to speak about it than

I am, but may I suggest that what may be possible for red deer may be possible also, on a different scale, and for a different market, for roe? On the Continent, again, the roe is a sporting animal, a tourist attraction and a source of revenue; here it is regarded as little more than a forest pest.

Our Scottish red grouse is a unique sub-species and represents, for a change, a natural resource which has already been farmed and marketed, but in no case has that farming been wholly successful for it has not been found possible to sustain the yield from year to year. The trouble would seem to be the difficulties inherent in all attempts at monoculture; there has been too much effort directed at building up big grouse stocks and little else, and too little attention to the exact requirements of the birds in terms of food and habitat. It is really only now that this aspect is about to be studied scientifically by the recently formed Unit of Grouse and Moorland Ecology attached to Aberdeen University, which, financed by the Nature Conservancy, is a natural projection of the original Red Grouse Inquiry initiated and sponsored by the Scottish Landowners' Federation. We still do not know exactly what the red grouse requires of its surroundings, but this moorland research may perhaps give us some of the answers. I myself have grave doubts, however, whether grouse can be farmed successfully on past lines. I would visualise, instead, some sort of multiple usage of the moorlands involved, yielding certainly nothing like the vast bags of grouse of some past decades but rather a mixed take-off, involving grouse as a sizeable and sustained proportion of the yield, but with a variety of other products too and with none of the rundown of the ground which in some cases at least appears to have been associated with past management.

Red deer, red grouse and golden eagles are perhaps the three Scottish animals which the average tourist to the Highlands most wants to see. But an appreciable and growing number of visitors are coming with the especial purpose of getting acquainted with our wildlife resource on far wider terms. That the interest is there cannot be gainsaid; it can be judged in part, as it relates to birds, by the number of people attracted during the past two years to the observation hides of "Operation Osprey" where 14,500 and 20,000 visitors signed the register in 1959 and 1960, respectively. Has any other single pair of birds anywhere else in the world attracted so much attention or produced anything like this tourist yield before? Their value to Scotland in hard cash must be assessed in many thousands of pounds.

Some measure of the current enthusiasm for the study of wildlife can be gauged from the success of the Scottish Ornithologists' Club, formed in 1936. With a membership of close on 1,000, and publishing its own magazine *Scottish Birds*, it and other local Natural History Societies, and National Societies such as the Royal Society for the Protection of Birds, have done an immense amount of good in fostering and directing the rather vague "interest in wildlife" which is latent in so many of our people. A love of nature and the outdoors is now almost a national characteristic, but it is a characteristic which must depend for its full development on the safeguarding and perpetuation of the resource in which it has its roots. We have already in Scotland a number of National Forest Parks and Local and National Nature Reserves. In these, wild country, wildlife and typical Scottish scenery are all preserved, and together—year in, year out—they attract steady streams of visitors. Here is another aspect of the conservation of our natural resources which we cannot afford to ignore. There are clearly limits to the number of people who can be accommodated in such areas without undue disturbance of the plants and animals involved. The Tourist Board has recently been considering giving greater publicity to Nature Reserves as a means of attracting still more enthusiasts and wealth to the Highlands. The idea is entirely laudable and has much to commend it, but for the reasons stated any such exploitation will require the most careful handling if we are to avoid the virtual sterilisation of an almost irreplaceable resource.

REFERENCES

1. Pearsall, W. H. (1960). Problems of conservation in the Highlands. *Institute of Biology Journal*, **7**, No. 1, 7-8.

2. Hunter, R. F. (1960). Conservation and grazing. *Ibid.*, 20-22.

3. Eggeling, W. J. (1960). Conservation and natural fauna. *Ibid.*, 22-26.

Outdoor Recreation Potential as a Natural Resource

WALLACE D. BOWMAN
The Conservation Foundation, New York

H. CUTHBERT DAVIS
Outdoor Recreation Resources Review Commission, Washington

The fastest growing land uses in the United States are urban and recreational. Pressures on outdoor recreational facilities far exceed capacity and a fact-finding group has been established by Congress to recommend a controlling procedure.

The relationship between urbanisation and outdoor recreation is examined and references to authorities noted. The demand for the outdoors can be assumed to be dynamic, sometimes highly individualistic, and demanding in terms of space and biotic life.

While man seeks change of environment for recreation, he simultaneously creates changes in the recreational environment that can modify the presence of recreational opportunity.

In Britain urbanisation had taken the form of dense population masses which were now being termed conurbations. Recreation resource in these units was destroyed as a result of resource converting techniques used for non-recreational purposes. Included in this destruction for instance were fish from streams and also natural swimming facilities. For this reason resource-converting techniques leading to efficient use of space should include recreation as a complementary facility to be integrated with other functions.

Research needs in the field of outdoor recreation are suggested and disciplines involved include economics, sociology, political science, biology, psychology and geography.

Perhaps the strongest research need, on which others hinge, is for a positive biological goal. Generally, conservation groups responsible for parks have been quiescent to nature displacement trends. We can keep biological affairs in order only if we maintain complex and varied wildlife communities. Stability of biological life is difficult to achieve where landscape is progressively simplified and there must be a re-examination of the assumptions and institutional approaches that have been used in guiding urban development.

Current trends of land use in the United States disclose two aspects of great significance. There has been a rapid rise in use of land to satisfy urban growth and an increasing importance of land needed for outdoor recreation. These two uses of land are not growing simultaneously by chance. One use is generating the other, for, in large measure, the rising demand for outdoor recreation is a reaction stimulated by conditions associated with urban development.

Outdoor recreation today is receiving the attention of many scholars. Government officials and civic-minded groups. Yet, only a handful have grasped the complicated relationships that exist between outdoor recreation, urban development, leisure and natural resources. Statistics and sophisticated analyses have not yet caught up with the reality of the situation even though it is apparent that pressures on many private and public outdoor recreation facilities and resources far exceed their planned capacities.[1] In 1959 the U.S. Congress established a fact-finding group, the Outdoor Recreation Resources Review Commission, and instructed its members to recommend guidelines and methods by which the process of wise development of outdoor recreation might come to be. Unfortunately, perhaps, the enabling statute restricts the Commission's purview; section 3 states that " 'Outdoor Recreation Resources' shall not mean nor include recreation facilities, programs or opportunities normally associated with urban development. . . ."[2] The question arises whether or not this is a serious oversight; Is it possible to dissociate outdoor recreation and urban development?

This paper will answer the question in the negative by examining the relationships between outdoor recreation and urban development; then a few avenues of needed research on this subject will be discussed.

Before turning to these matters it may be helpful to identify the distinguishing characteristics and broad limits of outdoor recreation.

OUTDOOR RECREATION, LEISURE AND NATURAL RESOURCES

A completely satisfactory definition of outdoor recreation is difficult to achieve partly because it involves activities that change rapidly with technology and invention of recreational equipment, partly because free time and the disposable dollars needed for outdoor recreation are being distributed more democratically today than ever. Both factors make outdoor recreation a highly dynamic use of natural resources.

Although the terms "recreation" and "leisure" are usually associated, the portion of leisure activities that should be classified as outdoor recreation is not easily comprehended. On this topic, Reuel Denney's analysis of leisure is of interest. During the first three decades of the century, Denney observed, leisure was considered to be primarily a concept of recreation. *Recreational leisure* meant "physical reconditioning, general reconditioning for the purpose of returning men to the normal load of heavy work and activities leading to the sublimation of impulses not purged in work".[3] The value derived from recreational leisure was assumed to be efficiency in work gained by relaxing from tension.

The last two decades have witnessed a rapid expansion of the opportunity for leisure. It has been necessary to develop broader dimensions to the concept. In addition to recreational leisure, two new types of leisure have been outlined by Denney.

The first emphasises identification. *Identificational leisure* refers to those activities in which one may involve psychological depths of himself as well as the personalities of others. Participation in a country club, youth organisation, spectator group or neighborhood gang gives an individual the opportunity for identificational leisure. The values assumed are those of social relationships.

The second type stresses authentication. The values assumed are not those of efficiency in work (as in recreational leisure) nor of social relationships (as in identificational leisure) but of art or science. One engages in *authenticational leisure* when he gratifies the demand for what Denney calls the "open questions" in our lives. The amateur astronomer, the student of nature, the gentleman farmer who enjoys applying conservation principles to the land, the collector of paintings are individuals who use their leisure for authentication.

If we accept Denney's classification, it appears to be desirable (in order to match terms) to speak of outdoor recreation as a subgroup under recreational leisure. Obviously, however, all three dimensions to the leisure concept may or may not involve the out-of-doors. For purposes of this paper, therefore, outdoor recreation refers to any type of leisure activity undertaken in the out-of-doors whether for purpose of physical reconditioning and relaxation from tension, associating socially with others, or studying nature and other phenomena of interest.

Since the characteristics of outdoor recreation are of this diversity, we are placed in an awkward position of shortsightedness in our attempts to design a desirable array of recreational facilities or to manage various resources for recreational uses. It is clear that outdoor recreation must be considered an important part-time function of man, necessitating special treatment of environmental resources; yet, a planned series of beaches, ball diamonds and amusement centres cannot fulfil the changing needs to associate socially with others; neither can ski-tows and country clubs satisfy the diverse needs to explore open questions in our lives or to recondition ourselves physically.

Most of us would agree with Glikson's observation that the most important means to achieve recreation is to find a change in the environment. "Whereas the townsmen migrate to the open country and to the seaside, the farmer looks for recreation in the city. As a counterbalance to the daily way of life, people may search for recreation either in solitude or in crowded centres of amusement, either in closed space or open squares."[4]

From this point of view, an enumeration of *spatial* changes in environment that have outdoor recreational value is broad and may include such facilities, amenities and resources as golf courses, gardens, historical sites and even entire river systems with their opportunities for fishing, boating, hiking, hunting, viewing of scenery and so on.

Change also has a *time* element: times of day, the weekend, seasons and the once-in-a-lifetime. Each time period, Glikson observed, can be related to the facilities, amenities and resources needed for outdoor recreation. Family homes and business centres should be planned so they satisfy recreational needs during the day. Open space, amusement centres, and gardens should be planned and distributed so they satisfy many of the daily and some of the weekly recreational needs. The forests, nature preserves, marshlands and flood plains of rivers within and surrounding the city should be planned for recreation on weekends. The region in which a city is located should be planned for various recreational purposes during different seasons of the year. Presently, there is a strong movement in the United States supporting the establishment of a system of inviolate wilderness areas in the hinterland. Those who support this idea argue that man should have the once-in-a-lifetime opportunity (his forty days in the wilderness!) to experience a relatively undisturbed environment, to discover an unfamiliar environment for whatever lost values it may hold.

This discussion gives ample evidence of the complexity of outdoor recreation as a use of leisure and natural resources. Here the assumptions to mark are as follows: (1) Outdoor recreation is leisure activity in which man engages during all periods of his life. (2) Outdoor recreation activities are extremely diverse, ever-changing and, in some instances, highly individualistic. (3) The demand for outdoor recreation consists of a broad spectrum of resources, facilities and amenities extending from the immediate environment in which we live to the environment of the region and on into the hinterland.

Now, we turn to the relationships between outdoor recreation and urban development.

URBAN INFLUENCES ON OUTDOOR RECREATION

The most spectacular characteristic of urban development is the distributional pattern of people and land uses which the process produces. These patterns evolve largely through application of *space-adjusting* techniques. Edward Ackerman explained these techniques as follows:

> The space-adjusting techniques either shorten the effective distance of travel and transportation or permit intensification of space employment beyond that possible on the land surface provided by nature . . . the modern city is a great engineering work which permits an astonishing intensification of space use.[5]

Space-adjusting techniques associated with urban development of the twentieth century have led to concentration of extremly large populations within limited areas (by adding levels) and a considerable widening of the resource base which sustains these urban areas (by improvement in transportation).

Improvement in transportation and a widening of the resource base have been paralleled by improvement in *resource-converting* techniques applied to the materials needed to sustain urban development. Ackerman viewed these techniques as follows:

> The resource-converting techniques are all those that turn the materials of the physical world and the life-products of the biotic world to satisfaction of the needs of men. Land-use technology, including the arts of agriculture and the sciences upon which they are based, constitute one phase. Mineral exploitation, metallurgy, chemical engineering, hydrology and hydraulic engineering, physics, mechanical and electrical engineering, and marine biology are illustrative of other phases.[6]

Provision of outdoor recreation opportunities involves the application of resource-converting as well as space-adjusting techniques although the differences are not always clear. The difficulty lies in making distinction between hinterland areas that are set aside as specialised recreation resource bases and the space and other resources within and immediately surrounding urban developments that are also used for outdoor recreation.[7]

Patrick Geddes, Artur Glikson, Christopher Tunnard and Lewis Mumford, among others, have contributed notably to our understanding of the problems of applying these techniques for purpose of achieving adequate opportunities for outdoor recreation.

Glikson pointed out that few cities in mediaeval times overtaxed local resources and there is little evidence that outdoor recreation was a problem. "Recreational land use and facilities represented a wholly integrated and therefore unrecognisable ingredient of the environment. Private gardens, the well, the streets and the nearby surrounding landscape, all in the context of but moderate housing density, generally provided for the recreational needs of the mediaeval citizen."[8]

In 1915 Geddes discovered that urban development in Britain had taken the form of dense population masses far greater than any of the cities of the past. A new configuration was formed by urban and industrial areas flowing together into groupings he called conurbations.[9] The outdoor recreation resources in these units, for the most part, were completely destroyed as a result of resource-converting used for non-recreational purposes. Industrial activity, for example, resulted in production of waste effluent which streams—formerly stocked with fish and suitable for swimming and other recreational activity—simply could not absorb. The same conditions of urban growth are found, of course, in the United States and other countries.

Long before most cities reach a million population, the displacement of outdoor recreation resources is fairly complete. A critical point is reached when local recreation resources are overtaxed and a city must reach beyond its immediate limits for recreation resources. In the United States, the reactions against these conditions have been something of a spectacle in recent years. Cities have expanded through a process of suburban and interurban overspill.

Up to 1920 it was mainly the upper-income group that could afford to adjust to the crowded city by moving to the outside to obtain its luxury of openness and opportunity for outdoor recreation. Since 1920 a large segment of the middle-income group has made the same adjustment, leaving behind most of the lower-income group.[10]

These adjustments have been made possible by improvement in commuter trains and the private automobile. Wave after wave of urban dwellers has made the shift to suburban living stimulated by heavy public investment in highways and feeder roads. Yet, the result of largely uncontrolled space-adjusting in suburban areas appears to be nullifying one of the main purposes that brought the movement about, namely, the search for a more desirable outdoor environment for leisure than the city provided.

Both Mumford and Glikson have championed the idea of guiding new urban development to promote an urban-rural balance. From this point of view, space-adjusting and resource-converting techniques would be applied to land use within urban areas in a manner that would produce an efficient use of space and more opportunity for outdoor recreation at the same time. They have suggested that natural environment, open space and various outdoor amenities should not be considered recreation specialities of a distant arc of land beyond present-day urban areas but, instead, as an integral and balanced portion of the urban scene.

A means of achieving this goal would be to consider recreation not primarily an exclusive function of any particular area, but a complementary one to be integrated with all other land development. There are trends in this direction, however slight they may be. "In the new urban pattern which is taking place," said Homer Hoyt, "emphasis is placed on uses that complement and supplement each other. Formerly, each parcel of land was valued separately and was an independent entity."[11] In the majority of cases this pattern of calculating land values will probably continue for a long time. But on the planner's board Hoyt foresees an increasing number of drawings of integrated suburban communities in which industries in parklike settings, shopping centres, schools, churches and recreation areas will all be built in one large area. Ideally, the value of each use will be enhanced by the others.

Christopher Tunnard, who heads the Graduate Program in City Planning at Yale University, has documented a recent trend of urban development which may very well frustrate such plans as Hoyt described. Most Americans, Tunnard wrote, will soon be living in fifteen great sprawling nameless communities that are changing the human geography of the country. He has given these the name "urban regions", the same name H. G. Wells gave cities of the future in his *Anticipations* which was published in 1902. Tunnard described one of the communities, the Atlantic Urban Region, as follows:

> Start driving down the coast from Bangor, Maine, along the old Post Road, and keep going until you swing out at the end of the journey at Norfolk, Virginia. You will have traveled through the heart of Anglo-America, the land-before-the-frontier, the financial center of the world, the heart of the communications industry, the part of the United States called by Westerners "older". The region has something of all 350 years of our history in it—historic houses and ranch houses, water-powered mills and steel rolling mills, farms and suburban estates, company towns and seaside resorts, the nation's capital and the world's largest city; drive-in movies, regional shopping centers, summer theaters. It has no mountains to speak of, but it has some picturesque scenery, especially east of New York where upland meets the drowned Atlantic plain, creating little bays and rocky harbors. From its appearance a great deal of the landscape through which you drive on this route still is countryside, but if you think of it as rural, in the strict sense of the term, you would be fooling yourself. By any scientific standard of calculation you have traveled six hundred miles through a giant city.[12]

Such strips of urban regions are not single communities with common interests. But the point is, as Tunnard suggested, the people living in these fifteen urban regions are being called on to work together and worry together about such problems as urban design, highways, water supply, recreation and so on. Tunnard objects to the drafting board concept of garden-type communities outside large cities that are designed to take the overspill of population, for it ignores what is actually happening to modern cities, that is, the merging of cities into urban regions. He sees the target growing bigger and bigger and suggests that planners must adjust their sights accordingly. "The urban region already shows signs of entering a new stage, even before most people are aware that urban regions exist at all. The land that is back from the urban strips, the 'interland', is filling in and is creating a merger of present regions."[13] The Atlantic Urban Region, for example, is linking up through the State of New York with other urban regions which include Cleveland and Chicago, thus creating a super-urban region.

The paths along which one urban region joins another can be traced along highways. As a result of considerable federal support that has been given to a planned New System of Interstate and Defense Highways, we are witnessing a rapid acceleration of this particular stimulus to urban development.[14] Apart from the effects on urban development, highways also have direct effect on outdoor recreation habits. A recent study of recreation in California showed that the automobile is fast becoming an extra member of the American family. The families which spend the weekend just driving for one or two hours turned out to be the single largest segment of the outdoor public.[15] In other statewide surveys, sightseeing and study, largely by car, ranked first or second in recreational interest. The automobile is so important for recreation in some states, planners are endorsing scenic-recreational highway systems with associated facilities such as wayside camps, picnic grounds, historical and educational markers.[16]

Theoretically, improvement in highways, in addition to affecting the space adjustment in cities, also tends to create conditions that lead to areal resource specialisation, to promote concentration and long hauls.[17] Thus we have a wheat belt, a corn belt, specialised manufacturing, tourist and recreation areas. Areal specialisation implies that particular production areas are tied to particular markets. It appears, however, that automobile-using habits of outdoor recreationists confirm the assumption stated earlier that the production area for outdoor recreation resources and facilities should be dispersed over the entire urban, regional and hinterland environment. Resource-conversion in the hinterland and space-adjustment in the city and urban region must somehow be balanced to provide a continuum of outdoor recreation opportunity.

In summing up this brief discussion of urban influences on outdoor recreation, two statements are in order:

(1) Through application of space-adjusting techniques (principally the addition of levels and improvements in transportation) urban development has progressively led to intensification of land use within cities, suburbs and urban regions to a point of displacement of a suitable outdoor recreation base for a wide array of daily, weekly and seasonal outdoor recreation activities. Resource-converting techniques, particularly those applied to water, have also destroyed many outdoor recreation resources within urban regions.

(2) Crowding and lack of suitable space, resources and amenities for outdoor recreation within urban areas have driven the recreationist farther and farther from his urban home into the countryside. In his search for outdoor recreation, the automobile has become one of the recreationist's most important recreational facilities.

These statements give substance to the argument that outdoor recreation and urban development should not be disassociated. The demand for outdoor recreation is stimulated by the conditions associated with urban development.

RECREATIONAL PLANNING: NEEDED RESEARCH

A listing of research needs focused on the relationships between outdoor recreation and urban development can easily be made lengthy. Conceivably, this field of study provides appropriate subject-matter for applying the research tools of such disciplines as economics, sociology, political science, biology, psychology and geography. Much research, in fact, has already been completed and more is on the horizon. The concepts and discussion presented in this paper suggest a number of questions for which we need more complete answers.

1. *On Problems Integrating Recreational Land Uses with Other Land Uses in Urban Regions*[18]

What are the differences in displacement and destruction of outdoor recreation resources among various urban regions? What forces are creating destruction and displacement in one region and not in another? What are the characteristics of demand for outdoor recreation in urban regions having differing degrees of destruction and displacement of outdoor recreation resources? What methods can be used to quantify a suitable balance between recreational land uses and other land uses within urban regions?

2. *On Problems of Organisation and Administration of Outdoor Recreation in Urban Regions*[19]

Means of providing adequate opportunity for outdoor recreation within urban regions must be sought by re-examining the assumptions and institutional approaches used for guiding urban development of the past.

What are the various alternatives for creating new regional alignments in outdoor recreational planning? Which types best "fit" the patterns of land ownership in different urban regions? Why is it that adequate recreational planning has not been achieved in urban regions? Is it a problem of legal means, communication, public support, tax redistribution, political organisation or faulty administration? How can communication between political and private interests necessary for achieving the objectives of recreational planning be established in urban regions?

3. *On Problems of Identifying Positive Goals for Preserving and Maintaining Outdoor Recreation Resources in Urban Regions*

A basic difficulty in gaining support for preserving and maintaining outdoor recreation resources in the urban environment is the lack of positive goals. Generally, conservation groups that have been responsible for preservation of parks, nature preserves, shoreline and similar amenities have recognised that the rate of displacement of outdoor recreation resources in urban areas is high and have simply reacted negatively to the trend. What positive goals can be established to justify preservation of more recreation resources in urban regions? Certainly, the field of ecology should offer some evidence of the need. Charles Elton, for example, stated that we can keep our biological affairs in order only if we maintain complex and varied wildlife and plant communities. His argument for maintaining open space and a diversified landscape is based on the need to promote a stability in which all kinds of compensatory pressures (that is, biotic pressures) will be exercised on local plant and animal communities. Stability is difficult to achieve where the landscape is progressively simplified. For rural areas, this argument makes sense if illustrated with case histories of insect eruptions in simplified habitats such as orchards or areas of single crop farming.[20] For urbanised areas, the best case histories documented so far have to do with epidemics and plagues. Much more evidence is needed before this argument can be used as a positive goal for preserving openness and a diversified outdoor habitat in urban regions.

The most fruitful areas to gather evidence for positive goals may well be in the field of sociology, psychology and economics. What effect does crowding have on the "sane society?" Can we identify normal and abnormal motives for outdoor recreation associated with different degrees of displacement of outdoor recreation opportunity in urban regions? Is the trend toward greater use of the automobile as a recreational facility a reflection of a psychological urge to find diversity in the landscape as a recreational activity? What are the social and economic costs associated with excessive use of the automobile as a recreational facility? What collateral benefits can be derived from maintaining open space and other recreation resources and amenities in urban regions?[21]

Additional research on these and similar questions is needed before the complex relationships between outdoor recreation and urban development can be fully comprehended.

REFERENCES

1. See, for example, Marion Clawson, *Statistics on Outdoor Recreation* (Washington: Resources for the Future, Inc., 1958). Also, U.S. National Park Service, State Park Statistics, 1959 (Washington: Department of the Interior, 1960).
2. Public Law 85-470, 85th Congress, S. 846, June 28, 1958. Actually, a review of the Commission's research programme shows that it has found it difficult to dissociate urban development and outdoor recreation. See: *Proceedings of the Third Joint Meeting with Its Advisory Council*, July 29-August 1, 1960 (Washington: Outdoor Recreation Resources Review Commission, 1960).
3. DENNEY, REUEL (1959). The leisure society, *Harvard Business Review*, May/June, p. 54.
4. GLIKSON, ARTUR (1956). Recreational land use, in *Man's Role in Changing the Face of the Earth* (Chicago: University of Chicago Press), p. 897.
5. ACKERMAN, EDWARD A. (1958). *Geography as a Fundamental Research Discipline* (Chicago: University of Chicago, Department of Geography Research Paper No. 53), p. 26.
6. *Ibid.*, p. 26.
7. CRAINE, LYLE E. (1960). Land use planning, in *Encyclopedia of Science and Technology* (New York: McGraw-Hill Book Co. Inc.), pp. 391-393.
8. GLIKSON, *op. cit.*, p. 897.
9. Cited in: Lewis Mumford, The natural history of urbanization, in *Man's Role in Changing the Face of the Earth* (Chicago: University of Chicago Press, 1956), p. 391.
10. *Ibid.*, p. 393.
11. HOYT, HOMER (1960). Changing patterns of land values, *Land Economics*, May, p. 116.
12. TUNNARD, CHRISTOPHER (1958). America's super cities, *Harper's Magazine*, August, p. 59.
13. *Ibid.*, p. 63.
14. See *The New Highways: Challenge to the Metropolitan Region* (Washington: Urban Land Institute, Technical Bulletin 31, November 1957).
15. ROMNEY, HENRY, (1960). Trail blazers in California, *Sports Illustrated*, April 4.
16. *California Public Outdoor Recreation Plan, Part 1* (Sacramento: California Public Outdoor Recreation Plan Committee, 1960).
17. ULLMAN, EDWARD (1957). *American Commodity Flow* (Seattle: University of Washington Press).
18. See, as examples of research on these questions, the following: William A. Niering, *Nature in the Metropolis* and Stanley B. Tankel, *The Race for Open Space* (New York: Regional Plan Association Inc., 1960).
19. See, as examples of research on these questions, the following: Shirley A. Siegel, *The Law of Open Space* (New York: Regional Plan Association Inc., 1960) and *California Public Outdoor Recreation Plan, Part 1* (Sacramento: California Public Outdoor Recreation Plan Committee, 1960).
20. ELTON, CHARLES (1958). *The Ecology of Invasions* (New York: John Wiley & Sons Inc.).
21. See, as examples of research on these questions, the following: *Annals* of the American Academy of Political Science and Social Science, September 1957 (entire issue is devoted to recreation) and Andrew Trice and Samuel Wood, Measurement of recreation and benefits, *Land Economics*, August 1958.

INTRODUCTION TO DISCUSSION

F. Fraser Darling, D.SC., PH.D., N.D.A., LL.D., F.R.S.E.
The Conservation Foundation, New York

The subjects of these two papers before us are in a way widely opposite. One has to do with the utilisation of natural resources and the other is concerned with recreation. Now, whether it was fortuitous that these two subjects should come into one session I do not know, but I am very glad that they have because here is one of the problems which we have to resolve and it is one very much before this Conference, as we have heard in this last session. Utilisation of natural resources and particularly of wildlife resource I feel to be one of the main foundations of its ultimate conservation. There is a very great deal of sentimental, very true, real public feeling for the care of wildlife, but ultimately that public feeling does not receive anything like so much regard from the Government as does the final practical "can we do it" and usually wildlife loses out. Certain forms of wildlife such as those which have been responsible in this country for a very real part of Scotland's economy, the game birds, the fish which we mentioned yesterday and the red deer. The utilisation of these, and particularly of the red deer, is one of the keys to its further existence as part of our wildlife. I am convinced that that can be done quite easily, but it is a problem that has not been tackled sincerely, I feel, in the past. Coming to recreation, which is one of multiple uses of land to which—we all follow this idea of multiple use—its actual application is a very much more difficult thing than to merely subscribe to it, it is a very difficult balancing on this cost benefit business and also of deciding what benefits are real although they cannot be costed. For the last twenty years in this country the notion of food production has just held everything—you have only to yell food production and you can ruin the amenity of the whole countryside perfectly happily. My view is that not only does man "not live by bread alone" or even by 90 per cent. of their good water which Mr. Lowe mentioned this morning, but that the amenity, the value of the tree, the value of the sheet of water is extremely real, and the fact that this country is increasing its population, that Britain as a whole is increasing fast, that we are getting so many more people coming into the countryside, the amenity value of a hedgerow tree for the public at large is, in my opinion, far greater than its value as timber, or as the amount of agricultural production which it is preventing by its being there. I do not accept any argument for a tractor not having to turn round, or for the little bit of extra shade or food that tree takes. I feel that the amenity value of hedgerow timber is a very real factor in the British scene, and the Scottish scene particularly, because we are so short of them, except in policy grounds. . . . Recreation is not always an opposite activity, it is also a quiet contemplation of our countryside. With more people, you say we have got to produce more food; there is also this necessity for realising that amenity is a greater value and that the enjoyment of that amenity is a possible natural resource which must be satisfied as a whole. The fact of so much of Highland land being now a place for recreation is a problem, a phenomenon which I do not feel that we have taken seriously enough. In 1773 Pennant could describe the Highlands as horrific mountains. By the turn of the century, with the influence of Rousseau and of Wordsworth and the rest of the romantic poets, Byron, Coleridge and so on, this attitude had changed, but it took again the best part of a century to find a full flowing of the people into the countr yside of Scotland to enjoy it, and this factor of recreation must now be considered in very different terms from what we have been prepared to think of it in the past. It is a problem, it is a phenomenon and I hope that this will be discussed this morning. I now turn us over to Dr. Eggeling.

STATEMENT BY THE REPORTER

W. J. EGGELING, B.SC., PH.D., F.R.S.E.
Conservation Officer, Nature Conservancy

Before speaking to these two papers, I would like to offer one or two general observations. Firstly, I do not know whether to be more frightened of the agriculturists and the foresters when they are in conflict or when they are, as today, on the same side as regards wildlife and recreation. We are perhaps in danger of forgetting that both these interests also involve the use of land and we might have done better to have had this discussion on conflicts in land use at the end of the session on multiple use, rather than in the middle of it. Secondly, there is this phrase "multiple use" itself. It has been at the head of our programme for the last two days and yet only this morning has the subject been mentioned. In almost the first paper presented to us—that on surveys—there was an excellent statement of what should be done in some of our Highland areas by way of integrated planning after preliminary survey, and the point was made that provision should be allowed not only for agriculture and forestry but also for wildlife management. I was privileged recently to attend a World Forestry Congress in Seattle, Washington, where the central theme was the multiple use of forest lands. I suggested that this title was far too limited because, if multiple use is to have any meaning, it must be applied to *all* lands and not, as an example, to forest lands only. Furthermore, multiple use is not simply the practising of a variety of uses in the countryside; it is the integration of these uses so that many usages are practised on each single unit of land. One of the usages will be a primary one, and the others will be secondary, but the land is planned to meet all the requirements in question. Multiple planning thus results in a landscape which has great variety and embraces many different habitats.

Now, sir, I have two papers to report on, and I would like to take the second one first; it is that by Messrs. Bowman and Davis, and it presents the case for regarding a countryside's potentials for outdoor recreation as one of the most important of its natural resources. The authors make a strong plea for the rational utilisation of that resource. They point out that in the United States today the two most rapidly expanding pressures on land are for urban development and outdoor recreation. Already in the States the demands for public outdoor recreational facilities and amenities far exceed capacity, and this is, of course, true also of parts of Britain, especially in the south of England. Here in Scotland, although the writing is already apparent on the wall, matters are not yet, in general, out of hand and need not become so if we are prepared to treat the problem as a research project involving the conversion of a natural resource. We must plan a study aimed at finding out the full extent of the recreational requirement as it is now, and as regards the future we must gaze into the crystal a little, and we must then indulge in some intelligent forward planning. Mr. Bowman and Mr. Davis have given us some definitions of recreation and leisure, and I think we will agree with them that what man is chiefly seeking from recreation is a change of scene. They stress, as others have done at this Symposium, that when human pressure builds up in a particular locality the environment will alter and may in the end lose just those attributes which initially rendered it attractive, so that it becomes sterile to man's interest. If this is not to happen we have got to spread the load or reduce the human impact by some means or other. Because so much of our population is urban, it is to the countryside that most people turn for a change of scene and they have now to travel great distances to get what they require, due to urban sprawl and adjacent development. Furthermore, they are travelling far farther than they ought to have to do, because we have been thoughtless about the recreational potentiality actually within our urban areas and their peripheries. To take one example, there is the thoughtless and needless sterilisation of the recreational potential of rivers and open freshwater surfaces by pollution. This has reduced their recreational value for fishing and other outdoor water sports including swimming and so on. Professor Yonge was hoping yesterday that it might be possible to restore oysters to the Forth; can we not go further and hope to get back some of its lost recreational potential? I hope there may be time later on for Mr. Bowman and Mr. Davis to speak themselves, but I think we can summarise their views by recording that because of lack of appreciation that recreation potential is a natural resource, far too little attention has been given to land use technology in the recreational field compared with the level of resource conversion which have been obtained by, for example, agriculture and forestry.

Now, one or two points about my own paper. We will be considering in our session tomorrow a paper by Mr. Fergus Williamson on marketing, in which he reminds us that the particular interest of 45 per cent. of the visitors to Scotland lies in scenery and countryside. This fortifies me in the belief that any evaluation of tourism must take into account the preservation of the attractiveness of the countryside, and an essential part of any countryside is undoubtedly its wildlife. I agree wholeheartedly with Prof. Wibberley that it is no use talking about hidden values: you must put some material value on them if you are to balance the requirements you are seeking against all the others involved in integrated planning. It is of interest that at Seattle there was a strong plea for the indirect values that accrue from forestry to be converted into £ s. d., for it was stated that only by so doing could the foresters of the world hope for a fair allocation of the moneys available for forestry extension in underdeveloped countries. I would therefore like to hope that we can get some cash figures for the value of that part of our Scottish resource which is involved when tourists view our countryside.

A part of my paper is concerned with the utilisation of what is only in fact a small fraction of the immense resource which includes sport, amenity, hidden values and the satisfaction of individual outdoor needs, the fraction capable of translation into an off-take of meat, sporting rents and so on. We have heard much already of red deer. I believe that the rational conservation of deer must include deer farming (I do not like the word "farming" in this context, but I think it expresses my meaning) and that red deer conservation in Scotland is little more than a problem in marketing. There is also the question of grouse. It has been shown that in general, although there may be exceptions, monocultures are sterile and unstable, and that one is pursuing a rather dangerous policy if one tries to build up a big population of, say, grouse alone. You might well be better off with a medium-sized population of grouse and a variety of other game, concentrating not on unrelieved grouse moor but rather on diversification of habitat, thus reintroducing into the Highlands more of that variety of wildlife which the tourist and I believe everyone here is seeking from our Scottish scene.

DISCUSSION

Dr. E. A. C. Chamberlain, *National Coal Board*

I wish to speak for a very brief moment on a matter which I think is of considerable recreational importance to Scotland, and that is small-boat sailing. My only excuse for doing so is that I happen to be the Secretary of the Scottish Dinghy Association, which represents some fifty sailing clubs and yacht clubs throughout Scotland. There are three reasons why the encouragement of small-boat sailing is of considerable importance to Scotland; first, because there is the opportunity of a new industry, that of building small boats, to be added to the traditional boat-building industries of Scotland; second, the promotion of the tourist trade; and third, the provision of safe recreational facilities for the youthful, and the not so youthful, members of the population. With the time available it would be improper of me to attempt to expand on these three aspects, but I will mention briefly some of the facts at the risk of missing out, perhaps, really important things.

It is of course the development of resin-bonded plywood which has led to sailing becoming a poor man's hobby rather than a rich man's hobby. The number of small boats built in Great Britain is probably in the order of 20,000 a year and relatively few are built in Scotland, in 1959 there were no Scottish producers of kits for building boats, and this, I think, is something which could be remedied. On the question of the tourist industry, I am frequently asked by Class Associations in England to arrange race meetings for class boats in Scotland. Individuals who have sailed on some of our better-known waters, such as Loch Earn, or on the Clyde or on the Forth, ask for permission to bring large numbers of boats here for national championships. This is not practical at the present time for reasons which I will mention later on. The value of such meetings is not inconsiderable, they would each attract some 300 to 400 people for a week, and the hotels would benefit by this influx of visitors.

The question of safe recreational facilities for the youth of the country cannot be overemphasised. In Scotland we have the best conditions in the world for sailing, and yet we have the poorest facilities. This is no exaggeration, and it is not a question of money. Sailing Clubs are not asking for financial assistance, but they are asking for some intelligent help from local authorities and from the Scottish Council for Physical Recreation and similar organisations for the provision of such things as simple concrete launching ramps and dinghy-parking facilities, at resorts on the Clyde, on the Forth and in the lochs of Scotland.

Mr. Ian Forbes, *Royal Caledonian Horticultural Society*

I had not intended to speak, but the Chairman greatly impressed me this morning when he said how much one thing affected another and how they overlapped. I would like to draw the attention of you today to a typical instance of this in horticulture.

The main supply of trained horticultural labour in the past was from the great estate gardens. There were large numbers of qualified gardeners produced from these estates—a very considerable export. One has only to think of many famous gardens throughout the world such as the Golden Gate Park at San Francisco and others which were established by Scotsmen. The change caused by the disappearance of so many estate gardens has led to an interesting situation. We have at present a great deal of amenity planting in towns and round factories, which is an excellent thing, but there are not the craftsmen available to maintain these areas afterwards. Another natural resource of Scotland might be considered to be golf. The source of greenkeepers in the past was largely the gardening profession. The problem of this sport, which is very popular with many visitors, is—where are the men going to come from to maintain the courses? There has been a considerable dilution of labour, and that, as a gentleman who is interested in fish mentioned yesterday, has reduced the social status of these craftsmen greenkeepers, and it is growing more difficult to encourage anyone to train. Facilities for advanced training in horticulture are available at the Agricultural Colleges, and in places such as the Royal Botanic Garden, but the basic knowledge required to benefit from this training is unfortunately lacking. It is of interest that a new school has been started by the National Trust for Scotland, this is the Gardeners' Training School at Threave. Taking young boys of 16 to 18 and giving them a basic training, it will provide at least some of the future craftsmen who are going to be so badly needed.

Professor W. H. Pearsall, *Nature Conservancy*

Might I make some rather general remarks? But before I do so I should like to point out what the gentleman said about the use of water is quite pertinent. I suppose most of us do not realise there are nearly 500 square miles of water in this country. It is quite a sizeable amount, isn't it? When we start to talk about resources we should, I think, definitely make plans for the use of that water. The main point that I wish to say something about, however, is this question of the integration of the varied uses of land. It is one which affects all of us, and I should say quite frankly as a scientist I am rather surprised that no one has referred to some of the prinicples which are rather generally accepted in deciding on the best use of land. From our present point of view we have had canvassed three sorts of problem in regard to land use. Firstly, utilisation and development; secondly, about which very little has been said, *conservation*—the first thing one learns once you start to use land is that you can get nothing out of it except what you put into it, and whether we are working on good farm land or a hillside that principle is true; thirdly, *recreation*. And each of these aspects of land use has to be considered in every area. If we are on the fertile Lowlands then we know that we are going to have high productivity, that we can maintain that productivity by manurial treatment. In fact, we have an excellent, highly experienced, long-established European system of agriculture which will handle our Lowlands well, and we cannot get out of the necessity for conservation by manurial treatment and cultivation. Thirdly, even if we have only to consider our wives, we must give something to recreation. It may be a pleasant road, it may be a place where she can grow flowers and we can admire them, it may be a place where we can go and picnic, it may be a golf course. All these things, you see, are part of every scene whether it is fertile, productive or non-productive. When we get on to our hillsides in Scotland we are generally dealing with land which has been very badly run down because these principles have been neglected and we may say, "Well, this should be a sheep walk, or it should be forest". What are the principles which decide which of those two we should choose? I think here again we have to ask "What is the effect of the treatment on the land and what will be its cost". If we put the land under trees we know that in the long run they will affect the character of the soil, and it is now perfectly practicable to improve the site or to maintain the level of the site by the proper use of trees. Trees have, however, one great virtue. The product that we take away is cellulose, literally carbon from the air. It costs very little. It takes nothing from the soil, indeed most trees to some extent build up the nitrogen resources of the soil and so do good. Because in cropping a forest you take away nothing but carbon, or very little but carbon, and restore some nitrogen to the soil, trees are in general the things that we should use on nitrogen-poor soils, and there is thus a strong case for using trees on much of the Scottish Highlands. Now if we go to, shall we say, sheep or animals, what do they require? They require vast quantities of calcium and nitrogen and we should only grow them where the soil is such that it can supply these vast quantities of calcium and nitrogen. Or else we must be prepared to conserve the site by adding those minerals as manure. There is no escaping this, you see, it is just plain economics; and at some moment that becomes so costly that it is not worth while on poor soils.

This brings me to the last point that I want to develop. All over the world there are these sites, these marginal sites, which are a world-wide last resource in terms of land. All over the world people are saying "Let us develop agriculture on them". Prof. Wibberley will tell you that this is nonsense. If you want a useful return you take a site which is productive and spend your money on that—this is plain common sense. You will get ten times as much at least for your money from the productive site as you will from the poor site. It is of that order of difference, you see. If you compare the Arctic Circle with the Tropics production is the the order of one hundred or one thousand times less, and this is the argument for tropical agriculture. You put your money where you get a return. Now, what shall we do with these marginal sites? Here the answer seems to be —I put this as a suggestion—it seems to be that there are a great many sites under natural, biological systems today which are producing more and are conserving themselves more under the natural system than under any system of land use we yet know. This is the case for saying that there are sites even in a country like Scotland which should be maintained in their natural condition as wildlife reserves. Now, I am a scientist, and I do not care two hoots which is the right answer, but I want us to use the right method of approach in tackling these questions.

Professor FRAZER, *Royal College of Science and Technology, Glasgow*

I just want to make a small point, Gentlemen, in connection with recreation. We tend to think of recreation to a certain extent as something strenuous, climbing up hills and that, but I would make a plea; we have some industry in the Highlands and I hope we will have more. Could these not be considered as part of recreation? I have only to stress the arrangements which have been made at Pitlochry for viewing the dam and the fish ladder there—the public are allowed free access. There is a proposal to build a pulp mill at Fort William, a centre of the tourist industry. It should not be very difficult to arrange the mill so that tourists and others, who are a bit tired of climbing up hills, or because it is a rainy day, could go there and see some part of the process. The ordinary townsman is very interested in that side of it. I remember once taking my students round one of the forests and meeting a Chartered Accountant in the hotel the night before. We invited him to come with us, and at the end of the day he said it was the most enjoyable and interesting day hc had spent on any holiday—it was something new to him. So on the recreational side I feel that where we have enterprises, they could have another use and fit into the multi-purpose scheme and encourage the public to come and see what is being done. I would instance Holland, where you have the appeal of the bulb fields in bloom, you are invited to see the auction room, and they explain to you how the bulbs are sold and all the rest of it.

Mr. R. GRIEVE, *Department of Health for Scotland*

I think it should be recorded at this meeting that there have been attempts to produce this kind of integrated planning of recreational and other resources. I should point out to you, as an example, the Scottish National Parks Commitee Report 1946 which had, as an appendix to it, a plan for the Glen Affric National Park. I think that was one of the first attempts to produce an integrated plan for a Highlands area. The Scottish National Parks Committee took a rather different line from the English National Parks Committee; they believed that, in Scotland, National Parks should be a kind of rehabilitation medium and, to illustrate the contention, they produced this plan for Glen Affric. I would commend you even now, after fourteen years, to read it because it does make an attempt to do the thing which I think we all feel needs to be done; to consider all these resources as one, including the important resource of recreational potential. The main difficulty, however, in all this kind of work is that the educational system does not yet produce the kind of man who can do that kind of integrated planning.

Mr. HUGH CUTHBERT DAVIS, *Outdoor Recreation Resources Review Commission, Washington, D.C.*

Gentlemen: I would first like to express my gratitude and appreciation for being asked to come here to participate in this meeting. It has been most interesting to learn how so many of the resource problems discussed here reflect those of our own in the States. I was impressed yesterday by what was said concerning the lack of adequate resource data and the pressing need for more and better resource information. In my particular job with a Federal government Commission studying problems of outdoor recreation, I would say that this is one of our most persistent problems. While we do have statistical measurements on many aspects of outdoor recreation, the quality of these data is often poor.

In the United States we have some very real problems in the use of our outdoor resources for recreation and it has only been in recent time, perhaps in the last five to ten years, that this kind of resource use has been studied with the emphasis similar to that which has been given forestry, hydrology, agronomy, and so forth. We are just on the threshold of developing what might be called an analytical approach to outdoor recreation resource use. There is much work to be done, and a great deal to be learned.

I should like to direct a few remarks to the application of the multiple use concept to recreation as I see it in my country. As you undoubtedly know, the major concentration of population in the United States is in the north-east quarter of the country—you might say in a quadrant running north of the Ohio River and the east of the Mississippi River. Perhaps 25 per cent. of the nation's population resides in this area. Most of this land is largely in private ownership, whereas west of the Mississippi, particularly in the eleven westernmost states, it is very largely in public or Federal ownership. It is this eastern portion of the country where many of our most critical recreation problems exist today.

Unlike your situation here in Britian, a large portion of our outdoor recreation takes place on public lands managed exclusively for that purpose. This situation is particularly true in the north-eastern quarter of the country. Here the demand for outdoor recreation is high and many of our parks are badly overcrowded. One state park for example, 45 miles from New York City, caters to over 155,000 persons on an avarage summer Sunday. There are many indications that this kind of pressure on the resources will continue to increase.

Speaking as an individual and not necessarily representing the view of my Commission, I see no other way of meeting the demand for outdoor recreation in the north-east other than actively pursuing a programme of multiple use. The high cost of buying new land exclusively for recreation, and the increasing competition stemming from other land uses, clearly indicates that the outright purchase of park areas in north-east United States, although important as one means of meeting the recreation demand, will not alone be sufficient in meeting the demands of the future.

Various types of recreation are well suited for integration with other types of resource use. Obviously hunting is compatible with many types of farming if the two are considered simultaneously as an objective of resource management. Another popular form of outdoor recreation is sightseeing. With proper highway and roadside planning this can be easily integrated with many other kinds of resource use.

I think, however, that before we can have effective multiple use management involving outdoor recreation, we must learn a great deal more about the various kinds of recreation and the combination of recreation activities that individuals engage in during specific outing periods. The forester when managing a wooded area has in mind the production of certain kinds of timber for rather specific uses. In managing an area for recreation or recreation in combination with some other resource use, we must also be able to identify rather clearly the kinds of recreation we expect the resources to provide. We have at present very little research and almost no information on this aspect of outdoor recreation.

I see no alternative to meeting our needs for outdoor recreation resources in the north-east part of the United States other than through a multiple use approach. In the next 30 or 40 years the cost of buying land and dedicating it solely to recreation is going to become a luxury our society can hardly afford.

I mention this because I believe it has some applicability to your situation here in Scotland. This is obviously something for you to decide, but for some time we have been preoccupied in the United States with the idea that we must put land into public ownership before it can be used effectively for recreation. In my very brief visit here, it seems to me that you have an opportunity to exploit the benefits derived through multiple use of resources by including outdoor recreation as one objective of land management plans.

JAMES MACAULAY, M.B.E., F.R.C.I.S., M.T.P.I., M.INST.R.A., *Chairman, Scottish Council for National Parks*

"The wild life of today is not ours to dispose of as we please. We have it in trust. We must account for it to those who come after."—King George VI.

Scotland still has a rich heritage of flora and fauna to be very carefully conserved. Wildlife in most countries is now being preserved in reserves of various types but also to enable the public to enjoy it in its natural habitat, and so that posterity may share the pleasure of seeing and knowing it as cultural subjects of education. To accomplish the full resources of wildlife conservancy requires control by careful development of selected areas of land and of public access and use.

Fish as a constituent of wildlife is also a resource for food and the basis of sport and recreation. As wildlife in the inland lochs, it is in danger of being seriously depleted and some species being exterminated. Fishing as a sport is in real danger of losing the title "angling", and poaching on the large scale is ruining many of the lochs. Fish is one of the finest foods in this or any other country. Continentals find Scottish fish shops one of the most attractive shops. Angling is one of the finest recreations.

Recreation takes many forms, and public outdoor recreation is growing faster than is realised. With the advent of the motor car the country can be covered and the adventurous motorist reach any point in reasonably short time. Once in the open he generally develops participation in some additional form of sport or recreation, caravanning, boating, mountaineering, swimming, skiing, etc. At present there are almost 100 organisations in Great Britain fostering over 40 games, sports and outdoor activities all of which are active in Scotland. Such organisations have acceptable standards of behaviour to be observed by their members. But there are large numbers of the public practising these outdoor activities who, under no form of proper control, are guilty of serious damage to the countryside and wildlife, and spoiling the true enjoyment and benefit to themselves and others. Mr. Krebs, U.S.A., said recreation is one of the greatest problems facing his country. It is and will be increasingly one in Scotland.

With these facts considered, what can be done to alleviate the problems referred to and what form of multiple land use can be advocated?

The answer was touched upon by Mr. Robert Grieve, Chief Planner, Department of Health for Scotland, when he spoke of National Parks for Scotland.

UTILISATION OF RESOURCES

WATER USE

The Pattern of Existing Water Use

R. M. CAMPBELL, B.SC., M.I.C.E., M.I.W.E.
Babtie, Shaw & Morton, Glasgow

The paper outlines the various forms of water use, sketches the historical background from which the present intricate pattern has emerged, and indicates current trends of development in the physical and administrative spheres. By the cycle of events there is again emphasis on power production, the quantity of water employed in hydro-electric projects being possibly twenty times that used for all other purposes. The public water supply services, administered by some 200 local water authorities, provide about 380 million gallons daily for domestic and industrial use. Future needs for such purposes are not likely to exceed say 600 m.g.d., representing only about 1¼ per cent. of Scotland's overall water resources of 50,000 m.g.d., of which nearly half may be classed as gravitational. Part of these reserves provide the hydro-electric potential.

The paper describes the factors influencing the various forms of scheme for water supply, and points to the advantages of upland impounding reservoirs in furnishing reliable supplies of favourable quality with the least effect on other stream users. General mention is made of untapped reserves and of the procedure to be observed in acquiring the requisite powers to harness them. There is reference to river pollution and the efforts being made to clean up the country's streams and estuaries, while the paper also touches on the inequalities of the present system of valuation and rating as affecting the development of water undertakings.

The past 200 years have witnessed marked changes in the country's economic and social structure, arising from the spread of industrial activity, the growth of the population and the progressive improvement of living standards. These developments created ever-increasing demands for water, and from the measures applied to meet such needs there has evolved over the years the present somewhat complex pattern of water use.

The word "use" itself covers a variety of purpose and may have different shades of meaning according to circumstance. Among the services rendered, water is employed as a driving force for the production of power, while it is also harnessed to maintain the level of navigable waterways, to irrigate crops, to act as a basic or ancillary material or cooling medium in numerous manufacturing processes and, in the more general sphere of water supply proper, to serve household, community and public health purposes, including water-borne sewage systems.

There are likewise differences in the methods which have been adopted to supply these various needs, the form of scheme depending on location and function and on consideration of quantity, quality and pressure. For general use underground sources such as springs, wells or boreholes are utilised in some areas, but the total quantity of water so derived is relatively small, primarily because Scotland's geological formations do not include extensive or readily accessible water-bearing strata capable of yielding adequate flows of satisfactory quality. By contrast, the average rate of runoff due to rainfall over the country's drainage basins gives prolific surface water flows in the streams and rivers, and as these sources can be most effectively harnessed or tapped they have naturally attracted development. It is of course these surface resources which provide the potential for the generation of power and it is from them, too, that most of the existing supplies for other purposes are derived, usually by means of upland impounding reservoirs but sometimes by means of intake works from which part of the natural flow in the watercourse is abstracted either by gravity from the headstreams or by pumping from the lower reaches.

The earliest use of the water resources on any substantial scale came with the Industrial Revolution, when mills and factories were established on the banks of the main streams and rivers where the flow could be utilised in water-wheels to provide power for driving machinery. Some of these low head run-of-river power schemes, especially those serving a series of mills along the course of a stream, incorporated upland impounding reservoirs based on lochs or other natural basins from which water could be released from storage to maintain the flow in dry weather. During this same period, too, a number of other impounding reservoirs were built to act as feeders for the canal systems which were then established as the readiest means of transporting raw materials and manufactured goods to and from the markets and ports.

As trade and industry developed, part of the natural or controlled stream flows came also to be drawn by firms for processing work, particularly in the textile, distilling and paper-making industries, and considerable quantities are so used today. The initial emphasis, however, was on water power, a trend which persisted even after there came into fairly common use the condensing steam engine as developed by James Watt. An example of some interest was the water power scheme installed at Greenock under Parliamentary powers granted in 1825, the works as designed by Robert Thom comprising a main and several subsidiary reservoirs, some five miles of open aqueduct and two lines of falls on which sites were made available for industries successively making use of the water as it dropped fully 500 feet to sea-level. These works may be said to have laid the foundation of Greenock's industrial development. They are still in use today, but are now controlled by the Corporation, who have expanded and improved them for public supply, although part of the output is still devoted to power development in modern turbines replacing the early water-wheels. The original scheme made allowance for serving the local inhabitants with water at the rate of 2 cubic feet ($12\frac{1}{2}$ gallons) per person per day, whereas Greenock Corporation now provide, in addition to the quantities delivered for water power, supplies for domestic and industrial purposes aggregating 110 gallons per person per day to a population which has increased close on tenfold.

The passing years, of course, brought other changes. The revolution in transport which followed the development first of the railways, and later of the roads with the advent of the internal combustion engine, led eventually to the virtual supersession of the canals as lines of communication. As a result many stretches of these works are maintained in being today primarily as purveyors of water to the industries which over the years were attracted to sites along their routes. Also within recent decades the more widespread availability and greater convenience of electrical power supplies have led to the abandonment of the water power facilities at the majority of the early riverside mills and factories—a process sometimes encouraged by other demands for the water. In some cases where up-to-date equipment has been installed the original rights are still enjoyed, but most of the river weirs, mill lades and water-wheels which were once features of the countryside have now fallen into disrepair or disappeared. Concurrently with that particular phase, however, the rapidly growing demands for electrical energy for industrial and domestic purposes throughout the country have once again brought into prominence the use of the water resources for power, this time in the form of hydro-electric development. Other factors contributing to this trend have been the advances made in the design of turbines and alternators and in the techniques of high-voltage transmission, whereby current may be efficiently generated and economically delivered over long distances from the remote Highland glens to the industrial areas, and even beyond for export south of the Border, coupled with the fact that a hydro-electric scheme incorporating upland storage is well suited to the special role of meeting the peak demands on the grid distribution system to which the base load requirements are supplied by coal-burning or nuclear power stations.

Specific instances of industries which require large-scale supplies of electrical energy being established where advantage could be taken of local hydro-electric possibilities are to be noted in the aluminium works at Kinlochleven and Fort William, which date from the first quarter of the century. The period between the two world wars saw the construction of three particular hydro-electric undertakings designed to supplement the public electricity supply system, namely the Clyde Valley, the Grampian and the Galloway water power schemes. The impetus to contemporary progress in the field of water power sprang from the Hydro-Electric Development (Scotland) Act, 1943, under which there was set up the North of Scotland Hydro-Electric Board with authority and responsibilities for developing the water power resources and for providing public electricity supplies throughout the Highlands and Islands. Since active construction started some twelve years ago, the Board have brought into commission schemes producing from water an average of 2,500 million units of electricity per annum, which represents about 40 per cent. of the target set in the Board's initial programme announced in 1944. In terms of flow, the quantity of water now being used or developed for power production in Scotland is possibly at least twenty times as much as is used for all other purposes.

The history of the public water supply service spans the last 100 years or so, since a start was made with the laying on of piped water to the houses of a community, in conjunction of course with water-borne sewerage. The first schemes were developed for service to the cities, burghs and other main centres of population, where distribution could be economically effected to a compact community, and where there was legislative provision for meeting the establishment and running costs through the medium of local rates. These independent developments proceeded with little regard for regional or long-term planning in the modern sense, the form of scheme in each particular case being largely dictated by the financial resources available. The cities and larger burghs could afford to plan with commendable foresight, as time has shown, but by and large the smaller communities had perforce to limit their service to immediate local needs. As a result there grew up throughout the country a multiplicity of small water supply schemes utilising numerous sources, some of which were tapped for small volumes of supply relative to their potential yields and by means of works which tended adversely to affect their ultimate full development. There also arose some degree of overlapping or duplication of services, particularly in cases where neighbouring authorities based their supply systems on adjacent upland catchment areas. As noted, these early schemes were developed for the benefit of the urban centres, and the prevailing practice of installing such filtration or other treatment works as were required in locations adjacent to the community being served, instead of at the headworks, militated against the ready provision of supplies to consumers in the landward areas traversed by the supply mains.

While the broader approach made nowadays to the solution of the country's water supply problems is doing much to remedy these early shortcomings, effective progress in the provision of piped water supplies to the landward and rural areas has only been achieved within recent years since Treasury grants were made available to help meet the high distribution costs involved in serving the sparsely populated districts. The modest start to this programme made in the 1930s with the aid of the then Unemployment Grants Committee was interrupted by the war, and real progress only came in the post-war years following the Rural Water Supplies and Sewerage Act, 1944, and subsequent legislation under which a fund of £20 million was made available for the development of such schemes in Scotland. With the assistance of this grant as administered by the Department of Health for Scotland, extensive works have been and are being carried out in the landward and rural areas hitherto beyond the range of the public water services, not least in the crofter counties where the provision of piped water simultaneously with electricity supplies to the outlying townships will no doubt play some part in arresting the depopulation trend in the Highlands.

In contradistinction to the position in England, where the supplies to many parts of the country are in the hands of Water Companies, all public supplies in Scotland come under local government administration and control. The County Councils of the counties and the Town Councils of the cities and burghs are the statutory local water authorities for their respective areas, although in a few instances neighbouring authorities have combined to form joint Water Boards having jurisdiction within defined limits of supply. Throughout Scotland today there are just short of 200 separate water authorities supplying in aggregate a total of some 380 million gallons of water daily for domestic and industrial purposes, of which about one-third is in the latter category. This figure does not include the considerable volumes of water also drawn for industrial use from sources outwith the sphere of the public services, such as the supplies circulated for cooling purposes at power stations or the supplies obtained independently from rivers, canals or boreholes by industrial firms for process work, about which statistical information is not readily available.

Under the Water (Scotland) Acts, 1946 and 1949, local water authorities are charged with the duty of supplying a pure and wholesome supply of water for domestic purposes to every part of their districts where such a supply is required and can be provided at reasonable cost, while they also have a duty to supply water for industrial use provided that this can be done without endangering the supplies necessary to meet present or future domestic requirements and subject to the reimbursement of the cost in certain cases. The enactments referred to, which also define the powers and obligations of authorities with respect to the acquisition of lands, the construction of works and the methods of charging for water, superseded earlier legislation relating to water supply and, in particular, introduced a simplified procedure whereby an authority intending to develop a source could seek the necessary rights by the submission of a Water Order for the approval of the Secretary of State for Scotland instead of, as formerly, by the promotion of a Provisional Order in Parliament.

As the statutory powers under which water authorities operate are not available to private firms, the current trend in areas of industrial development is for firms requiring water to obtain their supplies through the agency of the local water authority—a procedure having obvious advantages where several large water-consuming industries are involved. Water delivered from the public service for industrial use is normally measured at the consumer's premises and paid for at a meter rate fixed by the supply authority. Water supplied for domestic, community and some ordinary trade purposes is not individually metered but is charged for by the levying of rates on the valuation of the premises served, the main components being the domestic water rate and the public water rate.

With the improvement of housing standards and the greater use of water-consuming household appliances, a continuing upward trend is evident in the scale of domestic usage. The total unmetered consumption, which may be influenced by the habits of the community, the age of the supply system and the effectiveness of the measures applied to control leakage and waste, at present normally lies in the range from 40 to 80 gallons per person per day. This is about double the corresponding range in England but only about one-third of the average rate of consumption prevailing in America.

A favourable feature of supplies derived from Scotland's upland catchment areas is that the water, because of its relatively low content of calcium and magnesium salts, is inherently soft in character and so particularly suitable for general domestic and industrial use. Water derived from river intakes is usually noticeably harder, especially where the drainage basin contains limestone outcrops, while water obtained from deep boreholes, like that pumped from mine workings, is often not only extremely hard but also liable to contain sulphates and other deleterious constituents which render it unsuitable for general use without expensive corrective treatment. By their remoteness and freedom from direct polluting influences upland catchment areas also provide supplies of high quality from the bacteriological aspect. The water may be highly coloured where there are extensive peat deposits within the gathering ground, and in such cases clarification is effected by chemical treatment prior to filtration and sterilisation. In the provision of a clear, sterile and non-corrosive water for public supply purposes, the works of most major undertakings incorporate treatment plants based on the use of either the older slow-sand or the more modern rapid-sand type of filter. One notable exception is the Glasgow Corporation undertaking based on Loch Katrine, now a hundred years old, from which the supply is delivered to consumers without filtration because of the natural purity and clarity of the water.

The harnessing of the water resources has not of course been without effect on the natural regime of the country's streams and rivers. The early concept of a riparian proprietor being permitted to use the flow in a watercourse subject to the water being returned to the stream "undiminished in quantity and unimpaired in quality" represents an ideal having limited application in practice. By the reservoir and aqueduct works constructed for water power and water supply purposes flood discharges are impounded and major flows are often diverted from within their natural watershed to another, while water abstracted for use may be employed locally or conveyed over long distances to a supply area where, after serving community and industrial purposes, it may be returned to the same or some other watercourse as the carrier of highly polluting sewage and trade wastes. By such practices over the years, stretches of the lower reaches of many streams and rivers became transformed virtually into open sewers, despoiling the amenities and seriously injuring fishing and other interests. Since the turn of the century considerable improvements have resulted from the installation by local authorities of works for the treatment and disposal of sewage, either by means of purification works treating effluents before discharge to inland rivers or tidal waters, or by means of outfall sewers discharging to the sea. Before the country's rivers and estuaries are restored to a satisfactory condition, however, much still remains to be accomplished in the treatment of domestic sewage and especially of industrial wastes. The problem is now being tackled on a more effective basis under the influence of the several river purification authorities set up by Order made by the Secretary of State in terms of the Rivers (Prevention of Pollution) (Scotland) Act, 1951. These authorities may enact byelaws prescribing standards with which effluents discharged into non-tidal streams must comply, and their scope will no doubt eventually extend also to tidal waters as in the Forth Estuary where, by a recently promulgated Order, tidal waters have been brought under the control of the 1951 Act. The overall programme of works required effectively to clean up the country's rivers is a formidable one entailing substantial capital expenditure, and progress towards its attainment is likely to be slow. Meanwhile the polluted state of many rivers reflects adversely on the use and development of the national water resources.

In considering water as a resource, it is to be noted that unlike the other public utilities of gas and electricity which provide expendable media, water undertakings supply a commodity which is in itself indestructible but whose physical and chemical properties such as pressure, temperature and quality may be radically altered by use. Loss of head can be restored by pumping and the same water used again—a practice adopted in the special case of pumped-storage hydro-electric schemes where the water is lifted during off-peak periods for re-use at peak load hours. Temperature and quality changes can be corrected by appropriate treatment, so that water after use can be reconditioned for further use by another party downstream, as indeed applies in some places elsewhere. In theory, too, water could be used and treated for re-use over and over again by circulation within a closed circuit which would require only topping up from an outside source to make good the losses occurring through absorption, evaporation and leakage. Pursuing the same theme, the country's water resources could be regarded as limitless if distillation plants were installed to produce fresh water from the sea, as is done of necessity in some waterless areas abroad. For the conditions in Scotland, however, such considerations are merely of academic interest. The high establishment and operating costs of distillation plants rule them out as practical propositions in other than exceptional cases, while the costs involved in the continuous treatment of a polluted effluent to make it suitable for re-use in the public service would be prohibitive and quite unjustifiable in a country where, by accident of climate and topography, nature provides overall water resources on a copious scale.

The runoff from the whole area of Scotland in a year of average rainfall averages close on 50,000 million gallons per day, or roughly 10,000 gallons per day per head of the total population. If consideration be confined to the upland areas above the 500-ft. contour line from which gravitational supplies may be provided, the water potentially available for such use in a three-dry-year period averages over 20,000 m.g.d. By comparison, with an optimistic view of future increases in population and prosperity, the overall demands for domestic and industrial supplies are not likely to exceed 600 m.g.d., or only some 3 per cent. of the total gravitational resources.

The actual details of that very broad picture are of course affected in practice by a number of factors. Natural variations in the incidence and distribution of the rainfall cause stream flows to fluctuate within wide limits, with the bulk of the total runoff occurring as spates and with the flows falling off to relatively low values in periods of dry weather. As the total available flow in dry periods is of most value to all river interests, the permissible yield obtainable from a straight abstraction scheme is strictly limited. The overall effect on other stream users is of course least where the point of abstraction is in the extreme lower reaches, although in the case of salmon rivers provision must still be made to sustain adequate flows for the free passage of migratory fish. In one recent case in the north of England this is being achieved by returning sea water back to the point of intake to replace the fresh water abstracted, but such a method is not likely to find wide application until the problem of estuarial pollution has been resolved.

Where a substantial and reliable volume of supply is required, the advantages lie with the gravitational scheme served by an upland impounding reservoir. As the function of the reservoir is to collect and store flood water in sufficient quantity to tide over long dry-weather periods, this form of scheme normally interferes least with riparian interests and may indeed be beneficial under both spate and drought conditions, in the first case by reducing the effect of damaging floods and in the second by maintaining the stream at a level in excess of its dry-weather minimum with prescribed flows of compensation water discharged from storage. The feasibility of developing an upland catchment area in this way depends on the existence of a favourable reservoir basin with satisfactory foundation conditions for the construction of the necessary dam. Only a proportion of upland catchment areas contain sites fulfilling these requirements. Many streams fall too precipitously to be suitable for direct development, although in some such cases it is possible to divert the flood waters for impounding elsewhere.

Not unnaturally, the early water supply schemes were based on the cheapest or nearest sources, and the provision today of new or supplementary supplies usually involves consideration of the less favourable or more remote areas. In general, the main streams which lent themselves to ready development in the upland areas adjacent to the populous industrial belt, such as those in the Kilpatrick, Campsie and Ochil Hills, are already fairly well utilised and for major supplies it is accordingly necessary to seek new sources farther afield. There are considerable reserves as yet untapped within reasonable range of the main demands, some to the south throughout the southern uplands and in Ayrshire particularly, and more abundantly to the north in the foothills of the Grampians and of course beyond throughout the Highlands where, if need be, some of the many potential sources could be harnessed jointly for water power and water supply purposes. In all the possibilities mentioned, however, development can only be undertaken with the requisite statutory authority.

Any proposal to harness a source is liable to affect the legitimate rights or interests of numerous parties along the course of the stream, such as private fishings, Fishery Boards, river purification authorities, industrial firms, riparian proprietors or other water authorities, while in impounding works further private or public interests may be affected by the flooding of lands or the diversion of roads, etc. Under the prescribed procedure the promoters of a particular scheme must give notice of their intentions to all parties likely to be affected, and if opposition is encountered with conflicting interests which cannot be reconciled by negotiation, then the project becomes the subject of a public enquiry at which the case for the scheme has to be proved on the basis of need and technical feasibility, and the proposals modified if need be to satisfy objectors. The ultimate decision on the issue rests of course with Parliament—either directly or through the medium of the Secretary of State. Without invoking the procedure mentioned, any figure of yield attributed to a particular source or drainage area would be largely hypothetical, which puts a difficulty in the way of preparing a water map to delineate Scotland's available water resources, as is sometimes advocated. While a map based on rainfall records and stream gaugings could show the average or minimum flows in the streams draining the country's main basins, such information would be misleading if it conveyed the impression that the water was there for the taking. It may be observed, however, that the Department of Health for Scotland made a comprehensive survey in the post-war years of the resources and needs of water authorities throughout the country, and can therefore give general guidance as to the areas where there are surplus reserves available or potential sources worthy of detailed investigation.

Another recurring topic is the possible regionalisation of water supplies and the merging of authorities with common interests. There is no doubt that more economic construction and more efficient management and control can be achieved by authorities combining in the establishment and operation of joint works, and there is accordingly a case for amalgamation within defined geographical limits provided the administrative unit is not made too large, and provided like is merged with like, bearing in mind that the financial, administrative and maintenance problems on a large-scale municipal undertaking can be quite different from those on a rural supply system. In England, where the overall demands are large relative to the available supplies, the Ministry of Housing and Local Government as the controlling authority is forcing many undertakers to combine for the best use and proper conservation of the resources. Similar compulsory powers are available to the Secretary of State for Scotland, but official policy here seems to be rather to encourage the voluntary combination of authorities, a process which although slow is gradually having effect. In some areas burgh and county councils have combined to form comprehensive Water Boards having complete jurisdiction over the supply from catchment to consumer, while in other areas the trend has been towards the formation of joint Boards whose sole function is the provision of bulk supplies for augmentation purposes, the constituent authorities retaining control of local distribution. Recent examples of the latter type of authority are the Daer Water Board in Lanarkshire serving several burghs, the new town of East Kilbride and a widespread landward area with substantial industrial needs, and the Loch Turret Water Board providing supplies for general use in the Counties of Perth and Clackmannan and for industrial purposes in the Burgh of Grangemouth.

A review of the existing pattern of water use would not be complete without reference to the vexed question of the valuation and rating of water undertakings. It may be debatable whether the reservoir, filter station, service tank and pipe-line works of an undertaking should in fact contribute substantially as they do to the provision of other local authority services such as housing, education and police, but that point of principle apart, it so happens that the other utility services of electricity, gas and drainage have received special dispensations by way of relief or exemption from rates which have not been extended to water, and certain anomalies have thereby been created. The valuation of an undertaking, being calculated on the revenue principle, depends directly on the loan charges, which at current interest rates can be high especially where the works are built with reserve capacity against possible long-term needs. A new reservoir is therefore liable to carry an onerous burden of rates in its early years when it may be providing only limited service, whereas an older reservoir, constructed initially under more favourable conditions will, particularly as the loan periods lapse, contribute considerably less in rates although its total useful output may be considerably more. Moreover, a perhaps similar new reservoir constructed for hydro-electric purposes may make only a nominal contribution to local rates. As is perhaps less comprehensible, the trunk main supplying water to a community is subject to the full impact of rating, whereas the trunk sewer carrying the same flow to purification works for treatment is entirely exempt. The inequalities of the present situation have been ventilated in the Report of the Sorn Committee on Scottish Valuation Rating, and published in 1954, and in the Report of the Working Party on the Valuation for Rating of Waterworks in Scotland, published in 1955, but so far no official action has resulted from the recommendations and suggestions contained in these reports. Meanwhile the incidence of local rates has the effect of doubling the current loan charges on a project and so imposing a burden which is a serious bar to progress.

The Prospect in the Future Before Us

G. LITTLE, B.SC., M.I.C.E., M.I.MUN.E., M.I.W.E.
Dundee

In spite of the increasing demands for water from many quarters there is sufficient potential to satisfy all needs provided the problem is tackled in a realistic and co-ordinated manner.

Although the water potential varies from place to place owing to differences in rainfall, etc., there is no need for a water grid system analogous to the electricity grid.

To assess the water potential accurately in sources to be developed, more river and rain gauges must be installed.

The allocation of the water sources to be developed by the various interests should be the function of a Central Co-ordinating Committee who would also be responsible for the collection and collating of all data relating to the water resources of Scotland.

The individual sources would either be fully developed in the first instance or so designed that full use can be made of the source at a later date when circumstances so demand.

Domestic and industrial supplies would be developed and distributed by regional authorities.

Increasing attention must be paid to the prevention of pollution of rivers and the existing causes of pollution eliminated.

The rating and valuation of water undertakings must be altered and water mains and fittings should be completely de-rated.

Throughout Scotland there has been an increasing demand for water during the past twenty years and there is no indication that the demand will not continue to increase during the next twenty years. Industry continues to use more and more water and the expansive housing developments which have taken place, especially in all urban areas, have caused appreciable increases in the domestic demand for water, and the housing expansion programme is far from complete. The increasing demands of the past twenty years have been met by expanding existing sources and developing new ones. How are the demands of the next twenty years to be met?

It seems absurd that in a country like Scotland with such a high incidence of rainfall there should be any doubt at all about the sufficiency of the water supply in the future for all useful purposes—domestic, industrial and sporting, etc.

It has been calculated that in a year of average rainfall the runoff for the whole of Scotland is approximately 50,000 million gallons per day. About half of this could be used for gravitational purposes, giving 25,000 million gallons per day. With a population of 5 million people and allowing 200 gallons per head per day for ordinary domestic and industrial purposes, the need for water is only 4 per cent. of the available *gravitational* potential. In addition water could also be abstracted from the sea, underground sources, and the lower reaches of rivers by pumping, and the yield from these sources could be very great ideed.

With such an abundant potential of the raw material there should not even be the threat of a shortage of supplies provided careful consideration is given to the collection, storage and distribution of water. However, owing to differences of rainfall, geological formations, etc., the water resources vary greatly from area to area, and since the prosperity of a country depends on the use it makes of its material assets it is absolutely essential that the very best use should be made of the water resources of those areas which can best be developed for the ultimate benefit of the country as a whole.

Being essentially a democratic country and the Scot being naturally an individualist, there is no one method that could be suggested for the most efficient harnessing of water for its multiplicity of purposes.

Broadly, water is used for domestic, industrial (including the production of hydro-electricity) and sporting purposes and is developed from and by public and private sources. The sources and quantities used by public authorities are well known, but no such data are easily obtainable in connection with private supplies.

Under the Water Scotland Acts of 1946 and 1949 all domestic water supplies in Scotland are the responsibility of local *water* authorities, who are not necessarily local authorities although a great many of them are. The others are the Joint Water Boards. Their duties are fairly well defined by these Acts and their activities come under the jurisdiction of the Secretary of State for Scotland. Thus about 95 per cent. of the present domestic needs are or should be met by these public bodies; steps are at present being taken to meet the needs of the remaining 5 per cent. These public bodies are also empowered to supply other than domestic water, under certain circumstances, and this is done in all cases.

Industrial demand is met by various means—from public bodies, from private sources (without any statutory powers) and in the case of Hydro-Boards under their own Act of 1943.

A recent demand of enormous proportions has come from the Atomic Power Establishments. (It is estimated that the Hunterston Power Project will need 20 million gallons per hour for cooling purposes.) However, most of the water used in these establishments is returned almost undiminished in quantity but could be radically altered in quality or chemical composition, and there is no suggestion that any consideration should be given to the re-use of water returned from an Atomic Power Establishment. Owing to the enormous quantities used and the very doubtful quality of the effluents from such establishments it is strongly recommended that they should obtain their water from and return it to the sea at intake and outlet points which have been very carefully selected by a detailed study of the tidal flows.

Mass irrigation of crops is now being contemplated on an ever-increasing scale, but there are no statistics at present available for the actual amount of water that is being currently used for this purpose. Almost all the water used in irrigation is evaporated or transpired in plant growth and cannot be re-used, as is the case in hydro-electric schemes for instance. This is one of the very few uses of water where it is actually consumed. If the water were readily available for all irrigation purposes, then in dry seasons great use would be made of it to the decided advantage of agriculture and horticulture. As much as half an inch of water per acre is used in four hours for this purpose, and this used on a ten-acre holding amounts to a rate of 680,000 gallons per day. This water would be required only at times of greatest demand on a public undertaking (i.e. in the dry seasons) so it is imperative that the future requirements for irrigation purposes should be known well in advance if their requirements are to be met from properly prepared sources.

To meet the increasing demands for water from all sources—domestic, industrial, hydro-electric, agricultural—and to preserve the tidal estuaries, loch and rivers in a fit state for fishing, sporting and recreational activities it is essential that due consideration be given now to obtaining an overall picture of the water resources of Scotland and to draw up a plan for their most useful development.

It is difficult and undesirable to allocate individual sources to each of the above uses except in the case of Atomic Power Projects, which for various reasons should be situated near the sea.

How the water resources of Scotland will be developed in the future may well have a political solution and I am making no attempt to forecast political trend in Britain. Under the existing Parliamentary and Local Government structure and procedure it may well be that the future activities in the water supplies of Scotland will be determined outwith Scotland and even contrary to general Scottish opinion.

I am considering the future prospects from the *technical* aspect and completely divorced from political dogma.

Unlike gas and electricity, there is no economical method yet known for the production of water on a large scale or for the comparatively easy transference of water from one place to another. The sources must therefore be developed where they are found and not where it would be most convenient for them to be. Under such circumstances it would be most prudent to give very careful consideration to the location of any industry or project which requires large quantities of water.

To convey large quantities of water over long distances, high pressures and very large pipes or aqueducts are required. However, there is no real need to transfer water either from the north to the south of Scotland or from the east to the west or any other combination of transferences. And under such circumstances a grid analogous to the electricity grid is not necessary on account of need and prohibitive on the account of cost.

This inconvenience of transporting large quantities of water will have a telling influence on where and how the sources should be developed most usefully for all purposes.

The determination of this development should be by a Central Co-ordinating Committee composed of independent technical people who should have statutory powers and be responsible for the collection and collating of all data relating to the water resources of Scotland including the physical and chemical state of these resources, especially the lower reaches of rivers.

It is a great pity that the work of the Inland Water Survey was not continued and pursued more vigorously and effectively. That survey hardly rippled the surface of the problem of water statistics. It was truly a drop in the bucket, but I may add a very precious drop indeed—in fact a pearl of great price obtained in the bargain basement as far as cost was concerned. In such a technical country as Scotland it is ludicrous that we should be dependent on rainfall statistics obtained from voluntary readers. Their contribution up to the present has been invaluable, but their contribution should be merely supplementary to and not in substitution for organised readings which would be the Central Committee's responsibility.

Although rainfall records are necessary and desirable it is more important from the water supply aspect to know what water is actually available at certain places. This can best be done by gauging rivers, streams and underground sources, and a greater number of such gauges is necessary than those at present installed. The ideal, of course, would be to gauge every flow near or at the proposed point of draw-off of the water, but clearly this is financially impossible and not really necessary. However, a number of carefully selected and controlled gauging stations should be set up in certain areas and the results correlated to the readings from well-sited rain gauges in those areas. The information from these areas would be used as the basis for assessing the water potential of the country as a whole and give an indication as to what sources could and should be developed for particular purposes. It would be the Central Committee's duty to determine in general how a particular source should be developed. The actual development of the source and where applicable the distribution of water from the source would be controlled by a "developing" authority.

Unlike most raw materials there is no scarcity of water and there are almost unlimited possibilities of sources: the sea, tidal waters, rivers, streams, lochs, and man-made reservoirs and wells. As already mentioned, there are also many varied interests which use some of the waters of Scotland. However, with proper co-ordination there should be no competitive demand for one or more sources provided the possibilities of the sources are known in detail and administered by the Central Co-ordinating Committee whose only interest is the best use of each source, and it would be possible to satisfy all interests. There is no need for a source to be devoted entirely to one interest. With the use and ultimate state of the water being known the Committee would be in a position to allocate the several uses to the various interests in cases where there were rival claims for the same source.

By virtue of the use made of the water it can sometimes be used again; sporting activities and fishing merely use water as their area of operation, hydro-electric schemes do not consume or radically change the composition of the water, irrigation on the other hand "consumes" water in the sense that after use the quantity of water returned to the river is negligible; industry consumes some of the water, but the greater quantity is returned to the sea or river usually in a very different form either at a much higher temperature or greatly changed in chemical analysis; domestic water is drastically altered and eventually returned in some form of sewage effluent. Depending on the type and degree of pollution it might be possible, after purification, if so desired, to make further use of this water.

Once a source has been allocated it should either be utilised immediately to its full economic extent or so designed for partial use in the first instance that full use can be made of the source at a later date when circumstances demand. It is not unknown for a source to be only partially developed in such a way that its ultimate yield cannot be obtained because of the crippling restriction of the initial design, except at very great expense.

The source having been allocated, the development has then to be considered.

Hydro-Electric Schemes. These schemes merely use and do not consume water and the present arrangement under the existing Acts does not need to be altered as far as the development of an allocated source is concerned. The only interests which are affected by the hydro-electric schemes are those of the fishing industry, and I feel that this problem is exaggerated out of all proportion to its adverse effect on the community. The hydro schemes are being developed to provide power for all parts of Scotland (and some may even be exported to England) and great expense in time and money is devoted to the preservation of the fishing interests wherever a hydro scheme is developed. Under these circumstances no alteration is suggested for the future hydro schemes.

Water for Domestic and Industrial Use. In spite of the improvement which has taken place in the supply of water for domestic and industrial purposes during the past few years, I do not consider the present arrangements offer the best solution to the development and distribution of water supplies throughout Scotland. There are too many instances where duplication of distribution mains could have been avoided and where areas are not served from the most reasonable source, generally owing to local prejudice.

The most practical and economic method of developing water supplies for domestic and industrial use would be by regional schemes whose areas would be defined not by arbitrary lines drawn on a map such as parish, town and county boundaries but by the topographical outlines of the area. The limit of the regions would be the extent to which the water could be supplied within economic reason. This could easily mean, of course, that parts of the same local authority area as constituted at present would be supplied from different regional schemes depending on the topography of the local authorities' area; and a regional scheme would in all probability serve a number of local authorities. However, no area would be served by more than one regional scheme. The existing Joint Water Boards supply various areas but they do not supply *all* the areas they could economically supply. Those Joint Water Boards could function much more efficiently than they do at present if town and county boundaries could be forgotten and parochial prejudices submerged for the greater good.

Adjacent Regional schemes would be so interconnected that in emergencies, which must arise even in the best co-ordinated schemes, one region could help or be helped by the other.

It is certain that many small local sources could and should be developed to supplement the regional scheme. Private supplies would be used when these were considered to be the best method of supply. But local and private supplies would be developed only when sanctioned by the Central Committee. Whether local or regional sources should be developed would depend on the merits of each case and no limiting size—either upward or downward—should be placed on any development. At present some undertakings may be too small and others may be too large.

It would be encumbent on all concerns storing, using and/or distributing water to return an accurate account of their abstraction and use to the Central Committee at least once a year.

Co-ordination. Although over the years there is a plentiful supply of water for all purposes throughout the country, the rate of supply of water is so intermittent that some form of storage must be built for most purposes—the most common being an impounding reservoir to store water from the "wet" seasons to be used in the "dry" seasons. And to date all potential users have been working on their own without any great deal of collaboration with the other users. The hydro schemes use water as a source of power and the water which emerges in the tail race is the same water in quantity and quality as entered the turbines. Could this tail race water not then be used for some other purpose such as providing "consumable" water for domestic or irrigation use?

So far very little use has been made of water for "artificial" irrigation, but so much interest is now being taken in this aspect of plant and crop production that serious consideration must be given to the effect that abstraction of water for this purpose would have on loch levels and river flows as the case may be. Like domestic and industrial demands, irrigation demands are usually greatest when the loch levels and river flows are least. In times of overflowing lochs and flooding rivers there is no need for artificial irrigation. Such flooding can seriously affect agricultural interests. Since irrigation and flooding so directly affect agriculture there is no reason why both these problems should not be treated as one. Consideration at least should be given to the possibility of controlling the flooding of certain areas by the construction of flood control reservoirs which in turn could be used for irrigation in times of drought. Such reservoirs may even be combined with hydro-electric and water supply schemes.

Prevention of Pollution. Rivers and tidal waters are the usual depositories for sewage (crude and treated) and industrial effluents. Owing to the polluted state of the lower reaches of certain of our rivers it is only in the upper reaches of those rivers that fishing is possible and abstraction for domestic water supplies relatively safe. This necessitates long lengths of unproductive and expensive mains to be laid from those upper reaches to the premises to be supplied.

Reservoirs are mostly situated far from the mouths of rivers because they are usually used, at least partially, for domestic water supplies which must be free from pollution, and no river of any size in Scotland can be said to be pure in mouth—in other words they are all filthy mouthed to a greater or less extent. If the mouths of rivers could be used for domestic water supplies, great expense could be saved owing to the elimination of long lengths of unproductive mains. Extra expense would be caused by the necessity of pumping. The relative costs of the two types of scheme could easily be assessed and the more economic one used.

To ensure cleanliness in rivers, the river boards must act firmly and quickly, and deal not only with possible new offenders but eliminate those effluents which have been polluting the rivers for years. Surely progress can be made without pouring filth into rivers and the sea.

There are many uses for water mostly for utilitarian purposes, but it also provides facilities for various types of sport—fishing, swimming, boating, etc. All of those sports are much more enjoyable when practised in a clear unpolluted stretch of sea, loch or river. How often have we heard that the Forth and Clyde used to be fished for salmon at Edinburgh and Glasgow? Both those fine rivers are a disgrace to cleanliness and are now a challenge to their respective river boards which have been set up to try and restore them to their pristine glory. These boards should be given every encouragement in their endeavours in the future.

Most of the pollution is due to lazy, selfish industrialism; by certain industries and municipalities getting rid of their rubbish in the easiest and cheapest way to themselves without any regard to the ultimate consequences. No effluent or by-product should be allowed to be discharged into any estuary, river or loch without proper written authority.

Tourism is fast becoming a major industry in Scotland, and although the mountain and hill streams are beautiful attractions, similar beauty should be apparent in all our watercourses instead of the open sewers which the lower reaches of some of our rivers have become. How ludicrous the present position is that when a river, stream or loch is to be used for hydro-electric or domestic water supply purposes the fishing and other interests of those using such rivers are given due and rightful consideration to make sure that they will not be adversely affected by such schemes, even to the extent of an inquiry being held, whereas the disgusting condition of other rivers is not challenged because the damage to fishing, etc., has already been done. It has been truly said elsewhere in this connection that "we are the victims of appalling selfishness, timid governments and local authorities and excessive tenderness to established interests". The use and effect of the newly formed river boards will be awaited with interest and hope. Their task is an essential but difficult one.

Prevention of Waste and Re-use of Water. Although there is a plentiful supply of water which can ultimately be harnessed for human use and enjoyment, this is no reason why there should be wanton use or abuse of the processed article. There is no suggestion that the maximum use should not be made of water, but there is an urgent need for the public and industrial users to be made more water conscious, and thereby encourage them to eliminate all wasteful practices which at present prevail. Water undertakings in whatever form, public or private, should pay particular attention to the elimination of waste, and systematic "Waste Detection" should be practised and encouraged in all undertakings. With so much of their equipment underground (out of sight, out of mind) in the form of distribution piping, some form of continuous checking on the watertightness of the system should be the duty of all undertakings. Some of the present-day consumption figures given by water undertakings would be more correctly listed as "Consumption and Waste" figures. Particularly in old-established undertakings, considerable leakage takes place in worn-out and out-of-date fittings. In industry (including dairy farming) great savings could be made in the quantities of water used, and where practicable (even if causing some expense to individual firms) re-circulation of water—especially for cooling purposes—should be made obligatory.

Separate Systems for Domestic and Industrial Water. With the demand for water increasing annually, more sources will require to be developed or existing sources enlarged (as has been stated, in some cases this is impracticable). In the past the water supplies in Scotland have generally been derived from upland catchment areas and naturally those of easy access and least expensive have been developed, leaving the more expensive for future use. However if, as is hoped, the river boards can so improve the quality of the water in the lower reaches of the rivers, those lower reaches might be capable of being used as pumped water supplies with the great advantage of being near the centres of the greatest use of water. If this development does take place, then it would be possible on a greater scale than at present to separate domestic and industrial water, with considerable saving in the expense of water treatment, for usually industrial water does not require so much treatment as domestic water.

Water Charges. The vexed question of how water undertakings should be rated must be tackled and an answer found in the near future. It is incomprehensible that water mains and fittings in particular should be rated at all. Very often the lands in which the mains are laid are subject to considerable de-rating whereas the mains themselves are fully rated. There is no sense in such a contradiction. In the future, water mains and fittings should not be rated thereby bringing them into line with certain other services such as sewers and gas mains.

The rateable value placed on reservoirs should also be reviewed and their rateable value should bear some relation to the rateable value of the land surrounding the reservoir. With those two items considerably reduced, a water undertaking would be in a much better financial position to meet the developments which must take place in the future if all the increased demands for water must be met.

Since the supply of water for domestic purposes is rightly considered to be a public service, the present method of charging according to the rateable value of the premises supplied should be continued and all other water used should be charged for according to the quantity used.

Each regional scheme would be responsible for its own financial commitments, and although the method of charging would be the same throughout Scotland, the actual charges made for water could vary from region to region.

INTRODUCTION TO DISCUSSION

Professor W. H. PEARSALL, D.SC., F.R.S.
Chairman, Conservancy Policy Committee, Nature Conservancy

We go on this afternoon to the discussion of Water Use on which we have two papers and a number of speakers, but it has been thought that there may be some advantage in looking on another aspect of what we heard this morning. We are going to talk about multi-purpose, literally, use of water, and it would be very interesting if we could ask Mr. Bowman and Mr. Davis who have come quite a considerable distance if they have any reflections to offer on what they heard this morning. I wonder if they would like to speak?

Note. Since Mr. Davis's remarks were mainly concerned with recreation, they have been included with the immediately previous discussion.

STATEMENT BY THE REPORTER

Professor W. FRAZER, B.SC., PH.D., A.R.C.S.T., A.M.I.C.E., A.M.I.MECH.E.
Professor of Civil Engineering, The Royal College of Science and Technology

Gentlemen: I propose this afternoon to keep my remarks brief. I would just like to remark first of all that the two papers we are considering are both by practising and practical engineers. Mr. Campbell is a partner in a firm of consulting engineers in Glasgow, who have been responsible for very many designs of water undertakings of all descriptions from hydro-electric schemes, water supply schemes, right down at the other end to water purification schemes. Mr. Little is responsible for the supply of water to the City of Dundee. So both papers are not highly theoretical; they are the observations of men who are engaged in the utilisation and management of our water resources.

In his paper, Mr. Campbell has drawn us a picture of the existing water use. He points out that the present supply is mainly from surface sources—that underground sources are not developed, and that in point of fact Scotland's underground water resources are small compared with the surface resources. He has outlined the historic background which has given rise to the physical and administrative pattern of the present use of water resources, the greatest single users of water at the moment being the hydro-electric schemes, who use about twenty times the industrial supply. On the administrative side he points out that there are some 200 water local authorities administering about 380 million gallons per day. These authorities are all public bodies, as distinct from England, where you have a very large number of small private water undertakings. There are no private water undertakings in Scotland supplying water for domestic purposes. In considering the potential of water he estimates the potential as some 50,000 million gallons per day of which 40 per cent. is above the 500-ft. contour. In other words, there is in Scotland at the moment a very great potential from gravitational sources, but this does not mean to say that it is there for the asking. In development over the last 200 years or so, the most convenient and cheapest sites for dams and reservoirs and for river intakes have already been taken up; and for various reasons it is quite often impossible to enlarge such schemes. The water we have in Scotland is of extremely high quality in general, remarkably free from dissolved material. In fact, if I may for a moment speak from my own experience, we ran into serious trouble in our laboratory with a little gadget we obtained which measured flow by the conductivity of water. Glasgow water has practically no conductivity and the gadget would not work. It was developed down in the South!

Mr. Campbell draws attention to the effects of utilisation on rivers, and he stresses that the early concept that riperian properties were permitted to use the flow in the watercourse, subject to the water being returned through the stream undiminished in quantity and unimpaired in quality, has gone by the board. The abstraction of large quantities from rivers and streams has meant alterations of regime and the return of these quantities of water has led to the present state of some of our streams and estuaries from a pollution point of view. On the administration side he points out that there is a strong case for regionalisation. This is being forced in England by legislation on water undertakings, but in Scotland, although the Secretary of State has powers, this has not so far been enforced, the Secretary of State preferring to rely more on voluntary association, and he instances some very fine regional schemes which have taken place, such as the Daer Water Board in Lanarkshire where several of the burghs, the New Town of East Kilbride, and a widespread landward area, have co-operated in a regional scheme. Similarly, a scheme is being constructed at the moment by the Loch Turret Board which will provide supplies in the Counties of Perth and Clackmannan, as well as for the very important industrial purposes of the Burgh of Grangemouth. On the administrative side he raises the strange anomaly that rates are levied on practically every part of a water undertaking installation—the dam, the filters and the trunk mains—pointing out that the incidence of local rates has the effect of doubling the current loan charges on a project and imposing a burden which is a serious bar to progress. Other public undertakings such as sewage and electricity do not carry such burdens. If you build a dam for hydro-electric purposes you do not have to pay rates on it. I understand if you build one for water for domestic purposes you do have to pay rates—a very strange anomaly.

Mr. Little presents us with a provocative paper and raises several issues. He is confident that the increasing demand for water in Scotland can be met if the problem is tackled in a realistic and co-ordinated manner, and that the only problem is one of administration. He has considered the question of a water grid and points out that there is no need for a complete water grid; what is wanted is the development of regional schemes with a possibility of a transfer between them. He points out, of course, that it is an extremely expensive hobby to transport large quantities of water from point to point. In other words, the water must be used where it can be developed, which, of course, raises the whole question of location of industry. It is no good impounding water on the west of Scotland for use in the east—industry must go to the water, otherwise it becomes uneconomic. On the administration side he considers that the development of Scotland's resources should be done by means of a Central Co-ordinating Committee responsible for multiple purpose use of these resources.

A very provocative statement—he considers that the fish problem in Scotland has been greatly exaggerated. I will not comment on that any further. There are many people in the body of the hall who will.

I think the most important point he raises, and one which will give us great concern in the immediate future, is this problem of irrigation. Already yesterday someone mentioned that in East Lothian the equipment manufacturers have sold equipment capable of using 35 million gallons per day, while the dry-weather flows in the River Tyne can only provide 20 million gallons per day.

There is another factor which I would like to mention from my point of view. Some time ago I did a little calculation—it was not awfully accurate.I considered the scientific farmer who had read his Ministry of Agriculture publications and could work out heat balances and measure water contents, and did things by the book. He did all this and came to the point where his calculations indicated that he required to put water on his field—which he did. I then looked into the question of the number of times the weather forecast had been wrong, and I estimated that this very scientific farmer would use approximately 50 per cent. more water than was necessary, simply due to our climatic conditions and that we cannot rely on long-term predictions. If we then add a figure for the unscientific farmer who just sloshes water on the field, the potential for irrigation is absolutely frightening and is one which should be examined extremely closely as to whether from the overall point of view it is going to be economic. You cannot deal with irrigation unless you consider drainage; the drainage is just as important as an integral part of any scheme involving irrigation, and I think that this problem is an extremely important one. On the face of it, it is very attractive, if you do not get rain, in with the suction pipe and slosh the water on, but from an overall economic point of view I think the costs are going to exceed the benefits considerably.

DISCUSSION

Mr. R. W. Covill, *Chief Technical Officer, Lothians River Purification Board*

I wish firstly to congratulate the authors on their clear exposition of Scotland's present water resources and uses.

In the third paragraph of Mr. Little's paper, the author mentions the possibility of abstracting further supplies of water from the lower reaches of rivers. I wish to emphasise, therefore, the fact that abstractions for any purpose are matters with which the river purification boards are deeply concerned. The fact that the river boards at the present time, under Section 18.4 of the Rivers (Prevention of Pollution) (Scotland) Act, 1951, are only able to request information relative to the quantities and times at which abstractions are made stresses in my submission the desirability for the river purification boards, as the logical authority, to be able to control such abstractions. Mr. Little has raised the question of the spray irrigation of crops—a technique which is already placing a severe strain on the water resources in certain watersheds in the east of Scotland, and my Chairman yesterday stressed the seriousness of this problem in East Lothian alone. I should like to add at this point the fact that in many areas, particularly in the Forth-Clyde belt of Scotland, the rivers are being subsidised to a great extent by pit waters. Now, as and when some of these pits close it may well be that the quantity of pit water is reduced, and hence the position as determined by present gaugings and also future gaugings may not necessarily be realistic. However, with regard to statistics concerning the actual amount of river water being used for irrigation purposes, I can assure the authors that the river boards are actively engaged in collating this information. Abstractions from rivers for industrial and other uses are also the concern of the river boards, and requests are being made by the boards for abstractors to install gauging equipment which will enable the boards to assess the effect on the various rivers of abstractions. Some abstractors do not return any of the water to the watershed from which it is taken, and the serious effect of this can be judged when in one case within my Board's area, up to 60 per cent. of the d.w.f., i.e. dry weather flow, of the river has on occasions been abstracted and not a drop of this returned to the river basin.

It will be appreciated from the foregoing that unless control of abstraction is granted to the river purification boards, the contemplation of standards in respect of any discharges becomes ludicrous since the dilution factor will become less and less, and it is possible that some rivers or stretches of rivers will be or could be completely denuded of water.

It is generally agreed that increasing quantities of water will be required in the future for domestic, industrial and agricultural purposes, and both Mr. Campbell and Mr. Little have emphasised this, and the suggestion that all available and future information relative to water resources and requirements should be collated is very commendable, and I will go so far as to suggest that the river purification boards are bodies who should be directly associated with this. In other words, the organisations are already in existence, and provided that industry, local and central government departments, and river purification boards will continue to co-operate, I suggest the information will be forthcoming. Already the river boards are compiling useful data concerning the quality of river waters from the bacteriological, biological and chemical aspects, and this, coupled with the rainfall and river gauging networks which are being developed in the boards' areas, together with other available data, should establish a sound foundation on which to work for the future. In view of the fact that precise assessment of surface water resources can only be made if reliable flow measurement records are available for a period of years, and the same criterion applies to the assessment of water quality, then the urgency of the matter for Scotland is paramount.

I am particularly interested in the author's mention of the possible use of storage reservoirs in watersheds for flood prevention and also for industrial and agricultural usage. One was impressed by the employment of such reservoirs or lakes in the Ruhr area of Germany, and the River Dee scheme near Chester serves a similar purpose. It is thought that the principle may well be applied in the future in certain areas in Scotland.

With reference to Mr. Little's mention of the fact that industry frequently consumes some of the water abstracted and returns the remainder in a different form, this is, of course, very true, and the quantities of water used by some industries may be appreciated from the following. (These figures are taken from data available a year or so ago, and they may in certain instances have been lowered a little.) If we consider water required per unit of material produced:

Steel	55,000 gallons/ton
Oil from coal . . .	10,000 ,, ,,
Leather	10,000 ,, ,,
Sugar refining . . .	8,000 ,, ,,
Paper pulp . . .	30,000 ,, ,,
Butter	100,000 ,, ,,
Cheese	50,000 ,, ,,
Electricity . . .	1 gallon/k.W.h.

This, together with a statement that was published in the foreign Press referring to the possible development of United States industry when it was stated that in the Border cities it is understood that the demand in terms of gallons per head per day of water consumed may reach the phenomenal figure of over 1,000 gallons per head per day. We know from the development of industry in Great Britain that whereas thirty years ago 25 to 30 gallons per head per day were considered normal, these figures have been multiplied quite a little. It is therefore appreciated that water is one of industry's most valuable raw materials and it costs money to buy, to process, and to dispose of it as effluent; therefore, the strongest arguments for the re-use of water in industry can be found in the production costs. Good housekeeping within the industry is essential, therefore water use and effluent disposal must be considered technically and economically as integral parts of production costs.

Referring to the prevention of pollution, one has only to peruse the annual reports of the river purification boards to appreciate what improvements have already been effected by the co-operation of industrialists and local authorities, and one can be assured that this work is continuing.

The question of the re-use of water is raised by the authors, and in this connection may one suggest the possible further use of sewage effluent, i.e. sewage purified at least to the Royal Commission standard; i.e. 30 parts per million or less of suspended solids and a biochemical oxygen demand of 20 parts per million or less. Its application in agricultural irrigation could be valuable, bearing in mind the nitrogen and phosphate contents associated with such liquors. Moreover, for many years chlorinated sewage effluent has been used as cooling water in power stations and similar installations. Delegates will also be aware of the use of sewage effluent in the recharging of underground sources of supply. (These are just a few points which are of direct concern to the river boards and I know my colleagues wish to emphasise other matters.)

In conclusion, one would wish to emphasise the team work required to produce reliable data concerning water resources and water use in Scotland. The task is a formidable one, but that does not suggest that it is an impossible one, and therefore I would make a plea for all interested bodies to do their utmost to produce information which, as far as Scotland as a whole is concerned, may be collated by the appropriate authority.

Mr. E. W. GLOYNE, *Scottish Meteorological Office*

I would just like to comment briefly on the irrigation problem. I think Councillor Russell yesterday was right in suggesting that in irrigation we have a potential consumer for water which is very large and equal to many other existing sinks for this material, but I did wonder whether perhaps he overestimated the amount at this stage. You see, only in the most severe drought, such as 1955, is it likely that a whole range of agricultural crops will require water at the rate of one inch per ten days for sequences of ten days. Horticulture is in a different class that is more likely to be a constant consumer of water, whereas agriculture is more likely to be an intermittent one. Again, I think it unlikely that farmers will pull up in such a way to cater for the extreme maximum possible demand, because what it means is they will have great quantities of equipment lying idle for most of the time, and I put in the question as to whether in the computations of the Lothians River Board they have not gone into the trap perhaps of maximising each factor simultaneously and getting this tremendous figure. I think many of the other points I was going to raise have been raised, but we could quite rightly raise one, and that is—if legislation becomes essential, then river gauging becomes an absolute necessity.

Mr. J. I. WADDINGTON, *Tweed River Purification Board*

Mr. Chairman, Your Grace, My Lords, Ladies and Gentlemen: I call to your attention a publication issued recently by the Surface Water Survey Organisation entitled *Great Ouse Basin: Hydrological Survey*, which includes a water balance-sheet of the Great Ouse area and is a perfect example of how a river catchment should be surveyed. I submit that this type of survey should be undertaken in Scotland, and we have already begun to prepare a water balance-sheet for the Tweed. This will show all abstractions and all returns, and it is to be co-ordinated with a system of river-gauging stations.

I would like now to refer to one of yesterday's papers. The only excuse I can give is that one of the aims of this Conference is a cross-fertilisation of ideas. I do feel that Mr. Wilson, who is sitting beside me, was hitting a little below the belt when he suggested that river purification boards had made no significant contribution to gauging. The first of these boards was only set up six years ago, and he himself stressed it takes many years before reliable records become available. I can only say that in the Tweed catchment ten river-gauging stations are to be installed this year, mainly for full-range measurement.

One of the great problems on the Tweed results from the transfer of water into Central Scotland by three major water authorities. We have established an excellent relationship with these authorities and are carrying out joint river-gauging programmes. Now, differences of opinion will definitely occur between us. After all, they want to take water and we want to keep it! But any future negotiations will be based on carefully gathered information, so that at least there should be no disputes about the stream flow.

It is important that water quality and river-gauging studies are co-ordinated. During the last five years we have taken 6,000 samples on which we have carried out 80,000 tests and we now have a fair idea of the water quality of our area and can study the affects of altered discharges, land drainage schemes, abstractions, etc.

About three years ago we had a query about water quality from an industry interested in setting up in this area. On how many days of the year would the river water be usable?

At that time no comprehensive river-gauging equipment had been installed, but there was a height gauge on that river, and knowing the approximate load of suspended matter which the river could carry at various river levels, we managed to provide an approximate answer. We could also tell the firm the approximate minimum flow of the stream. That was in our very early stages. As we proceed with our gauging programme, we are endeavouring to co-ordinate water quality and river flow. This correlation is important for the textile industry in our area, who require very high quality water for dyeing.

My final point concerns Scotland's estuaries. Mr. Little stressed their importance and I am sure that a lot of industrial development will take place on Scottish estuaries simply because of the large quantities of water available, both for water supply and effluent disposal. If such developments are carried out sensibly there should be no opposition from river purification boards.

Mr. E. W. DENHOLM, *Stirlingshire and Falkirk Water Board*

Enough has been said yesterday by Professor Pearsall, then by Mr. Cranna, and today again by Professor Frazer of the importance of water supply to industry, and there is no doubt that the water supply is the life blood of industry and must be one of the major considerations when a site is being investigated. The existing resources must be developed to ensure that water supplies are available before industrial development commences, and not afterwards. A large factory can be built in one or two years, but major water supply works cannot be constructed under five or six years.

Mr. Little approves of regional water authorities—presumably large local water authorities with topographical boundaries. Mr. Campbell supports him. It is to these authorities that new industries will turn for their supplies but, as Mr. Campbell has stated, any reservoir development by a local water authority is likely to be opposed, firstly by industrial, private and agricultural riparian owners, secondly by private fishings, fishery boards, river purification boards and local authorities, and thirdly even by other local water authorities. I would like to stress that all these interests are in opposition to one another. Parliament always finds a compromise to the opposition and the net result is that the scheme cannot be fully utilised. Mr. Little's suggested remedy is a Central Co-ordinating Committee, but I shall come to that presently.

Firstly, the industrial and agricultural riparian owners seldom have any statutory rights of abstraction from the rivers unless by prescriptive right acquired over many years by use and wont. How many of them pass on the water, as Mr. Campbell puts it, "undiminished in quantity and unimpaired in quality"? In the test case of Alston *v.* the Town Council of Galston that position was upheld by Sheriff MacKenzie in Kilmarnock in the following words: "This is, in my opinion, a bad and untenable defence, the pursuer being entitled as a matter of legal right to have the water of the river sent down to him unimpaired in quantity without reference to the use which he makes or may purpose to make of it." Further, the British standard code of practice, CP/310, 1952, entitled "Water Supplies" states: "Generally speaking, no one, in the absence of special statutory authority, has the right to abstract water from a stream or river unless it is returned thereto, substantially undiminished in quantity and quality, before reaching his next neighbour's property." Yet the Department of Agriculture approves this apparently illegal land irrigation!

Secondly, let me examine the rights of private fishing, fishery board, river purification board and local authority interests. It is they with their friends under the first section above who have usually managed to cripple the utilisation of a site by insisting on compensation awards of up to as much as 40 per cent. of the average gross yield of a catchment area, when, in fact, the low summer flow of the river—that is during a dry summer—had the reservoir not been built, would have been of the order of 4 per cent. or 5 per cent. of the average gross yield for weeks at a time. If the river purification boards could, as Mr. Little puts it, restore the rivers to their pristine glory, the summer compensation water could be arranged to bear some relation to the flow which would have been in the river at the time had no reservoir existed. In other words, most industries who use the river merely want the compensation water to dilute their filthy effluent. By this means millions of gallons of water would be released daily for domestic and industrial use without in many cases having to construct additional works. At present the local water authority constructs part of every reservoir it makes for riparian and other river interests, with no financial contribution being made by these people for the storage provided.

Now, coming to Mr. Little's solution in the Central Co-ordinating Committee. I am not sure I like the set up of yet another committee to control our lives. Who is going to appoint its members and how many of the various interests will be pleased with either the set up or with the committee's decisions? The Secretary of State already has all the powers which could be vested in the committee, so far as the supply to the domestic consumer and to industry from local water authority is concerned. An extension of these powers to include control over abstractions of all kinds would appear to be a simple solution.

I am suggesting that the Secretary of State would be preferable to Mr. Little's proposed committee, not that I think that the Secretary of State has either carried out his statutory duties or that he even has made use of the powers given him. Professor Frazer yesterday was bemoaning the lack of records, but surely the Secretary of State has a duty under Section 1 of the Water (Scotland) Act, 1946, to secure the collection, preparation, publication and dissemination of information and statistics. There are many cases which could be quoted, showing where the failure lies, but in this case the Secretary of State would have to be prepared to carry out the duties placed on him. It is to the Secretary of State that this Symposium ought to direct its attention.

He has at present the same powers as the Minister of Housing and Local Government in England and Wales, but the Minister has already cut down the number of water authorities in England and Wales from 1,100 to 800, and he is proceeding apace to reach his goal of 500 authorities or fewer. This will give the average size of water authority in England and Wales a population of over 90,000 people, whereas in Scotland the average population per authority is less than 30,000 people, and there are only ten authorities supplying populations of more than the Minister's final figure of 90,000 persons in Scotland. The local water authorities in Scotland have an average income of about £1 per head of population supplied. It will thus be seen that the average size of Scottish authority with a 30,000 population cannot finance any work which would provide a water supply to attract industry. It is imperative that the formation of regional boards of economic size should be a first Government priority. If the Secretary of State is not to have his powers widened, can Mr. Little be satisfied that his all-powerful committee, which we would expect to have powers of action, will be composed only of people who will have no axe to grind because of their industrial or other allegiance? If it were composed of people with no other interests, would we not be in the hands of theorists?

Lastly, both Mr. Campbell and Mr. Little have mentioned valuation. Many water authorities are paying as much as 40 per cent. of their total income in local rates. I believe the average for other industry throughout Scotland is one-tenth of 1 per cent. of their annual income in local rates. No other industry could exist with a burden like this round its neck, and there was an assurance given four years ago that the Secretary of State would reconsider the matter before May 1961. We are still waiting on this reconsideration. This rating burden is one of the greatest current drawbacks to the utilisation of our water resources.

In furtherance of Professor Pearsall's, Professor Frazer's and Mr. Cranna's statements yesterday, it is to be hoped that one of the decisions reached as a result of this Symposium will be to ask the Government to press on by whatever means are available, to ensure immediate provision of water supplies to those areas to which industry may be attracted.

Mr. R. Cranna, *Scottish Meteorological Office*

Might I add one little bit to what has been said? I think, if you look closely at that, the Secretary of State's duties start with the collection of information, not with the making of observations or anything of that kind, but with the collection, scrutinising, publication and what have you. I don't think his terms of reference there include the making of observations.

Miss E. Mitchell, *Town and Country Planning Association*

I did not mean to speak at all, but yesterday it struck me that there was another subject among resources that might have a heading to itself, and that is the question of sewage and wastes generally as a possible resource. Today it came in along with recreation, clean beaches and so on, and pure rivers, and it might have a connection with the possible fertilisation of poor land or reclaimed land, or perhaps even of town gardens. I understand that Edinburgh is doing wonderful work with its sewage, and Kincardine-on-Forth with its waste ashes. Would it not be worth while to collect that under a heading also?

Dr. A. Lamont

I would like to make the comment that industrialists are often not told through lack of data that river waters in Scotland are often a good deal colder than in England. The English rivers heat up quite a bit in the summer and are unsuitable for cooling purposes, in dairies for example. I think that this factor of our having colder water in Scottish rivers and also the fact that we have quite a lot of underground cold water to develop should be put before industrialists coming or thinking of coming to Scotland.

Mr. JOHN L. KINLOCH, *Town and Country Planning Association*

You mentioned the rating of water supply pipes and you mentioned electricity, dams and so on, as if the same method of rating were used. It used to be that hydro-electric dams were rated on the whole area of the Hydro-Electric Board and pooled among various authorities. I wonder if that is still so or not? That used to be the case.

Mr. GILBERT LITTLE, *Dundee*

Well, Mr. Chairman, first of all I have got to thank the audience for letting me off so lightly, and I am going to start by telling them a story about a lawyer who told his witness, "Now, when you are explaining the explosion be brief." So the witness said, "The engineer was fu' and the boiler was empty." In this case the engineer is not fu' as yet, but I think it is very significant that generally speaking reservoirs are full in the winter but not so full in summer. I think as far as irrigation is concerned, although there is a great potential demand, that great demand is over a small period of time and that relativity must be taken into consideration. One of the greatest difficulties of supplying irrigation when it would be needed, as I have stated in my paper—it would be needed at the time when an ordinary supply would be least. Now, to supply irrigation with the amount of water it would require would have to be an insurance policy basis, because it would only be at times of real need that they would want it, not throughout the year, and after all if we have to build dams they are expensive and the cost is distributed over a great number of years.

The other point I would like to take up is on Mr. Denholm. I do not like being controlled, as he very well knows, but also I do not like to have debtors or gimmicks. I think this is what the Secretary of State is because it says here "the Secretary of State to secure the collection, preparation, publication and dissemination of statistics relating to such water resources and water supplies and to appoint an Advisory Committee to advise the Secretary of State on these matters". He may have appointed the Committee; they certainly have not advised. Mr. Denholm criticises himself very forcibly by saying something about the Secretary undertook four years ago to do something which is not done yet. Therefore, that is the reason why I would suggest a different approach to the problem—a practical approach to the problem. Let us have a Co-ordinating Committee—somebody that we can throw stones at, because we can't do that to the Secretary of State and get away with it.

On another point regarding the river purification boards—I tried, in my paper, to indicate that they were doing a reasonably good job of work, but again they are an individual concern and as far as water supplies are concerned no individual concern is big enough to be able to control the whole of the resources of Scotland. As far as water supplies on their own—I don't care who it is—we must have a committee and it is to co-ordinate these things. I do not say the river purification boards are not doing a good job of work. They *are* doing a good job, but as has been stated in particular with the Tweed that they will have notes of all the abstractions, all the legal abstractions (if I may say so); illegal abstractions you know nothing about, and I am afraid that is the difficulty.

Now, there are one or two other points, but time is getting on and someone else may want to speak. Professor Frazer is concerned considering the amount of water that might be used by very detailed calculations of a very well enlightened farmer. I would pass on in this connection advice I had from a Glasgow Professor when we were trying to work out things in very great deatail. He said, "Little, always remember that a judicious guess is worth hours and hours of useless maths." Now, it was this judicious guess, and judicious guessing can only come from practical experience—I think that is one of the things you tried to point out. In this detail of water supplies and with river gauging I do not think that we can get in the very near future any great degree of accuracy either from river gauging or rain gauging, but we can get a lot more information which would be useful to us at the right time. I think that is what is necessary.

I don't think I have any more to say on details as have been put to me. Just coming back to the Secretary of State, I have here in my notes the Secretary of State has so many multifarious duties—I don't think a Symposium on his duties would do any harm. I would state seriously in conclusion that there is a saying that an irresponsible man spends his money like water, but the time is rapidly approaching when a wise man will have to use the water as he spends his money to get as much as possible out of this necessity of life.

UTILISATION OF RESOURCES

ENERGY RESOURCES AND UTILISATION

Energy—Resources and Utilisation

J. Guthrie Brown, M.I.C.E., M.I.STRUCT.E., M.I.E.AUST., M.N.Z.I.E., and

J. K. Hunter, B.SC., M.I.C.E., M.I.MECH.E., M.I.E.E.

Sir Alexander Gibb & Partners, London

The paper stresses the relationship between the consumption of energy and the standard of living enjoyed. It discusses the various sources of primary energy which are available in Scotland and the manner in which the pattern of their use has changed over the years. Reference is made to the continuous fall in production from Scottish coalfields since 1913 and to the way in which present supplies of coal are divided among the principal classes of consumer.

Mainly as the result of steadily increasing efficiency in the use of coal the overall consumption of primary energy *per capita*, when expressed in terms of the coal equivalent, has not changed greatly over the past sixty years. However, the proportion of the total energy consumption of Scotland which is met from coal is steadily falling and has in fact declined from 90 to 75 per cent. over the past ten years.

Reference is made to the spectacular rise in the importation of petroleum, not only for road transport but for other uses for which its convenience and increasing competitiveness in relation to coal make it attractive.

A prominent feature of the changing energy pattern is the increasing use of electricity which over the post-war years has been advancing at a rate of about 7 per cent. per annum. At the present time approximately two-thirds of the total electricity used in Scotland is produced from coal and one-third from water power. This proportion will gradually change in the future partly through the inevitable slowing down in the rate of further hydro development and partly as the result of the increasing use of uranium to replace the coal now used in thermal power stations. This substitution of uranium for coal, while at present insignificant, is likely to be accelerated after the end of the present decade, by which time it is anticipated that nuclear power stations will be fully competitive with those burning fossil fuels.

The paper concludes that no rigid forecast is possible of the long-term changes in the use of energy resources since these changes are likely to be influenced not only by unpredictable economic factors but by government policies.

INTRODUCTION

A basic factor in the gathering momentum of the Industrial Revolution was the increasing application of natural resources of energy to manufacturing processes hitherto performed by human labour. Previously industries were sited where supplies of energy were at hand. Thus the first iron-works were found among the oak forests of Sussex and in the Forest of Dean, while the early textile mills were built along the streams of Yorkshire and Lancashire.

The substitution of coal for charcoal and steam for water which marked the beginning of the nineteenth century introduced a measure of flexibility in the location of industry and gave rise to the construction of the canals and later the railways for the transport of both raw materials and finished products. In Scotland the increasing industrial wealth of the lowland belt which was such a feature of the 1800s was due to the rich coalfields in the area.

The use of energy has long been associated with man's welfare and standard of living, and its availability has been a major factor in the material progress of civilisation. In fact, the national income of a country may be closely related to the consumption of energy *per capita*, while the number of horsepower at the disposal of each worker is a measure of their productivity. Thus if living standards are to continue to rise, an essential prerequisite is the availability of adequate and reliable supplies of energy.

Sources of primary energy are of two basic kinds. Those which are expendable and those which are continuously replenished by natural agencies.

Into the first class fall all the fossil fuels including coal, lignite and peat, oil and natural gas, and more recently the radioactive minerals such as uranium. In the second class the most important from the economic point of view is water power, which, like the wind and tides, is perpetually renewed.

Taking the world as a whole, the present overall consumption of primary energy is accounted for approximately as follows:

	%
Coal and lignite . .	46
Petroleum . . .	30
Natural gas . . .	11
Water power . . .	6
Other sources . . .	7
	100

Thus more than nine-tenths of the energy used in the world is represented by the consumption of capital resources.

In 1959 Scotland's consumption of primary energy was distributed among the principal sources of supply as follows:

	Million tons of coal equivalent	Distribution per cent.
Coal	17·478	74·4
Petroleum . . .	4·695	20·0
Water power . .	1·12	4·8
Other sources . .	0·25	0·8
	23·543	100·0

The overall consumption of energy in Scotland represents the equivalent of about 4·53 tons of coal per head of population and compares with 4·82 tons for the United Kingdom as a whole.

Although production from the Scottish coalfields has been falling steadily for nearly half a century, it still provides three-quarters of the country's overall energy requirements. The demand for imported petroleum, on the other hand, has been steadily rising at an ever-increasing rate to meet the needs of transport and other uses while the contribution made by water power in the form of electricity has, from small beginnings in the last decade of the nineteenth century, been increasing also especially during the past ten years.

Although water power at present accounts for no more than one-twentieth of the total energy requirements of Scotland, its contribution in terms of electricity—the form in which it is distributed—is more significant and it now provides a quarter of the country's electrical requirements.

SOURCES OF PRIMARY ENERGY

Coal

Since the earliest days of the Industrial Revolution coal has provided the energy needed by Scotland's expanding industries.

From negligible beginnings in the fifteenth century production from the Scottish coalfields expanded steadily until it reached its peak of 42½ million tons in 1913. Since then, however, production, although subject to considerable variation as between one year and another, has been steadily declining. By 1959 production had fallen to rather less than 19 million tons, a figure which it is believed the National Coal Board plan to maintain over the next two decades.

The spectacular fall which has taken place in Scottish coal production since 1913 may be attributed to a number of factors, amongst which are:

(*a*) Loss of export trade as the result of changing world economic conditions.
(*b*) Reduced internal demand for coal as the result of steady improvements in the efficiency of utilisation.
(*c*) Substitution for coal as a source of primary energy by other kinds of energy such as water power and especially by imported oil.

The fall of the internal demand for coal is all the more remarkable when it is remembered that it has occurred during a period characterised by a steady increase in the world's overall consumption of energy to meet the insistent urge for improved standards.

As already mentioned, the consumption of primary energy in Scotland at the present time is met by coal to the extent of 75 per cent. This compares with 90 per cent. ten years ago, and the downward trend is likely to continue in the future as the relative use of other sources of primary energy increases.

The following Table, which has been abstracted from the Annual Statistical Digest issued by the Ministry of Power, shows the consumption of coal in Scotland by the main classes of users in 1959. Exports and bunker coal are excluded.

	Millions of tons
General industry	4·06
Electricity	3·25
Domestic	3·42
Gas	1·96
Railways	1·34
Coke ovens	1·04
Other users—including colliery and miners' coal	2·40
	17·47

With the exception of electricity, which has been rising, and domestic demand, which has remained fairly steady in recent years, consumption by all these classes has been falling over the past ten years. This fall is particularly marked in the cases of industry and the railways, where to the effect of improved efficiency in the use of coal has been added the substitution of oil and electricity.

To the extent that the substitution of electricity for coal and gas represents an increase in the use of coal for electricity generation, the changing application of energy in industry and railway traction does not necessarily represent a net reduction in the demand for coal.

In general it may be said that future trends in the use of coal by the individual classes of consumer will be affected by a number of factors including:

(*a*) The overall level of industrial activity and changes in the gross national product.
(*b*) Improvements in the efficiency of utilisation of coal.
(*c*) The replacement of coal by other sources of energy on account of either economy or convenience.
(*d*) Development of new uses for coal or the extension of its present limited use as a raw material in the chemical industry.

The improvement in living standards to which we may reasonably look forward in the future can only be secured by a steady increase in the use of energy, and this factor must in the long run tend to maintain the present level of demand for coal—so long as its price is competitive with other sources of energy. It is this question of competitiveness which must provide the key to the future of the coal industry.

Deposits of coal are, like all other minerals, expendable, and once exhausted cannot be replaced. In the past it was the coal measures of Lanarkshire which provided the great bulk of Scottish coal. These rich deposits which once provided the best and cheapest coal are now largely exhausted and today provide little more than one-fifth of the total raised in 1913.

In 1959 the coalfields of Ayrshire, Fife and the Lothians, where geological conditions are far less favourable than those found in Lanarkshire, together accounted for 70 per cent. of all Scottish production, and the necessity to win coal in the future under increasingly difficult conditions is inescapable.

The latest accounts published by the Coal Board covering their operations for 1959 show that each of the eight areas forming the Scottish Division sustained a loss in that year. This loss, before allowing for the interest on the capital employed, varied from 3s. to 31s. 6d. per ton, the average for the whole of the Scottish Division being about 14s. 3d. per ton.

On the basis of the massive capital investment in the Scottish coalfields during the post-war years it would appear that these capital charges may amount to about 10s. a ton. Thus, taking the Division as a whole, it may be concluded that on the average coal is today being sold at a loss of some 24s. per ton, a loss which represents 28 per cent. of the average selling price of 86s. per ton. Losses sustained in 1958 were very similar to those in 1959.

Thus at the present time Scottish coal is being sold to the consumer considerably below its actual cost. The position may change for the better when the benefits of the heavy capital investment incurred by the Coal Board in recent years have been fully secured. But however this may be, the fact remains that in the long term—and subject to any revolution in the methods of winning coal—costs are bound to rise gradually as the more easily mined reserves are exhausted.

Petroleum

The petroleum industry may be said to have been founded in 1859 when the first oil well was sunk in Pennsylvania. In 1900 the total imports of petroleum into the United Kingdom amounted to just over 1 million tons, but by 1959 annual imports had risen to nearly 53 million tons.

Over the first fifty years of the century the imports of petroleum into the United Kingdom increased at an average compound rate of about 6½ per cent. Since 1949, however, this rate has shown a sharp increase and over the past ten years has averaged about 11 per cent.

At various times over the last forty years the early exhaustion of the world's reserves of petroleum has been predicted. Intensive exploration has, however, continually resulted in the discovery of fresh reserves, and today it may be said that in spite of the phenomenal increase in world consumption the proved and probable reserves are, in relation to consumption, greater than they have been at any time in the past.

In Scotland, continued expansion in the use of petroleum will be determined partly by economic factors and partly by political considerations, bearing in mind that outside the U.S.S.R. and Eastern Europe, 30 per cent. of the present world production of crude petroleum is derived from Middle and Far Eastern sources. It is from these sources that the great bulk of the petroleum consumed in the United Kingdom comes.

Water Power

Over the half-century preceding the passing of the 1943 Act which set up the North of Scotland Hydro-Electric Board, a number of schemes with a total installed capacity of 320,000 kW were carried out by private enterprise. The earlier schemes had as their object the production of aluminium, although many of the later ones were undertaken to give public supplies of electricity.

Since the Hydro-Electric Board was established it has pursued an active policy of developing water power within its area, and by the end of 1959 had completed forty-one separate schemes involving a total installed capacity of 866,000 kW, capable of producing in a year of average rainfall an aggregate output of nearly 2,500 million units.

At the present time the Board have further schemes under construction with an aggregate installed capacity of 582,000 kW, while additional schemes totalling some 550,000 kW are in various preparatory stages of study or promotion.

Thus when all these schemes are complete the Board will have at its disposal a total of some 2 million kilowatts producing an average annual output of rather more than 4,000 million units, equivalent to about 2·15 million tons of coal a year.

Electricity supplies in the southern part of the country are the responsibility of the South of Scotland Electricity Board, which possesses a number of hydro stations both in the Galloway area and on the Clyde having a total capacity of 122,000 kW and an output of some 300 million units a year. These schemes were among those carried out before the passing of the 1943 Act.

This short account of the present position of Scottish water power would not be complete without some attempt to place it into proper perspective in relation to the energy needs of Scotland. To do this it is necessary to consider the effect of some of the physical and economic factors which have governed development.

From the point of view of the development of water power, an important feature of the Scottish Highlands is the broken character of their topography and, as a consequence, the absence of large rivers or extensive elevated plateax. For these reasons individual schemes are, by world standards, relatively small and scattered and it is thus not possible to secure those economies which in more favoured regions result from the carrying out of engineering works on a very large scale.

One of the consequences of these physical characteristics is the frequent need for long tunnel systems to collect and concentrate the available water. This feature, combined with the scarcity of good really reservoir sites, renders many of the schemes more attractive economically when developed for operation at relatively small load factors.

Where, as in Scotland, hydro power resources are limited and can only meet a part of the country's demand for electricity, development must compete with other sources of energy. At the present time the coal-fired steam station presents the obvious alternative to water power, and the cost of producing power from a modern steam station thus provides a yardstick for estimating the value of a proposed hydro development.

The amount of electrical energy which can be obtained by developing the hydro potential of a region will depend upon the amount of money spent on its exploitation. By increasing expenditure on reservoirs and aqueducts more energy can be extracted from a given catchment until the point is reached where the cost of the additional energy is greater than its value as determined by the thermal yardstick. The exploitation of water power is thus subject to the law of diminishing returns.

So long as economic conditions remain constant the amount of water power which can be justifiably developed in a region may be evaluated. In practice, economic conditions do not remain constant and the position is often complicated by technical advances leading to a more efficient use of the resources employed in construction. For these reasons estimates of water power resources can never be final, but must be subject to review from time to time in the light of the changes which take place.

To make the best use of limited capital resources the policy of the Hydro-Electric Board has been to develop those sites which were economically most attractive, leaving the less favourable ones to the future. Inevitably, therefore, as the exploitation of the water power resources of a region proceeds, the residual resources tend to become less and less attractive and, in the absence of any changes in the economic balance, the possible rate of development must slow down.

At the present time it is not possible to say with any certainty how much of the residual hydro potential can still be developed economically. It is, however, clear that viewed against the rising needs for more energy the future contribution which can be made from hydro power is not great, and as time goes on the proportion of the country's overall energy needs which will be met from hydro power must fall. In spite of its ultimate limitations, however, the water power already developed within the Hydro-Electric Board's area of 21,175 square miles was not only responsible in 1959 for meeting 80 per cent. of their total requirements, but in addition it enabled them to afford substantial exports to the Southern Board. These supplies were given more economically than would have been possible by any other means.

Nuclear Power

The most recent appraisal of the economic position of nuclear power in Britain leads to the conclusion that even when confined to base load generation it will not compare favourably with power produced in a conventional coal-fired power station before about 1970. This assessment takes into account both the present and prospective costs of nuclear power stations and the spectacular fall in the cost of coal-fired steam stations which has been achieved as the result of technical advances.

The output from the Hunterston nuclear station which is expected to become available in 1964 will have an annual coal equivalent of about one million tons. This is about one-quarter of the total coal equivalent corresponding to the estimated production of electricity at that date, but less than one-twentieth of the overall energy requirements of Scotland.

The Hunterston station will carry the base load of the Southern Board's system and will provide the energy required by the new Loch Awe pumped storage plant belonging to the Northern Board. After 1970 present indications are that the increase in demand in electrical energy will in the main be met by building further nuclear stations of an advanced type in association with additional pumped storage plants to carry the peak load.

When this point is reached the use of coal for the generation of electricity will tend to decline as the base load now carried by the most efficient coal-burning stations is gradually transferred to the new nuclear stations.

MINOR SOURCES OF ENERGY

These include peat, indigenous sources of oil and natural gas, wind and tidal power.

Peat

After the war the coal situation in Great Britain appeared so unpromising that in 1949 a committee was appointed by the Secretary of State for Scotland to make a detailed investigation of the possibilities of using peat as a supplementary source of fuel.

This committee, which issued its report in 1953, estimated that peat covers about 1,625,000 acres, or 8 per cent. of the Scottish land area. After allowing for a moisture content in the bog of 92 per cent. it was considered that there might be about 180 million tons of dried peat available. For economic reasons only part of this would be usable.

In order to gain some experience of the technical problems involved in using peat as a fuel for the generation of electricity a small experimental plant has been installed in Caithness using a closed-cycle gas turbine. The plant which has a rated output of 2·2 mW was first commissioned in 1958.

Experience to date does not hold out much hope that even in the most favourable conditions the use of peat for the generation of electricity can compete with alternative sources of power at present available.

Oil and Natural Gas

Indigenous sources are not likely to make a significant contribution to the future energy requirements of Scotland.

In the South shale has been mined on a limited scale for more than 100 years. However, since the early 1920s when production of shale oil was in excess of 200,000 tons per year the industry has been declining, and in 1959 output fell to 60,000 tons.

Only one source of natural gas from a deep borehole has been found and is now used to supplement the local supplies of town gas. As a result of extensive exploration it has been concluded that the prospects of obtaining gas in considerable quantities from deep bores are not bright.

A limited supply of gas has recently been obtained by the draining of methane from coal workings in the Glasgow area, while a second and somewhat larger supply will shortly be available near Kincardine. In spite of these developments, however, it seems unlikely that natural gas, whether obtained from the mines or from deep bores, will ever provide an important source of energy.

Wind and Tidal Power

The amount of energy represented by the winds and tides around the Scottish coasts is both large and inexhaustible. The technical problems of harnessing these sources of energy, while presenting many novel and even formidable aspects, could undoubtedly be overcome. The crux of the problem is, however, an economic one since even where natural conditions are favourable the capital investment necessary to implement such projects makes them unattractive at present.

The exploitation of the winds and tides as a source of energy suffers from the inherent disadvantage that any output would not only be variable but intermittent. Under these conditions the only value which can be attached to such schemes is that represented by the fuel which would otherwise be used by a thermal power station to produce an equivalent amount of energy. For this reason such projects cannot be regarded as effective alternatives to the construction of conventional power stations, whether hydro or thermal.

The economic difficulties which beset tidal power schemes apply with even greater force to proposals to harness the ocean waves.

THE CHANGING PATTERN IN THE USE OF ENERGY

In 1900 coal provided virtually the whole of the primary energy consumed in Scotland and even in 1913 it accounted for 99 per cent. of the total requirements.

In that year the internal consumption of coal reached the record figure of 21 million tons, or nearly 4½ tons per head of population. By 1938 coal consumption had fallen to 18½ million tons, or 92 per cent. of the total internal consumption of energy. Twenty-two years later in 1959 only 75 per cent. of Scotland's energy requirements were met from coal, imported oil providing the greater part of the balance.

Since the beginning of the century the internal consumption of primary energy per head of population of the United Kingdom has, in terms of coal equivalent, varied as follows:

1900 . .	4·05 tons	1938 . .	4·00 tons
1913 . .	4·50 tons	1959 . .	4·82 tons

At first glance these figures suggest that over the last sixty years there has been no great change in the overall use of energy: their significance is, however, masked by the steady improvements in the efficiency in the use of fuel which has taken place over the past. Today the productive value represented by the consumption of a unit of primary energy is very much greater than it was at the turn of the century. This may be seen from Figs. 1 and 2, which show respectively the improvements which have taken place in the consumption of fuel in the production of electricity and pig iron.

Thus in terms of both industrial production and national income the consumption of energy equivalent to 1 ton of coal is today vastly more effective than it was in the past. In the case of electricity, for instance, the consumption of coal per unit sent out is less than one-half of what it was forty years ago, while over the same period the amount of coke used to produce a ton of pig iron has fallen by 40 per cent.

One of the most significant changes which has taken place in the pattern of the United Kingdom since the beginning of the century is the increasing use of petroleum, which from making a negligible contribution in 1900 accounted for no less than 25 per cent. of total energy consumption in 1959.

This spectacular rise in the use of petroleum is in the main due to increasing demand by road transport and by those other uses for which energy in other forms is either inconvenient or wholly unsuitable.

To a less extent the rise in recent years has been influenced by the increasing competitiveness of oil in relation to coal and its derivatives.

In a free society the user maintains the freedom to choose the form of energy most suited to his needs. Of all forms of energy electricity is the most convenient in application, whether as heat or as motive power to drive machinery, and above all for lighting. In the electrolitic industries it performs a function which cannot be carried out by energy in any other form. Moreover, technical advances in the production of electricity in steam power stations have led as we have seen to increasing economies in the amount of fuel consumed and to a steady reduction in the cost of electricity relative to the cost of energy in the form of coal or gas.

For all these reasons the use of electricity has been increasing at a greater rate than the overall use of primary energy.

This high rate of increase in the use of electricity, at present above 7 per cent. per annum compound, is attributable partly to the increasing mechanisation of industry, partly to the substitution of electricity for other kinds of energy such as coal or gas, and partly to the development of new uses for electricity in industrial and domestic fields.

ELECTRICITY

Because of the ever-increasing importance of electricity to the Scottish economy it is worth while reviewing some of the factors which affect its future expansion.

In the first place it may be said that the basic duty of an electricity undertaking is to provide adequate supplies of electricity to the consumer at the least possible cost consistent with an acceptable standard of reliability. This means in effect combining the various sources of energy available in such a way as to make the best use of their individual characteristics.

The choice of energy resources and the method of combining them must be made with a full knowledge of these special characteristics and of the often conflicting circumstances of the day. The choice has of necessity to be made on an *ad hoc* basis and the possibility must always exist that future changes in the economic background may subsequently show that the decisions taken were not in fact as wise as they seemed at the time.

The main sources of primary energy available to the two Scottish Electricity Boards are coal, imported oil and hydro power. To these nuclear power has been added in recent years.

The differing characteristics of these sources may be emphasised by dividing them into two broad classes:

(*a*) Thermal power employing the steam turbine combined with the expendable fuels, coal, oil or uranium.
(*b*) Hydro power using a non-expendable source—water.

The extension of electricity supplies by means of new thermal power stations—whether using fossil or nuclear fuels—depends primarily on securing the necessary fuel supplies, either imported or home produced. Extension by means of hydro power depends on the extent of hydro resources which can be developed at acceptable cost.

The ultimate development of Scottish water power resources will be determined not so much by the demand for power as by the cost at which hydro power can be produced in comparison with some alternative means—in this case thermal power.

Thus the gradual utilisation of the most favourable water power sites is inevitable, and as time goes on the development of water power will become more and more difficult to justify on a simple economic comparison with thermal power.

However, it has already been pointed out that one of the characteristics of Scottish water power resources is that in comparison with thermal power they tend to be more attractive economically when developed for peak load purposes. Thus a skilful integration between hydro and thermal power makes it possible to justify increasing the amount of generating plant in the water power stations beyond what would be practicable if such stations were considered in isolation. The combined operation of these two basically dissimilar sources of power enhances the intrinsic value of Scottish water power and enables it to make a greater contribution to the country's requirements than would otherwise be possible.

Increasing attention has been given recently to the concept of producing electricity directly by chemical or physical methods. While there are several lines of research which show promise, it would seem that a long time is likely to elapse before they reach the stage when they can offer serious competition to the well-established systems of the present day as exemplified by the steam turbine.

Practical studies for expanding electricity supplies in Scotland over the next ten to twenty years must therefore be based upon further development of the existing systems of coal- (or oil-) fired steam power stations, supplemented by nuclear power to the extent warranted by technical developments, and these methods must be combined with such further hydro power as may prove economical.

In this connection it is worth observing that the advent of nuclear power which is characterised by high fixed costs and low running costs has given rise to an increasing interest in the use of pumped storage. Where topographical conditions are suitable, nuclear power stations can be used at night to provide low-cost energy to pump water into high-level reservoirs from which it can later be released to drive hydro-electric machinery during the hours of maximum power demand. Such a scheme, already under construction on Loch Awe, will provide 400 mW of peak load power for use on the combined systems of the Northern and Southern Boards, and when completed will make an important contribution to the provision of electricity supplies at the minimum cost to the consumer.

ENERGY AND THE LOCATION OF INDUSTRY

Except in the case of some of the electro-process industries, such as those concerned with the production of aluminium and the ferro-alloys, the cost of the energy used in the majority of manufacturing industries represents no more than 2 to 4 per cent. of the overall cost of the end product. Thus the cost of energy is not usually one of the decisive factors in the location of industry. Of greater importance is the cost and availability of suitable labour and raw materials, access to markets for the end product, availability of land and water, and all the other services which contribute towards the establishment of a modern industrial community.

It may be said in fact that while the provision of adequate and reliable supplies of energy—whether as electricity or in some other form—is essential to the establishment of modern industry, such provision will not alone result in the setting up of new industries if the other conditions essential for their success are not favourable.

It is worth while observing that the power-intensive industries have in the past always been sited in areas where hydro-electric power could be developed at attractively low cost. It is for this reason that such industries are to be found in areas well endowed with water power resources such as the Alpine regions of Central Europe, in Norway, in Canada and in the U.S.A. which in the past offered them the opportunity of obtaining power more cheaply than could be obtained from fuel-burning stations.

As the demand for electricity increases, the lowest cost resources of hydro-electric power in the regions where industrial development has been intensive have of necessity to be supplemented by other and more expensive water power resources and these in turn by thermal power. Inevitably the average cost of producing electricity in such regions tends to increase and must in the long run approximate the equivalent cost of thermal power. Hence there has been a trend in recent years for expansion of the electro-process industries to take place in the more remote parts of the world which still offer the opportunity of developing large blocks of hydro-electric power on more favourable terms than those now available in the intensively industrialised regions.

CONCLUSIONS

1. In the past the rise of Scottish industry was based on the availability of ample and cheap supplies of coal. Until the beginning of the present century coal provided virtually the entire energy needs of the country.

2. For nearly fifty years there has been a steady fall in the annual production of Scottish coal—a fall which has been much more marked than that which has occurred in the coalfields of England and Wales.

3. Although the relative contribution made by coal to Scotland's total energy needs has fallen steadily, and this fall must continue in the future, it still provides 75 per cent. of overall requirements.

4. In the changing pattern of energy consumption which has marked the past fifty years the two most notable features are the ever increasing use of imported petroleum and the steady substitution of electricity for the direct use of coal and gas.

5. Future changes in the energy pattern will in the main be determined by economic factors tempered by political considerations—especially those relating to increasing dependence on imported sources of oil and uranium, and to the human and sociological problems arising from changes in the nature and location of employment.

6. Scottish water power at present meets about a quarter of the energy consumed in the form of electricity. Its real contribution to the country's economy is, however, of even greater significance since it performs certain functions which result in an overall reduction of the average cost of electricity to the community. Moreover, since the greater part of the cost of hydro electricity is represented by fixed capital charges on works possessing a long physical life, the relative value of the investment tends to appreciate with any fall in the purchasing power of money. An example of this is provided by the hydro stations in the south of Scotland constructed in the 1930s which today provide electricity at about one-quarter of the cost of the equivalent thermal power.

7. Continuous improvement in efficiency in the use of primary energy—especially coal—has made it possible to achieve a steady increase both in industrial production and in national income without significantly raising the overall consumption of primary energy resources.

8. Over the next ten years it would seem that Scotland's energy requirements will in the main continue to be met by maintaining or even slightly increasing the present level of coal production and by increasing imports of petroleum to the extent necessary to meet the needs of internal transport and in addition fill as much of the gap left by coal production as may be economically justified. The further development of water power will continue, especially in the northern parts of the Highlands, to the extent which may be justified by changing economic circumstances.

9. After 1970 it is reasonable to suppose that the same general pattern will continue, but as time goes on a steadily increasing proportion of the fuel used in the production of electricity will be in the form of imported uranium. The further development of water power is likely to be increasingly concerned with pumped storage schemes.

10. Except in the case of some of the power-intensive industries, notably aluminium,

the cost of energy used in the majority of manufacturing processes is not significant in relation to the overall cost of production. Thus the cost of energy is not usually one of the decisive factors in the location of industry. Of greater importance than the actual cost of energy is the availability of suitable labour, the cost of raw materials and access to markets.

BIBLIOGRAPHY

Annual Reports issued by:
(*a*) South of Scotland Electricity Board.
(*b*) North of Scotland Electricity Board.
(*c*) National Coal Board.
(*d*) Scottish Gas Board.

Digest of Scottish Statistics. April, 1960.

Government White Paper on Nuclear Power Programme, 20th June, 1960.

HENDERSON, J., and ALLAN, C. L. C. (1960). "Energy Resources and Growth of Consumption in Scotland." Proceedings of World Power Conference Sectional Meeting, Madrid, June 1960.

National Institute—Economic Review. July, 1960.

PARKER, Dr. ALBERT (1960). Cantor Lectures. *Journal of the Royal Society of Arts*, April.

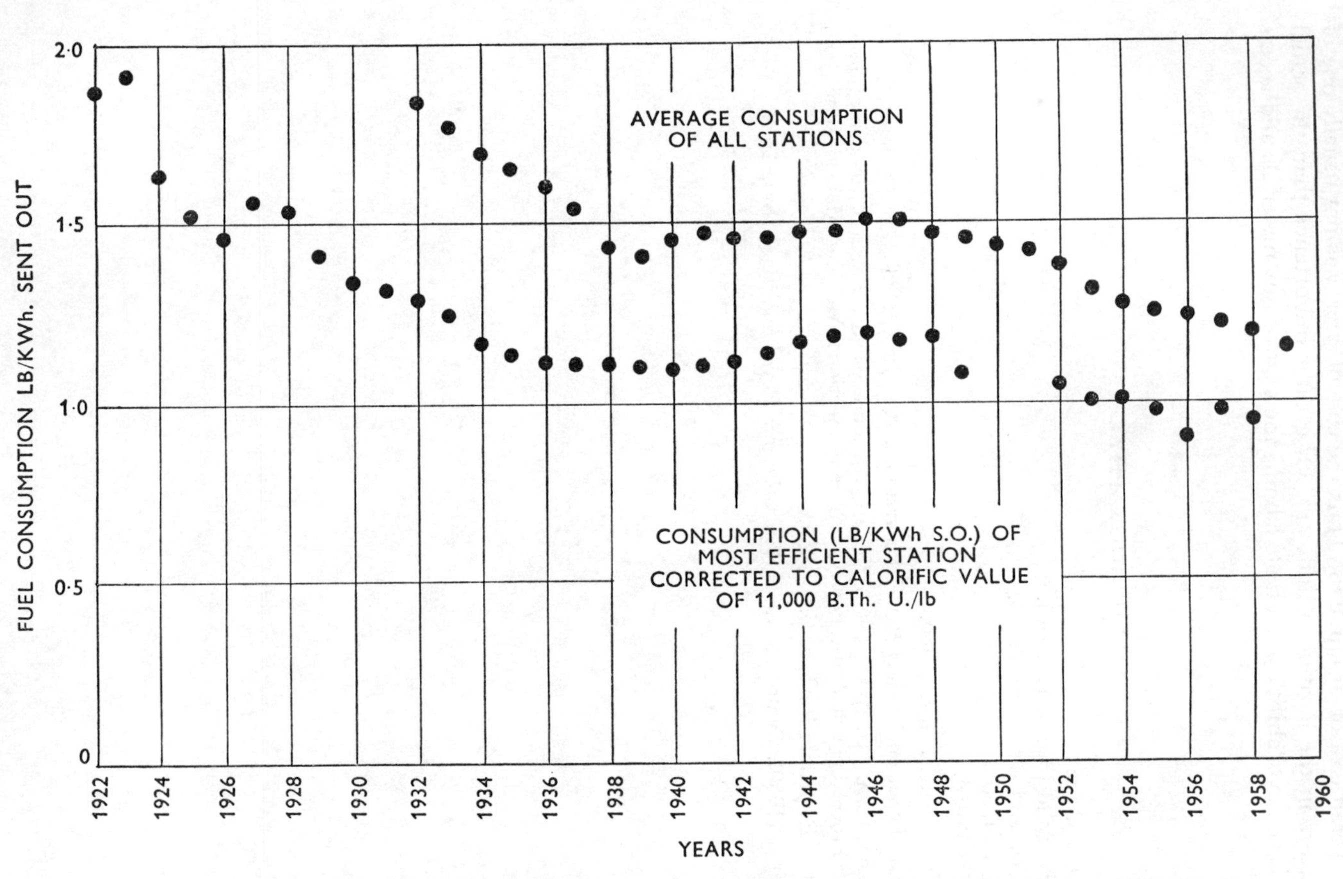

FIG. 1. Steam Power Stations—Great Britain—Coal Consumption per kWh sent out 1922-59 (figures adjusted to uniform calorific value of 11,000 B.Th.U./Lb.)

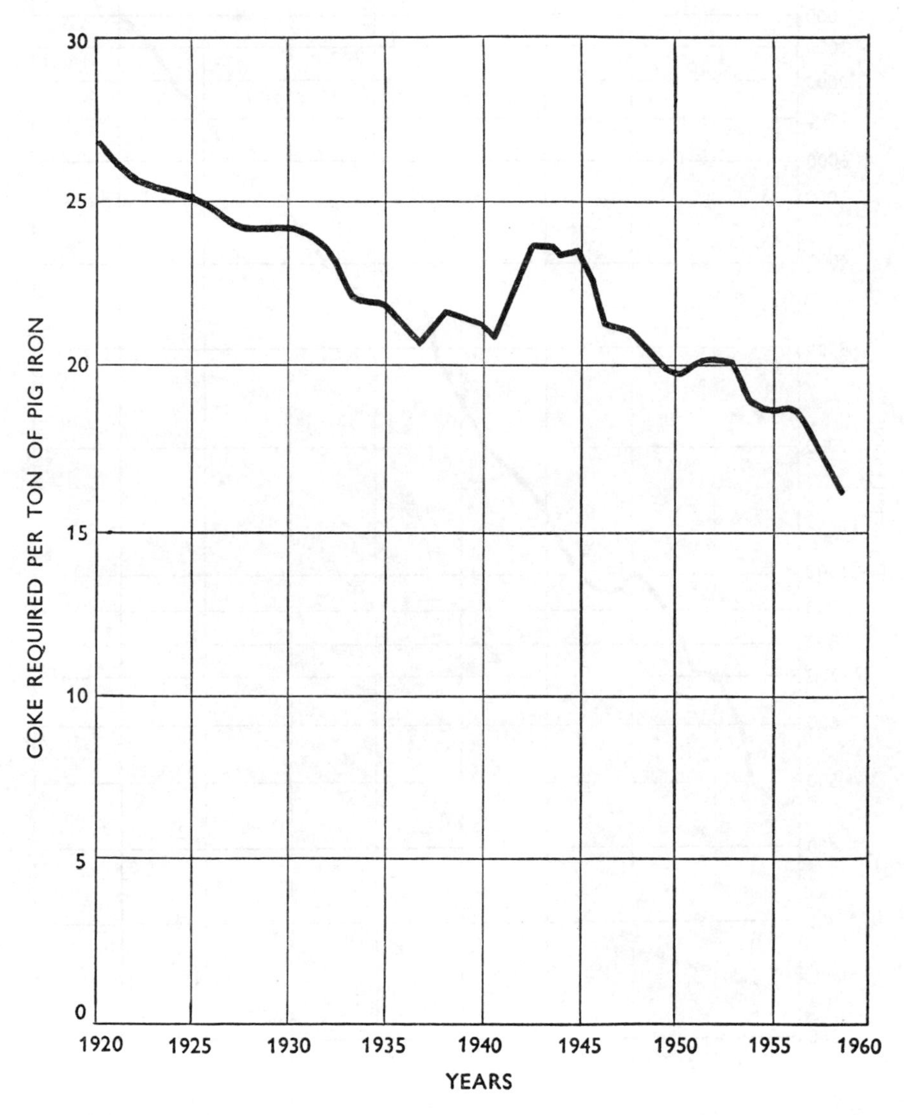

FIG. 2. Coke consumption (cwts.) per ton of pig iron produced Great Britain 1920-59

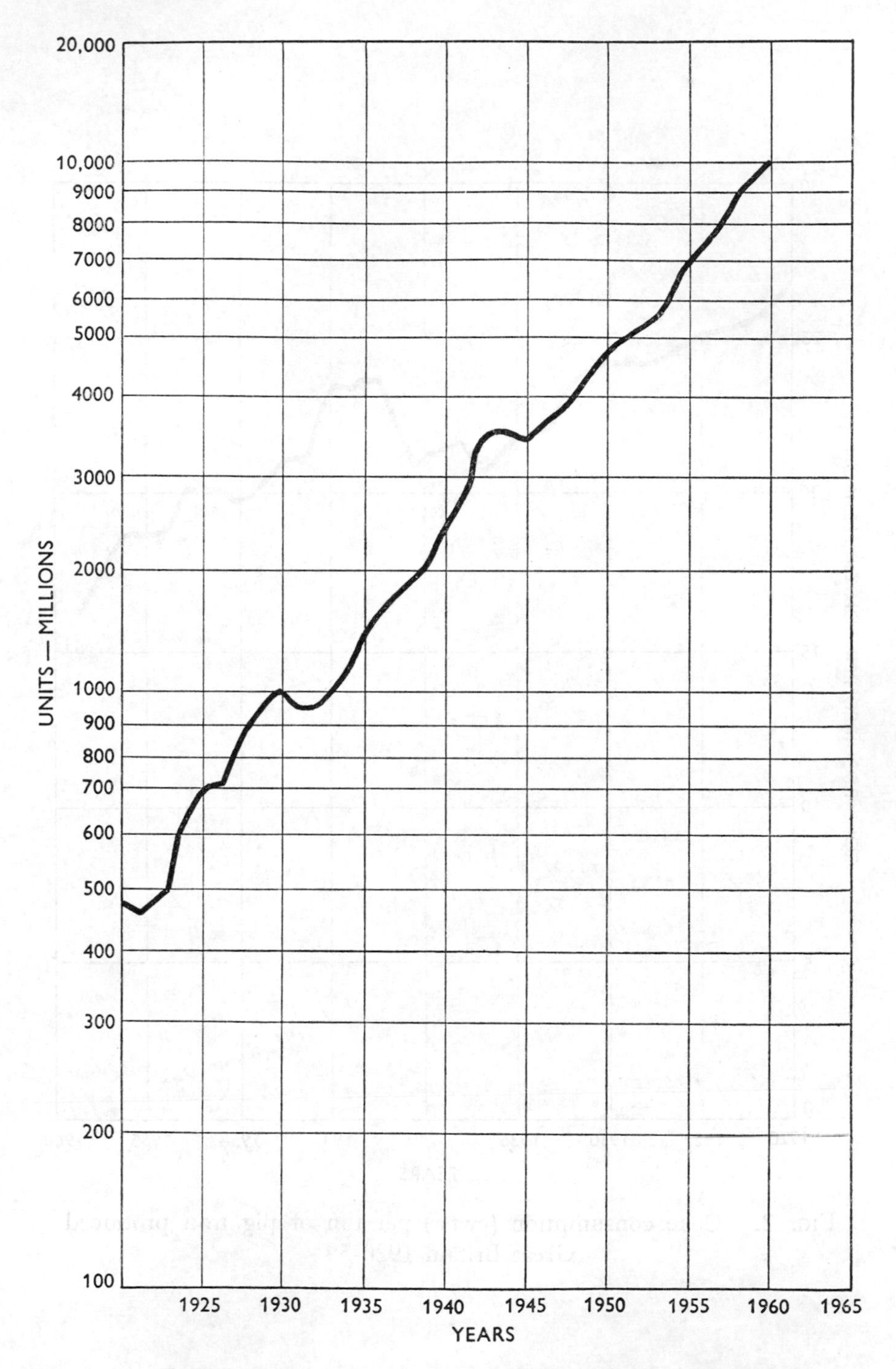

FIG. 3. Growth of Public Supplies of Electricity Scotland 1920-60

Coal and Gas from Coal Mines

E. A. C. CHAMBERLAIN, F.R.S.E., PH.D., D.I.C., B.SC., A.R.C.S., F.R.I.C., F.INST.F.
Divisional Chief Scientist, National Coal Board, Edinburgh

This paper reviews the reserves of coal in Scotland against a background of the estimated requirements of industrial and domestic markets up to 1980. It attempts to discriminate between total reserves and economically workable reserves in the development areas of the Lothians, Fife and Ayrshire; it indicates that the economics of coal production are constantly changing, on the one hand due to competition from alternative fuels and on the other the introduction of new methods of mechanical mining, loading and transport underground.

Major developments in coal utilisation are likely with the generation of electricity during the next twenty years, since it is considered that electrical energy from nuclear sources is unlikely to be strictly competitive with the new thermal stations now being built. In the gas industry the importance of the total gasification of coal is discussed in relation to the overall consumption of coal for gas making and the future availability of solid smokeless fuels to meet the requirements of the Clean Air Act.

For the steel industry, coking coal requirements should be met from indigenous resources.

While the coal industry in Scotland recognises the inherent problems of the next twenty years, it is confident that the basic energy requirements of the country will be met by coal and it has a planned programme of output, development and manpower to meet these requirements. On the subject of natural gas from coal mines, a small but useful contribution of energy is being made available from this source, but no large-scale developments appear likely.

INTRODUCTION

It was the discovery by Abraham Darby, at the beginning of the eighteenth century, that coal could be used as a source of carbon for the reduction of ferruginous ores to iron that led to the industrialisation of Great Britain. By 1700 iron production in Kent and Sussex had declined with the exhaustion of the timber resources of the Weald. The whole of south-east England, which had once been closely wooded, had become bare of trees and suitable only for agriculture or grazing. Contemporary historians record general hardship through lack of fuel and the only power available was from wind and water.[1]

The development of machinery, involving the use of iron, had virtually ceased.

Darby's discovery and the occurrence of coal, iron ore, limestone and green-sand in close proximity in Shropshire began a chain of events that completely changed the course of British history, the life of the people and the face of the countryside.

The ability to produce iron led to the development of machines and thence automatically to the need for energy to drive them. This energy was derived from coal. The consequential use of coal as a source of energy and the fact that it was abundantly available brought about the Industrial Revolution both in England and Scotland. It integrated the economies of both countries with coal, an integration that has existed for over two hundred years. It is only within the last decade that signs of any fundamental change have become apparent; how this change will develop and how fast are questions of paramount importance at the present time. The growing availability of energy, derived from sources other than coal, poses economic and sociological problems of great complexity which tend to overshadow the equally real problems of the economically workable reserves of coal. In a Brains Trust broadcast in December 1958, Sir John Maud, then Secretary to the Ministry of Power, said: "The future of coal is one of those things on which we should not be dogmatic."

With this warning in mind it is permissible to deduce from past facts and present trends the most likely pattern of the coal industry during the next fifteen to twenty years. After 1980, however, deduction tends to become merely prediction, and this is dangerous, for a close study of the literature on coal from the Royal Commission of 1871[2] to the 1950 Plan for Coal[3] fails to reveal a long-term forecast that has, by the event, been proved correct. This is not, of course, surprising. The coal industry is so closely integrated with the economics and politics of the country as a whole that cause and effect cannot be differentiated. The picture becomes even more complex when international relationships are involved. This is amply illustrated if we consider the part played in the national economy by coal exports during the heyday of British economic expansion up to 1914, the period of declining markets due to a variety of factors between 1918 and 1939, and the subsequent inability of the industry effectively to re-enter the export market after 1945.

Equally the sociological aspects of the industry present a complex pattern of cause and effect, profoundly affected by apparently simple and unrelated developments such as human transport facilities. Prior to 1914 the mining communities tended to be locally exclusive with strongly inbred traditions. The development of easier communications has effectively destroyed this insular exclusiveness and has tended to blur local traditions. This sequence of events has had considerable significance in Scotland, for there is little doubt that here mining communities have tended to remain rather more isolated than in England. Local traditions and family ties are more pronounced and the effects of any re-orientation of the mining industry tend to present greater human problems in Scotland than elsewhere, excepting perhaps South Wales.

Both economically and socially the future of the coal-mining industry in Scotland presents problems that must be given consideration outwith overall national considerations. It is not possible in this paper to do more than indicate them in order that they may be discussed and their importance assessed and noted for future action.

COAL PRODUCTION IN SCOTLAND, 1400-1959

Statistical information on coal production in Scotland is available from 1854, when the Home Department began publishing returns made by the coal owners. The Royal Commission on Coal of 1871,[2] however, made estimates from documentary records to 1660 and thence by "extrapolation" back to 1400. The returns from 1854 onwards are shown diagrammatically in Fig. 1. It is sufficient to summarise the estimated outputs before this by stating that by 1660 Scottish output was probably about 200,000 tons per annum and that by 1800 it had reached 1 million tons per annum. Thereafter the increase in use of coal by industry becomes apparent, and during the next hundred years output rose steadily to 33 million tons in 1900 and thirteen years later to the record maximum of 42·5 million tons. Throughout the period 1854 to 1913, Scotland produced between 13 and 15 per cent. of the national output. The graph in Fig. 1 also shows the general decline in output since 1913, the effect of the 1914-18 War, the coal strike of 1921 and the general strike of 1926, the recovery periods between 1933 and 1938, and 1944 and 1948 with the subsequent decline to approximately 18 million tons in 1959, when Scottish output was approximately 10 per cent. of the national output. The break in the curve in 1893, indicating a fall in production from 27 million tons to 22 million tons was caused by a prolonged strike and lock-out at the end of that year which affected all the coalfields of Great Britain. Since 1876 statistics of coal output by counties is available.[4] These have been summarised in terms of the four major producing areas, Lanarkshire, Fife, Ayrshire and Lothians, and expressed as percentages of the total Scottish output in Fig. 2. These curves clearly show the importance of the geographical redistribution of the coal industry that has taken place during the last hundred years between Lanarkshire and the three other areas, but does not indicate the full significance of the decline of the Lanarkshire coalfield in terms of actual tonnage. The peak production year in Lanarkshire was 1911 when 23·5 million tons of coal were produced; this output has fallen to 13 million tons in 1939 and 5·6 million tons in 1959.

GEOLOGICAL CONSIDERATIONS

When discussing Scottish coal production against the national background it must be recognised that geological conditions present greater difficulties to the mining engineer in the Scottish coalfields than in most other British coalfields. In England virtually all coal has been, and still is, won from the Productive Coal Measures; in Scotland more than half the present output is derived from the Limestone series.

Table I

Scottish Coalfield Output in terms of Productive Coal Measures Seams and Limestone Coal Group Seams

Coal Raised

Year	Productive Coal Measures Seams		Limestone Coal Group Seams		Total All Seams
	000 tons	%	000 tons	%	000 tons
1939	16,362	54	14,167	46	30,529
1949	10,626	44	13,427	56	24,053
1959	9,894	42	13,670	58	23,564

Table I gives the percentage coal output obtained from the Productive Coal Measures and the Limestone series for the years 1939, 1949 and 1959. Insufficient data is available to make precise calculations before 1939, but since the Lanarkshire coalfield almost exclusively worked Productive Measures it has been estimated that in the years of

Scottish peak production, 1900-13, about 80 per cent. of Scottish coal came from the Productive Measures. This is important because, in general, the Productive Measures are thicker and cleaner and less geologically disturbed than the Limestone series, and with the exhaustion of the Lanarkshire coalfield Scotland has been forced to produce coal under increasingly difficult and expensive conditions. This is perhaps best illustrated by the fact that the average life of a working section in Scotland is approximately six months, whereas in the major English coalfields the length of life of a section is measured in years. The coincidental problems associated with the Limestone series, variations in coal quality, the application of mechanisation to both coal mining and transport underground, and the need to establish a high percentage of reserve faces, all have a considerable bearing on the economics of the Scottish Division of the National Coal Board.

For the future, of the 13 major developments in course of implementation, 9 are in the Limestone series, 3 in the Productive Coal Measures and 1 (Seafield) in both.* Incidentally all the coking coal produced in Scotland comes from the Limestone series.

COAL RESERVES

It should not be necessary to stress the importance of discriminating between geological reserves and economically workable reserves. Failure thus to discriminate has, however, led to much confusion in the past, more especially as geological reserves consist of proved reserves and estimated "unproven" reserves. Apparently reassuring statements to the effect that Scotland has sufficient coal reserves for the next four hundred years[5] should therefore be subject to the closest scrutiny. In 1902 an estimate of workable coal in proved and unproved reserves was given as[6]:

Proven coal at moderate depths . .	4,634,785,600
Thin seams and deep seams . . .	5,994,327,120
Total	10,629,112,720

The report of the Scottish Coalfields Committee 1944[7] gives the estimated reserves as 7,652 million tons. The reasonable agreement between these two figures, taking into account coal production during the intervening 42 years, is, we believe, purely coincidental for in 1921 the Imperial Mineral Resources Bureau estimated the actual workable reserve of coal in Scotland to be 21,376 million tons[5]. The problem of deciding what are likely to be "economic" reserves is, of course, extremely complex. What may seem economic today may be quite uneconomic tomorrow, and vice versa. The introduction of new forms of energy from nuclear fission, the economics of which are also uncertain, and the growth of the use of petroleum fuels with equally complex economics, coupled with such uncertain factors as international politics, and its own uncertainties of economic reserves, must be considered as well as the possibilities of developing revolutionary mining techniques such as envisaged in a recent paper by B. L. Metcalf[8] (Thornton

* *Limestone series:* Rothes, Bilston Glen, Monktonhall, Valleyfield, Overton, Bedlay, Airth, Cardowan (Seafield).

Productive Measures: Glenochil, Barony, Killoch (Seafield).

Lecture A.M.E.M.E. June 1960). The most realistic assessment of reserves officially available is given in the "Plan for Coal"[3] published in October 1950 by the National Coal Board, and it is advisable that the relevant paragraphs should be quoted at length:

"Much knowledge of the coal measures of Great Britain has been built up over the years. Various estimates of the reserves of coal lying under Great Britain have been made in the past, but then the colliery companies were in separate ownership, data were not always comparable and it was hard to apply the same criteria everywhere. The latest estimate before nationalisation was made in 1946 by the Coal Survey (then under the Department of Scientific and Industrial Research and now under the Board). They considered that there was enough coal to maintain output for 100 years, but that in some places the 'economic reserves' would be exhausted earlier. However, the main importance of the Coal Survey's study was that for the first time an attempt was made to assess the 'economic reserves' by coal types. Since nationalisation the Board have obtained more information as the result of an extensive programme of borings and they have been able to assemble and collate much information formerly available only at scattered points throughout the industry.

"The Board's studies have led them to appraise the earlier estimates anew. They have not sought to evaluate total reserves; what matter are the reserves that can be worked economically. However, to assess the quantity of economically workable reserves is hard: no one can say precisely which are the reserves of coal that can be worked in 100 years' time or more and much more remains to be learned about reserves of coal still unproved.

"The Board have, therefore, expressed their conclusions in general terms. Their first main conclusion is that for many generations ahead there is likely to be no shortage of coal as such below the earth of Great Britain. However, because so much of the best and cheapest has already been mined there will be increasing difficulties in the way of mining the coal economically, and this applies particularly to certain special kinds and qualities of coal, notably those exceptionally well suited for the making of coke required by blast furnaces and foundries. There will for all kinds of coal be a general decline in the quality of the reserves, except for virgin areas still to be exploited. Technical advance and improvements in preparation technique may do something to mitigate the effects, but the hard facts of geology will remain. The cost of mining the special coals is likely to be high and will go higher unless demand for them can be curtailed by changes in the pattern of distribution and utilisation. Though it is unlikely that in the foreseeable future the reserves, even of special coals, will become exhausted, there is likely to be a growing scarcity of special coals which can be produced at a reasonable cost.

"The second main conclusion is that the scope for developing areas of coal as yet untouched is strictly limited. There can be much new development in parts of Scotland. Nevertheless, most of the output will still have to be got from those parts of the coalfields where mining is already concentrated.

"The Scottish coalfields are fortunate in having coal seams of economic importance in the Limestone Coal Group as well as in the Productive Coal Measures. The Fife and Clackmannan field consists of eastern and western synclinal areas, separated by a broad and complex anticlinal area. Large reserves exist in both the Limestone Coal Group and the Productive Coal Measures of the West Fife and Clackmannan syncline, particularly on the eastern flank. Parts of Central Fife have been worked extensively in the past. By far the largest reserves in Scotland, however, lie in the seaward extension of the East

Fife syncline which is no doubt continuous under the Firth of Forth with the Lothians coalfield. Seams in both the Limestone Coal Group and the Productive Coal Measures are well developed, and the undersea workings have so far given no evidence to suggest that the seams deteriorate seawards. It is true that the floor of the old valley of the Forth lies much deeper than the present sea bed and some of the upper coals will be unworkable because of this; that there is a certain amount of igneous intrusion; and that the steep dips on the flank of the syncline may carry the seams down too deep to be worked in the central parts. Nevertheless, the amount of workable reserves within reach of the coastal pits is certainly immense, representing one of the few really rich areas available for extensive exploitation in Britain. This richness is derived, not so much from the horizontal extent of the basin, but from the high proportion of coal in the strata available in the two geological groups.

"In the Lothians the seams on the western fringe have been exhaustively worked, but large reserves—particularly in the Limestone Coal Group—are very attractive and are available over most of the rest of the field. Steep on the flanks of the syncline, over a large central area of the basin, the measures are almost flat. Within the region which may be regarded as proved there is much coal to work, and the measures may extend in the same condition under the sea, where there are undoubtedly very large coal resources.

"On the other hand in the Central coalfield of Scotland the situation is unfavourable. A main cause is that a large area in the middle of the field is practically barren of seams in the Limestone Coal Group where these are concealed beneath the Millstone Grit and the Productive Coal Measures. The Limestone seams are well developed in some of the marginal areas and considerable reserves remain in parts of the field extending from the north-east of Glasgow to Denny-Stirling area and along the eastern margin of the coalfield around Bo'ness, Bathgate, Wilsontown and Carluke. In the north the measures are continuous under the Forth with those of the Clackmannan and West Fife basin. The thick upper coals of the Productive Coal Measures in the main Lanarkshire basin have been almost exhausted, and what is left of them is inaccessible at present owing to the danger from water in the old workings; the present dwindling output is derived mostly from thin seams—some of them very thin. In the shallower Shotts-Armadale basin to the east there are fewer seams, and remaining reserves are small and mainly in thin seams. The once important coal-producing region of Lanarkshire is virtually played out, and the future of the Central Field lies only in the marginal areas of the Limestone Coal Group, notably in those bordering on the Forth.

"In the Ayrshire and Dumfriesshire coalfield the Productive Coal Measures are of most importance, the Limestone coals on the whole being poorly developed in comparison with other Scottish fields. For the most part the reserves lie in scattered districts owing to much dislocation of the field by folding and faulting. One or two areas contain big reserves, including a large virgin field under the cover of Permian rocks in the Mauchline basin, the structure of which is not yet known in detail. The broken-up areas of this coalfield contain coal resources which are by no means unattractive and which in total are important."

Summing up, the National Coal Board are confident that the economic reserves of coal are more than adequate to meet the present planned requirements of slightly less than 20 million tons per annum for the next twenty years. After 1980, however, it would be dangerous to make a prediction in the light of economic changes, competition from oil and the developments in nuclear power. There are, however, indications that by the year 2000 coal output will tend to become restricted by the actual availability of economic reserves irrespective of the demand for coal or the capital available for new sinkings.

It is perhaps of interest to quote from the *Coalfields of Scotland* by R. W. Dron, published in 1902[9], in which it is stated: "on the basis of this estimate, all the proven coal in Scotland will be exhausted by the year 1994 and all the reserve coal will be exhausted by the year 2086. It is of course evident that long before these dates are reached the continued increase of the output will have received a check and that just as the output has gradually increased so also it will gradually diminish. The vital consideration is that within a comparatively short time the mines of Scotland will be unable to supply the necessary coal for the continuance of that increase of the trade and population of the country which has been so marked a feature of the last century. Assuming that the annual increment continues until 1941, when the Scottish output will have reached a total of 40 million tons per annum, there will be sufficient coal left to maintain the output at that rate until the year 2160, but even on this assumption, cheaply worked coal will only last until about the end of the present century".

Of course, Dron's assessments of annual consumption have proved to be nearly twice the actual outputs at the present time. Dron predicted an increasing export market, but he did not foresee the effect of two world wars and nowhere does he mention oil, and it it is unlikely that he even dreamed of power from the atom. It would, however, be more than a coincidence if his errors, through a lack of ability to foretell the future, were cancelled out by his errors in forecasting the economic reserves and the annual output from the Scottish coalfields.

MANPOWER

The present average output per man shift in the Scottish coalfield is 22·5 cwt. and the output for 1960 is expected to be of the order of 18 million tons with a labour force of approximately 72,000. After certain closures, the development of the new sinkings, and the advantages that will occur as a result of increased mechanisation, it is estimated that the output per man shift will increase to at least 27 cwt. by 1980, so that for a continuing output of about 18 million tons per annum the required labour force would lie between 60,000 and 65,000. In 1980 the output of coal from the Scottish Division will be fairly equally divided between the five main producing areas, Lothians, Fife, Alloa, the combined Central Areas and Ayrshire. Thus, while a certain degree of reorientation of the mining community will be necessary, careful planning by the Board, in consultation with the Unions, will ensure a minimum dislocation of family life. Controlled recruitment will obviate any real difficulties of redundancy so that for the foreseeable future the coal industry will continue to offer good labour and career prospects to the community.

THE MARKET FOR COAL

The consumption of Scottish-produced coal under seven main categories for the years 1949-59 is shown graphically in Figs. 3 and 4. These main categories are—Gas, Electricity, Coke Ovens, Railways, Domestic, Export and Bunkers and in total represent approximately 70 per cent. of the total consumption, the remaining 30 per cent. being consumed by General Industry. The overall breakdown, as given in the annual statistical Digest of the Ministry of Power for the years 1957-8-9, is shown in Table II.

TABLE II

Breakdown of Scottish Coal Consumption

	1957 (000 tons)	1958 (000 tons)	1959 (000 tons)
Iron and Steel	1,088	869	769
Engineering and Other Metals	293	284	262
Food, Drink and Tobacco	549	517	518
Chemicals and Allied Industries	504	439	389
Textile, Leather and Cloth	407	386	356
Paper, Printing and Stationery	775	736	733
Bricks, Tiles and Foundry	285	240	201
China, Earth and Glass	125	92	83
Other Industries	294	294	281
Mines, Quarries and Cement	32	26	27
Totals	4,352	3,883	3,619
*Small Establishments	519	494	440
Gas	2,299	2,148	1,959
Electricity	3,048	3,280	3,249
Railways	1,745	1,486	1,343
Coke Ovens	1,829	1,490	1,044
Miners' Coal	497	510	491
Merchants' House Coal	3,533	3,596	3,425
Anthracite	57	59	74
Collieries	905	789	630
Non-industrial miscellaneous	1,482	1,442	1,204
Totals	20,266	19,177	17,478

* Those consuming under 1,000 tons per annum.

In attempting to forecast the future trend of consumption it is convenient to consider separately the seven categories referred to above.

GAS

Since 1951 coal consumption at gas works has fallen steadily from 2·5 million tons to 1·78 million tons in 1959. While this fall is partly due to a decreasing market for town's gas, mainly in the domestic field, the main reason is that gas coke has not been readily saleable and thc gas industry has tended to make more carburetted water gas in order to reduce the coke make. We would have expected a reversal of this trend, with the introduction of smokeless zones and an increasing demand for solid smokeless fuel. Scottish low-rank coals are ideally suitable for the production of reactive solid smokeless fuels in traditional continuous vertical retorts and the potential demand for such fuels in fact exceeds the carbonisation capacity of the Scottish Gas Board. Unfortunately the economics of solid smokeless fuel production are directly controlled by the sale of the gas produced in making them. If the gas cannot be sold, the cost of the solid smokeless fuel is increased to a point when it is no longer competitive with the other alternative domestic fuels, electricity or oil. Moreover, because of difficulties in the coke market during the early 1950s the Gas Board were led to concentrate on gas production and decided on a policy of total gasification, resulting in the erection of the Lurgi plant at Westfield. In a paper to the Institution of Gas Engineers in May 1960,[10] T. S. Ricketts, the Chief Engineer of the Scottish Gas Board, estimates that by 1964 almost half of the gas produced by the Gas Board in Scotland will come from the Lurgi plant. Since all the coal required for the Lurgi plant will be obtained from the associated opencast site, the quantity of deep-mined coal required by the gas industry by the middle sixties is likely to be half the 1959-60 consumption, or approximately 1 million tons per annum. It is considered that coal consumption will continue at this level of 1 million tons for the planned future of up to 1980, but three modifying factors must be considered:

(1) The need to produce solid smokeless fuels, to meet the requirement of the Clean Air Act.
(2) A significant increase in the industrial use of town's gas as a supplement or alternative to oil in clean air zones.
(3) A continued decline in the domestic use of town's gas.

Factors (1) and (2) will tend to increase coal consumption and (3) to reduce it. It must be recorded, however, that suitable coals, in the quantity required, are available to the Gas Industry for the production of premium quality smokeless fuels.

The reduction in the carbonisation of deep-mined coal by complete gas-making process will in effect mean a reduction in coke production by the Gas Industry from approximately 770,000 tons in 1959 to 400,000 tons in 1965.

Electricity

Between 1950 and 1959 the coal consumption for electricity generation has risen steadily from 2·4 million tons to 3·3 million tons. While undoubtedly nuclear energy will contribute significantly to the increasing use of electricity, the present position appears to be that while nuclear power stations can operate competitively with coal-fired stations, the initial capital cost is some three times as great. This fact[11] has led to a cutting back of the nuclear power programme, with a corresponding increase in the thermal power programme. In Scotland this could mean a steady increase in the use of coal for electricity generation estimated at 6 million tons by 1970 and 8 million tons by 1980. Should this rate of increase be maintained we may expect a coal demand for electricity generation of between 10 million and 12 million tons per annum by the year 2000. We must, however, be prepared for major developments in nuclear engineering and even the direct conversion of nuclear energy to electricity. On the other hand there should be increased efficiency in the use of coal for electricity generation and even the direct conversion of heat energy to electricity. This would we expect improve the competitive position of coal so that it is difficult to predict coal requirements for electricity generation after 1980.

Coke Ovens

Like the coal industry, the steel industry closely reflects the prosperity of the country as a whole and if, as we anticipate, there is a steady rise in living standards in Scotland there will be a corresponding rise in steel production. This, however, may not mean an equivalent increase in the coal required by the steel industry. There has, for example, been a spectacular improvement during the last twenty years in the efficiency of iron production in terms of coke consumption per ton of pig iron produced, as the figures in Table III indicate.

TABLE III

Consumption of Coke in Blast Furnaces

(Cwt. of coke per ton of pig iron produced)

	Great Britain Average					Scotland
	1938	1956	1957	1958	1959	1959
Coke	22·6	19·7	19·0	17·9	16·8	14·53

It is also possible that the role of coal in iron production may become limited to its use as a source of carbon, for the reduction of oxide ores and the consumption of blast furnace coke for heat production may diminish significantly. These are however speculations, and while good coking coals for the production of coke are available, steel production in Scotland is likely to follow the basically traditional processes. Scottish coal consumption in coke ovens in Scotland in 1959 was 1·03 million tons and this is expected to rise to 3 million tons by 1970 and thereafter remain at this level for the plannable future. While the Coal Board will be able to meet this demand for coking coal, developments in the Iron and Steel Industry are proceeding on the use of weakly coking coals for blast furnace coke production, and the possible use of carbon prepared by the fluidised carbonisation of low-rank non-coking coals is also an important possibility. The successful outcome of these experiments should enable greater utilisation of the more easily available low-rank coals, with advantage to both the Steel Industry and the National Coal Board. It would also enable the release of the better quality coking coals for foundry coke production on which the light castings industry of the Falkirk area depends.

RAILWAYS

The general policy of British Railways to replace steam traction by diesel and electric traction is well known. Scottish coal consumption by the Railways has shown a steady decline since 1950, when the consumption was just under 2·4 million tons per annum to slightly over 1 million tons per annum in 1959. The expected future requirements of the Railways are 0·5 million tons in 1970 and 0·25 million tons in 1980 and thereafter a continued fall so that by the year 2000 virtually no coal will be used by them, at least for traction purposes.

DOMESTIC COAL CONSUMPTION

An assessment of the demand for coal in the domestic market is complicated by the fact that we do not know the rate at which the Clean Air Act is likely to be implemented, for this in turn tends to be unpredictable at the present time because the availability of solid smokeless fuels cannot be forecast accurately.

Up to 1939 domestic consumption had steadily risen to nearly 5 million tons per annum. The restriction, or rather allocation, of coal to the domestic market which continued until 1959 pegged consumption of raw coal at about 3·5 million tons per annum. If we could ignore the effect of the Clean Air Act we would have anticipated a slow, general decline in the use of raw coal for domestic heating; rising standards of living and a narrowing of the price differential between coal and the refined, "switched" fuels, gas and electricity, would indicate such a trend. To some extent, however, this trend would have been counterbalanced by the increased number of houses and the traditional preference for the open fire. The Clean Air Act, however, must accelerate the decline in the use of domestic bituminous coal at a rate which will be determined by the increased use of smokeless fuels, solid, gaseous, liquid and electricity. The most important factor, however, in this rate of decline is likely to be the availability of solid smokeless fuels made from coal. At the present time the only manufactured solid smokeless fuel produced in Scotland is gas coke, apart from a small quantity of paraffin coke, and we have already commented on the policy of the Gas Board to adopt complete gasification with the consequent decrease in the availability of gas coke. The Coal Board are urgently examining the possibility of producing smokeless fuels, and indeed this subject has been constantly under review since 1948. It has been reluctantly concluded that traditional methods of producing smokeless fuels by normal and low temperature carbonisation processes can only be economically acceptable if there is a market for the surplus gas produced. Up to the present it has not been possible to resolve this economic problem. New developments by the National Coal Board's Research Department at Stoke Orchard should enable the economics of solid smokeless fuel production to become independent of a market for surplus gas. The new process is suitable for Scottish coals, and if the pilot-scale plant at present being built at Birch Coppice is successful it should be possible for the National Coal Board to produce smokeless fuel from bituminous coal that would normally be supplied to the domestic market. In addition, research work on the design of domestic appliances to burn bituminous coal smokelessly may well prove successful. This would mean that the demand for coal in the domestic market, either processed or unprocessed, is likely to remain near its present level for the next ten years. The growing availability of electricity from the new stations at Kincardine and later in the Lothians, the increased use of town's gas from the Lurgi Plant at Westfield and to a smaller extent the use of oil by the higher-income groups will inevitably bring about a decline in the direct use of coal for domestic purposes so that we anticiptae by 1980 the domestic consumption of raw coal will have fallen to about 2 million tons per annum and to half this figure by the end of this century.

Export and Bunkers

The general recession in the use of coal is world wide and the export market for general purpose coals is restricted and highly competitive. Special difficulties exist when certain countries sell coal at less than cost price in order to obtain foreign currency. Scotland does not produce sufficient coals of a special type such as coking coal or anthracite to develop and maintain an effective export market for these qualities.

For bunkers, coal is used mainly in the smaller coastwise traffic and the fishing fleets. Both of these users are gradually changing to oil firing and the use of coal for bunkers will decline. In spite of the difficulties, the National Coal Board expect to be able to increase the export of coal from 0·5 million tons in 1959 to 1 million tons by 1970 and thereafter to maintain this level.

General Industry

If we exclude cement and ceramics from the list of general industry, the fuel cost element in the total make-up of the cost of manufactured goods lies between 2 and 3 per cent. This figure has remained constant since the beginning of the century, for while fuel costs have risen, raw materials and labour costs have risen proportionately, the low cost of fuel in the overall cost partly explains the reluctance of industrialists to invest capital for the the modernisation and improvement in the efficiency of fuel burning equipment. It also suggests that convenience and lower labour cost will exert an increasingly greater influence when an industrialist has to decide what fuel he should use. The convenience and lower associated labour cost of other fuels are particularly important to the small consumer using up to 50 tons of coal a week, especially in districts that are likely to be declared smokeless zones. While it is possible to have fully-automatic coal burning installations which will burn bituminous coal smokelessly and dispose of the ash mechanically, it is relatively more difficult and more expensive to do so in small installations, though we anticipate that these problems will be solved by the research work that is at present being carried out by the manufacturers of appliances and the British Coal Utilisation Research Association.

While for small installations the tendency in industry will be to use refined fuels such as oil, gas and electricity, in large installations coal will remain strongly competitive with clearly defined advantages.

For non-manufacturing purposes, such as large institutional heating in hospitals and schools, fully automatic coal-burning boilers have significant advantages over oil. In such instances and also for large-scale process-steam raising, as for example in the papermaking industry, coal can more than hold its own against oil competition. We must anticipate a decline in the use of coal in small units consuming 500 tons per annum and less, but a maintained market for consumptions larger than 500 tons per annum. Overall it is expected that coal sales to general industry will fall from the present figure of 5 million tons in 1959 to 3 million tons in 1980.

CONCLUSION

The Coal Industry in Scotland fully recognises the inherent problems of the next twenty years, but it is confident that the basic energy requirements of the country will be met by coal. The Coal Board has a planned programme of output, development and manpower to meet its commitments. The nature of coal mining, however, imposes difficulties in that an extractive industry cannot be as flexible as a manufacturing industry and coal production cannot quickly be changed to meet a fluctuating demand. We must accept the difficulties that arise from this fact and avoid regarding these difficulties as crises. They will arise from time to time and must be regarded as a challenge to rather than a criticism of the management of the industry.

Natural Gas from Coal Mines

Natural gas, firedamp or methane is commonly associated with coal mining. Normally the quantity of gas emitted into the ventilation system of a mine is small and in Scotland there are only a few pits where the drainage of methane in advance of coal working is either practical or necessary.

The first methane drainage installation in Scotland was at Cardowan, near Steppes, to the north-east of Glasgow. This has been in operation since December 1958, and the daily yield now is approximately 250,000 cu. ft. of methane. The gas is supplied by pipe-line to the Provan Gas Works of the Scottish Gas Board, where it is absorbed into the normal town gas supply. A second installation is at present under construction at Valleyfield Colliery in West Fife to the east of Kincardine Bridge. Here it is expected that the yield will be approximately 750,000 cu. ft. of methane a day. This gas will be used by the Scottish Gas Board either to enrich the Lurgi gas produced at Westfield or by reforming at Dunfermline Gas Works as a primary source of town's gas supply. Other methane drainage schemes have been examined, but it does not appear likely that further installations will be made in the foreseeable future.

The general position regarding natural gas from coal mines as a source of power in Scotland is that while it can make a useful contribution to the normal town gas supply equivalent to the carbonisation of about 70 tons of coal per day or 30 tons in complete gasification processes, it does not seem likely that natural gas drained from the mines will provide a major source of energy to the Scottish economy.

The same would appear to apply to natural gas bores for, in spite of careful exploration, only one useful source of supply at Cousland in the Lothians has been found. Like the gas from Cardowan and Valleyfield, the gas from Cousland is being used to supplement the town's gas supply. It has, however, been speculated from geological considerations that natural gas should occur in quantity in the vicinity of Glasgow and that this might be tapped by deep bores should the economic climate become favourable. At the present time, however, the cost of proving the existence of natural gas by deep boring is considered to be prohibitive.

REFERENCES

1. TREVELYAN, G. M. *History of England*, 2nd Ed. p. 528.
2. Report of the Commission to enquire into the several matters relative to coal in the U.K., 27th July 1871.
3. Plan for Coal, October 1950, issued by the National Coal Board.
4. (*a*) Coal Owners of Scotland—Output of coal raised from mines under the Coal Mines Act, as given in the Annual Reports of H.M. Inspector of Mines.
   (*b*) Outputs quoted by the Marketing Department of the National Coal Board, Scottish Division.
5. Imperial Mineral Resources Bureau, published in 1921.
6. DRON, R. W. (1902). *The Coalfields of Scotland*, p. 331. London: Blackie & Sons Ltd.

7. Report of Scottish Coalfields Committee, 1944, p. 100. H.M.S.O.
8. Thornton Lecture—Association of Mining, Electrical and Mechanical Engineers, June 1960.
9. Dron, R. W. *The Coalfields of Scotland*, loc. cit., p. 333.
10. Ricketts, T. S. *The Westfield High Pressure Coal Gasification Plant*. Inst. Gas Engineers, Publication 567.
11. *The Times* of London, issued 28th June 1960.

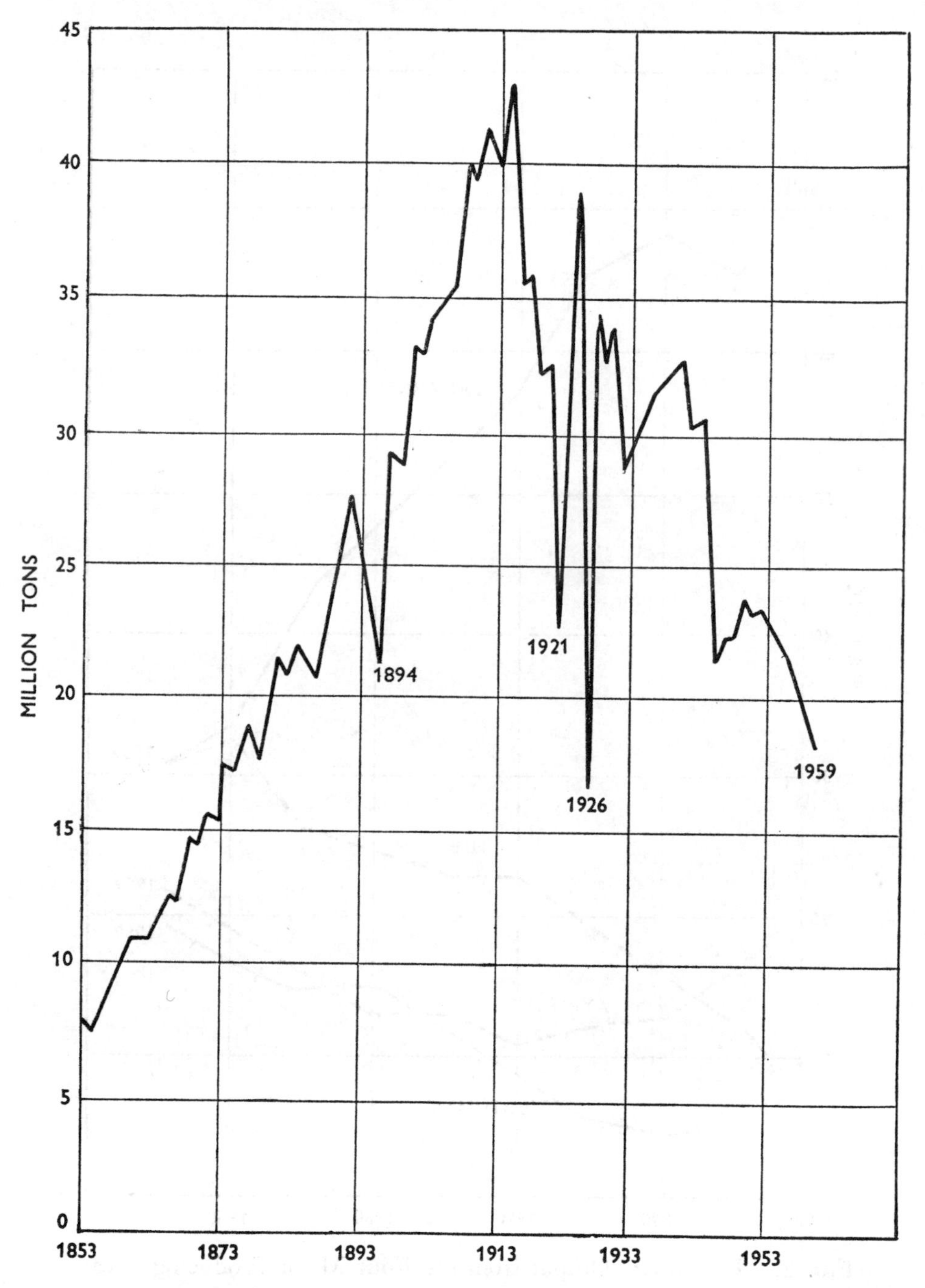

FIG. 1. Scottish Coal Saleable Output 1854-1959

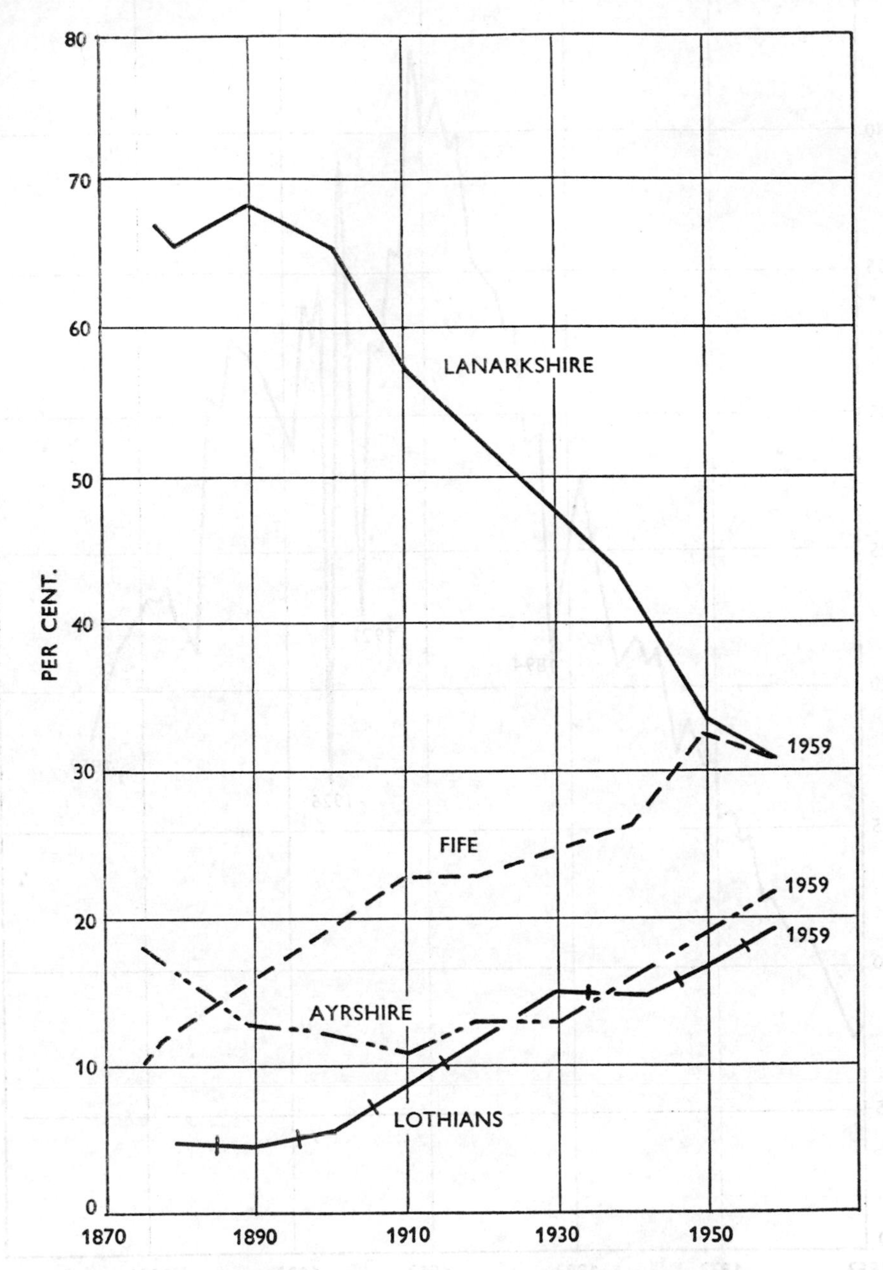

FIG. 2. Percentage Output from the Four Major Producing Areas

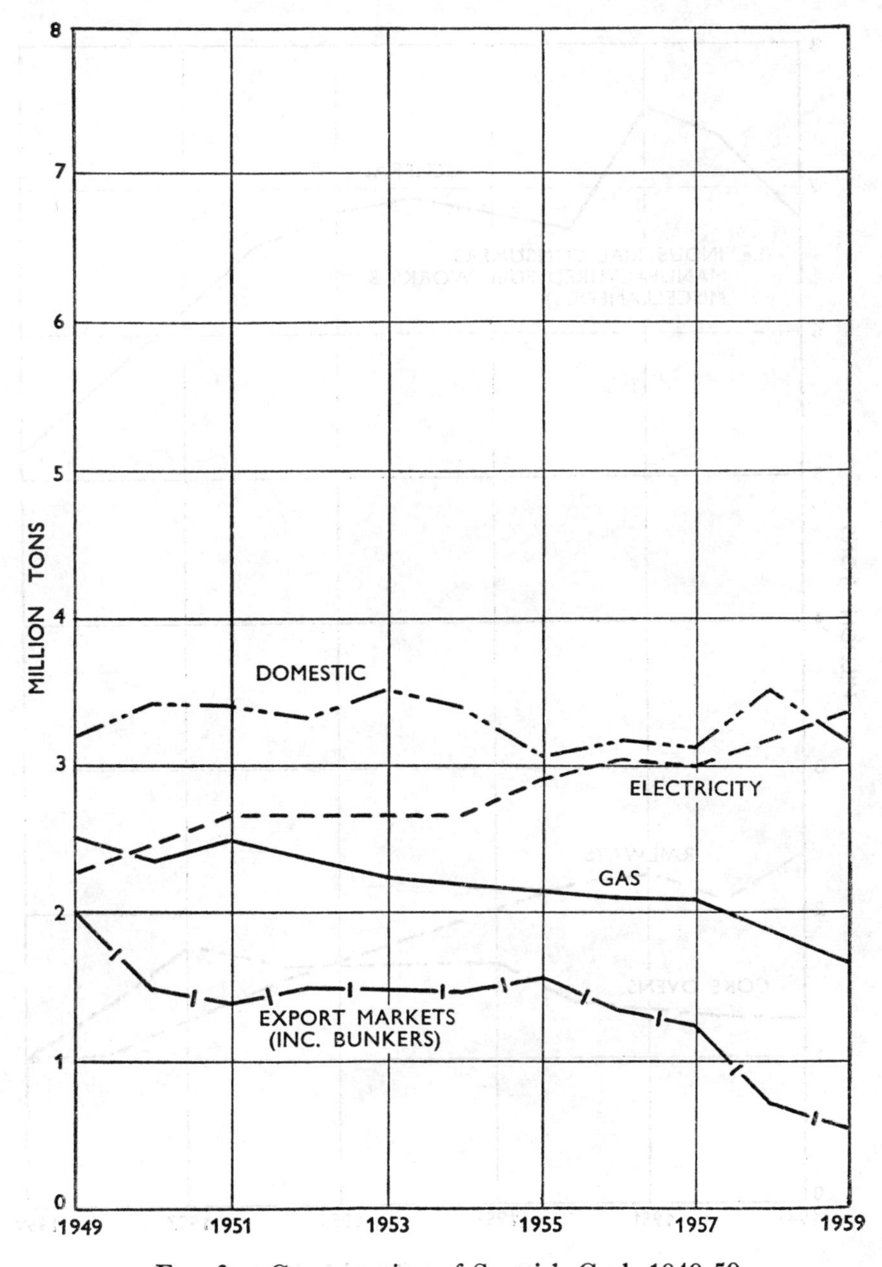

FIG. 3. Consumption of Scottish Coal, 1949-59

(From Marketing Department Records of The National Coal Board Scottish Division)

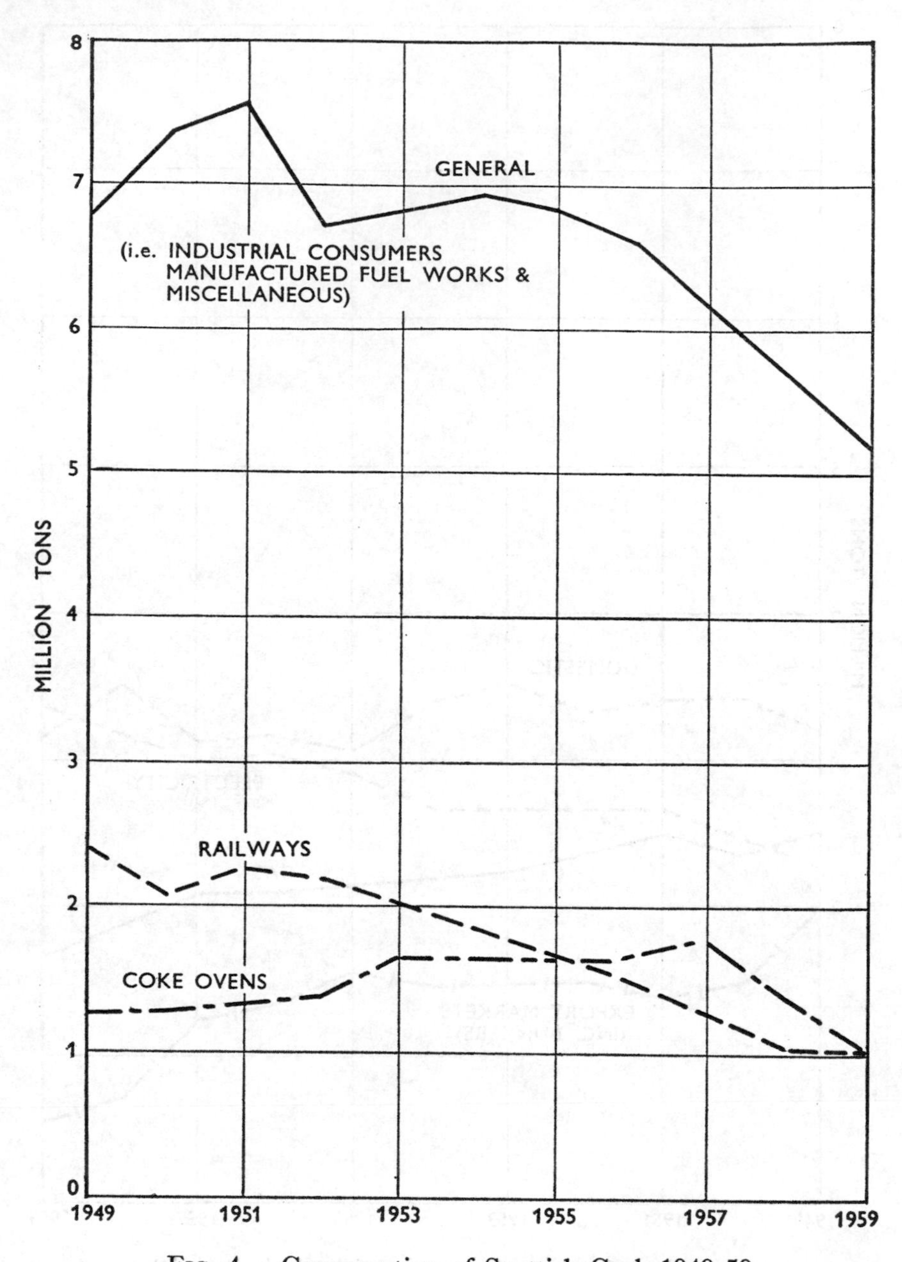

FIG. 4. Consumption of Scottish Coal, 1949-59

(From Marketing Department Records of The National Coal Board Scottish Division)

Natural Gas and Manufactured Gas

D. C. ELGIN, A.M.INST.MECH.E., A.M.INST.GAS E.

Development Engineer, Scottish Gas Board, Edinburgh

The development programme of the Scottish Gas Board envisages a revolutionary change in the approach to gas manufacture.

Conventional gasmaking has required the use of selected coals and the practice of manufacturing gas locally in relatively small units has limited the possible economies.

Linkage of small units to larger units has been carried out as far as has been possible economically.

Now a completely new approach has been adopted. All possible sources of surplus gas, coal normally unsuitable for gas manufacture; oil refinery surplus products, have been investigated. A supergrid about 140 miles long is under construction in Central Scotland; when completed the grid will supply undertakings as far apart as Montrose and Ayr. The grid will operate at high pressure; it will collect and distribute gas from a number of new sources including:

The Lurgi Pressure Gasification Plant being erected by the Board to gasify coal of high inert content from the Westfield opencast mine.

Methane from Cardowan Colliery, Lanarkshire, and possibly Valleyfield Colliery, Fife.

Refinery gas from Grangemouth.

Coke oven gas from Colville's Clyde Ironworks and Ravenscraig Steelworks; Bairds and Scottish Steel Limited, Gartsherrie Ironworks; National Coal Board, Dumbreck Coke Ovens.

The natural gas reserves in Scotland have been investigated. Gas from Cousland, Midlothian, has been distributed for about three years. The Cousland structure may be used as underground storage from the supergrid.

Costs at conventional works have been reduced. Plant has been modernised and technical control increased. "Light virgin naphtha" has replaced gas oil for enriching water gas; liquefied petroleum gases are being used to meet winter peaks.

The search for new methods continues.

In 1949 the Scottish Gas Board were made responsible under the Gas Act for providing an efficient gas supply throughout Scotland. They took over from local authorities and private companies a total of 196 gasworks which had been developed to meet local demands for gas in all the cities, towns and main villages of Scotland.

At most of the works taken over the basic method of gas production was by carbonisation of semi-bituminous coals, but the efficiency and cost varied widely from place to place. The small works with horizontal retorts were particularly expensive to run since labour requirements were high and the overall efficiency of gas production relatively low; in many cases also these works were in isolated positions and the cost of delivering coal was particularly high.

In the first few years after nationalisation the cost of producing gas for use by a number of these smaller communities was reduced considerably by interlinking them with larger and more efficient works. In these cases the local works were shut down and, by this method, the number of gasworks in operation in Scotland was reduced to 144 by the end of 1956. At the same time efforts were made to reduce the cost of gas production at the larger works; more modern and efficient carbonising plants were installed and technical control was increased. Due to interlinkage these economies were shared with many of the smaller places.

But despite these efforts the average cost of gas production continued to increase rapidly due to the steady rise in the price of the type of coal required for conventional gasmaking and also in the cost of manpower.

While conventional carbonisation of deep-mined coal remained the predominant source of gas supply, increases in coal prices and the quality of coal available were primary factors in the cost of gas production. Carbonisation can be carried out successfully only with coals containing sufficient volatile hydrocarbons to give a good gas yield on heating and capable of producing a strong coke with a reasonably low ash content. These properties are found in coals of groups 500 and 600 (in terms of the National Coal Board coal classification code). These coals are in demand by the iron and steel industry for the production of metallurgical coke; they command a high price relative to industrial and domestic coals and are in short supply. In Scotland, in fact, insufficient of these coals are available to satisfy all requirements and supplies to Scottish gasworks include large quantities of low-rank coals (in groups 700, 800 and 900) which show little or no tendency to "cake" during carbonisation. Although the coke produced from these coals is extremely reactive and is an excellent smokeless fuel for the domestic open fire, the proportion of small coke and "fines" (breeze) produced is relatively high; this affects adversely the overall revenue from coke sales and tends to increase the cost of gas production. Table I (which appears in the Appendix) shows the tonnages of various classes of coal (grouped in accordance with the National Coal Board classification code) received by the Scottish gas industry in 1959-60; the high proportion of weakly caking coals (groups 700, 800 and 900) will be noted.

It became evident that the various factors constantly operating to increase the cost of gas production could be counteracted only by bold and far-reaching changes. Two lines of approach appeared to offer attractive possibilities:

(i) further integration on a large and widespread scale in order to centralise gas production as far as possible on large works where the highest possible thermal efficiencies and the most advantageous use of manpower could be achieved;
(ii) exploration of every possible source of surplus gas or cheap fuel suitable for gas production in order to reduce dependence on a narrow range of high-priced coals.

During 1956 a comprehensive integration plan was drawn up. This included the construction of two major gas grids in Central Scotland; the West of Scotland gas grid was designed to serve Glasgow and Renfrewshire together with parts of Ayrshire and Lanarkshire; the East of Scotland grid covered the counties of Fife, Perthshire, Angus and Kinross-shire and also extended into Kincardineshire. It was envisaged that a total of 83 works would be shut down, following the provision of bulk supplies during the ten year period 1957-67. Undoubtedly the resulting centralisation of gas manufacture in itself would have produced worthwhile economies. About the same time, however, the Scottish Gas Board commenced investigations into the possibility of producing gas from the deposits of low-rank coal at Westfield on the borders of Fife and Kinross-shire. A rapid but detailed study showed that, provided long-term supplies of Westfield coal could be guaranteed at a satisfactory price, substantial economies, relative to orthodox gasmaking plant, could be achieved by gasifying this coal completely by the Lurgi high-pressure process. An agreement covering supplies of Westfield coal for a period of 20 years (from the date of first coal deliveries) was concluded in November 1957, and during February 1958 the Scottish Gas Board approved the erection of a major works at Westfield on a site adjacent to the opencast workings. Apart from the basic savings resulting from the complete conversion of low-grade coal into gas, an important feature of the Lurgi process is that the gas produced is available at high pressures. This means that Lurgi gas can be transmitted over comparatively long distances and in quite small diameter pipe-lines without further compression. The conception of a large pressure gasification plant close to the Westfield coal deposits therefore included the provision of a high-pressure "supergrid", 140 miles long and designed to supply Lurgi gas to Glasgow, Dundee, Perth and other places *en route* from Westfield. In effect, the supergrid will act as a link between the two sections (West of Scotland grid and East of Scotland grid) envisaged in the preliminary plans drawn up in 1956, thus forming a unified Central Scotland gas grid supplying places as far apart as Ayr in the south-west and Montrose in the north-east. The proposed extent of the supergrid and subsidiary mains systems up to 1966 is shown on the attached grid map which also indicates the progress made in this work to date. The supergrid will be commissioned at high pressure when the first stage of the Westfield works is ready for operation towards the end of this year. In order to meet this commissioning date an extremely fast rate of mainlaying has been necessary. Work on the grid was commenced during 1958 and the important section between Westfield works and Coatbridge is already complete; this includes the difficult underwater crossing over the bed of the River Forth near Airth which was completed successfully in November 1959 and is the longest river crossing by a gas main to be undertaken in Britain.

By the end of this year the section of grid heading north-east to Dundee will be completed up to the south bank of the River Tay; the crossing of the River Tay by a two-mile long pipe-line over the Tay railway bridge will be undertaken during 1961. The section of supergrid from Kilmarnock to Ayr is also under construction this year. This section will transmit supplementary supplies of gas from Kilmarnock gasworks to Ayr to meet rapidly expanding industrial demand there, pending completion of the Coatbridge to Kilmarnock section of the supergrid. The total length of supergrid completed by the end of this year will be about 80 miles.

Although Westfield is the most spectacular and novel of the new sources of gas to be brought into use by the Scottish Gas Board, a number of other important alternatives to conventional carbonisation have been found and are incorporated in the grid plans.

These include the following:

(i) Drainage gas from Cardowan colliery, Lanarkshire and Valleyfield colliery, Fife;
(ii) Refinery tail gas from Grangemouth refinery;
(iii) Additional coke-oven gas from
(*a*) Colvilles Limited: Clyde Ironworks,
(*b*) Colvilles Limited: Ravenscraig Steelworks,
(*c*) Bairds and Scottish Steel Limited: Gartsherrie Ironworks,
(*d*) The National Coal Board (Scottish Division): Dumbreck Coke Ovens.

A further important and interesting natural resource in the grid area is the natural gas well at Cousland in Midlothian.

The effect of the new developments on the overall pattern of gas supply in Scotland will be seen from Table II, which shows the progressive reduction in the numbers of works in the smaller size groups as a result of integration and rapid centralisation on larger units up to 1966. The original rate of closure envisaged in 1956, before the decision to proceed with Westfield, has been accelerated and it is now expected that between 1956 and 1966 a total of 107 uneconomic works will have been shut down. The total number of works remaining in operation after 1966 will be 49. Of these only 7 (the Westfield pressure gasification works; four large conventional gasworks at Granton, Edinburgh, at Provan and Tradeston in Glasgow and at Dumbarton; two coke oven-gas purification stations at Coatbridge and Uddingston) will remain in operation in the central industrial area; these will supply over 90 per cent. of the total gas demand for the whole of Scotland. With the exception of Aberdeen, the other 42 works in operation will be at small and isolated places, most of them in the north of Scotland (including the islands) and in the south-west, which are outside the range of economic linkage. Long transport hauls to these places inflate considerably the cost of gas production; due to their small size, overheads and labour costs tend to be high. Undertakings of this kind are a particular source of concern to the Scottish Gas Board since they believe strongly that these isolated communities should be able to enjoy the amenities of a modern and efficient gas supply at reasonable cost. For this reason the high costs in uneconomic undertakings are spread over the Area, through the medium of a uniform tariff structure. It can be expected, however, that with the existing gasmaking plant at these places costs will increase rapidly as coal and labour charges continue to rise and as plant becomes due for major repair and replacement. Alternative means of gas supply for these places is now being investigated as a matter of urgency. A promising possibility may be the installation of small butane or propane storage installations. These gases could be delivered to the works by lorry from Grangemouth refinery and stored in liquid form; before distribution through the mains system to customers the butane or propane would be blended with air to give a gas reasonably comparable with coal gas.

In total the new sources of gas supply which are being developed are capable of providing gas equivalent to about 40 per cent. of the total requirements for Scotland. The consequent reduction in the quantity of deep-mined coal carbonised may be up to 1,000,000 tons.

The Central Scotland gas grid and the other fundamental changes which have been made in the Scottish gas industry commencing only three years ago are among the latest developments in the British fuel industries. The Scottish Gas Board have been complimented in the technical Press and also by the national Press for the extent and diversity of their efforts to reduce costs and for the work they have done in adopting so many new processes for use under British conditions for the first time. In the following outline of the main developments and possibilities reference is made particularly to special problems which have had to be overcome in order to make the best possible use of the available resources and to the probable effects on the future fuel position.

WESTFIELD

Westfield lies on the borders of Fife and Kinross-shire to the north of the main coalfield of West Fife and just south of the Ochil Fault. It is estimated that the workable coal reserve there is more than 20 million tons. The coal occurs in four main seams within about 800 ft. of the surface. The seams each consist of a number of coal "leaves" of various thicknesses separated by "partings" of clay and dirt. The National Coal Board, Opencast Executive, will work this deposit by excavation and have built a washery for the preparation of clean single coals ($\frac{1}{2}$ in. to 1 in.) with a calorific value of just over 10,000 British Thermal Units a pound gross.

The Scottish Gas Board proposed originally to purchase from the National Coal Board unwashed coal containing over 40 per cent. of ash and moisture and having a calorific value of only about 7,260 British Thermal Units a pound. The initial agreement between the two Boards was on this basis and the plant installed at the new Westfield works is capable of producing gas from fuel of this extremely low quality. After further consideration and discussion with the National Coal Board, however, it was agreed that mutual advantages would be obtained if the basis of the contract were altered to allow for the supply of a uniformly sized ($\frac{1}{2}$ in. to 1 in.) mixture of washed coal and "middlings" comprising carbonaceous shale and ash discarded from the washery. The ash and moisture content of this mixture would be about 30 per cent. and the calorific value about 8,600 British Thermal Units a pound. This coal would still be unsuitable for gasmaking by conventional methods, but a quality more consistent than that of the unwashed coal could be maintained.

Due to the high inert content of the coal, it was considered essential for the proposed gasmaking plant to be situated as near as possible to the opencast coal site. After extremely careful investigation a site adjacent to the coal workings was selected.

The gas production plant at Westfield is based on the Lurgi pressure gasification process. This is a large-scale complete gasification system originally evolved in Germany in the 1930s for the purpose of making, from "brown coal", gas suitable for the synthesis of petroleum. The fundamental principle of the process is that the coal is caused to react with a carefully controlled mixture of oxygen and superheated steam under very high presssure (about 25 atmospheres). The oxygen in reaction with the carbon in the coal forms a mixture of carbon monoxide and carbon dioxide and releases heat. The steam reacts with the coal substance to form hydrogen, carbon monoxide and carbon dioxide absorbing heat. At the same time the high-pressure conditions promote a synthesis reaction between the hydrogen and the coal substance, resulting in the formation of methane which raises considerably the heating power (or calorific value) of the gas produced. The gasification process is complete and only ash remains; this is removed from the gasifier intermittently and at Westfield arrangements have been made for all ash produced to be driven back to the opencast workings; it will be dumped with the overburden and later used in restoring the site of the mine.

The Westfield works are being developed in two stages. Work on site was commenced in October 1958, and the first stage is now being commissioned; during this stage three Lurgi gasifiers will be available, two being normally in operation with one standing by, or under repair, giving a nominal gas production capacity of 15 million cu. ft. of gas a day. The second stage will be commissioned towards the end of 1961, one year ahead of schedule; this will bring the nominal gas production capacity up to 30 million cu. ft. a day. The works layout allows for easy extension up to a capacity of 45 million cu. ft. a day and, if necessary, this capacity could be doubled on the existing 45-acre site; a production capacity of 45 million cu. ft. a day is equivalent to about 25 per cent. of the total gas requirements for the whole of Scotland.

In giving the nominal daily gas production of 7½ million cu. ft. of gas a day, each Lurgi gasifier will use not only 240 tons of coal but at the same time 220 tons of high-pressure steam and 60 tons of oxygen; the steam boilers and oxygen plants had to be chosen specially to meet Westfield conditions.

The steam boilers had to be capable of burning small coal with a high ash and moisture content. The type chosen incorporates the special "Ignafluid" grate system developed by the French associates of Babcock and Wilcox Limited and never previously used in this country. In this type of furnace, air is admitted below the grate in a pulsating blast which burns the coal in suspension. This solves the problem of burning fuel of high ash and moisture content efficiently (5 per cent. higher efficiency than a normal chain grate) in units too small for the economic use of the pulverised fuel system.

The oxygen required at Westfield will be obtained by "air separation" and again the plants selected are the first of their type in Britain. The principle of air separation to produce oxygen on a large scale ("tonnage oxygen") is that air from the atmosphere is compressed to fairly high pressures (several atmospheres) and subsequently cooled by heat exchange and expansion. This causes the air to liquefy. The liquid air is then separated into oxygen of about 95 per cent. purity and nitrogen in a special distillation column. In the conventional type of oxygen plant the oxygen is recovered from the distillation column as a gas which must be compressed to very high pressures if required for pressure gasification. In the "Tonnox" type of oxygen plant installed at Westfield the oxygen is recovered from the distillation column as a liquid which can be readily pumped to give the high pressures required for gasification. The reasons for choosing this type of plant for Westfield is that up to 10 per cent. of the oxygen produced can be put into storage as liquid. An insulated liquid oxygen storage tank is provided; this has a capacity equivalent to the output of one oxygen plant over five days, and therefore provides an instantly available standby, safeguarding gas supplies in the event of a breakdown of one of the oxygen plants, and allowing routine repairs to be carried out without the need of a spare plant. The nitrogen obtained as a by-product of oxygen production is normally surplus and will be discharged to atmosphere although some nitrogen may be required for addition to the gas stream in order to produce the necessary burning characteristics.

Purification of the crude Lurgi gas includes a number of fairly conventional cooling and washing operations. Heavy tar, light oil and benzole are the main by-products and will be sold to the tar distillers and motor benzole producers. A weak aqueous effluent containing ammonia and traces of other chemicals is also produced; the ammonia will be recovered and concentrated to give a 20 per cent. product for sale to fertiliser manufacturers.

After removal of these products, however, Lurgi gas still contains two impurities which must be removed; these are carbon dioxide and hydrogen sulphide; the first is an inert gas and reduces the heating power of the gas produced; the second must be removed completely, to comply with statutory requirements. At Westfield these will be removed by washing with a hot alkaline solution in the Benfield plant, another process new to the British gas industry. After removal from the gas the carbon dioxide, containing 1 to 2 per cent. of hydrogen sulphide, must be disposed of. In the first stage of operation the hydrogen sulphide will be converted by burning to sulphur dioxide before discharge of the gases to atmosphere through a special chimney 275 ft. in height. A pilot plant is also being installed with a view to establishing a method of recovering pure sulphur from the waste gas stream.

After purification, the calorific value of the Lurgi gas will be about 410 British Thermal Units a cubic foot. Before distribution the calorific value will require to be raised to the new standard calorific value for the Central Scotland grid (450 British Thermal Units a cubic foot) by the addition of one or more of the following enriching gases:

Commercial butane—delivered by road tanker from Grangemouth refinery;
Refinery tail gas—by pipe-line from Grangemouth refinery;
Drainage gas—by pipe-line from Valleyfield colliery.

The Westfield gas will be dried by refrigeration before transmission to avoid the need for condensate removal from the grid and to prevent internal corrosion. In Stage 2 of the Westfield project a special plant will be installed to reduce the toxicity of the gas before distribution to customers. This will be achieved by the conversion of the carbon monoxide in the gas into carbon dioxide and hydrogen, by bringing it into contact with steam over a catalyst. This is another major advance in gas industry technique.

A data sheet showing approximate estimated production figures for the works is given as Table III; the estimated labour requirement for Westfield is 260 persons.

DRAINAGE GAS—CARDOWAN AND VALLEYFIELD

(i) Cardowan

Since the beginning of 1959, the Scottish Gas Board have received from the National Coal Board (Scottish Division) the whole production of drainage gas from Cardowan pit in Lanarkshire. This amounts to about 250,000 cu. ft. a day of drainage gas with a calorific value of about 825 British Thermal Units a cubic foot. This is transmitted along a special pipe-line to Provan gasworks, Glasgow, where it is mixed with the other gases produced and collected there (coal gas, carburetted water gas, butane, coke-oven gas) to give the declared calorific value of 450 British Thermal Units a cubic foot. The supply of gas from Cardowan is reliable and the calorific value is reasonably constant.

(ii) Valleyfield, Fife

The Scottish Gas Board may arrange with the National Coal Board (Scottish Division) for a supply of drainage gas from Valleyfield colliery in Fife. This gas either may be conveyed by pipe-line to Dunfermline or, alternatively, a main may be laid from Valleyfield to Westfield so that the drainage gas can be transmitted there, and pumped into the gas stream for enrichment purposes.

REFINERY GAS FROM GRANGEMOUTH

Negotiations are proceeding with Scottish Oils and Shell-Mex Limited for supplies of refinery tail gas—the surplus gaseous products of refinery cracking processes, probably with a calorific value of over 1,500 British Thermal Units a cubic foot. Several possibilities for utilising this gas are under consideration; the most attractive scheme may be to pump it to Westfield for addition to the Lurgi gas along with nitrogen as a diluent.

COKE-OVEN GAS

At vesting date the Scottish Gas Board were purchasing coke-oven gas from coke ovens in the west of Scotland at the rate of approximately 10 million cu. ft. a day. Negotiations with Scottish iron and steel firms and with the National Coal Board (Scottish Division) have resulted in additional supplies, including all coke-oven gas available for disposal from the new Clyde and Ravenscraig coke ovens of Colville's Limited and from the Dumbreck coke ovens of the National Coal Board. Coke-oven gas is now being received at the rate of about 20 million cu. ft. a day and the Board's plans allow for the collection and use of additional quantities which are expected to become available over the next five years. The supplies from individual coke ovens are utilised as follows:

COKE-OVEN GAS FROM

(a) *Colvilles:* Clyde Ironworks—purchased as unpurified gas and piped to Provan gasworks, Glasgow, for purification and mixing with manufactured gas;
(b) *Colvilles:* Ravenscraig Steelworks—purchased as unpurified gas, purified at the Scottish Gas Board's Uddingston station; compressed into the west of Scotland grid;
(c) *Baird's and Scottish Steel Limited:* Gartsherrie Ironworks—purchased as unpurified gas; purified in the important new tower purifier installation at the Scottish Gas Board's Coatbridge station; compressed into the west of Scotland grid;
(d) *National Coal Board:* Dumbreck Coke Ovens—purchased as unpurified gas; purified at the former site of Kirkintilloch gasworks.

As in the case of refinery tail gases and Lurgi gas, the purchase of extra coke-oven gas to replace coal gas manufactured by carbonisation could result in a direct reduction in the quantity of coke available for sale by the Scottish Gas Board.

NATURAL GAS

In recent times, discoveries of large reserves of natural gas have revolutionised fuel supplies in a number of countries abroad. For example, the large reserves discovered at

Lacq in the south of France have changed the pattern of the French gas industry and natural gas is distributed by high-pressure pipe-lines northwards as far as Paris and Nantes. Realising the potential importance of natural gas finds to the British gas industry, the Gas Council commissioned the B.P. Exploration Company Limited, formerly known as the D'Arcy Exploration Company Limited, to undertake a search for natural gas throughout Britain.

It was considered that one of the most promising possibilities was at Cousland near Dalkeith in Midlothian. In the early stages of the search it was thought also that worthwhile reserves might be found at Salsburgh in Lanarkshire, but preliminary investigations of that possibility were not encouraging.

The presence of natural gas at Cousland was first discovered in 1937 by the former D'Arcy Exploration Company Limited while searching for oil. The borehole sunk at that time showed that gas was contained in the layers of porous sandstone occurring at depths of 1,582 to 1,632 ft. and 1,720 to 1,735 ft. below wellhead level. The gas had remained in this position over the centuries, trapped between an impervious layer of rock above the sandstone and the natural subterraneous water which sealed off the lower edges of the formation at a depth of about 1,700 ft. One of the main difficulties which have been met in attempting to develop the Cousland reserve commercially has been in estimating the amount of gas likely to be available. From the original sinking and from the well drilled on behalf of the Gas Council in 1954 estimates ranging from 200 up to 3,000 million cu. ft. of gas were quoted. If quantities approaching the latter figure had been certain, the erection of a special plant to convert the natural gas into a gas suitable for direct distribution to customers would have been justified. The alternative possibility was to mix as much natural gas as possible with the coal gas produced at Musselburgh gasworks. A special pipe-line was laid from Cousland to Musselburgh in 1957 and since November 1957 more than 65 million cu. ft. of natural gas have been removed from Cousland at a steady rate, resulting in a fall in well pressure of about 50 lb. per sq. in. Over this period the composition and calorific value of the natural gas have remained fairly constant (the gas is principally methane and the calorific value is about 980 British Thermal Units a cubic foot).

From the pressure drop which has occurred so far, and other factors, the Cousland natural gas reserve is now estimated at about 1,000 million cu. ft.

Despite the limited gas reserve, the Cousland structure may be of great economic potential in restyling Scotland's gas supply. As will be noted from the grid map, it is planned eventually to extend the supergrid eastwards from the main Westfield-Coatbridge link to Edinburgh and Galashiels (which already is interlinked with Hawick). A connection may be provided between the supergrid and the Cousland natural gas well; the well then could be used as a large-capacity gasholder capable of eliminating the effect of seasonal demand variations on gas production plant. The rate of gas production then could be kept reasonably steady throughout the year, avoiding the need to keep retort benches heated up for long periods ready for use, or to keep special plant to meet seasonal peaks. Before the Cousland structure can be adopted as a seasonal gasholder, it would be necessary for most of the existing natural gas to be recovered for use; the water-level below the gas-bearing sandstone would then tend to rise and to fill the pores in the sandstone. Special high-pressure compressors would be required to pump grid gas down the well against the water pressure. The pressure energy required to pump the gas into storage would be available to force it back into the grid, as required, during the winter. The estimated potential gas storage capacity at Cousland is in total more than the combined capacity of all conventional gasholders in the whole of Scotland; the conventional gasholders still would be required in meeting daily and weekly variations in demand.

SUBSIDIARY DEVELOPMENTS

In addition to the major complete new projects in Central Scotland, the Scottish Gas Board have also taken advantage of the increased availability, at low prices, of light paraffinic products from the oil industry to reduce costs at existing works.

At Provan and Dawsholm gasworks, Glasgow, and at Granton gasworks, Edinburgh, "light virgin naphtha", an oil refinery surplus product, has replaced gas oil for enriching water gas.

At Provan gasworks, Glasgow, at Granton gasworks, Edinburgh, and at Aberdeen, large butane storage tanks have been installed. Liquefied butane is delivered by road tanker from Grangemouth. Butane with a suitable diluent (air at Provan, lower calorific value coal gas at Granton, chimney waste gases or producer gas at Aberdeen) enables sudden peak demands to be met at little notice and without the expense of keeping plant under heat in anticipation.

An interesting but small source of town gas is the supply of sewage gas from the Hawick sewage works. This gas, which is mainly methane with nitrogen and other diluent gases, is evolved from the "sludge digestion process" in which the solid matter in the town's sewage is broken down by the action of bacteria before disposal; the gas is mixed with coal gas to give the required calorific value.

SMOKELESS SOLID FUEL

In a conventional gasworks where most of the gas is made by carbonisation every ton of coal processed produces for sale say 80 to 90 therms of gas and perhaps 10 cwt. of coke plus breeze (after allowing for coke required for the manufacture of peak load water gas, and breeze used for raising steam for process and power requirements). Under these conditions the economics of gas production are influenced considerably by the revenue obtainable from the sale of coke and breeze. The replacement of conventional carbonisation by gas from complete gasification, gas purchased from coke ovens and similar sources is proceeding principally because the revenue from coke and breeze is insufficient to reduce the cost of coal gas below the cost of these other gases.

The consequent large-scale closure of works with conventional carbonising plants over the next five years and the reduction in the quantity of deep-mined coal carbonised will result in a considerable reduction in the quantity of coke and breeze available from a given gas production. During the past few years the demand for coke, for all purposes, has been less than the tonnage available, and large quantities of coke have had to be put into stock where further loss of revenue occurs due to break-down into fines.

It has been estimated, however, from figures provided by local authorities in Scotland that the demand for coke as a solid smokeless fuel for the domestic open fire is likely to increase substantially over the next five years as a result of the implementation of the

Clean Air Act. The Scottish Gas Board have carried out a study to determine what steps can be taken to meet this expected increase in demand for solid smokeless fuel as and when it arises and with as little alteration as possible to the development plan outlined in the foregoing. At the same time it is the aim of the Board in planning for, and achieving, economies in gas production to promote the use of gas as a main source of space heating and water heating in households everywhere, including the smokeless zones and smoke control areas. The advantages of these methods, particularly their high efficiency, flexibility and cleanliness, are widely recognised and the Board's latest tariff structure is designed expressly to encourage large-scale use of gas in the home.

The following special means are available to the Scottish Gas Board, however, in order to meet increased coke demand without departing materially from present plans. These methods are:

(*a*) restriction of the quantity of gas produced in water gas plants, thus reducing the quantity of coke used on gasworks for this purpose;
(*b*) restriction of the quantity of water gas produced by "steaming" during carbonisation in continuous vertical retorts. This increases the coke yield but would be accompanied by an increase in the calorific value of the gas produced;
(*c*) by reduction of the quantity of coke used for heating continuous vertical retorts by substituting coal gas for up to 40 per cent. of the heating requirements; this reduces the net gas yield per ton of coal carbonised and increases the coke availability for a given production of coal gas. By this means coke production capacity could be kept in operation which otherwise would require to close down following availability of cheaper gas from other sources.

It is important to note that although large quantities of additional gas can be made available economically without corresponding increases in coke production, for example by the Lurgi process of complete gasification, the quantity of extra coke which can be made available corresponding to a given gas demand is relatively limited.

The Scottish Gas Board believe that if increased demands for domestic solid smokeless fuel occur they should be met with a carefully prepared product of high quality. As the quantity of coal required by the Scottish Gas Board is reduced, following the adoption of gas from other sources, coals which are least suitable for the production of a reactive coke of low and consistent ash content will be eliminated from the works selected to produce domestic smokeless fuels. A special smokeless fuel known as "Gloco" has already been brought into production at works in Edinburgh and Glasgow with the specific aim of providing a superior fuel for the domestic open grate. "Gloco" is produced from selected coals under specially controlled conditions and with a stringent quality control procedure. A special investigation has been made jointly by the Scottish Gas Board and the National Coal Board (Scottish Division) into the possibility of increasing the allocation to the Scottish Gas Board of coals which are likely to be suitable for the production of further quantities of "Gloco" or of a premium type of smokeless fuel. Preliminary tests have been carried out on these coals and production trials are proceeding. The superior and consistent quality of "Gloco" and other controlled smokeless fuels which the gas industry can produce can command a higher price than ordinary coke. The increased revenue will require to offset the cost of the special measures which have to be taken in order to produce these fuels in the quantities required.

CONCLUSION

The work undertaken by the Scottish Gas Board during the past four years, and continuing in the immediate future is summarised in the Appendix.

Future progress may lead to the adoption of further new techniques and to even greater economies.

ACKNOWLEDGMENT

The Author wishes to thank his chief, Mr. T. S. Ricketts, Chief Engineer of the Scottish Gas Board, for permission to present this paper and for his advice and guidance in preparing it. The assistance received from members of the Chief Engineer's staff is also acknowledged gratefully.

APPENDIX

The programme of technical development undertaken by the Scottish Gas Board can be summarised as:

(i) *Reducing cost of conventional processes by:*

(*a*) modernising plant;

(*b*) increasing technical control;

(*c*) centralising on large units as far as the economics of short-distance, medium pressure interlinkage would allow;

(*d*) using cheaper feedstocks wherever possible, for example by the substitution of "light virgin naphtha" for gas oil in the enrichment of water gas. Used at Provan and Dawsholm gasworks, Glasgow, and Granton gasworks, Edinburgh.

(ii) *Collection of Surplus gases:*

(*a*) coke-oven gas from:

Bairds and Scottish Steel Limited—Gartsherrie,
Colvilles—Ravenscraig,
Colvilles—Clyde Ironworks,
The National Coal Board (Scottish Division)—Dumbreck;

(*b*) refinery gas from Grangemouth refinery;

(*c*) drainage gas from the National Coal Board (Scottish Division)—Cardowan and Valleyfield.

(iii) *Use of new materials:*

(*a*) addition of commercial butane for peak loads at:

Provan gasworks, Glasgow,
Granton gasworks, Edinburgh,
Aberdeen, Armadale, and Falkirk.

(iv) *Adoption of new techniques:*

(*a*) Lurgi pressure gasification plant at Westfield;

(*b*) development of Cousland natural gas reserve;

(*c*) providing flexibility in the quantity of solid smokeless fuel available, and improving quality.

TABLE I

Coal delivered to Scottish Gasworks during the Year 1959-60

Class Number	National Coal Board Classification Definition		Cannel and Unscreened	Large and Cobbles	Trebles and Doubles	Small Coal	Total	%
	Volatile Matter %	Caking Properties	(Tons)	(Tons)	(Tons)	(Tons)	(Tons)	
COALS RECEIVED FROM THE NATIONAL COAL BOARD (SCOTTISH DIVISION)								
301	20·1 to 30·0	Strong	—	13	108	300	421	0·4
306	19·5 to 32·0	Weak	—	—	7,145	—	7,145	
502	37·0+	Strong	—	311	95,454	—	95,765	5·1
601	30·1 to 37·0	Medium	—	8,516	48,115	—	56,631	23·2
602	37·0+	Medium	31	12,034	320,439	44,513	377,017	
701	30·1 to 37·0	Weak	—	1,698	16,552	11	18,261	14·5
702	37·0+	Weak	—	19,788	232,136	547	252,471	
801	30·1 to 37·0	Very weak	—	—	111,394	—	111,394	45·3
802	37·0+	Very weak	7,596	5,366	721,147	2,764	736,404	
902	37·0+	Non-caking	—	7	65,638	672	66,317	3·6
Total			7,627	47,733	1,618,128	48,807	1,722,295	92·1
%			0·4	2·6	86·5	2·6	92·1	—
COALS RECEIVED FROM ENGLISH DIVISIONS OF THE NATIONAL COAL BOARD								
501			—	—	2,218	2,803	5,021	0·3
702			—	—	136,645	6,776	143,421	7·6
Total			—	—	138,863	9,579	148,442	7·9
%			—	—	7·4	0·5	7·9	—
Grand Total			7,627	47,733	1,756,991	58,386	1,870,737	100·0
%			0·4	2·6	93·9	3·1	100·0	—

Table II

Number of Gasworks in operation in Scotland in 1949, 1956 *and* 1959, *also Programme for* 1966

Nominal Works Output Millions of Cubic Feet per Annum	1949		1956		1959		1966	
	Number of Works	% of Board's Output	Number of Works	% of Board's Output	Number of Works	% of Board's Output	Number of Works	% of Board's Output
0 to 50	107	4·7	79	3·8	57	2·4	33	1·5
51 to 100	30	4·3	18	2·7	9	1·4	2	0·3
101 to 500	41	17·6	38	17·4	23	11·1	6	2·4
501 to 1,000	9	13·1	8	12·4	7	10·7	—	—
1,001 upwards	9	60·3	11	63·7	14	74·4	8	95·8
Totals	196	100·0	154	100·0	110	100·0	49	100·0

Number of Works in Operation in September 1960=101

Table III

Westfield Works—Estimated Production of Gas and By-products

30 million cubic feet of gas per day at 450 B.Th.U. per cubic feet

Materials	Approximate Annual Quantities Produced
Gas	41 million therms
Nitrogen (from oxygen production), net . .	162,000 tons
Tar	47,000 tons
Light Oil	800 tons
Benzole	1,400 tons
Concentrated Ammoniacal Liquor (expressed as 100 per cent ammonia)	800 tons

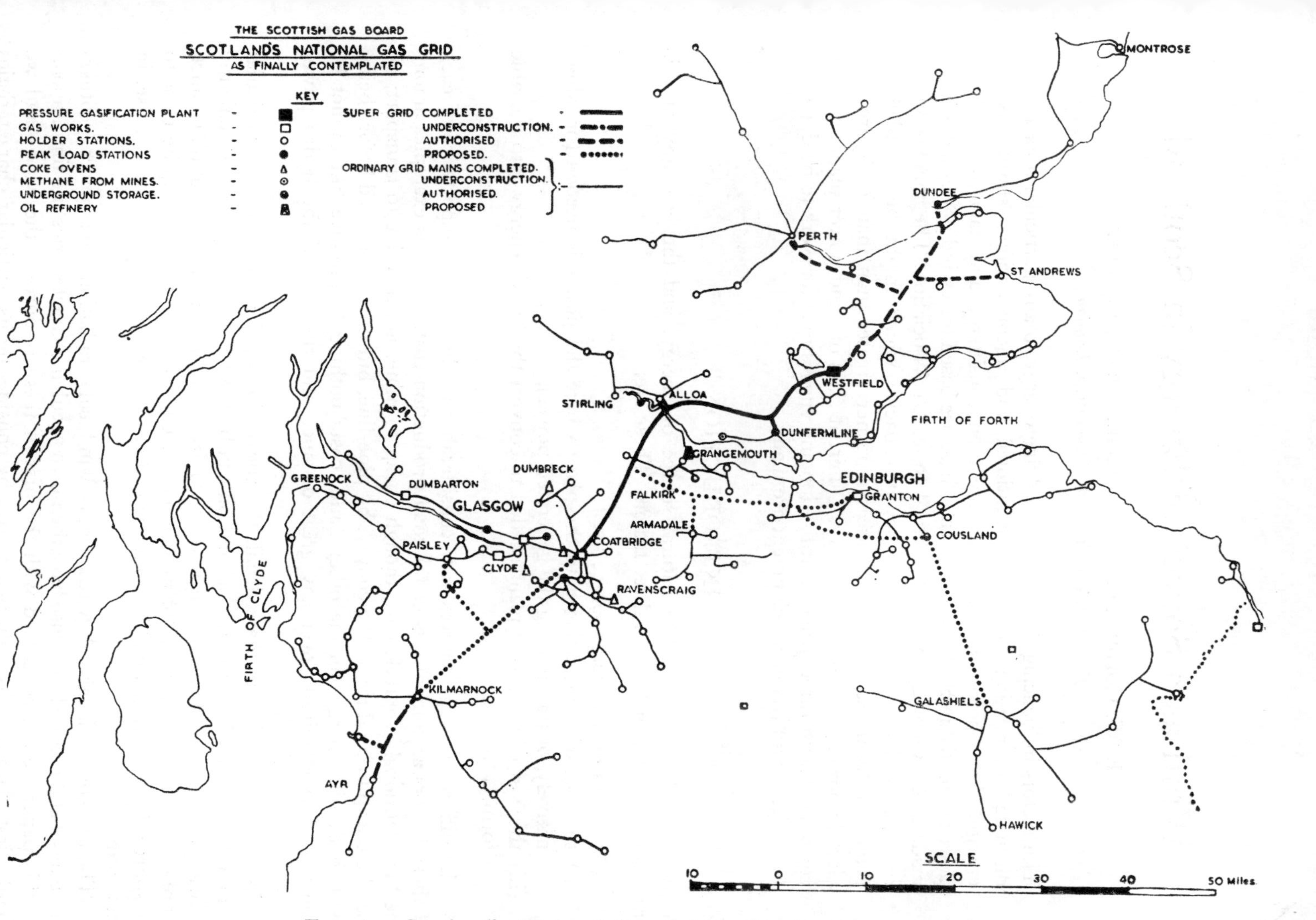

Fig. 1. Scotland's National Gas Grid as Finally Contemplated

Wind as a Source of Energy in Scotland

E. W. GOLDING, O.B.E., M.SC.TECH., M.I.E.E., M.AM.I.E.E.
The Electrical Research Association, London

The factors influencing the cost of supplying energy to any particular area are discussed in relation to both conventional and unconventional sources of energy. Wind power characteristics are then considered and data for wind power potential in Scotland are given. These are based on a wind power survey made a few years ago by the Electrical Research Association. The conclusion reached is that the total wind power capacity which might be installed economically in Scottish coastal areas is rather greater than that for hydro-electric power in the whole country. Different sizes of wind power plants are considered with three forms of utilisation and suggestions for work to be done to further wind power development are made.

INTRODUCTION

Power is produced from some natural source of energy, and the economy of this production depends mainly on three factors. These are:

(i) the cost of the energy source itself;
(ii) the cost of transporting it to the place where the power is needed (or, alternatively, of transmitting the generated power);
(iii) the cost of the power plant needed to convert the "raw" energy into a usable form.

The different energy sources vary considerably in the relative importance of each of these factors as components of the total production cost. Thus, as examples among the "conventional" sources, coal, though cheap to mine, is expensive to transport; oil may be cheap to produce and to convey, by pipe-line, but must be refined before being used; hydraulic energy, on the other hand, costs nothing to produce but cannot be transported economically over any great distance and the cost of the hydro power station is usually high.

When we consider, in more detail, the conversion of the energy into a particular form, other differences appear. Coal and oil can be used quite simply and conveniently as heat producers for domestic purposes, or to fire steam power stations, but oil is much more convenient as the source of mobile power. Unless power is needed quite close to its source, hydro power must be converted to electricity for transmission, and use, in that form.

The less conventional energy resources—wind, solar radiation, tidal power, geothermal energy and marine heat—also have their own peculiar characteristics and limitations.[2] In this paper we are concerned with the first of these resources—the wind—and we should first place it in its right perspective by considering its particular characteristics as a source of power. Later we shall discuss the potentialities of wind power, both in isolation and as part of an integrated power system in which it may be employed as a complement to the major, conventional power plants.

THE CHARACTERISTICS OF WIND AS A POWER PRODUCER

Unlike the conventional sources of energy in the form of fossil fuels, but in common with solar radiation, tidal power and inland water power, wind is an inexhaustible source. Like the latter group, or even perhaps to a greater degree, it is not continuously available and, at least in the temperate zones, its time of availability is unpredictable with any precision—it is undeniably a random source of energy. But it has some advantages over these kindred sources in that its regularity, on an annual basis, is often greater than that of solar radiation or of rainfall, while the installation of power plant to harness it creates much less disturbance to the area concerned, occupies less ground, and costs less for a given power capacity. There is no problem of transporting the wind energy to the site of the power station though, since it is important, economically, to select especially windy sites which may lie in remote areas, the question of transmitting the power, if generated in sufficiently great quantities, may arise as with water power schemes.

Although the installation costs for wind power may be low, the cost of the plant itself tends to be high because of the lightness of air. This means that the energy per unit volume in an air stream is low as compared, for example, with that in a stream of water. The wind power plant must therefore tap relatively large volumes of air to obtain its power.

For an air stream the power law is

$$P=\tfrac{1}{2}\rho AV^3,$$

where ρ is the density of air,

A is the area swept by the windmill rotor, and
V is the wind speed.

(This can be written, alternatively, as $P=\tfrac{1}{2}MV^2$, where M is the weight of air passing, per unit of time, through the rotor.)

If P is expressed in kilowatts, ρ in lb./cu. ft., A in sq. ft. and V in miles per hour, the expression becomes

$$P=0{\cdot}000005\,AV^3.$$

To produce any required power P, at a given wind speed V, A must be large because ρ is small. A large swept area is achieved by using long blades for the windmill rotor and the difficulties—due mainly to vibration—introduced by such long blades places a limit on the length which can be used in practice. This, in turn, limits the practicable size of a windmill power unit. The largest unit ever built had a capacity of 1,250 kW, though this was some twenty years ago and later developments in wind power techniques may allow machines of 1,500 to 2,000 kW to be constructed satisfactorily.

This restriction in the size of an individual machine means that a relatively large number of them must be installed if the total power capacity is to be significant, and to minimise operating costs such machines must run automatically so that only occasional attention, for routine maintenance, is necessary. The usefulness, or economy, of wind power should not, however, be judged solely from the viewpoint of large-scale production: quite small wind-driven plants can have a very important influence in retarding depopulation, and assisting development in remote areas, by providing electric light and other amenities which would be costly to supply by other means.

The exact value of a unit of energy at any particular place is very difficult to determine, but if such energy is to be supplied the relative costs of its provision by alternative methods are of interest. In general, wind-generated energy must be competitive with these alternatives and its potentialities can be judged by its success in this competition. The cost per unit of energy generated by a wind power plant is easily calculated from (*a*) the annual operating costs, including capital charges, for interest and depreciation, and maintenance costs (which, from experience in Denmark, should not exceed 1 to $1\frac{1}{2}$ per cent. of the capital cost of the machine), and (*b*) the annual output of energy. Assuming a rate of (say) 10 per cent. for the annual charges, the energy cost is directly proportional to the capital cost of the wind power installation.

The choice of site is very important because, with fixed operating costs, the unit cost of energy is inversely proportional to the annual output of energy. To take a simple example, if the capital cost of the installation is £50/kW, annual charges 10 per cent., and the annual ouput 4,000 units of energy per kilowatt installed, the cost per unit (in pence) is:

$$\frac{10}{100}\times\frac{50\times 240}{4000}=0{\cdot}30.$$

Obviously, if a worse site had been chosen, giving only 2,000 units of energy per installed kilowatt, the unit cost would have doubled to 0·6d. instead of 0·3d. The same doubling of cost would have resulted, of course, from a rise in the capital cost from £50 to £100. Having achieved—by careful design based on experimental data—the lowest possible cost for the wind power installation, and having chosen the best site, the only remaining question is whether the energy cost, calculated as above, compares favourably with that applying to other available methods.

The development of a satisfactory and economically cheap power plant must be left to the manufacturer, aided, in his design, by information resulting from research on experimental machines and from studies of wind behaviour referring particularly to the site of the proposed installation. But the potential user of the plant must be concerned with the choice of site and the assessment of relative economy. In considering the possible value of the wind as an energy source in Scotland, these two aspects of the question must therefore be studied.

WIND POWER SURVEYS

The most favourable sites for a wind power installation—judged by the annual output of energy produced for a given power capacity installed—must be chosen with two requirements in mind. These are:

(i) the district, in general, should have a high annual average wind speed;

(ii) the site itself should be so located that the average wind speed there is greater than that for the surrounding area.

In the first of these requirements one is limited (on a world-wide basis) by geography: the country concerned might not be very windy. Nevertheless, the principle that its windiest areas should be selected still, and obviously, holds good. The second depends upon topography: fairly steep (though not necessarily very high) hills, with rounded contours and without trees or other obstructions, give the best results. Because of the V^3 law for wind power, a gain of only one or two miles an hour in the annual average wind speed increases the annual output of energy from a given machine very considerably. This can be seen from Table I.[1, 3, 4]

TABLE I

Relationship between Average Wind Speed and Energy Output

Annual Average Wind Speed (in m.p.h.)	Annual Output of Energy (in kWh/kW installed) from a Machine giving full Power Output at 30 m.p.h.
10	600
15	1,800
20	3,150
25	4,350

How does Scotland stand in these respects?

Taking, first, the question of annual average wind speed, the western coastal areas of Scotland are among the windiest in the world. In a world-wide wind survey done by S. Petterssen[5] nine classes of area, in order of windiness, were recognised. Scotland was in the third group, and the only areas stated to have more wind were certain islands in the South Atlantic and South Pacific, and Iceland. Fig. 1 shows an isovent map prepared by the Meteorological Office from observations over the years 1926-40 and it can be seen that western Scotland has an annual average wind speed of 15 to 17·5 m.p.h. As for topography, the west of Scotland had literally hundreds of hills with contours favourable to wind power: they are steep, though smooth in outline, and their shape accelerates the wind passing over their summits so that the summit wind speeds have average values which are often 50 per cent. higher than those for the surrounding area. A few examples of such sites (selected in a Scottish wind survey made a few years ago by the Electrical Research Association) are given in Table II.[3]

TABLE II

Annual Average Wind Speed of Surrounding Area (m.p.h.)	Annual Energy per kW installed on Level Ground in the Area (kWh)	Site	Annual Average Wind Speed (m.p.h.)	Annual Energy per kW installed (kWh)
15	1,800	Costa Hill (Orkney)	25	4,350
		Meall an Fheadain (Wester Ross)	21	3,350
		Cruachan Treshnish (Mull)	20	3,150
17·5	2,500	Chaipaval (Harris)	27	4,800
		Sgarbhe Breac (Islay)	27	4,800
		Ben Tangaval (Barra)	24	4,200

The advantage in energy output to be gained from judicious choice of site can be seen from a comparison of the figures in columns 2 and 5 which assume a rated wind speed (i.e. wind speed for full windmill output) of 30 m.p.h.

At the author's request, Messrs. A. H. Stodhart and J. R. Tagg, of the Electrical Research Association, have estimated the total possible wind power installation and annual energy obtainable in Scotland and reached the conclusions given in Table IV. The bases of these estimates are as follows:

(i) The maximum admissible cost, per kWh, of wind-generated energy is 0·5d.
(ii) All hill sites, between 200 and 2,500 ft. in altitude, of suitable shape and well exposed, and lying within a coastal strip not more than 10 miles wide, could be used. Only those with annual mean wind speeds of 18·5 m.p.h. and over (at 100 ft. above ground) would be economic to use.
(iii) Four unit capacities of wind-driven generators, all of the same rotor diameter and basic design, would be used. The most relevant details of these are given in Table III:

TABLE III

Annual Mean Wind Speed of Site (m.p.h.)	Rated Wind Speed of Machine (m.p.h.)	Rotor Diameter (ft.)	Tower Height (ft.)	Rated* Capacity (kW)	Specific Annual Output (kWh/kW)	Cost† per kWh (pence)
26	35·5	150	100	1,400	4,000	0·3
23·5	34	150	100	1,280	3,700	0·35
21	32	150	100	1,070	3,500	0·43
18·5	30	150	100	880	3,300	0·50

* Assuming an overall efficiency of 35 per cent.

† Assuming a capital cost of £50/kW for the largest capacity,. and cost inversely proportional to (Rated wind speed)^3, and 10 per cent, capital charges

(iv) When more than one machine is installed at one site the minimum spacing between them would be 440 yards.

It should be noted that the 1,250-kW experimental aerogenerator built in U.S.A. had a rotor diameter of 175 ft., that a 640-kW machine, with a rotor diameter of 100 ft., is at present undergoing its preliminary operating trials in France and that a 100-kW machine installed for tests in the Isle of Man has a production cost of £50/kW.

The grand totals for the possible wind power installations and for the annual energy are quite striking. Thus, the possible power, at 2,285,380 kW, is some 14 per cent. greater than the total hydro-electric power given as "already in operation, at construction stage and under survey" in the latest report of the North of Scotland Hydro-Electric Board, while the annual energy figure is 42 per cent. greater than the estimated average annual output from water power. Corresponding figures for the rest of Britain are: Wales 371,000 kW and 1,180 million kWh; England 432,050 kW and 1,329 million kWh.

It is worth noting, also, that Meteorological Office records for the last 40 years show variations of annual average wind speeds between 85 and 120 per cent. of the long-term mean. Such variations would cause changes, in annual energy, from 65 to 125 per cent. of the long-term mean.

TABLE IV

Possible Power Installations and Annual Energy Outputs for Scottish Coastal Areas

Coastal Area	Possible No. of Machines of the Types given in Table	No. of Sites	Possible Total Power (kW)	Possible Total Annual Output (millions of kWh)
Outer Hebrides:				
Lewis	143	95	142,590	449
Harris	63	47	71,780	238
North Uist	36	21	36,330	115
Benbecula	1	1	1,070	3
South Uist	31	24	29,980	93
Barra	15	11	16,150	52
Inner Hebrides:				
Skye	135	60	139,970	446
Mull	85	42	91,820	295
Jura	34	19	41,350	141
Islay	51	29	61,380	198
Coll and Tiree	17	7	15,910	49
Colonsay	12	4	12,840	41
Arran	33	13	35,180	112
Orkney Islands	137	71	136,440	452
Shetland Islands	321	154	325,490	1,025
Caithness	76	30	69,030	210
Sutherland	191	99	185,360	577
Ross and Cromarty	179	76	181,280	578
Inverness	58	30	68,370	228
Morayshire	18	4	15,840	48
Banffshire	27	10	23,760	71
Aberdeen	30	7	26,400	79
East Lothian	24	8	21,120	63
Berwickshire	32	9	28,160	84
Fife	1	1	880	3
Argyll	226	85	237,590	759
Ayrshire	98	47	96,890	303
Wigtownshire	71	44	65,520	200
Kirkcudbrightshire	58	36	54,860	169
Dumfriesshire	9	6	7,920	24
Kincardine	31	16	27,280	82
Angus	13	2	11,440	34
Grand Totals	2,262	1,108	2,285,380	7,221

Picking out some of the more outstanding figures for the Scottish areas we have, in order of magnitude:

TABLE V

	Total Power, in thousands of kW	Annual Energy, in millions of kWh
Shetland Isles . .	325	1,025
Argyll . . .	238	759
Sutherland . . .	185	577
Ross and Cromarty .	181	578
Lewis . . .	143	449
Skye	140	446
Orkney . . .	136	452

The major possibilities for wind power development lie, therefore, in the remoter, and generally less developed, areas of Scotland.

UTILISATION OF WIND POWER

Three scales of use can be distinguished—large, medium and small. Wind-driven plant of unit capacity over about 100 kW is intended for large-scale use; medium-sized machines are those in the range 10 to 100 kW, while the small-scale plants are those under 10 kW.

The machines mentioned in the foregoing section ranged in capacity from 880 to 1,400 kW and, if built, they would be used connected to main electricity networks into which they would feed their energy output whenever there were sufficient wind to allow them to generate power. In this method of use no question of the storage of energy—usually an expensive process—is involved: the energy is quite random and its value, for an electrical network, lies in saving fuel, in the thermal power stations, or in giving the effect of increased rainfall with hydro-electric schemes. In view of the rainfall deficits experienced by the North of Scotland Hydro-Electric Board during recent years, and also remembering the Awe pumped-storage scheme, in which random energy could be stored, it would seem that wind power could play a useful part in the integrated electricity supply system. This might be especially useful if it could be shown, by analysis of wind and rainfall records, that the periods of availability of the two sources of energy—wind and water—were such as to have a complementary effect.

On the Scottish islands the position is a little different. There, generation of electricity is, in the main, by diesel engines, and the generating cost is much higher than that on the mainland. Wind power plants, feeding energy into island networks, could be economic fuel savers. The main apparent difficulty—from the figures in Table IV—would be in absorbing the very large wind power potentials in these islands. Unless wind-generated energy could be exported to the mainland or, alternatively, energy-consuming industries could be established, it would seem impracticable to cope with energy production on the scale which would be possible. This does not, of course, exclude limited use up to a conveniently large total power capacity. A very favourable position would arise if, as a result of studies such as those encouraged by this Conference, processes requiring large quantities of cheap, though permissibly random, energy were to be introduced on the islands.

Medium-sized wind power plants are for use by large houses or by remote communities, and with them at least a limited degree of energy storage, to cover calm spells, is needed. This adds to the energy cost because it increases the total capital cost of the installation and, therefore, increases the annual charges, but the final cost is likely to be competitive with alternative methods of electricity supply at remote places to which networks cannot economically be extended. The best economy, using wind power, is then achieved by using most of the available energy, without storage, through an automatic load-distributing device. A successful experiment on these lines has been made jointly by the Electrical Research Association and the Nature Conservancy during the last two years at Rothiemurchus, near Aviemore.[6] An 8-kW aero-generator has provided electricity for a wide variety of domestic purposes with very little support from a stand-by diesel plant. (In fact, during 3,726 hours of testing spread over the period June 1958 to June 1959 the plant produced 4,510 kWh of electrical energy while the stand-by plant was called upon to provide only 62 kWh.) The automatic load-distributor ensures the fullest possible use of all the energy becoming available, at random times, by passing it to one of the many loads which can be served without regard for precise timing: the order of priority for these loads can be fixed, in advance, by the user, through a system of small plugs which can be placed in a number of different positions on a distribution board.

This Scottish experiment can be regarded as a pilot scheme for larger ones, with wind power plants of greater total capacity—whether from single larger units or from a group of 8 or 10 kW machines—which could be installed to supply power for remote communities in many parts of the world, especially in the underdeveloped areas where electrical networks are non-existent.

The cost of such medium-sized wind power plants may be around £150/kW, and this, together with the fact that remote communities are not often located at especially windy places, may lead to an energy cost of 2d. to 3d. per unit, which would usually be considered low.

Small wind-driven generators—often called "wind chargers" because they are always used to charge an accumulator for energy storage—are a very familiar sight in many non-electrified areas all over the world. They provide valued amenities in the forms of electric light and a little energy for small-power domestic purposes in isolated houses. Their power output and operating voltage being low, they have to be installed very close to the house so that power losses are minimised, and this reduces the choice of site so that the annual output of energy may be rather small. If annual capital charges are assessed as for the larger machines, the result may be a cost of 6d. to 1s. per unit, depending upon the windiness of the actual site of the house. Generally, however, the initial cost of the installation—of the order of £100—is considered small enough to be able to dispense with such precise costing methods.

It should be pointed out, though admittedly it may not greatly influence the total figure for wind-energy resources in Scotland, that no account was taken (in Table IV) of the potentialities of medium- and small-capacity machines which might, in fact, be used in some inland areas as well as near the coasts.

CONCLUSION

Scotland's little-appreciated asset in the form of wind energy, amounting as we have seen to thousands of millions of kilowatt-hours per annum, could without doubt be used economically for many purposes. The research and development work which has been done by the Electrical Research Association, with support from the Ministry of Power and by a few interested manufacturers, has already given very promising results. The test figures for the latest 100-kW wind power plant now running in the Isle of Man combined with its low estimated cost of construction (about £50/kW) indicate that the problem of building a cheap enough machine of that capacity may be solved. What is now needed is support for further efforts towards the production of satisfactory, and at least equally cheap, wind power plants of other sizes and for studies on the most effective methods of utilising, to the fullest possible degree, the energy which the wind surveys in Scotland have already shown to exist in such ample quantity.

As for the expenditure involved, if the whole of the wind power capacity given in Table IV were to be built—admittedly an unrealistic assumption but one which can indicate an upper limit of cost—a sum of about £126 million would be needed for the machines themselves. In addition there would be the cost of constructing suitable roads to the windmill sites, of providing and housing control equipment and of extending existing transmission lines. To assess these costs accurately is not possible at this stage, but, as a guide, an average expenditure of £10,000 per windmill to provide these services would add about £23 million to the scheme and bring its total cost to nearly £150 million. The research and development costs to enable such a plan to be followed might be between one and two million pounds. These costs can be compared with an expenditure to date of over £141 million (excluding transmission line costs) on hydro-electric schemes by the North of Scotland Hydro-Electric Board, and a further considerable sum which has been expended, on hydro-electric development, in the south of Scotland.

REFERENCES

1. Golding, E. W. (1955). The generation of electricity by wind power. E. & F. N. Spon Ltd., London.
2. United Nations (1957). New sources of energy and economic development. U.N. Department of Economic and Social Affairs, New York.
3. Tagg, J. R. (1957). Wind data related to the generation of electricity by wind power. E.R.A. Report C/T115.
4. Golding, E. W., and Stodhart, A. H. (1952). The selection and characteristics of wind-power sites. E.R.A. Report C/T108.
5. Putnam, P. C. (1948). Power from the wind. D. Van Nostrand Co. Inc., London.
6. Walker, J. G. (1960). The automatic operation of a medium-sized wind-driven generator running in isolation. E.R.A. Report C/T122.
7. Golding, E. W. (1956). The combination of local energy resources to provide power supplies in under-developed areas. E.R.A. Report C/T118.

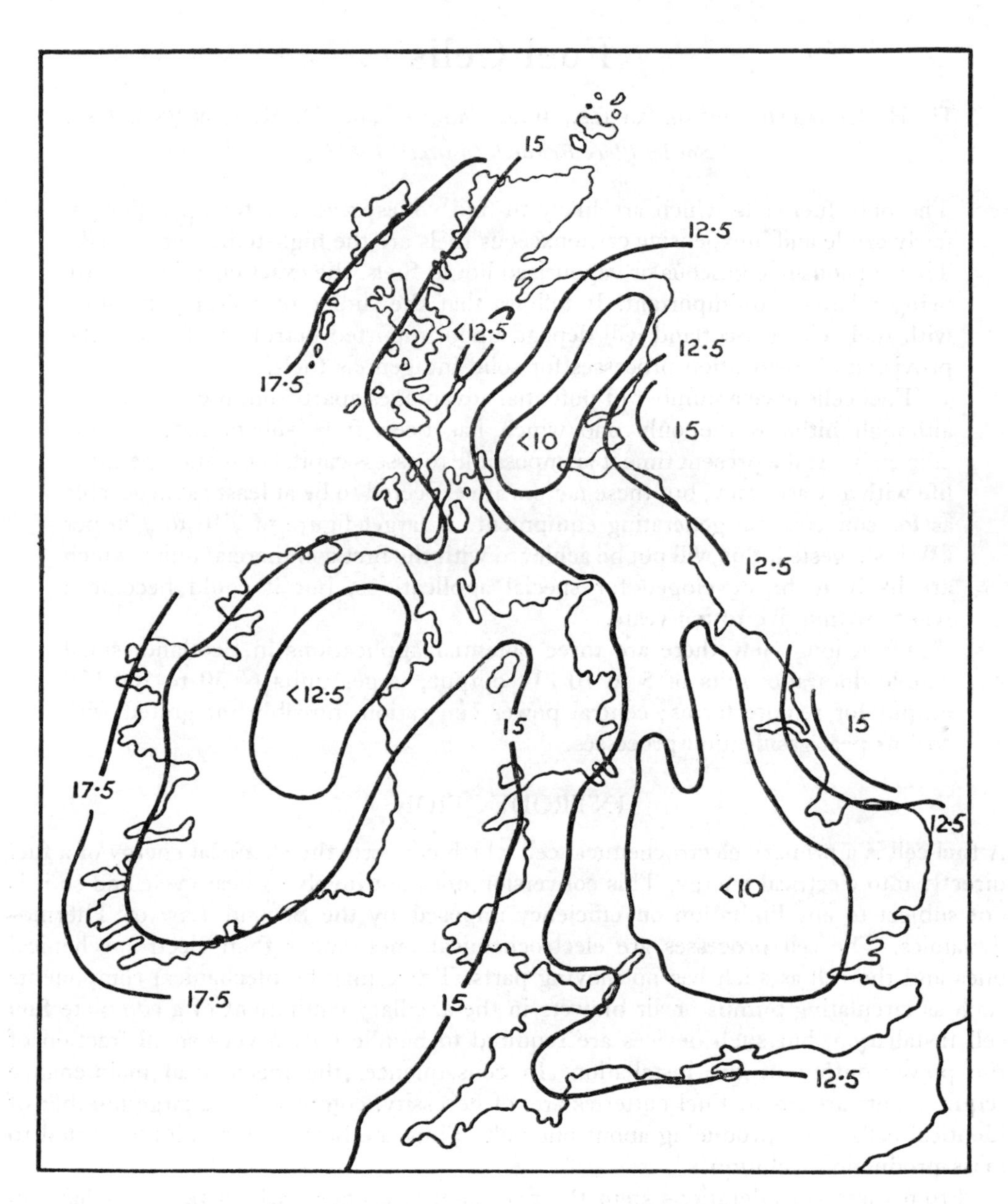

FIG. 1. Isovent Map for Great Britain

The figures on the isovent represent the annual average wind speed in miles per hour

Fuel Cells

H. H. Chambers, ph.d., a.r.c.s., d.i.c., a.r.i.c. and D. R. Corning, b.sc.
Sondes Place Research Institute, Dorking

The only fuel cells which are likely to find widespread use for operation on fairly crude and inexpensive carbonaceous fuels are the high-temperature cells. They all consume gaseous or vapourised liquid fuels, the exact chemical nature being relatively unimportant. It follows that the future of power generation with fuel cells in Scotland will depend upon imported petroleum fuels or the provision of gasification processes for solid indigenous fuels.

Fuel cells have a number of potential advantages apart from high efficiency, although hitherto the only one which has been fully substantiated is the efficiency. At the present time it is impossible to assess capital cost and operating life with any accuracy, but these factors are expected to be at least as favourable as for conventional generating equipment. A target figure of £10 to £20 per kW is suggested: this will not be achieved with the first commercial units, which are likely to be developed for special applications, but it could become a reality within five to ten years.

On a long view there are three potential applications in Scotland: small simple domestic units of 5 to 10 kW output; larger units of 50 to 100 kW output for remote farms; central power generation, possibly integrated with coal or peat gasification processes.

INTRODUCTION

A fuel cell is a primary electrochemical cell which converts the chemical energy of a fuel directly into electrical energy. This conversion does not involve a heat cycle and so it is not subject to any limitation on efficiency imposed by the Second Law of Thermodynamics. The cell processes are electrochemical ones rather than electromechanical ones and the cell as such has no moving parts. There may be mechanical components such as circulating pumps or air blowers in the ancillary equipment of a complete fuel cell installation, but such devices are required to handle only a very small fraction of the power output of the installation. In consequence, the mechanical maintenance requirements are small. Fuel batteries are, of necessity, composed of a large number of identical cells, each producing about one volt. Thus the battery is admirably suited to mass-production techniques.

From these considerations stem the five main advantages which fuel cells have in principle over orthodox methods of electricity generation:

(i) Substantially higher efficiency.
(ii) Ease of maintenance due to absence of moving parts.
(iii) Silent operation.
(iv) Simplicity of construction.
(v) Amenability to scaling-up by multiplication of identical modules.

The fuel cells under development at the present time may be classified according to operating temperature as low-temperature cells (less than 100° C.); medium-temperature cells (200° C. to 300° C.); and high-temperature cells (above *c.* 400° C.). There is another small class using exotic fuels such as hydrazine, but these cells have only highly specialised applications and need not be considered further. Successful low-temperature cells have been operated on hydrogen and oxygen or hydrogen and air. There has been no marked success at low temperatures with hydrocarbon fuels and the prospects are poor of being able to oxidise conventional fuels completely to carbon dioxide and water at anything approaching atmospheric temperature. On the other hand there is a fair chance that low-temperature cells will be developed for partially oxygenated fuels such as methanol. In the medium-temperature range impressive results have been obtained with hydrogen and oxygen, in particular by Bacon. The Bacon cell, however, is more suitable as part of an energy storage system than as an energy generator from primary fuels. Hitherto the only cells which have shown any promise for generating electricity from conventional fuels are the high-temperature cells which operate on gaseous or vapourised liquid hydrocarbons and on gaseous fuels such as producer gas. Nobody has yet succeeded in running a fuel cell on solid fuel, and in the absence of radically new developments the future for the utilisation of solid fuel in fuel cells is tied inevitably to gasification processes or processes for making oil from coal.

THE FUTURE OF FUEL CELLS

Fuel cells are only just emerging from the laboratory stage of development and any forecast is bound to be highly speculative. It is certain, however, that development will proceed along a number of parallel lines leading to more than one successful type of cell. An ideal unit equally well suited to all applications is unlikely because there are too many mutually conflicting requirements to be met.

The direction of development will be determined by three main factors: the nature of the fuel; the need for versatility with regard to fuel; and the operating temperature. The latter is largely dependent on the first two. If a relatively expensive fuel can be tolerated it may be possible to gain the practical advantages associated with low-temperature operation. These include greater freedom of choice of materials of construction and ability to start instantaneously from cold. Low-temperature cells are likely to require highly reactive and purified fuels, free from impurities which would poison the very active electrodes which are essential at low temperatures. High fuel cost does not necessarily rule out low-temperature cells for applications other than very specialised ones. Even the petrol engine uses a highly specialised and expensive fuel. If cells are required to run on cheap conventional fuels, particularly relatively crude ones such as fuel oil or producer gas containing sulphur and other impurities, it is fairly certain that the development will have to continue in the direction of high-temperature cells. Such cells are, of course, more difficult to start up rapidly from cold and therefore less suitable in principle for such uses as powering motor cars. They are considerably more versatile than low-temperature cells in the sense that the chemical nature of the fuel is much less critical and they may rightly be regarded as general-purpose units.

One aspect of operating temperature which is sometimes overlooked is the effect of temperature on cell cooling. All fuel cells develop waste heat on load and the higher the temperature the easier is the cooling problem. Moreover, the high-grade heat from a high-temperature cell may be usefully employed and one can visualise many potential domestic and industrial applications where a fuel battery could be used as a source of both electrical power and heat.

The hydrogen-oxygen cell is in a different category from carbonaceous fuel cells because hydrogen is less readily available and more difficult to handle and transport than other fuels. In special circumstances, e.g. where by-product hydrogen is available in an industrial process, the hydrogen cell could be used for power production. A more likely use is for electricity storage. This involves storage of oxygen and hydrogen obtained by electrolysis of water with off-peak power and recombination in a fuel cell. This might be an attractive proposition with the Bacon high-pressure cell, particularly if the cell could be made to run reversibly as a high-pressure electrolyser.

As we are taking a long view of the future we must consider briefly an aspect of the fuel cell on which very little work has been done hitherto, viz. its possible use as a chemical reactor. In electricity generation the object is to oxidise the fuel completely to carbon dioxide and water. Under certain conditions of operation it is possible to stop the oxidation at some intermediate stage where the oxidation products are olefines, alcohols, aldehydes, ketones, acids, ethers, etc. This promises a completely new method of synthesis of chemicals from hydrocarbons should it prove possible to control the oxidation in preferred directions.

Some of the potential advantages of fuel cells for electricity generation have been mentioned in the introduction. The only things which have been fully established experimentally are the high efficiency and the fact that unlike electromechanical generating processes the efficiency rises rather than falls at outputs lower than the maximum or rated output. This is not enough to make fuel batteries competitive with orthodox generating methods. We shall see later that fuel cost is not the only large factor in power production and in the long run the capital cost and operating life of the equipment may be more important. Here it is only possible to make inspired guesses because there is insufficient experience to draw upon. If the capital cost and operating life can be made to approach that of a diesel generator set, the future of fuel batteries is assured, because they will always score on efficiency, versatility, variation of efficiency with load and probably also cost of maintenance, even taking into account that ancillary equipment for d.c./a.c. inversion will be necessary for many applications. This target will not be reached overnight, but the essential simplicity of the fuel cell and its amenability to mass production lead one to think that it is not unattainable. There are many applications which would stand a capital cost many times higher than a diesel generator because of the other advantages: these are clearly the ones which will be developed first.

FUEL AND POWER IN SCOTLAND

It is not the intention of the authors to attempt a comprehensive survey of the present position as regards fuel resources and utilisation in Scotland. It is necessary, however, briefly to consider the various sources of energy in order to make some assessment of the contribution which fuel cells might be able to make.

COAL[1]

In 1959, the total coal output from the Scottish mines, at 18·5 million tons, was 3·8 per cent. down on the 1958 production. All the Areas in the Scottish Division had substantial trading losses. The average income per saleable ton of coal was 86s. 0·4d., which is equivalent to a pit-head cost of 3·8d. per therm. During the year, "small supplies" of methane were supplied to the Scottish Gas Board from Cardowan colliery. The Lurgi gasification of opencast coal at Westfield is referred to later.

The future of coal as a primary fuel is, of course, a very far-reaching question. Parker[2], in a paper presented to the Institute of Fuel, envisages a rather slowly rising demand for coal, the surplus requirement for power generation being obtained increasingly from oil and nuclear energy. This author estimates that the U.K. usage of coal in 1968-70 will be about 250 million tons per annum. It seems likely, therefore, that unless very large export markets are re-established the mines will continue to operate below their potential maximum and that alternative methods of using coal and coal products will be of great interest. This state of affairs may add considerable impetus to the development of gasification methods, etc., and fuels suitable for use in fuel batteries may become increasingly abundant from this source.

PEAT[3]

The Geological Survey of Scotland estimates that the total area covered with at least two feet of peat is of the order of 1,625,000 acres. Of the total weight of peat involved, probably about 600 million tons of dry matter are contained in mosses whose depth, accessibility and other factors make them likely to be suitable for utilisation. Much of this peat is of fairly high calorific value (*c.* 10,000 B.t.u./lb. dry matter) and in terms of energy these deposits would be enough to supply power stations of 2,000 MW capacity for about 50 years. However, because of the very high moisture content (*c.* 90 per cent.) and the low density of the peat as harvested, transport charges would be many times higher than those for coal.

In Ireland it has been shown that fairly large boilers can utilise peat.[4] Ferbane power station is equipped with 3×20 MW turbo-alternators and the boilers have been quite satisfactorily fired with milled peat containing 50 to 60 per cent. moisture: the fuel cost during 1959-60 appears to be about 0·60d. to 0·63d. per kWh sent out. An experimental 2,200-kW peat-burning gas turbine generator is being operated by the N.S.H.E.B. at Altnabreac in Caithness. This unit, during 1959, ran for 1,017 hours, producing 301,000 units of electricity and consuming 433 tons of peat.[5]

It is clear then that methods are available for the reasonably efficient and economical drying and handling of peat. Work has also been done on the gasification of peat with steam and air or oxygen and on the subsequent use of these gases in Fischer Tropsch synthesis. It is a possibility that the unique properties of the fuel battery could be utilised in a combined power plant and chemical work in which the fuel cells operated on gaseous products while some of the power developed was used for the production of oxygen which would be used in the process. Excess power and waste heat would then be available for the Fischer Tropsch plant.

NATURAL GAS[6]

A natural gas deposit, believed to contain at least 1,000 million cubic feet, is being worked at Cousland near Musselburgh. The gas occurs at 620 p.s.i.g., contains 90 per cent. methane and no sulphur, and has a calorific value of 930 to 960 B.t.u./cu. ft. At present this gas is being used to upgrade the town gas supply of Musselburgh. Obviously such a supply would be ideal for fuel cell operation, but the Cousland deposit appears to be the only one of exploitable size so far detected in Scotland.

GAS PRODUCTION IN SCOTLAND[7]

In the year ended 31st March 1959 the Scottish Gas Board sold 187·18 million therms of gas at an average price of 23·02d./therm. The amount sold was 5·1 per cent. down on the previous year. In addition to its own production, the Gas Board bought large quantities of methane from coal-mines, natural gas from Cousland and tail gases from oil refineries.

A large capital scheme in hand is the Lurgi gasification plant at Westfield in Fife.[8] Costing £6·6 million, with a further £8·5 million for medium- and high-pressure grid systems, this plant will eventually supply 30 million cu. ft. per day of gas. Opencast coal containing 25 per cent. ash and 16 per cent. moisture is used and the gas is upgraded with butane from the B.P. refinery at Grangemouth.

ELECTRICITY PRODUCTION IN SCOTLAND

In 1959 the North of Scotland Hydro-Electric Board sold to consumers a total of 1,421 million units, 5·8 per cent. more than in the previous year. The average cost of generation was 0·841d./unit while the cost to the consumer was 1·737d./unit. Average production costs by the three methods in use are shown in Table I.

TABLE I

Costs of Power Generation—N.S.H.E.B.[5]

Item	All in pence/kWh		
	Hydro	Steam	Diesel
Fuel	—	·677*	·880†
Lub. oil, stores, etc.	—	·002	·048
Operation and salaries	·021	·067	·149
Repairs and maintenance	·019	·094	·181
Sundries	·003	·006	·010
Rents, insurance, etc.	·001	·006	·008
Interest and amortisation	·743	·147	·562
Totals	·787	·999	1·838

* Average price of coal, 99s. 9d./ton.

† Average price of fuel oil, 14·53d./gallon.

Costs for diesel generation are high, but generally in line with other figures available (see, for instance, the Report on Heavy-oil Engine Working Costs 1958-59 of the Diesel Engineers and Users Association).

The South of Scotland Electricity Board,[9] in 1959, sold 6,435 million units, an increase of 7·4 per cent. over the previous year. The average cost of generation was 0·878d./unit and the cost to consumer was 1·500d./unit. The breakdown of costs for hydro and thermal generation is given in Table II.

TABLE II

Cost of Power Generation S.S.E.B.

Item	Hydro	Steam
Fuel	—	·577*
Lub. oil, stores, etc.	·002	·003
Operation and salaries	·072	·044
Repairs and maintenance	·045	·046
Sundries	·007	·002
Rents and insurance	·005	·002
Interest and amortisation	·125†	·217
Totals	·256	·891

* Average price of coal, 93s. 4d./ton.
† This is very low compared with Table I.

APPLICATIONS OF FUEL BATTERIES

The fuel battery offers a means by which the chemical energy in a fuel can be directly and efficiently converted into electric power. The absence of moving parts give continuous operation with minimum manpower and maintenance costs. The essential requirements are supplies of gaseous or readily vapourisable fuel and air at low pressures. These are fed directly into the battery, which can most conveniently be constructed on the "packaged unit" principle. For most economical operation, a cascade system of fuel feeding would be adopted and air or water cooling would be necessary with a large installation. The output from the cell is d.c. and for large-scale power generation and transmission an additional d.c./a.c. inverter would be required. Even so, the essential simplicity of the fuel battery compares favourably with the complexity of either diesel or steam generation.

Some of the fuels which might be of considerable interest in connection with fuel battery operation are:

Synthetic gases of relatively low calorific value, e.g. Producer and Water gas.
Liquified Petroleum gases. (L.P.G.).
Natural gases.
Liquified natural gas.
Sewage sludge digestion gas.
Synthetic gas of rather higher calorific values, e.g. from Lurgi processes or developments at higher pressures under slagging conditions.
Oil refinery tail gases.
Kerosene, T.V.O., or other light petroleum distillates.

Synthetic gases of widely differing compositions and calorific values can be manufactured by various processes: most of these would be well suited for use in fuel batteries.

It would be reasonable, however, to limit this use to gases of low calorific value (e.g. producer gas, 180 B.t.u./cu. ft.), which would nevertheless give completely satisfactory operation, and thereby release the higher grade gases for applications where their higher values could be used to maximum advantage.

L.P.G. is used very extensively in the U.S.A., where sales in 1958 were well over 10 million tons.[10] In the U.K., over the same period, sales were some 90,000 tons and the demand is increasing. The term L.P.G. covers commercial grades of both propane and butane, the former being favoured industrially while butane fulfils more domestic requirements. Most L.P.G. is obtained from oil refineries and obviously the relatively small scale of operations in the U.K. limits the supply and maintains a fairly high price.

Natural gases are not economically important in the U.K. and although supplies of liquified natural gas have been shipped to the U.K., where it has been reformed for admixture with town's gas, this material will obviously remain an expensive rarity until importations on a very large scale are undertaken. Sewage gases are used by some authorities in dual-feed diesel generating sets, the running costs of which appear to be generally similar to those using straight diesel fuel. Waste hydrocarbon gases of this type, particularly if methane is the major constituent, could be very effectively utilised in fuel batteries. The same considerations apply to oil refinery tail gases and it has been suggested that a large proportion of the power required for pumping, etc., at a refinery could be very economically generated by means of a fuel cell operating on these gases.

The use of light petroleum distillates such as kerosene and tractor vapourising oil could well be the most economical method of operating small fuel batteries under present conditions. The costs involved are considered in the next section.

SOME SPECIFIC APPLICATIONS

Domestic (5 to 10 kW)

Figures published by the Scottish Electricity Boards show that at the end of 1959 there were between 14,000 and 15,000 farms and crofts still unconnected to the mains supply, the great majority of these being in the Northern Area. In such outlying districts, therefore, there would be a very real market for a cheap, simple and reliable power generator with a capacity of 5 to 10 kW for domestic lighting and heating. The capital cost would have to be as low as possible and it is estimated that the acceptable maximum for such a generator would be in the region of £100, or, say, £10 to £15 per kilowatt output. This figure is unlikely to be reached in the immediate future, but it is by no means an unattainable target, taking a long view.

Such a battery as is envisaged would be of the simplest construction and it would probably be realistic to write the cost off over a short period of, say, five years. This rate of depreciation would be equivalent to fixed charges of about 0·274d./kWh if an average load factor of 20 per cent. is assumed. For a fuel battery of this type, light petroleum distillates such as kerosene or T.V.O. (particularly on farms already using tractors) would be convenient and economical fuels. At a retail fuel price of 2s. per gallon, the fuel cost would be 0·75d./kWh: if the fuel were obtained at bulk delivery rates, this cost would be reduced to 0·56d./kWh. An alternative fuel which at present rates would be rather more expensive but which might cheapen as demand increases is L.P.G., delivered in cylinders under slight pressure. At present, commercial butane is available to the domestic consumer at 67s. 4d. for 83 lb. or 9·73d./lb.: to the large consumer, however, this price reduces to 4·75d./lb. Consumption of a hydrocarbon gas in the fuel cell ranges from about 0·227 lb./kWh for methane to 0·254 lb./kWh for butane and the operating fuel cost with L.P.G. at the bulk price would be, therefore, 1·2d./kWh. Under the specified power load conditions, an 83-lb. bottle of L.P.G. would last about two weeks, if a 5-kW unit is considered: the consumption of kerosene would be about five gallons per week.

As stated above, a very simple unit battery is envisaged for this domestic duty. Kerosene would be held in a tank to which slight pressure could be applied, as in a blow-lamp or Primus stove. Heat from the cell could be used to bring about vapourisation and a very small auxiliary blower would be required to introduce air into the cell. In the calculations given above no account has been taken of labour charges since it is assumed that the householder would perform any required routine operations as a normal chore. Maintenance and replacements have not been included since the complete unit has been considered expendable over five years. It is unlikely, with a small unit of this type, that any utilisation of waste heat would be economically feasible.

Farm Use (50 to 100 kW)

A second possible use for fuel batteries is on farms and other sites where the maximum demand may be of the order of 50 to 100 kW. At present, diesel generators are extensively used for this purpose and it is suggested that fuel batteries might present an attractive and economical alternative. Automotive applications (e.g. tractors) pose special problems, particularly with respect to cold starting, and this aspect will not be dealt with in detail. In many cases, however, a stationary generating set is required to provide power to drive equipment (e.g. saws, hoists, etc.) and to provide light and heating for such purposes as hay drying, cheese ripening, broiler houses, etc.

It is in applications of this type that an outstanding property of fuel batteries shows to advantage, i.e. that the thermal efficiency increases as the load decreases. Under normal conditions of operation at say, 75 per cent. of maximum output, the efficiency may be 65 to 70 per cent., which is, of course, much higher than that of the internal combustion engine. If the load is reduced so that the fuel battery is as it were "idling", the efficiency increases appreciably. With an internal combustion engine, maximum efficiency of, say, between 30 and 35 per cent. may be attained at about 75 per cent. of maximum output, but the efficiency at low output may drop to about 20 per cent., with a corresponding increase of 50 per cent. in the specific fuel consumption. Quoted fuel consumption figures for internal combustion engines may, therefore, be very optimistic if the generator is required to run at low loads for long periods.

When the costs of fuel batteries for farm and light industrial applications are considered, it is probable that a rather higher unit cost would be acceptable than in the case of a very small domestic installation. On the other hand, the apparatus should be more robust, have a longer working life and should incorporate a degree of automatic control. A first cost of £15 to £20/kW should allow for certain refinements and would still be less than an equivalent diesel generator set. With amortisation over 10 to 15 years, the fixed charges on the fuel battery would be between 0·2d. and 0·3d./kWh, assuming a 20 per cent. load factor. Operating expenses such as wages, repairs and maintenance, sundry stores, etc., would be less than for an internal combustion engine and should not exceed 0·3d./kWh. The fuel cost, on kerosene or T.V.O., would be 0·56d./kWh, the total operating costs being therefore 1·11d./kWh, which is considerably less than that of a comparable diesel generating set.

A further point which might, under certain circumstances, count in favour of a fuel battery is the possibility of waste heat utilisation. It has been stated above that, in operation under good conditions, the battery converts some 65 to 70 per cent. of the chemical energy of the fuel into electrical energy. The remaining 30 to 35 per cent. of the energy appears as waste heat which is at a high temperature and which could probably, for little extra cost, be efficiently utilised. Hence at least 90 to 95 per cent. of the energy in the fuel could be recovered in one form or another. It should also be noted that for many domestic and farm uses (e.g. heating and lighting) d.c. would be acceptable and no additional alternating equipment would be required.

Central Power Generation

The use of high-temperature fuel batteries for central power generation may be technically feasible and is a logical alternative to other methods in use and in the experimental stage. Virtually complete waste heat recovery should be possible and would provide bonus energy which could be profitably utilised. The simplicity of the generating plant, the absence of moving parts and the ease with which full automation would be possible would reduce operating and maintenance costs to a minimum. Quietness of running, the absence of smoke and the complete elimination of ashes, etc., should be further attractive advantages.

For large-scale transmission, alternating current is preferred and, therefore, provision for d.c./a.c. conversion must be made if fuel batteries are employed. Orthodox vibrators or rotary converters have the inherent failings of electromechanical systems and the overall efficiency of the generating plant would be reduced. Recent advances in the field of semi-conductors, however, have led to the development of high-efficiency equipment such as the transistor inverter and the silicon-controlled rectifier inverter, and although at present these applications appear to be limited to loads of about 1 kW, it is to be hoped that the principles might eventually be applied to high-output types.[11]

Present costs of thermal power stations run between £30 and £40/kW sent out, compared with £110/kW for a large nuclear power station (e.g. Dungeness).[12] Of the total capital cost of a thermal station, the boilers and generators probably account for £15 to £20/kW, the remainder being due to transformers, switchgear, transmission gear, civil engineering, etc. The cost of generating plant is recovered by amortisation over a maximum period of 25 years. With a fuel battery station, however, it should be possible to reduce the civil engineering cost appreciably because of the smaller size of the fuel battery compared with the boiler-generator set and the elimination of coal storage and coal and ash handling facilities. Cooling towers also would either be eliminated or considerably reduced in size or number. It is probable, therefore, that if the fixed charges on fuel battery stations are to be comparable with those of thermal stations, the batteries themselves must not cost more than about £20/kW and must give trouble-free operation for at least 25 years. Considerable research on materials and methods of fabrication will be necessary, but these desiderata should not be considered unattainable.

If power is to be supplied to the consumer at an acceptable price, the total generating cost must not be more than 0·9 to 1·0d./kWh. If the fixed charges are 0·2d./kWh with operating labour, maintenance, stores, etc., totalling another 0·15d./kWh, the cost of the fuel must not exceed, say, 0·6d./kWh. This is equivalent to a fuel gas cost of approximately 12d./therm. In the year ended 31st March 1959 the net manufacturing cost to the Gas Boards of gas (town gas, water gas, oil gas, etc.) was 11·58d./therm.[7] It seems likely, therefore, that low-cost power could be obtained if a fuel battery station were supplied with synthetic gases produced at a nearby plant which might itself be able to effect economies by making use of the waste heat from the power station. If these combined power station/gas plants were situated near fossil fuel supplies—and peat might be useable—the consequent reduction in transport charges might also lead to quite considerable reductions in the overall cost of power generation.

It has been shown that the fuel cell has many advantages under a variety of conditions. Economic assessments under present conditions, however, involve uncertain factors and long-range forecasts and tend to suggest marginal savings only in some cases. More research and development is necessary before the operating characteristics, lifetime and costs of the batteries can be fully evaluated. It is considered that, for commercial exploitation, the cost of the battery must be reduced to £10 to £20/kW depending on the size and the degree of automation, etc. With mass-production techniques, however, these requirements should be met within five to ten years. The ultimate need then will be for cheap sources of gaseous fuels and, in the absence of natural deposits, it is likely that commercial development in the U.K. will depend on advances made in gasification techniques and possibly on increased supplies of lower hydrocarbons from oil refineries.

REFERENCES

1. National Coal Board, Report and Accounts, 1959. H.M.S.O.
2. *J. Inst. Fuel*, 1959, XXXII, No. 218, p. 98.
3. Report of the Scottish Peat Committee, 1954. H.M.S.O.
4. Cullen (1960). *J. Inst. Fuel*, XXXIII, No. 234, p. 317.
5. N.S.H.E.B. Report and Accounts, 1959. H.M.S.O.
6. *Nature*, 1957, **180**, No. 4600, p. 1944.
7. The Gas Council, Annual Report and Accounts, 1958-59. H.M.S.O.
8. *The Engineer*, Oct. 30th, 1959, p. 527.
9. South of Scotland Electricity Board, Report and Accounts, 1959. H.M.S.O.
10. Horner *et al.* (1960). *J. Inst. Fuel*, XXXIII, No. 230, p. 111.
11. *The Wireless World*, Aug. 1960, p. 399.
12. Sir C. Hinton, Lecture to Royal Society, July 1960.

A Survey of Electricity Supply in Scotland

J. HENDERSON, C.B.E., M.C., B.SC., A.R.T.C., M.I.E.E.
Chief Engineer, South of Scotland Electricity Board, Glasgow

C. L. C. ALLAN, B.A., M.I.C.E., M.I.E.E.
Chief Electrical and Mechanical Engineer, North of Scotland Hydro-Electric Board, Edinburgh

The responsibility for the public supply of electricity rests with the South of Scotland Electricity Board and the North of Scotland Hydro-Electric Board. The territories for which these Boards are responsible respectively lie to the south and north of the line from Arrochar to the Firth of Tay.

This paper reviews the operations of the two Boards, commencing with a brief historical review followed by a summary of the powers and duties of the respective Boards. Estimates based on past experience are given of the future requirements of electricity and the probable sources, i.e. coal, nuclear and water power, from which the requirements will be generated are stated. A description is then given of the existing generating plant, the high-voltage grid network and the development of the distribution system.

The capital expenditure over the last few years is surveyed and estimates are given of the expenditure to be incurred during the next few years.

A section is included to show how the type and location of future generating plant are governed by the energy resources available and details are given of the possible generating plant construction programme which will be required to cover the requirements up to 1970.

Finally, a section is given describing the social aspects of the electricity supply industry.

HISTORICAL

Before 1948 a public supply of electricity could only be given after a licence or provisional order had been obtained in accordance with the Electric Lighting Acts, 1882 and 1888. Such licences were non-monopolistic and included provision for the purchase of the undertaking by the local authority. Large-scale enterprise was thus discouraged and a number of small undertakings each with its own generating station grew up mainly in the urban areas.

Prior to the 1914-18 War the main undertakings were operated by the Corporations of Glasgow, Edinburgh, Dundee and Aberdeen, the Clyde Valley Electric Power Company, the Fife Electric Power Company and the Scottish Central Electricity Power Company.

Subsequent to the Electricity Supply Act, 1919, the functions of promoting, regulating and supervising the supply of electricity and for securing reorganisation by voluntary agreement became the responsibility of the Electricity Commissioners.

It was soon appreciated that considerable economies could be obtained by concentrating generation in a smaller number of large generating stations. This process was accelerated by the setting up under the Electricity Act, 1926, of the Central Electricity Board, whose functions were: (*a*) to construct a 132-kV grid interconnecting certain "selected" generating stations which remained in the ownership of the companies and local authorities, (*b*) to control the generation of electricity and to purchase energy from the owners of selected stations and sell such energy to local undertakings, (*c*) to arrange for the construction of new generating plant, (*d*) to standardise frequency. The original 132-kV grid was constructed during the years 1929-31 and, as a result, it was possible to close down a large number of the smaller generating stations.

There were also significant developments in hydro generation. In 1927 the Clyde Valley Power Company completed the Bonnington and Stonebyres generating stations on the Falls of Clyde. In 1936 the Galloway Power Company completed the Galloway scheme while the Grampian Electricity Supply Company completed the Rannoch station in 1930 and the Tummel station in 1933.

The North of Scotland Hydro-Electric Board, responsible to the Secretary of State for Scotland, was set up under the Hydro-Electric Development (Scotland) Act, 1943, to develop water power in those areas in the North of Scotland not already covered by statutory orders.

The electricity supply industry was nationalised in 1948 under the Electricity Bill, 1947. The industry in South Scotland came under the British Electricity Authority and the South-East and South-West Scotland Area Boards. The North of Scotland Hydro-Electric Board became responsible for generation, transmission and distribution of electricity in Scotland north of the line from Arrochar to the Firth of Tay. Forty-four separate electricity undertakings in Scotland were thus reduced to four. This arrangement continued until 1955, when under the Electricity Reorganisation (Scotland) Act, 1954, the South of Scotland Electricity Board was set up and became responsible to the Secretary of State for generation, transmission and distribution throughout the areas formerly administered by the Central Electricity Authority and the South-West and South-East Electricity Boards. The number of Electricity Supply undertakings in Scotland was thereby reduced to two.

POWERS AND DUTIES OF THE SCOTTISH ELECTRICITY BOARDS

The two Electricity Boards are charged by Act of Parliament with the responsibility for the development of generation of electricity and for planning and carrying out an efficient and economical distribution of supplies of electricity in their respective districts. In addition, the North Board have the duties of developing the hydro power resources in their area to meet the load in their district and to export power to the South Board. Income from this export is one of the principal means of financing the development of uneconomic electricity distribution in the sparsely populated areas. The North Board were also directed by the Act to collaborate in carrying out any measures for the economic development and social improvement of the North of Scotland. Each Board is accountable to the Secretary of State for Scotland. The arrangement differs from that of the Electricity Supply Industry in England and Wales, where the responsibility for generation and main transmission rests with the Central Electricity Generating Board and is separate from the responsibility for distribution which rests with twelve Area Boards—the Electricity Council providing co-ordination. These bodies are accountable to the Minister of Fuel and Power.

The North of Scotland Hydro-Electric Board has to serve an area of 21,600 square miles and a population of 1·2 million (55·6 per square mile) and the South of Scotland Electricity Board an area of 8,160 square miles and a population of 4 millions (490 per square mile). The area served by the South of Scotland Board by agreement with the North-Eastern Electricity Board includes Berwick-upon-Tweed and a small part of Northumberland, including Holy Island.

In the North Board's district there are no coal reserves and since it is cheaper to transmit electricity in large quantities than to transport coal, the coal-burning generating stations have been situated near the coalfields in the South Board's district. Close co-operation is required between the two Boards in the operation of the generating plant to ensure that the hydro and thermal plant are used to their best advantage. It would for example be wasteful to use limited water storage to generate electricity at night when the most efficient thermal stations are available, whereas it is most economic to reserve the water storage to generate electricity at times of heavy system demand when it would otherwise be necessary to use the older and least efficient thermal plant.

The agreement for supply between the two Boards provides for advance notice by the North Board of the maximum power and quantity of energy to be made available for export during the year and in each month of the year. To make maximum use of the output available from rainfall the export to the South Board can be increased on the basis of a weekly programme agreed in advance. Sometimes heavy and continuous rainfall may require the generation of extra quantities of energy at short notice if spilling of water from reservoirs is to be avoided, and in such cases arrangements are made to reduce thermal generation. A lower price per unit is then paid for this extra delivery at short notice.

Agreement has been reached between the two Boards whereby the South Board will provide supplies of thermal energy to the North Board during off-peak times. In the event of a shortage of water in the North of Scotland district during the summer months, additional supplies can be given.

When the South Board decided to build the nuclear station at Hunterston it was estimated that at certain light load periods more output than there was load in the district might be obtained from Hunterston, run of river hydro plant and the highly efficient new coal burning station at Kincardine. It was considered that a pumped storage scheme would absorb the surplus output at times of light load and supply energy at peak load times at an economic price. It was, therefore, agreed that a pumped storage scheme should be built by the North Board at Loch Awe.

GROWTH OF LOAD

The growth of the demand for and consumption of electricity in the whole of Scotland since 1949 is shown in Fig. 1. This indicates an average increase in consumption of approximately 7 per cent. per annum at compound interest. The growth has been so consistent that the trend may be expected to continue for a number of years, and in the graph the trend has been continued up to 1968. It will be noted that the consumption is expected to double in the present decade. The annual increase in the maximum demand is at a slightly lower rate, namely $6\frac{1}{2}$ per cent. The changing pattern of industrial life due to the five-day week and the reduction in the number of working hours per week tends to reduce the load factor. However, due to efforts to encourage the use of electricity at off-peak periods by special tariffs, the load factor, which is at present about 47 per cent., shows a trend to increase gradually.

The estimated requirements of the two Boards up till 1967 are given in Table I. This table shows the amounts which it is expected will be generated by coal, nuclear and water power resources.

EXISTING GENERATING PLANT

The situation of the coalfields and of water power resources are shown in Fig. 2 and the details of the existing generating plant of the two Boards are given in Table II, in which the plant is split into groups associated with specific coalfields or catchment areas.

In addition to the plant shown in the table, the South Board take a supply from the atomic energy factory at Chapelcross, which has a total output capacity of 184 MW and a firm output of 115 MW.

The Barony station in Ayrshire, completed late in 1957, burns colliery waste or slurry at the rate of about 200,000 tons per annum. The possibility of constructing a second colliery-waste station in East Fife is being actively pursued at the present time.

Kincardine generating station was designed by the British Electricity Authority, the South Board's predecessors, and was laid out for six 120-MW generating units. In 1956 the Board reviewed the generating plant construction programme and, after investigation, decided to instal two 200-MW generating units in place of the fourth, fifth and sixth 120-MW units in order to obtain a reduction in cost per kW and to obtain an increased thermal efficiency.

It is of interest to note that in 1959 the average thermal efficiency of the coal-burning stations in South Scotland, excluding the slurry-burning station at Barony, was 26·14 per cent. compared with a figure of 24·74 per cent. in 1955. Higher figures over 27 per cent. are expected in the future—the first generators at Kincardine are operating at an efficiency of over 33 per cent. and later units will be of a further improved efficiency. The significance of the improvement in thermal efficiency will be appreciated when it is realised that had the thermal efficiency remained at the 1955 level additional fuel requirements would have cost £690,000 in 1959.

There are two hydro schemes in the South Board's district, namely the Galloway scheme and the Lanarkshire scheme. The Galloway scheme was completed in 1936 and includes the generating stations at Tongland, Glenlee, Kendoon, Carsfad and Earlstoun, having a combined capacity of 102 MW and an average annual output of 220 million units. The Lanarkshire scheme was completed in 1926 and includes two run-of-river generating stations on the Falls of Clyde at Bonnington and Stonebyres having a combined capacity of 15 MW and an average annual output of 80 million units.

Hydro schemes have been developed in nearly every part of the North Board's area where sites are available. Some small stations enabled local distribution schemes to be started while larger ones met growth of load in the Board's system and provided for an

Table I

Estimated Future Requirements and Generating Sources in Scotland

		1960	1961	1962	1963	1964	1965	1966	1967
Requirements									
S.S.E.B.	Units $\times 10^6$	7,800	8,400	9,000	9,650	10,300	11,060	11,900	12,800
	MW	1,960	2,080	2,220	2,360	2,510	2,680	2,850	3,040
H.E.B.	Units $\times 10^6$	1,825	1,990	2,160	2,340	2,510	2,690	2,880	3,080
	MW	550	595	645	695	745	800	855	915
Combined	Units $\times 10^6$	9,625	10,390	11,160	11,990	12,810	13,750	14,780	15,880
	MW	2,510	2,675	2,865	3,055	3,255	3,480	3,705	3,955
To be met by									
Coal-fired Stations									
S.S.E.B.	Units $\times 10^6$	5,900	6,750	7,475	7,965	7,615	7,520	8,465	9,380
H.E.B.	,, ,,	85	135	85	85	85	85	85	80
Hydro Stations									
S.S.E.B.	,, ,,	300	300	300	300	300	300	300	300
H.E.B.	,, ,,	2,320	2,385	2,490	2,730	2,850	2,935	3,020	3,210
Nuclear S.S.E.B.	,, ,,	800	800	800	900	1,950	2,900	2,900	2,900
From C.E.G.B. and Sundry Sources	,, ,,	220	20	10	10	10	10	10	10
Total to be met from Statutory Undertakings	Units $\times 10^6$	9,405	10,370	11,150	11,980	12,800	13,740	14,770	15,870

TABLE II

Generating Stations (as at end August 1960)

S.S.E.B.		N.S.H.E.B.	
Station or Group	Capacity MW.s.o.	Station or Group	Capacity MW.s.o.
COAL-BURNING		HYDRO	
Lanarkshire — now largely worked out—supplies also from Fife, Lothians and Central Ayrshire:		Tummel Valley	243
		Conon Valley	177
		Breadalbane	117
		Sloy	181
Clyde's Mill	266	Garry-Moriston	100
Dalmarnock	246	Shin	38
Yoker	96	Isolated	18
Braehead	198		
Pinkston	63	Total Hydro	874
Stirlingshire—supply limited:			
Bonnybridge	60	COAL-BURNING—Supplies from Fife	
Fife—existing and being developed:		Aberdeen	57
		Dundee	76
Kincardine	336		
Dunfermline	20	Total Coal-burning	133
Central Ayrshire — supply limited:		DIESEL PLANT	
Kilmarnock	56	In full operation	38
		On Standby	10
Southern Ayrshire—Slurry—limited supply:		Total Diesel	48
Barony	56		
Lothians—existing and being developed:			
Portobello	244		
Total Coal-burning	1,641		
HYDRO			
Galloway Scheme	107		
Falls of Clyde	15		
Total Hydro	122		
Total Plant	1,763	Total Plant	1,055

Total Combined Capacity of Both Boards 2,818 MW.

export to the South Board which is now 400 MW. The largest scheme completed is Sloy with 130 MW installed. In the fourteen years before the North Board was set up six scheme promotions failed, but the powers and duties of the Board, with safeguards for protection of scenery, fisheries and other interests, have allowed development to go ahead more readily. Altogether 781 MW of hydro plant has been commissioned and 582 MW is under construction. Before 1943 85 MW had been developed for public supply and 114 MW for aluminium production.

A number of diesel stations are operated mainly on islands where they provide the cheapest means of local generation. A number of diesel stations on the mainland have been closed or relegated to standby duty as grid connections extended farther afield and enabled cheaper power to be delivered.

HIGH-VOLTAGE TRANSMISSION SYSTEM

The 132-kV transmission system which was inaugurated by the Central Electricity Board in 1930 has been extended and developed to meet increased requirements due to load growth. In 1948 the 132-kV system was as shown in Figure 3A. At the end of 1959 the system was as shown in Fig. 3B. In 1956 the 275-kV line linking Clyde's Mill to the C.E.G.B.'s 275-kV system at Karker, near Carlisle, was commissioned.

The total length of all 132-kV lines in existence in 1948 was

	Miles
S.S.E.B.	492
H.E.B.	246
Total S.S.E.B. and H.E.B.	738

At the end of 1959 the total length of all 132-kV lines and of the Clyde's Mill/Harker 275-kV line was—

	Miles
S.S.E.B.	1,006 (including 275-kV line)
H.E.B.	1,549
Total S.S.E.B. and H.E.B.	2,555

The South Board's 132-kV system has been developed during the last fivc years to enable twelve new bulk supply points to be connected, to reinforce seven existing bulk supply points and to link the generating stations, including the new station at Kincardine, with them in such a manner that the generating stations may be loaded in accordance with their order of merit.

In the North Board's 132-kV system the outputs from the hydro stations are collected at six major control points (Shin, Beauly, Fort Augustus, Errochty, Killin and Sloy) and, in addition, there are connections to the cities of Aberdeen and Dundee and to the South Board at Windyhill (near Glasgow), Bonnybridge and Abernethy; other radial feeders extend outwards to Caithness, Argyllshire, Moray, Nairn and Aberdeenshire. During the last five years thirteen new bulk supply points have been commissioned and three existing points have been reinforced. In addition, three new switching stations have been built to deal with extensions to the 132-kV network.

DISTRIBUTION DEVELOPMENT

The growth of the number of consumers connected to each of the Board's systems is shown in Table III in which the consumers are classified. New consumers have been connected during the last five years at the approximate rates of 21,000 per annum in the South Board's system and 12,000 per annum in the North Board's system: these were largely from new housing estates.

The North Board estimate that 90 per cent. of the total number of potential consumers in their district have been connected. Some of the remainder are on islands where expensive diesel generation or, alternatively, costly submarine cable connection to the main grid would be necessary to give supply. About 2,000 to 3,000 premises will be so costly to connect that it will be a long time before supplies can be brought to them. A small percentage of the remainder is near enough to existing distribution systems to enable supply to be readily provided if required. Rural schemes at present planned or in progress will provide supply to about 5,000 consumers.

The South Board's programme for rural development was virtually completed at the end of 1959, by which time 3,811 farms had been connected since the Board was formed. Many farmers limit their use of the supply to the farmhouse and the lighting of farm buildings, and efforts have therefore been directed towards the extended use of electricity in rural areas.

The L.V. distribution voltage is 240 throughout the area. Prior to 1955 there were certain areas supplied at d.c. and non-standard voltages, but the voltage has now been standardised throughout the area and all d.c. supplies have been replaced by a.c. supplies.

The Boards' distribution systems are being continually reinforced to meet the increasing requirements of consumers. The rate of extension can be assessed from the figures given in Table IV, which shows for successive years the total length of all overhead lines and underground cables at all voltages associated with distribution.

CAPITAL EXPENDITURE

The capital expenditure of the two Boards since 1955 under the headings Generation, Main Transmission and Distribution is given in Table V.

The South Board's expenditure on generation for 1958 and 1959 was high relative to the preceding years due primarily to the cost of the nuclear station at Hunterston. The total capital expenditure at Hunterston up to the end of 1959 was £20·41 million, of which £10·67 million was spent in 1959. The remainder of the capital expenditure on generation for 1959 was largely in respect of the Kincardine generating station, where expenditure amounting to £5·45 million was incurred. The total expenditure at Kincardine up to the end of 1959 was £21·03 million. It is expected that the Hunterston station will be completed by 1964 and the second half of the Kincardine generating station in 1963. Braehead generating station is also being extended by the installation of a 60-MW set due for commissioning in 1961. It is estimated that the total capital expenditure on generation during the years 1960-64 inclusive will be of the order of £60 million.

TABLE III

Consumers Connected

	1955		1956		1957		1958		1959	
	S.S.E.B.	H.E.B.	S.S.E.B.	H.E.B.	S.S.E.B.	H.E.B.	S.S.E.B.	H.E.B.	S.S.E.B.	H.E.B.
Domestic .	1,098,253	272,740	1,127,184	282,893	1,155,554	292,392	1,178,467	300,332	1,197,600	307,892
Crofts . .	—	11,329	—	12,082	—	13,008	—	13,266	—	13,544
Farms . .	11,419	9,223	12,186	10,715	12,863	11,854	13,821	12,789	14,488	13,966
Commercial .	113,122	37,699	115,552	38,497	116,642	39,482	117,590	40,302	118,763	41,199
Industrial .	11,224	6,841	11,296	7,016	11,450	7,143	11,468	7,179	11,494	7,282
Public Lighting	141	308	140	321	140	323	141	331	141	359
Traction .	2	—	1	—	1	—	1	—	1	—
Total . .	1,234,161	338,140	1,266,359	351,524	1,296,650	364,202	1,321,488	374,199	1,342,487	384,242

TABLE IV

Development of Distribution System

	Circuit Miles							
	S.S.E.B.					N.S.H.E.B.		
	1955	1956	1957	1958	1959	1957	1958	1959
Overhead Lines								
33,000 volts	643	741	905	953	1,003	1,771	1,841	1,991
22,000 ,,	248	240	237	248	235	305	312	315
11,000 ,,	4,655	5,054	5,445	5,967	6,417	6,444	6,908	7,431
6,600 ,,	370	397	399	387	388	20	19	19
Over 650 ,, and under 6,000 ,,	47	46	43	43	35	2	4	4
Medium and Low Voltage	3,064	3,223	3,357	3,508	3,609	4,187	4,371	4,522
Total	9,027	9,701	10,386	11,106	11,687	12,729	13,455	14,282
Underground Cables								
33,000 volts	155	176	194	226	272	52	54	62
22,000 ,,	252	247	242	194	193	2	4	4
11,000 ,,	2,590	2,690	2,772	2,891	3,015	407	425	444
6,600 ,,	878	900	926	966	983	366	369	378
Over 650 ,, and under 6,000 ,,	225	216	212	200	185	14	14	14
Medium and Low Voltage	11,130	11,456	11,823	12,096	12,421	1,676	1,732	1,773
Total	15,230	15,685	16,169	16,573	17,069	2,517	2,598	2,675

TABLE V

Capital Expenditure

	1956	1957	1958	1959	Capital Assets at 31st Dec. 1959
South of Scotland Electricity Board	£	£	£	£	£
Generation . .	8,457,122	9,760,981	17,589,326	16,563,846	96,419,368
Transmission . .	1,131,385	2,153,958	2,397,969	2,509,825	18,785,580
Distribution . .	6,827,501	6,691,018	7,075,023	7,728,288	93,048,895
Other . . .	517,906	632,770	555,858	575,033	5,997,299
Total	16,933,914	19,238,727	27,618,176	27,377,042	214,251,142
North of Scotland Hydro-Electric Board					
Generation . .	14,946,006	13,189,839	11,499,556	8,789,966	147,081,057
Transmission . .	1,579,741	1,319,146	1,420,491	1,469,178	16,604,697
Distribution . .	2,930,007	2,351,166	2,459,800	2,708,339	40,253,180
Other . . .	17,089	19,101	18,286	29,180	1,358,896
Total	19,472,843	16,879,252	15,398,133	12,996,663	205,297,830

Capital expenditure on generation by the South Board in respect of plant to be commissioned in 1965 and 1966 will be relatively small because for these two years it is intended that the increase in demand should be met by providing a pumped storage scheme at Cruachan, the expenditure in respect of which will be met by the North Board. The estimated cost of this 400-MW scheme is £38/kW excluding transmission and will require a capital expenditure of £15·2 million.

Plans are at present under consideration for a further new thermal generating station in the South Board's district to be commissioned in the period 1967-70. This station will have an output capacity of the order of 1,200 MW and will probably be situated in the Lothian coalfield. This new station will entail an expenditure of the order of £54 million.

It is expected that in the years 1960-64 inclusive the South Board's expenditure on the main transmission system will be of the order of £16 million, including an amount of about £10 million in respect of the 275-kV supergrid system which was released for construction at the end of 1957. Expenditure on the distribution systems will continue to increase at a rate consistent with the increase in load. The anticipated expenditure in the South Board for the years 1960-64 will be of the order of £43 million.

The large area over which the North Board have to supply electricity requires an extensive and expensive high-voltage transmission system; there has also been a large expenditure on distribution made particularly heavy by the high cost of distribution schemes in the thinly populated areas. Transmission expenditure during the years 1960-1964 inclusive will account for an expenditure of about £6 million. About £3 million of this will be in respect of 275-kV construction, including part of the expenditure on the transmission for the Cruachan scheme. Distribution expenditure for the same period is estimated to be £13 million.

Although the production cost of a hydro scheme is economic, the capital cost is considerably more than that of a steam station. Well over 90 per cent. of the operating costs are interest and depreciation payments, but there is, of course, no bill for fuel. Operating costs are, therefore, very nearly independent of future changes in costs so that investment in a hydro scheme, even if only marginally advantageous at the outset compared with other alternatives, is likely to be increasingly profitable as time goes on. The actual construction costs of individual stations vary over quite a large range depending on the situation of the scheme and the load factor. The relatively high cost of hydro development is the main reason for the large capital investment of the North Board amounting to £147 million up to the end of 1959. This includes £3·3 million on steam generation and £2·2 million on diesel generation. For the period 1960-64 inclusive it is estimated that the capital expenditure on generation will be £7·7 million. Apart from a small sum for diesel extensions, this expenditure covers hydro generation and early expenditure on the Cruachan pumped storage scheme.

ENERGY RESOURCES AND FACTORS AFFECTING THE TYPE AND LOCATION OF FUTURE GENERATION DEVELOPMENTS

Resources Available

In Scotland the most abundant indigenous source of energy is coal. It was estimated in 1942 that the total coal resources, located mainly in the Forth-Clyde belt, where 9,000 millions tons, of which about 2,400 million tons could be worked economically. In 1958 the total consumption of coal for all purposes was 19·2 million tons and it is expected to remain at about 18 million tons during the next ten years. Some of the coalfields, for example Lanarkshire, have been largely worked out, but new fields are being opened up, particularly in Fife and Lothians.

Water power resources are also considerable. It has been estimated that 10,000 GWh* could be produced annually, but the final extent will depend on economics. The total amount already developed by the North Board produces an average of 2,400 GWh per annum. The two schemes of the South Board have an average output per annum of 300 GWh.

In 1949 it was estimated that peat covered 1,625,000 acres or 8 per cent. of Scottish land area. After allowance for moisture and other factors it was estimated that 90 million tons of dry peat might be useable altogether. There are few peat areas sufficiently extensive to support a 30-MW generating station for twenty-five years. A small scale pilot experimental plant (approximately 2 MW) has been installed at Altnabreac in Caithness to test the possibility of milled peat for electricity production using a closed-cycle gas turbine.

Experiments in the development of wind generators have been carried out, but these are relatively small units and wind is not a firm source.

No known deposits of ore exist with a sufficiently high content of uranium to justify mining and, in consequence, nuclear development will be dependent on imported uranium or uranium ore. The purchase of uranium ore, its refining and fabrication into fuel elements is the responsibility of the United Kingdom Atomic Energy Authority.

* 1 GWh=10^6 kWh=the approximate amount of electricity which can be generated from 500 tons of coal.

In the North of Scotland the development of economic tidal power projects would be extremely difficult. This is because the range of tides at the likely sites is small, varying from 10 to 12 ft. at spring and 3 to 5 ft. at neap tides. The corresponding figures for the Severn Estuary, where a scheme has been under consideration for many years, are 40 and 20 ft. respectively. There are no possible tidal schemes in the Southern Area.

Factors affecting the Type of Future Generation Developments

The Lothians, Stirlingshire and Fife coalfields are now the economic sources of coal for new base load stations and the 760-MW Kincardine station in Fife will draw its supplies from pits within a ten-mile radius. During the period 1966-70 it will be necessary to instal generating capacity at a yearly rate of 200 to 300 MW. It would not be economical nor practicable to provide more than a small part of this by hydro and, in consequence, the bulk must be provided by thermal plant.

The cost of new coal-burning stations is approximately £45/kW and the estimated fuel cost would be about 0·37d. per unit. As there will be a surplus of coal produced in Scotland from 1967 onwards, a new thermal station is planned for the Lothians area to have a total capacity of the order of 1,200 MW, the generating sets being within the range of 200 to 300 MW.

Conditions in the North and West of Scotland favour water power development. The rainfall is sometimes as high as 150 inches per annum in places and the yearly pattern of its occurrence conforms generally with the seasonal variation in electrical load.

Rainfall varies from 70 per cent. of the long-term average in a dry year to about 150 per cent. in a wet year, so that a high load factor scheme requires considerable storage. The number of good reservoir sites is, however, limited and to obtain a very high degree of storage is almost prohibitive in cost in Scottish conditions. Low load factor schemes, however, require only moderate storage, and experience in the joint operation of hydro and thermal plants has demonstrated that surplus thermal energy available in the summer can economically make good the deficiency of hydro production in dry periods.

The characteristics suitable for pumped storage are relatively high head with limited upper storage capacity and short tunnel length. They should also have storage capacity at the lower level of adequate capacity to allow for the considerable flow of water required during the pumping and regeneration cycle without excessive level variation. A 400-MW pumped storage scheme to be commissioned in 1965-66 is to be built at Ben Cruachan, using Loch Awe as the lower reservoir. Another two schemes having a combined potential capacity up to 1,500 MW are possible, each of which would use Loch Lomond as the lower reservoir.

The growth of load in the Lanarkshire and Ayrshire districts required the provision of a base load station near these areas, and since no increased output can be expected from the Lanarkshire and Ayrshire coalfields it fitted in well with requirements when the possibility arose in 1956 of constructing the nuclear generating station at Hunterston having a capacity of 300 MW to be commissioned in 1963-64. Further development of nuclear generation on this site is possible in the future. A nuclear station is also envisaged on the North-East coast to meet the growth of load in that district, but this would not be before 1970.

In the North Board's district diesel generation on certain islands and in the remoter parts of the mainland has been carried out for some time as this was the only economic form of generation. Since diesel generation is costly the opportunity has been taken as the grid system extended to interconnect isolated mainland regions and lay submarine cables to the nearer islands. In the remote islands it is certain that diesel generation will require to continue for some considerable time.

FUTURE GENERATION PROGRAMME

The generating plant extension programme which is being considered for the years up to 1970 is shown in Table VI.

TABLE VI

Generating Plant Extensions Programme, 1961-70

Type	Capacity MW.s.o.	Capacity %	To be Commissioned	Remarks
Hydro	450	15·9	1961-70	Numerous Schemes
Pumped Storage	400	14·1	1965-66	Loch Awe
Nuclear	300	19·4	1963-64	Hunterston 6
	250		1970 or later	N.E. Coast or Ayrshire Coast
Coal	56	50·6	1961	Braehead
	376		1962-63	Kincardine
	1,000		About 1967-70	Lothians
Total	2,832			

The 450-MW hydro-electric plant is comprised of a number of separate schemes mainly in the North and West of Scotland.

The 400-MW Cruachan pumped storage scheme will comprise four 100-MW units and will be situated on the side of Loch Awe in Argyllshire. Pumping will be from Loch Awe to an upper reservoir on Ben Cruachan with a storage capacity of $7{\cdot}5 \times 10^6$ kWh and a head of 1,100 ft. It is hoped that reversible pump-turbines can be used for the first time at this head.

The 400-MW extension at Kincardine will bring the total installed capacity of this station to 760 MW, comprising altogether three 120-MW sets already in commission operating with steam at 1,500 p.s.i.g. 1,000° F. with reheat to 1,000° F. and two 200-MW sets to be commissioned in 1962-63 operating with steam at 2,350 p.s.i.g 1,050° F. with reheat to 1,000° F.

The nuclear station at Hunterston will consist of two natural uranium graphite moderated gas-cooled reactors and six 60-MW turbo-alternators operating with steam at 575 p.s.i.g. H.P., 145 p.s.i.g. L.P., at temperatures of 700° to 670° F.

The plant to be installed in the proposed Lothians station may consist of four 300-MW units, but the steam cycle has not yet been settled. The design will be such that the thermal efficiency of the station will be better than that at Kincardine by at least 2 per cent., giving a 6 per cent. saving in operating costs.

THE 275-kV SUPERGRID SYSTEM

To deal with the concentration of the thermal generating plant into fewer and larger generating stations in the South Board's district and the consequent increase in transmission flows, the South Board decided towards the end of 1957 to construct a new 275-kV transmission system to be superimposed on the existing 132-kV system.

The new lines will be constructed with extra heavy conductors and the carrying capacity will be five to six times the carrying capacity of the original 132-kV lines. The alternative policy of persisting with the 132-kV system would have resulted in the provision of many more new transmission lines due to their smaller carrying capacity.

The 275-kV supergrid which is now under construction is illustrated diagrammatically in Fig. 4. Broadly, the scheme comprises a ring of 275-kV lines encircling the central part of South Scotland with connections radiating to the North Board and to the C.E.G.B.'s system in England. New major sources of generation will feed their outputs into this main ring system and at other points large transforming stations will be constructed to feed into the 132-kV and 33-kV systems.

Although the lines from Hunterston to Neilston, near Paisley, will operate at 132 kV initially, they are insulated for 275 kV so that if additional capacity were ever required over this route this could be readily accomplished. The connection with the C.E.G.B.'s system runs from Clyde's Mill to Harker, near Carlisle, and consists of a double circuit twin 0·175 sq. in. 275 kV steel tower line.

In the North Board's district additional capacity is required between the concentration of hydro generation in the North and the load centre on the East coast. Consequently, contracts have recently been placed for 270 miles of 275-kV line between Beauly and Kintore and between Kintore and Tealing. These double circuit twin 0·175 sq. in. lines will be operated initially at 132 kV but will be raised to 275 kV working by about 1965. The South Board's 275-kV system will extend northwards to Abernethy, thus leaving a short section of 25 miles between Abernethy and Tealing to be completed in due course in order to link up the two systems. The North Board are negotiating at present for the route of the 275-kV double circuit line which will be required to connect the Loch Awe pumped storage scheme to the South Board's 275-kV network at Windyhill to the north-west of Glasgow.

SOCIAL ASPECTS OF ELECTRICITY SUPPLY

The population of Scotland is 5·2 million, of whom the working population is 2·4 million. The total numbers engaged in the electricity supply industries, that is the total number employed by the North Board and the South Board, was 15,800 at the end of 1959. The subdivision of this total between management, technical, accountancy, secretarial and manual workers is given in Table VII. The total employed in the industry amounted to 0·7 per cent. of the total working population, which is a remarkably small proportion.

Although the two Boards are not large direct employers of manpower, the rate of capital investment on plant is high and the South Board's thermal generating stations consume large quantities of coal. Both of these factors have a direct bearing in other sectors of industry.

TABLE VII

Numbers employed as at 31st December 1959

	S.S.E.B.	N.S.H.E.B.
Managerial and Higher Executive	117	69
Technical Engineering	1,127	380
Clerical, Accountancy, Sales, etc.	2,272	755
Manual	8,924	1,795
Technical Trainees and Apprentices	318	39
Total	12,758	3,038

The consumption of coal by thermal stations was 3 million tons in 1959 and it is estimated that by 1965 the quantity consumed will be of the order of 4 million tons, representing about 22 per cent. of the coal produced in Scotland.

The heavy engineering industry supplies boilers, turbo-alternators and associated plant for generating stations. Building and civil engineering work also make an important contribution to local employment. In the transmission and distribution of electricity transformers, switchgear, cables and meters are required. A large proportion of plant and equipment used is produced in Scotland.

Building of water turbines is now carried out in two places in South Scotland. To begin with orders were from the North Board, but the organisations expanded to deal with a considerable volume of export work.

Electricity supply in the North has been able to provide assistance to smaller industrial units, such as sawmills and small factories.

Great benefit has come to rural communities and the agricultural industry from the increased availability and use of electricity. Farm consumption of electricity has increased tremendously and development in the use of electric drives of various kinds, dairy sterilisers, grain and hay drying, has proceeded apace. In the North 66 per cent. of farms and 63 per cent. of crofts are now connected to the mains and in the South 94 per cent. of all farms have been connected. An electricity supply is a great asset to hotels and boarding houses and the growth of the tourist industry adds to the importance of this kind of development.

In the North Board's district there remains the problem of bringing supplies to the remote areas and islands where costs range from £400 per consumer upwards. At such high costs the return on the expenditure, even if the consumer makes a contribution, is quite uneconomic. Rural connections are still going on, but obviously a given expenditure per annum will connect fewer consumers each year as extensions are made into the more sparse areas.

During the years 1956-59 the two Boards have contributed payments in lieu of rates to the Secretary of State for Scotland. The payments over these years by the South Board amounted to £5·9 million and by the North Board £1·6 million. These sums were appropriately distributed among the local authorities in Scotland.

A large part of our present manner of living is essentially dependent on an abundant and reliable supply of electricity at an economic price and it would be difficult to imagine life without electricity as a service. Electricity gives to man the means to increase productivity and it is only by increasing productivity that we can continue to increase our standard of living. Electricity may, therefore, be regarded as the greatest single factor contributing to the well-being of any country.

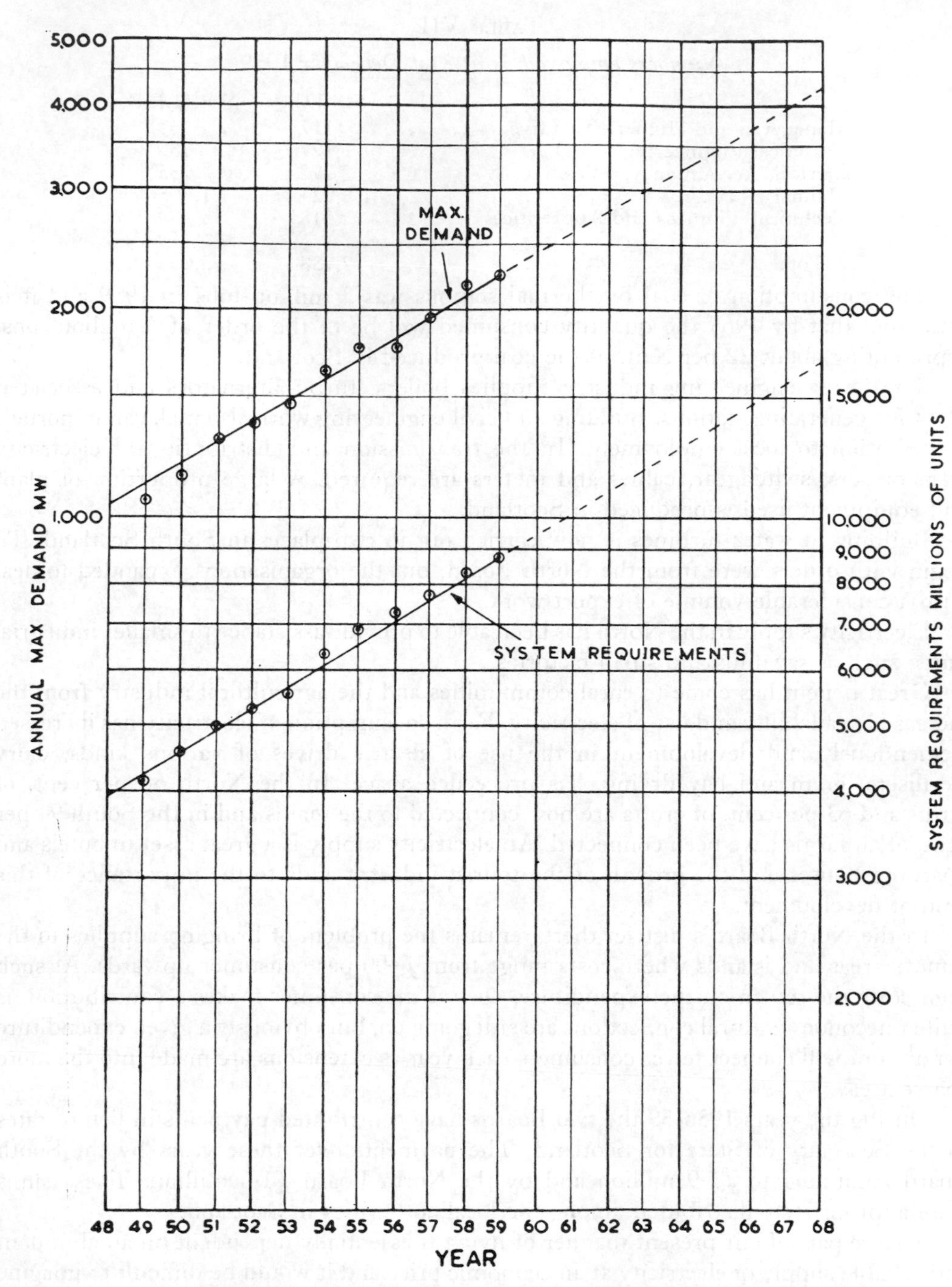

FIG. 1. Growth of Electricity Requirements in Scotland

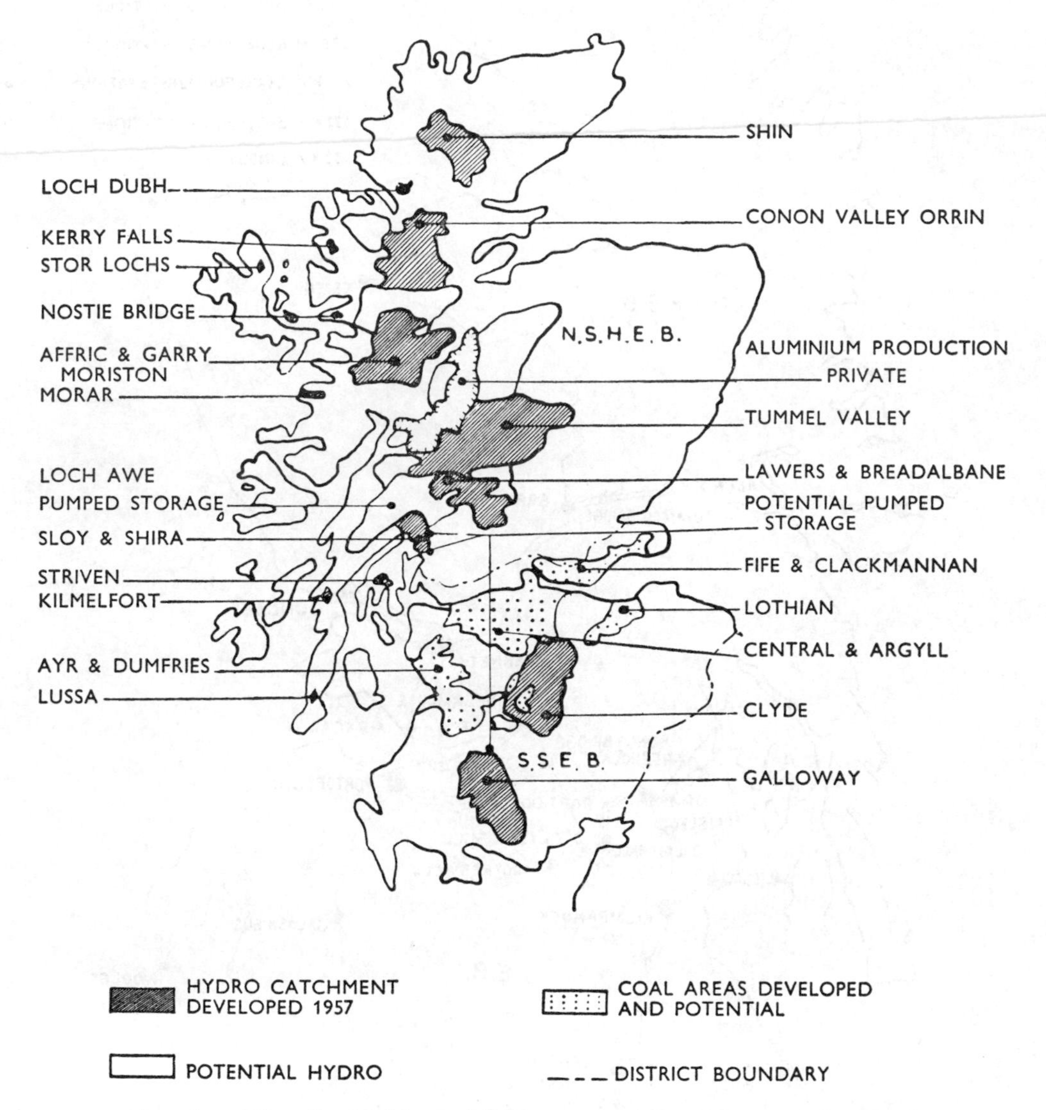

FIG. 2. The Coalfields and Water Power Resources of Scotland

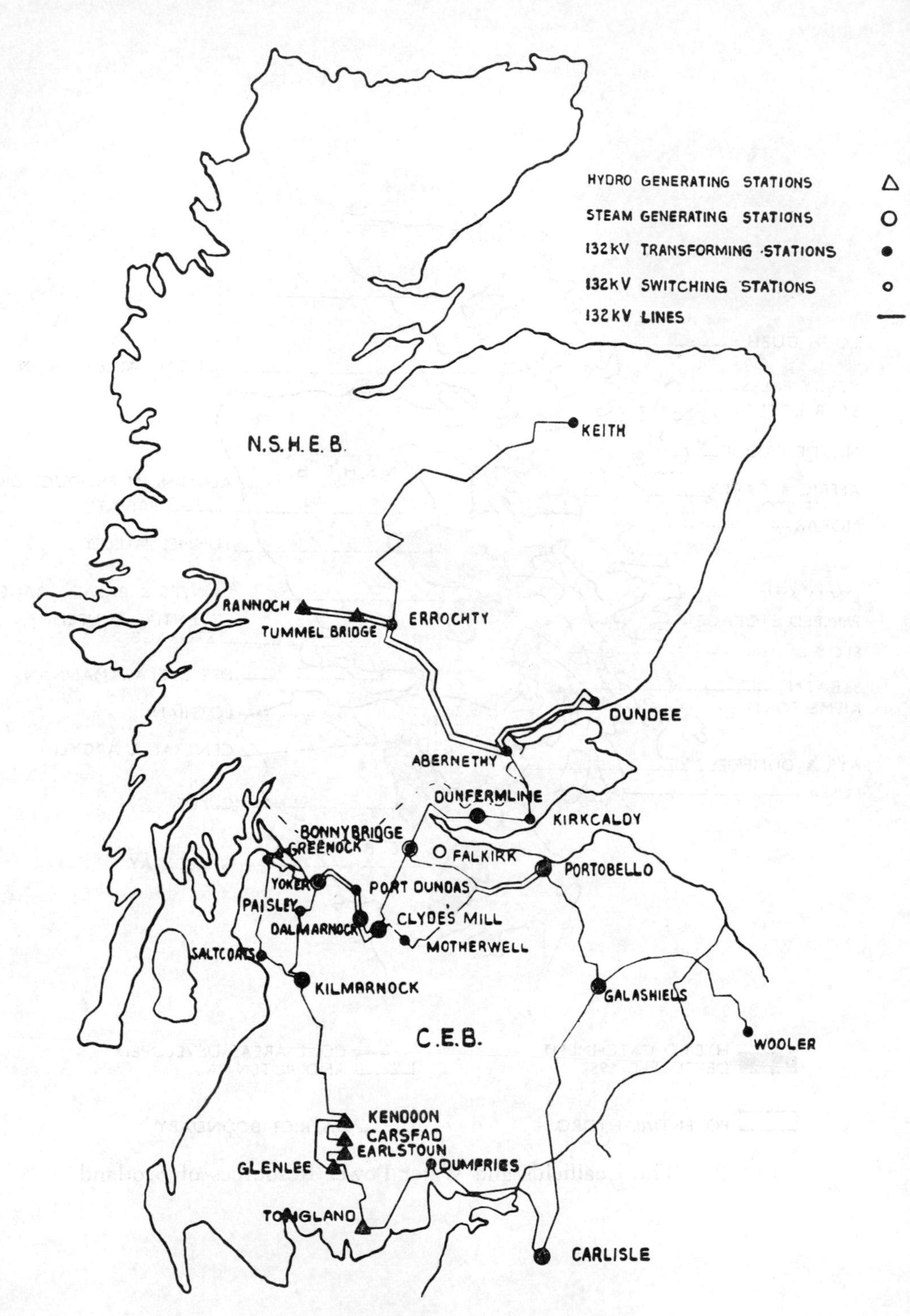

FIG. 3A. Grid System as in 1947

FIG. 3B. Grid System as in 1960

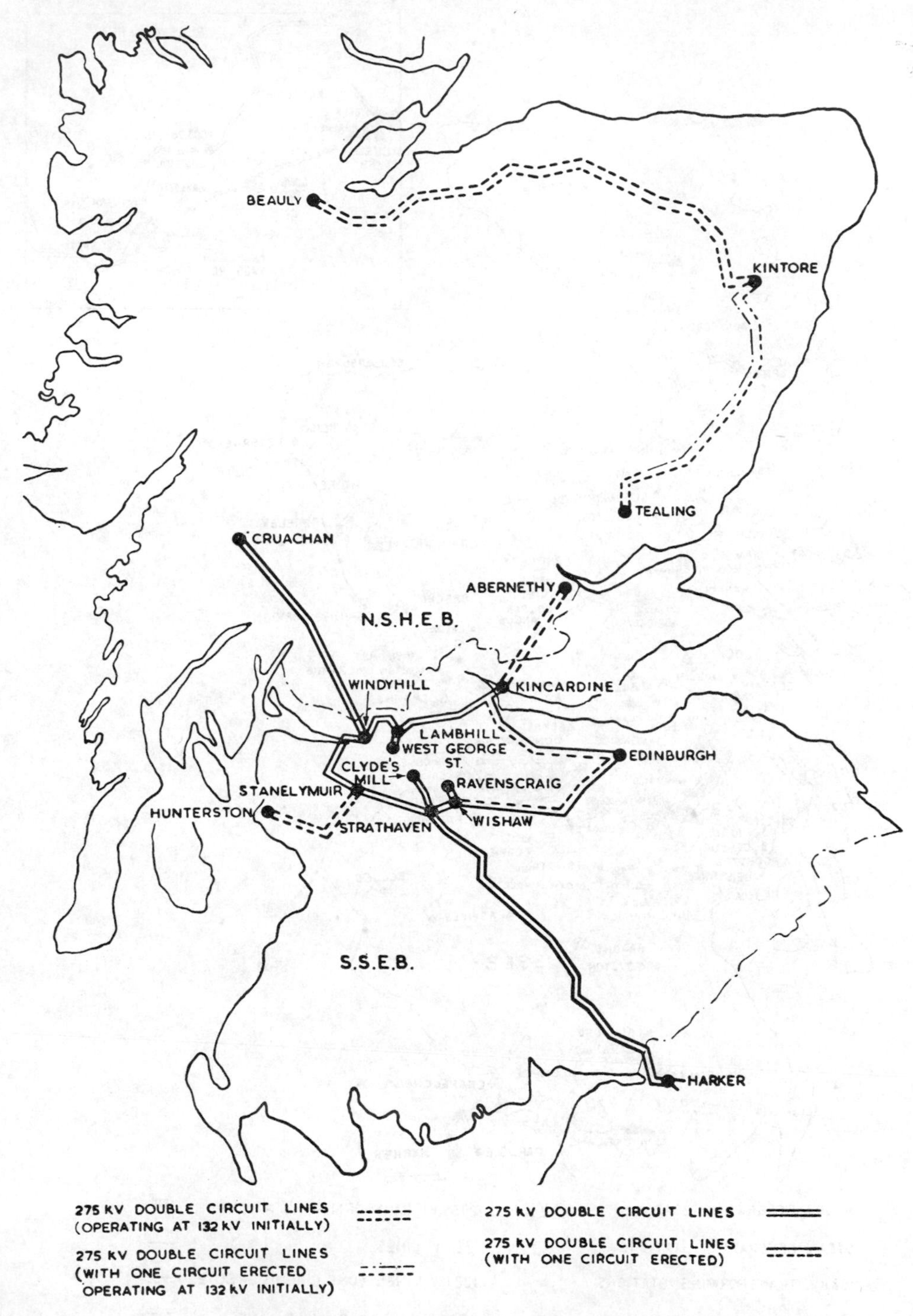

FIG. 4. 275 kV Super Grid to be Commissioned 1962/1965

Nuclear Energy

V. H. B. Macklen

Acting Head, Technical Secretariat, United Kingdom Atomic Energy Authority, Risley

As uranium, the essential raw material, does not exist in workable quantities in Scotland, nuclear energy must be considered from the point of view of assisting the full development of the country's indigenous resources and established industries.

At present the principal application is in electricity generation with radioisotopes as a by-product. Adequate power supplies are an essential pre-requisite for an expanding industry, and a wide range of applications of radioisotopes have led to important savings and improvements in many fields.

A promising future application of nuclear energy is to the propulsion of ships, which can have a major influence on one of Scotland's biggest industries.

In addition to the reactors and associated equipment at nuclear power stations, the ancillary plants in which fuel is manufactured and processed make heavy demands on special constructional materials and chemicals, while the instruments industry is called upon for a wide variety of products, both conventional and novel.

Thus, nuclear energy will bring to Scotland a new source of power, together with requirements from a number of different branches of industry; it will liberate coal and oil for use as chemical raw materials and will provide, through radioisotopes, a valuable industrial tool.

It may seem incongruous to discuss atomic energy at a conference which is primarily concerned with Scotland's natural resources and their utilisation, when uranium, the basic raw material, does not exist in workable quantities anywhere in the country. However, this is a situation not peculiar to Scotland. In the free world, uranium is mined in quantity by relatively few countries, but the energy available from this material is so much greater than from a comparable amount of any conventional fuel that most countries with industrial potential are planning to meet their increased demands for energy from nuclear power. Even for countries with established and relatively static industries, the use of uranium as a source of energy frees coal and oil for use as chemical raw materials, with consequent expansion of industries based on their by-products. For Scotland we must consider atomic energy from the point of view of augmenting the country's power supply and of assisting in the full utilisation of indigenous resources and of her established industries.

NUCLEAR REACTORS

You will all be familiar with the elementary principles involved in the production of heat from a nuclear reactor, how a small proportion of the uranium atoms are split by neutrons, releasing heat and more neutrons to carry on the chain reaction, and how the amount of heat generated can be controlled by governing the conditions within the reactor. In present-day plants, the heat is made to produce steam, which in turn is fed to turbo-generators to produce electricity. In this way energy derived from the nuclei of uranium atoms is converted into the more familiar form of electrical energy which lights our homes and runs our factories. You will also know that various types of reactor have been designed, and while it would be inappropriate to give detailed technical descriptions of them here, it will help in appreciating the potentialities and the limitations of this new source of energy to indicate the main differences between nuclear reactors and more conventional furnaces burning fossil fuels.

NUCLEAR AND CONVENTIONAL FURNACES

The vastly greater energy content of nuclear fuel has already been mentioned; in our current reactors one pound of uranium will produce as much heat as five tons of coal. This advantage, however, is offset to some extent by the fact that unless the reactor is bigger than a certain "critical" size, no chain reaction will take place because too many of the neutrons which help to maintain it will escape. In the first round of nuclear power stations, of which the station now being built at Hunterston is an example, this results in a reactor vessel some 60 to 70 ft. in diameter. Moreover, because of the radioactivity which is developed within the reactor, it must be surrounded by shielding to protect those operating the reactor from harmful effects; the biological shield, as it is called, consists of several feet of reinforced concrete. All this adds up to a massive construction which, when taken in conjunction with the elaborate and intricate mechanisms necessary for fuelling and controlling the reactor, represents over 50 per cent. of the cost of a nuclear power station, perhaps £27 million out of a total of about £50 million, which is the current cost of a two-reactor station.

Just as the nuclear reactor is much more complicated than conventional boiler-house plant, so is the care required in the preparation of nuclear fuel much greater than that exercised in the pre-treatment of fossil fuels. In the first place, uranium metal must be prepared from its ore to a standard of purity comparable with that demanded for pharmaceutical products; it must then be cast into bars, machined accurately to size, and hermetically sealed in special containers before it can be loaded into a reactor.

Similarly, the treatment of spent fuel is quite different. Whereas ash from coal-fired stations is valueless and often an embarrassment, fuel removed from nuclear reactors contains plutonium, which is a valuable by-product, together with fission products which, since they are lethally radioactive, must be separated, concentrated and stored indefinitely in heavily shielded tanks.

Another difference between nuclear and conventional furnaces is the temperature at which the fuel can be operated, and hence the temperature at which steam can be produced. The range of steam temperatures from our present reactors is about 600° to 700° F., compared with about 1,000° F. for conventional power stations. These lower temperatures result in lower thermal efficiencies, and a great deal of development work is being carried out with the object of producing fuel which can stand up to higher temperatures and so give better steam conditions. At the same time it is hoped to prolong the life of the fuel in the reactor and in this way extract more heat from a given amount.

A promising line of attack appears to involve the use of ceramic fuels based on uranium oxide in place of uranium metal rods, and the use of new cladding materials such as beryllium in place of the magnesium alloys used at present. Since the introduction of any material into a reactor tends to interfere with the chain reaction on which the smooth liberation of heat depends, some materials being more effective than others in this respect, the choice of cladding material is governed by nuclear characteristics as well as physical and chemical properties. These properties, too, can be appreciably altered by exposure to the intense bombardment by sub-atomic particles and radiation occurring within the reactor. Further, when withdrawn from a reactor, material invariably exhibits induced radioactivity, with the result that handling problems are set up and have to be surmounted.

Summarising, therefore, we can regard a nuclear reactor as a cumbersome device which will generate heat at a moderate temperature, which draws on a number of industries for its design and construction, and requires a full complement of fuel fabrication and reprocessing plants to support it, but which has a fuel consumption far less than that of a conventional furnace producing the same amount of heat.

As mentioned earlier, nuclear reactors are mainly used to produce steam, which in land-based power stations is fed to turbo-alternators generating electricity. In our gas-cooled reactors heat is transferred from the fuel to external heat exchangers where the steam is produced by carbon dioxide gas circulating in a closed system. If we review other possible uses of a reactor as a heat source, it is obvious that the usual applications can be eliminated at once because of radioactivity in the reactor and the relatively low temperature attained. Industrial processes such as ore smelting, steel production or pottery firing are therefore ruled out, and we find that we are driven back to using the heat of the reactor to produce steam. It is, of course, quite feasible to use the steam directly in chemical processes instead of driving a turbine, and in fact the small reactor at Halden in Norway is intended eventually to supply process steam to an adjacent wood-pulp factory. Similarly there have been proposals in Sweden to use steam from a reactor for district heating schemes, and from Australia and the Far East to use nuclear heat for sea-water distillation. But it is clear that, for the next few years at least, the main use for reactors will be as heat sources in nuclear power stations.

REACTOR DEVELOPMENT

The reactors in stations now in operation or under construction in the United Kingdom are developments from Calder Hall. Chapelcross, near Annan, is virtually a copy of Calder Hall and is at present supplying about 20 per cent. of the base load of the South of Scotland Electricity Board. As you know, Chapelcross is an A.E.A. establishment, and the prime purpose of the reactors there is to produce fissile material for defence; the electricity supplied to the S.S.E.B. is a by-product. On the other hand, the station at Hunterston, which is of improved design and optimised for electricity production, will be operated by the S.S.E.B. and should be on full load in 1963.

Further improvements for the next generation of reactors are now being sought and a prototype, known as the Advanced Gas-Cooled Reactor, and embodying our current ideas, is being built at Windscale.

It is hoped that the A.G.R. will be more compact, cheaper to build, and more efficient than previous reactors and that the fuel, which is uranium oxide in beryllium or stainless-steel tubes, will run at higher temperatures and be more durable than present-day fuels. The overall effect of these improvements will be a reduction in the cost of electricity generated and a narrowing of the gap between the cost of power from conventional fuels and from nuclear sources. If the prototype should prove successful, then a commercial power station based on a similar design could be built and brought on power in 1967 or thereabouts.

An even more advanced reactor experiment, known as the Dragon Project, is at present under construction at Winfrith in Dorset as an international co-operative effort under the auspices of O.E.E.C. This offers the prospect of reaching even higher temperatures, sufficient for the circulating gas to drive a gas turbine directly with satisfactory efficiency. To reach the temperatures required, specially developed graphite will replace the metal containers previously employed as cladding material. The advantages to be gained from this system are considerable, and the problems we have to face commensurately large.

The reactor system which holds our highest hopes for economic power generation, however, is the fast reactor, and our first experimental reactor is, as you well know, housed at Dounreay in Caithness. The fast reactor is quite different in type from those already outlined, and it is planned to fuel it with plutonium derived initially as a by-product from gas-cooled reactors. It is hoped that the reactor will produce more fuel than it consumes, thus being self-supporting and providing a surplus of plutonium fuel for other reactors. The experimental reactor at Dounreay will provide basic data in this entirely new field for the design of a prototype, which might be built in the late 1960s. With successful development, this could mean a commercial station employing fast reactors in the middle 1970s.

MOBILE REACTORS

So much for land-based power stations. The history of all prime movers in the past has shown that, starting with stationary machines with a large weight-to-power ratio, they have steadily improved in efficiency until this ratio is sufficiently small for the machine to become mobile. Nuclear reactors are already showing a similar trend, and indeed mobile reactors are now in use for specialised purposes, the American nuclear-powered submarines and the Russian icebreaker *Lenin* being the earliest examples. The main attraction of a nuclear reactor as the source of power in a submarine is, of course, the fact that re-fuelling is only required at long intervals, and the submarine is therefore operational for much longer periods of time. The reactors which so far have been fitted in ships are of the pressurised water type (P.W.R.), and we are purchasing one of these reactors from America for our first atomic submarine, *Dreadnought*, for installation in a British hull.

For submarines and icebreakers, economics are probably of secondary importance, but where merchant ships are concerned they play a much more decisive part. At present the economics of nuclear propulsion are being carefully assessed, and following an invitation by the Government, tenders have been submitted by selected firms for a nuclear-powered oil tanker of 65,000 tons dead weight. The outcome of this exercise will be governed by the relative costs of nuclear- and conventionally-fuelled tankers.

But in due course it is certain that nuclear-powered merchant ships will sail the seas, and in anticipation of this, international conferences are now being held to draft rules for their safe operation. These developments must have an appreciable influence on one of Scotland's most important industries, namely shipbuilding.

Other mobile applications, such as the use of reactors in aeroplanes or locomotives, may follow their use in ships. The prospect of employing reactors for space travel is under investigation in the United States and presumably in Russia also.

Comparable with the mobile reactors are the "package reactors", which are small units intended to meet the needs of isolated communities and generate a few megawatts of electricity. There is, of course, an economic penalty incurred by reducing the size of reactor, and the cost per unit of electricity generated is quite high, only acceptable for a remote site where essential supplies must be maintained. Thus, while the cost of generation at the first large stations of 300 to 500 MW capacity will be rather less than $\frac{3}{4}$d. a unit, the cost from a 20-MW station has been variously estimated as between 1d. and $1\frac{1}{2}$d. a unit.

RADIOISOTOPES

One application of nuclear reactors which we have been pursuing for a number of years is the production of radioisotopes for industry. The annual saving to British industry resulting from the use of these artificially produced isotopes is estimated to exceed £5 million, and this figure could be increased substantially.

The use of radioactive tracers in many fields is well known, and new uses are continually being found. Vast savings in the United States result from their use in oil-fields and mining. In our own country, sources for gamma radiography have been supplied to hospitals and labelled compounds produced for our biochemists striving to unravel the secrets of life processes. On a more mundane plane, isotopes are used to control thickness in metal rolling, to measure very thin surface coatings, to study the efficiency of mixing techniques, and to remove unwanted static electricity in the processing of fibres. In these applications the quantity of radioactive isotope is very small, and there is no possibility of harmful contamination of the products.

On the other hand, very large amounts of activity are used at the A.E.A.'s irradiation facility at Wantage. Here materials are subjected to intense radioactivity with the result that their properties are changed. In this way, for example, the heat resistance of plastics is greatly increased, and this technique offers the possibility of developing new uses for a variety of materials. Large sources of gamma-radiation are also employed for sterilising medical equipment and appliances unable to withstand high temperatures.

So far we have outlined the differences between nuclear and conventional heat sources, have summarised the stages in which future developments might proceed, and have surveyed possible applications of nuclear reactors. We should now consider the impact of nuclear power on the nation, the demands which it will continue to make, and the overall effect on industry.

EFFECT ON INDUSTRY

In making electrical power more readily available, nuclear energy will contribute to greater productivity in our factories and improved standards of living for our people.

By substituting for coal and oil as primary fuels, it will reduce industrial effluent and make for cleaner and better health in urban areas.

The first demand it will make will be for a steady flow of scientists and technologists into the industry and associated work. The range of activities is very wide, from thermonuclear fusion to the production of special steels. Some of this work will be conducted within the A.E.A., some in the Consortia, and the remainder in universities and in industry.

The other demands will be for new materials, new chemicals, new instruments, new methods of fabrication, new standards of accuracy and reliability. Because of the radioactivity inherent in a reactor, maintenance of many plant items is impossible, and complete containment must be ensured for as long as the reactor is in use. The pressure vessel must therefore be made of steel which will not fail over twenty or thirty years, in spite of the effects of radiation; and the welding of the separate plates of the vessel must be flawless. Similar stringent conditions apply in chemical reprocessing plants where spent fuel, which itself is highly radioactive, is treated for recovery of plutonium and removal of fission products. In this case the vessels have also to cope with the corrosive action of acid liquors, and with no possibility of carrying out maintenance, the reliability of the units must be exceptionally high. One direct result of this insistence on the complete integrity of vessels has been the development of new techniques in the making and examination of welds, improved techniques which have been passed on to other industries also. Similarly, the specialised instruments developed for the control and automatic safety devices in reactors have benefited other users and have resulted in a large expansion in the electronics industry. Chemical plants, too, have called for modified forms of standard instruments suitable for remote control and logging of data. New paints have been produced to help in the decontamination of active buildings. By applying a lacquer which could be removed as a sheet, the risk of contaminating the permanent structure has been much reduced.

The need for remote handling of radioactive materials and in particular for the examination of spent fuel presented a number of problems and led to the development of "master-slave" manipulators and machine tools which could be operated from a distance. Closed-circuit television has proved a most valuable tool, and special cameras have been designed small enough to pass into the fuel channels in a reactor so that direct inspection is now possible. Electronic computer manufacture has also been greatly increased by the demands made by atomic energy work.

On the chemical front, new compounds and solvents have been developed for the processes employed in our plants, and large demands placed on industry for the more common products, though often with more rigid specifications than usual.

From metallurgical firms the demand has been for better, purer metals and alloys for structural work and special duties such as fuel cladding. It is clear that in the future the overall effect of nuclear power on industry will be to act as a stimulant to progress, and as the basis widens so will the volume of business in all sections of industry increase.

SUMMARY

What can Scotland expect from nuclear power? Firstly, an increased proportion of her electricity will come from nuclear reactors, which will ultimately replace the present coal- and oil-fired stations. This will allow coal and oil to be processed as chemicals and industries based on coal tar distillation, the manufacture of chemicals from coal, oil refining, catalytic cracking and the synthesis of products from refinery gases will expand.

Secondly, Scotland will take her fair share of the construction of nuclear-powered ships.

Thirdly, the effect of the development of nuclear power will be felt by all industries producing basic materials, fabricated items and chemicals used in the construction of nuclear plant and the manufacture and reprocessing of nuclear fuel, many of which have already made substantial contributions to Britain's atomic energy project.

Lastly, this second industrial revolution can reverse the worst effects of the first by removing smoke and soot from the atmosphere of our towns, improve the health of the nation, and lead to a higher standard of living for all.

Chemicals for Industry from Fossil Fuels

A. McLean, B.SC., PH.D., F.R.I.C.

Chief Research Chemist, British Hydrocarbon Chemicals Ltd., Grangemouth

Coal and oil shale are the fossil fuels which occur naturally in Scotland, but in considerations of any products from these imported petroleum must, for economic reasons, figure largely. The competition throughout the world between these three raw materials as sources of fuel oils is surveyed briefly and it is concluded that under free economic conditions coal and oil shale cannot compete with petroleum at the present time and probably for some time to come. The direct utilisation of coal and oil shale for the production of chemicals (the coal tar industry being regarded as a by-product industry) is at present difficult to assess but seems worth investigation.

The rise of the petroleum chemicals industry in the U.S.A. and its post-1939-45 War development in Great Britain are outlined. Scotland has participated in this development in large measure by the establishment of British Hydrocarbon Chemicals at Grangemouth. The scope of the petroleum chemical industry and the variety of end-products stemming from its operations are briefly indicated, special mention being made of the products manufactured at Grangemouth. Suggestions are made for the development of Scottish light industries based on these products.

The fossil fuels which occur naturally in Scotland are coal and oil shale, but petroleum is now imported to such an extent that it must figure largely in any consideration of products useful to industry that can be made from hydrocarbonaceous materials. Indeed, during the past twenty years the manufacture of industrial chemicals from petroleum has, chiefly for economic reasons, so overshadowed their manufacture from other sources that petroleum chemicals will be the main theme of this paper, those from coal and oil shale being mentioned only comparatively.

The retorting of oil shale on a commercial scale to produce hydrocarbon fuel oil (paraffin or lamp oil) began independently in France and Scotland about the middle of the last century. In these countries, which have no indigenous petroleum, the industry has survived to the present time under Government protection. In the U.S.A. shale oil plants were in operation in 1859 when the first well was drilled for petroleum, but in competition with petroleum these rapidly became uneconomic and closed down. From about 1860 the industry started up in many parts of the world, notably Canada, Australia, Estonia and Manchuria, but since the advent of petroleum and the organisation of its transportation throughout the world, there has been no expansion except for very special reasons and in general the industry has contracted. Thus when Japan occupied Manchuria the shale oil industry expanded and was a major source of fuel oil for the Japanese navy during the 1939-45 War. However, in the U.S.A. and the U.S.S.R., both of which have vast reserves of oil shale as well as petroleum—the known reserves of oil shale in the U.S.A. are reported to be ten times the known reserves of petroleum—there is no significant shale oil industry. The general impression from a somewhat superficial review of shale oil production during the first half of this century is that the production of hydrocarbon fuel oils from shale cannot compete under free economic conditions with the production of similar oils from petroleum. Nor is this surprising when one considers the complexity of the operations involved in mining shale, retorting it and finally fractionating the liquid product compared with petroleum flowing from a well often under its own pressure ready to be fractionated.

The retorting of oil shale leads to a considerable amount of cracking, with the result that shale oil contains a relatively high percentage of olefinic hydrocarbons throughout its boiling range. Also the proportion of normal hydrocarbon chains to branched chains is greater in shale oil than in petroleum. The Scottish shale oil industry has taken advantage of these circumstances and from a selected fraction in the gas oil distillation range now manufactures an excellent detergent of the secondary alkyl sulphate type which competes successfully with similar products derived from petroleum. Again Scottish oil shale has a considerable nitrogen content much of which during retorting comes off as ammonia, which is worked up to ammonium sulphate fertiliser, whilst the remainder appears in the shale oil as organic bases. A preparation of the latter has shown promise as a corrosion inhibitor in applications such as oil well drilling and metal pickling. Although not directly connected with shale oil, it may also be mentioned that the Scottish shale oil industry makes use of spent shale to make good-quality building bricks by the sand/lime process. However, despite so much ingenuity in taking advantage of special properties of shale oil and in utilisation of by-products, shale oil as obtained at present could not, under the same economic conditions, compete with petroleum.

During the 1939-45 War the heavy drain on petroleum reserves caused the U.S. Bureau of Mines to carry out an extensive programme of research on the winning and retorting of oil shale and on the composition of the products. As a result of detailed costing it was concluded in 1950 that oil fuels from the shales examined could not then compete with similar products from petroleum but the opinion was expressed that if improvements continued to be made and the cost of finding new petroleum increased, the production of liquid fuels from oil shale could become a profitable industry in the U.S.A. From the point of view of the present paper a very interesting part of this investigation was concerned with the study of the chemical constitution of Colorado oil shale as a basis for developing more efficient methods for its conversion to useful products. A full report of this study does not seem to have appeared yet, but it may well be that in this field the potentialities of Scottish oil shale should be reviewed.

The major portion of all coal mined has always been burned direct to produce heat. However, towards the end of the eighteenth century in England high-temperature processing of coal to produce either gas for illuminating purposes or coke began to make available quantities of by-product coal tar. The increasing use of coal gas in the nineteenth century led to the development of the coal tar industry the story of which is well-known chemical history. Benzene, toluene, xylenes, higher aromatics, phenols and nitrogen bases all became available in hitherto unheard of quantities and were the foundation stones of the chemical industry in all the most developed countries. It is interesting to note that in 1951 the coal tar production in the four leading countries was:

	gallons
U.S.A.	795,000,000
U.K.	632,000,000
Germany	323,000,000
France	124,000,000

Such figures indicate the great importance of the coal tar industry in our industry and commerce.

Notwithstanding its importance, the coal tar industry is essentially a by-product industry, but during the past twenty to twenty-five years investigations have been carried out which could lead to the use of coal primarily for the production of chemicals. In this connection could be cited the hydrogenation of coal in the U.K. (Imperial Chemical Industries) and in Germany and the Fischer-Tropsch process. It is true that the original aim of these processes was the production of gasoline, but the former also produces methane and other low paraffins which were converted to synthesis gas (carbon monoxide and hydrogen), the gateway to many chemicals, whilst the latter can be made to produce olefinic gases, alcohols, ketones and organic acids as well as gasoline. Again much work has been done in several parts of the world on the underground gasification of coal, again with the object of obtaining the useful and versatile synthesis gas direct from unmined coal. At the present time it is difficult to assess the value of such processes, technically there is probably much promise but economically petroleum seems to have the advantage.

During the 1914-18 War the traditional sources of raw materials for the chemical industry as coal tar and coke oven distillate were severely strained and chemists had begun to look for new sources. It was then that the chemical constitution of petroleum and of the products from petroleum refineries, whose sole objective until then had been to make fuels satisfying physical specifications such as boiling range, began to be examined. At this time, as a result of the rapidly increasing operation of thermal cracking, refineries in the U.S.A. were producing enormous quantities of by-product gas which was found to contain large proportions of ethylene, propylene and butylenes. The chemistry of these as starting materials for a great variety of required chemicals had long been known, but many problems had to be solved before the long step from the laboratory to large-scale manufacture could be taken and the 1914-18 War ended without any chemicals from petroleum having been manufactured. However, the lesson was not lost and by 1920 the Standard Oil Co. of New Jersey had started the commercial production of isopropyl alcohol from propylene separated from refinery off gas and the Carbide and Carbon Chemical Co. were using ethylene from the same source to make ethylene glycol. This was the beginning of the petroleum chemicals industry which in the U.S.A. alone now makes over 20 million tons of chemicals in ever-widening variety.

In the U.K. we have no indigenous petroleum of any importance and up to the end of the 1939-45 War petroleum was imported mainly as refined products rather than as crude. For these reasons petroleum chemical development in the U.K. between the wars was insignificant compared with its progress in the U.S.A. A further reason was that in proportion to our total commerce our coal tar industry was much bigger than that of the U.S.A. and we did not feel the lack of chemical supplies to other industries so acutely as did the U.S.A. After the 1939-45 War the demands for chemicals of all kinds increased greatly and concurrently crude petroleum began to be imported and refined here. The petroleum chemicals industry for economic reasons makes its products in large tonnages, and the situation in the U.K. was now ripe for its development. This was quickly realised by petroleum and chemical organisations and shortly after the war petroleum chemical plants were planned and began to appear throughout the country. It should be mentioned that, due to the switch from thermal to catalytic cracking in the petroleum industry, the off gases from refineries were not now so rich in the olefines, ethylene, propylene and butylenes, and to obtain these it is the usual practice in this country for a petroleum chemical firm to make them itself by thermally cracking a cheap straight run petroleum cut. Scotland has in large measure shared this development with the establishment at Grangemouth of the complex of petroleum chemical plants centred on the thermal cracking operations of British Hydrocarbon Chemicals.

By 1959 the U.K. production of petroleum-based organic chemicals had risen steadily to 50 per cent. of the total organic chemicals production and it has been forecast that by 1965 the figure will be 70 per cent. Even so, the new industry does not use more than about 3·5 per cent. of the petroleum consumption of this country, and this figure is unlikely to be exceeded. There would appear to be no fear of shortage of feedstocks, and in this connection it is of interest that even during the Suez crisis the new industry was kept fully supplied. It is difficult to get up-to-date accurate figures for the products capacity of the U.K. petroleum chemicals industry, but the data in Table I taken from R. F. Goldstein, *The Petroleum Chemicals Industry*, 2nd ed. London, Spon, 1958, are probably the most reliable.

TABLE I

End 1958 *Actual or Planned Capacity in U.K. for Some Petroleum Chemicals*

	tons/year
Ethylene	25,000
Ethanol (synthetic)	75,000
Ethylene oxide and derivatives	75,000
Ethyl chloride and ethylene dichloride	25,000
Polyethylene	125,000
Styrene	40,000
Isopropyl alcohol, acetone, etc.	76,000-100,000
C_4 solvents	20,000
OXO Alcohols	30,000
Butadiene	50,000
Dodecylbenzene	60,000
GRS and other rubbers	70,000
Ammonia	135,000
Sulphur	40,000
Carbon black	75,000-100,000

At the present time the actual or planned capacities for ethylene, ethylene dichloride, polyethylene, styrene, OXO alcohols and butadiene are certainly higher than they were in 1958. However, it should be kept in mind that most of the ethylene shown in Table I appears again in the succeeding five entries whilst a large part of the butadiene appears also in GRS rubber.

Ethylene, propylene and the butylenes from the thermal cracking of liquid petroleum fractions were, as has already been indicated, the original primary materials of the petroleum chemicals industry. In the U.K. this is still largely the case and we shall now consider some of the uses of these olefines in order to obtain an idea of the diversity of chemicals produced from them and of their end uses. It should be emphasised that Figs. 1 to 4 indicate only a selection of use routes.

Of the chemicals shown in Fig. 1 ethanol, polyethylene and styrene are manufactured in large tonnages at Grangemouth and a plant to make ethylene dichloride will be built in the near future. Two plants make over 20,000 tons per year of two kinds of polyethylene in numerous grades for a variety of applications; these products are finding ever-increasing uses, particularly in light plastics industries making household hardware, wrapping foil, fibres, etc., but not to any significant extent in Scotland.

In addition to the uses of propylene shown in Fig. 2, throughout the world a growing use with great potential is polypropylene plastic. Of the propylene-derived chemicals indicated in Fig. 2 isopropanol, propylene tetramer and dodecylbenzene, isopropyl benzene (cumene), acetone and phenol are made in quantities of many thousands of tons a year at Grangemouth. Dodecylbenzene (detergent alkylate) is a hydrocarbon intermediate which when sulphonated yields the active agent in all the popular brands of packeted synthetic detergents and also in some of the liquid products. Phenol is a component of bonding and coating resins with a wide variety of uses. Apart from a very small consumption of detergent alkylate, Scotland makes no use of these intermediates, which are well suited for the manufacture of light industrial products, such as shampoos and other washing materials, plywood and laminated boards.

Of the products shown in Fig. 3 only butadiene is made in the pure state at Grangemouth by selective extraction from the C_4 fraction of the cracked product. Research is in progress with the object of utilising chemically the other components of this C_4 fraction, namely, the *iso*- and *n*-butenes. The alternative route to butadiene shown in Fig. 3, the dehydrogenation of *n*-butane (or *n*-butenes) is by far the most common source of butadiene in the U.S.A. but it is economic only on a large scale (25,000 to 50,000 tons/year). The greatest utilisation of butadiene is in GRS synthetic rubber which is a co-polymer containing about 75 per cent. butadiene and 25 per cent. styrene, but increasing tonnages are being used in special co-polymers with styrene for emulsion paints and long-wearing shoe-soling compositions.

As already mentioned the petroleum chemicals industry in the U.S.A. started on olefines in by-product gases. During its development, feedstock from this source became less plentiful and it had to look for other sources. The young industry developed its own thermal cracking as already seen, but the more paraffinic gases from catalytic cracking also received its attention and, from the results of research on these, its interest spread to the completely paraffinic natural gas obtainable in almost unlimited quantities at very low prices in Texas and adjoining states. The importance of the power paraffins, methane, ethane and propane in the development along these lines is illustrated in Fig. 4.

Vast quantities of the lower paraffins are converted catalytically to carbon monoxide and hydrogen mixtures (synthesis gas) by means of reactions such as

$$CH_4+H_2O \rightarrow CO+3H_2$$

The ratio CO/H_2 in the synthesis gas can be varied to suit the synthesis for which it is to be used by varying the proportions of methane and its higher homologues in the feed-stock. On the other hand pure hydrogen for, say, ammonia synthesis can be obtained by submitting the synthesis gas to the water gas shift reaction

$$CO+H_2O \rightarrow CO_2+H_2$$

and then removing the carbon dioxide. Over 3 million tons of ammonia are made annually by this route in the U.S.A. In the U.K. hydrogen for ammonia synthesis is obtained by the water gas reaction from coke and steam, but it seems likely that the methane/steam reaction will be employed in the future.

Natural gas has been found in Scotland, but not in quantities that could be economically used in processes such as those outlined in Fig. 4. At present the relatively small production from a drilling at Cousland, near Dalkeith, is blended with coal gas at Musselburgh gasworks; this is probably the best economic utilisation of the quantity involved. However, much larger quantities of the lower paraffins, especially methane, are available at Grangemouth from British Hydrocarbon Chemicals thermal cracking operations, and this company has announced its plans to build plants to produce synthesis gas and thereafter methanol from this source. Methanol probably does not find much application in light industries, but its near conversion product, formaldehyde does, particularly when phenol is also available, and a local demand for formaldehyde could probably stimulate interest in its production at Grangemouth.

The long known reaction between calcium carbide (from coke and limestone) and water is still the principal source of acetylene and seems likely to remain so in regions where coal and limestone are readily available and electrical power is cheap, but in regions where these conditions do not prevail it seems equally likely that this process will be displaced by acetylene from the cracking of lower paraffins at a high temperature as indicated in Fig. 4.

From this brief review so far of the activities of the petroleum chemicals industry it might appear that petroleum is mainly a source of aliphatic chemicals. In the U.K. this is true, the aromatic portions of some of the products shown in Figs. 1 to 4 being in this country obtained from coal tar. Petroleum contains considerable proportions of aromatics, and indeed aromatic rings having a greater thermal stability than aliphatic chains, aromatics are concentrated in thermal cracking operations but, being imported, benzene, toluene and xylenes in petroleum are not assisted by the Treasury allowance which applies to the same compounds in coal tar. This situation is likely to hold for some time, but it is probable that rising demand, particularly for benzene and ortho- and para-xylene, will in time lead to the extraction of aromatics from selected petroleum fractions. In the U.S.A. in 1958 about 65 per cent. (800,000 tons) of all the benzene used for chemical syntheses came from petroleum. This difference with regard to sources of aromatic chemicals is undoubtedly a reflection of the difference in the relative importance of the coal tar industry as compared to the total chemical industry in the two countries. Indeed, it has been suggested that because of this difference the development of the petroleum chemicals industry in the U.K. will be much more blended with the coal tar industry than it has been in the U.S.A.

Can a similar blending of the petroleum chemicals industry with an industry producing chemicals from oil shale be envisaged? With the situation as at present this seems unlikely. The annual output of oil shale in Scotland is about one million tons, retorting of which yields about 23 gal. of hydrocarbon oils/ton, that is about 80,000 tons of oils. Apart from the quantity being relatively small, oil produced in this way does not seem to have any special merit for the production of chemicals, an exception being its use in making secondary alkyl sulphate detergents already mentioned. However, it must be remembered that the commercial utilisation of Scottish oil shale has never had as a main aim the production of chemicals. It may be that breakdown of the oil shale by a process other than retorting could yield very different results. Experimental investigations along these lines have been carried out on American oil shales. The cost of this type of work is high and a preliminary to embarking on it would undoubtedly have to be an up-to-date assessment of the reserves of oil shale to determine if these warranted such expenditure.

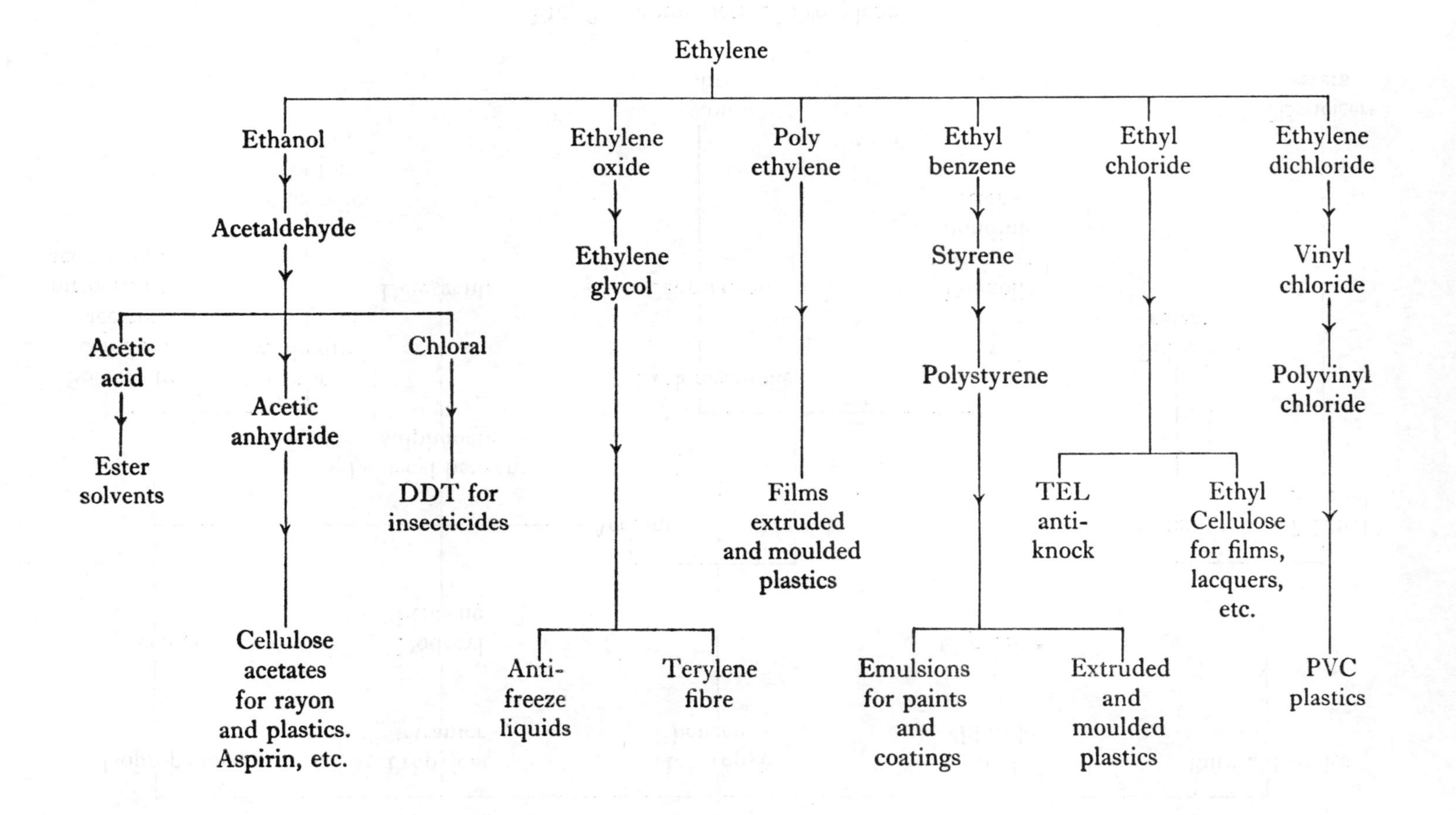

FIG. 1. Some uses of Ethylene

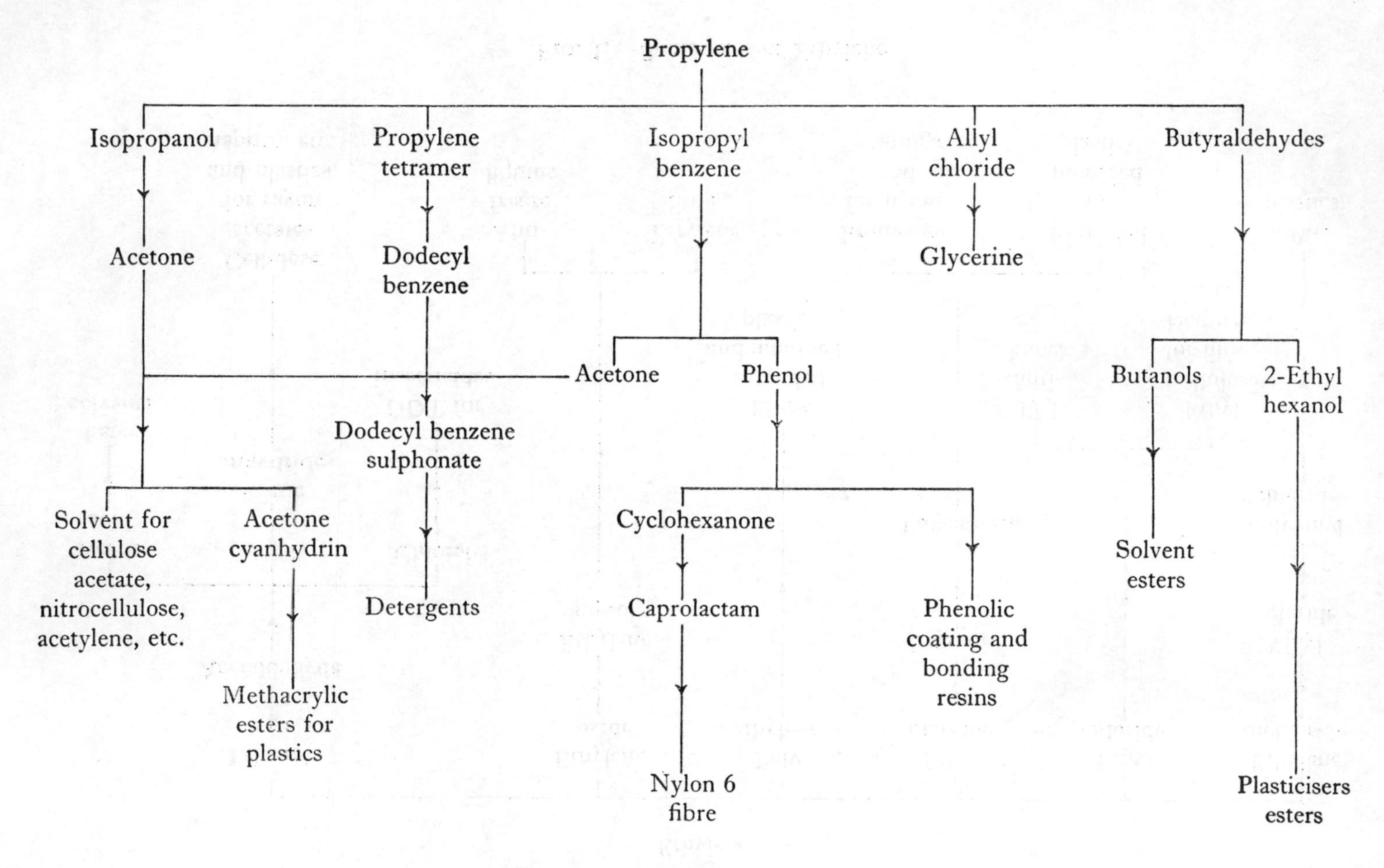

FIG. 2. Some uses of Propylene

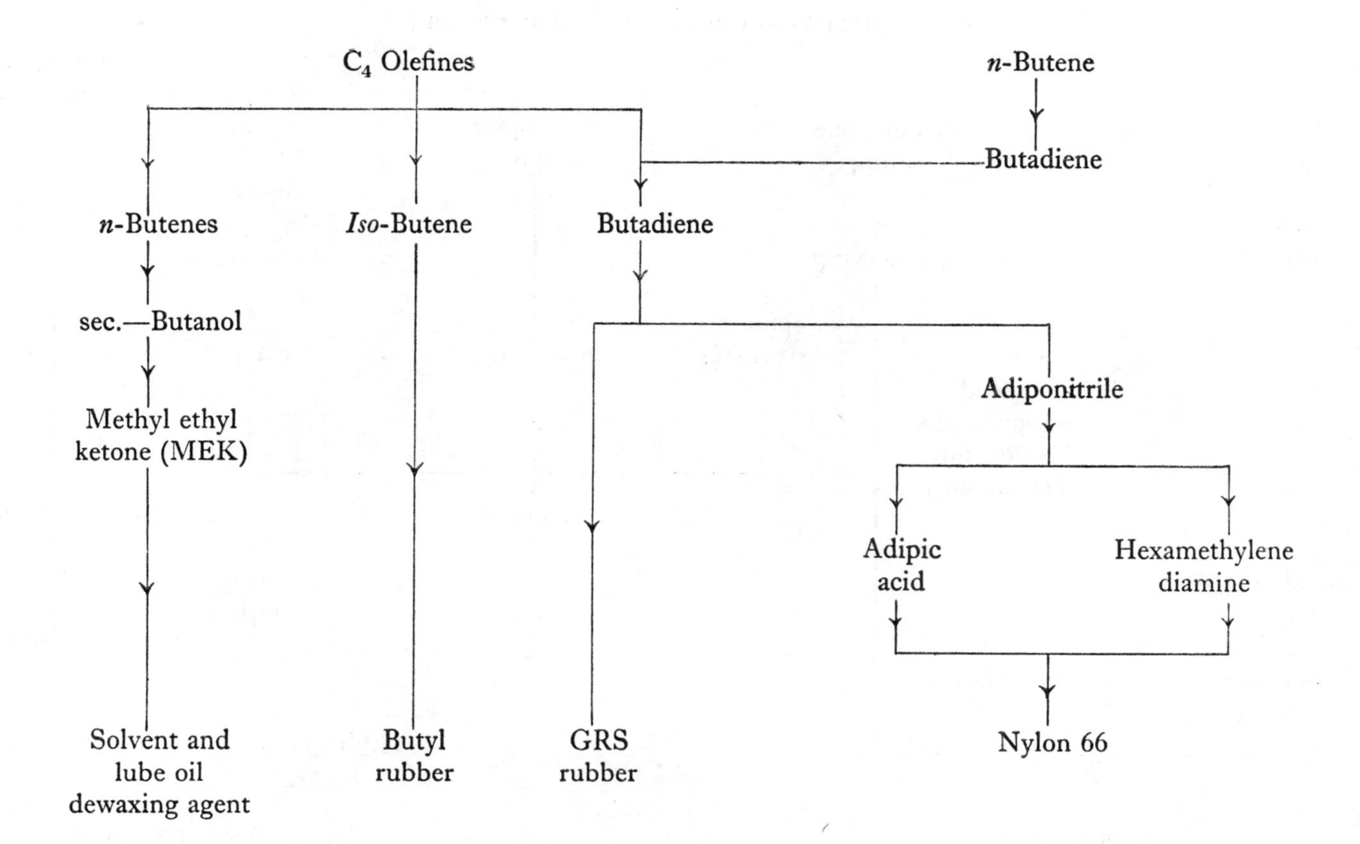

FIG. 3. Some uses of Butadiene and C_4 Olefines

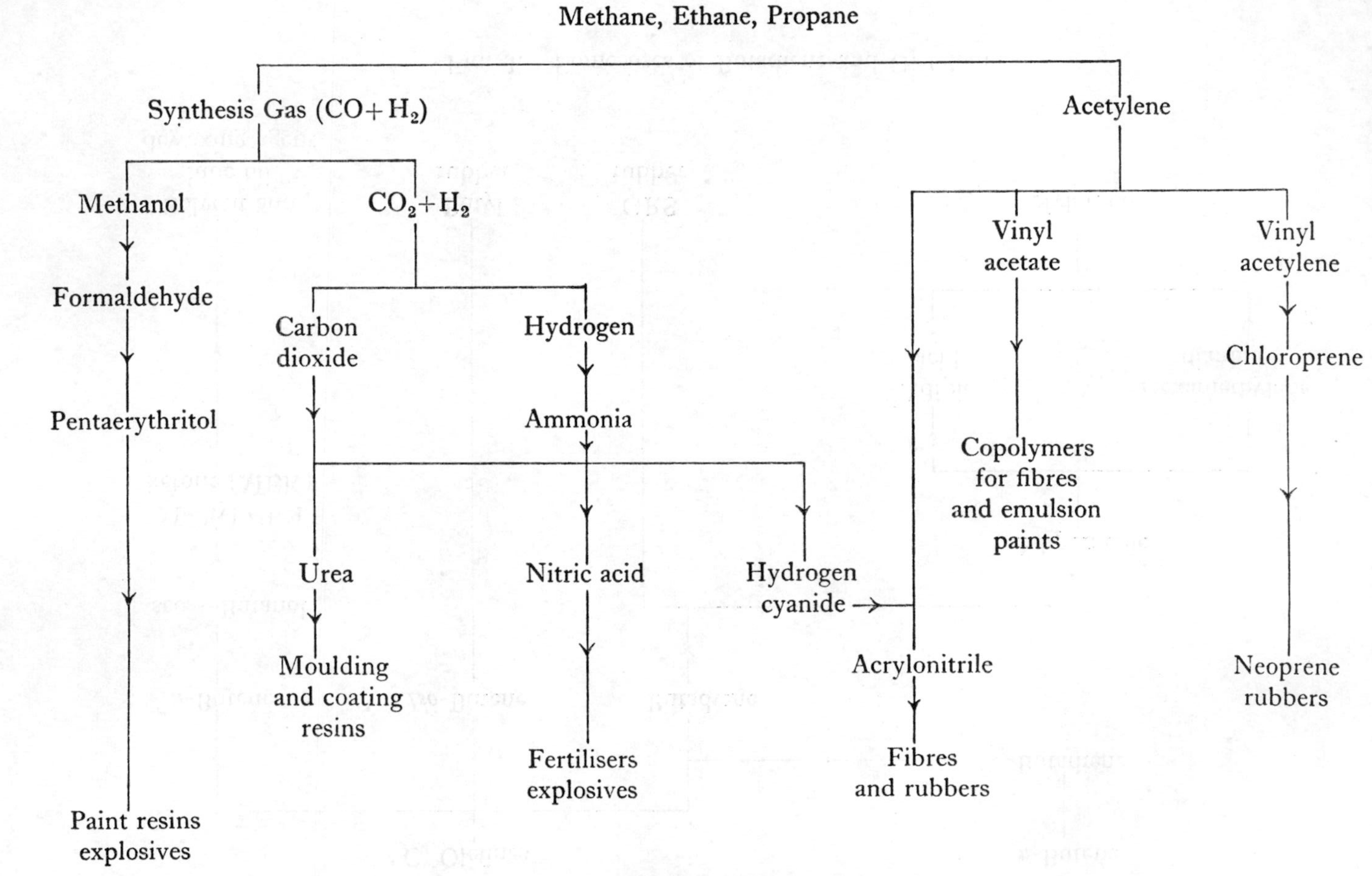

Fig. 4. Some uses of the Lower Paraffins

INTRODUCTION TO DISCUSSION

ALBERT PARKER, C.B.E., D.SC., F.R.I.C., M.I.CHEM.E.
Late Director, Fuel Research; Hon. Secretary, British National Committee, World Power Conference

I think I should begin by saying that though I am introduced as the late Director of Fuel Research, I am still active and I arrived on the platform on time. It is my first pleasant task to introduce to you the authors of the papers to be considered, who are acknowledged experts in their subjects. They are here on the front row and I shall ask them to stand up in turn. They are Mr. J. K. Hunter, co-author, of Sir Alexander Gibb and Partners; Dr. E. A. C. Chamberlain, Divisional Chief Scientist in Scotland of the National Coal Board; Mr. D. C. Elgin of the Scottish Gas Board; Mr. E. W. Golding of the Electrical Research Association; Dr. H. H. Chambers of the Sondes Place Research Institute; Mr. C. L. C. Allan of the North of Scotland Hydro-Electric Board; Mr. V. H. B. Macklen of the United Kingdom Atomic Energy Authority; and Dr. A. McLean of British Hydrocarbon Chemicals. These gentlemen are the authors or co-authors of the first group of papers on various aspects of Energy Resources and Utilisation.

There are two other divisions: Utilisation of Minerals—Mr. R. H. S. Robertson, Director of Resource Use Ltd.; Developing Uses of Biological Resources—Dr. W. A. P. Black, Deputy Director, Arthur D. Little Research Institute.

After my introductory remarks, Professor A. S. T. Thomson, our energetic Reporter, will summarise the subject matter of the collection of ten papers. I shall be brief in my remarks, as many delegates have signified their desire to take part in the discussion.

I would emphasise, as Lord Bilsland mentioned this morning that a measure of energy utilisation, in general, is also a measure of standard of living. For example, in the United States the amount of energy used is equivalent to rather more than eight tons of coal per inhabitant per year, and they have an average income per individual (when converted from dollars into equivalent pounds) approaching £800 a year. In Great Britain the average consumption of fuel and power is equivalent to roughly five tons of coal per person per year and the average income for each individual is about £360. The corresponding figures for Belgium are about four tons of coal equivalent and £330, and for France somewhat less than three tons of coal equivalent and £300 per person per year. Italy, with an energy consumption equivalent to only one and a quarter tons of coal, has an income of about £150 per person per year. Japan, which uses the equivalent of only about one ton of coal per person, has an income of only about £90 per person per year; and the corresponding figures for India are one-third of a ton of coal equivalent (including the large quantities of dung burned for cooking) and an income of only about £23. There is thus some correlation between the use of fuel and power and the standard of living, though there are other factors. Allowing for the amounts of fuel used for heating homes and other buildings, it seems that the average industrial worker in the United States has about twice as much power to assist him as the average industrial worker in Great Britain. It is not surprising, therefore, that productivity per individual in the U.S.A. is higher than in Great Britain. It must not be forgotten, however, that with the larger population and in consequence a larger demand for certain articles there is more scope for mechanised mass production in the U.S.A.

Another point of importance mentioned by Lord Bilsland is that the consumers in Britain spend rather more than 10 per cent. of the national income on fuel and power. In fact, the annual expenditure on fuel and power, excluding the tax on oils, is about £2,000 million. It is often said that the cost of fuel and power is not important because in many factories it is no more than 2 or 3 per cent. of the value of the product. In my view, that is a wrong conclusion. Life covers more than the factory. Houses require fuel and energy for heating and lighting and fuel is necessary for transport of passengers and goods; all these costs enter directly or indirectly into the overall costs of manufactured articles, sometimes in a demand for higher wages. Cost of fuel and power is definitely of great importance and will increase in importance as competition in world trade increases.

We must not be misled by the narrow economic view that it is better to use indigenous material at relatively high cost than to use imported material at lower overall cost. The overall economic effect must be considered.

In this country, with its large population and not so rich in natural resources as some other countries in relation to the size of the population, the aim must to be make the best use of brains and skill. Scotland is noted for having a high proportion of astute men of initiative, keen on education, and including a good share of highly skilled engineers.

I should like to make the position clear about the reserves of coal in this country. Before the nationalisation of the coal industry I was concerned with the Coal Survey under the Fuel Research Organisation. In 1946 the organisation published a paper on the quantities of the types of coal likely to be mined during the next 100 years. This did not mean that we were of the opinion that there was only enough mineable coal in this country for 100 years. In fact, there is enough for more than 200 years at the present rate of consumption. Similarly, the fact that Dr. Chamberlain has considered the coal position in Scotland over the next twenty years does not mean that the coal in reserve in Scotland will be exhausted in twenty years; there is enough in reserve for a much longer period.

Much is often heard about the possibilities of chemicals from coal, partly with the object of increasing the profitable demand for coal. The most recent document on the subject is the Report of the Committee, under the Chairmanship of Mr. A. H. Wilson, that was appointed by the Minister of Power to consider coal derivatives. Over a very long period, chemicals have been obtained from the products of coal carbonisation. Much of the coke used in the iron and steel industry is really a chemical reducing agent for converting iron oxide into iron. Large quantities of ammonia are made by synthesis from gases made from coal and coke, and many chemicals are extracted or derived from coal tar. But I do not see much hope of using many millions of coal a year more than are used at present for conversion to chemicals. A million tons of chemicals goes a long way, but a million tons of coal is relatively small in relation to a production of 200 million tons a year.

When this Symposium is over, the Scottish Council will, no doubt, carefully consider the papers and the discussions, with the object of suggesting action and priorities. There will surely be demands for action in various directions. Already, I have heard pleas for helping this and that from Government funds; we must remember that we all have heavy taxes. Fuel and power will certainly be required in increasing measure if profitable manufacturing industry is to be further developed.

With these observations in mind, I now have pleasure in calling on Professor Thomson to present his summary of the papers.

STATEMENT BY THE REPORTER

Professor A. S. T. THOMSON, D.SC., PH.D., A.R.C.S.T., M.I.C.E., M.I.MECH.E.

Head of the Department of Mechanical, Civil and Chemical Engineering, The Royal College of Science and Technology

In this session of the Symposium we cover three sections, namely, Fuel and Energy; Utilisation of Minerals; and Developing Uses of Biological Resources. As it is naturally desired to leave as much time as possible for discussion, the Reporter's time has been limited to approximately ten minutes (or one minute per paper). Under such conditions normal reporting of the contents of each paper is out of the question, and I can only hope to touch on some of the major points.

In the Fuel and Energy Section, the first paper, entitled "Energy—Resources and Utilisation" by Mr. Guthrie Brown and Mr. Hunter, gives an excellent summary of the energy sources available in Scotland—both expendable and replaceable—and the past, present and probably future pattern of energy utilisation.

The pattern of energy use has, of course, changed during this century. In the past, the rise of Scottish industry was based on the availability of ample and cheap supplies of coal, and at the beginning of the present century coal virtually provided the entire energy needs of the country. In 1913 the Scottish coalfields produced 42½ million tons. By 1959, however, the output had decreased to under 19 million tons—some of the reasons for this are given by Dr. Chamberlain in his paper. Thus, despite considerable increase in the efficiency of utilisation the proportion of total energy consumption in Scotland, which is met from coal, has dropped from 90 to 75 per cent. in the past ten years.

There has been a spectacular rise in the importation of petroleum, not only for road transport but for other uses for which its convenience and increasing competitiveness in relation to coal make it attractive.

As a result of the activities of the North of Scotland Hydro-Electric Board, our water power resources have been developed extensively.

Nuclear power is already with us, but even as a base load generation is not yet competitive with a conventional coal-fired power station, and will not be before about 1970.

The most prominent feature of the changing energy pattern is the increasing use of electricity which over the post-war years has been advancing at a rate of about 7 per cent. per annum.

Dr. Chamberlain in his paper "Coal and Gas from Coal Mines" discriminates between the total geological reserves of coal and the economically workable reserves. He concludes that there will be major developments in coal utilisation for the generation of electricity during the next twenty years since he considers that electrical energy from nuclear sources is unlikely to be strictly competitive with the new thermal stations now being built. The National Coal Board are confident that the economic reserves of coal are more than adequate to meet the present planned requirements of slightly less than 20 million tons per annum for the next twenty years. By then, it is estimated that the output of coal from the Scottish Division will be fairly equally divided between the five main producing areas, namely the Lothians, Fife, Alloa, and combined Central Area and Ayrshire.

In the gas industry the importance of the total gasification of coal is discussed in relation to the overall consumption of coal for gas making and the future availability, *or lack of availability*, of solid smokeless fuels to meet the requirements of the Clean Air Act. Coking coal supplies for the steel industry should be able to be met from indigenous resources.

Natural gas from coal mines will make a small but useful contribution to our energy requirements, but no large-scale development is likely.

In his paper on "Natural Gas and Manufactured Gas", Mr. Elgin outlines the development programme of the Scottish Gas Board. This includes the closure of small uneconomic units and the construction of a high pressure gas grid (140 miles) linking supply undertakings as far apart as Montrose and Ayr. The grid will collect and distribute gas from a number of new sources, including:

The Lurgi Pressure Gasification Plant being erected by the Board to gasify coal of high inert content from the Westfield opencast mine.

Methane from Cardowan Colliery, Lanarkshire, and possibly Valleyfield Colliery, Fife.

Refinery gas from Grangemouth.

Coke oven gas from Colville's Clyde Ironworks and Ravenscraig Steelworks; Bairds and Scottish Steel Limited, Gartsherrie Ironworks; National Coal Board, Dumbreck Coke Ovens.

An interesting paper on "Wind as a Source of Energy in Scotland" by Mr. Golding indicates that the total wind power capacity, which might be installed economically in Scottish coastal areas, is rather greater than that for hydro-electric power in the whole country. He refers to the successful operation of small 8-kW and 100-kW units. Further investigations would appear to be justified, although the stepping-up to large sizes would raise some formidable engineering problems.

Dr. Chambers and Mr. Corning contribute a paper on the "Fuel Cell", and it is fitting that in a Symposium of this type there should be a paper on this subject, although fuel cells are as yet only in the experimental stages, and much more research and development is necessary before the operating characteristics, lifetime and costs of the batteries can be evaluated.

We are indeed indebted to Mr. Henderson, the Chief Engineer of the South of Scotland Electricity Board, and to Mr. Allan, the Chief Engineer of the North of Scotland Hydro-Electric Board, for this most informative paper "A Survey of Electricity Supply in Scotland". It is symbolic of the close links existing between the two electricity supply authorities that this is a joint paper. The paper reviews the complete operations of the two Boards. Information in tabular form includes future generating requirements and sources: developments of distribution system; capital expenditure; and the Generating Plant Extensions' Programme 1961-70. During the period 1966-70 it is estimated that it will be necessary to instal from all sources, i.e. coal, nuclear, hydro power either normal or pumped storage, generating capacity at a yearly ratc of 200 to 300 MW. The previous combined capacity of the two Boards is 2,818 MW. Developments to 1970 include Hydro Developments (450 MW), Pumped Storage (400 MW), Hunterston Nuclear (300 MW), and N.E. Coast or Ayrshire Coast Nuclear, 1970 or later (250 MW); Coal station extension of Braehead (56 MW), Kincardine (376 MW) and Lothians (1,000 MW)—a truly mammoth undertaking! The paper concludes with a section on the social aspects of electricity supply.

The next paper in the Fuel and Energy group is by Mr. Macklen and deals with Nuclear Energy. The cost of electrical power generated from nuclear sources is, as already mentioned, at present greater than that from conventional fuels. The reactor development programme, which it is hoped will narrow and eliminate this gap, is described, namely the A.G.R.; the Dragon Project for O.E.E.C. and what Mr. Macklen thinks is the most hopeful of all, the fast reactor experiments at Dounreay which, if all goes well, could lead to a commercial station employing fast reactors in the middle 1970s.

What can Scotland expect from nuclear power? Firstly, an increased proportion of her electricity will come from nuclear reactors which should ultimately replace present coal- and oil-fired stations, thus allowing coal and oil to be processed as chemicals. Secondly, the development of radio isotopes and their application and assistance to many branches of industry. Thirdly, there is the future application of nuclear energy to the propulsion of ships, which could be of major influence in one of our largest industries. Here, however, while naval and "prestige" merchant ships are very necessary, for a large-scale construction programme of merchant shipping, the price, taking all the facts into account, must be competitive with other power systems.

The paper on Nuclear Energy, with its references to possible expansion in the coal and oil based chemical industry, leads naturally into the paper entitled "Chemicals for Industry from Fossil Fuels" by Dr. McLean. The paper outlines the enormous rise of the petroleum chemical industry in the U.S.A. and its post-1939-45 War development in Scotland by the establishment of British Hydrocarbon Chemicals at Grangemouth. Suggestions are made for the development of Scottish light industries based on the chemicals now produced at Grangemouth, such industries might include plastics, wrapping foil, films, detergents, shampoos, plywood and laminated boards, emulsion paints, long-wearing shoe-soling compositions. Very few of these are, in fact, at present being manufactured in Scotland. Here is indeed a challenge.

It is considered that Scotland's native fossil fuels—coal and oil shale—will find it difficult to compete with imported petroleum as sources of fuel oil. The direct utilisation of coal and oil shale for production of chemicals (the important coal tar industry being regarded as a by-product industry) is at present difficult to assess but seem worthy of investigation. There is doubt, however, as to whether under present conditions they could compete with petroleum.

In his paper on "The Utilisation of Minerals", Mr. Robertson calls for a new mental angle on resource development, and gives a list of basic rules and principles of raw material development. He contends that "by a comprehensive programme of survey and analysis, and research and development using a well-equipped central resource development laboratory, many new and valuable products would emerge. A 'poor deposit' for one application may be a 'rich deposit' for another." Several examples are given of by-products of a mineral nature with their present uses in industry.

The final paper in the section deals with the "Developing Uses of Biological Materials" and is by Dr. Black. Under the broad title "Developing Uses of Biological Material" a selection has to be made and consequently the paper is limited to the present uses and possible utilisation of brown seaweeds, wood, sugar beet and peat as being representative of biological material obtained from the sea and the land and from growing crops. Since the end of the 1939-45 War the seaweed industry has been revived and in 1959 approximately 40,000 tons of seaweed were processed, giving approximately 1,500 tons of alginates for use in dairy and other food products, pharmaceutical and cosmetic preparations, and other industrial applications, together with 5,000 tons of dried seaweed meal and fertilisers, the total value of the industry being of the order of £1¼ million per annum.

It is suggested that the other compounds in seaweed, such as *mannitol*, used in food products, inks, medicinal products, plastics, explosives and varnishes, and *laminarin*, source of glucose and with possible application as a blood anti-coagulent, could be exploited. Wood and sugar beet could also form the bases of new chemical industries.

Peat Solids in Scotland approximate to $1,000 \times 10^6$ tons. In 1949, the Scottish Peat Committee was set up to advise the Secretary of State of the commercial utilisation of these deposits and submitted a first report in 1954. As a member of the Peat Committee, I can confirm Dr. Black's conclusion that at present peat in Scotland would appear to have a future mainly in agriculture and horticulture. As a source of chemicals it cannot compete with cheaper, more readily available indigenous raw materials. However, its use as a soil conditioner and as a humus base for fertilisers could be greatly expanded.

Summary

Perhaps, in conclusion, I might summarise some of the main points from the paper and add one or two comments of my own:

1. Coal will remain the basic source of energy for at least the next twenty years and probably for a much longer period.

2. The demands for energy of all types will continue to expand; an ever-increasing proportion will be utilised in the form of electrical energy.

3. The high efficiency and relatively low capital cost of the very large new coal-fired electrical generating stations will make it more difficult for nuclear energy stations and the more expensive site hydro stations to compete. In my own view, nuclear energy stations will not become fully competitive with the best coal-fired stations before the mid 1970s. This will to some extent depend on the cost of uranium fuel.

4. As the more economically attractive water resources have already been developed, hydro-electric development will tend to slow down.

Integrated schemes of steam, nuclear, and hydro (peak load or pumped storage) will continue to develop.

5. This very large capital investment in power stations of all types will provide very considerable employment in all branches of the engineering and allied industries.

6. Oil imports will continue to increase. Indigenous sources of oil and natural gas are not likely to make a significant contribution to future energy requirements in Scotland.

7. The Clean Air Act calls for smokeless fuel. Under the Gas Board's present policy of a super high-pressure grid and complete gasification, will adequate supplies of solid smokeless fuel be available? Is it not possible that electricity will become economically attractive before the new plant installed to produce and consume solid smokeless fuel can be amortised? Might it not be better to base our smokeless fuel programme on electricity, supported by gas and oil?

8. Tidal water as a source of energy at first sight always looks attractive, but in addition to being variable and intermittent it suffers in most parts of Scotland from the basic disadvantage that the tidal range is small (of the order of 12 ft.). Under present conditions tidal schemes would not be economic.

9. Wind power is also variable and intermittent but would appear to be worthy of further development, especially for small power units.

10. Peat cannot at present compete with coal as solid fuel or for electrical generation, but might possibly have application as a smokeless fuel. Chemical extraction is uneconomic. Its chief outlet would appear to be in agriculture and horticulture.

11. As far as can be foreseen, Scotland's energy requirements over the next ten to twenty years will be fully met by the planned developments in the various sources of energy—coal, hydro, nuclear and oil.

12. Except in the case of some of the electro-process industries the cost of energy is not a decisive factor in the location of the industry. The cost of energy used in the majority of manufacturing industries is no more than 2 to 4 per cent. of the overall cost of the end production.

Similarly, in some cases, due to the extension of the grid, the availability of supplies of energy is not a decisive factor in the location of an industry.

13. There would appear to be scope for the development of new industries based on petroleum chemical, biological and mineral resources. Further research on the production of chemicals from coal might also prove rewarding.

14. One final point: The papers in this Symposium have illustrated the multiple utilisation of many of our fuel and other resources. For example, coal is a fuel and/or a source of chemical manufacture; water is used for hydro power, irrigation, or as a domestic and industrial water supply.

Might it not be advantageous to have under our Secretary of State a co-ordinating Minister of Energy and Resource Utilisation?

DISCUSSION

Dr. F. A. Williams, *Ministry of Power*

Mr. Chairman, your Grace, my Lords, Ladies and Gentlemen: You have had from your Rapporteur in the last few minutes such an excellent survey of the papers that he has already removed from my contribution to the discussion a great many points that I was going to make, so I won't have much difficulty in conforming with your Chairman's four minutes.

The first point I would like to refer to is in connection with the first paper by Messrs. Brown and Hunter, where they put a rather gloomy aspect on the cost of coal raised in Scotland for which they give a final figure of 24s. per ton as the loss. I don't know how they reached this figure. The actual figure which is published in the N.C.B. accounts is only about 14s. 3d., and they have extrapolated another 10s. for capital charges. Well now, the original 14s. 3d. includes some 6s. for depreciation so it is a bit difficult to see how the capital charges can amount to another 10s. My general feeling is that the position is not quite as bad as would appear. I may say that in Scotland the wages cost of raising coal is very much higher than anywhere else in the country. If you look at the last Annual Report of the N.C.B. the wages cost per ton of coal is 22 per cent. higher in Scotland than it is for the average of the United Kingdom, and no less than 70 per cent. higher than that in the East Midland Division. This, of course, is a reflection of the very difficult geological conditions which Dr. Chamberlain has described in his paper.

In discussing reserves, reference has already been made to Dr. Chamberlain's estimates for the next twenty years. Dr. Chamberlain has been inclined to regard as economic those reserves which demands will require to be mined over the next twenty years. Yesterday Dr. Bremner recommended great care in connection with this use of the word "economic" in regard to reserves, and I think it is particularly justified in this case because you have here competing sources of energy which are already making inroads into the coal market, and I think it is unwise to predict how those influences are going to make themselves felt. Another point is that what appears to be economic today may well be uneconomic in another ten years, and if one takes an extremely long view of, shall we say, towards the end of the century, reserves that may appear uneconomic in ten years time may again become economic. One reason why I say that is that, as is well known, reserves of petroleum in the world do not appear to be nearly so large as those of coal. Many times in the history of petroleum people have talked of a shortage of petroleum—that in another few years you would see it exhausted, but the petroleum geologists have immediately got to work and in a very short time they have succeeded in increasing the potential reserve very considerably. It is possible that the same thing may happen again, but as things stand at the moment, at the present rate of consumption of petroleum, towards the end of the century one might see some difficulties beginning to rise. This really behoves us not to render coal reserves incapable of being mined by allowing them to be flooded and that sort of thing. It is a problem which is very difficult, because obviously one cannot put mines on to a care and maintenance condition because of the costs which are involved. But I think it probably means that one has got to plan the way in which one works so that coal is left in a relatively virgin condition so that it could remain usable in the future.

I would now like to turn to one or two other points. I would like to refer first to the iron and steel industry, where the authors of the first two papers have pointed out the marked reduction in the coke/iron ratio which has already over the years occurred in the blast furnace industry, and which in the last year or two has accelerated. This is probably due very largely to the use of sintering, and Scotland is very well placed in the possession of vast quantities of breeze for the extension of the sintering of iron ore prior to charging to the blast furnace. It seems quite likely, therefore, that the demand for large coke in the iron industry will decrease very much more in the next few years than it has done already. And there are new techniques on the horizon for injection of pulverised fuel or oil into the blast furnaces which may have an even greater effect. If that does come about, then reserves of coking coal will become much more freely available. There will be more coke for use in the cupola industry around Falkirk; and the gas industry will probably have better coking coals available for carbonisation.

Mr. E. Hywel Jones, *South of Scotland Electricity Board*

We have already been told that the demand for electricity continues to grow and that there is no sign of saturation; in fact, our maximum demand is doubling every eleven years and our units demand is doubling every ten years. Increasing demands in the past have been met by using more of the available resources and also very largely by improving the efficiency of utilisation. Costs have been kept down by three methods:

(1) Adopting the newest technical advances in generating plant. There is less scope for this in the future—the rate of advance is slowing down.
(2) Building the largest units of plant practicable. For the time being we have pushed this almost to the limit, having regard to safety and the size of the system generally.
(3) Siting generating plant as near as practicable to the coalfields. We are now faced with the fact that units are getting bigger than the total available supply from local coalfields can support. At present, in Scotland, we depend on coal for our electricity with a very useful supplement from hydro plants. Before long Scottish coal will be unable to meet the rising demand. We are told that coal production will be stabilised at around 18½ million tons per annum. By 1980 our requirements for "electricity" coal would be of the order of 12 million tons per annum—two-thirds of the whole output. This would be a hopelessly uneconomic proposition. We should have to crack down large coals, but this would not crack down the price. Most people would agree that the scope for hydro development is limited. It cannot certainly continue to grow in proportion with the rate of growth of demand. Coal imports would be prohibitively costly because "electricity" coal is high in ash and moisture, all of which have to be transported. We must, therefore, attune ourselves to the idea of generating electricity by using alternatives to the two methods I have mentioned.

The adoption of oil as a fuel prevents the use of the most advanced ideas of high temperature and pressure steam cycles owing to "ash corrosion" on the metal surfaces. (Furnace additives are a palliative, but add to the cost and complication.) Oil, therefore, suffers from an economic disadvantage compared with coal unless the fuel cost is very low.

As an alternative, which is used in America, it might be possible in an area like this where refineries already exist to carry out a barter agreement whereby a generating station would receive residual fuel for nothing, and in return supply a refinery with free steam, no doubt with slight adjustments on either side. Electricity generated by this steam before it was passed to the refinery could be very cheap indeed.

Nuclear reactors are likely to make the largest contribution in the long-term future. They cannot compete with the best coal-fired stations just now, but this position will change. Meantime, in Scotland, we have a nuclear station being built which will be on full load by 1963. From then on we shall be learning the techniques of managing it at first hand and will have trained and experienced staffs available to deal with the advances of the future.

It is most unlikely that any single system of generation will oust all the others.

The various schemes are likely to develop in parallel and be complementary to one another. It would be a mistake to allow any particular vested interest to interfere with this process.

Mr. A. M. Wandless, *National Coal Board, London*

I want to say a very short word about this controversial question of reserves. There is enough coal in Scotland to supply the present output for longer than any of us here need worry about. But what matters, of course, is what are the economic reserves of coal, and that is a very much more difficult thing to assess. Obviously it depends on very many factors, factors which change from year to year, and certainly which change from generation to generation, and I am sure that it is that fact which has led Dr. Chamberlain in his paper not to speculate further than twenty years ahead. What matters is, can we continue to produce our coal at a cost that is competitive first with oil and then with nuclear energy? Only time will show this, and it does leave us, I think, with a clear challenge to keep coal competitive, and competitive on two fronts. First, obviously the front of cost which means, I think, exploiting to the full the potentialities of fully mechanised mining; the secondly, and no less important, that of efficiency of use to which I would also add amenity of use. Now these are the outstanding questions that will decide the future size of the coal industry in Scotland, and not the amount of coal that is left in the ground.

I would like to say a very short word about something that Dr. Chamberlain has hardly referred to, and that is the importance of coal type, or coal rank, in the Scottish context. Scotland is deficient in coking and coking coals which are traditionally used for coking and gas making. Nearly 80 per cent. of the Scottish output consists of low-rank, high-volatile, weakly coking or non-coking coals. Now, it is most important that the techniques of processing and utilisation should be developed to extend the field of use of these coals which has hitherto been too restricted. It should be remembered that these coals have remarkable properties of reactivity and combustibility which have not yet been fully exploited, and I believe that their abundance in Scotland define the research and development effort which is needed in the field of coal utilisation. Now, that is not to say nothing is being done. Already a three-pronged attack is being mounted. The Coal Board is working on the processing of these coals to provide high-quality smokeless fuels. The Gas Board is going ahead with pressure gasification at Westfield, a process for which these coals are particularly well suited, and I feel sure that the Scottish Electricity Board in common with their colleagues in the English C.E.G.B. are exploring the possibilities of new cycles of combustion which lead to higher efficiencies and hence which should help to keep Scottish coal more competitive. It may be difficult, as Dr. Chamberlain says, to say precisely what part coal will play in the second industrial revolution that we are now in the midst of. It had the field all to itself in the first Industrial Revolution and now it has to meet intense and virile competition, but none of us, and least of all those of us who are technicians in the coal industry, should grumble about this. The future indeed is full of interest and challenge for the coal industry as for other industries dealing with energy, and in the next decade or so we shall, I hope, see a fuel and energy policy hammered out in the way it should be hammered out, in the technical field rather than in the political field.

Mr. T. G. N. Haldane, *Merz & McLellan*

Mr. Chairman: I am rather sorry this Symposium does not contain a paper on the amenity problem faced by the power supply industry, possibly on the lines of the excellent paper by Sir Christopher Hinton which he presented to the Royal Society of Arts recently. This matter has been touched in our discussions, but I do not think it has been sufficiently emphasised. The dilemma is that we are a population of fifty million confined in a relatively small island and we cannot both maintain and increase our standard of living and at the same time have a countryside which is completely untouched. This is not possible, but unfortunately there is quite a considerable section of the public who do not realise the existence of this dilemma and are expecting to have a completely untouched countryside and also a rising standard of life.

Now, the particular problem which I want to refer to is the question of transmission lines. These are required whether or not you have hydro stations; in fact, if you did not have hydro stations you might possibly require even more transmission lines. They rouse fierce controversy, and there is very great difficulty in arriving at agreement about routes. Innumerable bodies have to be consulted. They have different ideas as to the route of lines, and the delay and the cost consequently involved are very serious indeed.

Now, I sometimes wonder whether it would be possible to have a single body of wise men to whom the amenity problem would be referred—the problem of routes for overhead lines—and from whom the final decision could be obtained, thus saving a lot of time and money. It might be very difficult to establish such a body and find such people, but perhaps something could be done to reduce the number of bodies which at present have to be consulted and to speed up the whole process. I think this is a matter to which attention should be very definitely directed. Public enquiries, where the atmosphere is liable to be highly emotional and partisan, are not necessarily the best solution of this problem.

I want to touch on one other matter out of the paper by Mr. Guthrie Brown and Mr. Hunter to illustrate the extreme complexity of arriving at economic decisions. You want to decide whether you are going to build a hydro station or steam station. You have got to make a very detailed analysis, and it is extremely complex—far more complex than most of the people who write letters in the Press realise. Its complexity arises inherently from the fact that you have to probe into the future in dealing with these matters. It is not a question of just how things stand at the moment. It is how things will stand over the life of the hydro station or the life of the steam station, and that involves our looking into the future; it is a difficult matter, and ultimately, even after you have worked out all the facts and statistics you can, it is a matter of judgment and common sense. The point in Mr. Hunter's paper which I want particularly to refer to is that it is now quite clear that the falling value of money which has been continuing for the past century or perhaps more is having a very big effect on the economics of long-term investments, particularly of hydro stations. As the value of money falls so, in effect, you wipe off the capital of your hydro station. I tried to illustrate this in a diagram which I presented in a paper to the Institution of Civil Engineers some time ago and the results were very striking, in so far as they showed the great difference between steam and hydro in this matter. This effect is far more marked for hydro than for steam and you could arrive at the conclusion, which may be approximately correct, that any hydro station—if it starts off somewhere approximately economic—will become highly economic in the course of its almost indefinite life. I would like to say more on this subject, but time does not permit.

For Mr. J. Henderson, *South of Scotland Electricity Board*

Mr. Chairman, Your Grace, My Lords, Ladies and Gentlemen: Mr. Henderson regrets that he is unable to attend, and with your permission, therefore, I would like to compress what he has written into the short space of time which has been allocated.

Only small contributions to the requirements of energy in the future will be made by peat and wind power, and therefore the major issues centre around coal, oil, water and nuclear energy. The electricity industry appears to be more associated with the future of the coal industry than any other industry. In Mr. Guthrie Brown's and Mr. Hunter's paper it is stated that in the long run costs of winning coal are bound to rise gradually as more easily mined resources are exhausted. In the event of all future generating stations after Hunterston being designed to burn coal, it is estimated that in 1985 the whole of the planned coal production would be required for the generation of electricity. It is clear, therefore, that practicable large-scale substitutes for coal must be available when required. The amount of electricity which can be produced economically by water power, although valuable, is relatively small compared with the total quantities which would be required, and therefore the only practicable alternatives which are available are oil and nuclear power. Unfortunately, neither oil nor uranium is indigenous to this country, but there is no escaping the fact that an alternative to coal will be essential within the next ten to twenty years. Oil may have to be used to eke out the coal supplies, but this may be considered as a transitional measure, and it is on the production of electricity from nuclear sources that we must rely in the future. The combined production of Chapelcross and the new Hunterston generating station in 1964 is estimated at 3,000 million units of electricity, in which year the total consumption is estimated at 12,000 million, so that in that year about one-quarter of the requirements will come from nuclear generation. Present trends in the design of nuclear generating stations, as described in Mr. Macklen's paper, indicate that nuclear power will not be competitive with coal or oil until about 1967. It may be that Mr. Macklen is somewhat optimistic and that the break-even date might not be until 1970 or even later. Nevertheless, with the help of pumped storage to maintain the load factor of the generation at Hunterston at a high average figure, probably of 70 per cent. during the whole life of the station, it is not unreasonable to expect that the average cost of generation at Hunterston will not be greater than that at Kincardine. The South of Scotland Board are at present surveying a proposed site for a new coal-burning station in the Lothians area for which ample supplies of coal must be guaranteed for twenty-five years at least. It is also important that the price of coal should remain reasonably stable in relation to other commodities during this period. The forward estimates indicate that the new generating stations will require to be commissioned in 1967 as described in the paper by Mr. Henderson and Mr. Allan. This station will be finished in 1970 and should be followed by the construction of a further nuclear generating station either on the Ayrshire coast or on the north-east coast of Scotland, provided the cost of production by this method is competitive with coal or oil. Oil most certainly must not be ruled out of comparison. The production of electricity by windmills in territory already served by an electricity supply system, or to which a supply could be economically taken from an existing system, could not be justified. Wind is a random occurrence and is not a firm source of energy. Other means must be provided, therefore, for generating the load on calm or windless days. For large-scale application in parallel with an electricity supply system it would be necessary to provide thermal or hydro plant of equivalent capacity to the wind generators in order to meet the system's demand with certainty. Mr. Golding suggests that the total capacity of 2,285 MW might be installed in Scotland, of which 618 MW would be on the mainland. The cost of this would be £150 million, which would be about £66 per kW. Assuming that the total cost per annum, including the capital charge and maintenance is 10 per cent. of the capital cost, the average cost per unit would be ½d. Now, for £150 million it would be possible to construct 3,600 MW of thermal generation which would generate at a cost below ·4d. per unit, and with the nuclear stations a cost of ·2d. is expected.

J. K. HUNTER, B.SC., M.INST.C.E., M.I.MECH.E., M.I.E.E., *Sir Alexander Gibb & Partners*

I think my task is a fairly simple and straightforward one if all you are looking for is an answer to any questions raised on the paper on energy. As far as my recollection goes, the only direct question was raised by the first speaker on behalf of the National Coal Board, who wanted to know how the Author had arrived at the sum of 10s. as representing the capital element in the cost of producing coal in Scotland. A search through the published records and reports of the Coal Board did not reveal any information on capital cost, except that there were details of the various sums voted for capital development over the post-war years. By summing these up and making certain assumptions with regard to the residual value of the capital expenditure over the historic past it was possible to arrive at a figure which we thought would reasonably fill the bill. If the Coal Board have a better figure, I should be pleased to hear it.

Mr. E. W. GOLDING, *Electrical Research Association*

Mr. Chairman, Ladies and Gentlemen: Obviously the figures which I gave in this paper, on what might be installed in Scotland in the form of wind-driven plant, is very much a question of "might". I did not suggest for a minute that you would put a windmill on every one of the hundreds of hills alongside the coast, but I think it is important to realise that a considerable asset, in the form of wind energy, does exist.

Mr. W. GUTHRIE, *Strain & Robertson, Glasgow*

The overall economics of generation and transmission as pertaining to the relative merits of the various sources of energy and their location has never been so uncertain as at present. Furthermore, there is the far-reaching question as to whether economics specific to these two items should be subordinated to gains of greater sociological consequence.

In the matter of coal, for example, the cost of Scottish coal, that is the "true" cost, is very high in relation to that available to the East Midlands of England, some 265 miles away. The lowest Scottish cost is £4, 11s. 0d. per ton: the East Midland's is £3, 1s. 0d.—30s. a ton difference. What does this mean to the Scottish electricity supply industry? It means that if economics were the only consideration it would be cheaper to have a very substantial proportion of the electricity required for Scotland generated near Nottingham and sent by transmission lines to the Central Scotland area. Would any of you gentlemen here care to support a proposal that we get half our electricity requirements from the Midlands of England? I do not think anybody would want to do so, bearing the overall sociological problem in mind.

As this Conference deals with natural resources, I would therefore like to comment on those available for the generation of substantial quantities of electricity—coal, water and peat—which I would, as a first approximation, place in that order of importance in the ratio 4 : 1 : 1.

I found Dr. Chamberlain's paper on coal a most readable paper; it recognises the unfortunate fact that geological conditions in Scotland make Scottish coal dearer, but I would like to suggest to Dr. Chamberlain that he should supplement his paper by a section on economics of future Scottish coal production against the national background. If we could have this addition it would be a very great help to those interested in economics. The present economics are extremely depressing in that the Scottish Division of the Coal Board has made very substantial losses in the last eight years, about £18 million in 1958 and £17 million last year, interest charges included. These losses are more than four times the losses in the worst English Division, and if Scottish coalfields had been required to be solvent it would have been necessary to add £1 per ton to all coal sold in Scotland. If we are to make reliable financial comparisons for future projects it is essential that the true cost of Scottish coal should be known, as it would be unwise to take decisions which ignore possible changes in Government or N.C.B. policy on the matter of solvency of the various Divisions. £1 per ton extra would add £3½ million to the annual cost of generation in Scotland at present, i.e. 16 per cent. of the total generation cost, interest, etc., included. Now, there is another point I would like to make at this juncture in order that one may compare the relative costs of the various resources. We read of excessive stocks of coal in the country—34 million tons, or approximately twice the annual output of Scottish coalfields; naturally we wonder if the use of other energy resources should be abandoned, substantially reduced, or placed in cold storage. This action would be most unfortunate because, of this quantity, there are only 1,100,000 tons of stock in Scotland, i.e. three weeks' supply.

I will have to pass over the section I had prepared on water power in view of the request to limit speaking for four minutes, but I would like to say a little about peat in view of the fact that it has got no champion. In the list of the Symposium papers there is no contribution dealing specifically with peat. What has happened to the Scottish Peat Committee that it has not stated its case? Has it become discouraged and frustrated after eleven years of effort? Compare the Scottish position with that now existing in Southern Ireland, as a result of effort over approximately the same period they generate 33·4 per cent. of their requirements from peat. The 60-MW peat station at Ferbane can provide electricity as cheaply with their coal-fired stations, and furthermore the cost of coal in Ireland is slightly cheaper than it is here in Scotland.

Dr. R. A. Mackay, *Mackay & Schnellmann Ltd., London*

Mr. Chairman, Ladies and Gentlemen: I am afraid that I condensed what I had to say to ten minutes—I can't say it in less. I sympathise with your position so that I think I will make my contribution entirely in writing.

What I wanted to say was based firstly on the theme that resources do not matter so much as the will to put resources to use. I was going to illustrate that by a number of examples around the world in various countries where I have been, where small countries have done something about it. Of course, Israel is an outstanding case. I was going on to deal with the cure for this—necessity in planning and occasionally ingenuity by individuals and companies. I can't do that either in the time, but I had some interesting examples. Then I was going on to say how certain countries had put it into effect; I wanted to pay tribute to geological surveys of the world and to say also that I thought it would be an unfortunate thing if this was put into their hands unless they had a special department created for it, because they are scientists, during wartime and times of emergency they are put on to the job of trying to discover how a certain commodity can be won, but they are not asked in those circumstances to see if it can be won in a paying way. Some of the most valuable experience and the happiest time of my life was with a geological survey, and my terms of reference have even been "Go and find that thing regardless of cost". Those are not the people we want to help us with development—the people who have got to carry out a scientific line of thought without regard to economics. We have got to take an entirely different line of thought so that if, as somebody said yesterday, it should be the geological surveys who did it, then it should be the geological surveys with a special department in which they recruit the men who have earned their living in industry, and not people who have just been to the university and then gone into what is basically scientific research.

A. A. Templeton, C.B.E., J.P., *Chairman, Building Materials Committee, Scottish Council (Development and Industry)*

Two points very shortly. My first one is—in my retirement I go about Scotland preaching for a return to the use of Scottish stone and Scottish slates in Scottish buildings and also for the manufacture of cement in Scotland from our lime deposits. I was asked why I had not put in a paper on these. The answer is that the Scottish Council are themselves pursuing these points very actively at the moment, and with some success. There is now more use of Scottish slates and Scottish stone going on than there was some years ago; and thank goodness cement has now broken cover at Dunbar, but that is *sub judice* at the moment.

My second point should possibly have been taken earlier. It arises in my mind from irrigation and talks on water. After their big fight over Loch Sloy, Dunbartonshire Water Authority *versus* the Hydro-Electric Board, they became fast friends and there was an agreement arrived at whereby the Loch should give the Hydro Board all the water it wanted, but it should also give local water authorities up to three million gallons per day. Before I left the County Clerkship of Dunbartonshire some eight years ago, I had gone to the Hydro-Electric Board and they were willing to discuss with the local authority that instead of taking the three million gallons daily throughout the year, we should take six million gallons during the summer months when we most needed it, and they should get that six millions in the winter when they most needed it. I mention that point, sir, to get on record that it may be well worth while for water authorities to think of the joint use of water supplies; and to say this to them, that I have never found the Hydro Board loath to discuss possible joint arrangements in the public interest.

D. C. ELGIN, A.M.I.MECH.E., M.INST.GAS E., *Scottish Gas Board*

I would like to draw particular attention to the stage at which the gas industry now finds itself. After many years of unspectacular development and consolidation we are on the brink of a "break through" which is likely to place the industry in a key position as a fuel supplier. We are now at the stage where we can change on a large scale from relatively small low-pressure plants to high-pressure technique centralised on large units. It is significant that even our traditional methods still make us the most efficient of the fuel processing industries. Modern techniques will take us even further along that line and in particular will allow the maximum possible conversion of low-grade fuels into useful energy. Nowadays our industry is going in for scientific methods of selecting its engineers. One useful criterion, and I may well be an example of this, is an effective bad memory so that past methods can be forgotten readily. For these reasons I would like you all to watch carefully what we are going to do with coal over the next few years as outlined in my paper. Concern has been expressed here for the future of the coal industry and in certain respects I consider that the processing of coal by the gas industry can assist them to achieve additional stability in the future. The support and active collaboration we have already received from the coal industry, both in planning our high-pressure gasification project and in seeking to meet clean air demands by the production of new high-grade smokeless fuels, has been a considerable encouragement to us. In fact, our Westfield high-pressure gasification project can serve as a prime example of the ready fund of support and enthusiasm which becomes readily available here in Scotland whenever a new enterprise is put in hand. This is probably a good advertising line for the Scottish Council because, although it may be argued that willing collaboration is usually available to cushion and encourage pioneer enterprise, here in Scotland it seems to me to be more channelled and effective.

I hope that in the paper and in these few additional comments I have shown that the gas industry is now on the threshold of an era during which its contribution to fuel conservation and to an improved standard of heat service, both in the home and to commerce and industry, will reach an even higher level than formerly.

WRITTEN CONTRIBUTIONS

W. GUTHRIE

The overall economics of generation and transmission as pertaining to the relative merits of the various resources of energy and their location have never been so uncertain as at present. Furthermore, there is the far-reaching question as to whether economics specific to these two items should be subordinated to gains of much greater sociological consequence.

As an example of this problem, the price of Scottish coal—the true cost as produced at the pit inclusive of interest and other overheads—is very expensive in comparison with that available in the East Midlands of England some 265 miles away; best Scottish price £4, 11s. per ton, East Midlands £3, 1s. per ton. What does this mean in the Scottish electricity supply industry? It means that if economics of that industry were the sole consideration, it would be cheaper to have a very substantial proportion of the electricity required in Scotland generated near Nottingham and sent by transmission line to Central Scotland for distribution. But would any of us here want this, knowing that many benefits would accrue to many people in Scotland by doing the generation within our own borders.

As this Conference deals with natural resources, I would therefore like to comment on those available to us for the generation of substantial amounts of electricity—coal, water and peat—which I would, as a first approximation, place in that order of importance in the ratio of 4 : 1 : 1.

Mr. Chamberlain's paper on Scottish coal is most readable and explains much, and it requests recognition of the unfortunate fact that geological conditions present greater difficulties to the mining engineer in the Scottish coalfields than in most other British divisions. May I suggest to Mr. Chamberlain that he should supplement his paper with a section on the economics of future Scottish coal production against the national background. This would be of great assistance to those of us who would deal in the economics of coal, water and peat.

The present-day economics are extremely depressing in that the Scottish Division of the Coal Board has made very substantial losses in the last eight years—about £18,000,000 in 1958 and about £17,000,000 last year—interest charges included. These losses are more than four times the losses on the worst English Division and, if the Scottish coalfields had been required to be solvent, it would have been necessary to add £1 per ton to the price of all coal sold in Scotland. If we are to make reliable financial comparisons for future projects, it is essential that the "true" cost of Scottish coal should be known, as it would be unwise to take decisions which ignore possible changes in Government or National Coal Board policy on the matter of the solvency of the various Divisions. £1 per ton extra would add about £3,500,000 to the annual cost of generation from coal as at present—that is a 16 per cent. increase in the overall cost of generation from coal.

Coming now to water, this is an extremely complex subject and in regard to Scottish conditions there is much misunderstanding by all section of the community—engineers included. As I see it, the scarcity of this resource will not allow of its providing any more than about 20 per cent. of the electricity in Scotland. Water is therefore not a major alternative or competitor to coal. Given suitable duties, the water power projects can more than hold their own with coal if financial performance is the criterion. The utilisation of Scottish water for base-load duty is uneconomic; for duty at or near the average load factor of the supply system it tends to be marginal, but for the peak work during the industrial week-day it is cheaper and very much superior as an operational tool to steam. So let us get on with our meagre 20 per cent. power from water, bearing in mind also that sociological benefits should be distributed.

At this point may I seek to clear up a situation which I am sure is much misunderstood at present. We read about the excessive stocks of coal in the country—34,000,000 tons or approximately twice the annual output of the Scottish coalfield. Naturally we wonder whether the use of other energy resources should be abandoned, substantially reduced or placed in cold storage. This action would be most unfortunate because, of the above quantity, there are only 1,100,000 tons in stock in the Scottish coalfield—that is a three weeks' supply. There is thus no excessive stock of coal in Scotland, and we should not therefore feel that it might be wrong to develop our other resources. The future of coal in electricity generation is excellent.

The list of Symposium papers contains no contribution dealing specifically and at length with peat. What has happened to the Scottish Peat Committee that it has not stated its case? Has it become discouraged and frustrated by eleven years of effort that in an important Symposium like this it has no progress or new information to give us since that excellent and interesting report published in 1954?

Compare the Scottish position with that now existing in Southern Ireland as a result of effort over about the same period. The electricity supply system has a load of the same order as the North of Scotland Hydro-Board, namely 2,000 million units, and 33·4 per cent. of this is generated by the burning of peat.

The 60-MW station at Ferbane, Co. Offaly, can provide electricity as cheaply as the coal-fired stations in spite of the latter's higher pressure and temperature and consequently better thermal efficiency. It should be noted that the coal, imported from England is slightly cheaper than Scottish coal.

There are fully 200 MW of generating plant in service using peat and a further 240 MW under construction or planned for completion by 1968-69. The foregoing installations involve an expenditure of about £25 million.

Do these figures indicate any lack of confidence on the part of the Irish Electricity Board in peat and its future?

And so the question must be asked as to why we stand still in Scotland. From the 1954 Peat Report we find that we are not without sizeable bogs; in the Flanders moss area fifteen miles from the Glasgow area 60,000 kW of base-load are lying dormant and in the main moss area of Caithness 200,000 kW could be obtained. The above Peat Report schedules 70 bogs estimated to hold 180 million tons of solids. If we select 8 only of the most likely bogs we find they contain about 56 million tons of solids or about one-third of the total estimated quantity available from the 70 bogs scheduled. The resources of these 8 bogs would give an output of 2,000 million kWh for 25 years; in other words, the same output as that from the Hydro Board at present.

Generation from peat would not play a major part in providing for the electricity requirements of Scotland as a whole, but the establishment of a few stations of the 60-MW size at suitable bogs would confer much benefit in their surrounding areas. For example, the Irish station at Ferbane and the associated work on the bogs give employment to about 350 permanent employees and during the peat harvesting the maximum number employed rises to around 600.

In regard to economics, the modern large-sized coal-fired plant with 200 to 300 MW generating units, with which the peat plants would have to compete, produces electricity at a very low overall cost, but few coalfields can support them. If these stations had to buy their coal, for the reasons of policy already referred to, at the true cost of production for the area in which they are located, the peat station of 60 MW could hold its own with them. Even if the economics were marginal the burdens would not embarrass the finances of the Scottish Electricity Boards which by 1970 should have a combined revenue of over £100 million.

In conclusion, I must strongly urge more action on peat. It might become as important as water power and I would hope with far less enemies.

C. L. C. ALLAN, *North of Scotland Hydro-Electric Board*

I am glad that Mr. T. G. N. Haldane has referred to the increasing value of a hydro scheme in future years. It is historically a fact that the value of hydro-electric stations has always increased during their lifetime in relation to the falling value of money and the rising cost of fuel for thermal stations. There are hydro-electric stations in Scotland today producing electricity at a quarter of the cost of their thermal counterparts although when built at the same time production costs were equal.

Critics of hydro schemes often use the argument that as the capital required for hydro schemes is more than for thermal stations they are too expensive. This argument ignores the fact that an electricity undertaking is concerned with getting its generation at the cheapest cost it can in the area where it operates. The capital charges on a hydro scheme are obviously higher than those on a thermal station, but the cost of fuel, the largest proportion of the running cost of a thermal station, is zero for a hydro station.

Mr. Haldane also referred to amenity difficulties and I can certainly confirm that the difficulties and delays which he has described are both costly and frustrating and it is to be remembered that in the end it is the price of electricity which gets loaded with extra costs arising from increased costs of construction or the consequences of delay.

I am afraid that a completely unrealistic picture about possibilities of wind power has been given in Mr. Golding's paper although possibly he did not intend this. Electricity generation on a large scale for public supply requires the use of equipment developed to a stage where its performance and reliability is well established. The paper shows only that a small experimental machine of 8-kW capacity has done some running at Rothiemurchus and that a 100-kW experimental machine has commenced operation in the Isle of Man. These experiments are in fact not the first, and the previous ones were not successful.

It is obvious that energy from the wind is quite random. Electricity loads must be met at all times and so other generating plant with firm output must be installed to meet the maximum loads and supply all the energy at times when wind power is not available. It would not be very attractive to Electricity Boards, after having provided this necessary plant, to consider installing further plant merely to get random production.

The cost of random wind power production was given as 0·5d./kWh, which may seem relatively cheap, but such a figure is by no means substantiated yet. Replacement of rainfall shortages in hydro-electric schemes could not be guaranteed from uncertain wind power, and as a speaker pointed out at the Symposium, the cost of additional thermally produced electricity made available on the Grid system would be more certain and probably cheaper to provide any additions above what is stored in reservoirs.

The production of the large amounts of power mentioned in the paper from machines as small as 100 kW would require such a large number of them that quite an absurd position would be created. There are serious problems too in the construction of bigger wind-driven generators. The design of the very large blades to operate with mechanical safety is difficult and the control of machine speed to regulate output to the Grid is difficult too.

Because of these facts and difficulties, it is most unlikely that wind power generation will be developed for public electricity supply.

H. R. HART, *Deputy Chairman, Scottish Gas Board*

In discussing the future pattern of fuel supplies in Scotland, an interesting conception emerged of the roles to be played by the major fuel industries. In particular there was forecast for the electricity industry a continued and spectacular expansion in output, regardless, apparently, of the extravagance in natural resources which this may represent, and ignoring developments which are placing other fuel industries in a strongly competitive position.

The transient role assigned to the coal industry in providing steam generating stations with all the coal they will need to meet this expansion in electrical energy until coal is finally displaced by nuclear fuels is hardly an enviable one. In 1959 about 3¼ million tons of coal were required for electricity generation in Scotland; figures were quoted during the Symposium to the effect that by 1980 about 12 million tons of coal, two-thirds of the output of the National Coal Board (Scottish Division), would be required for electricity generation; someone even suggested that by 1985 the entire output would be required for this purpose. But it is evident that a large proportion of Scotland's total coal output is vastly superior in quality to the relatively low-grade material which can now be sold at cut prices for power generation to avoid a glut. Several aspects of this arrangement appear to defy logical reasoning. Many of the coals in the Scottish output command prices which, although perhaps uneconomic, are high compared with the price of steam-raising coals; can these high-priced fuels be used in the relatively inefficient electricity generating process without upsetting radically the present economics, either of the buyer or the seller? But, economics apart, the ethics of consuming valuable reserves of high- and medium- grade coals merely for boiler firing are highly questionable and little less barbarous than the domestic open coal fire. More serious still in the long run: are the coal industry expected to devote all their resources within the next ten to twenty years to fostering a temporary market which may terminate with the advent of economic nuclear energy? How much better for Scotland and the National Coal Board to maintain a diversified allegiance, perhaps even modifying their present pricing policy to ensure that coals of different types are sold for the purposes to which they are best suited. For example, the reduction in coal price which would ensure the continued use of coal at isolated gasworks, which otherwise might have to be converted to some cheaper alternative, might be small in comparison to the overall loss sustained in downgrading such fuels by crushing them for power generation.

It is submitted that any worthwhile appraisal of the fuel situation in Scotland cannot simply aggregate the output estimates of a number of interested and competing industries and conclude that all is well because the total projected output appears to be adequate statistically. Success in the long run will be measured by the skill with which limited reserves are used in processes best fitted to conserve them, and inevitably will be reflected in the price to be paid for fuel of all kinds. The plans which are at this moment transforming the gas industry, traditionally a highly efficient processor of crude fuels, are based on these conservation principles. The time has come for their extension to the whole field of fuel supply and, in the absence of a national fuel policy, it is the hands of those who will assess the Scottish Council Symposium to recommend the first steps. Only thus can the prices of all types of manufactured fuels, including electricity, be kept within limits which will not interfere with the plans of industrialists seeking facilities in Scotland.

Belief in expanding opportunities for gas produced by the revolutionary new processes now being applied in Scotland and in particular by the Lurgi process as at Westfield is confirmed in the recent report of the Committee on Coal Derivatives (Wilson Committee) to the Minister of Power.

Further support for this view has been expressed from several other responsible quarters and I conclude with the final sentence of a searching feature article on the economics of gas production based on coal, which appeared in the *Economist* during 1958: "The chances are real and invigorating; as real as say economic nuclear power, no more remote, and eventually capable of providing energy a good deal cheaper."

J. L. WARRANDER, *Ministry of Power*

I congratulate Professor Thomson on his excellent review of the various papers on Fuel and Energy, but would dissent from his view that, because of a reduction in the carbonisation of deep-mined coal by the gas industry, less gas coke will be produced and it would therefore appear that there will be insufficient supplies of solid smokeless fuels for clean air schemes in Scotland.

This view is not supported by the statements in the papers "Coal and Gas from Coal Mines" by Dr. Chamberlain, and "Natural Gas and Manufactured Gas" by Mr. David Elgin. In reference to the need to produce solid smokeless fuels to meet the requirements of the Clean Air Act, Dr. Chamberlain has said that suitable coals, in the quantity required, are available to the gas industry for the production of premium quality smokeless fuels, and Mr. Elgin has referred to the means that are available to the Scottish Gas Board to meet increasing coke demands and the action that has already been taken to meet the demand for a superior fuel for clean air purposes. Furthermore, we should not exclude the possibility that other producers of solid smokeless fuels might also be interested in providing supplies in Scotland.

A. M. WANDLESS

I should like to amplify Dr. Chamberlain's valuable survey of Scottish Coal Resources in two respects—firstly as regards coal reserves and secondly as regards coal types and quality; and then to offer a few thoughts on the factors that will decide the place of coal in the Scottish economy in the future.

You may have felt that Dr. Chamberlain's treatment of reserves lacks precision. To those unfamiliar with the subject it would seem that now that the coal industry has been under unified control for some time it ought to be possible for us to say firmly how much coal lies in the earth's crust in Scotland and how much of the total amount is economically workable. After all, various estimates have been made in past years, and in the last thirteen years since nationalisation the Coal Board have undertaken in Scotland boring and explorative work on a scale and of a comprehensiveness unprecedented in any previous period of the long history of coal mining in Scotland. Very substantial new reserves of coal have been proved. But it is economic reserves that matter, and economic reserves depend on many factors which change from year to year, and certainly from generation to generation. There is enough coal in the ground in Scotland to meet the present output of coal for longer than we need worry about, but can it be produced at a cost that is competitive first with oil and then with nuclear energy? Only time will show and therefore I think that Dr. Chamberlain is wise and realistic to confine his forecast to the short spell of the next twenty years. What emerges, I think, is a clear challenge to keep coal competitive and on two fronts—first that of cost, which means exploiting to the full the potentialities of fully mechanised mining; and second that of efficiency of use, to which I would also add, amenity of use. These are the outstanding questions that will decide the future size of the coal industry in Scotland and not the amount of coal left in the ground.

It is self evident that the stronger the competitive position of coal the better the national interest will be served. For coal not only finds employment in a big way for Scottish people but it is also a source of energy and power that is entirely under our own control and that is independent of the vagaries of international politics and international finance. Further, every ton of it eases our balance of payments position, directly or indirectly, which is likely to remain critical for as long as one can foresee. Therefore there is a very powerful incentive, both for the producer of coal and the users, to make rapid progress in the related fields of costs of production and efficiency of use. It would, I believe, have been worth while to have had a paper at this Symposium examining prospects in these fields.

Tied up with efficiency of use is the question of coal types and quality of coal, about which Dr. Chamberlain has said little. As compared with England, Scotland is deficient in coking and caking coals which are traditionally used for coking and gas-making. Nearly 80 per cent. of the Scottish output consists of low-rank, high-volatile, weakly caking or non-caking coals. In this Scotland is unique, not only in Great Britain but in Western Europe as a whole. It is most important that techniques of processing and utilisation should be developed to extend the field of use of these coals, which has hitherto been too restricted. These coals have remarkable properties of reactivity and combustibility that have not yet been fully exploited and their abundance in Scotland should define the research and development effort that is needed. Already a three-pronged attack is being mounted: the Coal Board is working on the processing of these coals to provide high-quality smokeless fuels; the Gas Board is going ahead with pressure gasification at Westfield, a process for which these coals are very well suited; and I feel sure that the Electricity Board in common with their colleagues in the C.E.G.B. in England are exploring the possibilities of novel cycles of combustion, which should lead to higher efficiencies and hence make Scottish coal more competitive for electricity generation.

It may be difficult, as Dr. Chamberlain implies, to say precisely what part coal will play in the second industrial revolution that we are now in the midst of. It had the field all to itself in the first Industrial Revolution; now it has to meet intense and virile competition. But none of us and least of all those of us who are technicians in the coal industry should grumble about this. The future is full of interest and challenge and in the next decade or so we shall, I hope, see a fuel and energy policy hammered out in the way it should be hammered out—in the technical rather than the political field.

J. HENDERSON, *Chief Engineer, South of Scotland Electricity Board*

Although small contributions to the increasing requirements of energy may be made by peat and wind power, the quantities would be small in relation to the total quantities required and the major issues centre around coal, oil, water and nuclear energy.

Coal has been for many years one of the most important factors in the Scottish economy, and while the future of the coal industry will have an effect on all individually, the electricity industry would appear to be the most affected.

Certain disturbing facts are noted in some of the papers. In Mr. Guthrie Brown's and Mr. J. K. Hunter's paper attention is drawn to the loss which was made by the N.C.B. Scottish Division in 1959 which averaged 24s. 3d. per ton. These authors express the hope that the position will change when the benefits of the heavy capital investment incurred by the N.C.B. in recent years have been fully secured, but they go on to state that the fact remains that in the long run costs are bound to rise gradually as the more easily mined resources are exhausted.

In the event of all future generating stations (after Hunterston) being designed to burn coal, one-third of all the coal produced in Scotland would be required for generating electricity in 1970. In 1980 the proportion would have risen to two-thirds and in 1985 the whole of the planned coal production would be required for the generation of electricity.

It is clear, therefore, that the remaining reserves of coal must be used to the best advantage and that practicable large-scale substitutes for coal must be available when required.

The amount of electricity which can be produced economically by water power is relatively small compared with the total requirements. The only practicable alternatives which are available are oil and nuclear power. Unfortunately neither oil nor uranium is indigenous to this country, but there is no escaping the fact that an alternative to coal will be essential within the next ten to twenty years.

Oil may have to be used to eke out the coal supplies, but this may be considered as a transitional measure and it is on the production of electricity from nuclear sources that we must rely in the future.

The amount of electricity produced from the Chapelcross Atomic Energy Factory at the present time is about 1,000 million units per annum, and when Hunterston generating station is in full operation it will produce 2,000 million units per annum. Between these two, therefore, some 3,000 million units of electricity will be generated in 1965, in which year the total electricity requirements in Scotland are estimated to be 12,000 million units, so that about one-quarter of the total requirements of electricity will come from nuclear generation. If this amount of energy were produced entirely from coal, an additional 1·5 million tons of coal would be required.

Present trends in the design of nuclear generating stations as described in Mr. Macklin's paper indicate that nuclear power will not be competitive with coal or oil until about 1967. It may be that Mr. Macklin is somewhat optimistic and that the break-even date may not be until 1970 or thereabouts. Nevertheless, with the help of pumped storage to maintain the load factor of nuclear generation at a high average figure such as 70 per cent. during the life of the station, it is not unreasonable to expect that the average cost of Hunterston will be no greater than that of Kincardine.

The South Scotland Board are at present surveying a proposed site for a new coal-burning station in the Lothians area for which ample supplies of coal must be guaranteed for a period of twenty-five years at least. It is also important that the price of coal should remain reasonably stable in relation to other commodities during this period. Forward estimates indicate that the new generating station will require to be commissioned in 1967 as described in "A Survey of Electricity Supply in Scotland" and it would be completed by 1970. This should be followed by the construction of a further nuclear generating station either on the Ayrshire coast or on the North-East coast, provided the cost of production by this method is competitive with coal or oil. Oil must certainly not be ruled out of the comparison.

The fuel cell as described by Mr. Chambers is unlikely to affect the question of basic energy resources except in so far as efficiency with which heat is transformed into electricity may be increased. The fuel cell might, therefore, enable such coal reserves as there are to meet our requirements for a longer period of time. Unfortunately its development will be too late to extend appreciably the Scottish coal resources.

The production of electricity by windmills in territory already served by an electricity supply system or to which a supply could economically be taken from an existing system could not be justified.

Wind is a random occurrence and is not a firm source of energy. Other means must be provided, therefore, for generating the load on calm or windless days. For small remote establishments where the cost of providing a supply from the public electricity system is extremely high, a small windmill associated with a storage battery might be used. For large-scale application in parallel with the electricity supply system it would be necessary to provide thermal or hydro plant of equivalent capacity to the wind generators in order to meet the system maximum demand with certainty.

Mr. Golding suggests that a total capacity of 2,285 MW might be installed in Scotland and on the islands, of which only 618 MW would be on the mainland. The total number of units generated would be 7,221 million, of which 1,919 million would be on the mainland. He also suggests that the total cost of installing the whole of this plant would be £150 million, which is about £66 per kW. Assuming that the total cost per annum, including capital charges and maintenance, is 10 per cent. of the capital cost, as suggested, the average cost per unit would be 0·5d. For £150 million 3,600 MW of thermal generation could be provided which could generate at a cost below 0·4d. The proposals for utilising the wind, therefore, will not bear comparison with conventional plant.

The electricity generated by wind power at a cost of 0·5d. per unit. is not competitive with a fuel cost of 0·4d. per unit at modern thermal generating stations and still less so with a cost of 0·2d. per unit at a nuclear station.

R. GILMOUR, *Lochboisdale* (letter to Professor A. S. T. Thomson)

COAL 20 YEARS AS CHIEF FUEL

I have not been in touch with technical matters for ten years—although I was previously a research organic chemist and chemical engineer. Nevertheless, I cannot see eye to eye with you regarding your pessimistic view on the further outlook of coal. I am at a disadvantage, since I usually spend the winter here and my papers are in London. The figures I quote are from the Oxford Economic Atlas and many from U.N. surveys. They should be reasonably accurate for rough comparative purposes —and I think they have not doubled or trebled in the interval between 1952-53 and 1960.

Taking coal first—the estimated reserves of Britain are about 400 to 500 years at present consumption; not as much as we would like and getting more difficult to dig out. I dare say the Russians or Americans would dig it out for us. We have also to consider that as the world becomes federated into two halves anyway, those parts of the world which are rich in some particular material will supply those which are deficient in it, and vice versa. I do not think therefore that we need worry unduly about our supplies of coal in the future. No doubt some people might say that this is a Utopian idea, but as things are going in the world, the Utopian idea is the condition of survival. The coal reserves of Russia have been estimated as good for 3,000 years—and China 3,400 years; always keeping in mind the probable increase in consumption—which will have to be reduced eventually by stabilising the population: otherwise we face annihilation just as surely as by the H-bomb. Russia and China between them have considerably more than half of the world's coal supplies and no doubt in a decade or so they will be offering it to us at a knock-down price, which will topple all our Highland Hydro-Electric schemes and Nuclear Power Stations off their rather insecure pedestals.

As regards oil—the estimated world reserves are good for thirty years (1 per cent. of the coal reserves). Here and there more is discovered—but the chances of it overtaking coal are remote.

Some years ago the Government were cursing the miners for not digging out enough coal. Six months or a year later they said we must stock-pile and go over to oil—which they did, to the tune of millions of tons lying there deteriorating. Who was responsible for this incredible folly? We do not know, but the truth will come out gradually. Probably some financial group stand to gain. U.S.A. interest in the Middle East and ours too spells oil. For a time the U.S. was worried about her own supplies, and even contemplated large-scale production of oil from coal. Why should we close down so many mines on the plea that they are worked out or unworkable? I find it difficult to believe. It is a safe rule when any contradictory problem arises—or a situation which the man in the street cannot fathom—to assume that the answer is dollars or pounds.

When we come to water power we find that Asia and Africa have immense potentialities. (I leave out U.S.A. and Canada as they form another Continent, and have considerably less reserves than Asia and Africa.) Great Britain is in the unfortunate position of having very little water power. Pre-war the half-dozen reasonably possible sites for cheap power had already been developed, and there was little possibility of further cheap hydro-electric power. This statement was made by an eminent engineer in 1927, in an address to an Engineering Institution. During the years between 1927 and 1943 some bright boys must have tinkered with the idea of linking up watersheds by means of tunnels through the solid rock to a central watershed. The Government was interested and guaranteed interest on borrowed capital. The Hydro-Electric Board was formed and surveyed 102 sites—bringing into commission anything from a burn upwards. Everybody was happy. Engineering contractors were on velvet for twenty years. Why worry about dead beds of gravel in numerous valleys where once rivers ran? Why worry about effect on climate, husbandry, afforestation, salmon fishing, etc.? After all, it is only poor old Scotland. She has taken plenty in the past: no doubt she can take a bit more?

Eleven U.S. bases, depots and training grounds in Scotland—in addition to all those in England—and about forty bases scattered round the periphery of the Asian continent; such as the Mariana Islands, Guam, Okinawa, Formosa, Wake, the Aleutian Islands and many others.

When Russia suggests installing a base in Cuba, what a howl goes up—aggression, provocation, etc. Does the West have no sense of humour?—apparently not. The last priceless effort is the Holy Loch as a base for submarines armed with Polaris rockets to be fired from underwater. We are to have no control over these. They can cruise about in the Arctic or anywhere. There is some poppycock about the fullest possible discussion with our authorities before the missiles are used. This would not deceive a child. Possible seems a tricky word to introduce into agreements of this nature.

The Press are doing their best to show that our people do not object. They have interviewed local shopkeepers in Kirn and round about. These people, of course, know nothing and think it will be good for business. They have been told that bombs are so powerful that one falling anywhere would have just as much effect on the Holy Loch district as if actually dropped there. That, of course, is quite untrue. The radius of blast destruction of these bombs is known. An H-bomb dropped on London would have no blast effect on the Holy Loch district, ignoring radioactive after-effects, fall out, etc. It should be put before the people of this country that so long as we have U.S. bases and troops on our land we are a front outpost for the U.S.A. and would be the first to be completely wiped out. If the people are agreeable to that, it is up to them. But they should be told. It is difficult for the man in the street who has read modern European History to contact the public. The press is too powerful—and now appears to be passing into the control of three or four people. G. W. Keeton, the great lawyer, points out in his *The Passing of Parliament*, how close we are to the Soviet system of government—and no V.I.P. has answered him in book form.

On the other hand if we have *no* U.S. bases and missiles, Russia would not touch us—we should be in the same position as Eire. Russia has seldom, almost never, been an aggressor, compared with the rest of Europe. Her expansion East into almost uninhabitable land was similar to our expansion west in America. We did leave a few Maoris in New Zealand, but not many.

Russia and China together have 12,000 square miles of territory, very rich in almost all the materials they need. They want time and opportunity to develop their countries. China in particular is going to do in twenty-five years what Russia did in forty years. We must not stick our heads in the sand. Two historians (true historians, not writers of memoirs) unknown to the public, of course—K. Scott Latourette, an American who lived and taught in China, and Ping Chia Kuo, a Chinese and now professor of history in an American University—agree that China now has the strongest Government since the days of the Manchus, perhaps indeed the strongest ever. When I get an American historian and a Chinese historian agreeing I feel that I have got somewhere—I need no longer pay attention to the propaganda which is churned out day after day by the American and British Press, journals and political speeches. I know that the running down of Russia and China is propaganda, and the boosting of the Germans is a blot on our escutcheon.

African hydro-electric power, if fully developed, could give seven to nine times the power which could be obtained from the total coal used at present in the world for electric power production—or two and a half to three times what could be obtained from the world's total output of coal. I have not got my papers here, but I believe the figures are not far off the mark. Coal and the larger legitimate schemes will be the world's chief source of power for hundreds of generations.

T. G. N. HALDANE (extension of spoken contribution)

I am rather sorry this Symposium did not contain a paper dealing with the Amenity Dilemma in relation to power supply, perhaps on the lines of Sir Christopher Hinton's excellent paper published in the February 1960 issue of the *Journal of the Royal Society of Arts*.

This matter has, I know, been touched on in our discussion, but I do not think the basic character of the dilemma has been sufficiently emphasised. We are a population of 50 million confined in a comparatively small island, and if standards of life are to be maintained or raised it is impossible to avoid interference with the countryside through the construction of power stations, transmission lines and the like.

Unfortunately the existence of this fundamental problem does not seem to be fully realised and there is quite a number of the public who expect both an untouched countryside and rising standards of life.

The particular aspect of this problem I would like to mention is the building of power transmission lines. These are required whatever happens—whether or not hydro stations are built—but must increase in size and number the higher the level of industrialisation. The high-voltage lines cannot at present (or for a long time to come) be put underground.

The difficulties in arriving at agreed routes are at present very great and excessive delays and costs are being incurred because of the many bodies who have to be consulted and because of their differing opinion.

I have sometimes wondered if it could be possible to have a single body of "Wise Men" to whom decisions about overhead line routes—and perhaps hydro-electric schemes also—could be entrusted, but attractive though the thought may be, I doubt if generally acceptable "Wise Men" could be found. Perhaps, however, something could be done to reduce the number of bodies to be consulted and so reduce the very costly delays in reaching decisions.

Public enquiries, where the atmosphere is liable to be highly emotional and partisan, are not necessarily the best solution of this big problem. Mr. Nicholson (Director General, Nature Conservancy) has suggested that the value of all engineering works and the value of amenities can be reduced as in the U.S.A. to comparable £ s. d. I must admit to seeing a good deal of difficulty in doing this. Even the value of engineering works such as hydro stations is hard to express in definite figures. Almost always some element of gazing into the future is involved with its consequent uncertainties.

In this connection I would like to refer to a point touched on in the valuable paper by Mr. Guthrie Brown and Mr. Hunter.

If one assumes (fairly safely I think) that the purchasing power of money is going to fall in the future much as it has fallen during the past century or more, then the owners of long-life assets, such as hydro stations, are going to gain very greatly as time goes on. I attempted to show this gain graphically in a paper presented to the Institute of Civil and Electrical Engineers in 1955. The results were remarkable, showing far greater gain for long-life hydro-electric stations, than for the shorter life thermal stations, and it does not require any deep analysis to see the great profit now coming from hydro stations built some thirty years ago. It might therefore be concluded that practically all hydro stations are bound to pay handsomely in due course. Although this is probably correct it is not the whole story, because one must go on to ask who has lost due to the fall in money values and this raises very wide and difficult questions into which I cannot go now.

The point is that the purely economic assessment of the value of a scheme is complicated and could be ambiguous. In the long run an element of dispassionate judgment and common sense is necessary such as my "Wise Men"—if only they could be found—might supply.

From Mr. A. A. Templeton, *Chairman, Building Materials Committee, The Scottish Council (Development and Industry)*

1. My Building Materials Committee and myself personally are far more concerned with the expansion of traditional Scottish industries and the far greater use of her abundance of natural resources than with imported industries; this note will accordingly be overburdened with that slant.

2. The first and main point the B.M.C. wish to put before you is the difficulties they have encountered in bringing about a vast expansion of quarrying Scottish stone for building purposes; herein the Committee instruct me to send you a copy of the Report they prepared in 1953; From 1953 onwards the Committee have lost no opportunity in reviving the interests of Architects, Builders and Quarrymasters in this great Scottish traditional industry; but the whole affair is stuck and the industry is dying through the lack of Central Government appreciation and/or financial support; they rejected our modest request for assistance as set forth in paragraph 25 (*a*) and (*b*) of the Report; we in the B.M.C. have never understood why, unless it was because that as England and Wales did not need it, it could not be given to Scotland! Herein an important point of high policy—give any of our colonies all they need, but not Scotland!

3. The B.M.C. could put before you similar views on Scottish slates, home grown timber and plastic factory plants, etc., etc., in Scotland, but possibly we have said enough.

4. To give any personal views I may have to offer on broader issues, the first point arises from my giving evidence at the recent Public Enquiry on the proposals of Associated Portland Cement Manufacturers Ltd. to lay down a £4½ million cement plant at Oxwellmains, East Lothian; it was to use a very fine natural and local deposit of lime; it was to use East Lothian coal; it was to give employment to some 300 people (most likely displaced miners); and it was to produce 400,000 tons of cement annually. In the South of England the APCM would have got their consents almost right away; not so in Scotland. Immediately the proposed development was mooted the Secretary of State should have brought all concerned together informally so that there would be

no chance of this heaven-sent gift to Scotland being lost; but no; the poor soul is statute bound to order a prolonged and expensive Public Enquiry; and when a decision will be given goodness only knows; even then and if successful the consent may be burdened with conditions which are not reasonably capable of fulfilment. Little wonder industrialists turn away from Scotland.

5. My next point (almost the converse of the foregoing) is that Parliament has (and this is not just in recent years) clothed local authorities and others that matter with ample powers to promote the well-being of Scotland; but there is no local spirit or readiness to use these powers. The Scottish Council should never hesitate to send a member of its Executive Committee with one of its officials out to a local authority or other departmental office to convince, induce and plead for a certain line of action being taken. Examples of what I have in mind are as follows:

(*a*) Far too few local authorities use their powers to build a factory or to help a developer;

(*b*) local authorities have powers to provide houses for key workers and for managers; how often have I heard an incoming industrialist complain that he has been unable to get sufficient (if indeed any) such houses, and that even although his employees have offered substantial rents; he or his company are industrialists, not house-builders.

(*c*) Thirteen years ago it was provided, by Section 2 (2) of the Town and Country Planning (Scotland) Act, 1947, that two or more local planning authorities may combine for the exercise of their functions and they could be forced to do so by the Secretary of State if he thought it was of local or public advantage to do so; but nothing has been done in the North of Scotland; these powers are lying dormant; if the Highland counties had so combined and formed a "Highlands Planning and Development Joint Committee", what an authoritative body (thoroughly conversant with local needs and conditions) that would be; and an end would be put to all the cries for a new "Authority" in the Highlands.

6. I am not a keen supporter for the introduction of new or "foreign" industries to the Highlands; they are seething with natural resources crying out to be tapped, e.g. the marvellous development and prosperity of the Orkney Islands; the Highlands should (and they can) be brought to a state of exporting to the south of the U.K. and elsewhere vastly more quantities of beef, mutton, eggs, butter, wool, timber, whisky, fish, etc.; and all its needs are industries ancillary thereto, e.g. spinning and sawmills, boat building, agricultural machinery, etc.; more men are needed in the Highlands of the calibre of Lord Lovat and Mr. Hobbs (the Great Glen); better far that a crofter should be on the pay roll of such men at £10 a week than struggling alone to make £5; it is said you will never change the life and ways of a crofter; but that used to be said of the slum-dweller. And it has been said that it was the sportsman who caused the "eviction of the crofter"; nonsense—it was buying cheap beef from the Argentine and some similar stupid steps.

7. Apart from the far too many Government or quasi-Government bodies operating in the Highlands (e.g. Department of Agriculture, Crofters' Commission, etc.) there are a great many other more "voluntary" bodies, e.g. the Scottish Council (Development and Industry), the Scottish Council of Social Service, the Scottish Country Industries

Development Trust, the Scottish Tourist Board, the National Trust for Scotland, etc. Has the time not come to co-ordinate the work of such bodies? I would go the length of at least "enacting" that the Secretaries (no lower level) of these bodies should meet at least twice a year to ensure the avoidance of overlapping, etc.

8. Finally I would refer to the recent dinner we gave to the Lobby Correspondents; they informally and privately but clearly told us that Scotland gets a poor show in Parliament from her members therein. Is it not possible through our London Office to have regular meetings with the standing committees of all political parties to ensure that Scotland will always be kept on the map of the world and will be spoken of with the love and affection she deserves?

Note:—Certain of the written contributions included in this section duplicate the verbal statements made during the Symposium. In each case, however, there were included in the written statements points of fact or argument different from or additional to those in the verbal statements. For this reason and in order to give a completely accurate account of what was said at the Symposium, both have been included.

UTILISATION OF RESOURCES

UTILISATION OF MINERALS

Utilisation of Minerals

R. H. S. Robertson, M.A., F.G.S.

Director, Resource Use Limited, Pitlochry

Scotland is rich in mineral resources suitable for supplying the chemical, power, road and other industries. Many have made history (oil shale, blackband iron ore, alum, coal distillation), others have a great future if we approach the business of mineral development in a new way. By-products of a mineral nature (coal and oil shale bings, fly ash, slags, etc.) are regarded as deposits along with natural rocks and minerals. The relationship with other non-mineral raw materials is brought out by a few examples. The basic principles of raw material development have been stated, for without a clear understanding of these no new methods of development are likely to come about. Under "colonial exploitation" Scottish mineral resources do not excite much interest; but seen as part of Scottish economy by the new outlook (underdeveloped countries, please note) there is great scope for enterprise and much potential wealth to be released.

The raw materials for industry are animal, vegetable or mineral. Of the last, I shall consider only solids. These can be fairly pure—minerals, or mixtures—rocks, or the by-products of industry. Since the provenance of economic rocks and minerals in Scotland has been reviewed by Professor George, there remains to be added a list of the main by-products of a mineral nature:

By-product	*Source in Industry*	*Present uses*
Alum shales (spent)	Alum, nineteenth century	———
Blast furnace slag	Iron	Road metal, cements
Calcium carbonate	Paper, water, etc.	———
Coal bings	Coal	Common bricks
Coal bings (burnt shale)	Coal	Aggregate
Fly ash=powdered fuel ash	Electricity	Building material
"Gum"	Coal washery	Fuel
Gypsum—plaster moulds	Sanitary ware	———
Hydrated lime	Calcium carbide	Burnt lime
Iron oxide	Bauxite purification	Pigment
Oil shale bings	Shale oil	Facing bricks
Silts and clays	Sand and gravel washery	———

Now that the inventory of mineral resources in Scotland has been set down and Dr. Mitchell has recorded where we can find detailed information about many of them, we come to consider the problems of the utilisation of minerals. In this symposium we are concerned with the future; but a historical note here is useful.

The Industrial Revolution was so overpowering in its impact on men's minds that manufactured goods rather than raw materials became a central mental preoccupation. The mode of thought so induced was forward to the markets and backwards to the raw materials. In the "workshop of the world" one sought cheap raw materials by colonial exploitation. In the technical Press I have seen it stated that there are no unwrought mineral resources of consequence in Scotland, but what was meant was that the author knew of no minerals which could reach English centres of production economically.

If we are to make progress in this field we must subtend a new mental angle; we must look outwards from the natural resources and ask ourselves: "What can we make from the raw materials in this region?"; we should be concerned not only with improving supplies to old industries but with the creation of new industries. Today I shall attempt to formulate the basic rules and principles of raw material development and tomorrow to suggest some new techniques of research and development.

Few attempts have been made in Great Britain to think about the philosophy of resource development. It was in the United States, where the bad effects of ill-considered exploitation could be seen as early as 1900 and where much of the land was still virgin, that a philosophy of conservation was first formulated. In European countries the resources had been worked for many centuries, so there was no pressure on people to make them consider the subject. Yet by 1943 our legacy of bad resource development received the attention of Sir John Myres in a brilliant essay on "Devastation".[1] Within a few years a more progressive attitude towards mineral development was discernible in the Scott and Uthwatt reports and contemporary writings. Yet even then the attitude to the subject was still negative and regulatory rather than positive and creative.

Experience during the 1914-18 and 1939-45 Wars did not help towards forward thinking about resources. It was then of national importance to use effective hindsight by looking over one's shoulder, as it were, to see what raw materials we could find to replace imports. In the last war £1¼ million were spent in a search for home supplies of minerals; mica was extracted with the help of the army in the Highlands; feldspar was hand-picked in Lewis; and glass-making sand came from Lochaline. Of these, only the last remains in commerce, for in the case of mica and feldspar it was not the purpose of the wartime operators to create industries which would survive into peacetime.

Unfortunately in post-war Britain, not enough people in industrial and political life have a clear enough conception of the principles or rules of raw material development to make much impact on the country's economy.

SOME PRINCIPLES OF RAW MATERIAL DEVELOPMENT

The table below,[2] illustrates the most usually recognised stages in the development of an industrial project. Robert P. Russell,[3] who published the right-hand side of the table, had in mind what happens in a large firm.

TABLE I

Stage		
1	Survey	Natural and human resources
2	Analysis; laboratory-scale research	Scientific discovery, invention, research (test-tube)
3	Pilot-plant investigations	Development, pilot-plant; Engineering application of development
4	Factory-scale production	Production management and labour; sales and distribution; executive management
5	Region; World	Economic and political climate

Continuity of Development

By far the most important principle in raw material development is the maintenance of continuity of development. The table shows the successive stages of: (1) survey, (2) laboratory research, (3) pilot-plant investigations, (4) design, erection and operation of a factory or process, and (5) fitting the process into its general environment. Industrial success is achieved only when there is continuity between these stages; there must be no gaps.

Those who are professionally engaged in creating raw material industries are responsible for recognising gaps and seeking to fill them. The large firm can provide a wider range of services than a small firm, but no firm has sufficient scientific and technical resources to fill all the gaps completely. Consequently Government agencies have been created to do what industry is not equipped to do, nor should be expected to do.

Yet it is commonly supposed in Great Britain that the present industrial organisation is capable of developing without external help or pressure all economically sound raw material projects. The falseness of this notion can be seen by considering for example the industrial utilisation of bracken; for until research and development work has been carried out one cannot forecast what the chief uses of this raw material might be; consequently one cannot expect any one particular industry to take the lead. The case for Government and private research, to fill the gap, is clear enough.

Survey. Great Britain is served by surveying institutions such as the Ordnance Survey, the Geological Survey, the Meteorological Office, and by others of more recent establishment such as the Soil Survey. It is fair to say that the duties of the Geological Survey are somewhat narrowly circumscribed and it is only in wartime that any great effort is made to play a direct part in the development of new industries. Naturally, industries started only to replace imports at almost any cost seldom survive into peacetime. So it is clear that in ordinary circumstances there is a hiatus between the accurate mapping and geological descriptions of the Geological Survey and the next stage of development, analysis and laboratory investigations.

This particular hiatus has been more clearly recognised in other countries; in the United States it is partly filled by the Development Section of the U.S. Geological Survey and partly by the U.S. Bureau of Mines. If a relatively undeveloped area anywhere in the world is to be developed, the resources always have to be examined in detail; even the Tennessee Valley Authority[4] found that it had to multiply the survey work of the States before they could initiate development. The great importance attached to resource surveying in Russia is well known.

The need for botanical surveying is less often officially recognised. A fine exception, however, is the surveying of littoral and sub-littoral seaweeds in Scotland. Although the distribution of many botanical species has been determined by university research workers, there are no easily accessible sources of information concerning the occurrence of bracken, birch, fireweed and other plants which may have industrial uses. Peat, often considered as a mineral resource, is surveyed, but the reports, over thirty of them, are not published.

I should regard the Land Utilisation Survey as a valuable historical record, but what is needed is a series of maps which show the potentiality of the soil; or of minerals; or of vegetation.

The gap between survey and analysis can be partly bridged by conscious policy of the surveyors. Their work should be published in places where industrial scientists are likely to read about it. Information about resources gathered from all sources should be made readily available to the public by the use of modern methods of documentation; we believe that vast amounts of valuable information have been collected by various official bodies, but are lying unproductively in their offices. With a little rearrangement these documents could be made to assume a more vital role in resource development.

Some local and county authorities have indeed published brochures describing the resources of their area. These documents vary greatly in appeal; some are frankly dull. A good example of what can be done in this line is a brochure put out by Deadwood, South Dakota[5]; but then South Dakota has a Natural Resources Commission.

A similar document describing the natural resources of the Highlands would go far to converting a problem into a project of development. The West Highland Survey by Fraser Darling is of great anthropological interest, but needs to be backed up by a survey of material resources.

Analysis. Before one can suggest uses for a raw material one must make an accurate compilation of all its physical and chemical properties; the properties and the uses depending upon them can often be logged in a mineral utilisation diagram.[6]

Publicity should be given in the scientific and technical Press to the results of this kind of laboratory work, not only because more scientists become interested and enlarge the corpus of data on the raw material but also because the industrial technologists ask for samples, and applications unthought of by the raw material research workers come to light.

Laboratory-scale work on processes of extraction, refining, separation and utilisation should naturally follow; and promising unit-processes often require to be improved by *pilot-plant research*. This is where the chemical engineer comes in. Small companies are usually unable to carry out this class of work. They get some help from plant manufacturers, but this is usually limited to one or two days' test runs. Prolonged series of runs with a view to redesign of the plant to suit the raw material are seldom possible. In any case this class of work is expensive. Regional laboratories equipped with a good variety of unit-process plant would be a great help in the establishment of new industries or products.

Factory. The management of the factory development has been so well treated by Russell[3] that we shall not go into details here.

Regional Development. The siting of the works should be determined by social as well as by economic factors. This duality has been recognised both in Britain and in the United States; though it may be wise to say that the social factors should not cause the economy of the factory to be in any way impaired.

In raw material development in Britain it has for long been the tradition that anyone, however ignorant, can set up a plant with insufficient knowledge of the material, the process or the markets. A study of the many failures in this field proves the need for resource use education in Britain.

World Outlook. Man is slowly becoming aware of the evil effects of his devastation of resources, both human and natural, and is beginning to formulate, and even sometimes to practise, more ethical principles of resource development, taking a longer view than the previous generation of colonial exploiters. The trends of thought recommended today are towards unified resource development, regional long-term development, the principle of equitable participation by all nations in national surpluses as enunciated in the Atlantic Charter,[7] and the "Hot Springs" exhortation to make the best use of each nation's or region's resources, exporting only natural surpluses and, whenever possible, manufactured goods.

Multiple Utilisation

The aim should be to find the greatest number of different uses for a product, so that the discontinuance of one use will not jeopardise the industry. A one-use industry is as unstable as monoculture of the land. In the past many industries have failed because they relied upon a single major application. Thus for centuries the main use of fullers' earth was for the fulling of wool, for which purpose it was slowly ousted by soap. It is only since a number of uses have been found for this mineral that the industry has become safely established.

Seaweed was burnt at one time to kelp as a source of alkali, but tariff reductions and chemical discovery deprived the western seaboard of Scotland of its main source of income. Kelp was later used as a source of iodine, with potash as a by-product, but the extraction of iodine from Chilean saltpetre sounded the death-knell of the industry.

Limestone grinding was officially encouraged in Scotland during the last war for agricultural purposes, yet the price of ground limestone might have been reduced if other uses for the raw material had been found.

The slate industry in Scotland though urged by Lord Bilsland at the time of the merger to conduct research failed to do so, and failed financially. They had only one diminishing outlet—roofing slates—and tried to cut in at Stage 3 by doing pilot-plant investigations with a dense and unattractive brick which did not sell well.

Large firms frequently own mineral deposits so that they can make sure of their supplies. In many cases the mineral is well and economically worked in this way, but in others the economy would be improved if other uses were developed alongside the main one. In other words, the quarrying branch of the large firm should learn to become raw materials minded and to look around them for other outlets.

Varietal Utilisation

Deposits of minerals vary widely in purity and physical properties. Consequently they have different sets of uses. The aim should be to make use of varietal differences in raw material to the best advantage. Variation may occur within a deposit as well as between deposits. If it occurs within a deposit it may be wise to separate the grades, as in barytes mining, where white grades could be mined separately for milling to a high-priced product: usually it joins run-of-mine barytes for lithopone manufacture. Very often close collaboration between miner and processor is wanting, and this hiatus causes a weakness in the industry's economy.

Coloured terms such as "poor quality" sometimes prevent a deposit from being worked. Talc, which is poor in pharmacy, may be excellent in, shall we say, tile manufacture. A "poor deposit" was once bought and immediately abandoned by a firm who thought it was a commercial nuisance. Yet a few years later it was found by research that the poor raw material had some unique properties and these led to four applications for which it was much better suited than the better-known deposit.

Another example is the dolomite of Duror, Appin, which was regarded at one time as of little significance compared with the larger and purer deposits of Loch Kishorn, Durness and Loch Eriboll. Yet it was the first to be commercially worked because the impurities helped to give smooth melting in rockwool manufacture.

When several deposits, varietally different, are worked in competition by different firms, their products tend to find applications for which each is most suited, though geographical considerations will also favour the nearest; nevertheless, small or impure deposits are at a great disadvantage commercially unless the firm working them can have equal access to the scientific and technical knowledge available to larger companies, especially with regard to processing to improve the quality or widen the range of applications.

Complex Utilisation

In complex utilisation the raw material is broken down into constituent parts which are different from each other chemically or physically. Each product should then be treated by the rules of multiple and varietal utilisation. In the United States crude petroleum was once used only as a fuel, but today there, as well as in Scotland, the whole of the crude is processed, much of it into chemicals of high value. Seaweed now yields alginic acid and its salts in Scottish factories, and some other constituents of seaweed are beginning to come on to the market, such as laminarin; doubtless potassium, iodine, mannitol and other constituents will also be recovered in due course.

The complex utilisation of coal is well known and needs no elaboration here. Heating of houses by gas is sound when valuable chemicals including sulphur have been recovered at the gasworks. The complete gasification of coal is justified only when the coal is otherwise unsaleable, as in the new project in Fife. Peat undoubtedly lends itself to complex utilisation. When studying these organic raw materials, we see at once that there are several entirely different ways in which the materials may be broken down to yield a number of products. In other words, several different peat industries are possible. Thus wax can be extracted with solvents from certain peats and the residue converted into active carbon or destructively distilled. Steam distillation, low-temperature and high-temperature distillation yield different ranges of products.

The old-fashioned term "extractive industries" overstresses the main product in complex utilisation. It implies that the residue is waste or a nuisance. Iron and steel makers still find it difficult to believe that they produce a potentially valuable raw material in blast furnace slag. Few of them have conducted serious research programmes into the utilisation of this material. Electricity undertakings show the same kind of embarrassment over powdered fuel ash or "fly ash", also a most useful material—potentially.

We should go as far as to say that when a residue is accumulating because no use has yet been found for it, it should be kept clean and separate from other substances, so that it can be worked in the future when a use has been discovered for it. The whole subject of waste-utilisation needs to be continuously reviewed and not considered as a wartime necessity only. The world cannot afford to waste its substance.

Co-operative Processing

Many local resources could be worked if overheads could be reduced by sharing plant or management or laboratories. A simple example is a fine-grinding installation to which bulk lots of minerals go for treatment on their way to the consumers' factories. The requirements of finely-ground talc, feldspar, marble, limestone, dolomite, slate, mica, asbestos and so on, taken together, have on many occasions justified the erection of costly milling plant.

The production of basalt chips for road and concrete making and ground limestone for agriculture can sometimes be carried out under one roof or marble terrazzo chips and limestone powder.

Drying plant could be used for drying crops of seaweed, grass, oats, etc., in their season and special varieties of peat, sphagnum moss, fish meal and other things at other times. The drying programme would have to be worked out to conform with nature and her seasons.

Distribution and Size of Resources

For the sake of completeness I shall include some observations on the distribution of resources and on the scale of operation; for want of recognised terminology I allude to narrowly, moderately widely, and widely distributed raw materials. In addition we have large, medium and small deposits or occurrences. Even if we recognised only three types of distribution and three relative sizes, we should have nine groups to consider under this heading. I have space here to deal with a few extremes.

International Resources. If one country has more of a raw material than other countries which are deficient in it, the raw material assumes international importance. According to Atlantic Charter tenets these should be distributed fairly throughout the world according to the genuine peaceful needs of all parts. Moreover, the country of origin should benefit. Standards of health, feeding, housing and education can be raised by proper allocation of profits. In some countries reserves are set aside for financing the change-over to other industries when a deposit is finally worked out. Alternative occupations should preferably be found during the hey-day of the exploitation.

Regional Resources. We may also consider a middle group of medium-sized or well-distributed resources; these occur in many countries in quantities sufficient to supply national or lager regional needs. They are not all worked, because technical knowledge, unlike scientific knowledge, is not widely disseminated. Efforts of international agencies to provide technical knowhow to get industries started in underdeveloped countries have been prodigious.

To some extent modern technology has made countries less dependent upon each other's raw materials. Gum tragacanth meets competition in alginates; rare waxes obtained from leaves or insects or reeds are superseded by synthetic products; natural dyestuffs are scarcely used, but quinine still holds its own. But modern technology shows how to make fertilisers from a variety of raw materials widely distributed—so there has been no dependence upon Chilean nitrate for decades. The manufacture of chemicals from air, magnesium and bromine from sea-water, alumina from clay, alcohol from crops, paper from bagasse all point to the possibilities of greater self-sufficiency.

Local Resources. Small deposits also have their part to play, even though their interest is local. They provide alternative occupation, often where needed. They may be worked in conjunction with other resources. They provide training ground for technicians, and are a reserve in times of emergency. They should not be exhausted in a few years for quick profits, but should be made to last for one or two generations at least. It is significant that small deposits are worked even in countries possessing very great resources of the same kind, usually for local consumption or for a few specialised uses. Technical assistance should be freely given to small enterprises in this class.

Scale of Operation. Since any one with a little capital can acquire the right to work a mineral deposit, there is no guarantee that a potentially valuable mineral will be worked on a large enough scale. Many small firms' output is restricted when the owner is paying a high proportion of surtax. The incentive to make more money is not there. Even moderately large firms carry out no research and development if they have very lucrative main lines of business, such as sand and gravel which are nearly always profitable, since a pit is opened only when a demand arises. As a consequence many resources are not fully developed; individuals or firms should be trustees of the resources, but overriding guidance is often necessary.

REFERENCES

1. Myres, Sir John (1943). *J. R. anthrop. Inst.*, **73**, 17-26.
2. Robertson, Robert H. S. (1948). *Advancement of Science*, **5**, (17), 20-26.
3. Russell, Robert P. (1947). *The Organisation of Industrial Research.* London: Federation of British Industries.
4. Lilienthal, David E. (1944). *T.V.A.—Democracy on the March.* Harmondsworth: Penguin Books, S. 151.
5. *Industrial Survey of the Black Hills Region, centred on Deadwood, South Dakota.* South Dakota Natural Resources Commission, Pierre, South Dakota (1951).
6. Robertson, Robert H. S. (1960). *Mineral Use Guide, or Robertson's Spiders' Webs.* London: Cleaver-Hume Press.
7. Mineral Resources and the Atlantic Charter, A Conference, *The Advancement of Science* (1942), **2**, 187-252.

DISCUSSION

Mr. R. H. S. Robertson, *Resource Use Ltd.*

The only point I want to make is that I must apologise for not giving in my paper a great many examples of minerals which could be developed. There is a very good commercial reason for this; if I gave our private list of things that we were hopng to promote, then we would not be able to get them going so advantageously, because there is a right kind of publicity and a wrong kind. But, in fact, we have a private list of eight major projects and about a dozen minor ones which might grow, all of which in our view are very well worth investigating; from past experience probably a half of these would become industries if financed and developed.

UTILISATION OF RESOURCES

DEVELOPING USES OF BIOLOGICAL RESOURCES

Developing Uses of Biological Material

W. A. P. Black, D.Sc., Ph.D., F.R.I.C., F.R.S.E.
Deputy Director, Arthur D. Little Research Institute, Inveresk

Present uses and possible new uses are discussed for brown seaweeds, wood, sugar beet and peat.

The natural products from the brown seaweeds are those in which the dried milled weed is used as an animal food supplement, as a fertiliser, and as a constituent of liquid fertilisers, while the derived products are alginic acid and its derivatives. It is suggested that the other compounds present in seaweed such as mannitel laminarin and fucoidin should be exploited.

Wood is discussed in the light of its use as a construction material, as a source of wood pulp for paper making and as a valuable source of chemicals, capable of setting up a new industry.

The production of sucrose from sugar beet is regulated by International Law and cannot be expanded until an increased acreage is permitted. This depends on finding new large-scale non-food uses for sucrose, but fundamental research work is required to achieve this.

Peat in Scotland only appears to have a future in agriculture and horticulture. As a source of chemicals it cannot compete with cheaper readily available indigenous raw materials. However, its use as a soil conditioner and as a humus base for fertilisers could be greatly expanded.

A high proportion of Scotland's physical resources is of biological origin. A survey of the agricultural, forestry and fishery products in the United Kingdom and their utilisation, which was carried out in 1953[1] revealed a significant and increasing use by industry of such products and by-products. Under the broad title "Developing Uses of Biological Material" a selection must be made, and consequently this paper is limited to the utilisation of the brown seaweeds, wood, sugar beet and peat as being representative of biological material obtained from the sea, the land and from growing crops.

SEAWEED

Scotland with its 5,300 miles of coast-line offers ideal conditions for the growth of the brown seaweeds which clothe our shores between high and low water (i.e. littoral or rockweeds) and below low water down to 12 fathoms (i.e. sublittoral weed). The red seaweeds do not occur in sufficient quantity to justify their discussion here. Surveys have shown the presence of approximately 0·25 million tons of rockweed in areas where it could be economically harvested,[2] and 10 million tons of sublittoral weed, of which about 4 million tons could be economically harvested.[3] Allowing for regeneration every four years, it is reasonable to assume that one million tons could be harvested per annum and that a large-scale industry could be set up. The seaweed industry is one, however, which has undergone fluctuations in this country since its introduction in 1720. Since the end of the 1939-45 War, however, the industry has been revived until, in 1959, approximately 40,000 tons of wet seaweed were processed to give approximately 1,500 tons of alginate, while approximately 5,000 tons of dried seaweed meal went into foodstuffs and fertilisers, the value of the industry as a whole being now of the order of £1¼ million per annum. The products obtained from the seaweeds may be divided into two groups—natural and derived.

The natural products are those in which the dried, milled seaweed is used. Although the derived products are of primary economic value, the products for which the demand has grown rapidly in this country and more so in America are the natural products—animal foodstuffs and fertiliser. A review[4] of the value of seaweed in animal foodstuffs shows it to be a valuable source of minerals, trace elements and vitamins. This industry was practically non-existent ten years ago and it is noteworthy that about 5,000 tons of dried seaweed meal are now used in Great Britain as an animal food supplement. A greater realisation of its value in this field could lead to its more widespread use and create a considerable demand. As a fertiliser it has been used by farmers from time immemorial, but only recently have liquid fertilisers containing seaweed been available. Several of these are now on the market and sales are of the order of 100,000 gallons per annum, of a value of £50,000. This outlet can be a large consumer of seaweed if the market is increased, and there is every indication of this occurring.

The derived products are those manufactured from seaweeds by chemical processes. Historically, these products have included a wide variety of materials such as iodine, acetone and decolorising carbon, but at present the principal products are the alginates which are obtainable only from the brown seaweeds. Commercially the alginates are vastly more important than are the natural products. Their uses comprise:

1. Foods

(a) *Dairy Products.* Ice cream, dry ice cream mix, sherbet, cheese, cold sets, etc.
(b) *Other Food Products.* Bakery icings and meringues, salad dressings, frozen foods, candies, bread, puddings, dog and cat foods, etc.

2. Pharmaceutical and Cosmetic Preparations

Antibiotic tablets, penicillin suspensions, antiacid tablets, aspirin compound tablets, calamine lotion, haemostatic powders and dressings, bulking laxatives; toothpastes, dental impression compounds, surgical jellies, mineral oil emulsions, suppositories, ointments, hand lotions and creams, wave lotions, shampoos, etc.

3. Industrial Applications

(a) *Rubber.* Natural and synthetic latex, creaming and thickening.
(b) *Textile Products.* Size compound for cotton and rayon, textile printing pastes including use with reactive dyestuffs.
(c) *Adhesives.* Wall board, paper bags, gummed tape, etc.
(d) *Paper Products.* Food packages and wrappers, coating paper.
(e) *Other Industrial Uses.* Paints, ceramic glazes, leather finishes, auto polishes, welding rod coatings, boiler compositions, beer and wine refining, beet sugar processing, wax emulsions, etc.

The Scottish seaweed industry, based on the alginates from the brown seaweeds, has thus developed considerably in the last few years, due more to expansion of existing uses, in some cases stimulated by technical developments within the industry as with reactive dyestuffs, rather than to completely new applications. Sodium alginate, for example, has been found the most satisfactory thickener in the dye bath when reactive dyestuffs such as the cibacrons and procions are used, and in this field alone as much as 500 tons of alginate are now being used per annum.

Another new application of the alginates is in paint cores and the British Steel Castings Research Association has applied for a patent for the use of alginates in mould paints. The advantages of alginates in these paints are (*a*) only a small amount is necessary to give adequate suspending properties, (*b*) the paints are easier to prepare and (*c*) the tendency for the paint to crack during drying and chock heating is considerably reduced. Of interest, too, is the recent claim by the Japanese[5] for a mixture of sodium alginate, sodium chloride and glucose as a blood plasma extender.

Further research will no doubt lead to more widespread industrial use, and compounds like the recently introduced amine alginates, which are soluble in certain organic solvents and mixtures of solvents, will open up new outlets and lead to increased demand. These alginates are thus useful in organic solvent systems for applications corresponding to those where sodium alginate is valuable in aqueous systems. These include the effects of thickening a liquid, suspending fine solids in a liquid and film forming and binding.

Also of importance is the possibility of recovering the other chemicals present in the brown seaweeds, and methods have already been worked out for the preparation, as by-products of the alginate industry, of mannitol,[6] laminarin[7] and fucoidin.[8] Assuming that 1 million tons of *Laminaria cloustoni*, which makes up the bulk of our sublittoral weed, could be harvested each year, the tonnage of chemicals potentially available is given in Table I. This table gives the calculated quantities present in the weed in May and October and the average calculated for 24 samples over a period of two years.

TABLE I

Chemicals Potentially Available per annum from 1,000,000 *Tons of Fresh 'L. cloustoni' (whole plant)*

Chemical	Calculated Tonnage present in Weed		
	May	October	Average
Alginic acid	28,000	31,080	30,600
Mannitol	9,800	33,300	18,000
Laminarin	Nil	39,960	14,400
Fucoidin	5,920	9,400	7,620

MANNITOL

Mannitol is largely produced at present by the electrolytic reduction of glucose[9]; the tonnage used is small, although uses have already been established, e.g. in food products, inks, medicinal products, plastics, explosives, glyptal varnishes and soldering fluxes. As a result of the market created by the synthetic product, mannitol is now being produced in France from seaweed at the rate of 1 ton per day, giving a pure product with a market value of about £130,000 per annum. Recent work[10] has shown the potentialities of mannitol in the preparation of polymers.

LAMINARIN

This glucan, besides being a good source of glucose, and in this respect would have to be competitive with starch, has potential uses in the medical field. Although the sulphate has been found to be a blood anticoagulant, it has been found to be too toxic for clinical use. By adjusting the sulphate content, however, a non-toxic product has been prepared which is at present showing promise as an antilipaemic agent in a large-scale clinical trial.

FUCOIDIN

So far, no uses have been found for this polyfucose monosulphate, although its potentialities as a blood anticoagulant and antilipaemic agent are being investigated.

Although the seaweed industry is now well established and expanding, a considerable amount of the weed used for alginate production is imported from Ireland. The rockweed *Ascophyllum nodosum*, however, is now being collected at Loch Maddy, North Uist, and used for the production of the textile grade of alginate. Despite the fact that sub-littoral weed is available in Scotland, to support a large-scale industry and a commercial method of harvesting has been designed,[11] brown seaweeds to the value of approximately £66,000 are imported each year.

SUGAR BEET

Despite the fact that sugar, known chemically as sucrose, is one of the purest, most abundant and cheapest organic materials available for synthesis, little use has been made of it in this field. The chemical industry, based on petroleum, has grown from nothing to a major industry in the last decade. The sugar industry is basically in a stronger position, since the sugar cane and the sugar beet, the two sources of sugar, are renewed annually, whereas petroleum cannot be replaced in other than geological time. The world production of sucrose from the sugar cane and sugar beet is approximately 50 million tons per annum and this is controlled by international agreement to prevent flooding the market with surplus sugar. There is no doubt, however, that production could be doubled, or even trebled, if sucrose could be utilised in ways other than directly as a food. The authorised acreage for the Cupar factory of the British Sugar Corporation Ltd.—the only factory processing sugar beet in Scotland—is 16,000, which includes 1,400 acres in the North of England. In 1959 the contracted acreage was 16,000 with a clean beet yield per acre of 15·09 tons which was processed to give the following products:

Clean Beet
(241,440 tons)

White Sugar (32,300 tons)	Dried Molassed Pulp (15,900 tons)	Pressed Pulp (14,900 tons)	Molasses (11,100 tons)
Domestic and manufacturing consumption (confectionery, preserves, biscuits mineral waters, etc.)	Stockfeeding	Stockfeeding	Approx. 50% used in production of molassed pulp—balance to distillers for yeast making

The expansion of the sugar beet industry depends on finding new non-food uses for sucrose. Its price compares favourably with that of methanol, benzene and other chemical raw materials, while, if we consider molasses (the uncrystallisable syrup from beet or cane juice) as a source of sugar, the position is even more favourable, for at the current price of molasses, sugar could be available at less than 1d. per lb.

Despite the fact that the Sugar Research Foundation, Inc.—an international body of which Tate & Lyle Ltd., and the British Sugar Corporation Ltd. are members—has, since its foundation in 1943, spent over half a million pounds on research to find new uses for sucrose, no large-scale application has resulted from their work.

Although sucrose contains eight reactive hydroxyl groups, very few derivatives have been prepared and characterised, due to the extreme instability of sucrose towards acid reagents. The most important of these derivatives are:—

Allyl Sucrose. Prepared by treating sucrose dissolved in concentrated caustic soda with cheap and readily available allyl chloride,[12] this is an important ether from the industrial point of view. The monomer, containing 5 to 6 allyl groups per sucrose molecule, can be polymerised by heating and passing air through it to give a compound with potential applications, such as coatings for wood, metal or glass, adhesives for glass or laminates; coating and impregnation of paper, textiles and other materials for improving the tensile strength and grease-proofing properties. New products with increased properties may result from copolymerisation of allyl sucrose with various monomers, e.g. styrene, acrylates, methacrylates, maleates, maleic anhydride, acrylonitrile, etc.

Another interesting ether, octa-*O*-(hydroxypropyl) sucrose, prepared by reaction of propylene oxide with sucrose,[13] shows promise as an emulsifier and detergent and is claimed to be effective as a cross-linking agent for urethane foams.

Compounds which may be of importance in the detergent, pharmaceutical, plasticizer and synthetic resin fields have recently been prepared by catalytically combining petroleum distillates with sucrose.[14]

Sucrose Esters. The most important of the fully substituted sucrose esters is sucrose octa-acetate,[15] which can be used in making laminated glass or incorporated into synthetic resins.

Production has recently commenced of the mixed ester, sucrose acetate isobutyrate,[16] which can be used in extending solvent coating formulations, in hot-melt coatings, paper and cloth coatings and lacquers for plastics.

The most promising derivatives of sucrose from the utilisation point of view are the long-chain mono- and di-fatty acid esters which possess excellent surface active properties.[17] These esters are colourless, odourless, tasteless, edible, digestible, non-irritating detergents and emulsifying agents. Their detergent powers compare favourably with present detergents and there is reason to believe that they will produce far less foam in sewage disposal plants than the alkylaryl sulphonates and will be readily broken down by bacteria.

Fermentation Processes

Sucrose has found wide application in a number of micro-biological processes. Many micro-organisms can utilise sucrose to produce valuable chemical products such as ethanol, acetone, butanol, citric acid and dextran, and the last two still have large-scale application.

Sodium Sucrates

As the result of work recently carried out at the Arthur D. Little Research Institute on the alkali metal derivatives of sucrose, [18], [19], [20] a new route has been opened up for the preparation of a wide range of sucrochemicals which show interesting possibilities as polymers, pesticides, surface coatings, detergents, etc.

Sugar Beet Pulp

Sugar beet pulp, instead of being used in foodstuffs, can be processed into furfural and its derivatives, the first plant to process sugar cane waste—bagasse—into furfural having recently gone into full production at La Romana in the Dominican Republic.

It would appear, therefore, that in sugar beet we have, in Scotland, an indigenous, renewable, raw material capable of exploitation, limited only by the land available for its cultivation.

WOOD

Trees contain a large number of chemical compounds and are an excellent potential source of raw material for chemicals. Already approximately 5,000 products come from the forest, and the list of uses is being added to daily. In America, for example, the chemical utilisation of the tree has developed into an industry producing at an annual rate of the order of $110,000,000.

In Scotland the fortunes of the timber trade are essentially bound up with problems arising out of the softwood plantations created over the past years by Government-sponsored afforestation. This afforestation was not commenced solely on economic grounds but was partly social, partly the need to conserve natural resources and mainly, perhaps, strategic, for the purpose of ensuring a substantial reserve of timber in the event of a major conflict. The advent of nuclear warfare has largely discounted the strategic basis for forestry. A system has now been instituted which, by the very nature of its long rotation, cannot properly be arrested and the problem of disposal has become of commercial consequence.

Table II gives the current level of home timber production in Scotland.

Table II

Approximate Production of Home Timber in Scotland

Category of Production	Millions of cu. ft. (hoppus) (in round measure)
Mining timber	12·5
Pulpwood	1·5
Chipboard material	0·4
Fencing and other agricultural and estate uses	2·0
Sawn hardwood	2·2
Sawn softwood	4·6

Mining Timber

At present the main outlet for softwood thinnings is the coal mining industry. In Scotland we now supply 97 per cent. of the total requirements of the National Coal

Board, and in addition sell to the English collieries production which is surplus to Scottish requirements. In general, consumption of timber per ton of coal mined is decreasing, partly due to alternative means of roof control and support and partly to the more economic use of timber. In addition, the closing down of a number of mines has reduced the demand. There are two aspects in which the mining timber market can be improved: (1) by selling more to the English divisions of the National Coal Board, and (2) by establishing conclusively that timber should in many cases be used instead of steel and concrete.

PULPWOOD

No pulpwood is produced in Scotland at present, all the home timber used for this purpose being sent to Ellesmere Port. Recently a new company, sponsored by four of the largest paper companies in Britain, was registered to investigate the possibility of building a pulp mill near Fort William to produce bleached pulp from home-grown softwood. The project is intended to be a major one (cost approximately £10 million) with an annual consumption of pulpwood of the order of 12-15 million cu. ft. With this production thinnings from Scotland will no doubt be insufficient to meet the demand until about 1985, and until that time the balance will be met by imports. A wood pulp industry, of course, raises a challenge to exploit the potential by-products, and although considerable research in this field has been carried out in North America and the Scandinavian countries, it has not, as yet, been actively pursued in this country.

Theoretically, it is possible to convert the organic chemicals of the waste into valuable intermediates and derivatives. The oils, terpenes, lignins and aliphatic acids have tremendous unexploited possibilities, as has cellulose itself. One major application could be the preparation of suitably sulphonated lignin derivatives, now one of the three main types of anionic surfactants. The acid degradation of the pentose waste sugars derived from the hemicelluloses produces furfural and similar acid degradation of glucose and other hexoses yields hydroxymethyl furfural. Workers in America have already developed processes for the chemical utilisation of wood residues to both furfural and hydroxymethyl furfural, but with furfural, existing sources from corn cobs, oat hulls, and cane sugar bagasse can satisfy present demands, so that a future from wood sugars depends upon finding new applications.

The chemical industry is constantly finding new uses for the spent liquors remaining from the chemical pulping process, such as in making adhesives, road binders, tanning agents, plastics, dyes, rosin soap, acetic acid, alcohol, turpentine, fertilisers and as a substrate for Torula yeast. A recent process,[21] via the diacetone derivatives, has been worked out for the isolation of mannose, glucose, galactose, xylose and arabinose from sulphite liquors, while another process[28] with possible industrial application for the removal of these sugars from the waste is based on the solubility in organic solvents of a tertiary amine salt of the lignosulphonates. Commercialisation depends on finding markets for these sugars.

In addition to the waste liquors, a considerable amount of bark (which makes up 10 per cent. of the tree) will be available. The bark, in general, consists of lignin, phenolic compounds such as tannins, and other extractives such as wax, and is already being used in America for the manufacture of glues, plastics, fertilisers and insulating materials. Further research work, particularly on the chemistry of lignin, is required in order to find new uses for the bark. In Canada research on lignin has been more than justified by the industrial results achieved, notably the large-scale production of vanillin from lignin.

Chipboard

The world production of chipboard has risen from about 200,000 tons in 1954 to about 1½ million tons in 1960 (estimated). Although a good market already exists for chipboard in Scotland necessitating its importation, any large-scale development will depend on developing existing markets and finding new ones. The first chipboard factory in Scotland set up at Annan in 1955 now produces about a quarter of the total chipboard (80,000 tons per annum) produced in the U.K. This company plans to erect a second factory at Annan while another company will this year open a factory at Inverness (cost £500,000) to process, in the initial stage, about 20,000 tons of thinnings per annum.

Sawn Hardwood: Softwood

The bulk of the production of sawn hardwood is taken up by the furniture and allied industries with home production probably less than 10 per cent. of consumption. Railway sleepers, box and crate timber and house carcassing are the main uses for sawn softwood, and here also home production is not much more than 10 per cent. of consumption. There is at present, for example, an unsatisfied demand by the Scottish Region of British Railways for home-produced sleepers. This demand, in keeping with our afforestation policy, implies that new sawmilling capacity will have to be set up and follow the world-wide trend towards mechanisation of its operations. Sawmills already exist in Argyll (capacity, 3,300 tons per annum) and at Inverness (5,000 tons per annum to be increased to 12,000 tons), while a new company, comprising Scottish landowners and timber merchants, has acquired a site near Fort William to produce accurately sawn, well-conditioned, and graded home-grown timber for all markets, including house-building, shipbuilding and the packing-case industry.

In addition, timber merchants at Grangemouth have erected a factory, the first in Scotland, to produce laminated wood beams and arches. Today there are buildings in America with clear span timber structures of 250 ft. and wood towers spanning to 300 ft.

Chemically Modified Woods

Research is actively in progress, both in this country[10] and in America, to produce a wood stable to changes in atmospheric conditions, resistant to micro-organisms and fireproof. The problem here will be to create a market for this more expensive dimensionally stabilised wood.

The expansion of the Annan chipboard factory, the new laminated wood factory at Grangemouth, and the possible erection of a pulp mill at Fort William, are all clear indications of the changing nature of utilisation. The possibility of a new industry based on chemicals from wood offers challenging opportunities.

It has been said that forty years ago we saw a beginning of the coal tar industry. Twenty years ago we saw the beginning of petrochemicals. Today we are on the threshold of a new industry based on wood chemicals.[22]

PEAT

The Geological Survey of Scotland estimated that 1,625,000 acres of Scotland are covered with at least 2 feet of peat. This is equivalent, at an average moisture content of 92 per cent., to approximately 1,000 million tons of dry matter of which it is estimated, 600 million tons are accessible and suitable for utilisation.[23] In 1949 the Scottish Peat Committee was set up to advise the Secretary of State on the commercial utilisation of these deposits and has already reported the potentialities of the peat bogs.[23]

The utilisation of peat can be considered from four angles: (1) as a raw material for the extraction of chemicals, (2) in agriculture, (3) as a fuel and (4) its disposal in the bog by burning or through afforestation, but only (1) and (2) come within the scope of this paper.

Peat as a Raw Material for the Production of Chemicals

Very little is known of the chemical composition of Scottish peat. Preliminary investigations have been carried out and reported by Mitchell,[24] Tomter[25] and Black *et al.*,[26] but these only give the trace elements, total ash, crude fats, Kjeldahl nitrogen, cellulose, total reducing substances, reducing sugars and the individual sugars, glucose, galactose, arabinose and xylose. A polysaccharide was isolated but not characterised while the main sterol present was -sisosterol. Fig. 1 gives a flow diagram of the possible utilisation of peat and indicates its potential value as a source of chemicals. Although this diagram would appear to present peat as a potentially valuable raw material, a closer examination of the concentration in which the chemicals are present and the economics of their recovery practically rule out its exploitation in this way, e.g. despite work which has been carried out in Northern Ireland and in the Scandinavian countries on the waxes in peat, the percentage present is probably too low to warrant commercial exploitation.

The hydrolysis of the carbohydrates to the simple sugars, followed by their utilisation in fermentation, or conversion to yeast or fodder molasses, might be a practical proposition, but on account of their low concentration in the peat other cheaper sources no doubt exist, e.g. wood pulp waste liquors.

In Agriculture and Horticulture

The most noteworthy properties of peat moss are its high absorptive capacity for liquids and gases, resistance to decomposition and low heat conductivity. For these reasons it makes an excellent litter for cattle and is of especial value for poultry litter. Although not a fertiliser in itself, it is a valuable soil conditioner and it is also used as a packing material for perishable goods such as fruit and vegetables and is an ideal packing material for overseas shipment of articles that absorb moisture, fragile goods such as glass and crockery, and roots, bulbs etc.

In Scotland it is in horticulture where its increased use would help a natural resource and improve the general farm economy. There is an increasing need for organic matter for soil improvement due to the scarcity and high cost of stable manure. Humified peat, especially peat moss, provides a satisfactory and good substitute, and is capable of modifying the physical, chemical and biological properties of mineral soils. In horticulture alone a market for about 80,000 tons per annum has already been created in Britain with less than half of this produced in Scotland. This market could be considerably developed with increased production from Scotland.

The potentialities of peat as a source of power and chemicals were reviewed by Woodward in 1955,[27] and his conclusions still hold today, namely that considerable fundamental work has still to be carried out before a true assessment can be made of the value of peat as a source of chemicals.

ACKNOWLEDGMENTS

The writer is grateful to Mr. R. V. Andrews of the British Sugar Corporation Ltd., Mr. A. Tomter of the Department of Agriculture and Fisheries for Scotland, Peat Section, and Mr. A. Watt of the Forestry Commission (Scotland) for providing the figures in regard to sugar beet, peat and wood respectively.

REFERENCES

1. A Survey of Agricultural, Forestry and Fishery Products in the United Kingdom and their Utilisation, 1953. London: H.M.S.O.
2. Walker, F. T. (1947). *Proc. Linn. Soc., Lond.*, Session 159, Part 2, 90.
3. Walker, F. T. (1954). *J. Cons. int. Explor. Mer.*, **20**, 160.
4. Black, W. A. P., and Woodward, F. N. (1957). *Emp. J. exp. Agric.*, XXV, No. 97, 51.
5. Ikeda, K., and Moroe, T. (1959). *Tokyo med. News*, **76**, 209.
6. Black, W. A. P., Dewar, E. T., and Woodward, F. N. (1951). *J. appl. Chem.*, **1**, 414.
7. Black, W. A. P., Cornhill, W. J., Dewar, E. T., and Woodward, F. N. (1951). *J. appl. Chem.*, **1**, 505.
8. Black, W. A. P., Dewar, E. T., and Woodward, F. N. (1952). *J. Sci. Fd. Agric.*, **3**, 122.
9. Creighton, H. J. (1942). *Can. Chem. Process Inds.*, **26**, 690.
10. Arthur D. Little Research Institute, Unpublished results.
11. Hay, J. M. (1952). *Engineer, Lond.*, **193**, 814, 846.
12. Zief, M., Yanovsky, E. (1949). *Industr. Engng Chem.* (*Industr.*), **41**, 1697.
13. Anon. (1957). *Chem. Engng News*, **35** [22], 90.
14. Linn, C. B. (1957). *Chem. Engng News*, **35** [37], 84.
15. Linstead, R. P., Rutenberg, A., Dauben, W. G., and Evans, W. L. (1940). *J. Amer. Chem. Soc.*, **62**, 3260.
16. Anon. (1958). *Chem. Engng News*, **36** [16], 24.
17. Osipoiw, L., Snell, F. D., Marra, D., York, W. C., and Finchler, A. (1956). *Industr. Engng Chem.* (*Industr.*), **48**, 1459.
18. Arni, P. C., Black, W. A. P., Dewar, E. T., Paterson, J. C., and Rutherford, D. (1959). *J. appl. Chem.*, **9**, 186.
19. Black, W. A. P., Dewar, E. T., Paterson, J. C., and Rutherford, D. (1959). *J. appl. Chem.*, **9**, 256.
20. Black, W. A. P., and Dewar, E. T. (1960), *J. appl. Chem.*, **10**, 134.
21. Anon. (1958). *Chem. Engng News*, **36** [28], 40.
22. Luke, D. L. (1960). *Tappi*, **43**, [5] 12A.

23. Report of the Scottish Peat Committee, 1954. Edinburgh: H.M.S.O.
24. Mitchell, R. L., Proc. Intern. Peat Symposium, Dublin, Eire, July 1954, Section B.3.
25. Tomter, A., Proc. Intern. Peat Symposium, Dublin, Eire, July 1954, Section B.1.
26. Black, W. A. P., Cornhill, W. J., and Woodward, F. N. (1955). *J. appl. Chem.*, **5**, 482.
27. Woodward, F. N. (1955). *Indust. Chem.*, **31**, 219.
28. Ontario Research Foundation, Annual Report 1959.

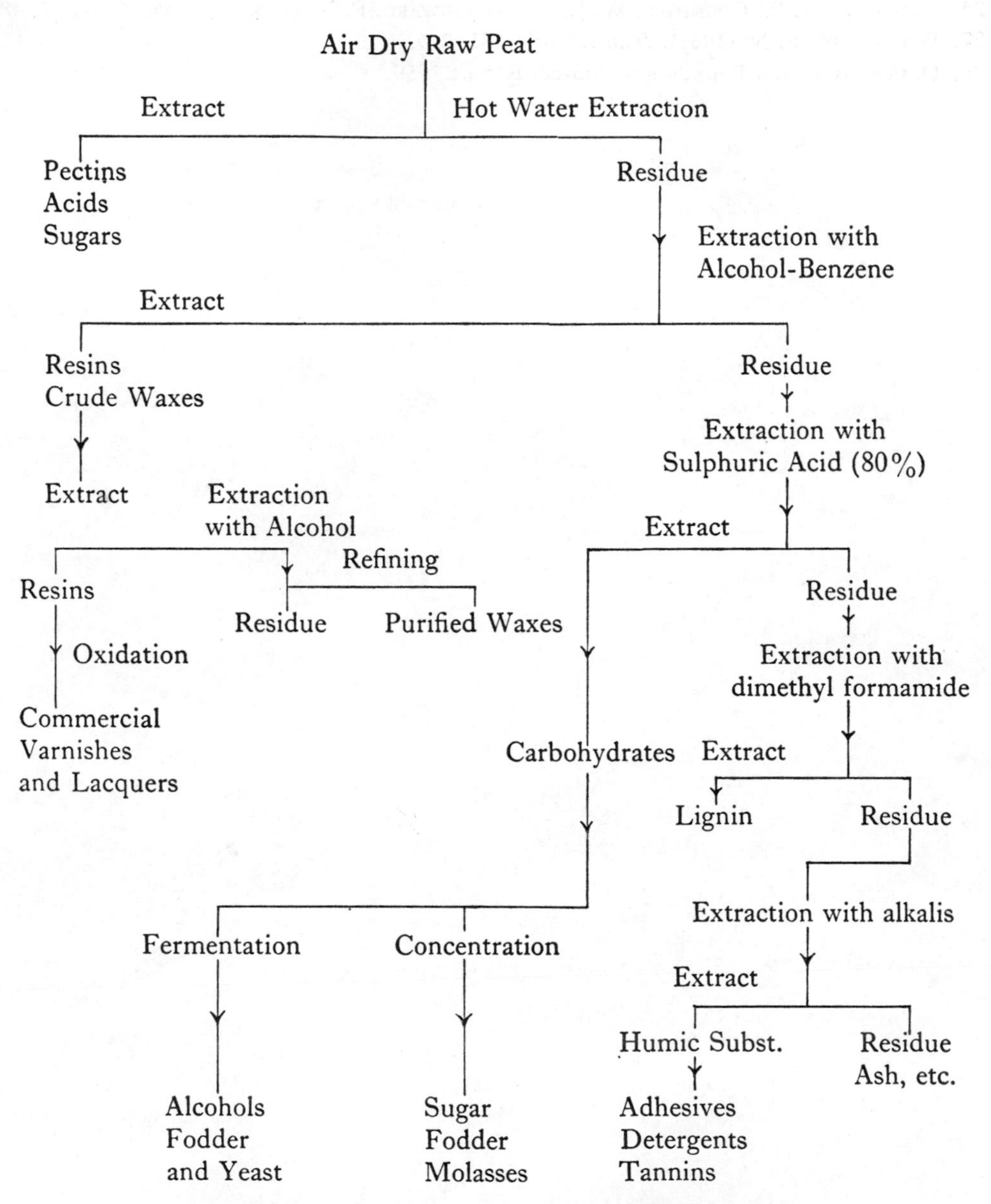

FIG. 1. Some Derivatives of Peat

DISCUSSION

Dr. Blodwen Lloyd, *Department of Biology, The Royal College of Science and Technology, Glasgow*

Professor Thomson has already covered Dr. Black's highlighting of the four major industries derived from biological materials. One of them—peat—has proved itself refractory; sucrose as a non-food substance is not yet fully developed; manitol, perhaps fucoidin and laminaarin also, we are told, need to be developed. These have not been developed in the ordinary way and may take time. May we not perhaps hasten matters by something non-traditional? If traditional research methods do not produce the answer, may we not (and in saying we, I exclude myself personally), might we not offer a prize of some sort? The Napoleonic armies were unable to march except on their stomachs and a prize of 12,000 fr. was offered for preserving food, and from the prize money given to Nicholas Appert in 1812 stemmed the whole industry of preservation of foodstuffs and tinning of foodstuffs. Might the Scottish Council please take note of that?

A second point: I was amazed in reading of the skilled detail of the chemists' work in developing biological materials. Now, on the whole, very few chemists have any biological training, and on the whole very few biologists have chemical training. There is a gap as between biologists, chemists, ecologists (pure and simple) and conservationists. Can the Scottish Council produce some spark that would bridge that gap? Possibly another committee—I believe that might be useful.

Another point: These major industries may not lead very much farther; they may have been fully exploited, but can we look at the little things, because they may produce something. Forgetting the major industries, peat as a source of chemicals is refractory, but the scent of peat—can we smell that? Can we sell it, having smelt it? Only a fortnight ago in the Press came the story of an Australian who took some peat all the way back to Australia just to burn it. Cannot we just pack it up and sell it that way overseas and save the chemists a lot of trouble? During the summer I was travelling on a bus tour and we were looking at the scenery. An American lady said, "My, I can just smell those mountains. I wish I could take it home with me." The thing she was smelling was the bog-myrtle right at her feet. Well, bog-myrtle apparently, although it has an aroma, is not going to be very useful commercially, but cannot we pack up bog-myrtle and sell it? Can't we do little things like that? For an old-age racket I would put on an apron myself and sell sprigs of it at 6d., or do as my grandmother did—take off the leaves and dry them and fill a pillow; a bog-myrtle pillow is supposed to be a country remedy for insomnia. Let us not forget the little things.

There are a number of other little things that I have brought, but I hope the Chairman will be very firm and cut me off. Look at this horrible shell thing—it came all the way from Hong Kong and somebody in Scotland is prepared to buy it. Some of these shells are sub-tropical, but some sub-tropical current has cast up a shell beach in Scotland—and I have been very careful not to ask where it is—which is practically wholly these little Turritella shells. I am afraid to mention where it is in case some farmer will bring his tractor for the comminuted fragments, break them up and use them for limestone. A little sifting and a little sorting out, and we have the raw materials for a rural shell industry. Here are some Turritella shells which anyone may look at. If they do not come back to me I will know at least there is a demand in Scotland for these things.

Dr. F. N. Woodward, *Arthur D. Little Research Institute*

Mr. Chairman, it seems almost improper to talk about the possible use of biological resources after all we have heard based on the use of non-renewable resources, but I am encouraged by the success attending Dr. Lloyd's efforts, and also I do not think we should let Dr. Black's most stimulating paper pass without comment, because he and his colleagues at Inveresk have done and are doing work which I personally believe is of great importance and certainly is of great significance to Scotland.

Many of you may have heard me speak previously about the need for examining our biological renewable resources as possible raw materials for industry, although this idea is not popular in many circles, certainly not with the Advisory Council on Scientific Policy. I am very happy, however, that others are becoming more enlightened, as is evidenced by the success of our small but growing group at Inveresk, where 70 per cent. of our effort is currently being devoted to a study of biological raw materials, wood, sugar and cereal grains in particular, with this objective in view. I regret to say that none of the support for this work is coming from Scotland, or for that matter from Britain. We are currently spending about £50,000 per annum on this type of work which is provided by foreign government departments and industrial firms, and with few exceptions the results are available to everybody.

If I may have one more minute, Mr. Chairman, I would like to do something which perhaps I should have done yesterday, namely, briefly to highlight the main steps in the development of seaweed utilisation in Scotland in the post-war era. Obviously I cannot give these in detail now, but if I were to recapitulate briefly the steps taken to bring this about it would be useful because I believe this may well be looked upon in the future as a classic example of indigenous resource development in Scotland.

The idea that the old seaweed industry could be resuscitated on a sound scientific basis first occurred to the late Professor J. Masson Gulland and Mr. E. D. MacPhee in 1944, and for different reasons they approached Sir Stephen Bilsland, now Lord Bilsland, to see where something could not be done to the benefit of the crofting communities. Due to the efforts of Sir Stephen Bilsland and the Scottish Council of the day, and the very great help of many interested individuals and Government Departments, the Scottish Seaweed Research Association was formed which later became the Institute of Seaweed Research. It was given a very simple remit—"Find all you can about seaweed, where it is, why it is there, what is in it, how do you get it, and what can you do with what is in it; pass this information on to *bona fide* enquirers in the hope that they, the industrialists particularly, will develop industry based on this hitherto wasted resource in the more remote parts of the crofting counties of Scotland." Stimulated by this operation, an industry has been built up by independent firms which, as Dr. Black has explained, is now worth £1¼ million per annum; although this is not large on a national basis, it is a development of considerable significance to the crofting communities.

WRITTEN CONTRIBUTION

Dr. B. Lloyd, *Department of Applied Microbiology and Biology, The Royal College of Science and Technology*

The possibility of exploiting smaller resources whose sum total might be effective in Scottish economy does entail preliminary survey and assessment of potentialities. But there is one field which does not appear to have been developed, and should most certainly be enquired into. It is the following:

As far as I am aware, there is no commercial undertaking which sets out to provide material for biologists, and biologists are among the regular consumers of biological material. This particularly refers to material required for teaching, both in schools and in advanced institutions, and as Britain on the whole is poorly served in this respect, there might well be scope for initiating or encouraging the formation of a Biological Supply House, not only to satisfy Scottish needs but also to purvey those plants and animals which could with special ease be collected or grown in Scotland.

THIRD DAY

RESOURCE ADMINISTRATION AND DEVELOPMENT

PROGRAMME

Introduction

RESOURCE ADMINISTRATION AND DEVELOPMENT

Sir EDWARD V. APPLETON, G.B.E., K.C.B., M.A., D.SC., SC.D., LL.D., LITT.E., F.R.S.E., F.R.S.
Chairman, Third Day

Deputy Chairman
T. G. WATERLOW, C.B.E.
Deputy Chairman and Director, William Thyne Ltd.

11. *Human Resources*

Deputy Chairman
F. N. WOODWARD, C.B.E., B.SC., PH.D., F.R.S.E.
Director, Arthur D. Little Research Institute

12. *The Mechanics of Resource Development*

INTRODUCTION

Sir Edward V. Appleton, G.B.E., K.C.B., M.A., D.SC., SC.D., LL.D., LITT.E., F.R.S.E., F.R.S.

Chairman, Third Day

On this the third day of the Conference on Natural Resources in Scotland we come to what I would claim to be the heart of the matter—human resources. And I imagine that, as today's discussion develops, we shall find ourselves thinking and talking about the gifted human resources—and also the talented brains, rather than the skilful pairs of hands. For I would have thought that there is no special shortage of skilful pairs of hands in Scotland. Now, the great advantage of being an opening speaker is that you can raise—you can ask—questions without being obliged to answer them. In a recent television programme "Ask Me Another" none of the experts knew the meaning of *Sermocination*. Neither did I, until it was explained, when I learned that it means "Asking a question yourself and immediately answering it, yourself". Well, as I say, I do not intend to be bound by the need to observe sermocination. As a University Principal, developing and sharpening human resources is my business. The higher education of young people of talent is, by a long and splendid tradition, a major activity in Scotland. Of course, one ought not to justify it on simple economic grounds, but I may point out that it does bring money and business to Scotland. For, as you will have read in one of the documents presented today, the Scottish Universities educate as many as 17 per cent. of the undergraduate population of the United Kingdom. And, in the case of medical students, as many as 25 per cent. are educated in the Scottish Medical Schools. Both figures, you see, are much greater than the population of Scotland expressed as a percentage of that of the United Kingdom. And we see, in these figures, one readily understandable reason why some Scottish graduates—the majority of whom are, of course, born in Scotland—go to seek their fortunes elsewhere. Now Mr. Kyd's fascinating paper on "the effects of migration on the economy of Scotland" gives numerical concreteness to these matters. I do not mind in the least being classed by him as an "immigrant", to use his phraseology for people who come from England to Scotland, but I would like to assure him that I have never felt like one—least of all when I have been invited to this Conference. Now I know it is customary for people in Scotland to lament the fact that so many young people of great ability leave its borders. And one question which will have to be discussed today is this: "Why does this happen?" But I want to suggest to you that an even more important question than this is "Why, when they have gone away, don't they come back?" I say this, because I am convinced that a Scotsman can be notably useful to Scotland if he has been away, done well while he has been away, and wants to come back. Let me remind you of a lament in Mr. Kyd's paper. He says, "It's a sombre thought, but I sometimes wonder if a large proportion of English people are filling posts for which no suitable Scots can be found." Now I suspect that we are dealing here not with people like the newly fledged graduate but with Englishmen with some experience who are fairly senior. I doubt whether any English graduates come to Scotland immediately after taking their degrees. However, in University circles we *do* manage to attract *some* people back who started their academic careers in Scotland—who have gone south, have distinguished themselves and who then want to come back. I cannot think of a better prescription than that for a Scottish University teacher. Now, if we can do it to some extent in Universities, why can't it be done in non-University life? As regards the migration to the south of people like the newly fledged graduate, surely that is understandable. England is nine times the population size of Scotland—there are nine times as many people with ideas and at least nine times as many opportunities for rewarding careers. Look at the advertisements in the daily and Sunday papers, detailing jobs for trained people. They are almost all for English posts. I have only once seen such an advertisement from a Scottish organisation. The great majority of these advertisements are for people with scientific qualifications. And I ask another question, "Has Scotland, and notably Scottish Industry, yet come to terms with this age of science and technology?" Now, it is very odd that people who bemoan the fact that so many talented people leave Scotland seem, in some way, to blame England for it; whereas I am sure you will agree that the fault is clearly that of Scotland herself. We want to make Scotland a place where ability can flourish. And some of us, in our various ways, are feeling that we can best serve Scotland by doing precisely that. Why haven't Scottish geniuses in the scientific world made their discoveries in Scotland but have had to go to England to make their "break-throughs" on the scientific front? Take your Sir Alexander Fleming in biological science and your James Clerk Maxwell in physical science. Where did they find the stimulating conditions which led to the flowering of their genius? As you will have seen, Sir Alexander Fleck, both a great scientist and distinguished industrialist, seems to think the right text for *his* therapeutical sermon is "Ye must be born again". Whether that is the right prescription, I wouldn't know. But I do suggest that you should examine the activities of the people I call "negativists", the "no change at any price" brigade, the people who say, "Because we were wonderful in the past, it's not necessary to make any effort to be wonderful today." These are certainly the enemies of progress. Now I know that, in an electric circuit, you can overcome resistance if you put enough electromotive force in the circuit. But, Gentlemen, it takes time to do this, and time is precious. Some years ago I experienced the situation of people refusing Professorial Chairs in Edinburgh, including Scots, because the material conditions were "appalling". I use the words used by one of the Scots. But that has been changed. And we are now in process of achieving conditions which are fit for a genius to flourish in, fit to keep people in Scotland and, in my view—better still—fit to attract exiled Scots back to their own country.

RESOURCE ADMINISTRATION AND DEVELOPMENT

HUMAN RESOURCES AND EDUCATION

Emigration and Depopulation and Scotland

J. G. Kyd, C.B.E., F.R.S.E., F.F.A.
Late Registrar General, Scotland

In the first half of this century Scotland's net loss by emigration was over a million. The rate of Scottish migration loss is sixteen times that of England and Wales. Up to 1931 the major flow of Scots was overseas, but since 1931 more than twice as many Scots have crossed the border as have gone overseas. Is the migrant Scot now content to take his share in the expanding industries of England, rather than going to the far corners of the earth to continue the work of Scots of earlier times who were largely responsible for building the Commonwealth?

Since the date of the census in 1951 Scotland's loss of young men by migration exceeds the number of Scots killed in the two world wars.

The majority of migrants are young and trained in the professions and in industries, and it is now difficult to find skilled personnel in Scotland to supply Scottish needs. The number of English in Scotland has increased greatly. Are they filling the posts for which trained Scots are not available?

The population of Scotland is unevenly spread. In the central belt comprising one-seventh of our area no less than three-quarters of our population live under congested conditions. North and South depopulation is so great that many counties are so sparsely populated that public administration is almost impossible. In some counties emigration has produced a distorted age distribution of the population which results in the deaths exceeding the births—this means eventual complete depopulation.

We must try to keep our creative ability within our own shores.

EMIGRATION

Before one can begin to measure emigration or depopulation in respect of a particular country it is necessary to obtain a broad picture of the population trend both national and local.

The first official census of Scotland was taken in 1801. Since then there has been a census at decennial intervals, with the exception of 1941—during the 1939-45 War.

A national register of the people was however taken in September 1939 which gave a precise picture of the numbers in the civilian population of Scotland and in each area thereof. At the census of 1801 the population of Scotland was 1,608,420. The following table shows the population at each census up to 1951.

TABLE I

Census Year	Population	Intercensal Increase (or decrease)	Percentage Increase (or decrease) of previous Census Population
1801	1,608,420	—	—
1811	1,805,864	197,444	+12·3
1821	2,091,521	285,657	+15·8
1831	2,364,386	272,865	+13·0
1841	2,620,184	255,798	+10·8
1851	2,888,742	268,558	+10·2
1861	3,062,294	173,552	+ 6·0
1871	3,360,018	297,724	+ 9·7
1881	3,735,573	375,555	+11·2
1891	4,025,647	290,074	+ 7·8
1901	4,472,103	446,456	+11·1
1911	4,760,904	288,801	+ 6·5
1921	4,882,497	121,593	+ 2·6
1931	4,842,980	−39,517	− 0·8
1951	5,096,415	253,435	+ 5·2

Prior to 1801 there was one definite enumeration of the inhabitants of Scotland. In the year 1755 The Rev. Alexander Webster, D.D., who was Moderator of the General Assembly of the Church of Scotland, instructed all the parish ministers to enumerate the inhabitants of his parish. The resulting total was 1,268,380, which was about 340,000 less than the number at the official census taken 46 years later. This was an increase of some 27 per cent. in the intervening period.

Earlier estimates of the population of Scotland were made from time to time; these were however more of the nature of educated guesses and do not concern us in connection with the present investigation.

It will be observed from the figures in Table I that the population of Scotland increased from 1801 to 1951 by 217 per cent.—more than three times.

During the same period the population of England and Wales increased nearly five times.

In a community from which there are no departures other than death, and no entries other than by birth, the population changes are due to what is known as "Natural Increase"—normally the excess of births over deaths. In modern times, however, with the vast development in countries overseas and with the greatly increased facilities for travel, the natural increase of the population is affected powerfully by movements into and out of a country.

I have stated that the population of England and Wales has proportionately increased much more rapidly than that of Scotland, and this is notwithstanding that the rate of natural increase in Scotland is normally in excess of that in England and Wales. The slower increase in the population of Scotland as a whole is due to its much larger proportionate loss of population by emigration. National Statistics in Britain are rather lacking in facilities for the precise measurement of migration either to or from the country.

This is so in regard to overseas migration, but the position is even less satisfactory in measuring the flow to and from Scotland across the border. Precise measurement of *net* population movement is possible only between census dates. If the excess of births over deaths is added to the enumerated population at one census and the resulting total is greater than the enumerated population at a later census, the difference is accounted for by net loss of population by migration. If the later census poulation is greater than the previous population plus the natural increase, the difference is the net gain by migration.

But the figure of net migration loss or gain does not in fact give information as to the number who leave, or the number who enter, the country but shows merely the net loss or gain by migration. Before making an estimate of the actual number of migrants in each direction it is interesting to compare the relative position of Scotland with that of England and Wales. It will be seen from Table II that Scotland's loss is much greater than that south of the border. The following Table II shows the net loss (or gain) by migration in England and Wales and in Scotland respectively during the first half of this century.

TABLE II

Period between Census Date	Loss by Migration England and Wales	% of Earlier Population	Migration Loss Scotland	% Earlier Population
1901–1911	501,000	1·5	254,000	5·7
1911–1921	620,000	1·7	239,000	5·0
1921–1931	172,000	0·5	392,000	8·0
1931–1951	gain 745,000	1·8	220,000	4·5
Net loss 1901–51	548,000		1,105,000	

It will be observed that in the first half of this century Scottish net loss by emigration was 1,105,000. In England and Wales with a population eight times as great the loss was 548,000, less than half Scotland's loss. This indicates that the average rate of net loss by migration from Scotland was sixteen times that of England and Wales during this century. Scotland's loss by migration is not only much greater than that of England and Wales, it is also greater than that in the countries of Europe, as is shown in the following Table III.

TABLE III

The net Migration Rates for 1921-31 *in various European Countries*

Country	Net Migration Loss per cent. of Population
Scotland . . .	8·0
England and Wales .	·5
Italy	2·6
Norway . . .	2·9
Sweden . . .	1·5
Denmark . . .	1·2

Both France and Belgium had a gain of population by immigration.

I have stated that no satisfactory machinery exists whereby we may measure the actual numbers moving to and from Scotland. If we take as an example the movement across the border between Scotland and England I understand that any estimates which are made are based on the transfer of medical cards from the lists of doctors under the National Health Scheme, in Scotland and England and Wales respectively.

This is probably the best available means, at present, of making an estimate, but I feel that it is not altogether a very reliable basis. I should imagine that many who move from one country to the other do not register with a doctor at their new address until they, in fact, require medical attention. There may therefore be considerable lag in obtaining the information by this method.

If we consider the period 1931 to 1951 in respect of migration both within the United Kingdom and abroad we find in the report on the 1951 census that the net loss to Scotland by migration was about 220,000. This figure completely obscures the size of the movement of population into and out of Scotland respectively during these twenty years. To appreciate the position it is necessary to examine the periods in the pre-war years and the post-war years separately. In the period from the 1931 census to the outbreak of war in 1939 Scotland gained by immigration from overseas by about 77,000. This was due partly to the world-wide economic depression which not only practically put a stop to emigration from Scotland to countries overseas but also resulted in many who had emigrated previously returning to Scotland as their hopes in establishing themselves in countries overseas had been disappointed.

During the war period in 1939 to 1945 overseas migration was practically at a standstill. But in the period between the end of the war and the date of the 1951 census—less than six years—Scotland's net loss by overseas migration was no less than 88,000.

In regard to migration to other parts of the United Kingdom, the net loss to Scotland between the 1931 census and the end of the war was 116,000 and between the end of the war and the 1951 census was 93,000. These figures exclude those who were evacuated to Scotland from England but who returned after the cessation of hostilities. Put into tabular form the migration figures between 1931 and 1951 are shown as follows:

	Overseas Migration		U.K. Migration	
From the date of 1931 census to end of the war	Net gain	77,000	Net loss	116,000
End of war to date of 1951 census . . .	Net loss	88,000	Net loss	93,000
	Net loss	11,000	Net loss	209,000

Total Net loss to Scotland 1931-51 220,000.

It is instructive to examine the subdivision of Scotland's loss by migration during this century as between overseas and to other parts of the United Kingdom.

In the first decade of the century Scotland actually gained by immigration from other parts of the United Kingdom. The following Table IV shows the position during the first half of the present century:

TABLE IV

Net Loss of Population from Scotland

	To other parts of the United Kingdom		Overseas	
1901–11	gain	27,000		281,000
1911–21	loss	10,000		229,000
1921–31		63,000		329,000
1931–51		209,000		11,000
1951–60	about	120,000	about	120,000

It will be seen that in the first thirty years of this century Scotland's loss by migration was mainly to countries overseas. Since 1930, however, the loss to other parts of the

United Kingdom—mainly England—is greater than the overseas loss. Has the wandering Scot become a mere cog in the great industries of England rather than the pioneer of overseas development which, the whole world knows, he was in the past?

As is shown in Table IV, loss of population by emigration is still continuing. Each year the Registrar-General in his annual report gives an estimate of the net loss and since 1951 it has averaged about 24,000 a year, which is almost equally divided between overseas and United Kingdom migration. During the last ten years the loss by migration of men has exceeded the loss of women by about 14,000 for the decade. Of the total of 243,000 in the ten years no less than 156,000 were between the ages of 15 and 44, which represents the most vital and energetic cohort of the whole population. Slightly less than half of the women were married and thus Scotland loses not only the emigrants but those who will be their children born away from Scotland. Of the men, about half are obviously highly trained belonging as they do to the professional and non-industrial executives, builders, carpenters, miners, quarriers, engineers and metal workers. One-quarter of the migrants were children under the age of 15 who would have provided the skilled worker of the future in Scotland. Where did these emigrants—who average about 24,000 a year—go? About half crossed the border to other parts of the United Kingdom—mainly to England. Of the other half the following gives a rough estimate of the average annual loss to the following countries:

Canada . . .	7,000	United States of America .	1,000
Australia . . .	3,000	South Africa . . .	200
New Zealand . .	1,000		

These figures may not signify anything very alarming to the ordinary citizen, but when it is realised that Scotland has lost in the last ten years population of half the size of the city of Edinburgh, and further that two-thirds of the loss consisted of young people between the ages of 15 and 44. The number in this age-group represents 68 per cent. of the total. Whereas in the whole population this age-group represents 43 per cent. of the total. It is evident that emigrants are heavily weighted by people in this vital age-group. In this age-group the average annual loss by migration is at least four times the loss by death. Further, Scotland's migration loss among men since 1951 is greater than the number of Scotsmen who laid down their lives in the two world wars.

It is interesting to make an attempt to gauge from where the inflow of immigrants to Scotland came. A rough guide is to compare the number living in Scotland at the two censuses 1931 and 1951 who were born in other countries.

The following table gives some information on this point:

Country of Birth	Enumerated in Scotland	
	Census 1931	Census 1951
England	164,299	222,162
Wales	4,341	9,632
Northern Ireland / Irish Republic . . .	124,296	89,007
Isle of Man and Channel Islands .	1,104	1,286
Commonwealth and Empire .	23,567	28,810
Foreign Countries . . .	29,435	49,689
Total	346,952	400,586

It will be seen from these figures that those born outside Scotland who were living in Scotland at the date of the 1951 census were more than 50,000 greater than at the census of 1931. It is an interesting fact that Scotland notwithstanding its high emigration rate seems to have an attraction for those born elsewhere.

Of our population in 1951, 8 per cent. were born elsewhere. In England and Wales the proportion born elsewhere was 5·8 per cent. In actual numbers just over 400,000 of the Scottish population were born elsewhere—of these 230,000 were born in England and Wales. South of the border 2,500,000 were born elsewhere of whom just under 600,000 were born in Scotland. The increase since 1931 in the number born in England who were resident in Scotland amounted to 58,000. Unfortunately the census reports do not give information as to the occupations followed by these immigrants. It is a sombre thought, but I sometimes wonder if a large proportion of them are filling posts for which no suitable Scots could be found.

DEPOPULATION

I suppose, however great the migration has been within a particular area, if in fact the population has not decreased then it may be said that there has been no depopulation. During this century 18 of our counties have shown increases in population and in 15 there has been a decrease. With the sole exception of the county of Bute, every county of Scotland has suffered loss by emigration since 1901. Depopulation has taken place mainly in the Highlands, but the Border counties have suffered material loss by the drift away either to the cities of Scotland or to lands beyond our frontiers. As I indicated in the earlier part of this paper, each Scottish census has shown an increase of population from the date of the previous census, with the one exception of that of 1931. These increases occurred notwithstanding that there has been a large migration of Scots away from Scotland. Looking at the population figures of this century, we find that the population in 1901 was 4,472,103. Up to the date of the 1951 census there was

an excess of births over deaths of		1,757,762
With this amount of natural increase and had there been no migration into or out of the country the population would have been		6,229,865
In the fifty years, however, Scotland's net loss by migration was	1,104,591	
and it is estimated that at the date of the 1951 census National Service personnel living away from Scotland increased since the previous census	28,859	
		1,133,450
Giving the population recorded at 1951		5,096,415

This shows that notwithstanding a loss of over 1,100,000 by migration in the past half-century Scotland's population has increased by over 624,000.

This increase has, however, been very unevenly spread throughout the country, and in order to give a clearer picture of regional population changes I have divided Scotland into three parts, comprising

(1) the central industrial belt, which includes the counties of Ayr, Dunbarton, Lanark, Renfrew, Clackmannan, Stirling, the Lothians, Fife and the City of Dundee;
(2) those counties north of this belt which may be called the Highlands;
(3) the lowland counties lying to the south which we may call the Borders.

To show the profound changes which have taken place in the geographical distribution of our population I have included figures of the population of these three areas at three points of time: (1) in 1755 when Webster took his census, (2) at the census of 1861, and (3) at the census of 1951. The central belt, and also the Border counties lying south of it, comprise approximately one-seventh of the area of Scotland. The counties lying north of the Central belt make up the remaining five-sevenths.

The following Table V gives facts relating to population distribution in the three areas at the three points of time.

TABLE V

District	Size of Area in Square Miles	Fraction of Total	Population in Thousands	% of Total	Density—Persons per Square Mile
1755					
Highland	21,330	$\frac{5}{7}$	652	51	31
Central	4,269	$\frac{1}{7}$	464	37	110
Lowland	4,196	$\frac{1}{7}$	149	11	36
	29,795		1,265		42
1861					
Highland	21,330	$\frac{5}{7}$	1,020	33	48
Central	4,269	$\frac{1}{7}$	1,769	53	414
Lowland	4,196	$\frac{1}{7}$	273	9	65
	29,795		3,062		103
1951					
Highland	21,330	$\frac{5}{7}$	1,000	20	47
Central	4,269	$\frac{1}{7}$	3,840	75	900
Lowland	4,196	$\frac{1}{7}$	256	5	61
	29,795		5,096		171

It will be seen that in the middle of the eighteenth century more than half of the population lived north of the central belt, but by 1951 only one-fifth of the population were in this district which constitutes more than 70 per cent. of the area of Scotland. More dramatic still, however, is the fact that by 1951 three-quarters of our population were concentrated, with a density of 900 persons to each square mile, in the central belt which comprises but one-seventh of our area. These figures indicate the profound changes which have taken place in the last two hundred years in the regional distribution of the population of Scotland. This concentration of population in the central belt means that a large proportion of our people live under congested conditions which are certainly not good for health nor for social welfare and render the industrial potential of Scotland extremely vulnerable.

The coalfields, the iron ore and the shipping facilities are the primary causes of the extreme concentration of population in this area, but its rapid increase is mainly due to the fact that although all areas in Scotland have suffered from emigration, the main movement of population within the country has been from the north and the south to the centre, so that, notwithstanding that large numbers have left this industrial area to seek their fortunes away from Scotland, these losses have been made good by the natural increase in the population and by immigration from other parts of Scotland.

It is unnecessary for the purpose of this paper to analyse the loss by migration in every county where the population has decreased materially since its maximum.

I shall, however, take a typical county in the Highlands and in the Borders and analyse the population trend of each. I have taken Sutherland as representing the Highland problem and Berwick county for the Borders. Sutherland attained its maximum population in the middle of last century. In 1861 the population was 25,241. In the ninety years which have elapsed to 1951 there was an excess of births over deaths of 5,433. During the same period, however, the net loss of population by migration was approximately 17,000, leaving a population of 13,644, which is only slightly more than half of the population of the county in 1861.

The 1951 total represents seven persons for each square mile of the area against a figure of 171 persons per square mile for Scotland as a whole. The county showing the maximum density is Renfrew, where on the average 1,445 persons are concentrated in every square mile. I do not suggest that the intense pressure of population in Renfrewshire is desirable either from the social or personal point of view, but with a population of only seven persons to the square mile in Sutherland the difficulties of carrying on the normal day-to-day affairs of life and of administrating the services of the local government and the State must be very great. It is a sad thought that the shrinkage of population in Sutherland has occurred notwithstanding that the married women of the county are among the most fertile in Scotland. Their fertility is exceeded only by the married women of the neighbouring county of Ross and Cromarty.

Even with the high fertility in Sutherland the deaths in each census period since 1911 have exceeded the births. If the present trend continues it does not take much imagination to envisage the eventual total depopulation of the county.

Looking now at the county of Berwick, which gives a typical example of the depopulation which is occurring south of the central belt.

The population of the county reached its maximum in 1861 when it was 36,613. At the 1951 census it was 25,060.

In the intervening ninety years the births exceeded the deaths by 21,015, but during the same period there was net migration from the county of approximately 32,000, so that the natural increase was only two-thirds of the migration loss. From an examination of the census volumes it would appear that there was a considerable influx of people from Berwickshire into the capital, but large numbers must have found their ways overseas or crossed the nearby border into England. Strangely enough there was practically no increase in the English-born recorded in the 1951 census over the number in 1931. In fact, Berwickshire showed the smallest proportionate increase in the English-born recorded in any county during the last census period.

As a matter of general interest it is worth mentioning that fertility of the married women of the county of Berwick is at the other end of the scale from Sutherland, being the lowest of any Scottish county.

FINALE

I was asked to write a paper on emigration and depopulation and I understood that there was to be another paper on the biological effect of these forces. I am told that no one could be found who was willing to venture on this uncharted sea. My observations on this aspect of the subject are merely points which have occurred to me as a student of Scottish Statistics for more than half a century and have no biological foundation.

I have given a general outline of Scotland's loss by migration which had its beginnings after the break-up of the clans in 1746.

It seems to be inherent in the nature of the Scot to take his skill to the far corners of the earth. At the beginning of the flight away from Scotland emigration was practically enforced and the flow seems to have continued almost without interruption for over two centuries.

There can be no doubt that the men and women who left Scotland have taken a major part in the building of the British Commonwealth as we know it today, and the enormous development in the industries of England is due in no small measure to the skilled engineers, craftsmen and administrators who have crossed the border from their native land. But what is the effect on the economic life of Scotland? Looking at the matter in the crudest sense—in terms of the financial loss to Scotland in respect of each trained person who leaves Scotland to take up work in another country.

It is difficult to place a precise figure on the cost of the nurture, upbringing, education and training of an emigrant, but let us assume a figure of £3,000, which is probably a gross understatement.

Taking an average number of emigrants as 20,000 a year, the financial loss to Scotland would be in the neighbourhood of £60,000,000 a year and the potential loss to Scotland's industrial development must be much greater.

Incidentally, a prominent Scottish nationalist once said to me that Scotland should charge a transfer fee for each emigrant across the border or overseas on the lines of professional football clubs!

It is difficult to put one's finger on a particular shortcoming of the Scottish industrial scene and say "this is due to emigration".

There is little doubt that the much higher rate of unemployment in Scotland than in England is due to the fact that we have not a sufficiently large reservoir of skilled men, either in science or in crafts, to support the large industrial development which would absorb our unemployed. As I have already stated, I have a shrewd suspicion that the large influx from England come north to fill the posts for which we have not the trained Scots available. As I have already indicated, the census report does not reveal the occupations followed by the large number of English who now reside in Scotland. They are fairly evenly distributed throughout the industrial parts of Scotland. The city of Glasgow, however, shows a decline in English-born since 1931. Edinburgh, on the other hand, shows an increase which seems to indicate a transfer of brain power from across the border. There are increases in the English in Ayrshire, Renfrew county,

Dunbarton county and Fife, thus indicating an inflow of trained industrial personnel. Is this a symptom of lack of trained Scots and is it due to emigration?

Investigations were made earlier this year which show that leaders of industry and professional bodies are finding the greatest difficulty not only in getting suitable recruits from the schools, Colleges and Universities, but also in filling the higher posts in industry and in the professions.

These observations are mainly based on my own views and are put forward primarily to give a lead to discussion.

It seems to me that the paramount duty of those responsible for the welfare of Scotland and her people is so to plan our educational policy and our industrial training and development that Scotland may be able to keep her own creative ability within her own shores.

Interrelations between Material Resources, Human Resources and Human Culture

Professor C. Macrae, C.B.E., D.PHIL.
Residential Centre for Management Studies,
The Royal College of Science and Technology, Glasgow

Life cannot exist without resources. The more resources, or the utilisation of them, can be extended, the more abundant, in a material sense at least, life should be.

Whatever man can use to overcome his difficulties, meet his needs or satisfy his desires is a resource. Coal, when used, is a resource, so are dexterous fingers, so is the ability to use them profitably. Resources therefore include things, persons and knowledge, or, as defined for the present purpose, non-human material resources, human resources and culture. Human beings and therefore human resources incorporate body, mind and spirit, and any culture which neglects any of these does so at its peril. Culture may be broadly defined as what man makes of himself and nature, or even as education in the broadest sense. Formal education is only part, but a supremely important and potent part, of culture.

Just as human beings cannot exist without material resources, so human culture cannot exist without human beings. The efficiency of use of natural resources will depend on the quality of the human beings utilising them, and that in turn will be determined very largely by the culture of these human beings.

Resources are continuous, like the sun, the winds or the waters, or renewable, as in the case of animal and vegetable life, or, like the fossil fuels and other minerals, exhaustible. Obviously, it is important to develop as much as possible the use of continuous and renewable resources, as it is also to seek substitutes for exhaustible resources, particularly those of which known supplies are dwindling. If, however, efficiency of use of a supply of material is doubled, the same yield can be obtained as if the supply were doubled. Thus the search for improved efficiency in utilisation of materials, especially materials in short supply, can be even more rewarding than the search for additional supplies of these materials, for several reasons, including the fact that the achievement of progressive efficiency in utilisation can conserve materials without diminution in yield. By human ingenuity, resources in themselves static can be made, for all practical purposes, dynamic.

The incentive to maintain continuous search for improved efficiency and the productiveness of such search will be determined very largely by culture. For this, as for other reasons, culture is at the generative centre of resource utilisation and any programme directed to improved utilisation of resources must concern itself fundamentally with culture.

It is submitted that on so wide a front the most speedy and effective way of making progress would be, while neglecting no possibility of advance anywhere, to concentrate on those sectors of activity which influence most powerfully the condition and fate of the community. These obviously include Government, the Civil Service, and management in industry and affairs. The conditions of the future will require in all these fields, and others, alertness and flexibility of mind, initiative, perceptiveness, rapid response to challenge and change, wisdom and leadership of a high order.

The ultimate importance of leadership and resource utilisation lie not in themselves but in the purposes they serve. Accordingly, the final arbitrement lies in essential values. True values must be based on truth. The search for truth should be also the primary objective of scholarship; the dissemination of truth and the cultivation of minds to receive it should be main objectives of education.

Education is the predominant lever which can determine what mankind will make of themselves and their environment. It is therefore in education above all that major thought and effort should be consistently and urgently applied. Education must move with the times or preferably ahead of them, and it must be true education. Bad education can be worse than none at all. Possibly the greatest danger facing civilisation today arises from the rapid spread of imperfect knowledge. If so, salvation can lie only in the even more rapid cultivation and dissemination of truer, more perfect knowledge. It is to education primarily that we must look, both for cumulatively and constructively expanding utilisation of resources, and for the inducement of conditions which will make such utilisation an agent for more abundant life, as against the grim but very real alternative of destruction.

Animate existence on this planet is dependent on the derivation by the living organism of aliment from outside itself. In other words, life of the kind we know cannot exist without resources. The limit of available resources is the limit of life. It follows that the more resources or the use made of them can be extended, the more abundant, in a quantitative and material sense at least, life should be.

It is undoubtedly true that man cannot live by bread alone and that richness of life is not necessarily synonymous with material prosperity. It is even more evident that man cannot live without bread, or food of some kind, and that want is not in itself conducive to fulness of life. The interrelation and relative values of the material and the immaterial, the rewards of the life of the flesh and the life of the soul, the functions and needs of body, mind and spirit, the blessings, the limitations and perils of material well-being, are subjects of supreme importance, calling at this tense period in history perhaps more than any others for earnest and naked thought, but they are not the subject of this paper. Nevertheless, it must be submitted that they cannot be ignored in any but the most superficial discussion of material resources, human resources and culture. Indeed, one fruitful basic classification of resources is to embrace them in two comprehensive but interacting categories—material and immaterial.

What can scarcely be doubted is that the level of material prosperity attained by any community or individual is in direct relationship to the extent to which they, he or she make or makes constructive use of available resources. The highest possible degree of material prosperity will be attained by any society, any country, or humankind as a whole, only by making the maximum and most rewarding use of all resources available to them. Resources can be defined, grouped, classified in many ways and in intricate detail. One basic classification has already been adumbrated—material or immaterial. Another, more germane perhaps to immediate practical purposes and probably more congenial to those who will accept only what is generally thought by human beings to be directly known, is this: at bottom resources known to be available to mankind are of two types, material and human. Yet, strictly regarded, this classification, though convenient and useful, is not by any means an exact one since human beings are themselves partly material and partly immaterial. It would be more correct, but tedious, to say "non-human material resources and human resources, the latter including all constituents, material and immaterial, of human personal entities". It is with these connotations that the words "material resources" and "human resources" are used in this paper.

A standard dictionary definition of "resource" is: "a means of supplying some want or deficiency", or, in the plural, "the collective means possessed by any country for its own support or defence". Another is "capability in adapting means to ends or in meeting difficulties". The last is an interpretation of the word in a signification somewhat different from that represented by the first, but resource as capability is also included in resource as means; in fact, resourcefulness is one of the most important and potent of all resources, and without it other resources are of little avail. Resources are more than things. Coal is a resource, but it is not a resource—or at most not more than a potential resource—until it is used. Dexterous fingers are a resource, and so is the knowledge to use them profitably. Whatever man can utilise to overcome his difficulties, meet his needs or satisfy his desires is a resource. Resources therefore include things, persons and knowledge; or material resources (regarded for the purposes of this paper as excluding human beings but including material things made, or assembled, or shaped by human beings), human resources and culture. Moreover, these all interact and condition each other. They also fructify each other. The process of utilising resources is not delimited, static or mechanical; it is organic, responsive, vital. It is the human element which makes it so and the quality of the human element is determined largely by its culture. Culture, then, emerges as the proximate, determinant factor in the utilisation of natural resources.

Material resources can exist without human beings, but human beings or other living creatures cannot exist without material resources. On the other hand, material resources without human resources are, from a human point of view at least, sterile or unused. Therefore in a dynamic context, even on the material plane, human resources are more important than material, and on the quality and vigour of the human resources will depend the extent and yield of the utilisation of the material resources. Effort, ingenuity, inventiveness, knowledge, skill, prudence, persistence, can wring rich rewards even from meagre and intractable material resources. Ignorance, sloth, myopia, stupidity, can make even the richest material resources unfruitful: prodigality can dissipate and waste them. By ingenuity man can make the desert blossom as the rose; by impenetrable ignorance he can die of starvation in the midst of potential plenty. The Dutch made a muddy, waterlogged delta into rich farm and garden; the Red Indians wandered in search of a hard living amidst the vast resources of America. Surely no theme in human existence is more persistent, more repetitive than this: the triumph of human effort and ingenuity in harsh circumstances; the fructification of scanty or unpromising resources; the transmutation of obstacles into assets: on the other hand, the failure through ignorance or refusal through prejudice to utilise abundant resources; dearth in the midst of the profuseness of nature; dissipation of resources once vast. Man has seen often the prolific garden wrested from the wilderness. He has also often seen neglected, wasted, run to seed, the garden once prolific—a wilderness worse than primeval.

The way in which human beings make use of the resources available to them, the extent and quality of that utilisation depend on the knowledge, outlook and character of these human beings. The usage of material resources will be governed by the innate capabilities as developed by culture of the human beings using those resources. There are many who would leave innate capability out of the reckoning. The overall capabilities, they would argue, of any major groups of people, given the same assets, conditions, compulsions, outlooks, knowledge, aims, education and equipment, both physical and mental, are so similar that they can be regarded as basically constant. In that event, differing attainment in utilising similar resources would be entirely attributable to differing cultures. Whether this view—which has much in common with the claim that the shaping of human character is attributable to environment rather than heredity, or perhaps that heredity itself is a long-term product of environment—be adopted or not, there can be no question of the capacity of all human beings to learn, to imitate, to release power in themselves previously latent and unsuspected. Without any doubt and on any basis of assessment, the nature of the culture of any group of people will very largely determine the kind of use they will make of the resources to which they have access.

Just as human resources cannot exist without material resources, so human culture cannot exist without human resources. Just as what material resources will yield is determined by the quality and knowledge of the human resources applied to them, so the fruitfulness, the potentialities, of these human resources are in turn conditioned by their culture. Culture is therefore at the generative centre of the process of resource utilisation. It is the leaven which leavens the lump. If material resources be the soil, human resources the plant, it is culture which provides for the preparation of the soil, the application of fertiliser and water, the adjustment to weather conditions, the protection of the plant, and the fostering of growth.

If—as is assuredly the case—the utilisation for human purposes of natural resources requires the existence and involves the interaction of material resources, human resources and culture, the extent and yield of such utilisation depend critically on the culture applied to it. From another angle, too, culture is of supreme importance since it is through culture that human beings can be changed and rendered more fruitful, as they in turn can change material resources and render them more fruitful. Under the impact of human endeavour and ingenuity, themselves largely shaped by culture patterns, stimuli and values, even static natural resources (minerals, for instance) can be made, for all practical purposes, dynamic.

As has already been said, natural resources can be classified in many ways; for instance, animate and inanimate; organic and inorganic; animal, vegetable and mineral; primary and secondary; things and the functions of things; substances, souces of energy, living beings, sciences and arts; and so on. One distinction which is of primary concern to man is that between continuous or renewable resources on the one hand and exhaustible or non-renewable resources on the other. Minerals, including the fossil fuels, are exhaustible and non-renewable; in the case of some of them known deposits are nearly used up. On the other hand, short of a cataclysm on a cosmic scale, the powers of the sun, the rivers, the sea and the winds are indefinitely continuous, though sometimes with intermissions; animal and vegetable resouces are renewable.

There are still on this planet enormous reserves of many minerals; others have not yet been tapped. But in the end all mineral resources are expendable. This obviously enhances the importance of the continuous or renewable resources, of the sciences investigating them—for instance, Chemurgy—and of their products, such as hydro-electricity or synthetics.

When known supplies of any useful mineral are nearing exhaustion, obviously, if there is not to be loss of what that mineral can provide, a new source of supply or alternative materials of equivalent capacity or some other device must be found. Possible future sources of supply as yet untapped, or almost so, of many minerals are the sea, common rock, or other planets, though the prospects of efficient and cheap extraction are in all three cases at least open to question. The world has already seen many striking examples of replacement of one substance as a primary resource by another; for example, the substitution of coal for wood as a major fuel and source of applied energy; the subsequent replacement, in considerable measure, or supplementation of coal by petroleum and hydro-electricity; the current prospect of supplementation and perhaps ultimate replacement of all of them by atomic energy. No doubt this process will continue, but it is prudent to remember that wood, coal, petroluem and fissile materials are all expendable; water, including the sea with its tides, the winds and the sun, which is the ultimate source of most of the energy existing on this planet, will last as long as our world endures.

Whatever may be found possible in obtaining new sources of or substitutes for exhaustible materials, it is undoubtedly wise to make the most of what we have. Conservation demands the most careful attention. There is, however, much more that can be done than mere conservation. The yield and duration of even exhaustible materials can be extended by improvements in use. If I burn in a domestic fireplace 1 cwt. of coal per week, and have a supply of a ton of coal, that supply, if there is no change in conditions, will be exhausted in twenty weeks. If, however, I instal, before I begin to use my ton of coal, a new type of fireplace which will give the same amount of heat for half the consumption of coal required by its predecessor, my ton of coal will last for forty weeks if I continue to produce the same amount of heat as before. In other words, doubling the efficiency of my fireplace has precisely the same immediate effect as doubling my supply of coal. If I should be able to double the efficiency of my fireplace every week, my ton of coal would last indefinitely. So it could be, if we could make ourselves sufficiently clever, with all resources. The situation, which is one of vital importance, can perhaps be illustrated by the first three graphs, the base line in each representing material, the vertical line representing time.

If the extent and efficiency of usage both remain constant, one unit of material being consumed in the space of one unit of time, the graph of consumption of the material will be as Consumption Graph 1.

If the extent of usage remains constant, but efficiency of usage is doubled (i.e. twice as much as before can be extracted from each unit of material) the graph will become as Consumption Graph 2.

If the extent of usage remains constant, but efficiency of use is doubled by the end of each unit of time, the graph will be as Consumption Graph 3.

Thus, if usage could remain constant and if efficiency in use, or yield of material, could be doubled within the span of each unit of time, even the second unit of material would never be exhausted. It is of course very unlikely that usage would remain constant, and those who believe in expansion would not wish that it should, while the possibility of doubling efficiency of use progressively and regularly within limited periods of time *ad infinitum* is so remote that it can be discounted. Nevertheless, it is abundantly clear that major improvements in utilisation of materials are not merely as valuable as obtaining new sources of those materials in the same ratio, but even more so, since, in addition to extending the usage or yield of the materials, improved efficiency can simultaneously conserve them. Moreover, there is a far better prospect of continuing indefinitely to improve efficiency of use of materials than there is of continuing for ever to secure new supplies of the materials.

There is also the obvious and important consideration that many materials can be used over and over again. Steel is used to make a battleship. In time the battleship, if she survives to outlive her usefulness, is broken up and her steel plates return as scrap to the steel mills, where they are used again in the production of new steel which may go to build another battleship, or a motor car or any other article made of or incorporating steel. And so on again and again. Of course, in each transformation and in each period of use there will be some loss—battleships, for instance, can rust—but again human resourcefulness can progressively limit the amount of loss. In the natural economy as a whole there is no ultimate loss, only change: sometimes cycles of transformation such as water, cloud, water again, or steel, battleship, steel; sometimes "a sea change into something rich and strange".

Thus by human ingenuity the yield of even exhaustible materials which are in limited supply can be extended indefinitely, or, what amounts to the same thing, resources in themselves static can be made, for practical purposes, dynamic by the application of the human factor. The capacity and potency of the human factor will be determined by the culture which has moulded and equipped it.

Discoveries can be, have been, and sometimes are still made by chance and often in unlikely circumstances, but sustained improvement in efficiency is not only, nor indeed usually, the result of new-dimensional discovery but rather of technical proficiency and of the patient, sedulous application of knowledge and experiment. Even discovery in the traditional sense of the word results much more often from sustained investigation and research than from sudden illumination, or intuition, or chance.

Clearly, then, progressive efficiency in the utilisation of natural resources is more likely to occur in a society sympathetic to change and avidly in pursuit of knowledge, of exploration in all directions, and of material advance, than in a society committed to the *status quo*, governed by tradition and averse to enquiry. The nature of the society, its capacity and conduct, its proneness or hostility to change and to material progress will be governed by its culture.

Though each individual human being is different from any other, the similarities between all members of the human race are much greater than the differences they exhibit. The salient fact is that every human being, whatever his origin, colour, race or experience is a trinity of body, mind and spirit. Any culture which neglects any of these will do so at its peril. Each of them requires reasonable scope and fulfilment and there will be effective utilisation of resources—material and human—only when body, mind and spirit act and interact rightly and harmoniously.

This, too, involves culture.

Man is a gregarious animal; our world is a social world. Only by effective social effort can extensive and intricate use be made of natural resources. Only if there are good human relations can there be really effective social effort. Human relations will undoubtedly be better in a society whose culture induces all its members to try—not merely to say that people should try—to follow the ancient precept, so often and so authoritatively recommended at least since Confucious enjoined it, of doing unto others as they would that others should do unto them, than they will be in a society whose culture demands persistent aloofness, invariable aggression, or the glorification of thwarting the efforts of others.

It is accordingly clear that if we wish to improve the utilisation of natural resources the most apposite and fertile area for application of effort to do so is culture. Even so, the field is vast, for culture is as wide as life. It could be defined as the outcome, which in a progressive society should be continually developing of what man makes of himself and nature; it is the accumulated and cumulative product of man's experience of his interaction with nature, of his perception of existence, of his reflection on himself, on his experience, on nature and on perception, and of the interplay of all of these. It could be equated with education in the very broadest and deepest sense—total education, of which formal education is only a part, though a very important part.

On so wide a front the most speedy and efficient method of making progress would seem to be, while neglecting no possibility of advance anywhere, to concentrate on the improvement of those aspects or segments of human activity or aspiration which exercise the most powerful influence on the condition and fate of the community—the focal or control areas. In the remainder of this paper an attempt will be made to suggest, very briefly, what appear to be the essential and determinant features which should be given primary consideration in any discussion or programme directed towards the enhancement of culture, of human resources through culture and of the utilisation of material resources as a consequence which can be confidently expected.

Obviously the power and influence of Government are of dominant effect. It could be asserted that in a democracy as we know it the ordinary citizen can do no more than vote every five years or so for two or three aspirants to membership of Parliament, all of whom he may dislike and of whom even the successful candidate can only, apart from possibly participating from time to time in debates or asking occasional Parliamentary questions, vote as he is directed or become a voice in the wilderness. But the citizen can express opinions, criticise, exercise his judgment. While Governments have to face the electorate every few years, while an alternative Government is possible, no Government can flout the general public opinion too often or too long. The situation is rather different under a dictatorship, but even there public opinion, once awakened, is not without its influence. If we are to have responsible and intelligent government we need a responsible and intelligent populace. The essential requirement is for good and widespread education. In a properly educated community the electorate should be able to choose their representatives with reasonable wisdom and the representatives themselves Members of Parliament and Ministers, should be equipped to at least the current level of knowledge and capacity to think. It must never be forgotten, however, that just as the half truth is the most dangerous of lies, so imperfect or distorted knowledge is more dangerous than ignorance. Inadequate education may be worse than none at all.

The increasing weight and complexity of international and national, government and public affairs will demand ever expanding and progressively expert knowledge on the part of those who direct, promote and administer these affairs. No ordinary Member of Parliament, no normal Government Minister can possess all the knowledge and skill that will be required. Accordingly, apart from and in addition to the continuously growing Government control which must be expected, a far heavier and more demanding burden will fall on the Civil Service. The question is therefore of great consequence whether the Civil Service as at present organised is as competent as it can be made to carry this vast and critically important load.

Most unbiased people would, it is thought, agree that the typical civil servant is, as a person, admirable. He is often very able, usually hard working and conscientious, frequently dedicated. There are civil servants who are entirely outstanding in ability, character and administrative skill. There may be others who become corroded by the dreary round of workaday entanglement or repressed by constant care not to be passed over in promotion. Still others may be frustrated or even embittered by the ways in which things are done, or, perhaps an even more inhibiting consideration, not done. It seems legitimate at least to consider whether the citizens of this country have adequate guarantees that from among those who administer their public affairs the best are always chosen to occupy the senior posts; whether the present Civil Service system, with its reverence for precedent, its somewhat cumbrous methods of dealing with business, its emphasis on caution and conformity, its eye always alert to political expediency, is happily fitted to the conditions of our time; whether it is adapting itself readily to meet the needs of the future. A century ago, when the action or influence of the Civil Service extended to only a limited number of sectors of national life, when the British economy was robust, when expansion was the dominant motif, when the pace of life was more leisurely, it was right that the Civil Service should set itself assiduously to check imprudence and to safeguard the public purse, to avoid, so far as possible, making mistakes. Today conditions are very different; we need to move quickly; we require enterprise and drive; we must try to be ahead of events, not struggling behind them. It is certainly wrong to waste money, but it is wasting it to keep it lying unused, just as it is waste to spoil a ship for a ha'p'orth of tar. What conditions in this country at present require, it is submitted, is not the scrimping of ha'pennies but the judicious investment of all available pounds.

It might be worth considering whether public employees, including particularly civil servants, have sufficient living contact with life at large. Might it not be profitable to have more interchange between, say, the Civil Service and Industry, and to incorporate into the Civil Service new types of skill and knowledge? At any rate it seems unquestionable that our future national efficiency will require of Government and public officials alertness and flexibility of mind, rapidity of response to challenge and change, versatility, perceptiveness, awareness, resolution, understanding, foresight, large-mindedness, integrity, and ready, wise, insistent action.

These are also, it is suggested, the types of qualities and attributes which will be needed in the management of industry and in general administration. In the economic sphere, probably the dominating issues in the years to come will be, firstly, continuing and expanding scientific discovery with consequent rapid technological change, and, secondly, ever-increasing pressure, owing to expanding world population and general demand for higher standards of living, on the resources of this planet, many of which are, as was stated earlier, expendable and already dwindling. A country like the United Kingdom, which has to obtain so high a proportion of its food and materials from outside its own borders and which requires much larger markets for many of its major industries than its own limited population can provide, must sell heavily in export markets. It must do so in the face of stark and merciless competition from other countries—competition which must be expected to become ever more relentless as more and more countries already industrialised have to seek greater outlets in world markets for more and more of their products, and as countries not yet industrialised become so, thus cutting off what are at present relatively easy markets, and in due course no doubt becoming competitors in world markets themselves. In this struggle to sell there are and will be ranged against us other countries with resources in home populations and natural wealth much greater than our own. Large populations and lavish natural wealth are assets of magnitude, but they have not always, nor indeed usually, been, and they need never be, entirely decisive. Goods produced in any country will sell continuously in world markets only if people want to buy them. The goods therefore will have to be attractive in kind, quality and price. Above all, they should have something the others have not got—goods of novel type and novel types of goods. This will require constant ingenuity, the best efforts of our brains and skill.

Brains are the most productive, the most important, of all resources. If the maximum output is to be obtained from them they must be developed in the best way, which will require sound education, and they must be deployed in the best way, which will necessitate good management, since managers are persons who control, direct, activate or influence other people. Thus management emerges as one of the most important, perhaps, in terms of material well-being, the most important of all current pursuits. Can it then be left to random selection, rule-of-thumb methods, amateur endeavour? It is submitted that it cannot. Very much has been said and a good deal has been done in recent years in the field of management development, some of it ill conceived and injurious, much of it partial and of limited value, a portion of it judicious and of high worth. Much more is required.

In all sectors of national life and along the whole front there will be needed, if advanced national efficiency is to be obtained, leadership of the highest order. Leadership is the subject of another paper from an eminent hand which is before this Symposium. It would accordingly be otiose and improper to discuss it here. It should however be remembered, which too often it is not, that the function of the leader is to lead, not to drive, and that there can be leadership for evil as well as for good—leading and following (for without following there can be no leading) into disaster as well as into triumph. The ultimate importance lies not in leadership itself but in the objectives it seeks to attain. Leadership in itself is neutral; it is the goal to which it tends that gives it its true significance. The real avail of leadership and of natural resources lies not in themselves but in the purposes to which they are put. It is not what human beings direct or control that will decide their fate and the measure of mundane happiness they may achieve, but what guides their direction and what use they make of what they control. The decisive arbitrament, the fulcrum of destiny lie in ultimate values.

It is obvious that without values of some kind no society can survive. There must be honour of a sort even among a band of thieves if they are to remain a band. Does it not then follow inexorably and manifestly that the better the values by which society is guided, the better will society be? If this be so, the conclusion is ineluctable that even on the most utilitarian assessment the best values should be sought and cherished, more eagerly, more zealously, than anything else.

The best values should be self-evident to those who do not wilfully obscure or distort their vision. These values need no artificial buttresses, no adventitious gloss; they cannot be found in what does not cohere with the best we know and think, whatever tradition, dogma or eclectic asseveration may claim. They cannot be inconsistent with the evidence of experience, though they can transcend it. They can have no true part in what has been honestly and adequately tried and failed, however venerable the authority for it. They can be found only in the zealous, single-minded and unremitting pursuit of truth, and they can and must be developed or clarified as truth progressively reveals itself, however painful the revelation may be, whatever cherished illusions it may dissipate, whatever hallowed institutions it may overturn, however incomplete the vision of truth may be. Nothing less will suffice than the greatest measure of truth which can be attained by humanity.

The search for truth should also be the primary objective of scholarship. The dissemination of truth and the cultivation of minds to receive and seek it should be main objectives of education.

If the motive force in the constructive utilisation of natural resources runs through human beings from culture, culture itself is primarily moulded by education. Repeatedly in the submissions made in this paper the primary practical importance of education has asserted itself. Education is the ultimate lever which will determine what mankind will make of themselves and their environment. It is in education that if advance in both human and material resource utilisation is sought the major effort should be directed.

We are unlikely to get education of the highest quality unless we are prepared both to pay for it and to honour it. At present in this country we spend on education less than 5 per cent. of our national income. The question is not merely one of finance but of status also. It can scarcely be expected that many of the best people will be prepared to be teachers in schools and universities unless they can be assured that conditions will be such as to enable them to have primary control over their own destinies and to preserve their fundamental independence as self-respecting human beings. In the interests of real and lasting progress, the promotion of the best attainable education is manifestly essential. It follows as a principal and pressing need that the whole content and administration of education in this country should be searchingly and continuously reviewed. If the function of schools, colleges and universities be to cultivate minds and to increase and disseminate knowledge, as surely it is, then all aspects of academic life should subserve the primary academic function and should therefore in the end be answerable to and controllable by those who exercise that function.

Education must move with the times or preferably ahead of them. The educational needs of the future undoubtedly call for earnest consideration at the highest levels of constructive thought. We must have specialists—this is the way of rapid material progress

—but a world composed of specialists who were only specialists would be a grim and arid place. Yet knowledge in any individual discipline is already so voluminous and is in most cases increasing so rapidly that it is difficult for the student to look outside his own subject, or narrow range of subjects, unless he is forced to do so. He must then be so forced. Over-narrow and increasingly delimited specialisation would cause in the long term cumulative distortion of human personality—a very sinister development indeed; moreover few would, it is believed, dispute that the best specialist is not the man who knows his own subject and nothing else, but the man who knows his own subject supremely well and a great deal else besides, and the more "besides" the better, because all knowledge bears upon, illumines and fortifies all other knowledge. Specialisation therefore should be built upon and augmented by a true and full general education. Only so will there be obtained the rich and rounded personality which humanity needs so much. In education, as in other fields, the best that has come down from the past should be retained and cherished, and on it there should be built what is required to meet the needs of the future.

The spread over the world of partial, imperfect, ill comprehended knowledge and its fermentation into injurious assertion and pernicious action constitute perhaps the greatest of all the dangers facing civilisation today. The great hope, the great need for humanity must then be to promote and fortify wisdom, to spread better and truer knowledge sufficiently widely and sufficiently quickly to prevent the imperfect from erupting into irreparable disaster.

It is, then, to education above all that we must look for both the cumulatively expanding fructification of natural resources and the inducement of conditions which will make them agents for advancing well-being, sustained progress and more abundant life, instead of the grim but unfortunately very real alternatives of destruction, devastation and death which they could also serve.

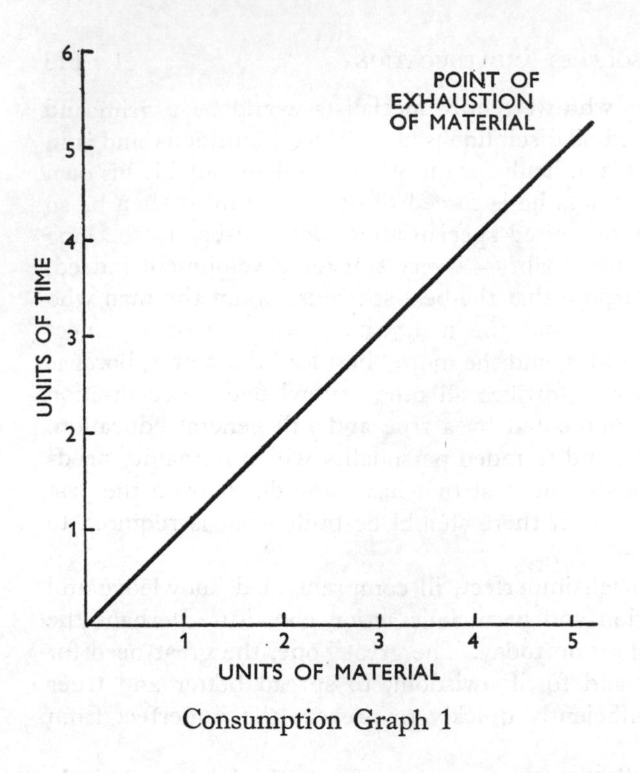

Consumption Graph 1

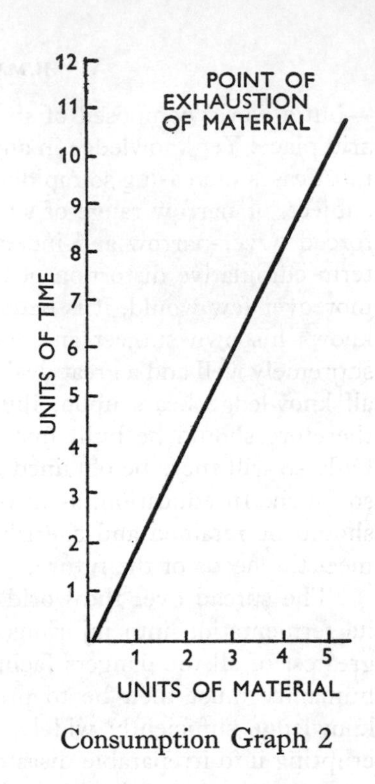

Consumption Graph 2

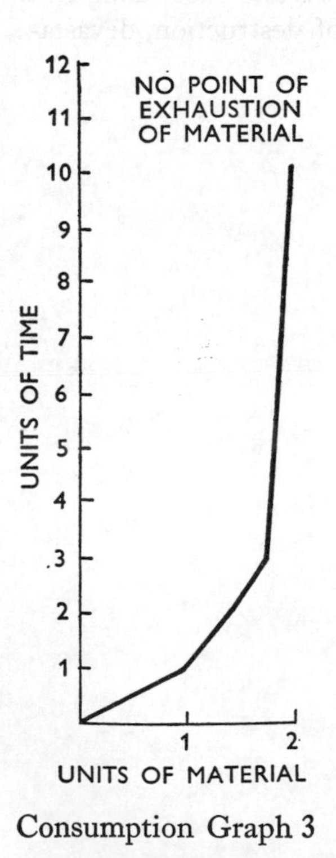

Consumption Graph 3

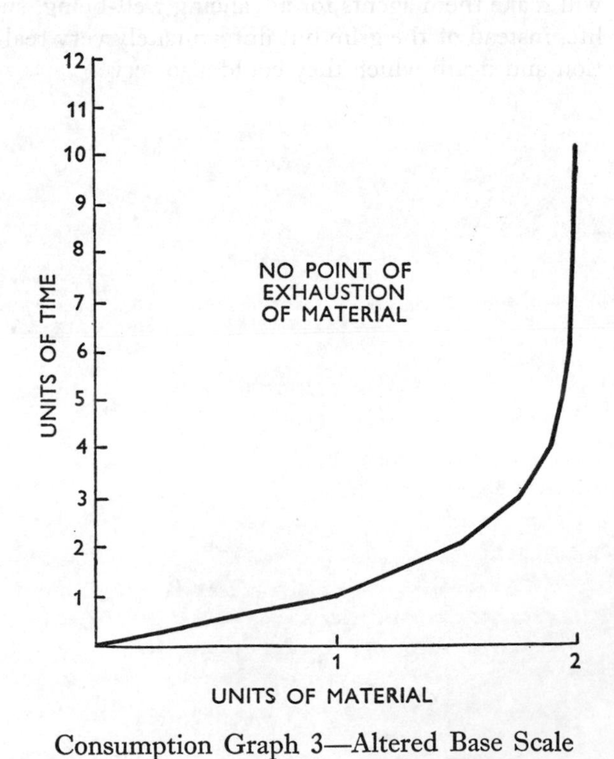

Consumption Graph 3—Altered Base Scale

Leadership in the Scottish Industrial Scene

Sir ALEXANDER FLECK, K.B.E., F.R.S.
London

Scottish industry has a wealth of diversification, and educational establishments seem to be broadly based. Therefore one would expect Scotland should provide as complete an industrial community as could be found in this world.

However, the picture is not so satisfactory as one might think, and three sets of comparative figures given in the text are of great importance: unemployment, industrial disputes and technical education. These figures indicate an unfortunate state of affairs.

As directors in established techniques we hold an almost unchallenged position: in fact, any situation requiring shrewdness, straightforward logic and strength of character. However, our educational method requires to produce people with good scientific or technological imagination. Modification of teaching method is required to effect this.

For more immediate improvement in effort, advice to management and union might well be "Ye must be born again". Rebirth in industrial terms is difficult. It appears to be the case that on the one hand management could show a more enthusiastic belief in such things as Joint Consultation; on the other hand the Scottish workman tends to be uninterested in Joint Consultation, because basic matters such as wages are not normally involved. There is readily room for mutual accommodation on methods, and on points, where a spirit of mutual understanding can readily be developed.

The case for better leadership to meet present-day needs is briefly sketched with the hope that there will be thrown up people strong enough to give specific reforms some chance of success.

There is, I understand, to be held in Edinburgh in the autumn of 1960 a conference on Scotland's Natural Resources, and as part of the background of that meeting I have been asked to give my views on Leadership and its place in relation to the people as part of the human resources of the country. As one who has retired from the day-to-day responsibilities of industrial and commercial life I am happy to do so, since under those conditions I can possibly take a more detached even if maybe a more controversial view than would have been likely hitherto.

It is possible that what I write may be regarded as provocation to an unwarranted degree. If so, I can only hope that my incursion will be productive of a higher and wider appreciation of the true position of leadership in Scotland than is available to many like myself who survey things from a distance.

It is a subject in which I have long had some considerable interest even although I never have had many immediate responsibilities in Scottish industry. It is some forty odd years since I left the Glasgow area as a place of work: even so, in the intervening years my contacts have been considerable in number even though they have in general been restricted in length. Naturally, therefore, my comments are given with a degree of hesitancy but, that being overcome, they are put forward with a desire to advance, as I conceive it, the well-being of the Scottish industrial scene. I believe that my contacts have been diversified enough to enable me to generalise beyond the chemical industry which is naturally the one industry where I have been concerned with some of its details.

I have before me as I write Oakley's book on industrial Scotland published in 1953. What a wealth of diversification it shows in every type of industry. For good measure I have just recently read an article in the *Scottish Field* on the Burgh of Arbroath. That article presses home for a particular town the lessons I deduced from Oakley's bigger volume, namely, diversification of industry in Scotland is a very real thing. It would seem that in that direction Scotland has achieved a goal that is still the envy of many regions.

I turn from diversification in industry to diversification in education. There again, as I look at the broad picture, I see much that I can only conclude is most excellent. The secondary schools and the academies in the various townships and in the cities have excellent records of achievements. The Technical College system is broadly based and supported by such excellent organisations as that whose Chairman is my friend, E. P. Hudson, the Scottish Technical Education Consultative Council.

The Royal College of Science and Technology is recognised as fully up to its responsibilities as one of the eight colleges of Higher Technology for the United Kingdom. Our universities, with their historical tradition of broad based learning extending much longer than those of any other university in the kingdom except Oxford and Cambridge, need no praise song from me. With all these benefits, one would think that Scotland should be as satisfied and as complete an industrial community as could be found anywhere in this world. True, there is a dearth of natural resources of a material kind, apart from coal and apart from a measure of very good agricultural land. Scotland should on this analysis be about level pegging with Switzerland, a country of similar size and of the same order of numbers of people.

Most of us, however, are aware that the picture we see of industrial Scotland is not so satisfactory as we might think it should be if we merely concentrated on the aspects sketched above. It is, of course, impossible to measure these kinds of things in absolute standards: the best we can do is to make statistical comparisons with England, where ways and means of doing industrial work arc, in spite of some differences, more or less the same.

I do not wish to imply that England should be upheld as having reached a satisfactory level in all these matters. I would wish to see progress throughout the whole of the United Kingdom: there is certainly room for it in every direction.

I am going to quote only three sets of comparative figures: unemployment, industrial disputes and technical education. Others writing on this subject might be able to quote other figures which conceivably could be equally significant, but to me the three sets I give herewith are of much importance.

The figures I have are as follows (those for Industrial Disputes come from the May 1960 number of the Ministry of Labour *Gazette*):

	1959	
UNEMPLOYMENT:	Scotland	England and Wales
Average for year	94,877	380,280
Estimated number of employees at May 1959	2,145,000	19,725,000
Percentage of unemployed against employed	4·4	1·9
INDUSTRIAL DISPUTES:		
Total number of workers	2,145,000	19,725,000
Number of workers involved in stoppages	127,000	497,600
Percentage of workers so involved	5·95	2·52
Number of working days lost by stoppages	781,000	4,399,000
Number of working days lost per 1,000 workers	364	223
Total man work days	536,500,000	4,693,500,000
Percentage man days lost by stoppages	0·14	0·09
TECHNICAL EDUCATION (Day Release):		
Total boys and girls in employment	162,000	604,000
Day Release	17,263	187,541
Percentage	11·0	31·0

I know that it is easy to be critical of figures, but from all the observations I can make I believe that these figures represent correctly the general situation and I make the deduction in spite of many good aspects, some of which I have indicated in the earlier part of this paper, that there is an unfortunate state of affairs in industrial Scotland to which we should pay attention to see if it can be corrected. Here I enter the most difficult part of my paper because I must leave the statistical side and give what is an opinion, and the best I can say is that it is based on a summing up of observations from numerous varied sources.

On Joint Consultation, for example, my enquiries lead me to believe that on the one hand the management shows a less enthusiastic belief in it than does his English counterpart, and he is encouraged in this by the Scottish workman who has an uninterested approach, since normally none of the basic things like wages are involved and only fringe conditions can be influenced by these discussions (basic conditions like wages being fixed nationally).

This illustrates a well-established and in many ways a good aspect of Scottish character, when it readily asks: Do the ancillaries really matter?—let us rather concentrate on discussions that deal with our pay packet. This is a good and reasonable philosophy up to a point. Beyond that it is bad, because it tends to concentrate discussion on matters where there is likely to be disagreement and gives no opportunity for discussion on points where there is readily room for mutual accommodation in methods and where a spirit of mutual understanding can readily be developed.

From the information that comes to me in my position as President of the Industrial Co-Partnership Association, I have the impression (which I cannot prove statistically) that relatively fewer firms in Scotland than in England go in for profit-sharing schemes, or go in for plans designed to make stock holding by employees a relatively easy matter.

From all these figures and factors, what deductions should be made? The degree of unemployment may under certain circumstances stem from some far-away Governmental policies: in general I do not think this is a major consideration—"the fault is not in our stars but in ourselves" is more often true. They emphasise the general conclusion that all is not as well as it should be. Stoppages with their accompanying sense of frustration, with the inevitable waste of time on everybody's part, with the loss of rhythm sustained by production, the wasted effort, with the loss of wages, show equal lack of leadership with the failure of vision which cannot grasp the need for fuller education.

The conclusion I am driven to is that industrial leadership in Scotland is not as good as it might be, and is in fact less satisfactory than it is in England. Further, I would say that it is not as good as it must be if Scotland is going to maintain her erstwhile position as a leader in the industrial development not only of the United Kingdom but of the world as a whole.

Is it necessary for me to say something to support my plea that industrial leadership in the world, or at least Western civilisation, is worth while? To me the answer is unhesitatingly, yes. We in Scotland have a long heritage of achievement in some form of Arts. Our poetry, our painting, our prose, our philosophy all show that nationally we have risen to great heights. Our Watt, our Black, our Hutton, our Kelvin and so on show that in the parallel fields of science and technology we have made great contributions and these were all part of the foundations that made our industry in Scotland so useful to the world at large as one of its leaders. That leadership not only brought us mental satisfaction and mental renown, it also brought us material prosperity and enabled us, up to recent years, to maintain universities and an educational system which ought by all the rules of the game to have enabled our high mental level to be maintained indefinitely and our high level of industrial leadership to be self-perpetuating. And so to me at least it is well worth while struggling and striving to see if we cannot recapture the leadership of the Golden Age of Scotland of 1780-1830, or even that secondary zenith of the Kelvin, Tait and Clark Maxwell period and the high activities of the latter part of the nineteenth century when in most sections of industry rough and ready technology was adequate for leadership: before, that is, the application of exact sciences and their full development came to be one of the essentials of all good, successful and progressive industries.

And so I now address myself to the question: What suggestions have I which I would hope would improve the position of industrial leadership in Scotland?

My first suggestion is a very long-term one involving some modification in our educational system. I have already said that our educational system has many good points and in several respects it produces people with many excellent qualities. As managers and as directors in established techniques we hold an almost unchallenged position: in fact, any situation where shrewdness, straightforward logic and strength of character are the main requirements. In one respect, however, our educational method is to my mind notably deficient. It is failing to produce a proper proportion of people who have good scientific or technological imagination. We used to be able to do that, but since the latter part of the nineteenth century we have been deficient in this respect. I support my conclusion here by my own examination of Fellows elected to the Royal Society who have taken their degree in Scotland. Something of the order of only one-third of Scottish science graduates seem to gain an F.R.S. compared with a like number of science graduates from the Red Brick Universities of England, i.e. English Universities other than Oxford, Cambridge or London. I find that my general conclusions on the facts of the matter are similar to those arrived at by R. H. S. Robertson and given in *The Eugenics Review* of July 1960* although our deductions from the facts are by no means the same.

* "The Output of Scientists in Scotland 1600-1950."

I would be the last person to suggest that because our methods are not producing imaginative scientists of the high degree required by the Royal Society for its Fellows that we should scrap our educational methods lock, stock and barrel. My plea is for modification. I know of no cut-and-dried certain method that would stimulate the imagination of the Scottish science graduate, but my hope would be that out of the process of university growth and development which is going on now we can set less store on uniformity and more weight on *individual teaching*—and that requires greater numbers of university staff *per capita* than at present—then we might make progress towards a bigger output of imaginative scientists. I have called them imaginative, but the men I am referring to are often referred to as creative scientists—to me the one has the same characteristics as the other. I have raised this problem in the context of relativity between Scotland and England. That is in many ways just an accident, and I know that the fundamental problem of how to maintain the informed imaginative faculty or the power of scientific and technological creation is one that gives concern to all progressive Western nations. I would like to take here some sentences from a recent (May 1960) issue of an American journal *News Front*. They quote Mr. Thomas Watson, President of I.B.M., "Encouraging creativity is one of the most important responsibilities of any management. It is also one of the hardest": and again William Brady, President of Corn Products Co., "Creativity must be instilled in our managers if we are to meet successfully tomorrow's challenges." These quotations show their anxieties just as I have tried to indicate here. I find that they can express their remedies only in the broadest of terms just as, I must acknowledge, my suggestions for improvement are general and lack specificness.

A personal view that I put briefly forward, not as one based on a logical mental process that I can state but as one that my observation tells me might be worth experimenting with, is that if we could introduce mathematics in a more comprehensive way and if we could teach mathematics more as a straight development of logical thought, we might be able in the fulness of time to produce a higher quota of creative, imaginative scientists. But it is and must be a long-term programme. The prize is great, and given the achievement of the goal we would, as a direct consequence, have new industries which would give us leadership in a wide industrial field, not in a narrow but in a world-wide sense.

Now, however, I would direct attention to what might be done in a shorter term effort. I have drawn attention to the relative frequency of stoppages, to the relative paucity of day releases for education, to what I believe to be a reluctance to share to an adequate extent the fruits of industry. There is to my mind no one section of Scottish industry on whom the blame for this varied and multiple situation rests. I would wish to see an improvement all round both from my management and my union friends. The question is, Where do we go from here? In some religious circles when reformation is wanted, the remedy is given "Ye must be born again". I am inclined to give that advice to Scottish industrialism, and if I thought it would easily happen I would be inclined to conclude this paper here and now, with the hope that an outstanding industrial leader will emerge who would weld all sections of industry into a whole with the one purpose of making such industries as we have (and they are many and great) into productive machines to give benefit to all who are concerned with them.

Productive machines for the benefit of all—is that merely a pipe dream? I think not. For the scientist it is a creative, developing, organic growth worthy of the tradition of science; for the skilled craftsman it is an opportunity for the practice of skills and art that have given satisfaction through the ages; for the manager it is an occasion for leadership and rhythm of production which contribute to material good of large numbers of people, and for the man whose skills and education are limited from whatever cause, it is an opportunity to take a legitimate and proper place in a productive society. That is but a very generalised picture: but whether it is direct production or service work to that end, there is no doubt in my mind that the Industrial State is a worthwhile one and one that should be developed with idealism much in the foreground of our thinking.

Rebirth, however, in industrial terms is a difficult and by no means a straightforward process and so my friends at a Conference on Natural Resources might be inclined to ask for some more practical proposal.

In 1927-30 a noble effort was made to make some progress in industrial matters when the Mond Turner Conference deliberated on how greater unity of effort could be made towards industrial development, in particular "the need for effective machinery of joint conference to speak for industry as a whole". There was a joint conference between "a Representative Group of Employers" and the General Council of the Trades Union Congress. It was called a Conference on Industrial Reorganisation and Industrial Relations, and at its second but not final full conference in July 1928 it agreed statements on "Trade Union recognition, victimisation, National Industrial Council, prevention of disputes, rationalisation, gold reserve and its relations with industry". The detailed history of the Conference activities is long and cannot be given here—it must suffice to say that the outcome was the "establishment of machinery for consultation on agreed questions". These were by no means the same agreed matters which are set out earlier in this paragraph as being the outcome of the July 1928 full discussion. The Conference came to an end "even though the agenda that was planned has not been completely covered in our reports".

If I may sum up, I would say that that Mond Turner Conference of 1927-30 was well worth while. It made some progress, but in colloquial terms it failed to provide machinery with teeth. Is the time ripe for an active industrialist, be he a factory payroll worker or a member of the management, or an owner of a business, to take up the case in Scotland and see if a new spirit or a wider vision can be brought on to the Scottish industrial scene and with a missionary and visionary sense make effective a gospel of improved industrial efficiency?

I have sketched very briefly the case for better leadership to meet present-day needs and asked if there is any hope that a new conference on Industrial Relations would throw up people strong enough to give specific reforms some chance of success.

This is not the occasion to be specific as to the type of organisation through which I would hope a set of leaders might work; whether it would be a highly centralised one or whether, as I believe, decentralised as much as possible consistent with preserving the character of effective leadership. The choice is a relatively minor matter, since what is important is not the form but the spirit of the organisation. I quote Crawford Greenewalt, President of the Du Pont Company, when he says "Organisations do not make men—men make organisations".

And so I conclude with the hope that from the study of the Scottish industrial scene there will emerge a collective sense of leadership which will result in growing industrial prosperity.

Education of Scientists and Technologists on Interlinking their Work in their Respective Fields

Professor BRUCE R. WILLIAMS, M.A.
Faculty of Economic and Social Studies, University of Manchester

In industry the object of research and development is to produce new or better processes and products. Successful innovation depends on effective communication and co-operation between the research, development, production and sales departments. In practice this means that there must be qualified scientists or technologists in these various departments with an understanding of the others' disciplines, and that there must be an operational approach to development problems.

Because of our small output of qualified scientists and technologists there are too few of them in industry to get an effective interlinking of their between-department work. On the other hand industry has failed to see clearly just how much the application of research requires the employment of these people in production, selling and in general management.

Formal and informal training in industry depends on the supply of scientists and technologists and the number of difficult problems they have to solve. In Britain there are better opportunities for industrial training on the research side than on the development side and training has been made less effective by a failure to manage innovation well.

The greatest need is for more technologists, and thereafter to improve the management of innovation. Particular regard must be paid to informal training within industry to get the appropriate form of co-operation. Informal training in industry can lead to a better understanding of the others' problems, to an increasingly efficient use of scientific personnel, and to improved direction of innovation. In universities more stress is required on teaching how to tackle fresh problems and to analysing how effective they are in meeting a need for vocational training.

Scientists and technologists are educated at universities and colleges of technology, in formal training schemes within industry, and by formal training on the job. The efficiency and range of informal training depends on the capacity of leading members of the groups involved, on the types of tasks undertaken and on the form of organisation provided by the firm or institute concerned. In public discussion of education in this field informal methods of training have been rather neglected. Because Britain has been weak in, for example, chemical development engineering it is very difficult to get good informal training in it without going to Germany or the United States. Because the management of innovation is often poor, industrial scientists and technologists are not provided with the opportunity or pressure (and both are needed) to link their work. Indeed, when management is poor there is often considerable conflict between scientists and technologists in research, development and production; a conflict that is sometimes explained in terms of different methods of formal training, which are often in fact much less important than the current conditions of work and the opportunity for good post-graduate informal training.

Before examining the qualitative problems of training I will look first at the available statistics and then at the reasons why we expect scientists in various fields to co-operate.

AVAILABLE STATISTICS

Statistics on the supply of scientists and technologists of various kinds is given in *Scientific and Engineering Manpower in Great Britain 1959* (Cmnd. 902). The term "qualified scientist or technologist" includes university graduates, holders of the Diploma in Technology or graduates or corporate members of professional institutes such as the Institute of Mechanical Engineers.

Qualified Scientists and Engineers, 1959

	Industry	Government	Education	Total
QUALIFIED SCIENTISTS:				
Analogists	681	1,511	4,194	6,386
Chemists	15,945	2,251	6,410	24,336
Geologists	318	282	243	843
Mathematicians	2,049	971	9,955	12,985
Physicists	6,434	1,666	5,445	13,545
Others	—	—	2,719	2,719
Total	25,427	6,681	28,966	60,814
QUALIFIED ENGINEERS:				
Metallurgists	3,409	189	—	3,598
Chemical	1,875	60	—	1,935
Civil and Structural	6,278	7,378	—	13,656
Electrical	16,733	3,256	—	19,989
Mining	4,523	117	—	4,640
Mechanical	29,939	4,063	—	34,002
B.Sc. (Tech.)	1,316	58	—	1,374
Engaged in teaching	—	—	3,270	3,270
Total	64,073	15,121	3,270	82,464
Total scientists and engineers	89,500	21,812	31,966	143,278
Holders of H.N.C. and H.N.D. only	37,363	3,465	1,460	41,488

Of the qualified scientists and engineers in industry 41·2 per cent. were engaged in research and development. This percentage varied considerably between industries—being highest in "electronics" (66 per cent.) and "precision instruments" (59 per cent.), and lowest in "shipbuilding" (9 per cent.). Of course, these percentages may not mean much where the total number of scientists and technologists employed is very small. Thus in "shipbuilding" only 142 were employed, which is 0·4 per cent. of the overall employment in shipbuilding. Scientists and engineers as a percentage of total employed varied between 7 per cent. in "mineral oil refining", 3·7 per cent. in "chemicals and allied trades", 0·1 per cent. in "cotton and wool textiles" and 0·02 per cent. in "clothing".

What general conclusion about total supply, the balance of supplies and the use to which we put our scientists and technologists, can we draw from these statistics? Very few of a precise nature; but we can use them in a comparative way to help in reaching a judgment.

In Britain, qualified scientists and technologists are roughly 0·6 per cent. of working population. International comparisons are difficult because of differing standards and methods of training, but it seems reasonable to conclude that comparable percentages in the U.S.A. and the U.S.S.R. are 0·9 to 1·0 per cent. The discrepancy is mainly explained by the higher *per capita* output of engineers, the greatest discrepancies being in mechanical and chemical engineering.

The distribution of engineers between industry, government and education was much the same in Britain and the U.S.; 75 per cent. of the engineers were engaged in industry in both countries. The distribution of scientists was very different: whereas in Britain 50 per cent. were in education and 38 per cent. in industry; in the U.S. 60 per cent. were in industry and 20 per cent. in education. The activities of scientists and technologists within industry varied considerably. In Britain, 41 per cent. were engaged in research and development; in the U.S. only 32 per cent. It follows that in production, selling and general management Britain employs relatively few scientists and technologists.

It is often argued that our effort in research and development is much too small for a country that desires a high material standard of living and is very dependent on foreign trade. We do spend a slightly higher percentage of our output on research and development than do the Americans, but their output per head is double ours and their population three times greater. Their quantitative effort is much greater than ours and yet they use for it less than one-third of their scientists and engineers. With our present supplies we could only increase our research and development by pushing up our already high concentration of qualified scientists and technologists on it. There is good reason to believe that this would reduce the effectiveness of research and development.

THE USE OF SCIENTISTS

The use of scientists in "education" is obvious. In "industry" (which here includes building and contracting industrial research associations, nationalised industries and public corporations) they are used for research and development, to provide technical services such as work study and production planning in production departments, to control production departments, to engage in technical selling and in general management.

The object of industrial research and development is to produce new or better processes and products. There is no point in producing solutions to industrially unimportant problems. Nor is there any point in working out new processes which would be uneconomic in operation; or evolving new products for which there is no market. The right choice of projects entails considerable knowledge of markets, production problems and possibilities, the financial resources of the firm and so on. But even if the choice is "right" the outcome will be disappointing if the production department is incapable of handling the new process or suspicious of the long-haired university types and unwilling to co-operate, or if the sales force is incapable of providing worthwhile technical information on some new process and of what contribution it could make to the potential buyers' problems. Successful innovation depends on effective communication and co-operation between research, development, production and sales departments. In practice this means that there must be qualified scientists or technologists in these various departments and that there must be an operational approach to development problems. Thus in deciding what applied research and development problems are worth while we need to ask the following questions (the answers to which should become more precise as we reach the end of the development stage):

What is the industrial objective? Is it relevant to the firm or industry concerned?
How long is the project expected to take?
Does it require significant changes in personnel?
What is the consequential investment?
What is the likely pay-off period?

Obviously, to answer these questions, as well as to draw up a good list of possible projects, requires considerable co-operation from other departments.

Successful development is not just a matter of choosing the right problems and solving them. If the production department is not capable of using the new development or of using it successfully it will fail and in failing will make the future work of the research department more difficult. If, on the other hand, there is the appropriate technical skill in the production department it will be possible for the production engineers to keep in touch with the development engineers during the process of development to ensure that the problem of going into production is not needlessly complicated by inappropriate design or specifications. When the production engineers are able to talk clearly and precisely to the development engineers and vice versa there is a chance for effective communication, and trust, to develop.

Selling is often important too. A new piece of electronic equipment, a new chemical or a new process machine may require technical selling of a high order to get it established. Failure at the selling end can be just as important as failure at the production stage, and more expensive. A technical competence in the sales staff may also be important in giving the research and development people sound technical information about trends in their markets.

It follows that success in applying science to industry depends on having a balanced distribution of scientific and technical manpower between research, development, production and selling. Of the many cases of successful process and product development that I have studied less than one-third appear to have originated in the research and development department.

Does a balanced distribution require scientists and technologists in general management? Sir Alexander Todd has argued that the scientist is needed in the Boardrooms as well as in the Laboratories of modern industry: "the decline in the pioneer spirit (in British industry) was associated with a decline in the participation of the scientist in policy matters". Certainly some companies have failed to see the industrial potential of some new scientific or engineering developments, but not only in companies that have no scientists on the Board. The main questions here are: What arrangements does the

Board make to get periodic appraisals (from within and without the firm) of possible lines of development? What is the Board's attitude to risk? How capable are the executive directors in overcoming managerial difficulties that arise from a policy of innovation?

It is not true to say that scientists are necessarily better prepared to take calculated risks or more able to manage innovation. But it is true to say that if a firm employs scientists and engineers in an efficient way then it is natural and inevitable that some scientists and engineers should become directors.

INTERLINKING WORK

So far I have written in a general way about the interdependence of activites in the various departments of the firm and of the need to employ scientists and technologists in production departments to convert the output of development departments into a useful production input and so on. What of the more direct problems of interlinking work in various fields?

Pure research, where there is no foreseen or intended industrial application, is generally departmental. That is to say members of, say, a chemistry department in a university conduct research in chemistry. Some of this research is conducted by individuals, some by groups. The scope of a subject changes as work on old problems leads to new problems and as new techniques are created. Such change often leads to the growth of new subjects and new departments to house and facilitate the work of the new specialists. In pure research the emphasis is on specialisation, and in lively branches of science there is a continuing tendency to grow new specialisms. What co-operation there is is mainly between specialists in the same or closely related fields.

In applied research also the emphasis may be on research within a particular branch of science. The difference between pure and applied research in this case is that the practical goal sets a standard by which to judge the course of the research: an applied problem may be dropped because it ceases to give promise of application even though it is still very interesting as a scientific problem. Because of the practical goal applied research often requires the co-operation of scientists from different disciplines. Such co-operation may be planned from the outset as in the case of early applied research on atomic energy, though this is usually too wasteful and expensive. Alternatively, the interlinking may be allowed to grow out of the work in progress—a method typical of medical research.

In development there is a much more definite stress on team work. Basically this is partly because the degree of uncertainty is less than in research and advance planning becomes more possible and useful. For example in the chemical industry, at the pilot plant stage the main problems are usually so well known that the remaining work can be foreseen in some detail. A fairly comprehensive organisation is also needed to prevent waste of time and frustration later. Unless the production and sales staff have a chance to express their views during development they may bring up important new points when arrangements have already been made to invest in new production facilities. This is indeed a frequent cause of loss and delay with planned process innovations. The appropriate interlinking of the work of development engineers and production engineers is by no means easy. Their interests and their basic approach to design problems may often conflict. Design engineers may be interested in getting the best technical solution, production engineers in the most economical solution or in getting the least interruption to existing production arrangements.

Conflict and failure to interlink development and production activities appropriately is most likely when:

(*a*) The production and development engineers have been trained in radically different ways. This is most likely to happen when the production engineers are simply "qualified by experience", but it can happen also when the balance of basic training and approach is tipped heavily towards the science element of technology in the development department and the art element in the production department. Such basic training can be counteracted in large firms by appropriate training schemes.

(*b*) There is an inadequate provision for development facilities and the development engineers are dependent on production facilities for their work.

(*c*) The overall organisation of the development and production departments is poor and they are allowed to work in excessive isolation of each other.

TRAINING

After this consideration of what we expect from scientists and technologists and of how their activities may need to be interlocked it should be fairly easy to say just what the problem of training is.

The main problems are these:

1. Because of our small output of qualified scientists and technologists there are too few of them in industry to get an effective interlinking of their work. We have too few industrial scientists and technologists outside research and development departments to make the best use of research. Industry has failed to see clearly just how much the application of research requires the employment of scientists and technologists in production, selling and service departments and in general management.

2. Much of our training in Universities and Colleges of Technology is very highly specialised. People with such training are often not very adaptable and lack of adaptability is a serious handicap, especially for development work. This may be less of a problem when we have a more plentiful supply.

3. Whereas in science it is possible to be taught by very eminent scientists, this is difficult in technology. The universities' departments of technology have lacked close links with industry and the technical colleges have had difficulty in attracting really able staff. The element of "art" in their training has been excessive and that art not always of an inspiring kind.

4. Post-graduate training in science is sometimes rather trivial and in technology very rare. Scientists taking Ph.D.s learn something of co-operating with other researchers, but sometimes at too low a level. In any case such training tends to be a more specialised version of undergraduate training. There are some research institutes attached to universities where there may be opportunites to take part in problem-orientated team research, but the opportunities here are very limited.

5. Both formal and informal training in industry depends on the supply of able scientists and technologists and on the number of difficult problems that they undertake and solve. In Britain there are better opportunities for industrial training on the research side than on the development side. This weakness tends to be self-perpetuating. Training

within industry on this level has, however, been made less effective than it could be by the failure to manage innovation well.

Where a research and development department fails to choose the right problems there will be conflict between it and other departments. The research people will be sure that the production people are stuck in the mud of tradition and the production people will be equally sure that the research people are impractical college types. Under these conditions scientists and technologists cannot learn to interlink their work.

Where the production people are not capable of taking up the output of the research department or of giving some guidance and impetus to the research, the conditions for a productive interlinking of work will not exist. There will be a strong sense of frustration and isolation.

SOME POSSIBLE REMEDIES

1. The most important thing is to increase the supply of scientists and technologists. The greatest need is for more technologists. (In saying this it is important not to forget the crucial shortage of technicians.)

2. The next most important thing is to improve the management of innovation. The economics of research and development is a very much neglected subject in research and development departments. Even more significant is the failure to study seriously the forms of organisation required to get the appropriate form of co-operation between research, development and production departments. I stress these first two because I am convinced that both formal and informal methods of training within industry are of crucial importance. We have had too little of the formal training and too much poor informal training.

3. I come now to universities and colleges of technology who have received an undue share of the advice and criticism in this field.

Universities should not be purely vocational, but they are inevitably involved in it (for law, medicine, teaching, research and so on). Because universities are reluctant to recognise the degree to which they are involved in the business of vocational training, they are reluctant to analyse how well, or ill, they are doing it. A good deal of Ph.D. work is simply a passport to industrial research, and yet it may be a poor training for it. Much might be achieved by allowing students to find suitable Ph.D. work in industrial research associations and establishments. At the undergraduate level students, both as undergraduates and later, could derive great benefit from the opportunity (and the pressure) to undertake a substantial research or design project. Universities have tended to place too much stress on a standard of performance in examinations and too little on ensuring that students know how to tackle fresh problems.

It is difficult to say much of colleges of advanced technology. My main worry here is that through lack of opportunity those teaching technology will not be drawn sufficiently into making contributions to the art and science of technology. It may be that we need some Government-sponsored institutions to conduct commercial work in development engineering to overcome our backwardness in this field and that such institutions could be linked to universities and colleges of technology. If this could be done, we would put up our standards of both formal and informal teaching in technology.

The Case for a New Scottish University

R. B. KERNOHAN and J. HOLBURN
The Glasgow Herald

In Scotland we have 10 per cent. of Britain's population and 17 per cent. of its students. Within a decade we have to increase our university capacity by 40 per cent. Two-thirds of Scottish students take pass degrees; in England two-thirds take Honours. Let us make Honours the rule.

Scotland had five universities when England had two. We believe the universities, as well as their potential customers, should be prepared to revise some of their traditional views; and, in particular, that they should welcome the stimulus and the new ideas which a new foundation could provide. There is a place for an upstart. It would attract an adventurous staff and students, and offer a home for new ideas.

East Stirlingshire, Inverness, Ayr, Dumfries, Perth are runners. Inverness is the centre of the only Scottish regional hospital not linked to a university; advanced technology is applied near by at Dounreay.

The successful efforts of Brighton, York and Norwich were supported by enthusiastic local authority promotion committees. Local authorities give financial support. Those interested in getting a new university must know what they want, and what they can offer.

It is 400 years since a university was founded in Scotland. In founding a new one now we should look twenty or thirty years ahead.

The location for a new university would be a natural regional capital with a hinterland not already bespoke by other universities. The University should gain from, and contribute to, its hinterland.

A residential university in the less fertile Highlands, at Inverness, could be a major stimulus and contribution to the correction of the economic and demographical imbalance of Scotland.

SUPPLY AND DEMAND

We propose to deal in this paper with the case for a new Scottish university, with the opportunities which it offers, and with the question of its location. We cannot argue at length the case for university education; to do so would be the work of a term, perhaps of a lifetime. Nor can we debate how far university education should be regarded as vocational training and how far it should be a glimpse of eternal values.

We assume that university education is a good thing, for the sake of the community, which looks to the universities for a high proportion of its leaders, and for the sake of the students, who are equipped to earn a living and to lead a richer and fuller life. We regard universities as necessary higher vocational training centres and as something more: the source of an intellectual irrigation system which spreads clear thinking, respect for culture, and liberality of mind throughout our society.

In doing so we are merely following our national tradition—for Scotland had five universities (two of them in Aberdeen) when England had two. Not only do we think that the universities have served Scotland well in the past; we believe that they might serve Scotland still better if their graduates were scattered more widely throughout Scottish life, and especially Scottish industry, than they are today. But we believe the universities, as well as their potential customers, should be prepared to revise some of their traditional views; and, in particular, that they should welcome the stimulus and the new ideas which a new foundation could provide.

One sometimes hears that England is merely catching up with us in education. It is argued or hinted that Scotland need not match the enthusiasm and thorough planning which has led to the foundation of the three new universities at Brighton, Norwich and York, and which may bear more fruit later this year when such places as Gloucester and Kent put their cases to the University Grants Committee. (This body is the academic advisory commission to the Treasury who bear by far the greater part of the cost of modern university education.)

It is true that the proportion of students in the population is still higher in Scotland than in England, even when allowance is made for the English students in our universities. We have 10 per cent. of the country's population and 17 per cent. of its students. Yet there is no doubt that the Scottish universities, too, are likely to feel the impact of the high post-war birth rate, the tendency for pupils to remain longer at school, and the growing belief that a university education is a passport to material success in life. There have been complaints that Glasgow and St. Andrews are turning away qualified Scottish students in favour of English men and women. Scottish teachers are already alarmed at the prospect of the English scramble for university places spreading to Scotland.

The most reasonable estimates of the country's needs bear out these gloomy forebodings. Scotland's minimum needs have been conservatively estimated at 22,000 places by 1965 and 25,000 by 1970. Within a decade we have to increase our university capacity —now about 17,000 to 18,000—by at least 40 per cent. It may well be that the number of really good students will not increase in the same proportion; but the man with the minimum qualifications ought not to be turned away.

It is worth noting that the University Grants Committee, in their latest return, published this month, reported that the "potential university population in the early 1970s is likely to be very much higher than previously estimated". The Treasury has authorised them to work on the basis of providing 170,000 to 175,000 places for the whole of Britain. If Scotland is to maintain her present relative position this would mean at least 29,000 places—12,000 more than today. But even if we take the more conservative estimate and accept that the proportion of Scottish students must continue to decline slowly, it is reasonable to plan on the basis of 8,000 new places being required: the equivalent of a new University of Glasgow, which many teachers and students believe to be already too big for either efficient tuition or corporate feeling.

We believe that this is a conservative figure if the Scottish universities are:

(*a*) to accommodate all properly qualified native applicants who might reasonably be expected to make good use of a university education (we do not question the universities' right to select by interview where they are in doubt);
(*b*) to accommodate the present proportion of overseas students (10 per cent.) and possibly to increase it in the Arts faculties;
(*c*) to accept properly qualified English men and women who think highly enough of Scottish education to seek it.

It is, of course, possible that each university could do what Aberdeen are doing: prepare to take another 2,000 students. That, however, would give Glasgow (even without the Royal College of Science and Technology) and Edinburgh 7,600 students each. We believe that this would mean overloaded classes and would make it more difficult to provide any tutorial system. It would also presumably mean that both universities would have to consider further physical expansion (which might well arouse public opposition) on their present sites.

An alternative which we have heard suggested is that they should establish satellite colleges in such places as Stirling, Ayr and Dumfries. We believe that such colleges might stimulate personal contact between staff and students and promote more contact among the various groups of students themselves: Scottish and non-Scottish, black and white, Arts men and scientists. But we see nothing which they could offer which could not be offered better by a new university. If Norwich, York and Brighton can offer their own degrees from the start (like the young University College of North Staffordshire), we see no reason why such an experiment should not succeed in Scotland.

We believe that a new university would attract adventurous staff and students and not merely those unable to find places elsewhere and that it would naturally offer a home for new ideas. We have four ancient universities, conservative in their ways and proud of their traditions. We believe there is also a place for an upstart.

We suggest, for example, some ideas which a new university would or might take up. If it did, we believe that it would contribute more to the human and intellectual resources of Scotland than could be offered by any other expedient for absorbing the increased number of students in the next decade.

NEW IDEAS

In suggesting that a new university might break with some Scottish customs (and in doing so might revert to some older Scottish traditions) we are not—so we hope—being destructive in our criticism. We believe that some of our complaints against existing practice have been voiced not only by alumni like ourselves but by many university teachers, and even by principals.

More Residential Accommodation

Indeed, our first point is almost academic orthodoxy. We believe that there is a strong case for more residential accommodation and for another predominantly residential university. The tone of Glasgow, in particular, is set by the 70 per cent. of its students who live at home: student commuters. Most travel by bus morning and evening, though we have heard of some who, to save the cost of lunch, went home after morning lectures.

Such students might be better advised to take some other degree by correspondence course.

We believe that communal university life develops individual self-confidence. It also allows the student more time to combine extra-curricular activities with his studies; and we believe that sporting activities and student societies, cultural or political, are an important part of university life. If they flourish in Glasgow and Edinburgh, we believe it is in spite of, not because of, the number of students who live at home.

It may be Utopian to suggest the creation of a university where every student would "live in", especially as we should like a university much larger than North Staffordshire. But we believe that it would be possible to establish one where every student "lived in" for a part of the course and could seek congenial lodgings for the rest of it.

Courses of Study

We are not convinced that our students should be submitted to what the Glasgow ordinance calls "not less than 75 meetings of the full class on separate days" in each subject, each session, with additional, but very few, "meetings for tutorial or other supplementary instruction". We believe that the lecture system in its present form is a strain on the lecturer; if it is not, we believe that the lecturer is giving the class what they could find conveniently in a standard textbook. We do not know whether to pity more the conscientious student, with notebook, who never dodges a lecture, or the conscientious lecturer who tries to put something of his personality, opinions and scholarship into every lecture. We have noted a small but significant divergence in Scots and English language. An Oxford man says "I read history"; a Scot says "I do it", perhaps because he never reads a book unless he means to take Honours. Perhaps he should say "I listen" or "I note-take history". We hope that a new university would give less weight to lectures; more to tuition and private study.

General Studies

We believe that lectures have a place, especially in introducing students to a new subject and giving them the fruits of specialised study by the lecturer. The University College of North Staffordshire uses a lecture system to give all its first-year students an introduction to the sciences and the humanities. We believe that this experiment might be repeated in a new Scottish university and that an attempt might also be made to allow Honours students to offer an Arts and a Science subject instead of a pair of kindred subjects. There is undoubtedly a demand in industry for the man who has a liberal education and a scientific training. There is also much to be said for such an education for its own sake.

Degrees

Approximately two-thirds of Scottish students take pass or "Ordinary" degrees; in England two-thirds take Honours. This means that a majority of Scottish students debar themselves from some of the most vital positions open to graduates: the Higher Civil Service, the Foreign Service and post-intermediate secondary teaching among them. We are not sure whether this is because they are poorly trained at school, because the higher proportion of students in Scotland inevitably includes more "minimum qualifiers", or merely because too little is asked of our students. If the Ordinary degree did not exist, would all those students who now take it fall by the wayside? We hope that a new university would make the Honours degree (not necessarily in its present form) the rule rather than the exception.

New Approaches

A new university would find it easier than an old one to plan a curriculum to keep pace with events in the outside world. In history, for example, it might put the emphasis less on Europe than on Africa, Asia and the Commonwealth. In English and other literatures it would be more likely to include modern trends as well as established traditions. Some subjects, such as Scottish history and literature, which are relatively unimportant in larger universities, might flourish more readily if cultivated in this new environment. There would also be an opportunity to create Chairs in new subjects. Why not a Chair of Industrial Relations? Or of modern Political Institutions? Or of Town Planning?

These are a few of what we believe are exciting possibilities. We believe that, taken in conjunction with the statistical evidence, they justify the creation of a new university now.

LOCATION

The location of the new university is an important consideration if a new foundation, supported by public funds, is to make the maximum contribution to the social as well as the intellectual welfare of Scotland. The extent of local enthusiasm and initiative, however, is a factor which the Government and the University Grants Committee are bound to consider. We have decided that at this stage we should assume that all the areas interested are equally anxious to have a university, equally prepared to support it from local resources, equally well advised and organised in their campaigns.

Four areas are definitely in the running as a result of civic or private initiative: East Stirlingshire, Inverness, Ayr and Dumfries. We have also seen the claims of Perth argued, and we have considered that city as likely starter. We have also heard suggestions that Elgin and Peterhead might be interested, but have not taken these vaguer aspirations into account.

In considering them we have taken account of the criteria listed by the Secretary of State for Scotland in a letter to Mr. Malcolm Macpherson, M.P. Apart from local enthusiasm and support, these include cultural background, reasonable proximity to learned institutions and libraries, good communications, housing and social facilities for staff, and a supply of lodgings for students.

Since we advocate a largely residential university we have also considered the question of environment. This is not merely a question of landscape and architecture, though we believe that students are more likely to develop good taste if they live, perhaps for the first time in their lives, in pleasant or elegant surroundings. It is also a question of what the university can offer its hinterland. Students might work harder in an academic monastery, even a co-educational one, in some remote glen. But a university should gain from its environment and contribute to it.

East Stirlingshire

If the new university is expected to draw its students from its immediate vicinity,

East Stirlingshire has an overwhelming case. Falkirk and Grangemouth are expanding and may become one city the size of Dundee. We are opposed, however, to the creation of another university dominated, as Glasgow is, by students living at home. We also believe that if the Government accept the Anderson Committee's recommendations that all students should have public grants there will be fewer students who unquestioningly apply to the university nearest their homes. We have also noted that the idea of the local university seems to be on the way out in England, largely as a result of the competition for places which forces students to apply to six or seven universities. We deplore the need for this competition, but we welcome its consequence.

East Stirlingshire has first-rate communications with the rest of Scotland and a direct link with London. One consequence of this, however, is that students can live at home and attend classes in Glasgow or Edinburgh only twenty-five miles away.

The area includes much ugly, scarred countryside with straggling towns, but it could, like North Staffordshire, find a site in congenial surroundings which would provide the 200 acres a modern university needs. In Stirling it has a town which is the historian's delight, while dons might turn Bridge of Allan, for better or worse, into another North Oxford.

The area is a centre of industrial expansion. If the new university is to be largely scientific or technological, it has a strong claim. We note, however, that the Royal College of Science and Technology, Glasgow, has its own claim to be regarded as the fifth university of Scotland. It, too, may wish to expand and to secure not only degree-granting powers but, eventually, a new site in a less crowded area. The Heriot-Watt College would also expand, while other colleges might reasonably seek advanced status. We are told that in Paisley the technical college students take London external degrees and even wear London University scarves.

Were an East Stirlingshire university situated in Falkirk, there might be difficulty in finding congenial lodgings. There is also a risk that the staff might look to Glasgow and Edinburgh for their social and cultural life.

Perth

Perth has history, dignity and grace. It would make an excellent centre for a residential university and could probably offer good lodgings. Its communications are good. It is, however, very close to Dundee, which contains a large part of the modern university of St. Andrews.

Ayr

Ayr, like Brighton, can offer excellent accommodation during the tourist off-season. In intellectual and cultural life it would be easily dominated by Glasgow, through which it has reasonable communications with the North and East of Scotland.

Dumfries

Like Ayr, Dumfries could no doubt offer a Chair of Burnsology. It is the centre of a wide area whose life and development would be stimulated by a university. It should be able to provide lodgings, though its tourist trade may not be as developed as that of Ayr or Inverness. It might attract students from the English side of the border, and it has good rail communications with much of England. Lovers of tradition may also note that Dumfries has tried twice before to obtain a university—in the seventeenth and nineteenth centuries—and has twice failed.

INVERNESS

We admit that we strongly favour Inverness's claim. Like Dumfries it is a regional capital, but it has a still vaster hinterland. We are not arguing for a Highland university, however, to keep Highlanders from the corrupting Sassenach Lowlands. We expect West Highlanders to continue to look to Glasgow, and the East and North to maintain their traditional ties with Aberdeen. We should much prefer to see a university in Inverness attracting Lowlanders and Englishmen to the Highlands.

Like Perth, Inverness offers a university a congenial environment: a town which would gain new life from a university but is large enough not to be overwhelmed by it. It has a well-developed tourist trade to supply lodgings and has ample room for university development. It can offer mountaineering, sailing and other forms of open-air recreation to its students.

It has a major hospital and is the centre of the only Scottish regional hospital board not linked to a university. It could also, in planning its scientific research, take note of the relative proximity of Dounreay, where a very advanced technology is being applied.

Communications are an obvious but far from insuperable drawback. The rail journey from London, though direct, is tedious. But ought we not to look ahead to a time when internal air transport is commonplace? The Western Isles already feel themselves an hour or two from Renfrew. Inverness can look forward to a day when it is a mere two hours' journey from London, most of it spent on the Great West Road. And is it unrealistic to think in terms of a motorway from Glasgow and Edinburgh?

It is public policy to revive the Highlands and make depopulation give way to population. A university can play its part in that. In welcoming Aberdeen University's expansion plans the city's Lord Provost called them "the equivalent of a new industry for the city". A university brings an increase in population, permanent as well as temporary, and it brings trade; yet this is a form of industry where it may even be beneficial to set down the factory a considerable distance from its market of potential students. But we believe that a university might also pave the way for other commercial and industrial development.

A university can thrive in Inverness. We believe that it will attract an adventurous type of student from Lowland Scotland and beyond. A decision, however, should be taken within the next eighteen months if the new university is to help meet the probable demands of the late 1960s.

CONCLUSION

It is essential, however, that the Scottish applicants for Government assistance should match the successful efforts of Brighton, York and Norwich in enthusiasm and planning. They should form promotion committees supported by every local authority in the area and including both prominent local figures (some of whom may command substantial financial resources) and people of some academic experience and distinction.

It should go without saying that the local authorities will be expected to give financial support. In England the yield of a penny, twopenny or even threepenny rate is usually offered. Trust funds may also be available as well as grants from local industry. (York starts off with nearly £500,000 promised as a result of help from the two independent Rowntree Trusts and the Rowntree firm.)

We have heard the prospect of competition between different Scottish areas deplored as undignified. Those interested have been urged by one M.P. to wait till the Government and the existing universities agree to sponsor a new university. We fear, however, that if there is not local initiative, backed by interested and informed public opinion, Inverness, Dumfries and the rest may have to wait till Doomsday. Those interested must know what they want and what they have to offer.

It is 400 years since a university was last founded in Scotland. The founding of a new one will be a momentous event. In deciding where it is to be we should look not five or ten but twenty or thirty years ahead: to the day when industry needs to overspill from the industrial belt in Scotland, where already much too large a proportion of its population is concentrated. It will surely be Government policy to guide that overspill as far as possible away from the rich farmlands of the Borders, East Lothian, Fife, Perthshire and Angus into the less fertile and empty vastness of the Highlands. A university in the Highlands could be a major stimulus and contribution to the correction of the economic and demographical imbalance of Scotland. It would nourish and share the intellectual, cultural and scientific life of the revivified North-West. The Lowlands, and the Lowland universities, have drawn liberally on the human resources of the Highlands in the past. They have now a chance to put something back.

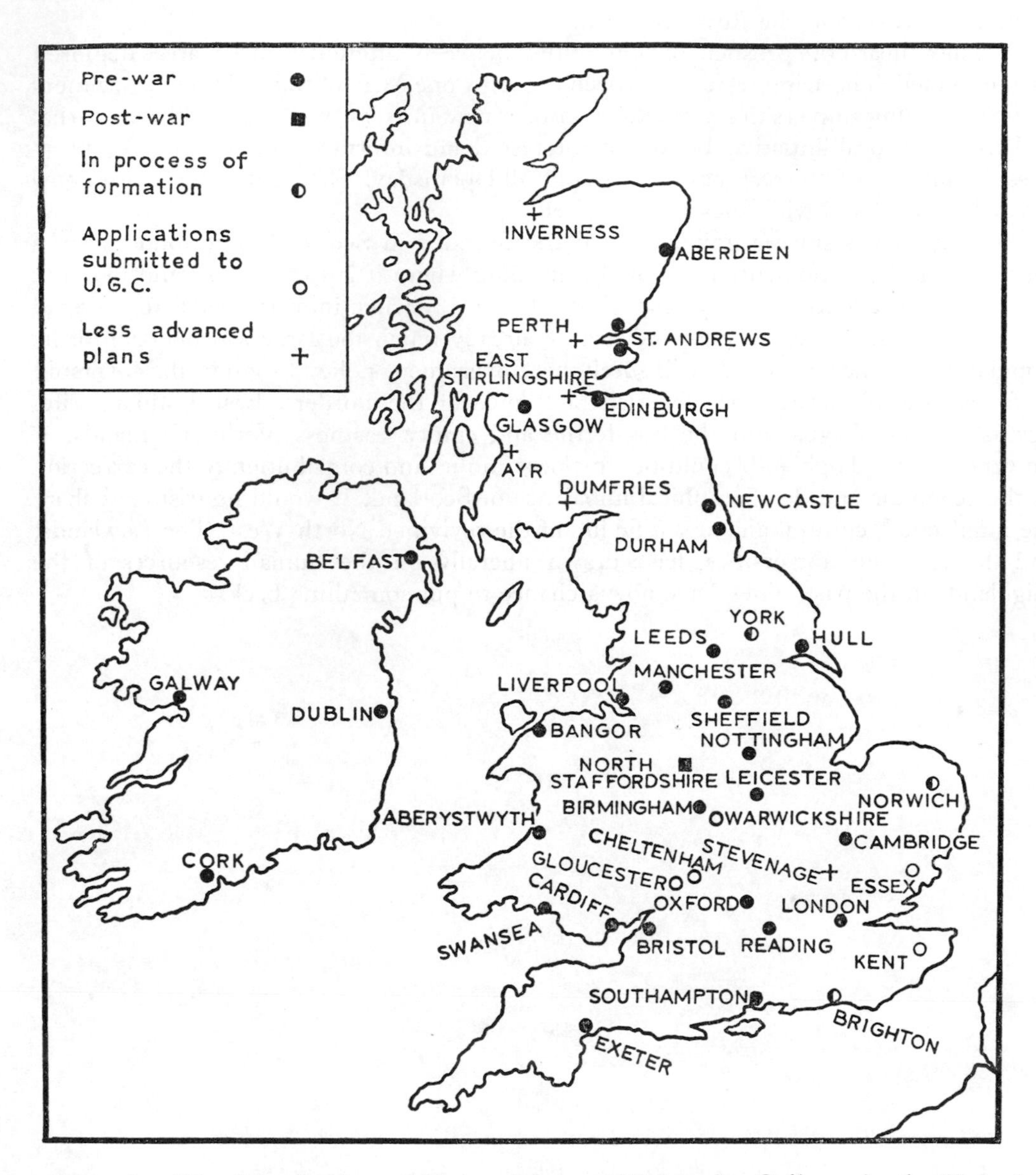

FIG. 1. The Distribution of Universities and University Colleges in the United Kingdom and the Irish Republic

INTRODUCTION TO DISCUSSION

T. G. WATERLOW, C.B.E.
Deputy Chairman and Director, William Thyne Ltd.

Statement by Mr. ELGOOD

The first Deputy Chairman today is Mr. T. G. Waterlow, Deputy Chairman and Director of William Thyne Ltd., a Director of Standard Life Assurance, and he is also a colleague of mine on the Board of the Royal Bank of Scotland and of Westclox. I have pleasure in calling on Mr. Waterlow.

Mr. T. G. WATERLOW

Ladies and Gentlemen: We have not a great deal of time this morning for some very important papers. I cannot think why I have been asked to be one of the Deputy Chairmen, except for the fact that the Chairman is an immigrant to Scotland, and I am also, and I suppose there has been some thinking in view of Mr. Kyd's paper. [A few words on procedure.] We have had a most inspiring address from the Chairman, and the best thing I can do is to call on Mr. Wilson, who is Technical Secretary of the Scottish Council (Development and Industry), our Reporter.

STATEMENT BY THE REPORTER

H. M. WILSON, B.SC., A.M.I.MECH.E., A.M.I.E.E.
Technical Secretary, Scottish Council (Development and Industry)

The papers we have to consider today are as follows: "Emigration and Depopulation and Scotland" by Mr. J. G. Kyd; "Interrelations between Material Resources, Human Resources and Human Culture" by Professor C. Macrae; "Leadership in the Scottish Industrial Scene" by Sir Alexander Fleck; and "Education of Scientists and Technologists on Interlinking their Work in their Respective Fields" by Professor Bruce Williams—a necessarily complicated title and a subject which is shown in the paper to depend somewhat on the management of innovation in industry. I tried to get a basis from which to measure innovation and from Bacon's Essay there is this sentence, "It were good that men and their innovations would follow the example of time itself which indeed innovateth greatly but quietly by degrees scarce to be perceived." I interpret from Professor Bruce William's paper that time now catches us on the hop. We have much to do in a very small period of time. We have in a given industrial unit a department which forges ahead and one which lags, depending upon the people in these departments, and the problem is to bring them together so that they go ahead with force as a block. From the point of view of education of scientists in interlinking, the problem lies in finding suitable informal training fields within industry, since so few firms have advanced far enough in the management of innovation to provide good case material. Lastly, there is a paper by Mr. Holburn and Mr. Kernohan on "The Case for a New Scottish University".

Throughout all these papers references to education come up regularly, but none are contradictory; they all tend to be complementary. The last paper gives a good summary of all the views in the other papers. Basically there are three main recurring points: (i) the need for individual teaching, (ii) breadth of education, (iii) teaching designed to stimulate imaginative thinking.

Now, I would like to bring some points from Mr. Kyd's paper. The population of Scotland increased from 1801 to 1951 by 217 per cent. that is, more than three times. During the same period the population of England and Wales increased nearly five times, although the rate of natural increase in Scotland is normally in excess of that of England and Wales.

On emigration, the first half of this century saw Scotland lose just over one million people, net. In terms of comparison with other countries Scottish loss was 8 per cent. of her population, England and Wales was 0·5 per cent. That is, Scotland's loss was sixteen times that of England and Wales during this century. Corresponding losses by some European countries were: Italy 2·6 per cent.; Norway 2·9 per cent.; Sweden 1·5 per cent.; Denmark 1·2 per cent.—compared with Scotland's 8 per cent. The population of Scotland in 1951 was just over five million. If there had been no net loss it would have been 6¼ million people. The loss of population by emigration since 1951 has averaged about 24,000 a year. In kind, 60 per cent. were between the ages of 15 and 44, the most vital cohort of the population, and there are other significant features recorded by Mr. Kyd concerning the kind of people who are leaving Scotland. In terms of balance of population, this century shows eighteen of our counties with increases and in fifteen there are decreases. In the middle of the eighteenth century more than half the population lived north of the central belt in 70 per cent. of the area of Scotland. By 1951 one-fifth of the population was in that district, three-quarters of our population being concentrated in the central belt, which comprises one-seventh of Scotland.

Mr. Kyd has hazarded a shot at cash values and he presents us with a figure of £3,000 covering the nurture, upbringing, education and training of an emigrant. Taking the average number of emigrants at 20,000 a year, the financial loss to Scotland would be about £60 million a year, and the potential loss to Scotland's industrial development must be much greater. I notice from another paper, Mr. Nicholson's on the tourist industry, that he estimates the income from tourism is £60 million a year, exactly the same as the estimated loss due to net emigration.

I now come to Professor Macrae's paper, and I will start by a quotation from it. "By ingenuity man can make the desert blossom as the rose; by impenetrable ignorance he can die of starvation in the midst of potential plenty. The Dutch made a muddy, waterlogged delta into rich farm and garden; the Red Indians wandered in search of a hard living amidst the vast resources of America".

If material resources be the soil, human resources the plant, it is culture which provides for the preparation of the soil, the application of fertiliser and water, the adjustment to weather conditions, the protection of the plant and the fostering of growth. Under the impact of human endeavour and ingenuity, shaped by culture patterns, even static natural resources such as minerals can be dynamic; thus, doubling the efficiency of one's fireplace has precisely the same immediate effect as doubling one's supply of coal. If one should be able to double the efficiency of one's fireplace every week, one's ton of coal would last indefinitely. Such would be the trend, if we could make ourselves sufficiently clever, with all static resources. There must be a limit to conservation through efficiency and this enhances the importance of the continuous or renewable resources.

The capacity of the human factor will be determined by the culture which has moulded and equipped it. Culture itself is primarily moulded by education. It is in education that, if advance in both human and material resource use is sought, the major effort should be directed.

Then Professor Macrae touches upon the management of our affairs through the Civil Service and maximum use of brains, which is the most productive of resources. He finishes up in describing the need for a goal, a goal for a leader to aim at. There is no point in leadership without a goal.

Yesterday there was a goal described in terms of balance of biological resources in the form of wildlife, growth on the land, and human activities associated with the multi-cultural use of the land. This afternoon there is a paper which hinges the goal on the health and happiness of people; Sir Alexander Fleck's is a hard-headed spearhead of a goal, such as would take our industry vigorously forward. He says it is well worth struggling and striving to see if we cannot recapture the leadership of the Golden Age of Scotland, of 1780 to 1830, or even that secondary zenith of the Kelvin, Tait and Clark Maxwell period, when in most sections of industry rough and ready technology were adequate for leadership; before, that is, the application of exact sciences and their full development came to be one of the essentials of all good, successful companies. Our educational system produces people with the effect that as managers and directors in established techniques we hold an almost unchallenged position; it is failing to produce enough people who have good scientific or technological imagination. He gives us some figures of results (Scotland compared with England, simply because that standard of comparison is useful). Percentage of workers involved in stoppages—5·95 per cent. in Scotland, 2·52 per cent. in England and Wales. Number of working days lost per 1,000 workers—364 in Scotland, 223 in England and Wales. Technical education day release—11 per cent. in Scotland, 31 per cent. in England and Wales. He ties that 11 per cent. with the lack of realisation by industrialists that they can do more in pushing education even within their own establishments. These figures represent correctly the general situation, and the deduction follows that there is an unfortunate state of affairs in industrial Scotland. Then he gives us two general points on joint consultation and on profit-sharing schemes—we could do more in Scotland. He mentions some other points which I will just mention quickly. Individual teaching to cultivate the imaginative faculty. He associates with that the teaching of mathematics in a more comprehensive way, which might in the fulness of time produce a higher quota of creative, imaginative scientists, which in turn would lead to leadership in the industrial field. His goal is the kind of leadership which would place Scotland where it was in the last century, among the other countries.

Now I come to Professor Bruce William's paper. Innovation depends on communication and co-operation between the research, development, production and sales departments. In practice this means that there must be a balanced distribution of qualified scientists or technologists in these various departments with an understanding of the others' disciplines. In fact, this distribution does not occur in industry as it should. Of many cases of successful process and product development which have been studied less than one-third appears to have originated in the research and development department.

Professor Bruce Williams gives the percentage distribution of scientists—I will not repeat these. Because of our small output of qualified scientists and technologists there are too few of them in industry to get an effective interlinking of their work. On the other hand, industry has failed to see clearly just how much the application of research requires the employment of scientists and technologists in production and the other departments. In Britain there are better opportunities for industrial training on the research side than on the development side. This weakness tends to be self-perpetuating, because scientific and technological people cannot get the informal training in industry required to balance properly the training they might get in colleges and universities.

The most important need now is to increase the supply of scientists and technologists; the next most important thing is to improve the management of innovation.

Universities require to press more on ensuring that students know how to tackle fresh problems. Universities should not be purely vocational, but they are inevitably involved in it.

I come now to the last paper—"The Case for a New Scottish University"—The writers (to whom I will refer as "we") regard universities as necessary higher vocational training centres, and as something more; the sources of an intellectual irrigation system which spread clear thinking and respect for culture throughout our society. Scotland had five universities when England had two. We think universities have served us extremely well, but there are several points we think could be considered and can be associated with the new university:

1. We believe there is a strong case for more residential accommodation.
2. We believe the lecture system in its present form is a strain on the lecturer; if it is not, we believe that the lecturer is giving the class what they could find conveniently in a standard textbook.
3. An attempt might be made to allow Honours students to offer an Arts and a Science subject instead of a pair of kindred subjects. There is a demand in industry for the man who has a liberal education and a scientific training.
4. Two-thirds of Scottish students take pass degrees; in England two-thirds take Honours. Let us make Honours the rule.
5. A new university would find it easier than an old one to plan a curriculum to keep pace with events in the outside world.
6. A university should gain from its environment and should contribute to it.

Finally, I would take a point from Mr. Kyd's paper on education which he touched upon. In his view there is little doubt that the much higher rate of unemployment in Scotland than in England is due to the fact that we have not a sufficiently large reservoir of skilled men, either in science or in crafts, to support the large industrial development which would absorb our unemployed.

DISCUSSION

Lt.-Col. ROBERT GAYRE OF GAYRE AND NIGG, *The Mankind Quarterly*

The Principal, Sir Edward Appleton, has anticipated some of the things I was going to say. Nevertheless I think some of the points might well be underlined in the paper about to be put into print. I approach this matter from the genetical point of view. No country can afford to have a continuous loss of its more inherently able, whatever country that may be. This high emigration which is going on from Scotland is, as a consequence, extremely dangerous to the country. There is no magic formula, by waving a wand, whether it is industrial redeployment or anything else, to put back inherent ability once it has been largely exhausted from a stock. I am not saying the Scottish stock is absolutely exhausted—please do not misunderstand me—but we are in a position of danger, and therefore this must be corrected. I am glad the Principal made a point about the return of Scots to Scotland. I think that is extremely important, and I think what is being done in Edinburgh University in bringing back many Scots to the University is an extremely valuable contribution to Scottish demography. In the same way, the immigration of people of high quality from south of the border who are not Scots, or other people ethnologically closely related to the Scottish people, is a valuable contribution to the bank of genes of high ability which we must begin to build up again in our own country. At the same time, we must not forget the fact that all immigration is not necessarily good, and there have been in the past large-scale immigrations into Scotland which have not been at all beneficial from the purely genetic point of view. It could well be that large-scale immigration could come on the redevelopment of industry again, and the danger might well arise of a mass immigration of people whose inherent ability is low, and who, as a consequence, are not likely to assist the replacement of the genes of high quality which we have already lost. Immigration from certain quarters of the Commonwealth might not be at all helpful. In other words, we do not want to see an emigration of our best for an intake of somebody else's poorer stocks. Therefore it is necessary to have a redevelopment of highly skilled industrial and scientific work in Scotland which can prevent the emigration of our best, and in so far as it brings in immigrants, brings people of quality. In this connection the Government should locate in Scotland far more in the way of scientific laboratories and other organisations which will help to keep the educated Scot at home. Furthermore, steps should be taken to provide employment at advanced grades so that even where we have allowed our people to emigrate elsewhere they will be drawn back again to their own country. A return of the best of the Scottish *diaspora* should be part of our policy.

Professor R. RUGGLES GATES

I would like to reinforce what Colonel Gayre has said. I think the question of depopulation in Scotland, particularly of the more intelligent elements is an extremely serious problem. I may mention two or three facts in relation to migrations generally of human kind. The successful migrations have always been in the same climatic zone. For instance, the Eskimos originated in Siberia. Thousands of years ago they successfully migrated right across the Canadian Arctic for two or three thousand miles to Greenland. I do not think anybody has pointed out the significance of their success. It was successful because they continued in the same climate in which they had originated. The most successful of all emigrations has been from Europe to North America—again in the same climate, in this case a temperate climate; but most, if not all, attempts at migration from one climatic zone to another have been unsuccessful. For instance, the Normans moving from Normandy to Sicily; the Hyksos invasion of Egypt; the Abyssinian invasion of Egypt—they were either driven out or absorbed. Rome was unsuccessful in colonising Britain; they were equally unsuccessful in the colonisation of North Africa. If you go to Algeria you will see whole cities which have been deserted for 2,000 years as a result of unsuccessful colonisation by Rome. There is another relationship I would like to point out, and that is the north and south. This is emphasised by Baron Ehrenfels in an article in the *Mankind Quarterly*. Scotland and England occupy this relationship, north and south. You have the same thing in North America—Canada and the U.S.A.—and similar situations all over the world. It seems that there is generally a drain from north to south—larger populations, and so on. In this connection I might refer to one particular country—one in which I was born—Nova Scotia. That was populated (eastern Nova Scotia in particular) from Scottish sources, beginning in the first attempt in 1612, but later, in the eighteenth century and early nineteenth century large numbers of, for instance, Highlanders came to Cape Breton which is now part of the Province of Nova Scotia. They retained their Gaelic language as well as their customs. Eastern Nova Scotia is largely of Scottish descent. Now, Nova Scotia is in a similar position to Scotland in the fact that her population has been drained mainly southward since the middle of the nineteenth century. So I would just like to say that this problem is very similar—this north-south relationship—and requires special methods for dealing with it. Finally, I would like to refer to an article by Mr. Robertson in the current issue of the *Eugenics Review* in which he shows clearly the statistics of how the best elements of Scottish ability have been drained in the last century, and I hope he will show us a few figures to illustrate this result.

Mr. R. H. S. Robertson, *Resource Use Ltd.* (Illustrated with slides.)

I shall start straight away with the slides because they were referred to by the previous speakers. In this diagram I have tried to quantify certain results. You have here (Fig. 1) what are called "inventors" but what are really the cream of Scottish inventors and scientists and innovators in science and technology for the last 350 years, and it is expressed in the numbers of them per million per decade. You can see that the bottom scale is the time scale and represents the centuries. The actual numbers represent per million per decade. It is the actual output of bright people ("Genius" is a word I do not like to use), and it went up to the famous peak, the Golden Age. The Golden Age of Edinburgh we know of, but it affected the whole of Scotland. It has been falling at the most appalling rate until today the output is quite likely less than it ever was. In the early days there were few opportunities; then there was the rise of opportunity, when the clever people showed up and brought about the early Industrial Revolution, but today the downward portion of this slope is a real depletion of genes. The second picture (Fig. 2) shows the Fellowship of the Royal Society from its beginning until today, rising to a

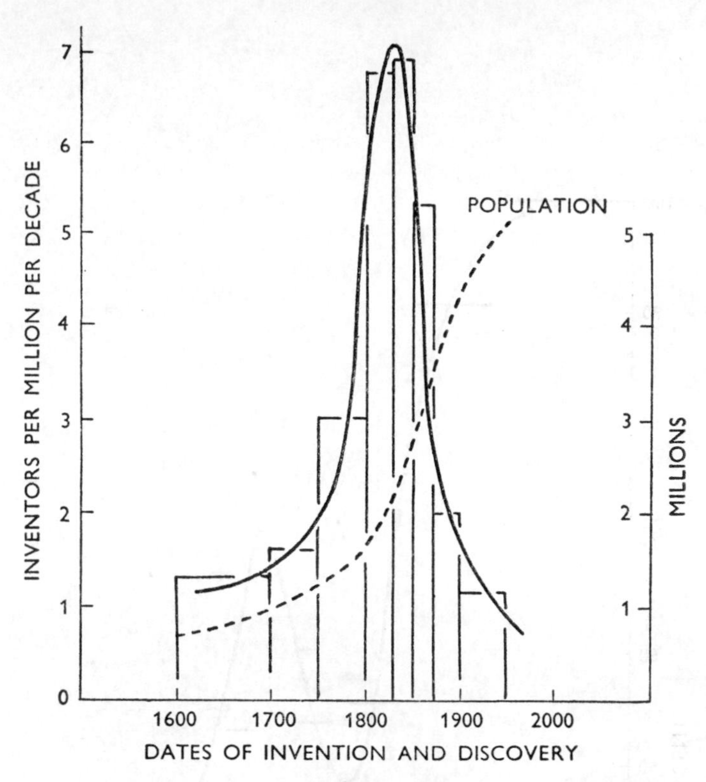

FIG. 1. Inventors per million per decade

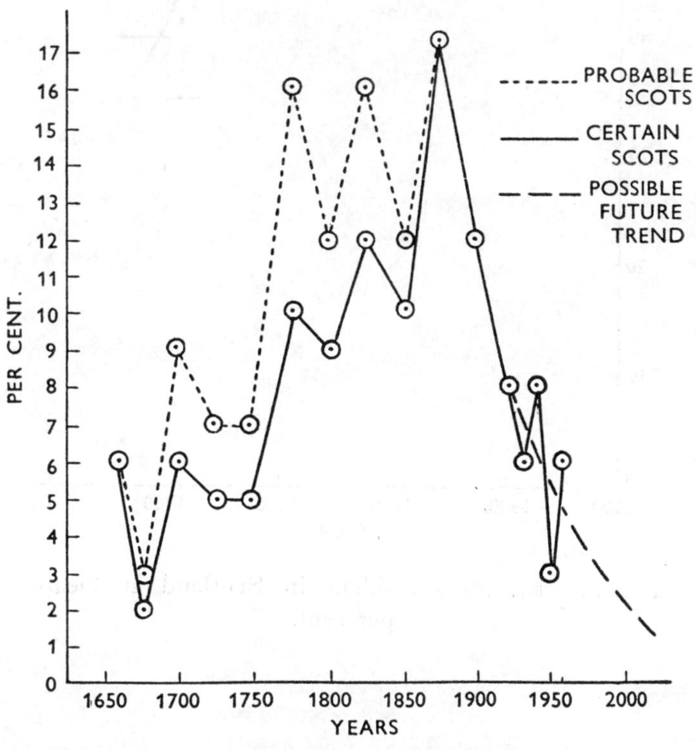

FIG. 2. Scottish Fellows of the Royal Society as a percentage of British Fellows

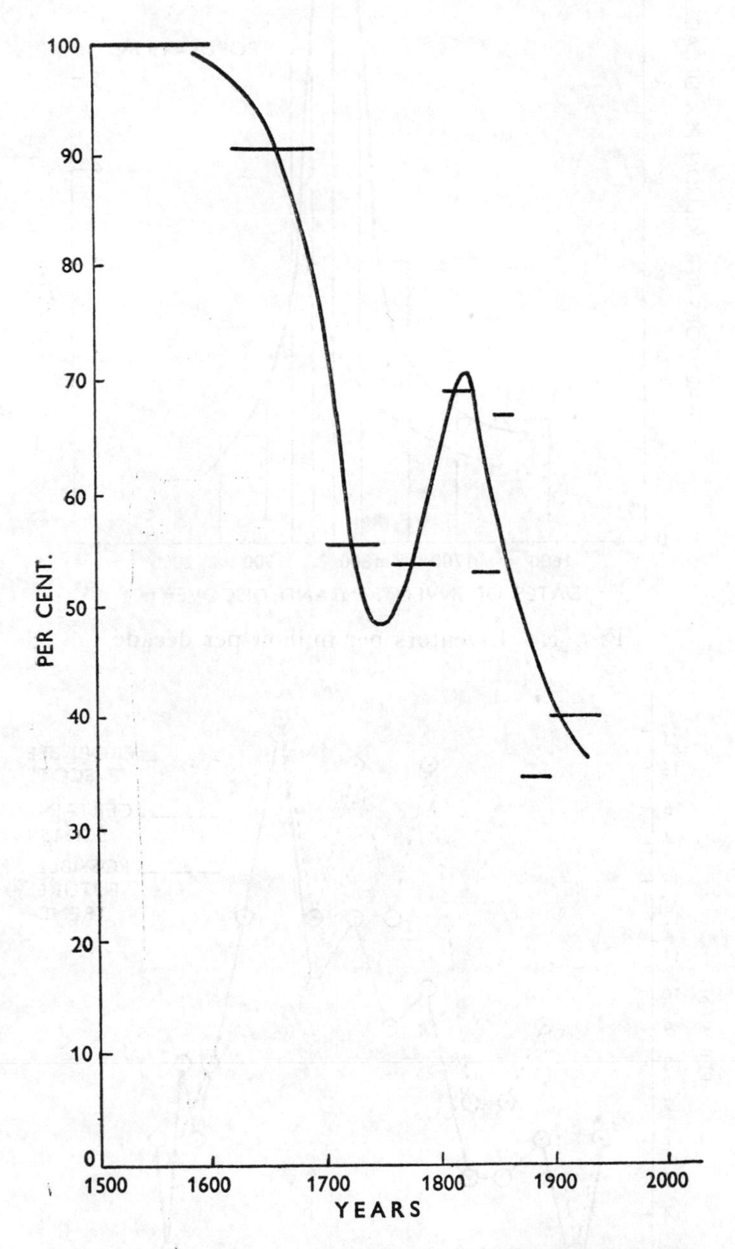

FIG. 3. Inventors resident in Scotland at Death, per cent.

peak of 17 per cent. of Scots, an astonishing figure for a small nation like Scotland. But since 1875, where that peak is, it has been falling steadily, and with inescapable statistical veracity, downwards until by the year 2000 we shall be lucky if there can be 2 per cent. of Scots in the Royal Society of London. This is a result of the genetic decline of Scotland. We cannot produce the great men to build up our industries if this goes down any further, so we have got to bring them back. The last slide (Fig. 3) shows the retention of Scots from a very high percentage in early days. From 1600 it starts coming down with the people taking sinecures in London; the Royal Society is the steep part on the left hand of the curve; curiously enough it starts to come back about 1750 and rises to a peak in about 1815; the maximum retention being 71 per cent. Since then it has declined with a bit of a wobble, today suggesting that there might be a slight arrestment. However, this must be given a really good push upwards again.

Dr. S. C. CURRAN, *Royal College of Science and Technology, Glasgow*

I would like to make two very simple points. One is concerned with the figures produced in the paper on the Fifth University, that is, the 17 per cent. and 10 per cent. figures to which Sir Edward has already referred. First of all he too has in a sense pointed to one difficulty in dealing with these figures; the fact that I do not believe they take into account the very large number of medical students. I do not know if you call these students Honours or Ordinary degree students. Again there are exceptions to the figures. Our own college, the Royal College of Science and Technology, has a figure of close to 70 per cent. of Honours qualifications, degree and associateship. Indeed most of the Ordinary qualifications are third-class Honours in essence. It is, of course, a very young institution. Perhaps an upstart, in the language of the paper. It is indeed hoping, I think it is fair to say, to do some of the things suggested in the paper, that is, to increase its accommodation greatly in the next decade when it looks as if university population must rise, and to increase its residential accommodation. I wondered indeed if these differences—there are, of course, a very large number of Ordinary Scottish graduates—are due to the difference in linkage between the school system in the south and the university and linkage in the north. The English school system tends to make the English schoolboy pick his strong subject at a relatively early stage, and perhaps the Scottish system of the broadly-based education works to the disadvantage of the student wishing to prove fit for Honours. If we analyse the figures it can be argued that the Honours made per thousand of the population, for instance, is very similar in England and Scotland at the moment and this makes the question a proper one, I think, as to whether or not increased population at universities will show the same ratio. In other words, we cannot assume they will all be Honours men, those coming to universities in the next decade. Regarding lectures as against private study; the second is an extremely expensive matter—providing tuition, private study—but it is the strength, I am sure, of the great universities of Cambridge and Oxford. However, there are very good staff to student ratios already available in institutions in some parts of this Scottish region.

Turning to Sir Alexander Fleck's paper and the lack of Fellows of the Royal Society who have taken Scottish degrees: there are many interesting points to be raised in that connection, but again I would begin to ask a question—I am not prepared to answer it—as to whether or not the Scottish system fails to give the young student his head for fear of narrowing his education. I believe that men who are going to be F.R.S. in due course do not need to have spoon feeding in regard to their culture; they will prove to be able to look after that themselves throughout the course of their careers. But there is a very important stage about 15 or so when the potential F.R.S. should be given his head and not criticised too much for narrowness, and again the residential system is extremely valuable here. In my own case I deliberately went to St. John's College, Cambridge, from Glasgow University (at St. John's in those days we had 450 students). I went there because our own Chairman this morning, Sir Edward, Sir John Cockcroft, Dirac, Jeffries and Kopitza were all members of that College and some were Nobel Prize men. This raises the question, "Can you in fact encourage potential F.R.S.s if Fellows are too thin on the ground?" They are very thin on the ground and I am delighted to hear Sir Edward say that conditions are appropriate—and I am sure they are now—in Edinburgh for the coming of the rewards which result from the creation of the right environment; this has not been right for some time in Scotland.

Mr. JOHN ROLLO, *Rollo Industries Ltd.*

This cataract of humanity which Mr. Kyd has shown us is frightening and appalling I think it is an elementary axiom when you are dealing with floods of any kind, that if you are unable to stop the main flood, if you can stem a tributary you are at least doing something. I can show you quickly, I think, that we have it in our power to stem quickly and effectively one of the tributaries of flow from Scotland, and that is from the Highlands. Twenty years ago I was christened a crank and a fool because I set up a little satellite industry in the Highlands. I have done it four times since. Ten years ago I was called a foolish enthusiast. Today the excuse made is that I am a freak and perhaps there are not enough freaks around. But, Gentlemen, that is all wrong. I want to quote some quick figures to show you how this can be achieved. At Inverasdale in Wester Ross my little factory there, working ten years now, employs five men, local men, all crofters, married since they became employed with me. The school population in Inverasdale in 1937 was 65, in 1950 it was 13, today it is 18. Now I have devised what I call a population retention factor which is an index of the number of people who can be employed, who will retain the population. In Wester Ross and, in fact, throughout the rural parts of Ross-shire, that figure is 3; 5 men employed retain 15, with their children, wives and other people who stay. Well now, let us go to Sutherland, which Mr. Kyd has quoted. The population today is 13,400. The population loss in Sutherland is between 4 and 5 per cent. per annum. So that somewhere about 680 people leave the county of Sutherland every year. If Sutherland has a population retention factor of 3, you only require to retain one-third of that to stop the flow or, in other words, 226 people given work in the county of Sutherland in small satellite factories will stabilise the population. That is, if 10 people in industry in Lowland Scotland will do together throughout the county of Sutherland what I have done individually over the Highlands in the last twenty years, you can stabilise the population of that county. In fact, 100 firms doing it could stabilise the population of the mainland crofting counties.

Mr. I. F. CLARKE

I think Scotland faces a most serious educational problem. All the papers so far undoubtedly point to that, and whenever I hear from industrialists and people engaged in university education, the same answer is given to the question "Where stands Scotland?" She stands in the middle of the nineteenth century waiting to make a leap forward in education. I would put two simple points. All civilisation depends upon a technological base, and unless we have an adequate technological base we will never advance. Therefore we must create the conditions to produce the right number and the right quality of technologists. Western Germany in fifteen years has recreated a completely shattered economy. The reason—the present figures for the eight great technical universities of Western Germany are at present 46,000 students at university level working for degrees in applied science. Compare the corresponding figures for the University Grants Committee for the whole of Great Britain—15,000. For Scotland 3,000. Look at Aachen Technical University, which feeds into the Rhineland and into the Ruhr, and is at the moment educating 9,000 technologists—Scotland's population at university level of technologists is exactly 3,000 in the latest figures. So I would submit, Mr. Chairman, the first thing we must do, amongst others, is to create an adequate supply of technologists in number and in quality. Unfortunately, the papers *all* point to the fact, the central British problem, that our technologists are not of the right quality. The Appointments Committee of Oxford University of 1959 had made this point: "Three-quarters of the engineering graduates entering the engineering industry make competent technical men, but are not up to leading teams in difficult times." This is the point, of course, made by Sir Alexander Fleck and Professor Bruce Williams and others. Now, I think we will undoubtedly be able to tackle the problem of numbers, but the problem of quality is a much more difficult question. And here I would suggest that it will do Scotland no harm to look outside to see what other countries are doing about this problem of quality. We have two things to consider. First the creation of those many special rare geniuses, the type of Fellow of the Royal Society of whom Dr. Curran spoke—that requires one method. But the mass of people who are going to develop that creative scientific imagination mentioned by Sir Alexander Fleck, and demanded by him by the condition of Scotland today, will have to be created by something wider than the present narrow technological education. The University Grants Committee has already spoken out against the intense specialisation of technologists, and it has demanded a wider education. In England, hard-headed industrialists have demanded a wider education in the new colleges of advanced technology, and here they are getting at least four hours a week of general education and the industrialists say that this is the type of education which they want. Abroad you have in Germany eight great technological universities, all with large Arts Departments devoted to the general education of the technologist. Why should Scotland not look to Germany, not look to great institutions like the Massachusetts Institute of Technology to see if perhaps our 150-year-old educational system may not be adapted to a type of technological education suited to the modern age.

Mr. E. P. Hudson, *Scottish Agricultural Industries Ltd.*

In the line of duty I was called upon to address the Symposium two mornings ago. I am now under another compulsion—to say this morning something which Sir Robert Urquhart said yesterday, which was that he was going to declare publicly that he would not take umbrage at the failure of the organisers of this Symposium to deal adequately with one particular subject. My subject is technical education, or rather, further vocational education. It is touched on by the papers we are discussing at the present time, but I feel that it does require some rather more adequate treatment which I propose, if I am allowed, to contribute in writing. I would like to say, however, that the situation at the present time in regard go further vocational education in Scotland is not anywhere near as good as it should be. It is, in fact, deplorable. There is an equilibrium between the demand for such education and the supply of the facilities for it, including the amount of public money which public opinion will tolerate to be spent on it. But this equilibrium at the present time is at a dangerously low, indeed a deplorably low level. Now, I only want to make one point whilst on my feet on this, and that is in regard to the time-scale. Yesterday and the day before there were occasionally references to looking ahead ten years, or twenty years, or thirty years, as the case may be, on some kind or another of natural resources. I want to suggest to you that in this matter of education our time-scale has got to be both immediate, because it is urgent, and at the same time long distant. I would remind you that the mature working citizens of this country that are going to take us into the twenty-first century are already entering our primary schools and the junior levels of our secondary schools. It is they—the people who are starting their educational processes just now—who are going to be the working leaders of our community in A.D. 2000—forty years ahead. I ask you to recall for a moment 1880. I can only think of it by recollection through what my father told me. I ask you to recall 1920. Then today; and then go ahead another forty years and I think there is no evidence whatsoever so far that the curve of change has lost its exponential shape. Therefore we have to provide today for a situation in which it is almost impossible to imagine what technical skills may be needed. But we have got to provide for them; and here, with great respect to Sir Edward (I have had inspiration from you over many years since I sat at your feet as a student) I would take issue with you on your use this morning of the words "skilled hands". The skilled hands that we are going to need during this next forty years are not hands, but brains operating hands, and not operating muscles, but operating machines. But over and above the technical skills that we are going to need in the developments of the next forty years, there is something else we are going to need that is just as important, and that is an education for good citizenship the kind of citizenship that is going to be needed, the kind of qualities of citizenship that are going to be needed in this world that lies ahead of us.

Dr. R. W. GLOYNE, *Meteorological Office, Edinburgh*

I would just like to make a very quick plea that the universities should accept obligation to would-be students outside their walls. May I illustrate by three examples? It came to my notice about two years ago that a group of teachers of mathematics in Edinburgh wished to improve their qualifications by taking Honours degrees. The only theoretical possibility nowadays is London External, but neither Heriot-Watt nor the University could offer them any assistance towards that end, again leading perhaps to a small but significant trickle south. Secondly, I have a Press cutting from *The Scotsman* whereby it notes that Glasgow University have changed the regulations for their LL.B. so that "no longer will it be possible for graduates or others in industry, administration or professions other than law to study part-time for the LL.B. degree". A thoroughly retrograde step, I suggest. The third example concerns Ph.D. regulations. At most, if not all, our universities they are far too rigid. Professor Williams mentions on page 636 of his paper "much might be achieved by allowing suitable Ph.D. work in industrial research associations and establishments". In *The Guardian* of 2nd May I noted, at a Conference in Glasgow, where a prominent industrial scientist suggested that this degree should be thoroughly reformed and made into a sort of junior D.Sc. obtained by presentation of a series of papers. I will not take any more time in amplifying these points. This audience will quickly see the gist of my remarks, but I would like to echo the last speaker. I am very surprised that in this Symposium there is no mention whatever of the implications, social and material, of advanced automation, cytogenetics and decision-making computers. I think they have social consequences which are really very frightening unless we look ahead.

Deputy Chairman

I do feel, before we end this session, we would like to hear if any authors would like to say anything arising from contributions made to the session.

Professor Bruce R. Williams, *Faculty of Economic and Social Studies, University of Manchester*

One point about what Dr. Curran said about the relationship in Scotland of the proportion of Honours to Arts degrees, in which the Royal College of Science and Technology in Glasgow is an outstanding exception to the usual Scottish practice. What I want to take up is that the root of the trouble—trouble because it affects the quality of education and the prospects of the students once they have got it. I am not sure that it follows that you cannot have a broadly based education in schools and a very good specialised education later in university. I think the root of the trouble may well be that perhaps we should have given more attention to schools, which are the root of so many troubles—I do not think our students stay long enough and do not get their basic qualifications early enough in their school career. One of the points we might have made in our memorandum had we had space is this. On the average the Scottish student goes up to University a year sooner than his English counterpart and only the Honours student stays a year longer to make up for it. The second point is, I think, that we have spent time in the past few years readjusting our basic senior secondary courses but have not got round to the point of adapting to modern conditions what one might call post Leaving Certificate point, and I find very often that those who do study at school for a sixth year are in fact making up what would have been regarded as basic qualifications to be obtained in fifth year. So that in fact I think the sooner we get round to again having either a revival of University bursary competitions, which have lost some of their point and purpose with the better financial conditions of students, or the introduction of something like the "A" level, the sooner the better, and I think we might then see this imbalance in the Universities corrected. The only other point—if I might touch on the main theme of the discussion this morning—the drift south from Scotland to England. There is a point which comes in if you consider possible sites for a university that this same process has been going on for several hundred years in Scotland itself. In Scotland we have been packing more and more into a small area of Scotland, and in Glasgow particularly not only our University, but city are bursting at the seams. There is coming a point when either population will continue to drift south or we shall have to form a drift north in Scotland itself.

DEPUTY CHAIRMAN

We will have to close now. I would like to thank the authors for their papers and all those who have contributed to the discussion. I apologise for having to be ruthless.

WRITTEN CONTRIBUTIONS

E. BOOTH

A REGIONAL DEVELOPMENT SCHEME FOR THE HIGHLANDS

The Great Glen bisects the Highlands and could be developed to give a viable industrial belt in the very centre of the crofting counties. The raw materials of this area are timber, cattle and sheep; sea freight from Inverness would provide cheap freight to East Coast ports as far south as London. Projects already in existence, i.e. the site of Scotlands fifth University and the wood-pulp mill at Fort William, provide a basis for a more ambitious regional development scheme which, with careful planning, could be carried out without any loss of amenity value to the area.

The depopulation of the Highlands is, and has been for many years, a source of concern, and a number of official, semi-official and private bodies are working to arrest the steady migration from this area. There is no need to enumerate the achievements in this area because many individual efforts come readily to mind, but all suffer from the same disadvantage—each effort is too remote from the rest of the area to have more than a local effect. On the other hand, an effort to bring a limited amount of industry to a central area of the Highlands would benefit the "hinterland" if the industrialisation of the central area is based on the raw materials of the "hinterland". Other industries would be attractive but less vital to the area as a whole.

The Great Glen, a narrow valley about 70 miles long running from Fort William to Inverness, is at the centre of gravity of the crofting counties; at its north-eastern end, the port of Inverness has good sea communications with markets as far south as London. (Sea-freight is cheap and vessels usually sail south without any cargo; currently, for instance, seaweed is transported from Orkney to Wisbech at £2 per ton in small coasters taking 300 ton loads and it is probable that Inverness-London would have similar freight rates.) The West coast is not so well served with shipping routes. Road and rail communications exist between both Fort William and Inverness with Edinburgh and Glasgow and there is a regular air-service to Inverness. The area is well supplied with water and power, and would be attractive for development. Amongst the disadvantages of the area, from an industrial viewpoint, are the need to provide housing as well as factory sites, and the amenity value of the area is so great that special care would be necessary to avoid damaging the scenic beauty of the area. At first glance it would appear that existing legislation, e.g. assistance schemes and control of pollution, are adequate both to preserve the amenity value and to offer financial assistance for extra building costs which may be incurred in preserving the area from industrial spoilation. If necessary, special consideration could be given to any problem of additional costs arising from the development of this area. In any case, amenity must not be allowed to interfere with the livelihood of the district, but there is every reason to suppose that a measure of industrialisation could be planned without loss of amenity. A special organisation should be established to study possible developments in the Highlands; this body should be similar to the "Regional Laboratories" which have proved so successful in Canada and the U.S.A.

There is already some industry at Fort William where the aluminium works is expanding and the construction of a pulp mill is under consideration by a group of paper manufacturers. Inverness has a chipboard factory in course of construction, has opened a Technical College and has been mentioned as a possible site for a new university. The university should be, if necessary, directed to the area as a matter of policy; it would infuse new life and thought into the area, be a major employer of labour and a major contributor to the rates of the area, i.e. in economic terms, it is the equivalent of a major industry. Remoteness and rural isolation have not been considered any disadvantage to, for instance, the Universities of Cambridge or St. Andrews and should not be any disadvantage to siting Scotland's fifth university at Inverness. The pulp mill must be an economic venture and is currently being assessed. It is hardly necessary to point out the benefits this venture could bring to the area, but paper and/or paperboard would be natural developments and chipboard and hardboard are possible developments. It is obvious, however, that a university and a pulp mill would have a great direct influence on the Great Glen and every effort should be made to establish them.

The economic resources of the area are timber, cattle and sheep; the pulp mill can be assumed to require all the timber in the area which is not already processed by sawmills or required for the Inverness chipboard factory. Thus only cattle and sheep need consideration. At present the Highlands are essentially rearing areas which supply stock and wool to the South and import feeding-stuffs, sheep-dips and veterinary products. There is, therefore, a reasonable market in existence for feeding-stuffs, etc., which should be used to induce one of the larger organisations to set up a subsidiary factory in the area. The annual wool-clip in the Highlands must be very considerable, and experience in the Outer Hebrides and the proposed spinning mill in Shetland prompt the broad proposal that the processing of this wool could be carried out in the area and thereby add to the commerce of the Highlands.

Frozen meat is certain to reach Britain and it is very probably in the planning stage today. This region is at the very heart of the stock-rearing area and could be a "fattening" area. With the large London market, the East Coast as well as Glasgow and Edinburgh within the range of cheap freight, the Great Glen would be a good centre for meat processing. Some effort should be made to point out the advantages of this area so that any interested firms could be acquainted with the advantages of which, to many, is a remote inaccessible region. With meat processing the by-products of the slaughter-house automatically suggest such outlets as tinned meat, sausages, leather, glandular products, pet foods, gelatin, etc.

Thus it is possible to visualise a development scheme in the very heart of the crofting counties which would draw its raw materials from them and export its products by cheap sea-freight to the East Coast of Britain. Such a scheme would be of direct benefit to the whole of the Highlands as well as bringing prosperity to the central valley. It is realised that there must be a minimum sacrifice to the amenities of the area and that some time must elapse before the scheme could be put into effect. It is therefore recommended that immediate consideration should be given to siting the fifth university at Inverness and all support given to the development of the pulp mill at Fort William. Prompt action on these two items would alone bring great benefit to the area and would also minimise the effect of any delay in the execution of the general plan. An organisation should be established to study the economic, technical and sociological aspects of planned development in the Highlands; it is possible that this Unit could obtain financial support from the Development Commission. This is an opportunity which will not recur; it gives hope for the development of an area which has hitherto appeared impossible to view as a whole and, for that reason, should be given every consideration.

N. G. KENNEDY, *D.S.I.R., Edinburgh*

During the course of the discussion on this session, grave concern was expressed at the high rate of loss by emigration of new graduate population. Further, it was stated, that something much more realistic must be done to attract graduates who had emigrated and found fame and favour abroad to return to these shores, bringing with them all the wealth of their experience. A suggestion that the setting up of Government research laboratories and institutions in Scotland would go a long way to solving these problems met with general acclaim by the Symposium. I should like to suggest that the general acceptance of this principle without due and careful consideration could well lead to grave disappointment.

Take, for instance, the case of the National Engineering Laboratory, the actual building of which was commenced at East Kilbride in 1949. The Laboratory now employs approximately 600 staff, of whom 51 are first- or second-class Honours graduates, or possess senior degrees. The disappointing facts are that only 14 of this group are Scottish and that, in spite of repeated advertisements and attendance at appointments boards, there are many vacancies unfilled. It appears that the salaries offered by the scientific civil service now compare very favourably with those offered by industry with the exception of a relatively few very senior posts. Further the conditions of service at East Kilbride are very attractive, housing is guaranteed and the equipment available and the working spaces provided are of the highest quality.

If the experience of the Laboratory can be taken as representative, then it would seem that Government action alone cannot possibly solve the problem. I believe a much broader concept is necessary where Government, universities and industry get together to create a climate, sympathetic to scientific thinking and attractive to those who originate, innovate and apply scientific principles. The Government might well be the catalyst but, unless the other elements are ready to combine, the reaction may be disappointing in the extreme. I feel that Mr. Krebs of the Arthur D. Little, Inc., of Massachusetts, U.S.A., in his contribution to Session 12, was thinking along very similar lines.

N. G. KENNEDY, *D.S.I.R., Edinburgh*

ADMINISTRATIVE REQUIREMENTS FOR OPTIMUM RESOURCE DEVELOPMENT

During the final session of the Symposium the Government was once again criticised for not carrying out sufficient research in Scotland. In particular the Department of

Scientific and Industrial Research was singled out by Dr. Woodward, who said that the Department had only two national stations in Scotland and one research association. I should like to point out that, apart from these, the Department has Scottish Branches of the Road Research Laboratory, the Building Research Laboratory and the Warren Spring Laboratory. Further, a Geological Survey of Scotland is operated with headquarters in Edinburgh, whose senior officer is an Assistant Director of the Geological Survey of Great Britain. A Radio Research Station Sub-Laboratory is maintained and next year a Sub-Station of the Water Pollution Research Laboratory will be instituted at Thorntonhall. All these additional activities represent the employment of a further 120 persons approximately, many of whom are highly qualified scientists. Of the total grant which the Department receives for the maintenance of its stations, *circa* 17 per cent. is spent in Scotland. This is a very fair proportion.

With regard to research associations, the trend has been, since the inception of the co-operative research scheme, immediately after the 1914-18 War, that the headquarters of a research association, partially sponsored by industry and partially grant-aided through D.S.I.R., should be sited in the largest concentration of the industry which it serves. It happens that this occurs mainly in England, with, of course, the obvious exception of jute. This in no way implies a slight on Scottish industries, which have equal right and freedom to join any association considered beneficial. It may mean a longer journey, but is this such a real problem in this modern day and age? It is fairly generally known that the research associations find greater difficulty in attracting members from Scotland than from other parts of the U.K. and, in order to stimulate interest, two have opened branches sited in Scotland.

Professor Matthew of the Chair of Architecture, Edinburgh University, criticised the Scottish Branch of the Building Research Station for being inadequate to cope with the research requirements of the building industry in Scotland. He suggested the Branch was merely a post office. Professor Matthew is apparently under some misapprehension as to the function of the Branch; it has undertaken and continues to conduct studies of Scottish materials and building; it is not a post office.

Once again I must refer to my remarks in my contribution to Session 11. Unless there is a genuine sympathy towards research and development, which is broadly based throughout the interested community, further Government action will have far less impact than it could have, given the right conditions.

N. G. Kennedy, *D.S.I.R., Edinburgh*

Having attended the Symposium for the three days, one cannot but marvel at the mass of information which has been presented over a wide variety of subjects. The task of those whose duty it will be to sift and analyse this information is indeed Herculean. It has interested me to note that, in many of the fields covered, the Department of Scientific and Industrial Research has a vested interest. A number of the Department's stations and research associations has been engaged on work closely associated with the discussions. It appears to me that the wealth of information and experience which these stations and associations must have could well be of value in the analysis of the Symposium material and I am sure they will all give freely should the need arise. I, therefore, list those whose work is considered particularly pertinent in a separate appendix.

I should also like to highlight the fact that the Department administers grants for studentships, fellowships and advanced course studentships, as well as for researches of special merit at universities and colleges. Grants are also made in the human sciences. The Department is also in close touch, through the Office of the Minister of Science, with the Medical Research Council, the Agricultural Research Council, the Nature Conservancy and with certain important functions in relation to the promotion and development of atomic energy. These points are worthy of note, particularly as regards human resources.

APPENDIX

List of D.S.I.R. Stations and Research Associations

Stations

Building Research Station (Scottish Branch at Thorntonhall).
Forest Products Research Laboratory.
Geological Survey and Museum (Scottish Headquarters in Edinburgh).
Hydraulic Research Station.
National Engineering Laboratory.
National Physical Laboratory.
Road Research Laboratory (Scottish Branch at Thorntonhall).
Torry Research Station.
Warren Spring Laboratory (Scottish Branch at Thorntonhall).
Water Pollution Research Laboratory (Scottish Branch to be established 1961 at Thorntonhall).

Research Associations

The British Coal Utilisation Research Association.
The British Coke Research Association.
Coal Tar Research Association.
British Cast Iron Research Association.
British Iron and Steel Research Association.
British Non-Ferrous Metals Research Association.
British Steel Castings Research Association.
British Jute Trade Research Association.
Wool Industries Research Association.
British Ceramics Research Association.
British Glass Industry Research Association.
Research and Development Committee of the Timber Development Association.
Water Research Association.
British Electrical and Allied Industries Research Association.
British Hydro-Mechanics Research Association.
The four food research associations could have fringe interests. They are:
Baking.
Flour Milling.
Food Manufacture.
Fruit and Vegetable Canning.

SCOTTISH COUNCIL OF SOCIAL SERVICE

The Scottish Council of Social Service, through its Rural Community Development Committee, is interesting itself in the fuller use of material and human resources in rural areas, especially in the Highlands and Islands.

Community development methods to promote healthy and balanced development through local action are in use in very many countries throughout the world today, in towns and rural communities not only in underdeveloped countries but in countries with planned and developed economies. National programmes are being worked out and successfully operated in countries as widely differing as U.S.A., Canada, Peru and Ceylon. Everywhere the process is designed to create conditions of economic and social progress for the whole community with its active participation and fullest possible reliance upon the community's initiative. Self-help and co-operative action on the part of the community itself are fundamental, with of course the availability of technical knowledge from Government and voluntary agencies. The approach must be comprehensive, dealing with the economic, social and cultural life of the community.

Community development programmes that have been successful in other countries have certain basic elements common to them all:

(1) Activities undertaken must correspond to the basic needs of the community; these needs must be discovered, discussed and given expression to by as many as possible of the members of the community.

(2) In the early stages, changed attitudes in the people are as important as material achievements. Defeatism and apathy must be overcome and a feeling awakened among the people that life is improving primarily through their own efforts.

(3) Community development aims at increased and better participation of the people in community affairs. Voluntary organisations mobilising non-official support for community projects will help local government.

(4) Local initiative is a first condition of community development; the identification and encouragement of local leadership should be a basic objective.

(5) Greater reliance on the participation of women and young people invigorates development programmes, establishes them on a wide basis and secures long-range expansion.

The Scottish Council of Social Service is considering whether and how a programme on such principles might be adopted in rural areas in Scotland, more particularly in the first instance in the crofting communities, so that human and material resources may be discovered and fully developed and the population stabilised. There are many Government and national voluntary agencies at work providing aid, financial and otherwise, and the Secretary of State for Scotland, with the help of the Highlands and Islands Advisory Panel, endeavours to co-ordinate operations. But co-ordination is possible and necessary too at lower levels, and a district or regional Council of Social Service can be of great help in the area it covers and through its constituent associations in each small community; they can study all the aids that are available and determine how local resources could best be made use of co-operatively to obtain full value. The local Council of Social Service can help to provide the national services with up-to-date information on the wants and needs of the people, and inform the people what services are available and how they can obtain them.

The system best suited to Scotland must be worked out; the conception of community development applied in U.S.A. is not necessarily applicable in this country with its advanced system of social services, nor is it likely that methods used in underdeveloped countries, say in Africa, would fit. Something can be learned from all of these, but it would appear to be a matter of urgency that serious consideration be given to the formulation of a policy and programme for rural Scotland. Planned community development in hitherto "forgotten corners" is now being undertaken by the Governments of a number of Western European countries, for example Denmark, Netherlands, Norway and Germany. The European Productivity Agency of the Organisation for European Economic Co-operation is carrying out pilot comprehensive development schemes in various places including Greece and Sardinia.

The Scottish Council of Social Service is studying ways and means of developing the best approach to this problem in our more difficult rural areas. Meantime, as a beginning it is helping in the setting up of regional Councils of Social Service which it feels will prove to be an integral part of the plan. One of these Councils, the Skye Council of Social Service, has been in operation for some years and has yielded good results in developing leadership and in the assistance it has given towards the improvement of transport services, the development of tourism, Old People's Welfare and development of industry.

The Scottish Council of Social Service has been interested in, and encouraged by, many of the contributions, written and verbal, in all sections of the Symposium on Natural Resources in Scotland. "Educating the individual to leadership having regard to an integrated approach to resource development"; "the need for voluntary expression of what people want and think about"; "a national development strategy to get a combined coherent approach"; these are a few of the many phrases which had a relevance to the subject of this paper. Particularly interesting was Professor Macrae's paper on "Interrelations between Natural Resources, Human Resources and Human Culture", with one sentence of which it is perhaps appropriate to conclude this paper: "Progressive efficiency in the utilisation of natural resources is more likely to occur in a society sympathetic to change and avidly in pursuit of knowledge, of exploration in all directions, and of material advance, than in a society committed to the *status quo*, governed by tradition and averse to inquiry."

Professor C. H. WADDINGTON, *Institute of Animal Genetics*

In the discussion of the value of the natural beauties of the Scottish landscape as a tourist attraction not enough attention was paid to the advisability of making good artificially the points in which Nature falls short of everything the tourist required. The utilisation of Outdoor Recreation Potential not only requires some indoor potential as well, in the form of hotels, motels, etc., but the outdoors itself often needs the provision of something which it lacks. Scotland has what should be an asset of enormous value in the possession of the North-West Highlands, which are almost unique in Europe in combining extreme beauty with unspoilt solitude. There is room for enormously more tourists to visit the Highlands without spoiling them (provided the roads were improved).

But there is a large snag—the comparative absence of sun and prevalence of rain. Now, many countries which have developed the tourist trade have done so on a basis of having the sun but providing most of the rest artificially. For instance, in Jamaica a good many of the famous hotel beaches are made up every year from specially laid sand; and inside the hotels are air-conditioned. Would it not be valuable in Scotland to do some "sun-conditioning"? That is, roof over one or two even fairly small isolated stretches of beach with a light plastic or shell concrete roof, and install ultra-violet lamps and infra-red heaters such as are used for heating the pavement cafés in many continental cities. If potential tourists knew that even on rainy days they could get some fresh air and perhaps bathe, and would not be faced with the alternative of sitting indoors or making a semi-arctic expedition, it would surely tempt many more of them to come north.

Lt.-Col. R. Gayre of Gayre and Nigg

An Indication of Material available for ascertaining the Extent of Migration from Scotland

The extent of Scotland's loss by way of emigration has been put at a matter of 20 million to all parts of the world—that is 80 per cent. of those of British descent live furth of Scotland.

The writer, in his capacity as Chief of a Scottish clan, has in the course of years built up a card index of persons all over the world who are descended from it. While this is by no means a complete tabulation of *all* of that clan, it is a record of the more or less successful members of it who reside outside of Scotland. That is of persons who appear in directories, or who, because of their education standards and interests, have made it their business to communicate with the Chief and become enrolled in the card indices which are kept. As far as Scotland is concerned, because of the accessibility of the Chief, who is known locally to many of his clan, there is a tendency of people of a lower stratum of society to become known to him, and so recorded on these indices.

Consequently, it may be concluded that the figures at disposal include nearly all of the clan in Scotland, but are less comprehensive where they deal with those located farther afield. Consequently, these figures are likely to minimise the extent of the migration rather than to exaggerate it.

In order to ensure that only those of the blood of the clan are included, as far as is possible, only those having the chiefly surname (Gayre or Gair or its variants) are tabulated, and in most of these cases the persons concerned have been at one time or another scrutinised, and even their pedigrees examined in many instances, so that the amount of error due to recording people who have no right to the surname must be very slight.

Owing to the need for accuracy the number of persons involved in this has thus been reduced to approximately 1,100 persons, represented by 280 householders. It is not argued that from such a small number an accurate estimate of the proportions of Scottish emigration can be ascertained. But if a number of clans and other surnames were similarly investigated, the material necessary in order to reach fairly accurate instead of guesswork figures on Scottish migration would become available.

It should be pointed out that this survey is only concerned with the movements due to the mass-migrations from the eighteenth century onwards from Scotland, and is not concerned with the earlier and substantial migrations of Scots to France, Denmark, Russia and Sweden, and other countries. A large proportion of the noblesse, for instance, of Sweden has Scottish ancestry through these causes. This migration of military adventurers to European countries affected largely the nobility of Scotland only, and was not by any means as absolute as that which has resulted from the mass-migrations of a later period, since large numbers always returned to Scotland after their services with the foreign states had run out.

From the figures at my disposal the following percentages have been obtained. Of the clan members with the Chiefly surname (excluding all septs, and dependers and followers of the clan) there resides in

SCOTLAND—16·80 *per cent. of the whole clan*, of which
3·22 per cent. is located in Edinburgh,
3·93 per cent. is located in Glasgow,
9·65 per cent. is located in the Provinces;

ENGLAND, IRELAND, WALES and MAN—25·71 *per cent. of the whole clan*, of which
11·79 per cent. is located in the English Province of York,
8·21 per cent. is located in the English Province of Canterbury, excluding London,
4·64 per cent is located in London,
0·35 per cent. is located in Wales,
0·35 per cent. is located in Man,
0·35 per cent. is located in Ireland;

EUROPE—0·35 per cent. of the whole clan;

U.S.A.—31·07 per cent. of the whole clan;

CANADA—9·29 per cent. of the whole clan;

AUSTRALIA—6·78 per cent. of the whole clan;

NEW ZEALAND—5·0 per cent. of the whole clan;

S. RHODESIA and S. AFRICA—4·28 per cent. of the whole clan;

THE REST OF AFRICA—0·70 per cent. of the whole clan.

It will be observed that the United States of America contains the bigger proportion of this Clan than any other single country, and we suspect that the same thing is true so far as most of the Scottish *diaspora* is concerned. This population is a total loss to Scotland and the Crown. In the case of this name, the relatively small showing of Canada is explained by the fact that on examining the antecedents of many of the American clansmen it was found that they were of Canadian origins, although they now regarded themselves as Americans. It will be observed from this that Canada's immediate gains from Scotland have been off-set by a drainage of people to America. As those of the name in America appear to contain relatively more prominent and prosperous clansmen, one suspects that there is a genetic drainage of the more able from Scotland to America through Canada.

Another striking fact which emerges from this limited survey is that England has absorbed more members of this clan than are left in Scotland, and, again, it can be said as a general principle that the English clansmen tend to have proportionately more prosperous members than those left behind in Scotland, and while lack of opportunity in Scotland may be claimed as the cause of this, we suspect that it is due, in part at least, to a genetic loss—the more able migrating, and the less able staying at home.

In so far as one can compare the results from such a limited number of migrants with the national population figures as a whole, it can be concluded that it is possible that the total Scottish blood in the world is not less than 33 million, and since these figures are weighted on the conservative side, as we have pointed out earlier, it would not be surprising if further investigations of this and any related kinds did not lead to the conclusion that 35 million was the correct figure.

In that event the constantly reiterated figure that Scotland has lost by migration 20 million may very well be a substantial understatement of the tremendous loss of people the country has in fact suffered. As these number the most able, the most energetic and progressive, it is a drainage of population of which no country can stand the strain indefinitely. The gain of the goodwill of people who because of Scots ancestry are sentimentally inclined towards Scotland does not offset the losses of that very goodwill which can arise from the country becoming backward, unprogressive and derelict as a very consequence of that excessive loss of people of high quality by emigration.

In an otherwise gloomy position perhaps the percentage one has quoted for settlement in England of 25·71 per cent. is the least alarming feature. This could represent a settlement of between seven and eight million Scots in England. Since many of these are of recent settlement, and many more are sincerely attached to Scotland, a Scotland which once more became the centre of economic, industrial and cultural vitality would become attractive to many of them. Consequently, it is to be hoped that a part, at any rate, of these Scots might be drawn back to their fatherland. They are, at least, not so irretrievably lost to Scotland as are those who settled overseas.

R. G. L. McCrone

Natural Resources and Economic Development

If we may assume that this Symposium was held primarily in answer to widespread dissatisfaction over Scotland's economic development, the collection of data on Scotland's natural resources should be undertaken not so much for its own sake, as to see what light it can shed on the development of the Scottish economy. Scotland's economic growth has been unsatisfactory for much of the last forty years: this has been illustrated by the decline of the older industries and the comparative failure of new industries to take their place. As a consequence unemployment is generally higher in Scotland than in the United Kingdom as a whole and there is a steady flow of emigrants to the south.

The collection of data on natural resources can be of value in the search for a solution to this problem, if it illustrates possible lines of development which have hitherto been neglected. It may also be useful as a means of publicising the existence of exploitable resources in Scotland, for so often, even when resources are known to exist, their exploitation takes place only when attention is focused on them.

But it is clear that an abundance or a shortage of natural resources cannot of itself explain the success or failure of a country's economic development. It must be emphasised that the problem is primarily an economic question and that, although an abundance of natural resources may be a considerable advantage, development will only take place if the economic and social conditions are such as to encourage it. If these conditions were right, it would be perfectly possible for the inhabitants of a desert island to enjoy a fast rate of economic development and a high standard of living by importing fuel and raw materials and exporting manufactured goods. A glance at the situation in countries all over the world confirms this: apart from the United Kingdom, the countries with the highest living standards in Europe are Sweden, Switzerland and Denmark; and none of these can be said to be rich in exploitable natural resources. In Asia, Japan has the highest standard of living and the fastest rate of growth; and she, apart from being one of the most densely populated countries in the world, is very poorly endowed with natural resources. The United Kingdom herself, although originally developing mainly from her own natural resources, now has to rely to a great extent on imports of raw materials and to an increasing degree on imports of fuel; but there is no reason to suppose that this must cause the pace of economic growth to fall or development to give way to unemployment and stagnation.

To understand the problem of Scotland properly it is necessary to remember that Scotland is not an economic unit on its own, but is part of the wider economy of the United Kingdom. The problems facing Scotland are much more comprehensible if examined in this wider context than if they are looked at in isolation.

There are two aspects of the United Kingdom's development which have a bearing on the Scottish problem: The first is that the pace of economic growth in Britain as a whole has not been high, certainly not nearly as high as in Western Germany or France. Had Britain's growth been at this higher rate, it is likely that some of the impact would have spread to the Scottish economy; indeed, such a rate of growth could probably have been achieved only if the idle resources in Scotland were mobilised, since the economy of the southern part of England is fully loaded already. Secondly, this situation in the South and Midlands of England is itself the inverse of the Scottish problem: here instead of unemployment and emigration there has been a constant shortage of labour which has been partly responsible for the tendency towards inflation. This in itself creates a serious problem and the measures the Government have taken to combat inflation have themselves probably impeded economic growth. Meanwhile the southern part of England becomes constantly more congested and the social costs caused by this inconvenience are constantly increasing. These may take the form of traffic congestion, of the destruction of the countryside and its amenity value or simply of personal wear and tear caused by longer journeys and more travelling. Thus it may be suggested that the ever-growing concentration of industrial development in areas which are already crowded, some would say too crowded, is as much a problem in need of a solution as is the reverse situation in Scotland.

To understand this curious imbalance between the north and south it is necessary to discuss the forces which govern the distribution of industry. Britain's industrial areas are still largely determined by the pattern evolved in the nineteenth century. At that time industrial growth took place mainly on and around the coalfields, where power could readily be obtained, or near a port, from whence trade could be conducted with the rest of the United Kingdom, with America or with Europe. But the twentieth century brought very different conditions. Britain now relies very much more on imported raw materials, and even coal is giving place to electricity and oil. The transport system is more developed and the process of manufacture much more complicated than in the industry of the nineteenth century. As a result it would seem that the cost of raw materials and their transport represent a much smaller proportion of the total cost of a finished product. These developments have lessened the need for modern industry to be located where natural resources are available; indeed many modern industries seem to be more concerned about proximity to a wide market. The more complicated processes of manufacture involve a colossal expenditure on capital equipment and very often this leads to huge economies of scale. To exploit these, firms tend to settle near the widest available market, and this leads them to the south.

The most important aspect of this is that the process is cumulative. If firms go to the south because the market there is larger, in doing so they attract more labour, generate more income and make the market in the south still larger. As the drift of population to the south continues, the advantage of the south over the north will increase. Indeed it may be wondered if there is any limit to this movement short of the occupation of all possible sites in the south. But of course if the movement could be halted and if satisfactory growth was started in the north, then correspondingly the handicap of the north would diminish.

Very probably the root of the problem is that there is a net exodus of funds saved in Scotland to investment in projects elsewhere. This would account for the lack of economic dynamism in Scotland; but at the same time the comparatively depressed state of the country is a discouragement to the starting of new projects. This vicious circle can only be broken if some sort of action is taken to attract capital to the north.

One major problem is that no Government has yet been able to devise an economic policy which is sufficiently flexible to meet the diverse needs of all parts of the economy at once. If unemployment is widespread, the Government can adopt budgetary and monetary policies which stimulate demand throughout the economy and increase purchasing power. But in Britain at the present time unemployment is not widespread, it affects only a minority of the country and it is confined to particular areas. The problem affecting the main part of the economy is "overfull employment" and the danger of inflation. The Government is therefore obliged to adopt policies which damp down demand, reduce purchasing power and very probably slow down the economy's rate of growth. Yet these policies are precisely the reverse of what should be applied in areas where there is unemployment and inadequate growth such as Scotland. Clearly the Government has to some extent to try to counteract its own policy in areas where that policy is not applicable. And even if purchasing power could be successfully stimulated in Scotland in contrast to the restraint on the rest of the economy, Scotland is so dependent on England for consumption goods that most of the impact would be transmitted to the south and add to the inflationary problem there.

But whatever the difficulties may be, there seems to be no escaping the fact that the problem is mainly a matter for the Government. It is not sufficient to blame it on the lack of enterprise in Scotland or on the investors who allow their money to be spent on projects in the south. If the right economic climate could be created, there would be no shortage either of enterprise or capital. And if some more selective policy could be found for controlling the economy, it seems likely not only that Scotland's economic development would be encouraged but that the pace of economic growth for Britain as a whole would improve. This would be made possible by utilising the parts of the economy where idle resources existed instead of applying the same anti-inflationary policy to all areas alike.

It would seem that there are two particular ways in which the study of natural resources may help this problem. The first is where there is a clash of interest over the use of a particular resource. This occurs, for example, over forestry and agriculture. It would seem most valuable to carry out a survey of the country to find out which areas could be most suitably devoted to forestry and which should be left for agriculture. It would be important to consider for this not only the land in question but the relative profitability of the two industries over the long period, taking into account the balance of payments contribution of each and the effect of agricultural subsidies. Similar work could very usefully be done to plan for the future of the tourist trade or for the futher development of hydro-electricity. The second way in which a study of this sort could contribute to the Scottish problem is in the examination of the facilities required for the satisfactory running of industries in Scotland. This applies to the whole range of industry from motor cars to tourism. In many cases development may only be held up by the unsatisfactory state of some basic service, and if this is so it would be well worth some initial expenditure on harbour facilities, on roads or on finance for new hotels.

RESOURCE ADMINISTRATION AND DEVELOPMENT

THE MECHANICS OF RESOURCE DEVELOPMENT

Management of Resource Exploitation

TEODORO MOSCOSO
Administrator, Economic Development Administration, Commonwealth of Puerto Rico

Nearly twenty years ago the Government of Puerto Rico concluded that achievement of a decent standard of living would require industrialisation of the island. It was also decided that accelerated economic growth would require extensive Government intervention in economic affairs. The first five years (1942-47) of the effort were primarily devoted to construction and management by Government of several plants. While by no means a failure, the experiment in Government ownership of plants was short-lived. This approach was abandoned because it became apparent that our economic goals could not be realised through State ownership.

The Government-owned plants were sold and the programme was re-directed to emphasise the attraction of private capital to invest in Puerto Rico. Simultaneously, a programme to promote tourism in Puerto Rico was initiated.

Organisationally, both the devices of a public corporation and a regular agency of Government have been employed.

The programme has had some success as measured by the fact that *per capita* annual gross product, in constant dollars, has risen by about 50 per cent. during the past decade; has more than doubled since 1940.

Initiation of industrialisation in a primarily agricultural area characterised by chronic unemployment in turn has generated many problems—economic and social. Achievement by 1975 of Puerto Rico's basic economic objective—a minimum family income of $2,000 annually—will be difficult. Its attainment will probably require both a more vigorous effort by the Commonwealth Government and favourable external circumstances—particularly a peaceful and prosperous U.S.A.

The Government of Puerto Rico has been pursuing an active programme of economic development for eighteen years. I have been associated with this effort since its inception. What I will say is mainly derivative from this experience.

My remarks must be prefaced with two general notes of caution. Geographically, Puerto Rico is a small, densely populated, tropical island—3,500 square miles with a population of slightly less than 2·5 million—670 persons per square mile versus Scotland's 174. Politically, Puerto Rico is uniquely associated with the United States of America. Both geographic fact and the nature of this political association impose limitations on the transferability to other regions of Puerto Rico's experience in resource management for economic growth.

I do not propose here to catalogue what I regard as Puerto Rico's material and non-material resources. It is not that such a catalogue would be lengthy—quite the reverse. It is our paucity of resources of all sorts which has imposed and continues to impose on us in Government an extraordinarily difficult task of management and exploitation.

Some twenty years ago, approximately forty years after Puerto Rico's annexation by the U.S.A., the decision was taken that only by extensive Government intervention in economic affairs was there any hope of changing Puerto Rico from a stagnant or even decaying economic backwater into a growing economy. I would not wish to be misunderstood. What I have just said does not imply that Puerto Rico's economic backwardness was exclusively or even primarily the result of some forty years of, initially, military occupation and of, subsequently, civil government dominated by the Federal capital. I believe the primary reason for our backwardness was our own inertia. What was initiated in the early 1940s could and should have been initiated at least twenty years earlier—shortly after the conclusion of the 1914-18 War.

By far the most important economic result of U.S. rule was that Puerto Rico became basically a one-crop economy—sugar. In economic terms the experience was bitter; in human terms, degrading.

Sugar culture meant a substantially absentee-owned plantation economy affording low-paid job opportunities for about six months each year: a January-June "live" season; a July-December "dead" season. The instability of the sugar market further compounded the problem. From a post-1914-18 War high of 12·6 cents per pound the price fell to 3·9 cents in 1921; to 1·6 cent in 1932 and then rose, under the influence of U.S. farm price support legislation of the mid-1930s, to a price of 1·9 cent in 1940.

In 1940 Puerto Rico could be, as it has been, properly described as "the stricken land". Nor did the wartime economic boom, which was then getting under way in the continental U.S., promise any amelioration of Puerto Rico's economic plight. Indeed, as events were to prove, the active entry of the U.S. into hostilities in 1941 exacerbated, on balance, Puerto Rico's economic difficulties. True, sugar was at a premium in almost every market, but both the quantities which could be shipped and the prices at which they could be sold were controlled by governmental forces external to Puerto Rico. The machinery, equipment and most of the raw materials needed for initiating industrialisation could not be produced locally—they had to be procured and shipped from the U.S. mainland. And, shipping stringencies apart, the machinery and the materials required were most difficult to obtain. These could be procured only if Federal Government priorities could be secured. These were difficult to obtain when it is borne in mind that the production thereby made possible would make no direct contribution to the Allied war effort.

I have referred to the characterisation of Puerto Rico as "the stricken land". I have categorically stated our belief in the necessity of Government intervention to remedy this state of affairs. As a Government official actively associated with the effort to promote economic growth in Puerto Rico, I could hardly be expected to be unbiased in judgments such as these. Let me therefore quote the considered judgment of one whose predilections about Government intervention in economic affairs can, I think, be fairly said to have run in somewhat different directions. I refer to the opinions on Puerto Rico's plight and the need for Government intervention as they were expressed at the beginning of our development effort by the late Senator Robert A. Taft.

The Puerto Rico Development Company which I headed was created in 1942.

In that same year Senator Taft, then a member of the U.S. Senate's Interior and Insular Affairs Committee, visited Puerto Rico.

I now quote the written support given by the late Senator Taft to a priorities request of ours. In a letter dated 12th March 1943, to the late Donald M. Nelson, then Chairman of the U.S. War Production Board, Senator Taft wrote as follows:

> Dear Mr. Nelson,
>
> I understand that the Puerto Rico Glass Corporation, in part financed by the government-owned Puerto Rico Development Company, has applied for priorities on glass-making machinery.
>
> I have just been in Puerto Rico with the Subcommittee of the Senate Territories Committee, investigating social and economic conditions there. In view of the number of people crowded into a small island, I believe that the only possibility of a decent standard of living lies in the industrialisation of the island. The construction of a glass factory will not only give employment to many who would otherwise be out of employment, but it will make it possible to continue other industries now shut down for lack of glass containers and cans. The rum industry and the canning industry must have some assistance, and glass containers can no longer be shipped from the United States because of the shortage of shipping.
>
> The situation in Puerto Rico is not like that in the United States because there is no war work to which the employees of these industries can turn. Furthermore, in view of the shortage of food, canning is essential to provide more food for the people themselves. I have never been very strong for government-supported industry, but the situation in Puerto Rico is such that I believe the government has a proper function in promoting the development of new industry.
>
> I hope that every consideration will be given to the application of the Puerto Rico Glass Corporation.
>
> Sincerely yours,
>
> Robert A. Taft.

May I suggest that the Senator's views about our problems and the necessity for Government intervention for their solution should carry far more weight than any opinions which I might express? I would draw your attention in particular to that part of his letter which reads as follows: ". . . the situation in Puerto Rico is such that I believe the government has a proper function in promoting the development of new industry".

Beginning in 1942-43 and continuing to the present time, our efforts to promote the development of new industry have probably been a special variant of what Professor Galbraith of Harvard University has called "bumblebee economics". The first sentence of a book of his published several years ago reads as follows: "It is told that such are the aerodynamics and wing-loading of the bumblebee that, in principle, it cannot fly."

In principle, the economist counterparts of the aerodynamicists would, no doubt, had they then been interested, have expressed the judgment that Puerto Rico was an "economic bumblebee"—it could never get off the ground. I think that we have gotten off the ground as demonstrated by the fact that in the Western Hemisphere, south of the Rio Grande, Puerto Rican *per capita* national income at $511 annually is second only to that of Venezuela—the world's second-largest producer of petroleum. But getting off the ground, while not easy, is probably not the most difficult of the tasks. If one starts from an appallingly low base, as we in Puerto Rico did, the early rises both in absolute and relative terms are both impressive and dramatic—possibly delusorily so. The very process of initiating economic growth in turn engenders problems—economic and social—of no less severity than those encountered in the initiation of the process, and to some of these I shall allude later in this paper.

To peruse the analogy of aerodynamics, I recall reading the story of Lord Cherwell and the problem of the airplane tailspin during the pioneering aviation days of the 1914-1918 War. Cherwell, so the story goes, satisfied himself by formulas and his slide-rule that a pilot could pull his plane out of a spin. But a workroom demonstration was hardly sufficient. Cherwell learned to fly; put a plane into a spin; then demonstrated that the plane could be pulled out of the spin to climb again.

Puerto Rico is now at a point in its economic growth where we feel insecure about going into a tailspin. The rates of climb are no longer so rapid as in earlier days. And the problems are not such as to be susceptible of workroom solutions via formulas and the slide-rule. Nor were such workroom solutions available either in the earlier days. But at least some of the first steps were reasonably straightforward. Reference has been made to the glass plant. As in most backward countries an early step (1942) was that of Government purchase of a cement plant (in addition to silica sands for the glass plant, one of the few raw materials available in Puerto Rico in a measure of economic abundance is limestone).

But because, as I have noted, Puerto Rico could do nothing of consequence by way of industrial war production our efforts to industrialise could not assume significant proportions until the conclusion of hostilities and the elimination of the critical materials shortages of the immediate post-war period.

Looking back, it was possibly just as well that external circumstances held back our effort during the period 1942-47. During those five years we had purchased and expanded one plant and had planned and built four others. Additionally we had had only the most limited success in promoting private industry to build new plants—fewer than a score.

In summary, the Development Company had created of the order of 2,000 new jobs and its investments were generating perhaps $4 million of new income annually.

But as we are all dead in the long run these rates of progress, if such they can be called, were wholly unsatisfactory. The dimensions of the task were estimated to be as follows: more than 200,000 new jobs had to be created; new income to be generated must exceed a thousand million dollars annually. At the rate of the first five years of our development effort the task would have taken five centuries; we were and remain determined to compress this effort into a quarter-century.

The ambitiousness of our goals or, perhaps more accurately, the imperatives derivative from our gloomy prospects required that our efforts be re-directed.

At this point it may be useful if I interpolate briefly both on our first five years of experience and more generally on our mode of grappling with our problems both then and now. The method of operation both then and now essentially is one of "cut and try". In more elegant language it can perhaps be described, at least so far as I am concerned, as empiricism tempered with impatience. The empiricist is almost certain to make mistakes—I know that we have made a number. But I also submit that there was and is no body of theory—no comprehensive set of basic principles—to which one in my position could or can turn for guidance. We have read and heard much during the recent past of phrases such as "take-off", "achievement of sustained growth", etc. But these phrases, more particularly the evaluations underlying them, provide no guidance for solution of the problems with which I must cope. They do not help in accomplishment, for example, of the desirable diversion of a part of the substantial amounts of local savings now going into real estate speculation to productive industrial investment.

By experience, both failures and successes, we have been able to distill a few helpful principles. Basic services such as electric power, for example, must be in the van of the pace of economic growth generally. Otherwise the actual pace of growth will be slower than the possible pace of growth. Commercial services, branch banking and supermarkets as examples cannot be neglected. A growing tourist industry interlocks with and strengthens the effort to industrialise. Special attention and effort must be given those industries and plants capable of both backward and forward integration into the economy —a modern slaughterhouse and packing plant, for example, which will both stimulate healthy local livestock and poultry industries and give the final consumer more value for his money.

Such principles, I repeat, are derivative from empiricism. And in my own case, as I have said, it is an empiricism tempered by impatience. I have often had the experience, for example, of one or another of the economists on my staff advising me that a project under consideration was not feasible. When given such advice my inclination has invariably been the same: do not abandon the project; replace the economist. Do not mistake my meaning. One of the necessary occupational hazards of my job is that of listening frequently to the jargon of the economists on my staff. When the jargon is translated into straightforward, generally understandable language, I have often found that it makes surprisingly good sense.

To revert to 1947 and the re-direction of our efforts, one wholly negative conclusion stood out. Our experience to that date had demonstrated that we could not achieve, within a reasonable time, our economic and social goals through Government purchase, or construction, and operation of industrial plants. Quite apart from the inherent institutional problems of Government as producer, employer and wage negotiator, caught in the cross-fire of producer and consumer interests, the fact was that the financial resources available to Government were wholly inadequate for the task at hand. Another negative conclusion was also derivative from our experience: local private capital would probably not be forthcoming, at least initially, in other than small amounts to invest in new industrial enterprises. By elimination, therefore, the bulk of the investments required to create more than 200,000 new job opportunities must be outside venture capital attracted to Puerto Rico.

A footnote may here be in order. The supply of capital, public and private, is in greater or lesser degree always short everywhere. That is no doubt why there exists that phenomenon known as the rate of interest—sometimes described as "the price of time".

Time is particularly short in a backward area such as Puerto Rico; capital, Government capital in particular, is scarce; rates of interest are high. The competition, and I use the word advisedly, within Government for scarce financial resources is severe. At present, and for some years past, about 50 per cent. of total Commonwealth Government budgetary expenditures have been accounted for by health, education and welfare disbursements. Such expenditures are an integral part of the essential foundation of any economic development programme.

Then there is the matter in our case of an adequate road network—the privately owned railway once serving Puerto Rico has been liquidated by court action and while sea and air intra-island transport are technologically feasible and such services do in fact exist our basic dependence for intra-island movement of people and goods is on our road network. Highway construction and maintenance are expensive. Then there are the usual functions of Government such as police and fire protection and the administration of justice. When a balance-sheet is struck, little is left for other purposes, including financial support of an agency devoted to promotion of economic growth.

We in Puerto Rico have therefore used the instrument of the public corporation extensively to ease the pressure on scarce Governmental financial resources. By legislative authority, for example, the Puerto Rico Industrial Development Company is empowered to sell revenue bonds in the private capital markets; to make both loans and equity investments. Of course, to sell such bonds a prospective earnings record is necessary; a microscopic scrutiny of the existing balance-sheet inevitable. These are not easy tests to pass.

I believe that without the device of the public corporation our economic growth would not have been possible. There were not and are not sufficient Government financial resources to cover all the problems. Education is without doubt the prime case in point. Illiteracy and economic growth are simply not compatible. As a precondition of substantial economic growth the attack on illiteracy must be massive and as such it is necessarily expensive. Today the official statistics show that 15 per cent. of the Puerto Rican population ten years of age and older is illiterate. This is probably an underestimate in that literacy is a symbol of status, as is well realised by many of those living in this particular darkness who in confronting the census enumerator are at pains to profess even though incapable if put to the test of demonstrating their proficiency in this "cabalistic" art. The highest of priorities has properly been accorded in the allocation of Government resources to eradication of this blot of shame: illiteracy.

The calls on Government resources were and are such that such of these as could be devoted directly to economic growth had to be and continue to be directed primarily to the promotion of private capital to invest in Puerto Rico. I have already alluded to the attraction of private local savings to real estate speculation. By elimination, we concluded thirteen years ago that Puerto Rico's economic salvation could be achieved on our compressed timetable only by attraction on a massive scale of outside capital. This meant, in our case, primarily one source—the U.S. mainland investment community.

I referred earlier to the fact that during our first five years our record of attracting private industrial investment capital was unimpressive. Two things seemed required. First, we had to make the mainland business community aware of Puerto Rico's existence. If asked, probably no more than one in a hundred adult mainlanders could place Puerto Rico within one thousand miles of its actual location. Almost certainly Cuba a dozen years ago was far better known to far more Americans than was Puerto Rico. Second, it was judged unlikely that a potential mainland investor, once made aware of Puerto Rico's existence, would choose to locate in Puerto Rico, a strange and different area—in a cultural sense at least largely alien territory—unless positive inducements were offered him. I will turn in a moment to our attempts to reach a mainland audience and the matter of special investment incentives.

Now I want to try to explain the interrelationship between our effort at industrialisation and that specialised form of commerce known as tourism. We were aware of the success which some of our Caribbean neighbours, Cuba notably, were having by way of attracting visitors from the U.S. mainland. Why could not Puerto Rico do the same? One obstacle was apparent—where could such visitors be housed? There was nowhere in Puerto Rico a hotel of the first class as measured by mainland standards.

Availability of hotel accommodations of the first class had in fact, we believed, a significance extending beyond the attraction of tourist visitors as such. It seemed unlikely that any potential mainland investor would choose Puerto Rico as a factory location without making an advance, on the spot, survey of local conditions. The potential mainland investor, particularly one with an expense-account mentality engendered by the annual depredations of the U.S. Collector of Internal Revenue, would expect, as a matter of natural right, to stay in hotel accommodations of the first class. Our concern about housing the potential investor went deeper than this. Were he forced to stay in the dreary, inefficient commercial class accommodations then available, might not his initial impression of Puerto Rico be so sour as to bias him against a decision to locate in Puerto Rico? We believed this concern to be soundly based.

Our sense of urgency about the matter was such that we decided that reliance upon private investors would be both too risky and too time-consuming. We decided that the Industrial Development Company would finance the construction of a hotel of the first class.

The result was the Caribe Hilton Hotel in San Juan. Hilton is the more significant word in the hotel's double-barrelled name particularly in view of the fact that the hotel fronts on the Atlantic Ocean rather than on the Caribbean Sea. The geographic licence involved is, I suggest, legitimate. Caribe has something of an exotic savour to it (at least to those unfamiliar with the word's literal meaning, and these must be legion; the only exceptions probably being some mainland professors of Romance languages and it is most unlikely that any of these can afford the rates associated with hotel accommodations of the first class). To have named the hotel the Atlantic Hilton Hotel would have been impossible. Imagine the image created by this name in the mind of the New Yorker examining the travel supplement of his copy of a Sunday issue of the *New York Times*. Could the initial image be other than that of the boardwalk at Atlantic City, New Jersey?

But, as I have said, the name Hilton is more significant than the geographic part of the hotel's name. Site selection, the securing of competent architects, detailed scrutiny of architectural plans, financing of construction; all of these constituted for us a big project indeed. But hotel accommodations of the first class have both management and physical dimensions. The former is probably more critical to success than the latter. In any event we realised that the managerial skills did not exist in Puerto Rico to handle the multitude of problems involved in operation of a first-class hotel.

Some twenty-five years ago Sinclair Lewis wrote a book called *Work of Art*. I believe that the literary critics did not regard it as one of his better books, but to me, if I grasped it correctly, Lewis's theme was interesting. What I thought he was trying to say boils down to about this: it is true that America has not produced say an El Greco, but is not a well-managed hotel, an enterprise in which the Americans have demonstrated their competence, in some sense a work of art?

One thing at least was and is clear: the hotelkeeper who would impose his tastes on his guests rather than cater to theirs, particularly guests from the U.S. mainland, has taken a long forward step in the direction of bankruptcy proceedings.

After a careful evaluation of several possibilities the Industrial Development Company entered into a contractual agreement with the Hilton Hotels Corporation whereby the latter assumed full managerial responsibility. The hotel, including a substantial expansion, has now been in successful operation for some eleven years. The Caribe Hilton has done and continues to do both of its jobs well. It has provided pleasant tourist resort accommodations; it has provided a home away from home for the mainland businessman with whom we are in negotiation in an attempt to persuade him to invest in a Puerto Rico plant location.

And the success of the Caribe Hilton accomplished something else. The old adage has it that nothing succeeds like success. This seems to have been proved true in the case of the Caribe Hilton. There are now in operation in the San Juan metropolitan area several hotels of the first class. Several more hotel projects for this area are in advanced stages of negotiation. There is now in operation to the west of San Juan a hotel of the luxury class and a similar one is under construction east of San Juan. On Puerto Rico's south coast overlooking the Caribbean Sea and Puerto Rico's second-largest city, Ponce, there was opened early this year a hotel of the first class. This last fact, together with the fact that several hotel projects distributed about the island are under active consideration, is encouraging. Our aim has been and is the decentralization of tourism. Another encouraging fact is that the bulk of the financing for the hotel projects subsequent to the Caribe Hilton has come from private, not Government, sources.

My account of the promotion of tourism in Puerto Rico would, however, be incomplete were I to fail to note the expressions of local concern, usually based on cultural and philosophic grounds, that promotion of tourism is a nasty business. I regard objections on these grounds as nonsense. The culture unable to withstand the impact of transients is not worthy of the name.

There are two things, however, which we will not tolerate. First, we will not permit any of our beach fronts to be solidly lined with concrete blocks varying in height from, say, six to twenty floors. Second, we believe that the ordinary Puerto Rican has as much right to enjoy a beach as the tourist who is paying, say, $20 to $60 a day for hotel accommodations. Public beach facilities available either at no cost or at a nominal cost to the user have been and will continue to be developed. Government has a responsibility to conserve and to develop such resources for the benefit of all its citizens; not merely the affluent—whether visitor or native.

My remarks on tourism may strike you as having been a digression from the story of Puerto Rico's attempts to industrialise. I do not believe this to be the case. Some at least of the transients visiting Puerto Rico do not spend all their daylight hours taking the sun on the beach or fishing. We estimate that about 10 per cent. of the industrial plants of mainland origin in Puerto Rico directly or indirectly resulted from transient visits.

Moving from estimate to personal knowledge, let me note our experience with our first petroleum refinery (we now have two). Promotion of a petroleum refinery was a major objective of our early attempts to attract private mainland capital to Puerto Rico. These efforts to secure a petroleum refinery were unsuccessful even though two major U.S. oil companies and a major British company (nominally identified with a nation across the North Sea) had each marketed petroleum products in Puerto Rico for many years. A transient in Puerto Rico, an executive of a U.S. oil company, with whom I came in casual conversation, was told of our unsuccessful efforts to secure a refinery. He expressed some interest and enquired whether it might be possible to look at possible sites (need I say that I was only too delighted to put an automobile at his disposal?) and in due course (which roughly translated meant a lot of hard work both by private industry and the Puerto Rican Government) in 1955 an oil refinery began to process crude oil in Puerto Rico—the initial investment of $12 million being the largest single investment to that time in an individual private industrial plant in Puerto Rico. But our industrialisation effort, or rather the achievement of our ambitious economic goals, could not be and is not based upon casual conversation with transients.

We have attempted to institutionalise (horrid word) our work in economic development by bringing and holding together as its core several groups of professional civil servants. I use the word groups advisedly because of the diversity of the tasks involved. Perhaps the diversity of these tasks can be gotten at by noting that I wear not one but several official hats.

Within a short time after re-direction of our efforts from Government ownership and operation of plants to attraction of private capital it became apparent that the tasks were too many for our then-existing organisation even though all the formerly Government-owned plants had been sold to private investors and we no longer had any direct responsibility for their management.

One of the hats which I have worn for the past ten years has been that of Administrator of the Economic Development Administration, a Government agency and not a public corporation as was, and is, our original development company. The assumption of this hat did not mean the liquidation of our development company—far from it: its assets are today worth over 85 million dollars. And it may be of interest to note that in origin this company was floated on a "tidal" wave of 1939-45 War rum shipments to the U.S. mainland as indeed were most of the public corporations now operating in Puerto Rico. Given our unique political relationship with the U.S.A., the U.S. Internal Revenue Code (excise, personal and corporate income taxes), with relatively minor exceptions, is not applicable to Puerto Rico. One feature of this unique relationship as it applies to fiscal relations is that rum distilled in Puerto Rico and marketed in the U.S. mainland results in remission to the Treasury Department of the Commonwealth of Puerto Rico of the Federal excise tax on such distilled spirits. Such remissions were the basis of the capitalisation of our development company. While I have no acquaintance with the relevant figures, I imagine that if a similar fiscal relationship obtained as between Scotland and England in the matter of Scotch whisky sales there would be no dearth of industrial promotional capital here. Particularly when it is considered that the quality of Scotch whisky is a fact long established while quality control of rum, on which we are working hard, is of comparatively recent development.

The company had developed by 1947 and continues to exercise valuable and essential skills in the specialised fields of finance and physical planning—site selection, site preparation and building design and construction. What was lacking ten years ago was a professional organisation equipped to locate and attract the private investor. The experience of the past ten years has demonstrated that the activities of the two organisations—the development company and the development administration—interlock. If the activities in fact interlock, why then not a single rather than a dual organisation? The answer emerges from definition of the rather different tasks involved. Financial and real estate operations require a degree of flexibility which is most expeditiously achieved through the corporate form of organisation. More than this is involved—it is not really a matter of comparative efficiencies so much as the need for an instrument which can tap the private capital market so as to ease somewhat the ever-present pressure on scarce Government budget resources. The public corporation with specialised functions, however, tends to be self-contained and as the development effort touches intimately upon most parts of the social fabric it seemed to us desirable to make basic policy functions an integral part of the regular Governmental apparatus. Additionally, the daily operations of our development effort are dependent for their success on close working relationships with most other agencies of the Commonwealth Government.

That the duality of organisation fuses into a singleness of purpose can be illustrated by the Spanish names of the two organisations. The development company is called *Compania de Fomento Industrial.* The development administration is called *Administracion de Fomento Economico.* The key word in each title is of course *Fomento,* a word which can be rendered variously: *promotion, encouragement, development, aid.* In verb form *fomentar* either in Spanish or when rendered into English has a more urgent, and appropriate, overtone.

Promotion, encouragement, development, aid—all of these are a part of our job. To do these jobs the full-time clerical and professional staffs of the Development Company and the Development Administration total approximately 675 persons, including 125 stationed on a full-time basis in the U.S. mainland. But these staffs do not comprehend all the technical skills required to do our job. A substantial part of our work is contracted out to consulting firms both on a retainer basis and a spot contract basis to handle particular problems which seem, incidentally, to have a nasty habit of arising frequently.

Such activities necessarily involve financial outlays. I therefore summarise below the amounts budgeted for the Development Administration (figures relating to the Development Company are excluded because financially it is self-sustaining) for the fiscal year which began 1st July 1960:

1. Advertising	$1,970,000
2. Staff salaries	1,690,000
3. Travel and communications	230,000
4. Consultant fees	225,000
5. Rent	225,000
6. Other	1,350,000
Total	$5,690,000

In the disposition of our budget I believe that I can fairly claim to have defied that law formulated by Professor C. Northcote Parkinson concerning Government activities:

"Expenditure rises to meet income." Indeed, to be applicable to our case I believe the law would have to be reversed, plurals substituted, and then expanded to read as follows: "Incomes rise as functions of expenditures, and at rates many times that of unity." The word which properly characterises our budget is *investment*, not *expenditure*. For every dollar so invested we believe that our experience to date demonstrates a twenty- to thirty-fold return for the economy of Puerto Rico as a whole. For every dollar so invested there is at least a five-fold return to the Treasury Department of the Commonwealth of Puerto Rico.

Because of its magnitude, the advertising item in the budget is worthy of comment. The item provides for several distinct programmes linked, however, by a central theme—that of telling the story of Puerto Rico. For the most part the audience we are trying to reach is the U.S. mainland, which accounts for more than 90 per cent. of our advertising budget.

What immediately follows is concerned with our U.S. mainland advertising programmes.

First, our industrial promotion advertising. This is hinged to the incentives, principally exemption from the Puerto Rican corporate income tax which the investor may qualify for, which the Puerto Rican Government offers. Direct mail campaigns are used. The bulk of our industrial advertising expenditures are, however, accounted for by series placed both in the daily Press and in periodicals.

Second, our tourism advertising. We prepare and distribute brochures, but the bulk of our expenditures are again accounted for by series placed in the daily Press and in periodicals.

Third, our rum promotion advertising. Specialised and localised promotion efforts are undertaken. For example, the tourist arriving at San Juan's International Airport is offered a drink while waiting for his luggage to be brought into the terminal. Localised promotional campaigns are mounted in selected mainland metropolitan centres. The bulk of the expenditures are accounted for, however, by series placed in periodicals.

Fourth, our cultural-scenic advertising. This series is placed exclusively in periodicals. This series is, I suppose, what the Madison Avenue practitioners regard as a "soft sell" by way of contrast to the "hard sell" of the other three campaigns.

Initially we were self-conscious if not actually squeamish about mounting advertising campaigns. Was it dignified (the Spanish "dignidad" probably has subtler overtones than its English equivalent) to funnel the Puerto Rican story through the account executives and the copy writers of the professional New York City advertising mill? From my own experience I should like to venture two comments. First, the caricature popularly known as "the huckster" is, as are all caricatures, a gross distortion of reality. Second, and once again from personal experience, there is no one so amateur as the amateur who fancies himself competent to prepare effective advertising copy. So for a number of years our advertising has been in the professional hands of a firm with New York headquarters (Fifth not Madison Avenue, however)—Ogilvy, Benson & Mather, Inc. I might note in passing that the president of the firm is by birth a Scot.

Let me dispose of the matter in this way. I have described myself as an empiricist. I also regard myself as a pragmatist and as such I firmly believe that such progress as we have made would have been impossible without our professionally directed advertising campaigns. In the popular, inelegant, but apt Mainland phrase—advertising has been the instrument by means of which we have gotten most of the "customers into the store".

Getting the customer into the store is essential. But ours is not a bargain basement operation—the customers do not elbow their way to a counter to snatch up a bargain. The potential investor, if he is prudent, and we do not wish to attract imprudent ones, wishes to investigate for himself and to ask innumerable questions—and properly so.

This means that there is no such thing as a typical industrial promotion case. And in turn it follows from all this why we must maintain a substantial full-time staff. The hard and protracted work begins only after the customer is in the store. More often than not he will make more than one visit to Puerto Rico in addition to enquiries by mail. We have found that the large industrial project in the multi-million dollar class will almost invariably require an investigative period measured in years; not months. Then, of course, the ultimate failures far outnumber the successes achieved. But failures as well as successes involve hard work on our part—we estimate that of all mainland visitors to Puerto Rico who investigate industrial investment possibilities there are six whose decisions are negative in relation to one whose decision is positive.

And the volume of work is compounded in that our job is far more than that of an enquiry-answering service. We seek, for example, to exert an influence on the potential investors' choice of a specific site location. One reason for this is Puerto Rico's geography. On its east-west axis Puerto Rico is cut by a mountainous spine with peaks ranging to heights of over 4,000 feet. The mountains are beautiful to look at from a coastal plain or from an airplane. Economically, a decent living cannot be scratched from their soil.

We have therefore tried and continue to try to influence the potential investor to consider an inland site. We have had only limited success, and for understandable reasons. Roads are in poor condition, telephone service is either non-existent or unreliable, schools and hospitals are inadequate, commercial facilities are primitive, social amenities virtually non-existent. The prospects for the foreseeable future of creating job opportunities in the mountains for the unemployed and the underemployed are poor, even though we have offered and continue to offer special inducements to the potential investor to locate his plant in these areas.

There are limits to the influence which we can appropriately bring to bear on the site location decision of the potential investor. The poor, after all, cannot afford to be too choosy. If the potential investor insists on a coastal plain, metropolitan location then we must defer to his wishes even though we would prefer that he choose an inland location or a non-metropolitan coastal plain location. Though I regret it very much, the conclusion seems inescapable that in most cases unemployed workers must move to their jobs because it seems most unlikely that it will prove possible for us to bring the required job opportunities to them.

An even more intractable but fortunately, in human terms, much smaller problem exists in the case of our off-shore islands. About 10,000 persons are involved; less than $\frac{1}{2}$ of 1 per cent. of Puerto Rico's total population. No matter how wretchedly poor their economic environment, these people are stubbornly attached to the places of their birth; and I admire them for the depth of their attachment. The problem is what can be done now for the people now living there. The direct benefits which they have derived from Puerto Rico's industrialisation have been insubstantial.

We believe that development of tourism is probably the only practicable solution to the otherwise likely alternative of economic strangulation via depopulation. One of the several hats which I wear is that of a one-man board of directors of the Puerto Rico Ports Authority—a public corporation charged with the responsibilities of developing and operating commercial seaports and airports. Our off-shore islanders benefit, of course, only indirectly and marginally from general revenue expenditures for highway improvement. Their highways are necessarily either the sea or the air. As a basic tenet of our Government is that there is no such person as a second-class Puerto Rican citizen, the Puerto Rico Ports Authority is currently subsidising reasonably efficient transport by sea in hydrofoils and is actively investigating subsidisation of air transport as a necessary condition for development of off-shore tourist centres.

There is another dimension than that of geographic location which substantially increases the volume of our work. We cannot simply mount a direct mail campaign or insert a series of advertisements in U.S. publications and then wait for the enquiries to come to us. There are some plants and industries which we go after by the "door-bell-ringing" method. This is of course enormously time-consuming and can be afforded only when the result sought promises to be unusually rewarding. To illustrate, during the past year I spent a considerable amount of time, including several trips to the mainland, in an effort to secure location of a major petrochemical operation in Puerto Rico. The magnitude of the investment involved—$30 million—was consequential but in my judgment the least of the considerations involved. Two other considerations seemed far more important. First, the petrochemical plant would serve to redress one of Puerto Rico's inherent weaknesses—our scarcity of indigenous raw materials. Second, expansion capabilities (with the exception of one artificial limitation to which I shall allude in a moment) are limited in petrochemicals only by the growth of the market—the market in this case being not primarily Puerto Rico but Western Europe and the mainland U.S.

Now let me touch on another case which we have worked on, which has not come to fruition and is unlikely to do so. We have done some "door-bell-ringing" in an effort to secure a major shipyard operation for Puerto Rico. The industry people to whom we have talked have had two major concerns. First, practically all the materials, machinery and equipment would have to be shipped into Puerto Rico. Second, could a skilled labour force be trained and then held together in view of the highly cyclical character of the industry? The matter of dependence on outside sources for materials and equipment could probably be solved at tolerable economic costs. It was and is the matters of training and retaining a skilled labour force which posed the great uncertainty; or, rather, uncertainties. For the industrialist the training of shipfitters, welders and carpenters is expensive, and these skills are transferable to other industries. Could he hold together his labour force in slack times? And on our side this uncertainty was viewed from a somewhat different angle. There were and are considerable risks in investing heavily in an industry which is not only subject to sharp cyclical fluctuations but is also heavily influenced by the caprices of U.S. Government action. With tanker rates, for example, at Scale—60 per cent. or even lower, I think that we shall continue to concentrate our efforts, as we have been doing recently, on promoting a ship-breaking rather than a ship-building operation.

Let me touch on another case which has not come to fruition. I refer to an integrated steel mill. The economists on my staff think poorly of this idea. My answer to them has been that if Japan can import coking coal and iron ore from thousands of miles away why cannot Puerto Rico do the same? The resolution of the question lies not in cost of supplies and technological feasibility. These matters could be resolved, but the question of markets dominates. We have gained some insight into the problem of markets in this industry by virtue of the fact that there exists in Puerto Rico a firm which produces reinforcing bars by the electric furnace process using locally generated scrap as its basic raw material. In normal times the firm can undersell U.S.-fabricated bars in the Puerto Rican market and make a profit. But in the 1957-58 business recession the firm found the going very rough indeed as a result of very sharp price competition from continental European suppliers—and I use the plural advisedly. On balance I think that we shall confine our activities to promotion of sufficient capacity to supply the local market for reinforcing bars. We shall leave the far more ambitious project of an integrated steel mill to our Venezuelan neighbours in the Caribbean who, if financial losses should occur, can presumably cover them with oil royalty revenues.

Implicitly in my discussion of the shipyard and the integrated steel mill projects I think that the fundamental question for Government policy has been and is that of shelter behind a protective wall. This is what our Venezuelan friends have done and I think are doing in the case of their nationalised, integrated steel industry. I have no objection in principle to such protectionism. Quite the reverse; I believe that a necessary condition for success of a poor area's industrialisation effort is a measure of protectionism. What I do insist upon is that such protectionism shall not be open-ended. Protectionism must be limited in time. It must be limited in financial amount.

Our industrial investment incentives—exemption from corporate income taxes, exemption from local property taxes, financial grants for location in rural areas, grants for worker training—are a special kind of protectionism. In every case that protectionism is limited both in time and financial amount. And this is, I suggest, as it should be but rarely is in the world today. Few of the firms which locate plants in Puerto Rico are from infant industries, but all which so locate are, at least initially, infant plants in Puerto Rico. If they manage to grow up, which we always hope they will do, they automatically lose their protection. If they falter, their protection will have been of no avail.

While Puerto Rico is an integral part of the U.S. tariff area, I must note with regret that the concept of protectionism which obtains generally and is practised in Washington is of the open-end variety. It has been alleged, and not without reason, that Washington's foreign economic policy is schizoid in character. On the one hand, thousands of millions of dollars are annually extended as foreign aid from Washington. On the other hand, Washington always jumps to attention when domestic producer groups point a finger at a threat of foreign competition.

Let me sketch a recent case in point and one which I believe to be of substantial and growing consequence. In 1959 the U.S. imposed strict quantitative controls on all imports of crude oil and its derivatives. The stated reason for such action was that the prospective levels of such imports threatened the national security. However, the suspicious mind cannot dismiss the possibility that the restrictions imposed were in fact the result of a working alliance of the moment between the U.S. producers of domestic crude oil and of bituminous coal. I say a "working alliance of the moment" because these two groups are most unlikely to agree for long on anything.

The domestic oil producers were in the van of the restrictionist movement. Dull or sharp, the scissors of economic forces can cut. In this case one blade is the fact that the average price of U.S.-produced crude oil at the well rose from about $1.20 per barrel at the close of the 1939-45 War to over $3.00 during 1958. The other blade of the scissors is the rapid rise during the same period of proved reserves of very cheaply producible Middle East crude oils. Such oils, even though they must be transported many thousands of miles, can be delivered in the U.S.—even into the heart of Texas—at prices substantially cheaper than those for comparable quality domestic crudes.

It has been stated that the direct and immediate cost of these restrictions to U.S. consumers is of the order of $10 million daily. If this estimate is anywhere near the mark, then on an annual basis this is a tidy sum even for the U.S.—roughly the equivalent of the amount now annually being granted by Washington in the form of foreign aid. And the indirect costs resulting from retaliatory actions taken by other countries will no doubt steadily increase in amounts.

I would be less than frank if I failed to note that these particular restrictions are prejudicial to our efforts to industrialise.

First, an assured supply of commercial energy selling at reasonable prices is a necessary condition for successful prosecution of our development effort. This means in our case residual fuel oil preferably derivative from imported crude oil refined locally. Under normal marketing relationships as they have obtained in the past, with residual fuel oil selling at a lower price than the crude from which it is refined, coal is not competitive with oil as boiler fuel in Puerto Rico. Oil has two inherent economic advantages over coal: greater ease of handling and a B.Th.U. content of about 40 million per ton as compared with about 25 to 26 million for U.S. bituminous coal.

Second, I referred earlier to our promotion last year of a major petrochemical plant. The feedstock for this plant must be imported petroleum products. More generally the work of the organic chemists with hydrocarbons is full of promise for Puerto Rico where commercially exploitable raw materials are few. Technologically, it is equally feasible for the organic chemist to move from hydrocarbons in solid form (coal) to liquids or from hydrocarbons in liquid form (oil) to solids. For economic reasons which I have noted such future as our synthetic organic chemical industry may have is likely to be a function of the availability of imported oil.

Let me turn now to a project which is linked to U.S. trade restrictions generally and which may also serve to illustrate both the diversity and the time-consuming nature of our work. A few months ago the U.S. Secretary of Commerce approved the creation of a foreign trade zone in Mayaguez—Puerto Rico's third-largest city and a commercial seaport. This approval was the culmination of more than six years of active planning and negotiations.

Briefly, a U.S. foreign trade zone functions as follows. An importer can bring his materials into the zone without restriction as to quantities and without payment of import duties. The product or products fabricated within the zone will then presumably be sold either in foreign or U.S. markets. If the former, no U.S. import duties are levied. If the latter, U.S. duties are assessed, but not on the product as such but at rates appropriate to the contained raw material content of the product. To illustrate with an example of possible practical utility, the U.S. has in effect a stiff tariff-quota applicable to imported woollens. Such fabrics could be brought into the Mayaguez zone without limitation and there fabricated into garments. This could of course also be done in any one of the several U.S. mainland foreign trade zones. But there is one possibly important difference. If such a manufacturing operation were to be located in the Mayaguez zone, it might well qualify for ten years' exemption from corporate income taxes together with other possible incentives.

I should like to make one other comment on this matter. San Juan, both as commercial centre and seaport, is far larger than Mayaguez. Would not the prospects for ultimate financial success of the zone be better were it to be located in San Juan rather than in Mayaguez? The answer to the question is undoubtedly *yes*. But there were other matters to consider in making the locational decision. For a number of years it has been apparent that Mayaguez has been declining as a commercial port. Unless some stimulus could be applied, it appeared to us likely that Mayaguez would eventually die as a commercial port. To illustrate, preliminary 1960 U.S. census returns indicate that both San Juan and Ponce registered substantial population gains while Mayaguez registered a loss. I doubt that creation of the zone will be Mayaguez' economic salvation; I very much hope that its creation will help to arrest the declines of both city and port.

I am afraid that I have already imposed too greatly on your time and patience and that much of what I have said has been fragmentary and episodic. However, if you will bear with me, I would like to attempt to formulate some generalisations about our basic objectives, our economic point of departure, where we seem to be now, where we hope to be fifteen years hence and some of the problems we now foresee.

As to basic objectives, the demands of our daily routine in promoting economic growth are such that we tend to forget that most things we do are means; not ends in themselves. We therefore try to remind ourselves, and frequently, that the justification of what we do lies not in the number of new plants promoted but rather in making possible a decent standard of living and a modest amount of comfort for an ever-increasing number of human beings. I believe that the only thing we are doing which could be characterised as an end in itself is our sponsorship and management of the annual Casals musical festival in San Juan, initiated in 1957 and inspired incidentally by your own Edinburgh festival.

I have spoken earlier in qualitative terms of our point of departure during the early years of the 1939-45 War. I now invite your attention to certain of the quantitative data annexed as Tables I and II to this paper. In particular, note that twenty years ago our estimated *per capita* annual gross product (expressed in 1954 dollars) was $269 and that estimated illiteracy of the population ten years of age and over was in excess of 30 per cent. These are no doubt disgraceful figures for an area which had then been a possession of the U.S.A. for forty years. But it is also probably true that our point of departure was an advantaged one as compared with the areas, for example, of equatorial Africa and those of most of Asia which have recently initiated economic development programmes. Ours was probably a more advantaged point of departure than that of most countries of the Mediterranean basin—a relatively rich area extending from the "fertile crescent" of ancient times through the Straits of Gibraltar to the Atlantic coasts of the Iberian Peninsula on the north and Morocco on the south. I commend to your attention in this connection an excellent survey article, prepared by a technician of the United Nations' Food and Agriculture Organisation, which appeared in the July 1960 issue of the *Scientific American* on the problems and prospects of the Mediterranean basin—the

Government	*	44	50	55	57	62	65
Other	*	170	169	175	170	166	171
Unemployment	66[2]	69	97	85	84	82	90
Per cent. of labor force	11[2]	11	15	13	13	13	14
Consumers' Price Index (1947-49: 100)	*	*	113·1	112·7	116·2	120·1	122·7
E.D.A. promoted and assisted factories in operation as at the end of the year (cumulative since 1947)[3]:							
Promoted plants Num.	*	50	292	354	423	468	533
Assisted plants Id.	*	2	32	53	65	80	96
Agriculture:							
Value of production (millions of dollars)	84	192	212	222	205	216	228[p]
Transportation and Communication:							
Number of registered motor vehicles as of June 30	26,847	57,258	105,413	116,346	127,930	140,197	156,563
Number of telephones in service as of June 30	16,778	30,852	47,789	53,452	58,360	63,607	68,438
External Trade:							
Exports (millions of dollars)	92	204	353	406	446	467	503
Per capita (dollars)	49	93	156	179	196	202	215
Imports (millions of dollars)	107	351	575	633	710	728	807
Per capita (dollars)	57	160	254	279	311	315	345
Banking as of June 30 (millions of dollars):							
Bank deposits	76	251	323	357	404	446	508
Private checking accounts	28	84	112	119	134	149	169
Private savings accounts	17	49	77	86	103	129	139
Government accounts	27	88	89	90	98	89	103
Other	4	31	47	63	70	79	97
Loans	33	119	217	266	310	331	387
Debits	73	275	418	427	448	535	705
Assets	93	326	414	475	518	552	619
Investments	4	138	117	125	116	120	133
Vital Statistics:							
Population (thousands)	1,869[4]	2,185	2,263	2,267	2,281	2,317	2,340[p]
Net migration	497	−34,011	−31,182	−61,647	−48,284	−25,956	−37,212

Note—See p. 686 for Explanatory Notes

Table I (*continued*)

Item	1939-40	1948-49	1954-55	1955-56	1956-57	1957-58	1958-59
Birth rate (per 1,000 population)	39·0	39·0	34·9	34·2	33·3	31·8	31·9
Death rate (per 1,000 population)	18·2	11·4	7·4	7·1	6·9	7·2	6·8
Life expectancy (years)	46	61[5]	68[5]	68[5]	68[5]	68[5]	68[5]
Number of physicians[6]	509	855	1,419	1,510[r]	1,744[r]	1,804[r]	1,644
Persons per physician	3,672	2,556	1,595	1,501[r]	1,308[r]	1,284[r]	1,423
Education:							
Enrolment, total[7]	*	452,960	668,019	700,398	698,360	717,871	*
Public day	286,113	386,229	529,226	545,195	553,683	564,443	568,804
Private accredited	11,328	20,962	38,969	42,752	44,947	48,847	57,984
University of Puerto Rico[8]	4,987	11,105	13,232	14,292	15,176	16,753	18,222
Other schools of college level	*	761	3,129	3,553	3,691	3,969	*
Literacy of population ten years old and over (per cent.)	68·5	75·3[9]	80·4	81·5	83·2	83·8	85·0
Number of teachers	6,294	8,716	10,717	11,504	12,189	12,302	12,959

[r] Revised.

[p] Preliminary.

* Data not available.

[1] Includes construction, transportation and communication, finance, insurance and real estate, services and net factor income received from abroad.

[2] Figures for April 1940.

[3] A promoted plant received some kind of assistance from E.D.A. and/or P.R.I.D.C.O. during its establishment while an assisted plant received it subsequently.

[4] Figure as of April 1, 1940.

[5] Figures for fiscal year 1949 correspond to an average estimate for period 1949-51; figures for fiscal years 1955, 1956, 1957, 1958 and 1959 correspond to life expectancy for calendar year 1955.

[6] Figures for calendar years 1940, 1949, 1955, 1956, 1957, 1958 and 1959.

[7] Includes private and public schools, vocational groups, literacy program, special course for adults, and schools of college level. Does not include English teaching to emigrants, with an enrolment of 5,714 for 1954-55.

[8] The University of Puerto Rico includes the enrolment of the University of Puerto Rico at Rió Piedras, School of Medicine, College of Agriculture and Extramural Courses.

[9] Data for 1950.

Source: Puerto Rico Planning Board, Bureau of Economics and Statistics, Division of Statistics, Economic Indices Section.

TABLE II

Data Sheet on the Fomento Programmes

	1956-57	1957-58	1958-59	Preliminary 1959-60
Employment (fiscal year averages in thousands):				
Total labor force	636	637	636	625
Unemployed	84	82	90	82
Per cent. of labor force	13·2	12·9	14·2	13·2
Employed	552	555	546	543
Manufacturing	79	79	78	82
Fomento promoted plants	33	35	37	44
Industrialisation program:				
Plant Promotions—				
From external sources				
New plants[1]	121	81	124	112
Other	11	7	17	44
Expansions	6	6	13	34
Changes in ownership	5	1	4	10
Of local origin				
New plants[1]	27	27	27	28
Other	1	—	4	12
Expansions	—	—	2	9
Changes of ownership	1	—	2	3
Promoted plants—				
Starting operation during year	89	96	105	111
Closed during year	25	47	37	27
In existence at end of year	428	477	545	629
In operation at end of year	422	464	524	594
In process of establishment at end of year	92	85	95	109
Assisted plants—				
Assisted during year	16	19	18	16
Closed during year	5	6	2	1
In existence at end of year	64	77	93	108
In operation at end of year	62	76	88	100
Employment and earnings in Fomento promoted plants at end of year:				
Total employment	34,700	33,141	41,572	46,000
Production workers, number	31,800	29,953	37,533	41,200
Production workers weekly payroll ($ millions)	0·9	0·9	1·3	1·5
Average hourly earnings	$0·78	$0·86	$0·90	$0·94
Average weekly earnings	$28·97	$30·53	$33·72	$35·42
Employment in Fomento assisted plants at end of year:				
Total employment	3,419	3,610	4,855	5,172

Table II (*continued*)

	1956-57	1957-58	1958-59	Preliminary 1959-60
Investment in industry ($ millions):				
Investment, total	322	380	465	500
Investment, Government	34	40	51	55
Investment, private	288	340	414	445
Tourism program:				
Number of visitors	187,321	218,840	274,767	344,000
Expenditure ($ millions)	28	34	44	53
Number of rooms available[2]	1,595	2,093	2,518	2,890
In tourist hotels	1,029	1,502	1,890	2,102
In San Juan commercial hotels	566	591	628	788
Hotel registrations	109,548	125,104	166,224	220,000
Resident	25,221	25,814	28,404	30,000
Non-resident	84,327	99,290	137,820	190,000
Hotel employment (average)[2]	1,511	1,978	2,588	3,100
Rums of Puerto Rico:				
Number of cases shipped to the mainland	812,759	777,509	901,598	978,000
Tax collections ($ thousands)	18,333	17,172	19,815	21,036
International Airport:				
Number of passengers	909,555	998,476	1,171,595	1,416,158
Cargo movement (000 lb.)	38,107	42,790	40,842	50,560

[1] Includes additional units of firms operating in Puerto Rico.

[2] Relevant figures for commercial hotels operating outside of the San Juan metropolitan area are not included.

Research and Development Techniques

R. H. S. Robertson, M.A., F.G.S.
Director, Resource Use Limited, Pitlochry

Ways and means—techniques—of promoting research and development, with the object of creating new products, processes or industries in Scotland, are discussed under many headings, such as regional development, management, raw material development as a profession, a national corporation, a multiple development scheme for raw materials, investment, publicity and information, Government assistance, and ownership of resources. A case is made for the establishment of a number of research and development laboratories (or workshop factories), for industries other than electronics where the system is already in operation. For raw material development a regional laboratory in the Highlands is advocated; for other industries other sites are suggested. These suggestions are discussed in the light of investment.

MAN'S PLACE IN RESOURCE DEVELOPMENT

David Lilienthal[1] said that the greatest single factor in resource development is the people. The inhabitants of a resource-bearing region should have some control over its management; in Scotland this includes the concept of the resumption of parliamentary control; they want some interest in it and fun out of it. Moreover, it is in their interest to preserve their heritage, whereas outside organisations of consumers are less concerned with long-term continuity of supplies and regional welfare than with getting the cheapest source of supply.

Since the last war vast sums of money have been spent on technical assistance to underdeveloped countries. The art of giving and the art of receiving have yet to be refined; the difficulties are well discussed by Alec Dickson[2] in an address given to the British Association in 1957 entitled "Technical Assistance and Idealism: Misgivings and Mistakings".

Even at the grass-roots, it is very important to give local people a genuine feeling of participation and endeavour; but the feeling must be based on reality. Scottish landlords often refuse permission for minerals to be exploited on their lands, though they might favourably consider forming a company to exploit the mineral, with others' help, as part of estate management. Work-people in districts unused to highly industrialised life can sabotage a project; Lord Leverhulme met a difficulty of this sort in Harris. In Unified Resource Development the aspirations and wants of the people are taken care of by "people's participation in planning".[1] Development of the Highlands, civilisationally different from the rest of Europe, demands "a deep respect for the indigenous culture of those that are to be helped—maybe even a deeper respect than is possessed by many of them themselves" (Schumacher).[3] Thoughtless development can have the "withering touch".

REGIONAL DEVELOPMENT

Owing to the interdependence of resources and their applications in natural regions, thought should be given to regional administration of resource development. We shall restrict ourselves to raw material development. In this part of the work, all the resources should be kept under constant review. It is no use writing a report on a resource once every twenty-five years or more. It is necessary to have a regional laboratory in which raw materials, whether animal, vegetable or mineral, can be investigated at any time in the laboratory. Sectional division into road research, ceramic research and so on has certain advantages, but it does not lead to regional development. However, the existence in Britain of dozens of specialised laboratories makes it possible to run regional laboratories, for example one in the Highlands, very economically. The regional laboratory in this case would to a great extent be a preparative laboratory; specimens selected and examined and not very elaborately treated (e.g. dried, ground, calcined) would be sent elsewhere for further scientific research or for technical tests. It has been shown that it is possible to offer to industry a very full service of chemical, X-ray, thermal and electron-optical analysis, in which all the work apart from sample preparation is extra-mural. Indeed, my company has a very high coefficient of extramurality! In the same way the first stage of many projects in the Highlands or indeed in the countries overseas could be thus accomplished.

MANAGEMENT

It is essential to preserve continuity of development. Consequently someone must be continuously bringing each project forward through its various stages; the whole process can take as much as five years or more, though in other cases one or two years might be enough to establish an industry. Committees and advisory bodies do not create industries. Curiously enough, industrialists very seldom do either.

RAW MATERIAL DEVELOPMENT AS A PROFESSION

We have come now to the point where it should be stated that there is a profession of starting industries. Those who practice this profession may be in industry, but we are more concerned with the quite large field of enterprise which lies outside industry's immediate comprehension.

If raw material development were left to industry and to private individuals practising this new profession as Consultants, there would still be many projects which would not be developed. The reason for this is that the private professional man has not the capital to carry the project far enough to make it clear to an industrialist that it is worth backing, and very few industrialists will pay for research and development which, at an early stage, look nebulous and unrealistic. Yet hundreds of worthwhile projects have to go through these early humble stages, which if well-organised lead in a surprisingly large number of instances to lucrative enterprises.

There is another class of project which the professional man could initiate and that is the local industry which is not quite large enough to be a safe investment by faraway industry. Here a blend of effort by Government and consultants might be very fruitful, particularly if a regional research station had been established.

Projects in this class might be started thus. The raw material would first be surveyed, sampled, analysed and tested thoroughly. If the initial tests were promising, someone bright living near the raw material and who wanted to be associated with its development would go to work at the regional research laboratory as an experimental worker, with or without assistants. Under training supervision he would develop the project in pilot-plant with his own hands and would become master of the technique. If the economics of the process warranted the establishment of the new industry, he would return home and start work. The Laboratory would assist him to begin with in sales and other essentials. Loan capital could be repaid under agreed terms and under a simple form of contract.

It cannot be assumed that a Governmental or industrial research station is always capable of developing its own discoveries in the field of raw materials. Nor if this discovery is a fairly novel one can it be assumed that the research association will find among its member firms one or more who have the will or the means to develop the project.

In the raw material field, therefore, there is scope for development in (*a*) large-scale new enterprises not at present attracting the attention of industry; (*b*) smaller enterprises which could lead to economic local industries; (*c*) industries which would follow from work done in Government research stations which cannot constitutionally carry the work beyond stages 1 and 2.

A NATIONAL CORPORATION?

The Edinburgh Junior Chamber of Commerce have proposed a national corporation, financed by the Scottish people, to promote research and development and to invest in new projects in Scotland.[4] The main managerial divisions would be a research and development centre; a market research and economic intelligence unit, and a new project investment department. The Corporation would in effect be a highly efficient factory for producing new industries for Scotland.

Such a scheme seems to me to be right in principle, but it would benefit by being divided into at least six workshop factories: (*a*) one for electronics already exists at Ferranti's, thanks to the Scottish Council; (*b*) one for mechanical engineering might be established in Glasgow; (*c*) one in chemical engineering nursed by George Scott, Leven; (*d*) one in instrument making; (*e*) one for the chemical industry and (*f*) one for raw material development at present in embryo at Pitlochry.

A MULTIPLE DEVELOPMENT SCHEME FOR RAW MATERIALS

This has the advantage that unpromising projects can be discontinued as soon as their true nature becomes apparent, while successful schemes can easily pay for the abandoned ones. The bias is more favourable than the traditional "swings and roundabouts". Formerly such projects had to be offered individually, as mere ideas perhaps, to separate firms. There were failures, and at the best there was seldom very good control of the development by the introducer. Many industrialists prefer to have brought to them a well-worked-out idea; it costs them more initially, but as the risks are greatly reduced they are much more ready to take them up commercially. The case for the externalisation of development work from industry and its concentration into specialised development factories rests not only upon investment advantages but upon the provision of far better management and investigational resources than could be afforded by many small or medium-sized firms in Scotland. Management may well be the most important factor in resource development, for it is only by maintaining continuous full-time research direction for several years that industrial ideas will be brought to life and reality.

INVESTMENT

As an investment a well-thought-out multiple development scheme has this advantage: that as one cannot foresee who will want to buy or invest in the process in several years' time, it is advisable to pay for the development work first and then to sell the idea most profitably to the firm or group who need the process most, at the time when it has been proved. Even if a process designed for Scotland failed to find a buyer, or further investor, it could be offered to other countries where conditions were more favourable.

GEOGRAPHICAL RESTRICTION?

Although a multiple development institute in Scotland would naturally seek to promote new Scottish industries, it should not restrict itself to developing industries in Scotland; it would be best to serve the world. One can imagine that some useful work might be sponsored by firms or countries all over the world, and valuable training could be given to people from the so-called underdeveloped countries.

PUBLICITY

For many projects the work should be carried out in confidence, in order that it can give to an eventual buyer a private advantage. I do not favour indiscriminate publicity in the later stages of development, but it can be most helpful in stages 1 and 2. If the chemical and physical properties of raw materials were published in such journals as the *Chemical Age*, or the *Chemical Trade Journal*, large numbers of technologists in industry would become aware of a potential raw material. A standard data sheet form would encourage people to collect them.

INFORMATION

Since resource development is coming into the public mind, the regional centres of research and development should receive all official reports on resources, so that they may encourage the unified approach to resources and be available to research workers in resource development.

GOVERNMENT ASSISTANCE

Since only 2 to 3 per cent. of all Government expenditure on research and development is spent in Scotland, it is reasonable to ask that this figure be increased to 10 per cent., the population percentage. We do not recommend a duplication of research effort, though a little competition does no harm. The allocation of Scotland's fair share of research money would have to be determined after much further thought and discussion, but I would suggest that priority should be given to financing organisations in Scotland capable of creating industries. Even if private finance is attracted to this task, I strongly advocate the use of Government funds also for this purpose. Since so many Government research stations have been set up in England, Scotland has been drained of scientists and technologists capable of creating new industries[5]; it is consequently a matter of great urgency that the six development stations mentioned above should be set up soon.

OWNERSHIP OF RESOURCES

In Scotland mineral development can interfere with sporting and other interests; but quarrying can often be done during a few months in the year when no damage would be done to wildlife. In the Highlands especially, mineral developments are prevented by unsympathetic landlords even when the mineral worker is willing to go to great lengths to preserve the other estate values. In another case an English firm has been known to buy a mineral deposit in Scotland to prevent its being worked and thus to eliminate a competitor. All quite legal. But Scots would do well to study the status of resource ownership in the U.S.A.

In May 1908 a conference of State governors was held at the White House on behalf of conservation. Roosevelt then appointed a national conservation commission to *prepare an inventory*, the first ever made for any nation, of all the resources within the territory of the United States. "Roosevelt's official acts and the influence of his speeches and messages led to the adoption by both citizens and government of a new theory regarding natural resources. It is that the Government, acting for the people who are the real owners of public property, shall permanently retain the fee in public lands, leaving their products to be developed by private capital under leases which are limited in their duration and which give the Government complete power to regulate the industrial operations of the leasees."[6]

In the last fifty years this philosophy has become widely disseminated and accepted in the United States, partly through observation of the works of the various conservation agencies and the Tennessee Valley Authority, Franklin D. Roosevelt's masterpiece, but also through conscious schemes of Resource Use Education.

It has been said there[7] that "natural resources cannot be brought into effective productive relationship until individuals have the skills, attitudes and motivation to organise working and living arrangements. Therefore, it seems that the future of the South" (and here we can substitute the Highlands, Trinidad or anywhere else) "largely rests on the development of dynamic educational procedures which will help the people to see *what is* as a stepping stone to *what can be* and who view and accept problems as challenges." Even in the U.S.A. there is need for professional personnel with the resource-use concept; but in Britain the need is scarcely recognised at all.

It has been said that some of the philosophy we are discussing here is inherent in the teaching of scientists and administrators who subsequently take up colonial appointments; but we must make it very plain that we have seldom met anyone who has taken up such appointments and who has had a clear concept of the principles we have enunciated. Yet among educated Americans we have frequently found that we think the same way as they do about resource development. Nor have we found comprehension of the principles of raw material development among industrialists, even among those who are working deposits of raw materials. The philosophy is equally rare among Government administrators who are concerned with various aspects of resource development.

I am therefore strongly of the opinion that it is very much in the country's interests that wide publicity should be given to this new way of thinking about natural resources and raw materials. I should like to see a Government White Paper on the subject, as this would have a more rapid effect than many courses of lectures at Universities. Moreover, what we say and do in Scotland on resource development will be watched with keen interest by countries all over the world.

REFERENCES

1. LILIENTHAL, DAVID E., T.V.A. (1944). *Democracy on the March.* Harmondsworth: Penguin Books, S. 151.
2. DICKSON, ALEC G. (1957). *Advancement of Science*, **14** (55), 177-182.
3. SCHUMACHER, E. F. (1960). London: *The Observer*, 21st August, 17.
4. *The Scotsman*, 28th April 1960.
5. ROBERTSON, ROBERT H. S. (1960). *The Eugenics Review*, **52**, 71-82.
6. HAGEDORN, H. (1929). Conservation under Theodore Roosevelt, 1902-1909, London and New York: *Encyclopaedia Britannica*, 14th Edition, **19**, 538-539.
7. BURNHAM, REBA (1950). Resource-Use Education in Georgia: Progress, Plans, Problems; *Georgia Geological Survey Bulletin*, No. 56, Atlanta, Ga., 27-34.

Marketing

A. Fergus Williamson

Director, Balfour, Williamson & Co. Ltd., London

Various examples are reviewed from Scottish natural resource developments and Scottish industries where marketing has had a profound influence on the courses which these developments and industries have taken.

Some achievements of Scotland's outstanding industries are listed as examples of what can be done with foresight, well-planned sales campaigns and energy.

Co-operative marketing is advocated for agricultural communities. Scottish horticulture would appear to be a field for development where the natural conditions of soil, climate, etc., are most suitable and with more effective marketing strides could be made.

The scope for the application of professional marketing techniques to the tourist industry is explored and Government marketing schemes and subsidies are discussed. Throughout the paper the various points have been illustrated with examples taken from Scottish natural resource developments and industries.

Marketing has a very important function to perform in the development of any natural resources. This function must not be looked on merely as the means by which the product is disposed of. Full weight must be given to the problem of marketing from the very earliest stages of development and in this way the end-product is planned, produced and presented not only to the convenience of the producer and his production unit but also to the wants and requirements of the customer.

In the paragraphs which follow there are reviewed various examples from Scottish natural resource developments and Scottish industries where marketing has had a profound influence on the course which these developments and industries have taken.

The examples which are given have been divided into three categories:

(i) Development of markets for natural resources whose level of production would not appear to be economic.
(ii) Enterprising marketing as a means of combating declining sales.
(iii) Marketing as a means of achieving new or larger markets.

However, before examining these actual cases, some of which are the record of industries which have fallen on difficult times for one reason or another, we would do well to remember that Scotland has attained remarkable successes in its marketing efforts in the past and today the marketing achievements of some of Scotland's industries are amongst the most outstanding in the country.

Scotch whisky sales have grown larger every year since 1947, and the exports alone reached, in 1959, the fabulous figure of £62 million. Contrary to the belief that Scotch whisky sells itself, this success has only been achieved in the face of import restrictions and increased tariffs, and credit must be given for the very successful marketing and advertising which has gone to build up these sales.

The success of the Scottish knitwear industry both at home and abroad is truly outstanding, being a field of business where the high quality of material and workmanship alone are not enough; these qualities must be combined with clever designing and alert marketing in order to meet the fickle changes of fashion. There are many other highly successful Scottish industries who are marketing their products in the world markets today and reaping profitable rewards for their foresight, well-planned sales campaigns and energy. To mention a few:

Woollen cloth (£8 million worth exported in 1959);
Carpets (£2½ million worth exported in 1960).

Industries manufacturing watches, clocks, cash registers, calculators, typewriters and computers are all new industries in Scotland since the war and now Scotland accounts for half the total British output of these products.

Earth-moving equipment manufacture was unknown in Scotland until very recent years, but now Scotland is the biggest centre for the manufacture of this type of equipment in Western Europe.

MARKETING ORGANISATION

The planning of a marketing programme, the preparation of market surveys, advertising and the management of a sales force have today become professional studies in themselves, and in planning each one of these constituent parts of a marketing programme it is now possible to consult sound professional advice of proven ability and considerable experience. Unfortunately, there is a certain reluctance in this country to make use of these professional services and consultant firms. Two good examples of the employment of such firms are:

The employment by the O.E.E.C. of the Canadian firm of consultants, Messrs. Sandwell, to survey Scotland and report on the possibilities of establishing a pulp factory. This consultant firm was able to bring to bear a wealth of experience and practical knowledge on the subject and investigated all the relevant factors on the spot, from which the Report was made. Even if this Report did not give the idea of the establishment of a Scottish pulp factory quite the unqualified and enthusiastic support which many had hoped for, it did show the problems involved and introduced the layman to the capabilities and requirements of the different processes which might be considered. (Small Pulp Mill Survey by Sandwell & Co., Consulting Engineers, Vancouver, B.C., Canada, February 1959.)

The National Farmers' Union together with the Tomato and Cucumber Marketing Board employed the services of the firm Produce Studies Ltd. to report on the functioning of Tomato and Cucumber marketing in the U.K. The first report was published in February 1960, and though much of the information which this report used for evidence was figures already available from the National Statistics, it also quoted from the many private investigations made by this consultant firm and produced in a most fair and understandable form a presentation of facts from which recommendations were based. (Tomato Marketing, a first report by Produce Studies Ltd., February 1960.)

Good planning with the help of the best professional advice can do no more than design the marketing programme, and even the best marketing programme can be rendered of little consequence and a poor return on money spent unless it is executed with energy and resourceful thinking.

The examples of enterprising, resourceful and energetic selling are not qualities exclusive to the West German, Japanese and Italian salesmen. There are plenty of Scottish firms and organisations who do an excellent job at selling, the only problem is to increase their numbers.

Finally, marketing must take its rightful place in co-operation with production design and all other constituent departments of any industry as it not only provides the outlet for the finished product but it is also the means by which the customers' requirements are made known to the industry.

DEVELOPMENT OF MARKETS FOR NATURAL RESOURCES WHOSE LEVEL OF PRODUCTION WOULD NOT APPEAR TO BE ECONOMIC

Many of the attempts at natural resource development in Scotland have ended in the decision that due to some apparent fault in the raw material or its location, economic development would not be possible. However, there are occasions where resourcefulness applied in marketing has been able to turn such an apparently uneconomic proposition into profitable channels.

An excellent example of such resourcefulness in marketing and its influence on the further development of the business is to be found in the firm of W. A. Baxter & Sons Ltd., of Fochabers—"Makers of Fine Foods from Scotland since 1868". The development of a commercial enterprise from the sale of any one such Highland fruits as Rowan berries, Blaeberries, Cranberries, or the small wild Highland strawberries would surely in each case have been shown to be an uneconomic proposition.

However, the Baxter family have, by manufacturing preserves made from each of these Highland wild fruits, made an overall economic production unit. Then, having found acceptance for these unusual jams and preserves in the market for speciality foods they proceeded to develop this market with other unusual lines of Highland origin such as vintage marmalade matured in old whisky barrels, and canned grouse, pheasant and partridge. By such enterprising planning they have not only increased the lines of speciality foods which they can offer on the market but they have added to the volume of throughput for their jam factory and their cannery.The Baxter family are not only resourceful but their energy is prodigious, going forth to meet their customers both in this country and abroad, so that it is not very surprising to find that between 1946 and 1960 their overall output increased by 2,500 per cent.

A further example where resourcefulness and a proper presentation of facts in the right quarter resulted in finding a market for the product of an otherwise derelict local industry appeared in the *Oban Times* of 8th October 1960.

The Luing and Balvicar Slate Quarries produce a perfectly good but undersized slate which is unpopular with building contractors, who prefer to use bigger slates, on which, for local buildings in Argyll, they have to pay considerably more haulage. The quarries were threatened with having to close down and so cause serious unemployment in the district. A far-seeing County Councillor presented the facts of this case in proper perspective to the members of the Scottish Home Department and the Argyll County Council, whereupon the Scottish Office agreed to provide an additional subsidy when local undersized slates were used for public works. As a result the Council specified local slates for all their building schemes. This has resulted in such demand for these slates that the stockpiles of slates at these quarries have literally melted away; new machinery has been installed and employees are now working full time to keep up with orders.

ENTERPRISING MARKETING AS A MEANS OF COMBATING DECLINING SALES

This example is taken from the history of the jute industry, and though jute is certainly not a natural resource of Scotland it has been manufactured in and around Dundee since the 1840s. It was then that Dundee witnessed the conversion of most of its flax mills into jute mills as the market for flax products declined in the face of increasing competition from Lancashire cotton goods.

Annual imports of raw jute climbed steadily from 37,000 tons in 1860 to 277,000 tons in 1895, which has come to be regarded as being the Golden Age of the jute industry.

From 1900 to the outbreak of the 1914-18 War the annual imports of raw jute maintained a level of about 215,000 tons per year. By 1930 the imports of raw jute declined to an annual figure of about 100,000 tons, but with the advent of the 1939-45 War the annual imports rose to 176,350 tons in 1939.

After the 1939-45 War the consumption in U.K. raw jute rose from 99,990 tons in 1949 to 143,310 tons in 1955, and since that date there has been a decline:

1956. U.K. consumption 139,850 tons per year;
1957. U.K. consumption 137,450 tons per year;
1958. U.K. consumption 124,450 tons per year.

It can be appreciated from these figures that in spite of several rises and falls there has been a general downward trend in raw jute imports since 1895 and therefore a somewhat similar decline in manufactured jute goods in Dundee. The jute industry has had to face many exigencies, such as the disturbing effects on its supplies following on the partition of India and Pakistan; competition from the import of cheap manufactured jute goods and a decline in some of the traditional uses for jute.

In the face of gloomy prospects great resourcefulness in its marketing has been shown by the industry as a whole, and the formation of the British Jute Trade Federal Council in 1947 did much to centralise the work of co-operation between mills. Modernisation of machinery has taken place throughout the entire industry and in 1946 the British Jute Trade Research Association was set up in Dundee in order to centralise scientific research for all sections of the industry, including quality control and research into improved uses and new uses for jute.

The industry faces a hard future with further declines likely in some of the more traditional uses for jute products. However, there have been considerable developments in the more specialised uses for jute such as the backing of tufted carpets, underlays made by combining jute backing with foam rubber, etc. While more of the market for standard jute products may be lost to the Asiatic mills who can compete at considerably cheaper prices, it is to these more specialised uses as well as customer service and the highest quality of product that the Dundee jute manufacturers look for their opportunities.

MARKETING AS A MEANS OF ACHIEVING NEW AND LARGER MARKETS

The problem in this category would appear to be purely one of selling, but in most instances the active co-operation of other departments of a business are necessary in order to break into new markets successfully or counter the relentless attacks of competition.

Some industries have set up scientific research and advisory establishments which are supported by the member firms where experimental work in improved uses for their products or new uses are developed. It is in co-operation with such technical assistance that the marketing organisations of these industries are able to pioneer new markets and give better customer service.

The example of the jute industry has already been quoted. It was through the British Jute Trade Research Association that a jute cloth was developed especially for backing the new tufted carpets, thus opening up yet another market for jute products. This is only one instance of the active co-operation between the marketing organisations and the Research Association—there are many more.

The Scottish woollen industry has already been mentioned as having an exceptional record of sales both at home and abroad, but the marketing of its products is always meeting strong competition. In order to assist the marketing organisations of its member firms the National Association of Scottish Woollen Manufacturers formed the Scottish Woollen Publicity Council to help sales in the home market.

The Scottish Woollen Designers Group was formed towards the end of last year in order to assist woollen cloth manufacturers to improve designs and pool their ideas. Here again is a case of a well-organised industry co-operating together and sharing the costs of technical assistance in order to improve the competitive position of their products.

The Flaxspinners and Manufacturers Association of Great Britain have had to meet intense competition in marketing their products, and with the help from the Linen Industry Research Association Laboratory at Lambeg, N. Ireland, they have managed to market new types of proofings for both canvas and fire-fighting hose and new types of light-weight tarpaulins. The annual exports from the Scottish member firms of this Association have now risen to about £3,000,000 worth per year. Some idea of the importance of the Scottish trade can be gauged from the fact that over the past ten years the Scottish industry has used an average of about 15,000 tons of fibre annually compared with 25,000 tons by the Irish industry.

The above examples have been of highly industrialised industries who, through the co-operation of their member firms, have had the foresight to pool resources and assist their sales forces with publicity and their customers with technical know-how. Armed with these two most valuable aids, their salesmen have had an effective weapon with which to meet competition and develop new uses and new markets, besides being able to give more effective customer services.

The example of Scottish Timber Products Marketing has not reached such a high state of development. In recent years two of the largest buyers of Scottish home-grown softwoods have been the National Coal Board and British Railways. Unfortunately, the requirements of these two buyers are likely to decline slowly in coming years. Meanwhile the Government is encouraging private woodland owners to plant more trees and are doing so themselves through the Forestry Commission. There is now a growing volume of thinnings to be disposed of.

The firm of Airscrew and Jigwood Ltd. (now a subsidiary of British Match Corporation) have established a chipboard factory at Annan and Michael Nairn & Co. are about to go into production with their chipboard factory at Inverness. These two factories will help to absorb a certain amount of thinnings from the areas in which they are situated. There is a team set up by some of the leading British Paper companies which is looking into the possibility of a Pulp Mill in the Highlands. These are all interesting developments, but in all these investigations of the raw material supplies as well as the findings of the Sandwell Report and Watson Report (Report of the Committee on the Marketing of Woodland Produce, 1956), have discovered that the marketing of Scottish timber products is extremely haphazard.

There is a huge market for softwoods in the U.K., as is borne out by the following figures for softwood imports compared with U.K. production:

	Figures in Thousand Standards of 165 *cu. ft.*			
	1958	1957	1956	1955
Softwood: Home production .	38·0	43·1	44·7	49·6
Imported . .	1374·2	1462·5	1461·6	1547·1

In order to help organise better marketing of Scottish Woodland Produce the Scottish Woodland Owners Association was set up in 1959 with regional branches in Edinburgh, Perthshire, Aberdeenshire, Inverness and Kirkcudbrightshire.

CO-OPERATIVE MARKETING IN SCOTLAND

Producer co-operatives especially in agricultural communities are to be found in many very different parts of the world and a great number of them, more particularly the ones we hear about, have proved a great success. Our neighbours the Danes and the Dutch have developed their agricultural and horticultural co-operatives over a considerable number of years and the efficiency of these co-operatives at marketing their produce at home and in the U.K. is only too well known to us. The Channel Islands have organised efficient producer co-operatives and in more recent years farmer co-operatives have appeared in England. In Scotland the Scottish Agricultural Organisation Society has made valiant efforts to help organise co-operative marketing, but material achievements have been small so far. Some reasons for such little progress towards co-operative marketing can be found in the report by the firm Produce Studies Ltd. which was published in February 1960 and was made for the National Farmers' Union and the Tomato and Cucumber Marketing Board. The troubles of the Tomato and Cucumber Marketing Board have been numerous, but this report has managed to avoid becoming too involved in some of the smaller issues and has given a very factual survey of the industry as well as some clear indication as to where this attempt at co-operative marketing has fallen down—if one assumes that the Dutch and Channel Islands co-operative schemes are the ones to follow.

There is probably a great deal of controversy over the recommendations made by Produce Studies Ltd., but their facts and comparisons should provide some useful advice for setting up any new co-operative marketing scheme in Scotland.

The opportunities for horticultural development in Scotland are numerous and the favourable conditions for such development have been touched on by others in this Symposium. There is one unfortunate fact that the Scots eat considerably less green vegetables than the inhabitants of any other region of the U.K., but one should not forget the 470,000 tourists who are estimated to have visited Scotland in 1959 nor the £14½ million which they spent, during the best vegetable and fruit harvesting months of the year.

Scottish horticulture would appear to be a field for development where the natural conditions of soil, climate, etc., are most suitable and with more effective marketing strides could possibly be made. That conditions are right can be borne out by the existence of raspberry growers in Strathmore and vegetable growers of the Lothians and Clyde Valley.

This should not be read as an elegy on the attempts to organise agricultural and horticultural co-operatives in Scotland, and the "few" successful co-operatives which are mostly in the islands and the Orkneys must be given full credit for having succeeded where others have failed. The failures of the past, the evidence of the Tomato Marketing Report by Produce Studies Ltd. and the examples of efficient producer co-operatives in Denmark, Holland and Guernsey can all provide useful lessons in setting up co-operatives in the future.

CO-OPERATIVE MARKETING FOR EXPORT

With the help of various trade associations several consortia of manufacturers have banded together in order to sell more efficiently and more economically in the export markets. The Harris Tweed Association Ltd. is possibly an unusual example, but their trade mark of an orb stamped on all the tweed they produce has been a most effective emblem and through the Association's publicity campaign is now known and respected as a mark of quality all over the world.

In the peak year of production, 1957, over 6,500,000 yards of orb stamped Harris tweed was sold, of which more than 70 per cent. was exported.

More recently consortia of light engineering firms and consumer goods manufacturers have pooled their efforts in the export field in an attempt at more economic marketing.

THE TOURIST INDUSTRY

Year	Overseas Visitors to Scotland	Expenditure in Scotland £	Total Visitors to U.K. as a whole
1951	215,500	5,727,750	696,000
1952	231,500	6,103,000	732,828
1953	260,600	7,196,000	818,690
1954	305,270	8,837,010	898,580
1955	351,250	10,340,000	1,035,545
1956	380,000	11,550,000	1,105,560
1957	405,000	12,000,000	1,178,440
1958	430,000	13,300,000	1,250,360
1959	470,000	14,400,000	1,385,600

The above figures supplied by the British Travel and Holidays Association together with the Scottish Tourist Board give some indication of the size of the market. A market survey of the Tourist Trade in Scotland was carried out in 1956 for the British Travel and Holidays Association and the Scottish Tourist Board by Social Surveys (Gallup Poll) Ltd., and is available at the cost of 5s. The information contained in the booklet is so comprehensive as to the likes and dislikes of the tourist, his nationality, the class of accommodation which he stayed in, what he spent his money on, etc., that it is almost essential to study its statistics before venturing any guess as to how to attract the tourist to Scotland or cater to his wants.

Scotland's deficiency in meeting the comforts and personal wants of this large number of tourists are only too familiar to us. The need for more and better hotels, better garages, wider and straighter roads, etc., etc., are being constantly repeated, but catering for the tourist industry is largely an accumulation of individual efforts and these improvements can best be produced by the one individual improvement encouraging the other, e.g. by improving the standard of the local hotels, so the shops in the vicinity are encouraged to raise their standards, and so on.

One point stands out in the survey of the Tourist Trade in Scotland 1956 and that is the high percentage (45 per cent.) whose particular interest in Scotland was the scenery and countryside. Many of the older admirers of Scottish scenery, sportsmen and amateur naturalists will rankle at the idea of "commercialising" the natural beauty spots and wildlife of Scotland, but unless there is some control and organisation which will both show off these natural amenities to their best advantage to the tourists as well as protecting them, it will not be long before the natural beauty spots no longer exist, the wildlife is driven off elsewhere and subsequent tourists are disappointed.

What finer example was there of how to achieve this than the work of the Royal Society for the Protection of Birds, who arranged an observation hut with powerful binoculars from which tourists could watch the pair of Ospreys nesting in a tree on the shore of Loch Garten early this summer. No fewer than 20,000 people visited this observation hut while the Ospreys hatched the eggs and raised their young; without such enterprising presentation and protection by the members of the Society who kept constant watch there is no doubt that the eggs would have been stolen long before they could be hatched.

There is need for similar enterprising ventures whereby nature and wildlife are protected and, at the same time, the interests of the tourists are met to the best advantage.

Catering for the tourist trade is a specialised field of marketing which has been developed successfully in many other countries, and we would do well to learn from their experience. The National Parks of Canada and the U.S.A. have, for many years, provided interest and enjoyment to vast numbers of tourists and, at the same time, protected the National Parks and their wildlife.

GOVERNMENT MARKETING SCHEMES AND SUBSIDIES

There is no purpose in discussing those Government-assisted schemes where the producer is paid a subsidy and the problem of marketing is left entirely in the producer's hands. This occurs in the "Cereals Deficiency Payments" where a producer of, say, wheat markets his own wheat at the market price and receives a "deficiency payment" from the Government should this price be below the Government's standard price.

In the following cases the Government is practically the only buyer:

Wool; this is bought from the wool growers, who must have registered with the Wool Marketing Board, by authorised merchants who act as the Wool Marketing Board's agents.

Sugar beet; the grower must first arrange a contract with the sugar beet factory (Cupar in Fife is the only one in Scotland), who tells him how much acreage he may grow. The grower sells his entire crop when harvested to the sugar beet factory (British Sugar Beet Corporation).

In the cases of milk and eggs, the producer is paid a guaranteed price for his products by the Milk Marketing Board or Egg Packing Station as agent for the Egg Marketing Board. Both these Marketing Boards look after the distribution, manufacturing and selling of these products, which of course entails the marketing and encouragement of further consumption.

The Milk Marketing Board have shown themselves to be well aware of the need to increase outlets and existing sales, and their efforts have been praiseworthy; however, the farmers would like the Milk Marketing Board to buy even more milk by developing sales of milk products. In view of the figures for imports of butter, cheese and milk powder, it would appear that there would be plenty of room for development by the M.M.B. in the field of milk products. Somewhat the same situation exists regarding the attitude of the egg producers and the figure for imported eggs. However, it is not the Government's policy to subsidise home production to the extent that it will squeeze out the imports which come principally from Dominion countries and Denmark. The Milk Marketing Board and Egg Marketing Board are left to tread an unenviable path between the Government policy with regard to imports of milk products and eggs and the cry of the farmers for better prices at the expense of these imports.

CONCLUSION

Throughout this paper an attempt has been made to illustrate various points with examples taken from Scottish natural resource developments and industries, and in checking the figures and authenticity of these examples which have been omitted would have provided even more surprising instances of enterprise, ingenuity and the over-coming of difficulties, but unfortunately time, space and the smallness of some of these ventures has required them to be pruned from the text. For this reason many intriguing examples have had to be left out, including:

The export of periwinkles to France.
Curling stone manufacture in Ailsa Craig.
The export of table delicacies such as pigs' snouts, trotters and tails.

Mention has been made in the early paragraphs of a reluctance to seek professional advice from consultant firms and others on marketing problems and more particularly export marketing. Preliminary advice is available from Trade Associations, the Scottish Council (Development and Industry), from their offices in Edinburgh and London, the Board of Trade and others. These neutral bodies have gone to great lengths to accumulate and catalogue a vast amount of helpful information and advise on how to obtain more. This is part of the object of their existence besides being a satisfying reward for their efforts in seeing that the best use is made of all the information they have collected.

Scottish Transport

Sir Ian F. C. Bolton, Bt., K.B.E.

Late Chairman of Scottish Area Board, British Transport Commission, Glasgow

The Scottish transport problems revolve round road and rail. They are accentuated

(*a*) by the distribution of the population in the centre of Scotland with large areas only sparsely populated in other parts of Scotland;
(*b*) by the location of all the main industries in the same central area.

In view of the population and industrial position of Scotland, cross-subsidisation of one part of each form of transport with another part thereof has always been essential. This question runs through all public service transport.

The minimum rail system required to be retained in Scotland should be agreed and modernisation should be pushed ahead as far as possible.

All out-of-date restrictions on the railway should be abolished. There is no fear of unfair competition resulting, because the competition of private car and lorries will automatically prevent it.

If free competition is considered by those in authority the best policy for Scottish economy, then it should be allowed to take its course, resulting if necessary in closing down unnecessary transport.

If for social or political reasons the economic effect of free competition is not practicable, then a subsidy of some sort appears inevitable, which may lead to considerable inefficiency.

The whole transport question in Britain is now a Governmental one. Transport questions should be removed from the arena of party politics.

1. Transport in Scotland comprises:

A. ON LAND

(*a*) Passenger:

(i) Rail—British Railways.
(ii) Scottish Omnibuses Ltd., including Highland Omnibuses Ltd., David MacBrayne's Bus Service and some small local operators.
(iii) Municipal Transport.
(iv) Private cars.

(*b*) Freight:

(i) Rail—British Railways.

(ii) Road Haulage Lorries—

1. British Road Services.
2. Private Road Hauliers, including Furniture Removers, Livestock Carriers, etc.
3. "G" Licence holders.

B. ON SEA

(*a*) Ocean-going in and out:

(i) West—from and to Glasgow and Greenock on the Clyde.
(ii) East—from and to Grangemouth on the Forth.

(*b*) Coastal:

(i) West—Clyde—Glasgow—B.T.C.
Caledonian Steam Packet Co. (Irish Services) Ltd.
MacBraynes Ltd.
Burns & Laird Lines Ltd. (Ireland).
Clyde Shipping Co. Ltd.
Gourock—Ayr and Ardrossan.
"Puffers".
(ii) East—Aberdeen to Orkney and Shetland.
Dundee to London.
Forth Area—Burntisland, Methil and Leith.

C. AIR

(*a*) B.O.A.C. and foreign lines:

Inwards Prestwick and London, and
Outwards Prestwick and London.

(*b*) Internal B.E.A. Lines:

Glasgow	—	London and Ireland.
Edinburgh	—	London.
Glasgow	—	Inverness with Stornoway, also Western Islands and Orkney and Shetland.
Glasgow	—	Aberdeen.

D. UNDERGROUND

(*a*) Pipe-line for crude oil—Finnart to Grangemouth.

(*b*) Gas pipes now being laid from Westfield in Fife to Dundee and Coatbridge.

Notes

(1) Apart from special local conditions in Glasgow and Edinburgh, and to a lesser degree in Aberdeen and Dundee, municipal transport is covered by Scottish Omnibus Group.

(2) Air competition with rail is increasing for passengers and will become more and more acute with reduced fares, but is still dependent on weather, especially in the winter. Air services are mainly competitive for 400 miles and over, subject to population and industry.

(3) The underground pipe-line for crude oil to Grangemouth does not effect inland transport very much as otherwise the oil could be brought to Grangemouth direct in smaller ships.

(4) The gas pipe being laid from Westfield will mean a considerable reduction in carriage of coal inwards to works and coke outwards as many smaller gas works will be closed and production concentrated at Westfield which is fed by conveyor belt from opencast coal working.

(5) For the purpose of this paper, freight carried by sea transport may be mentioned only because coastal shipping has a preference with regard to rates.

(6) The main problems for Scottish transport are fares and freight charges by road and rail.

2. (*a*) Scotland is a receiving region for goods and has neither the population nor the industry to sustain the present railway transport at wages rates applicable to England. This has been accepted since 1920 and, so far as I know, is still unchallenged.

(*b*) The population of Scotland is 5·2 millions ("working" 2·2 millions). Broadly speaking, the central area, i.e. the Forth and Clyde valleys, carry the economy of Scotland with a population of 3·4 millions or 66 per cent. ("working" 1·4 millions, 64 per cent.). They are the passengers and produce coal, steel, shipbuilding, heavy industries, etc., on the freight side, with, of course, agriculturists as basic producers and consumers throughout Scotland. Thus profit, if any, on transport, passenger or freight, whether by rail or road, is likely to arise in this area. It has always been the mainstay of Scottish Railways: in other words, transport in many other parts of Scotland has been indirectly subsidised from the centre. This cross-subsidisation, of course, goes on daily through all public service transport. Probably the most profitable passenger services are to London from Glasgow and Edinburgh, but resistance to higher fares is being felt from first-class daylight travellers.

(*c*) Tourism, of course, effects the bus and rail problem at certain periods of the year. Hundreds of buses tour the country, a large proportion of them coming from England.

3. Road

(*a*) Pre-war the bus and road haulage, as roads improved, brought the railway monopoly to an end and the Railways' attempt at a "square deal" got nowhere owing to the war. In 1947 road haulage was nationalised: after 1953 denationalised in so far as the previous owners and others would buy lorries back. Far more lorries were left with British Road Services than anticipated. Competition is now very severe, particularly owing to the growth of "C" licences, which were never nationalised. It is worth noting that the granting of licences for buses and lorries creates a certain monopoly value and railway objections may or may not be accepted by the Licensing Authorities. These Authorities grant licences by areas on behalf of the Ministry, while the railway fares and rates are controlled nationally by a Tribunal.

(*b*) The enormous growth of "C" licences taking freight from both rail and road hauliers is worth noting:

Year ended 31.12.48:

Vehicles . .	590,516
Operators . .	311,811

Year ended 31.12.59:

Vehicles . .	1,137,897
Operators . .	357,991

It is doubtful how far they are really economical in many cases, but private traders dislike nationalised haulage for various reasons, including strike possibilities. Thus individual control of lorries weighs heavily in the balance and in many cases owners whose lorries were nationalised became the transport managers of companies and carried on with "C" licensed lorries.

In Mr. Gunter's recent maiden speech in the House of Commons he said, "Everybody knows that the Institute of Civil Engineers—not the Research Department of the Labour Party—has estimated that the cost of congestion on the roads in Britain in 1967 will be £2,000 million."

In less than 11 years there has been a 390 per cent. increase in "C" licences for lorries of 6 tons unladen weight and over.

Commercial vehicle fleet in this country has doubled between 1949 and 1960.

(*c*) Buses in Scotland, apart from David MacBrayne's Bus Service and some small local operators, are controlled by Scottish Omnibuses Ltd. (purchased after 1947 by the British Transport Commission) with road services throughout Scotland based at various local headquarters:

Scottish Omnibuses Ltd.—Edinburgh.
Walter Alexander & Co., Ltd.
Central S.M.T. Ltd.
Western S.M.T. Ltd.
and north of Inverness—
Highland Omnibuses Ltd.

4. Railway:

(*a*) The main lines of Scotland are:

Glasgow —London, west coast via Beattock and Kilmarnock.
Glasgow —Edinburgh.
Glasgow —Aberdeen.
Glasgow —Dundee.
Glasgow —Inverness and Thurso (joins at Larbert with traffic from the south via the west coast).
Glasgow —Oban.
Glasgow —Fort William and Mallaig (coming from the east via Glasgow).
Glasgow —Stranraer via Ayr and Girvan.
Stranraer —Carlisle.
Inverness —Kyle and Dingwall.

Edinburgh—London, east coast.
Edinburgh—Glasgow.
Edinburgh—Aberdeen, east coast.
Edinburgh—Dundee, east coast.
Edinburgh—Inverness, via Aberdeen and north-east coast.
Edinburgh—Mallaig, west coast via Glasgow as above.
Edinburgh—Carstairs.
Edinburgh—Carlisle.

(*b*) The re-appraisal of the *Modernisation Plan*, page 43, stated:

"In Scotland the route mileage open to passenger and freight traffic in 1948 was over 3,000 miles. Since that date passenger services have been withdrawn from 50 branch lines totalling around 500 route miles, and freight traffic has been withdrawn from some 170 route miles. Closures on this scale have brought the Region fairly close to the point where the curtailment process, although it will certainly continue, must undergo a change of emphasis. This will lie in the shift from route closure to the selective abandonment or conversion of individual stations and facilities in order to further the concept of concentration at railheads."

N.B. In the first 10 years of nationalisation 92 branch lines and 165 stations were closed, resulting in economies of £559,890 per annum. To the end of June 1960 these figures have been increased to 109 branch lines and 294 stations, yielding a total annual saving of the order of £734,000.

(*c*) The railway is forced to keep up the track to a high standard for obvious safety reasons and to provide signalling. Roads and police for signalling are provided for their competitors from local rates or the Government, to which the railways contribute. It has been estimated that to equalise the railways with road haulage and buses, British Railways in the United Kingdom should receive about £70,000,000 a year.

(*d*) Charging provisions under a statutory maximum have been to some extent freed by the 1953 Act. This, while allowing the railways to compete for more traffic, does not offset the competition of road lorries.

(*e*) Scottish rail receipts are particularly dependent on traffic in coal and the heavy industries.

(*f*) After Nationalisation in 1947 the Government severely restricted capital to the railways they had nationalised. The Government in 1954 agreed to a modernisation scheme to cost £1,200 million for projects to be begun within 5 years and finished in 15. Much of this is literally deferred repairs from pre-war, war and post-war periods when nothing could be done owing to lack of capital. Much has been done, e.g. on the passenger side, inter-city diesels introduced between Glasgow and Edinburgh and diesel cars in various parts of Scotland. Large diesel electric locomotives will gradually replace steam. In 1960 the first phase of Glasgow Suburban Electrification should be complete. On the freight side modern marshalling yards, new waggons, etc. But inflation, recession and resultant economies, including a complete change of policy by the National Coal Board in closing down pits, and rises in pay—especially those which will result from the Guillebaud Report—have overtaken the modernisation scheme and the result is in the balance. Only 5 years have elapsed out of the 15 and projects cannot be generally accelerated.

(*g*) In 1960 rail is essentially a long-distance means of transport both for freight and passenger, leaving short distance to lorry, bus and private car, but if for reasons of free competition the railways are expected to be competitive and earn a working profit, the modernisation scheme must first be completed, a decision having been made exactly what minimum railway system must exist to serve the country's needs. Railways should also be allowed, apart from safety rules, to compete for traffic free from interference, have power to close down stations and lines and have freedom to charge rates of fares as desired, with the corollary, which is implicit in free competition, that the weakest goes to the wall. In normal course a railway line which cannot be made to pay its way under these conditions should close down and follow the stagecoach into oblivion.

This also applies conversely where the bus is the uneconomic form of transport. The bus can be transferred elsewhere, though the railway cannot.

(*h*) If these results are not acceptable, the alternative is a subsidy of some sort to keep uneconomic lines in being. This is a national question, may amount to a considerable sum, and is an obvious danger to all efficiency.

(*i*) The Government authorised the modernisation plan and at the same time is spending millions on roads to make them fit to carry not only an ever-increasing flood of private cars, but of lorries, both "A" and "C" licences, carrying goods which should be on the under-used railways.

(*j*) The whole question is in the political arena, firstly from the angle of party politics and secondly from the fact that the Government is finding the money.

The Tourist Industry in Scotland

W. A. NICHOLSON, O.B.E.
Manager and Secretary, The Scottish Tourist Board, Edinburgh

Post-war developments in transport and the improvements in social conditions, including the provision of holidays with pay to large masses of the population, have opened up vast new markets for the development of tourist trade.

Scotland, with an excellent reservoir of facilities existing from pre-war years, has been able to take advantage of the increasing tourist traffic of recent years and some remarkable results have been achieved. Notwithstanding the lack of capital for development, building restrictions and other serious handicaps which prevented the promotion of new constructions and extensive modernisation, Scotland's hoteliers, by making greater use of the country's natural resources and introducing schemes to make longer use of existing facilities, have shared to a continuously growing extent in holiday trade both from inside Britain and from overseas.

Prospects for the tourist industry are good, but if Scotland is to get a share of the great and growing market available in the near future, those engaged in this industry must be freed from restrictions, capital must be made available and basic facilities in the form of better roads, modern transport and local produce must be provided.

A co-ordinated and fully developed tourist industry in Scotland could add many millions of pounds to present trade, increase the use of all natural resources, enlarge considerably the demand for basic food products, provide longer and guaranteed employment for thousands of workers, bring a new measure of prosperity to rural areas, and benefit all classes of the community.

The tourist industry has made a substantial contribution to the greater use of Scotland's natural resources.

In the expansion which can be anticipated in tourist trade, the contribution which the industry can make towards the fuller use of the country's natural resources, and particularly to national economy, should be considerable.

In the years immediately prior to the 1939-45 War a restricted programme of tourist development was embarked upon, but it was not until 1945 that any really serious consideration was given to the part which tourist traffic might play in Scottish economy.

Changing social habits, the great improvements in transport which were accelerated by the war, the extension of holidays with pay to growing masses of the population, the introduction of shorter working weeks and the consequent increase in leisure, contributed to a recognition of these facts: (1) that some national effort had to be made to provide adequate facilities for the increased leisure of the people, particularly at holiday time, and (2) that through the higher spending power available to increasing numbers of people, both at home and overseas, and the astonishing improvements in transport, particularly in air travel, the tourist industry was fast becoming a major development requiring substantially augmented facilities for its proper expansion.

In 1945, when the Scottish Tourist Board was established, an initial survey made showed that there was in Scotland at that time accommodation for 73,056 persons per night in hotels, boarding houses, hostels and camps.

In 1948, when a fuller survey was made, the following accommodation was recorded as being available:

Hotels (Licensed)		*Hotels (Unlicensed)*		*Boarding Houses*		*Camps, Hostels, etc.*		*Total Nightly*
No.	*Capacity*	*No.*	*Capacity*	*No.*	*Capacity*	*No.*	*Capacity*	*Capacity*
1,165	37,274	865	21,642	1,929	14,659	102	9,761	83,336

Comparative figures for 1960 are:

1,402	44,972 (persons)	742	18,616 (persons)	2,629	19,579 (persons)	142	10,713 (persons)	93,888 (persons)

A straightforward comparison between the figures of 1948 and 1960 suggests that there was a substantial increase in the number of new hotels, but this in fact was not the case.

While it is true that between 1945 and 1960 a considerable number of hoteliers improved and modernised their premises, not more than five new hotels, all of them of a small size, were built throughout the whole of Scotland in that period.

The increase from the total of 2,030 licensed and unlicensed hotels in 1948 to a total of 2,144 in 1960 was due almost entirely to the fact that many people who previously were satisfied to call their premises boarding houses changed the names of these premises to hotels.

The absence of new construction was due to many factors. Building and other restrictions prevented any expansion of the industry over the period from 1945 until 1954. In 1954 there was some sign of expansion, but this was largely restricted, as it was in the years subsequent to 1954, to the provision of more private accommodation in cottages, crofts and apartments, many of them benefiting for the first time from the modern amenities of piped water supplies and electricity.

Financial restrictions officially imposed over many years prevented in part the construction of any new hotels or of any substantial expansion to existing hotels. During the period from the end of the war up to early 1958, hoteliers in many cases were quite unable to obtain capital either from their own business activities which previously had been restricted to a three months' season, or through banks and other financial organisations. It is only in the past two years that there has been any new or additional accommodation built in Scotland, and, as is stated earlier, this has been of a minor character and far below the requirements of many centres.

It is only now in the present year, 1960, that there are any definite signs that financiers, and bankers, are prepared to regard hotel and tourist trade development as a reasonable risk and there are prospects that in the near future some new hotel construction will be undertaken in Scotland.

It is important to emphasise, however, that despite the serious handicaps under which the existing hotels have had to operate in the past fifteen years, and of the almost total absence of capital for expansion, the industry has made tremendous progress. This expansion has been achieved primarily through the longer use of existing accommodation and facilities. While the amount of accommodation available in Scotland for holiday purposes has increased from a nightly capacity of 83,336 persons to only 93,880 persons, the use made of accommodation has increased substantially in recent years through a lengthening of the season and by the fuller use of existing facilities.

Evidence of this is provided in the fact that between 1954 and 1959 the number of persons accommodated in hotels, boarding houses, apartments and camps rose from 3,723,364 to 5,052,895.

In that same period the number of overseas visitors to Scotland rose from 305,000 to 570,000.

Over a substantial part of Scotland, where the peak season of tourist trade is from mid-June to mid-September, demand in recent years has, at times, exceeded all normal available hotel and boarding house accommodation. In such cases, and practically every area is becoming increasingly affected as the flow of tourist traffic rises, it has only been possible to meet this excessive demand by encouraging private householders to grant visitors the use of their spare bedrooms on a temporary basis.

In a limited number of areas, where, with the co-operation of hoteliers, boarding house keepers, traders and others, it has been possible to extend holiday trade outside the normal peak season, some remarkable results have been achieved. Two areas, the island of Skye and Speyside Valley, are outstanding examples.

In 1950 when the island of Skye had no electricity and many villages had no piped water supplies, the existing hotels on the island could accommodate approximately 739 persons per night, and the season extended from July to mid-September, a period of not more than 12 weeks. In 1950 a total of 21,608 motor cars were carried over the ferry between Kyle of Lochalsh and Kyleakin.

As Skye obtained hydro power and as piped water supplies were provided, crofters and cottagers were encouraged to cater for visitors and from 1954 onwards did so to an increasing extent. No new hotels have been built in Skye, but largely through the opening up of croft and village homes, the island can now cater for 1,308 visitors per night.

Through the promotion of events, chiefly Skye week, the better organisation of road transport services, and publicity, Skye now enjoys a tourist season from mid-April to mid-October. Last year (1959) motor cars carried over the Kyle of Lochalsh and Kyleakin ferries had risen to 43,825.

Today the tourist industry is the largest employer of labour on the island and has been a most valuable supplement to the livelihood of the crofting population.

Ten years ago the majority of the 48 hotels and boarding houses in the Spey Valley closed down in the late autumn, winter and early spring months. Workers seldom received more than a three-month guarantee of employment. The hoteliers themselves contrived to live for twelve months on a three-month income.

Encouraged by the Scottish Council of Physical Recreation and the Scottish Tourist Board to make use of the great natural resources around them by promoting outdoor holidays at out-of-peak-season periods, a few hoteliers, with some reluctance, agreed to experiment.

When, through experience, it had been established that a public was available, even in mid-winter, for organised and at times energetic outdoor holiday pursuits, other hoteliers joined in. Pony trekking holidays from Newtonmore, ski-ing holidays at Carrbridge, Aviemore, Kingussie and Nethybridge, fishing training holidays at Grantown-on-Spey and Boat of Garten, and mountaineering from Glenmore, are now but a few of the outdoor activities which in a few years have transformed this area into the greatest sporting holiday centre in Britain.

A new mountain highway built into the Coire Cas from Glenmore and a chairlift now under construction, together with the construction of new hotels and the provision of restaurant facilities, promise to make this area one of the boom holiday centres of our country.

The effect of the transformation has been tremendous. The majority of hotels now remain open all the year round, workers are getting up to 10 months' guaranteed employment, hoteliers with a bigger and nearly all-the-year-round turnover are refurnishing, modernising and even extending their premises; local tradesmen are getting increased orders, plumbers and builders are being given increased employment, shopkeepers are happier, more money is circulating.

Some idea of the effect which tourist traffic can have on the demand for the food products of Scotland and the contribution which a growing tourist industry can make to farming and fishing economy can be obtained from the results of a restricted enquiry made by the Scottish Tourist Board in 1958.

At the request of the Tourist Board the owners of 14 hotels and boarding houses in various parts of Scotland kept a record of the chief food commodities, all bought in Scotland, required to feed their guests in that year.

The combined purchases of these 14 hotels were:

Butter	24,327 lb.
Poultry	113,157 lb.
Beef and Mutton	182,404 lb.
Milk	59,300 gallons.
Eggs	51,206 dozen.
Bacon	48,909 lb.
Potatoes	560,780 lb.

The hotels participating in this survey were: the Broadford Hotel, Broadford, Skye; the Royal Hotel, Portree, Skye; Sligachan Hotel, Skye; Carrbridge Hotel, Carrbridge; Nethybridge Hotel, Nethybridge; Craiglynne Hotel, Grantown-on-Spey; Cluny Hill Hotel, Forres; Marine Hotel, Oban; Royal Hotel, Dundee; Carlton Hotel, Edinburgh; Park Hotel, Edinburgh; Peebles Hydro Hotel, Peebles; Victoria Hotel, Rothesay, and Mayfield Hotel, Kirkcudbright.

These 14 hotels between them have a total of 844 rooms and can accommodate 1,355 persons per night. They enjoy, on the average, peak trade for five months of the year.

It is obvious from the food purchases of these 14 hotels that even in the present limited development of Scotland's tourist industry the annual requirements of the industry in home-produced farm and fish products must be considerable.

The producer of a B.B.C. programme has computed that it now requires the productivity of 500,000 laying hens and 25,000 milking cows to meet the annual requirements of the tourist trade in eggs and milk.

The duplication of the Skye and Speyside examples in other parts of Scotland and the promotion of new schemes designed (*a*) to meet the changing habits and desires of holiday makers, (*b*) to cater more adequately for the ever-increasing numbers of visitors and (*c*) to make fuller use of Scotland's extensive natural resources over a longer period of time, are now being carried into effect by the Scottish Tourist Board with the co-operation of many local and national organisations.

It is only possible in this paper to summarise a few of the developments taking place or planned.

At the request of the Secretary of State for Scotland and under the leadership of Mr. Hugh Fraser, one of its members, the Scottish Tourist Board has embarked on an extensive scheme, initially restricted to three years but likely to extend beyond that period, to secure a substantial increase in tourist trade and facilities in the Highland counties. This scheme involves the creation of more hotel and restaurant facilities, the establishment of a finance corporation to make loans available for hotel and other development, the promotion of events and the fullest possible use of existing facilities.

Supplementing this, and coincident with it, the Scottish Tourist Board is now actively engaged in the promotion of a national angling scheme under which it is hoped to make fuller use for tourist purposes of the great variety of angling facilities that now exist, or could be made available, in lochs and reservoirs in all parts of Scotland, including the Orkney and Shetland Islands and the Hebrides.

The promotion of further pony trekking holiday activities in all parts of Scotland in winter and spring time, ski-ing in the Braemar, Glenshee and Glencoe areas, deep-sea angling along the western seaboard, sailing and water ski-ing both in the open sea and in lochs, and golf tours for visitors including the facility to hire clubs, are among the many other schemes now being introduced or encouraged.

In co-operation with the National Farmers' Union in Scotland and the leading food marketing boards and organisations, the Scottish Tourist Board is actively encouraging hoteliers and caterers in all parts of Scotland to serve Scottish-grown or produced food to visitors.

In co-operation with the National Trust for Scotland and the Ministry of Works, the Board is promoting schemes to encourage increased visitation to centres of historic interest.

Consultations are taking place with officials of the Nature Conservancy to arrange organised visits to areas controlled by the Nature Conservancy. These visits will be designed to stimulate public interest in the work of Nature Conservancy and to encourage a public appreciation of the purpose of conservation and a respect for the natural resources being preserved.

Notwithstanding the handicaps and frustrations which it has faced in post-war years, the tourist industry is on the verge of even greater development. Air and other forms of transport will bring ever-increasing numbers of visitors to Scotland and the Scottish Tourist Board is convinced that provided adequate facilities can be made available there is no reason why in the next ten years at the most, the tourist industry of Scotland should not double its present turnover and be worth at least £100 million per year to Scottish economy.

Of the estimated £60,000,000 which Scotland now obtains from its tourist industry, approximately £45,000,000 is spent by Scottish residents and English visitors on holiday in Scotland and the balance of £15,000,000 is spent by overseas visitors to Scotland.

If the expectations of the Board are fulfilled, the effects of this expansion will be felt in all parts of the country and among all classes of the community.

The market for Scottish-produced foods through hotels, boarding houses and catering establishments could be doubled.

Through the greater use of such natural facilities as lochs, rivers, moors and mountains, local economies will be improved.

Hotel and boarding house owners, by operating a seven to eight months' season in all parts of Scotland, which should be possible, and in many areas an all-the-year-round season, will be able to modernise their premises and provide employment for many categories of trade.

Employment in the industry itself and in ancillary industries, particularly the souvenir industry, will increase.

Demands for other products such as tweeds, hosiery and whisky will increase.

Longer and more effective use will be made of transport services.

In the developments embarked upon, or envisaged, the Board does not anticipate any conflict so far as access to beauty spots is concerned, or any serious infringement on agricultural or existing sporting activities. There will be need for the provision of some new roads to provide links between beauty spots or to provide access to undeveloped areas, but Scotland has so many beauty spots with access to them that the expansion of the tourist season over a longer period of time will in the main bring only increased trade to existing centres.

In the majority of cases new hotel construction will be in existing centres and should not lead to any serious encroachment on agricultural land. What the new hotels and the fuller use of existing hotels will do will be to increase substantially the demand for Scottish-produced foods.

The demands of the growing tourist industry and those of other industries and activities should in no way conflict. The activities of the tourist industry should, in fact, be complementary to practically all other industries and developments. Transport facilities both in the form of services and roads should be improved as the demand increases. So far as roads are concerned, there is immediate need for major improvements and for the construction of new highways to meet present and future requirements.

Experience has proved that where modern and adequate transport services are provided there is a public demand for them. For example, in 1953 when the Clyde steamer services had no modern facilities for the transport of cars, and when cars could only be transported if tides were suitable, approximately 400 cars were conveyed annually on these services. Following the modernisation of these services, beginning in 1954, and the introduction of lifts to take on and discharge cars at any state of the tide, public use of these services increased enormously. Last year (1959) the Clyde steamer services handled a total of 87,754 cars.

This modernisation process is urgently needed in respect of other Scottish areas served by sea services, notably the Hebridean Islands and on the Mallaig to Armadale (Skye) route.

Scotland's biggest markets for her tourist customers are not from her own natives enjoying holidays in their own country, however welcome and necessary this may be, but are first in England and Wales and secondly in overseas countries.

Of the 5,000,000 people who it is expected will make use of Scotland's tourist facilities in 1960 at least 3,000,000 of them will be from England and Wales, 500,000 will be from overseas countries and the balance will be Scottish people.

There is no reason in the view of the Scottish Tourist Board why, the facilities being available and the growing trend towards out of season holidays continuing, the numbers of both English and overseas visitors to Scotland should not double in the next ten years.

The introduction at an early date of jet air services across the Atlantic and from the Continent of Europe will certainly double the potential from overseas countries in less than ten years, and it is interesting to note in respect of this that American and Canadian hoteliers, anticipating a coming boom in overseas travel to Scotland, are now contemplating the construction of hotels in Scotland.

It may take longer to achieve double the present volume of English traffic to Scotland, but as our roads are improved, as the transport facilities between English centres and Scotland are increased, and as more and more people living in the crowded south want some freedom to motor in comfort, the volume of English visitors can be expected to go on increasing.

All this growth inevitably means an increasing demand on Scottish services and brings to the doorstep of Scottish manufacturers a vast annual market for the products of our country.

But while the prospects for the future are undoubtedly bright, Scotland must find a solution to a variety of problems if she is to benefit to the extent she could from tourist trade.

Past developments in Scotland's tourist trade, which have not been inconsiderable, have been largely based on what is known as home holiday traffic—that is traffic from inside Britain, and while overseas traffic to Scotland (now one-third of the total overseas traffic to Britain) is of considerable economic importance, its development until now has been prescribed by the availability of facilities acceptable to overseas visitors and their travel agents.

In catering for home holiday visitors who provide the bread and butter of their existence, hoteliers in the areas outside the main cities and towns of Scotland and such centres as Turnberry and Gleneagles have had as much traffic as they could handle at peak holiday periods and there has been no widespread distribution of overseas visitors to those areas.

One primary reason for this lack of movement of overseas visitors to all areas is that the bulk of overseas trade is controlled almost entirely by travel agents who sell round-ticket facilities to their customers, facilities which include both transport and accommodation. These travel agents will not risk sending their clients to areas where they have been unable to make prior reservations or where the bulk of accommodation offered to them is of the bed and breakfast variety in private homes and cottages. To do so would kill their own business.

In the areas outside the large cities and luxury-type hotels, large numbers of hoteliers in the rural areas of Scotland and especially in the area north of Perth are unwilling to pay commissions to travel agencies and many do not realise the great potentialities of this branch of trade.

The control of travel by travel agencies will undoubtedly increase and as the facilities for all classes of travellers in Scotland are improved and extended, consideration will require to be given by hoteliers to the need of co-operating more with travel agents. As this co-operation grows, so will the range of travel of overseas visitors throughout Scotland increase.

One thing which is certain is that there is ample room for the expansion of overseas tourist trade to Scotland.

Yet another matter which must be taken into account in the anticipated expansion of tourist trade is the need to co-ordinate with that expansion the marketing of goods and produce. There are many rural areas where agricultural, horticultural and other productions could be increased to cater for the bigger needs of the hotel industry. More adequate means than are now in operation must, however, be found in the better development of road, rail, air and sea services, first to encourage higher production which should be possible and secondly to ensure that such production is more easily marketable on a local and national basis. Provided marketing facilities were available, the benefits that could flow to the remoter areas could be considerable.

One fundamental requirement in the adequate provision of the services which the tourist industry must provide if Scotland is to benefit from the wave of tourist traffic flowing towards her is capital.

The limited capital being invested in the industry now is not sufficient to meet the expansion that is needed. Apart from the new hotels that are required, many hotels and boarding houses in all parts of the country must be modernised if Scotland is to cater adequately and efficiently to modern tourist trade. The hotel and boarding house keepers themselves, having existed so long on a limited income occasioned by the previous shortness of the season, which left them no reasonable balance with which to improve and extend, cannot by themselves face the costs required. If capital could be made available to them, even at normal terms, many, I am sure, would gladly improve and extend.

The immediate results to financiers and investors might not be measurable in profit percentages which would attract a Stock Exchange expert, but on a long-term basis the results achieved would be enormous. Visitors would get facilities of which, as a nation, we could be proud, the flow of trade to other industries would mount by leaps and bounds. Areas like some of the remoter parts of the Highlands and Islands would not be dependent for their survival on the industrial south, and the effect on national and local economy would be substantial.

Finance Available for Developing Resources

W. R. BALLANTYNE

General Manager, The Royal Bank of Scotland, Edinburgh

The development of resources and of technological skills and of new inventions and processes requires a sufficient volume of savings to provide capital formation for the desired rate of expansion.

In the public sector of industry, finance for development is secured from

(1) the operating surpluses, if any; and
(2) borrowings from the Government.

Industries in the private sector obtain new finance from

(1) retained earnings;
(2) public issues of Capital or Debenture Stock; and
(3) borrowings from the Joint Stock Banks and other financial institutions.

Small and medium sized Companies lack the facilities open to the larger Companies for obtaining capital. Special problems also arise in the provision of finance for the commercial development of new inventions and innovations of techniques, because the risks in the commercial exploitation of technical innovations are likely to be greater than those in expanding existing lines of production.

The Joint Stock Banks are the most important source of credit for industry.

Among other financial institutions concerned in the provision of finance for industry are:

Finance Corporation for Industry, Ltd.
Industrial & Commercial Finance Corporation, Ltd.
Charterhouse Industrial Development Company.
Glasgow Industrial Trust.
Insurance Companies.
Investment Trusts.
Unit Trusts.
Hire Purchase Companies.
Ship Mortgage Finance Company.

The essential ingredients for the growth of any economy are, as I set out in a paper which I read to the British Institute of Management Scottish Conference in April:

(1) the availability of natural resources;
(2) The supply and efficiency of labour and technologists;

(3) the availability of savings for capital formation; and
(4) the management of financial and economic policy.

On that occasion I was examining the problems involved in financing an expanding economy and I stressed—as I do again—that the maximum utilisation of the natural resources of a country and the full potential of the technological skills of its workpeople and of new inventions and processes, etc., can only be secured if there is available also a sufficient volume of savings to provide the capital required for the development of these assets.

When considering the sources from which finance can be procured for development, it is very important that we should remember that in the ultimate the money must come from savings of one kind or another. If development undertaken is not matched by an adequate volume of savings, inflation is the inevitable consequence. The experience of the past shows that economic expansion can be achieved by inflating the money supply, but this has such harmful effects and causes such great hardship to sections of the people that it is a policy which we should resolutely endeavour to avoid. The truth of the matter is simply this, that a nation which desires to expand its economy and raise the living standards of its people must be prepared to forgo current consumption to whatever extent is necessary in order to provide new capital of the amount required to achieve the desired rate of expansion.

At the outset of this study we should note that our industries are grouped in two sectors: (1) the public sector comprising the organs and activities of the Central Government, Local Government and the public Corporations, and (2) the private sector comprising a great number of concerns of widely different size and character owned and managed by private individuals or groups of individuals.

It is with the financing of the private sector industries that we are mainly concerned, but inasmuch as the public sector contains the nationalised coal, gas, electricity and transport industries—industries which are of basic importance to our whole economy and all of which are continually engaged in carrying out large schemes of development—we should note the sources from which these development schemes are financed.

The first source is their operating surpluses, if any. In so far as the expenditure on capital account is not covered by these surpluses the balance is borrowed from the Central Government. The loans granted to them are now included among the "below the line" items in the Budget and brought into account in determining the net Budget surplus or deficit.

We should remember also that the Local Authorities are responsible for large investment programmes on housing, schools and roads. The net cost of these programmes is very largely financed by Exchequer Loans from the Government or loans from the Public Works Loans Board or by issues of Stock or long- or short-term Mortgages in the capital market.

Turning now to the private sector, the first source from which finance is obtained for capital development, including the development of new resources, is retained earnings which comprise depreciation allowances and profits not paid away as interest or dividends. A substantial part of the investment programmes of industries in the private sector are financed out of retained earnings. Whereas, however, the Government provides the public sector industries with the additional funds required by way of loans out of money raised by taxation or by borrowing, private sector concerns have to depend on private sources for any new money which they require to raise. Established and successful concerns can generally obtain additional funds by:

(1) issues of new Capital or Debenture or Loan Stocks to their existing Shareholders or the public; or
(2) by borrowing from the Joint Stock Banks or other financial institutions.

Such concerns can, as a general rule, satisfy their needs without undue difficulty, except perhaps in periods of acute credit stringency. New issues can be made to existing Shareholders or new Stock or Debenture or Loan Stock issued through the market to the public or placed privately with Pension and Superannuation Funds, Insurance Companies, Investment Funds and Unit Trusts, all of which are recipients on a substantial scale of private savings. The situation of the small business, the private Company and more particularly concerns formed to exploit new inventions, technical knowledge or new processes is quite different. They do not have access to the new issue market and in the main they do not have the investment status to interest the Investment Trusts and other institutional investors. It is, nevertheless, very important that such concerns should have access to funds for expansion and development when the investment of new money can be justified on its merits. This was one of the matters to which the Radcliffe Committee gave consideration and they stated that "there is a danger, which it is socially as well as economically desirable to avoid, that the growth of small firms may be impeded because they lack some of the facilities open to larger Companies for obtaining Capital".

The Macmillan Committee set up some thirty years earlier to examine the gap which then existed between the needs of industry for capital and the sources available recommended the setting up of new institutions from which small and medium-sized concerns, which could not satisfy their capital requirements through the normal capital market, might obtain long-term credit and from which enterprises of all sizes might obtain credit for a period which would normally be too long for Bank finance and too short for the capital market. It was some fourteen years later that the Finance Corporation for Industry and the Industrial & Commercial Finance Corporation were formed but they owe their origin to this recommendation of the Macmillan Committee. The Radcliffe Committee, when it in its turn came to consider the matter afresh in another era, came to the conclusion that although something had been done as a result of the Macmillan Committee's recommendations, there was room for some further improvements to meet the requirements of small businesses. They considered that rather than set up a proliferation of new institutions, whether financed by public or private money, the problem could be met by making certain modifications to the existing institutions, and they made two recommendations :

(1) "that the Banks should be ready to offer term loan facilities within reasonable limits having due regard to their liquidity requirements as an alternative to a running overdraft for credit-worthy industrial and commercial customers"; and
(2) "that the upper limit of the Industrial & Commerical Finance Corporation, Ltd., which was fixed at £200,000 in 1946, be reviewed in the light of the change in the value of money since it was first fixed and that the facilities of the Corporation be made more widely known than hitherto".

The Committee also referred to "special problems about the provision of finance for the commercial development by small businesses and private companies of new inventions and innovations of technique".

The main problem here arises from the fact that "the amount of capital required to finance a development may be larger in relation to a small Company's capital structure and apparent earning prospects than financial institutions would ordinarily feel justified in putting up" and that "the risks in the commercial exploitation of technical innovations are likely to be greater than those in expanding an existing line of production or extending into existing types of business". The Committee suggested that an Industrial Guarantee Corporation with Government backing might be set up to "guarantee, for a commission, an agreed proportion of loans made by existing financial institutions to borrowers wishing to finance novel processes or the manufacture of new types of product" but not "the financing of the initial stages of research and development".

They recommended that the Guarantee Corporation should "not lend directly to manufacturers or to financial institutions nor give guarantees directly to manufacturers". Guarantees would be given "only to financial institutions which would themselves lend the money".

The Committee went on to say that "the essential merit of a scheme of this kind would be that it would put the main responsibility for assessing the commercial possibilities of an application on existing financial institutions, so that a manufacturer would be able to approach a wide variety of institutions, some of them already familiar with his capabilities and affairs, for the finance he required. By limiting the losses which such institutions could incur on any single project, the Corporation might induce them to take a more venturesome attitude towards new developments that would otherwise fail to obtain financial backing". Their view "that no proposal can be lightly disregarded which may help to accelerate technical development in British Industry" is one which will be widely endorsed by all who are concerned to see a more imaginative and vigorous development of our resources. Although there are differing views about some of the Committee's ideas as to how the Guarantee Corporation would operate, the recommendation generally is one which merits further consideration for the difficulty of a new business in obtaining finance at the outset of its career, particularly if it is proposing to exploit some new invention or embark on some development of a novel character, is very much greater than the difficulty encountered by a successful concern in obtaining finance for the expansion of existing lines of production. Even the Board of Trade Advisory Committee, whose purpose it is to advise the Board of Trade in regard to applications for financial help under the Local Employment Act for the establishment of new industries and the re-equipment of existing industries in areas where there is an abnormally high level of unemployment, have usually to be satisfied, even if a project would not stand up to the normal commercial tests, that there is a reasonable prospect that it is capable of being made a commercial success. They do not believe—and I agree with them—that there is any virtue in investing money in projects which have no prospect of surviving, even if it provides some temporary short term alleviation of unemployment.

I have already referred to the fact that the large and successful concerns in the private sector can generally find the additional finance required for expansion with much greater ease than smaller concerns. Financial institutions are generally found to be much more ready to help the larger Company and where the Company concerned is a Public Company with its Stock quoted on a Stock Exchange it has the added advantage of being in a position to obtain at least part of its requirements from its own Shareholders by means of an issue of new Capital Stock on bonus terms. There are also available to the larger Companies the facilities of the Finance Corporation for Industry which was established to provide bridging finance in amounts of £200,000 and upwards to Companies which for the time being are unable to raise the long-term capital they require through the normal channels. The Corporation was set up in 1945 at the instigation of the Government, 30 per cent. of its capital being subscribed by the Bank of England, 40 per cent. by the Insurance Companies and 30 per cent. by Investment Trust Companies. This capital has only been called up to the extent of £500,000, but the Bank of England has paid an additional £5 million in advance of calls. The Corporation obtains the remainder of its loanable funds by way of advances from the Joint Stock Banks. The amount borrowed at 31st March 1960 was just over £39 million. The total of loans made by the Corporation at that date was approximately £44½ million.

The Industrial & Commercial Finance Corporation was also set up at the instigation of the Government at the same time, the Share Capital in this case being subscribed by the Bank of England, the London Clearing Banks and the Scottish Banks. Whereas it was the intention that the Finance Corporation for Industry would provide only bridging or short-term facilities, the Industrial & Commercial Finance Corporation was set up to provide small and medium-sized industrial Companies with long- or medium-term capital in amounts of between £5,000 and £200,000 by way of loans and/or Share Capital, in the form of Preference or Participating Preference or Ordinary Shares according to the circumstances in each individual case. The setting up of the Corporation fulfilled one of the recommendations of the Macmillan Committee, and the upper limit of £200,000 placed upon the amount which it could provide to any one concern was the limit suggested by the Committee on the reasoning that amounts above that figure could normally be raised by a public issue. The Radcliffe Committee recommends that the upper limit of £200,000 should now be reviewed "in the light of the change in the value of money since it was first fixed", and this seems an eminently reasonable suggestion.

It was not intended that the facilities of the Corporation should supersede the facilities provided by other lenders and other financial institutions and in its fifteen years of existence it has worked closely with the Joint Stock Banks both in England and Scotland in supplementing, where appropriate, lending by the Banks. The assistance provided by the Corporation generally takes the form of loans or the subscription of Share Capital and sometimes by a mixture of both. The loans granted are normally for periods of from fifteen to twenty years, repayable by yearly instalments very often not commencing until a period of three or five years from the granting of the loan in order that the borrower may not be burdened with the necessity of making repayments before the benefits of the expenditure are felt. Although the Corporation has an impressive record, it has frequently been criticised on the score that the help given to Scottish concerns has been disproportionate to the help given to concerns south of the border. In defending itself against this criticism the Corporation states that the situation is due simply to a lack of demand from Scottish concerns rather than any lack of willingness on its part to make advances in Scotland, and it has declared itself as anxious to increase the size of its business in Scotland. As an earnest of this desire it has increased its Scottish representation by the opening of a new office in Glasgow. Why then has so little use been made of the Corporation's facilities in Scotland? Is it because they adopt a more stringent attitude to applications than other lenders? It may be that the facilities of the Banks have been so readily made available to small businesses and the approach so easy that borrowers have preferred to rely upon the Banks rather than go to a Corporation with which they have had no personal relations. It may perhaps be due simply to the fact that the help which the Corporation is prepared to provide has not been made widely enough known. The Corporation has, however, a part to play in financing small businesses with their long- and medium-term requirements. It has substantial funds at its disposal, having, in addition to its own capital resources and the proceeds of a Debenture issue made last year, borrowing facilities from the London Clearing and Scottish Banks, and I feel that concerns which have plans for expansion in mind and for which they require longer term finance than they should normally expect the Banks to provide should put their problems to the Corporation. They will, I am sure, find it most sympathetic and helpful. They need have no fear that it will interfere in the management of their businesses. The Corporation is not interested in taking over the management, nor in obtaining control, by direct or covert means, of any customer's business.

Another organisation of a somewhat similar nature is the Charterhouse Industrial Development Company formed in 1934, which specialises in financing promising smaller business. The policy of this Development Company is to nurse businesses along until such time as they can make a flotation of capital on the Stock Market. The issue is at this stage handled by an issuing house member of the Charterhouse Group. Loans for development are also made by Credit for Industry, which is a member of the United Dominions Trust Group.

Then there are a number of institutions, of which the leader in Scotland is the Glasgow Industrial Trust, which specialise in the marketing and placing of blocks of Share Capital. These institutions arrange the flotation of blocks of Shares through the ordinary machinery of the market or place Shares privately where a flotation through the market is not possible. They can be of great help to a private family Company which wishes to spread the ownership of its Share Capital or obtain fresh money by the issue of additional capital, for not only are they experts in handling the technical matters connected with issues of Stock but they also have access to other institutions and individuals who are prepared to invest money in the smaller and medium-sized Companies.

Among the large providers of capital through the market are our Investment Trusts and Unit Trusts and I consider that Unit Trusts which attract a regular flow of savings mostly from the small capitalist and salary and wage earners are likely to play, as time goes on, an increasingly important part in providing finance for industrial concerns.

Then there are the Insurance Companies which are today one of the great reservoirs of private savings, through their life assurance business and superannuation schemes. In addition to providing capital through the acquisition of Shares in the Stock Markets, Insurance Companies are generally found willing to provide mortgage loans on properties and have participated on a large scale in the purchase and lease back type of transaction, which enables industrial Companies to unfreeze for productive purposes funds formerly tied up in properties.

Hire Purchase Companies are a source from which financial help can be secured for the purchase of industrial plant and machinery, but in this case their facilities, being generally of a short-term character, are not so capable of satisfying the needs of industry as the loan facilities from longer term lenders. There has, however, been an increasing tendency lately for Hire Purchase Companies to grant loans for periods of up to five years and some have introduced straight hiring schemes whereby industrial Companies, particularly those in the contracting field, may hire industrial plant rather than purchase it themselves.

Although it operates in rather a specialised field I feel I should mention the loan facilities which the Ship Mortgage Finance Company are prepared to grant to shipowners to assist in the building of ships in British yards. This Company, at present a private Company, was formed in 1951, the Shareholders being the Shipbuilding Conference, certain Banks and Insurance Companies and the Industrial & Commercial Finance Corporation. The main function of the Company is the provision of medium-term finance, but Lord Piercy, the Chairman, says that the Company has taken part in several instances in longer-term projects, including tanker fleet finance. He has also indicated that plans are in hand for the conversion of the Company into a Public Company since the Company "may find it desirable and practicable to raise additional funds at a future date". As at 30th June last, advances and investments by the Company amounted to just over £6 million.

A review of this nature would not be complete without some reference to the facilities which the Scottish Banks provide. I think I may safely claim without running the risk of being accused of being unduly biased, that throughout their long history our Banks have made a truly significant contribution to the economic development of Scotland and today, except in so far as they may be prevented by official credit policy, they are just as ready and willing as they have always been to provide their customers with loans and overdrafts for trading and business purposes. The Banks are, however, essentially short-term lenders, a circumstance which is dictated by the fact that the major part of their loanable funds consist of Deposits which are repayable on demand. Therefore, the traditional function of the Banks in the sphere of lending has been to grant short-term advances to augment the working capital of a business rather than loans of a long-term character for capital purposes. Their policies are, however, not so rigid and inflexible as may appear from this statement for, as they acknowledged in their evidence to the Radcliffe Committee, they frequently, in granting loans, have a tacit understanding with their customers that these loans will, in the absence of events and circumstances of an unforeseen nature such as a serious deterioration in the financial position of the customer, be continued for a period of years at the original or reducing limits. Also in recent years at the request of the Government they have been granting medium-term loans for exports covered by policies of the Export Credits Guarantee Department. And although the period for which the Banks have been granting loans under their own small Personal Loan Schemes is relatively short, these also are an instance where the Banks have departed from the principle that all their advances are repayable on demand. In their evidence to the Radcliffe Committee the Banks were questioned closely about their arrangements in regard to farming loans and they admitted that, while the Banks did not give up their right to call for repayment on demand, there was often an understanding with the farmer customer that, in the absence of unforeseen circumstances, the loan would be continued at the same level or at a reducing level for a stated period. On this basis the Banks, by far the largest institutional source of credit for agriculture, have been making advances to farmers for the purchase and re-equipment and improvement of farms as well as for their seasonal requirements. These informal arrangements for the continuance of the loan for a period of years are not, of course, binding upon the Banks, who retain the right to call for repayment on demand if they should feel this necessary for any reason whatsoever, and there is usually an arrangement for annual review. The Radcliffe Committee said that the evidence submitted to them left them with the clear impression that the farmer who borrows from his Bank on the basis of an informal understanding that the money is required to finance medium-term or long-term expenditure need nowadays have no fear that the overdraft facility will be prematurely withdrawn because of changes in circumstances which are beyond the farmer's control. They were referring particularly to loans to farmers, but arrangements and understandings of a similar character are also frequently made with industrial concerns, and the Banks have in fact on their books loans to customers in all fields of industry which have been renewed from year to year over long periods.

I have already mentioned that one of the recommendations of the Radcliffe Committee is that "the Banks should be ready to offer term loan facilities within reasonable limits having due regard to their liquidity requirements as an alternative to a running overdraft". They thought that because Bank overdrafts "are legally repayable on demand and in practice subject to annual review" borrowers are inclined to look upon Bank credit as being "too unreliable a form of credit for medium or longer term purposes". Borrowers, they suggested, sometimes want something more than the informal assurance which a Bank is often prepared to give and the Committee thought that the Banks could go further and grant "term loans repayable either by regular instalments over a fixed period or in full at a given date".

I had previously myself, in a Presidential Address to the Institute of Bankers in Scotland, suggested that the Banks should openly offer to lend for longer terms than had been conventional in the past. At the same time, I said that the Banks could not ignore the short-term character of their Deposits and therefore if they were to launch into longer term lending it would be necessary to confine such lending to a definite and not too large proportion of their deposits. They must also take account of their liquidity requirements and the possibility of frequent changes in monetary policy, for if they had substantial sums out on term loans at a time when it became necessary for them to reduce the total of their advances, the full weight of the restrictions would fall on the other borrowers.

Whatever one's views may be on the future role of the Banks, they remain, and will I am sure continue to remain, the chief source to which business and industrial concerns of all kinds will first turn when they are faced with financing problems, and I can say that within the limit of their resources and policies the Banks will not be found wanting.

It has been possible in this survey only to refer briefly to the main sources from which capital for expansion and development can be obtained. There are many other smaller institutions and agencies which offer facilities of a like nature. Sometimes they operate only in a specialised field. There is, for instance, the Scottish Agricultural Securities Corporation which provides long-term loans for up to twenty years and quite frequently for longer periods for the purchase and improvement of farms. The Shareholders are three of the Scottish Banks, who also provide the Corporation with advances pending funding issues of Debenture Stock.

In concluding I get back to the point I made at the beginning that all the finance for expansion and development, whether provided by way of loans or fixed capital, must come out of savings. The institutions I have referred to are, in the final analysis, only agencies whereby savings are ingathered and made available to those who need and can use them for productive purposes.

Natural Resources and Economic Development

Professor ALAN T. PEACOCK, D.SC., M.A.
Department of Economic Science, University of Edinburgh

This short paper is concerned with certain principles of economic analysis and their application to the problem of determining the place of natural resources in economic development. It is realised that the survey is concerned with resources in a wider sense and very sensibly includes human resources within its scope. However, particularly important misunderstandings arise about the economic significance of natural resources, and, therefore, attention will be concentrated on them.

A basic assumption of the analysis is that the present survey is meant to have some bearing on the present and future economic condition of Scotland. The commonly accepted objective in economic discussion is to raise the standard of living in Scotland to a comparable level to that found in the United Kingdom as a whole coupled with the objective of maintaining a comparable rate of economic advance as measured, for example, in income per head of population. Built into the general scheme of objectives may be many others, including the prevention of depopulation of the Highlands and the reduction of unemployment to the national average, not only in Scotland as a whole, but in specific areas.

Granted this assumption, it will be the contention of this paper that while surveys of natural resources of a general kind provide primary data about the economy, they cannot of themselves give an accurate picture either of the present state of the economy or of its future economic development. The implications of this thesis, if accepted, are that the collection of data of direct relevance to economic policy in the widest sense, while it must comprehend information about natural resources, should be steered towards a different direction than that seemingly believed by the natural scientist to be useful.

THE ECONOMIC VALUE OF NATURAL RESOURCES

The *economic process* is essentially that of producing a flow of goods and services (often computed annually and called the *national income*) in response to the "signals" of consumers through the price system. This process is common to all societies, although they differ in the extent to which the price system is influenced by Government action, e.g. through subsidies to producers or consumers, and the extent to which goods are produced by private as distinct from public enterprise.

Economic organisation consists essentially in the transformation of natural resources into the goods and services demanded by the community by processes requiring enterprise, technology, capital equipment and labour of varying degrees of skill.

Economic progress, at least in the narrow sense of increasing output per head, presupposes a continuing improvement either in the quality or quantity of one of these "factors" of production or in a combination of factors. It is to be noted, however, that in the case where the quantity of labour increases through an increase in population, both the numerator (output) and the denominator (population) in the measure of progress will alter.

This highly simplified description of economic activity is sufficient to enable us to outline the forces which determine the economic value of natural resources.

The economic value of natural resources, then, depends on the availability of complementary factors of production necessary to transform it into goods and services,* and on the valuation placed by the market on the final products for which it is used. The fact that the economic value of a natural resource depends upon the availability of complementary factors, such as capital and labour, means that it is also dependent not only on the products produced from it but also on the prices of other products which can be produced by these co-operant factors. For example, the value of farmland suitable for crops depends not only upon crop prices but upon the remuneration in the alternative employments open to farm labourers, e.g. in manufacturing industry, and thus upon the prices of manufactured articles, which they could help to produce as an alternative to crops. In short, the influences on the economic value of a natural resource are often complex and difficult to discern.

Several important conclusions follow from this analysis.

The first is that the economic value of a natural resource may fluctuate very considerably over time, according to the relative importance of the influences we have described. In Scotland we need look no further than shale oil in order to find an example, where a combination of high labour costs affected by remuneration of alternative employments and the competition of substitutes has virtually killed the industry. The social problems which may follow from a situation of this kind do not need stressing. Important policy problems arise, however, if it is to be assumed that uneconomic working of natural resources must be maintained on social grounds, so that the economic value of resources is to be disregarded.

The second conclusion is that a purely physical description of natural resources gives little indication of its economic value. This must follow from the fact that the value of a natural resource depends on the value of co-operant factors of production. It follows that a simple inventory of natural resources in isolated categories including human resources, as an indication of economic endowment and, therefore, as a guide to future economic policy may be misleading. This point will be discussed in more detail below.

NATURAL RESOURCES AND ECONOMIC DEVELOPMENT

It would hardly be denied that information about natural resources gives us pointers towards the type of economic activities which will promote economic development. The nature of the soil, the topography of the country, and the location of minerals are

* Transformation is used here in a wider sense than purely physical change in the natural resource. Coal is not transformed physically in order for it to be sold. But it involves complementary factors in order for it to be made available as an economic good. What the consumer wants is not coal in the ground but coal in his cellar. The force of this distinction will be clear in later analysis.

obvious examples of the kind of information which will be useful to have. In this respect, a great deal is already known about Scotland, enough, I would submit to give us sufficient indication for the purposes of economic policy. However, only in extreme cases, such as desert or polar regions, are natural resources likely to be the dominating influence on economic conditions. It would be foolhardy to claim that relative scarcity of natural endowment is the main factor in explaining the lower rate of economic growth in Scotland compared to the rest of the United Kingdom.

This point can be put in another way by emphasising the role of the other factors of production. Many areas of the world richly endowed with natural resources have remained underdeveloped for centuries, the U.S.A. being the best known example. The indigenous Indians could not be regarded as having reached more than a very primitive level of living. It required foreign immigration and skills as well as foreign capital to bring rapid economic advance. Even agricultural development has often depended on both foreign "know-how" and foreign labour. The author's main practical experience as an economist has been in East Africa and in the Pacific, and in these areas there are many examples of this. The sisal industry in East Africa not only required foreign capital and enterprise, but even the plant itself, a member of the daffodil family, was introduced in Tanganyika and Kenya in the form of plants from Kew. The same is true of the sugar industry in Fiji, which was developed by the Australians, not with indigenous labour and plants but by indentured Indian labour and imported plants.

In the case of Britain, even the absence of particular natural resources has not been a serious handicap. Some of our most important and (formerly at least) most prosperous industries have relied on imported raw materials which could never have been produced at home, given our natural resources. Obvious examples are cotton and jute. Indeed, even the exploitation of natural fibres which could be produced at home depended at one stage upon the stimulus given by the "know-how" brought by the Flemings and Huguenots! The classic case of a country with a relatively high standard of living and practically no "exploitable" natural resources is Switzerland.

Indeed, there are many examples of countries where, had there been a survey of natural resources available at a particular moment of time, it would have given little idea of future economic development. Hence, such a survey of Malaya at the turn of the century would hardly have indicated that that country would be one of the principal producers of rubber, a plant which was not even indigenous; and rubber today is a major component of the national income of Malaya. The same is true of the countries mentioned above and the crops associated with them, sisal in Tanganyika and sugar in Fiji. Coming nearer home, would a survey of natural resources in Scotland in 1948 have suggested the possibility of bulb-growing in Tiree? I doubt it.

Of course, there are special circumstances in which particular attention needs to be paid to natural resources as a factor in our economic life. These are in situations where force of circumstances, such as war, or deliberate nationalism, make a country depend entirely on its indigenous resources. For a country such as Britain, which is still heavily dependent on overseas trade, an autarkic policy is hardly possible. Some attention needs to be paid to the traditional arguments which link strategic requirements to the problem of conserving natural resources. After all, it was Adam Smith who remarked that "defence is of much more importance than opulence!" Many of these arguments, however, are no longer relevant in an atomic age, and it is not always certain that even if we assume that conventional warfare is a possibility they are still fully applicable to present-day conditions.

NATURAL RESOURCES AND ECONOMIC POLICY

Two kinds of argument concerning natural resources and their supposed relationship to economic progress will now be considered. These are, firstly, the argument that economic progress depends on the "fullest possible use of natural resources" and, secondly, that it depends on "conservation of natural resources".

It is often believed that vast tracts of unused land and forest means that a country has a vast economic potential and that the very fact that these natural resources are unexploited implies economic inefficiency. There is only one important case where this may be true and this is where institutional arrangements such as the existence of monopoly or the prevalence of custom prevent the use of natural resources which would otherwise be brought into production through the response to the market. It is perfectly rational, if we are concerned with economic progress, to leave natural resources unused if the co-operant factors of production are more effectively employed in other uses, e.g. manufacturing articles using imported raw materials.

Another way of putting this is to say that a natural resource is without value, in the economic sense, if the cost of employing the factors of production and the costs of transport of the product to markets exceeds the price of the product in the market. There are countless examples of natural resources which, in technical terms, are considered of high quality whose extractive costs or location mean that co-operant factors would be used unproductively so that these resources, in an economic sense, are valueless unless market conditions change.

In the case of Scotland, even with a relative abundance of technical know-how, a relatively high rate of capital formation by industry and Government, and skilled labour, large areas remain uncultivated and unexploited. This is not necessarily an irrational state of affairs, in terms of economic policy at least. Despite the existence of factors of a relatively high level of efficiency, these factors, as is universally the case, are scarce and, if not used in optimum fashion economically, it is highly doubtful if they would be better used by being transferred to relatively unproductive uses in the Highlands.

In any case, it is arguable whether use of natural resources necessarily implies transformation of these resources by physical means. In one sense the natural resources of the Highlands are quite intensively exploited—as scenery which attracts tourists. This is not quite what many supporters of the "full exploitation" school have in mind!

It must be noted, especially by those who favour economic planning and controls on a more extensive scale than those found in this country, that this problem of the effective use of natural resources transcends the forms of economic organisation. Computing "rates of return" on different economic projects is carried out in Soviet Russia by economic planners, and there is every reason to believe that Soviet economists are well aware of the fact that efficient employment of factors of production is not the same thing as the fullest possible use of natural resources.

Of course, what may be the most effective use of factors of production will change, often rapidly, over time. Tastes may change, at home and abroad; the supply of savings available for investment, technical knowledge, the supply of labour may alter. Consequently, the demand for domestic natural resources may increase or diminish, and the nature and extent of this change may be extremely difficult to forecast.

Nothing in what has been said so far is meant to suggest that there are no cases where investment which might lead to more intensive exploitation of natural resources should be undertaken by the State. There are certain types of productive investment which private enterprise is unwilling to undertake either because they are too risky in themselves or because there is no means possible for charging for the use of the service (the common example is the lighthouse, whose beams cannot be directed solely to guide the ships willing to pay for its benefits!). There is fairly general agreement on the role of the State in the provision of roads and of power as means of promoting economic development. However, in terms of economic policy, that is no argument for equalising charges for these services, ignoring differential area costs, except in very special circumstances such as those relating to a defence programme. In general, therefore, the justification for the improvement of basic services in the Highlands must depend largely on non-economic arguments.

A special aspect of the argument for State investment for economic development purposes is presented in the demand for conservation of natural resources. Obviously, if we take such an argument seriously, its implementation through policy requires an inventory of the various natural resources we wish to conserve, and detailed surveys are necessary. However, concerned as we are only with the economic aspect of conservation, we have to be careful in our assessment of the particular value of conservation measures as often advocated.*

It can be readily agreed on economic grounds that the conservation of certain natural resources because they provide amenities, e.g. historical sights, places of scientific interest, beauty spots, etc., may be necessary. These amenities are desired by the community, but, as in the case of roads mentioned above, it may be technically impossible to charge a price. These amenities, which may be of some importance also in attracting foreign tourists, may therefore have to be financed by taxation.

The really difficult question is that of deciding on the *amount* of these services. If they were provided by private enterprise, their scope and size would depend upon market demand. As it is impossible to charge prices, then some other method of making the decision must be found. It is a common fallacy to assume that those concerned with the technical operation of these kinds of service "know best" what should be spent. Any estimate by them has to make an assumption about the *standards* of service to be provided, and common observation suggests that they will generally assume that the

* The strong hold of conservationist arguments in the U.S. and Canada has been commented on and roundly criticised by their economists. For example, J. K. Galbraith formulated the following definition: "The conservationist is a man who concerns himself with the beauties of nature in roughly inverse proportion to the number of people who can enjoy them" (see *Perspectives on Conservation* (ed. Henry Jarret), Baltimore 1958, p. 92). Scott Gordon in a forthright attack on "conservationism" remarks that the term "conservationist" is "replete with honourable and admirable connotations, designating one who is unselfish and forward-looking, rational and public-spirited, energetic and self-denying. These are rich psychological comforts, and it would seem a poor bargain to exchange them for the ambiguous satisfaction of knocking old icons off their pedestals" (see his "Economics and the Conservation Question", *Journal of Law and Economics*, Vol. 1, October 1958, p. 110). While conservationists do not appear to be so active or so belligerent in this country, the words of President Taft apply here as well as in the U.S.: "there are a great many people in favour of conservation, no matter what it means"!

standards are not good enough! We are all very good at suggesting how other people's money should be spent. If we accept democratic principles, then in these cases the Government is acting as the agent of the electorate, and expenditure on amenities requiring a conservation policy must not only be weighed against one another but against other forms of government and private expenditure. What the expert can tell us is what standards of service can be provided, *given* the finance available.

It will also be agreed that conservation through state regulations may be justified on economic grounds where the exploitation by individuals and enterprises of some resource has "neighbourhood" effects. The common example given is that of the effect of the exploitation of the soil by individual farmers on general level of fertility.

However, conservationists often mean much more than simply the general principle of substituting alternative arrangements for cases in which the price mechanism does not do its job. They mean that the stock of particular forms of natural resources should either be preserved intact or replenished up to some given absolute level. A common example of this view is found in the support for extensive forest conservation. Again, thinking in terms of economic efficiency, there is nothing to support the view that the total stock of any particular natural resource should be maintained intact. Any natural resource is simply part of the total stock of resources. Resource conservation, therefore, is simply a form of capital investment, and like all forms of capital investment it must be judged in terms of its productivity compared with other alternative forms of investment. For example, any extra expenditure on forest conservation by the Government must be judged in terms of the alternatives foregone, viz. either the other forms of public expenditure or the private expenditure which would otherwise take place if the extra taxes to meet the cost of this investment were not levied. If we extend the investment in conservation beyond the point where the return is less than that which the capital would produce in other uses, then the income stream is reduced below what it would otherwise be. It has been well said the "conservational who urges us 'to make greater provision for the future' is in fact urging lesser provision for prosperity".[1]

So far only reproducible resources have been considered. What of irreplaceable resources, such as minerals? It is important to distinguish between the use of the word "irreplaceable" in a physical and in an economic sense. In a physical sense, what is meant is that a particular resource, once used up, cannot be replaced in physical form. In an economic sense, what is meant is that it is impossible to find competing substitutes whatever the physical form. An intelligent economic decision about the use of a particular irreplaceable resource in the physical sense presupposes some estimate of future prices of the resource, and this will depend in turn on forecasts of future technological developments in respect of substitutes and of future discoveries of the same resource. Moreover, in an "open" economy such as ours, the relevant price levels are international ones. The economist at this stage can only stress the difficulties encountered in deciding whether the conservation of this type of resource is desirable or not from an economic point of view. It is clear, however, that the case for conservation is weakest, the greater the expected technological advance.

Economists, like many natural scientists, have been impressed by the falsification of the pessimistic forecasts made at the beginning of the century regarding future fuel and other resources. It has been pointed out, for instance, that Chile would have been much better off had its natural deposits of nitrates been exploited more rapidly before the competition of synthetic nitrates began. Professor Hayek in his recent book[2] argues that "industrial development would have been greatly retarded if sixty or eighty years ago the warning of conservationists about the threatening exhaustion of the supply of coal had been heeded; and the internal combustion engine would never have revolutionised transport if its use had been limited to the then known supplies of oil . . .". These views are backed by hindsight and implicit faith in "argument by extrapolation". Is it sensible to project the rate of technological progress relevant to the discovery of commercially exploitable substitutes at the same rate as over the last fifty years? I should not care to give an answer. What we can say is that once again one has to be careful in deducting any precise conclusions about the future economic value of a resource from a survey of the stock of resources at one point in time.

CONCLUDING REMARKS

This paper has endeavoured to show that while a survey of natural resources may have a variety of uses, its use in economic policy is very limited, once the general pattern of natural resources has been established. The limitations arise from the fact that indigenous natural resources are not the only ones which may be transformed by domestic production, and that a country's economic development is a function of many other factors. These limitations, it may be noted, are in no way a product of any particular view of economic policy and operate independently of the organisation of the economy, i.e. whether it is a planned economy or not.

It is always tempting to assume that because one has discovered where particular natural resources are located and how they may be transformed technically one has in doing so made a statement about potential economic development. This is far from being the case, because the implicit assumption is usually being made that the co-operant factors, and particularly capital are unlimited in supply. The fact that they are generally limited in supply to the economy as a whole means that their use in one direction means denial of its use in another. Thus, to repeat, the value of any particular natural resource depends on the alternative uses of the co-operant factors and the structure of the demand for the products which the community and (very important in the case of the U.K.) foreign buyers want. The structure of demand may alter overnight, the supply of the co-operant factors may alter much less rapidly. Over even a short period of time the economic value of a natural resource may move from a high level to zero.

It is unrealistic in a country such as ours which is not going to be anywhere like first in the queue for international aid to begin an analysis of economic development assuming that there is a relative abundance of capital privately or publicly provided, to conform with the requirements of "developing our natural resources to the full"—whatever that means. A much more realistic approach is to confront the technician—the agricultural expert, the engineer, etc.—with the question, what can you produce and at what cost can you produce the product in question if the capital available were £x and what difference would it make if the capital available were £$(x-1)$ or £$(x+1)$?

Nothing in what has been said is designed to denigrate other objectives than that of increasing output per head. All that has been attempted is a sorting out of the general policy issues so that we are made aware of the important distinctions between economic and non-economic objectives. It is to be noted, however, that non-economic objectives have their economic implications, so long as resources are not unlimited; for the more we choose to subsidise particular areas for commendable motives such as the preservation of rural life, the less we may be able to fulfil other objectives which are bound to require the use of resources. The final judgment of the aims of policy and their relative priorities is not within the competence of the economist. The most he can claim is that he may help to detect inconsistencies in policy which may arise from a neglect of the economic facts of life.

ACKNOWLEDGMENTS

Economists in this country have paid scant attention to the subject of the use of natural resources. Apart from the literature quoted in the text, this contribution owes much to the excellent brief discussion in Chapter IV of the *Economics of Underdeveloped Countries* by P. T. Bauer and B. S. Yamey (Cambridge, 1957). I am also indebted to my colleagues Mr. I. G. Stewart and Mr. Innes Smith of the Department of Political Economy, University of Edinburgh, for comments and criticism.

REFERENCES

1. Scott, A. D. (1955). *Natural Resources: The Economics of Conservation*, p. 97. Toronto.
2. Hayek, F. A. (1960). *The Constitution of Liberty*, p. 370. London.

INTRODUCTION TO DISCUSSION

F. N. Woodward, C.B.E., B.SC., PH.D., F.R.S.E.
Director, Arthur D. Little Research Institute, Inveresk

Mr. Chairman, Ladies and Gentlemen: For the third time this morning you will find yourselves under the Chairmanship of an immigrant. Like Sir Edward, I am quite happy to be described in this manner as I have been told on several occasions that I have now earned my residential qualifications! In any case, I prefer it to the description which was often tagged on me, and I suspect on Dr. King, when we used to go to Canada quite frequently, namely that of a "friendly alien".

Now, this session is rather different from all the others that we have had so far in that it brings together a number of contributions which, in many respects, appear to be disconnected. We have given as the title of this session "The Mechanics of Resource Development", which is an accurate description although I do not think any of the authors of these papers would have looked upon themselves as experts in resource development before this session. I may be wrong in that, but I think that I am correct as I found on looking through the list of authors of papers for the Symposium that I knew at least 60 per cent. personally, but when I was faced with the names of the seven authors of papers in this session I found I only knew two of them. So I have had to do my homework and I have been able to meet each of these gentlemen prior to this session and have had very stimulating talks with them, and it has been very greatly to my benefit as I hope and know it will be to you when we come to discuss what they have said.

This session is different also in another respect in that our Reporter is not working locally and he therefore requires some introduction from me. He has just whispered that he is an emigrant: I would describe him somewhat differently as a local boy made good, but more of that in a moment. And also there is going to be an exception to our previous practice in that amongst our contributors we have one, namely Mr. Moscoso, who is going to be invited to speak, but I will tell you more about that and about him in a moment.

So, Ladies and Gentlemen, before I introduce the Reporter formally, I think I should ask the authors of papers to identify themselves: Mr. Moscoso—I think you all know he is the Administrator of the Economic Development Administration in Puerto Rico, and is here as our guest today; Mr. R. H. S. Robertson, the Director of Resource Use Ltd.—a very old friend of mine and one of the foremost protagonists in the post-war period of resource assessment, development and conservation in Scotland; "Marketing" by Mr. Fergus Williamson, a Director of Balfour, Williamson and Co. Ltd.; "Scottish Transport" by Sir Ian Bolton, lately the Chairman of the Scottish Area Board, British Transport Commission; "The Tourist Industry in Scotland" by Mr. W. A. Nicholson, Manager and Secretary of the Scottish Tourist Board; "Finance Available for Developing Resources" by Mr. W. R. Ballantyne, General Manager of the Royal Bank of Scotland; and last but not least "Natural Resources and Economic Development" by Professor A. T. Peacock of the Department of Economic Science, Edinburgh.

Well, Ladies and Gentlemen, my duties at this stage are complete when I have introduced Dr. King. He was born in this country, although he received his formal education in the south and he has had a distinguished career in many fields. He first came to eminence at a very early age as a lecturer in Chemistry in the Imperial College, London. Then came the war and he held a number of very important engagements, starting with the Ministry of Supply, then passing on to the important post of Assistant Scientific Adviser to the Minister of Production. He was then appointed Director of the United Kingdom Scientific Mission in Washington, D.C.; eventually he became the first Scientific Attaché at the British Embassy there and had much to do with the formation of the British Commonwealth Scientific Office. On his return to this country after the war he was appointed Head of the Scientific Secretariat in the Lord President of the Council's Office; then he became Chief Scientific Officer in D.S.I.R., and more recently he moved to Paris where he holds the very important position of Joint Director of the European Productivity Agency of O.E.E.C. In this connection he has, and has had, much to do with almost every topic which is up for discussion today.

STATEMENT BY THE REPORTER

ALEXANDER KING, C.B.E., D.SC.
Joint Director, European Productivity Agency, Organisation for European Economic Co-operation

It is a very great pleasure to be here and particularly to take part in this Symposium because as you may suspect I have a great deal of interest in the subject and I am particularly interested in this latter part where technological, economic and sociological matters are to be considered together. Dr. Woodward hinted that this last session was a sort of rag bag, but I think it will appear after the discussion that there is a continuity, a coming together and a coherence in the subjects we are now to discuss. Furthermore, I think that many of the subjects discussed today have an important bearing on the central theme and especially on the mechanics of resource development. I shall say little about the paper by Mr. Moscoso because he is going to speak to it himself, but I would like to stress that all over the world Puerto Rico is now regarded as a pilot case of integrated development, and I know from discussions in the United Nations, my own Organisation and elsewhere of the esteem in which it is held as an important workshop for the shaping of the methodology of economic development. His paper is extemely interesting and we look forward to a highlighting of it by Mr. Moscoso himself.

Mr. Robertson's contribution is interesting in quite a different way. In the process of making a case for the creation of a series of research and development laboratories for Scottish raw material resources, Mr. Robertson introduces many other ideas; some of them are clearly matters which he regards as extremely important and I share with him a sense of that importance. For instance he has a lot to say about the need for a fresh approach to the educational problem. He has a great deal to say on the necessity for the direct participation of the people in developments in their area and their own land and I think it has been shown in most of the successful development schemes in other parts of the world that participation and community development are major sociological questions. In discussing a suggestion from the Edinburgh Junior Chamber of Commerce, Mr. Robertson gives some straightforward and useful proposals for the creation of an economic intelligence unit. He also suggests (perhaps by the way) that this unit and the group of laboratories he is advocating would be useful training places for people from the underdeveloped countries of the world. I want to make a little aside there, Mr. Chairman, because I think there is in Scotland the potential for an extremely important invisible export. It is interesting that Denmark, for instance, which is not a very big country, is deliberately and consciously educating and training engineers and scientists above its domestic requirements in order to provide this export of specialists which will be required in ever-increasing numbers in other parts of the world, and I suggest this is a matter which might be highlighted in the conclusions as something from which Scotland could very well profit, although it is only implicit in Mr. Robertson's paper. In Mr. Fergus Williamson's paper we have a completely different approach and I am very glad that the organisers of this Conference included the subject of Marketing because this again is an important feature of all integrated schemes which is often forgotten. In many parts of the world you can improve the crops and products of farmers, foresters and others, but unless you teach them how to sell these products you do not get very far. Again and again and again one has seen in schemes that a critical threshold for property is reached through improved marketing and distribution. We had observed this in our O.E.E.C. schemes for the Island of Sardinia and Epeirus in Greece where marketing is the critical feature which tipped the balance to success in increasing the real cash incomes of the local people. Mr. Fergus Williamson's paper gives a tremendous wealth of practical case detail which I recommend for thorough study. Incidentally I think his paper foreshadows what some people will regard as unholy alliance which is becoming important in industry and at times dominant, namely, between the marketing man and the research man. To my mind the trend in future in industry is that development will be through this symbiotic relationship between, if you like, these two extremes with production more and more the service function in between. Research application and marketing advance will certainly go hand in hand. We ought to give this paper particular attention for that reason.

Next we come to Sir Ian Bolton's paper on Scottish transport, which is a careful and very close analysis of our transportation systems and their economy; it is written from the economic point of view and the question of rail/road balance and other problems are clearly stated. The place of transportation in a coherent scheme of development is of course very important and hence the place of this paper is significant. Mr. Nicholson's paper on the tourist industry comes next. I would hardly regard this as a mechanism of development, but rather as a major industry for Scotland as in many other parts of the world. This is a very readable paper and the case is very well made. There is a rather unhappy story of tourist development since the war suffering from lack of capital, etc.; however gratifying new plans are put forward. It seems to me that the outstanding need is for capital and again good marketing methods. The need for capital in tourism should be understood far more widely as also its general investment value for the economy. An important case of this was quoted from Southern Italy, where a chain of hotels created by an industrialist as a patriotic duty had not only brought tourism profits but opened the way for new industrial enterprise. Mr. Moscoso has also great experience of the importance of tourism in Puerto Rico in the same way. Capital acquisition for tourism must be looked at in a new way and far more incisively as an extremely important national economic investment. Publicity and marketing are of obvious importance here, and as an emigrant Scot roaming about in Europe and North America I must say I have been appalled in the last years to find the great ignorance of Scotland in most parts of the Continent. There is a tremendous amount to be done in connection with making the touristic splendours of this country as well as the facilities much better known and perhaps separately known from those of the U.K., as a whole, but that is another story.

Now to the paper by Mr. Ballantyne, on the availability of finance. I do think that this is one of the clearest statements I have read for a long time on the different methods of industrial financing. He makes a point, of course, that most of these resources of finance apart from the Scottish banks are of United Kingdom institutional origin and have significance for the island as a whole. He also has a great deal of interesting comment on recommendations of the Radcliffe Report which interested me personally very much.

Now I come to the paper of Professor Peacock. From the point of view of the conservationist this is a difficult and, I think, salutory paper. As an economist he hits out, though very politely, at the excess naivety of the natural scientist and conservationist who so often look at natural resources on the ground as an economic potential without really taking into account the vast number of other facets of the problem of economic development which are represented by many of the other papers in this session. I think it is very important that this point should be made, and I think it has been made very clearly. Professor Peacock sums up by asking technicians, agriculturalists and engineers what they can produce for a certain capital expenditure and at what cost. He raises also the question of alternative investment and the need for looking at alternative investment possibilities on the basis of a reasonable economic assessment rather than through a sentimental attachment to a single resource, or a feeling that resource development as such can be successfully exploited without taking into account the many many other factors which lead up to the overall economic assessment. I suggest that conservationists, of which there must be many here, should not be damped by this approach, on the contrary they should answer back, but they should profit by this all-round economic approach and be willing to look at the development of Scotland as I think Lord Bilsland did in broad terms of investment possibilities. One thing I take from Professor Peacock's paper is the need for a concentration of effort and enquiry as to how to use Scotland's greatest human natural resource, her human intelligence and skills in the various alternative methods either by digging things from the ground and fishing from the sea, or by creating great new industries, exporting brains, and a hundred and one other ways.

I think that this series of papers illustrates very clearly the complexity of the problem of economic development whether of natural raw materials or otherwise. Not only are we interested in the existence of minerals in the ground, fish in the sea and capital to exploit them, but the availability of men, skills and education. There is a need to create an expert and trained management, to achieve the willing co-operation of an interested and knowledgeable labour force together with their unions, to encourage research and development and manage them well, to encourage and expand market research, to improve the distribution system and to encourage the application of techniques of economic assessment. This includes the study of the general economic climate in relation to development, looking into the fiscal and legal conditions favouring development, and the building up of an enlightened trade policy; in addition to all this is the necessity for progressive background social policies without which such developments are unlikely. We are facing a situation characteristic of our age, where scientific, technological, educational and social factors are interacting and must be considered together. We will hear a great deal more from our Speaker Mr. Moscoso and others about the integrated approach to this problem which to my mind is its essence. We have heard so much of the shortcomings of United Nations and other technical assistance schemes because they concentrate on individual actions—a soil scientist here, an irrigation expert there and a mineral advisor somewhere else: in the enormous vacuum of underdevelopment, these things are just diluted to infinity and very little results. It is important then to look at experiments which have taken place by means of a combined, many-faceted approach. In highly developed economies such as that of the United States there is more and more concentration on the question of how to accelerate economic growth to study of factors which favour it, including, of course, education, research, management development, management-labour relations and things of that sort. There are also by now many examples of the integrated approach to development of regions which we can profit by. I need not mention Puerto Rico. We have also the classic example of the Tennessee Valley Authority, and here in Europe much is being achieved and much experience is to be gained which could be of value for Scotland; in France this has been done extremely well, for instance the company, the nationalised company, for the development of the Bas Rhone Langedoc in the Southern part of France, concerned with agricultural land utilisation, industrial problems, etc., has been an outstanding success and is a first-class pilot example, visited by people from all over the world. In the European productivity area agency where I work we have at the moment pilot developments of an integrated type in Sardinia, in Greece and in Turkey.

In the Greek one, for example, it is hoped to make all the inevitable mistakes on a very small scale by concentrating on a small area first, and looking at the social education, management, community, land utilisation, agricultural, forestry, small industry problems, etc., before the main development plan for the whole province of Epyrus is put into effect. Even very near here we have the Shannon Scheme, which started as a straight trade scheme thought up by the Irish because of the excellent sales of duty-free whisky at the Shannon airport. Now there is a free-trade manufacturing area, plants have already been erected and many more are on the way. But the Irish have been clever: they have thought about it in a rounded way, and with advice from us they are setting up vocational training schools for accelerated vocational training so that farm labourers can be trained very quickly to make very intricate transistor radios, etc., and complicated equipment of all kinds. This is based of course on the idea of a Free Trade Port where there is free import of components and raw materials, no export quotas or difficulties. The hope is to give much new employment to Irish labour, but it is hoped that it may become a model not only through its advanced training methods but also its management-labour relations, thus becoming a pilot example for management-labour co-operation in Ireland as a whole. I must mention one more point before stopping: human resource planning is one of the most important aspects of the whole thing. We have talked a lot about education this morning. We have heard some extremely interesting things. In many of the economic development plans of various parts of the world human resource planning has been forgotten. Plans go into effect, the infrastructive work is completed, but there are too few skills to operate the new industries. It takes a long time to educate a man—longer than to build an atomic power station—and yet this is too often left to the end. O.E.E.C. is now working with six of the Mediterranean Governments first of all to assess the skilled manpowers, scientific, managerial and otherwise, which will be required by their economic development plans in each case and from that working out what the institutional needs are for education from the schools upwards so that the pre-planning of the human resource and education is done in such a way that there will in fact be men available when they are required by the schemes. I want to end on this note. To my mind what is required in Scotland is probably not the seven-year plan of the conventional Russian type, but I would suggest initially what we badly need is a national development strategy and that as a beginning towards the creation of such a strategy we should create a technical-economic Intelligence Bureau to look at many of the problems that have been under discussion this week, which would pull things together and provide the basis for a coherent integrated approach to future development —but I think that many of the points will come out in the discussion of the papers and in the speech of Mr. Moscoso.

SPECIAL PAPER BY TEODORO MOSCOSO

Dr. Woodward, *Arthur D. Little Research Institute, Inveresk*

As I indicated earlier, this session is slightly different to those which preceded it in that we are to have one of the papers read, and this is to be by Mr. Teodoro Moscoso. Right from the outset the Committee felt that it would be an extremely good thing if they could invite somebody here who has had personal and considerable experience in the field of resource development particularly in a country which until recently might have been described as underdeveloped. The name of Mr. Moscoso was suggested to the Committee, who extended an invitation to him to participate in the Symposium which I am delighted to say he accepted despite the fact that our air-mail letter inviting him to come took over four weeks to reach him.

I think it only right that you should know a little bit about Mr. Moscoso's background.

I will only touch the highlights as I want to spare his blushes. He is a graduate of the University of Michigan and has had a wide experience mainly in his own country of Puerto Rico. In the early days from 1932 onwards he was General Manager of a firm which bears his name; 1936-39 a President of the Puerto Rican American Drug Co.; from 1938-42 he was Chairman and Executive Director of the Ponce Housing Authority; from 1942-50 he was President and General Manager, Puerto Rican Industrial Development Co., which changed its name in 1950. In addition to his various responsibilities as Administrator, Economic Administration, Puerto Rico, he also holds a number of Directorates, included amongst which are the Puerto Rican Glass Corporation, the Puerto Rican Cement Corporation, the Pulp and Paper Corporation and the Government Development Bank for Puerto Rico.

You will all have seen and doubtless read the very interesting paper which Mr. Moscoso has submitted which tells us something of the development of his own country under his skilful management. On this occasion he is not going to talk about that but is going to speak on the topic of management resource exploitation.

Mr. T. Moscoso, *Puerto Rico*

I wish I were allowed to speak in Spanish. I am afraid that my Spanish would be as unintelligible to you as your Scotch accent is sometimes unintelligible to me, and speaking of Scotch accents I just developed a theory about this wonderful story which Dr. King has told about his daughter in Moscow. I am quite sure that she has a Scots accent and that when she was asked where she came from what the Russians understood was that she came from Togoland instead of Scotland.

Now having come from further away than most of you I feel doubly pained at being unable to contribute very much of a theoretical nature to this Symposium. However I must say I am taking back with me a most agreeable experience of having been stimulated beyond words by the quality and quantity of brain power available to you here in Scotland. Were we fortunate enough in Puerto Rico to be able to marshal the intellect, the wisdom and the experience of those assembled right here in this room, we would cease to be an underdeveloped country in a very few years.

I don't wish to fly under false colours in making my remarks on the subject of resource management. My observations are those of an interested layman on matters which, particularly during the past fifty years, have increasingly become the province of specialists.

Rather than trying to set forth the principles or the elements of resource management, it seems wiser for me to try to formulate the questions which must be at least partially answered as a condition of establishing resource management policies. My layman's questions are these:

1. What are the region's resources?
2. Of the resources discovered, which, if any, have utility in the economic sense of the word?
3. With due regard both to present and prospective demand and, always bearing in mind considerations of human welfare, how can each of the resources judged to possess utility be most efficiently exploited?
4. What is the best possible balance, as between coercion and education, in securing efficient resource exploitation?

I will now comment very briefly on each of my questions.

Regional Resources

It is a truism that knowledge is the basis of resource exploitation. Yet the truism is probably as often ignored as observed.

To illustrate, eight years ago the Royal Institute of International Affairs published a brief survey of world raw materials. The survey estimated that as of 1950 only 11 per cent. of the surface area of the U.S. had been adequately mapped geologically. The Institute's estimate is, I suggest, borne out by the activities of the Bear Creek Mining Company, an exploration subsidiary of the Kennecot Copper Corporation—one of the world's largest copper producers. In the post-1939-45 War period the Bear Creek Mining Company systematically explored for copper all along the U.S. east coastal region from Maine to Florida—the area of initial settlement by European migrants.

Economic Utility

In the matter of resource economic utility, I believe that I can illustrate the meaning of my question by recalling an account of one of his early professional experiences by Sir Dudley Stamp, the distinguished British geographer. Stamp had been engaged to survey for oil in Burma. While beating his way into jungle back-country, Sir Dudley discovered what he believed to be a mountain of high-grade iron ore of high quality. Excited by his discovery, Sir Dudley made haste to the nearest telegraph office, many days away, to inform his superiors of his discovery. Much to Stamp's chagrin, the telegraphed reply of his boss read, as I recall, about as follows: "Of what use is iron ore in the Chindwin? Get on with your work."

Iron ore deposits have been discovered in Puerto Rico, but should an integrated steel industry ever be developed, a most doubtful possibility, it would have to be based on imported ores, probably from Venezuela.

Efficient Resource Exploitation

Efficient resource exploitation has, I believe, both an economic and a human dimension. I believe that I can illustrate both dimensions by reference to our neighbouring Caribbean island of Jamaica with whom we have very friendly relations.

Jamaica has large and rich bauxite deposits. But Jamaica, just as Puerto Rico, has no low-cost source of energy. Large-scale electrolytic metallurgy, such as is necessarily involved in the production of aluminum (I suppose that I should have said aluminium) production, is not economically feasible in Jamaica or in Puerto Rico. The intermediate stage between bauxite mining and aluminum production—alumina—is another matter. Here, I believe, that we and our Jamaican friends may possibly be in competition with one another. The essential point is that an area should process its raw materials through the most advanced stage of fabrication which is economically feasible.

The Jamaican bauxite deposits also illustrate, I believe, the human dimension of efficient resource exploitation. The initial bauxite mining contract signed by the Jamaican Government did not give a fair share of protection to Jamaican interests. An outside observer commented to me several years ago that at the end of the contract all the Jamaicans would have obtained would be a big hole in the ground. The contract has since been re-negotiated so that a reasonable share of the mining operations' profits are now going to the Jamaican people.

I believe that I can illustrate the dual dimensions of the problem in the case of Puerto Rico by reference to bagasse—the pithy residue produced in crushing sugar cane. Traditionally, bagasse has been consumed as fuel by the sugar mills. But the value of bagasse as a material can be upgraded by using it for other purposes and substituting another energy source—in our case fuel oils. Our first paper plant using bagasse as its basic raw material was opened last year with a consequent increase both in Puerto Rican jobs and income.

Balance between Coercion and Education

Let us talk for a moment on the proper balance between coercion and education. The cupidity of man is, I am afraid, an essential element in the achievement of economic progress. If this judgment is correct, then I would suggest that the police powers of the State must be used to maximise the efficiency of resource utilisation and to enhance human welfare.

The mining of the U.S. Great Plains soils and many of the rich U.S. timber stands are familiar stories. Less familiar perhaps is the pollution of major U.S. rivers and the despoiling of marine life. Of these only the mighty Columbia River, the headwaters of which are in Canada, has managed to defy the well-nigh infinite capacity of man to foul his own nest. Only Government is able to curb the cupidity of, for example, the paper mill operator who forreasons of economic gain would prefer to discharge his raw effluent into the river near by. Only Government is able to stop the selfish operators who, in the case of the Columbia River, would destroy the spawning cycle of the salmon.

But the essential questions are: How much coercion? How much education? I am sorry I must confess to pessimism in this matter. I believe that the major reliance must be placed on coercion—on the police power of the State.

I would now like to comment very briefly on human resources. As a matter of fact, these are about the only resources we really have in Puerto Rico.

In Puerto Rico with our population density of about 685 persons per square mile human resources are necessarily a subject of continuing interest. It is not our population density *per se* which is a cause of concern: after all, the population density of, for example, the Netherlands is substantially greater than that of Puerto Rico. Our concern is with a high and rising population density together with a high level of chronic unemployment, and I am afraid that this pairing of conditions is all too common in the world today.

Just a few minutes ago we discussed very briefly a very fine paper on migration. We have a migration problem in Puerto Rico also. We have lost in twenty-five years over 700,000 Puerto Ricans who have moved to the United States. I think the migration has to a certain extent been successful, and here is a case where there has been success in migration from a tropical climate to a temperate climate. However, by the way, 700,000 emigrants must be considered in relation to the population of Puerto Rico. We have $2\frac{1}{2}$ million inhabitants, a little less than half of your population. I understand you have lost a little over a million in half a century. However, the best trained minds in Puerto Rico have not migrated, and the reason for that is that we have made it a point to create the necessary job opportunities in Puerto Rico for them. As a matter of fact most well-trained Puerto Ricans can obtain better salaries in Puerto Rico than in the U.S. That is why we retain the best-trained minds.

I also read the paper yesterday and heard the brief discussion today on this movement to the south out of Scotland. Well, that movement is no different than the movement to the south from the north-eastern United States, particularly from the New England area. However, the New England area has not taken it sitting down. They have developed very aggressive programmes of industrial promotion and right now New England is the United States centre for electronic research and development and the number of job opportunities open in New England today is many times higher than they were twenty-five years ago when most of the textile industry of the United States was located there. Now, reading a paper last night on the number of scientists and technologists available to you I envied you the 150,000 engineers and scientists available in Scotland. Proportionately we should have 75,000 in Puerto Rico on the basis of population. Well, we hardly have 3,000 now. That has not however prevented us from doubling our net income *per capita* in the last ten years. Because brains can be hired; brains can be brought from outside. I must take a moment to comment on the fact that Mr. Woodward's very fine organisation, for instance, has been one of the sources of brains for us in Puerto Rico for almost eighteen years. We have been picking their brains; they don't have to necessarily live in Puerto Rico, they live in Cambridge, Mass., but we make use of them.

One of the few things I would like to mention because I believe it is one of the few contributions that I could make to the Symposium is that we have kept in mind a target date and a goal for Puerto Rican economic development. Ten years ago we decided that by the year 1975 the great majority of the population of Puerto Rico, the great majority of the families in Puerto Rico would have reached a personal income of $2,000 per family. Now we keep that goal and that target date continuously in mind in all our economic development programmes on the island.

Finally, I should like to comment on weather and climate as resources. In ordinary usage these two words are used synonymously. But I would like to suggest that there can be a valid distinction drawn between them. For example, I would say that in Puerto Rico the weather is good but the climate is bad. As a freshman visitor to Scotland I would suggest that your weather (at least in the autumn) is bad but that from what little I know of your sustained, diversified agricultural production, your climate must be good.

Let me try to clarify these elliptical statements. The December tourist in Puerto Rico who has fled the rigours of at least a part of a, say, New England winter has a different view about our brilliant sunshine than the local sugar-cane grower who may for weeks have been praying for those rains which may well be the difference between hunger and comfort.

An aphorism of the American humourist Mark Twain was that everybody talks about the weather but nobody does anything about it. Today things can be and are being done about both weather and climate.

We of course need to expand our knowledge in the conventional fields of resource management. But I would suggest that it is no less important to intensify our efforts in adaptation to and control of such natural phenomena as weather and climate—phenomena generally regarded as "Acts of God" but ones which I believe, while not fully controllable, can more often than not probably be converted from curses into blessings.

In spite of its almost total lack of raw materials and absolute lack of fuels, in spite of its meagre domestic market of only 2½ million people, Puerto Rico has been able to double its net income *per capita* in the last ten years to just under $600 per head. This achievement of our people has led us to accept as truthful the dictum that there are really no underdeveloped countries but only underdeveloped brains. Thank you.

Dr. Woodward, *Arthur D. Little Research Institute, Inveresk*

Thank you very much indeed, Mr. Moscoso, the warmth of the applause speaks for itself. As a member of the Committee I take some pride in this as it is in effect a vote of confidence you have given us in our choice of guest speaker. I would like to congratulate Mr. Moscoso not only for the subject-matter of his paper but also for the excellent way in which he presented it and his masterly control of our language.

I have had the opportunity already of having a chat with Mr. Moscoso and I have been greatly impressed by his ability, by his modesty and by his enthusiasm, and I would suggest that if you can corner him for a few minutes it will be very much to your advantage. I am sure Mr. Moscoso would welcome the opportunity of talking with as many of the delegates as possible.

Again I am going to be an exceptional Deputy Chairman in allowing one of the authors to speak, but I have a very good reason for this. If you look at the titles of these seven papers you will notice that five are really factual statements which although very valuable would not be particularly profitable to discuss here. The two exceptions are the paper on Research and Development Techniques by Mr. Robertson and that on Natural Resources and Economic Development by Professor Peacock. This latter contains rather a novel approach to what we are doing here and one of which we should certainly take notice, and Professor Peacock has asked for an opportunity to speak not to his paper but to participate in general discussion which I am sure you will agree to.

DISCUSSION

Professor PEACOCK, *Department of Economic Science, Edinburgh University*

My first point is that it is a fallacy to assume that economics is concerned purely with economic development in a very narrow sense. It is artificial to separate economic policy and social policy; there are simply certain policy objectives and all of them have economic implications. Therefore, to say that the economist is merely concerned with material development is wrong. The important conclusion which follows from this is that you cannot dodge out of a discussion of economics by saying that a particular resource ought to be developed "for social reasons". Any resource use implies the denial of use of those resources in other directions.

I have the feeling that those people who have put forward very interesting technical devices do not realise their economic implications; they seem to assume that capital resources and human resources, particularly know-how, are free goods which are there for the asking. For example, in only one case has any writer actually calculated the capital cost of one of these devices. We are told that the capital cost of utilising wind as a source of energy would be roughly £150 million. Unfortunately, we do not know the annual rate of capital investment in Scotland—it is a most extraordinary thing that one of the basic statistics regarding economic development in Scotland is simply not known—but assuming the same rate of capital investment per head of the rest of the country this £150 million would be equivalent to something like two-thirds of the total amount of capital investment in Scotland in one year! You may have seen in the papers today that the total public investment for Britain in 1960-61 is put at something like £1,700 million per annum. If you take the appropriate *per capita* figure for Scotland, £150 million would exhaust the total amount of public investment in Scotland in one year! Therefore, the difficulty is that if you totted up the likely capital costs of all the various schemes you would find that the costs would far exceed the capital resources which are likely to be available, and if capital is scarce the question of choosing between projects arises. You do not provide an answer to the problem of choice by simply giving an account of the technology of a particular process.

My second point relates to the requests for Government help, and is closely connected with the first. I think it would be thoroughly dangerous for our democratic system to assume that resource use problems should be "taken out of politics", whatever that means. Resource use involves the spending of public money, other people's money, and if resource use were taken out of politics, those who pay the price would have no choice in spending. You have, therefore, got to convince people that this spending is worth while, that the extra taxation which these various schemes imply is worth raising.

My third point is based on the assumption that this Conference is meant to have some bearing on the problems of less-developed countries. If my own experience is any guide—I had in fact to draw up a development plan for the Fiji Islands last summer—it is that stable political and developed financial institutions are as important as technical innovation in furthering economic development. We must not repeat the schoolboy explanation of the Industrial Revolution—"a wave of gadgets swept Britain". In fact, the Industrial Revolution was made possible by important institutional innovations in banking, financing and government, and these innovations are on a par with technical or scientific innovations. There is hardly a less-developed country in the world where it has not been brought home that one of the most important things in economic advance is stable government, and the creation of an environment which will attract capital.

Mr. C. J. M. Cadzow, *Scottish Agricultural Organisation Society Ltd.*

I rise, Mr. Chairman, to make a few remarks on Mr. Fergus Williamson's paper on marketing. While there may be many well-organised and efficient business concerns engaged in the marketing of agricultural products who are well able to speak for themselves if they feel that their activities have been overlooked by him in his paper on marketing, I wish to refer particularly to his comments on agricultural co-operative marketing and marketing boards. He has singled out co-operative marketing for some quite caustic comment and mentioned my own Society's efforts in this field, adding—and I quote—"material achievements have been small so far". I fear, however, that the writer's conclusions regarding marketing of produce have been tempered and probably based entirely on his reading of a report on tomato marketing prepared by Produce Studies Ltd., and many readers of his paper may have drawn unfair conclusions therefrom. There are some 70 agricultural co-operative societies trading in Scotland today, and of these at least 40 are engaged in the marketing of produce of one kind or another. During 1959 the turn-over of all trading societies was just short of £40 million, and of this total, sales of produce reached nearly £32 million plus the Scottish trade of the Fatstock Marketing Corporation, which is also producer controlled, but whose figures I have been unable to obtain since Mr. Williamson's paper was circulated. I leave these figures, sir, to speak for themselves.

In the co-operative movement in Scotland we are well aware of the gaps still to be covered and of the need for market research, but we are particularly proud, sir, that more than 50 per cent. of all eggs produced in Scotland are marketed through producer-owner packing stations.

But this is not the only bone I have to pick with Mr. Williamson. A section of his paper is headed "Government Marketing Schemes and Subsidies". In this section Mr. Williamson, I feel sure, must have caused considerable misunderstanding to arise in the minds of his readers. In the main he is of course referring to agricultural marketing boards, established and brought into being in terms of the enabling legislation passed by Parliament in 1931 and later years. He lists wool, milk and eggs but overlooks potatoes as being commodities for which, I quote "the Government is practically the only buyer". It is, sir, quite a few years since this was so. Today our wool, milk and egg marketing boards are certainly most actively concerned with the marketing of their respective products, and are doing a good job of work. Perhaps that job needs improvement. Since cessation of war-time controls these boards may have been very convenient instruments to use for the implementation of the Government's agricultural policy, but their position and activities are very different from those pictured by Mr. Williamson. It must not be forgotten that they are farmers' organisations, devised by producers, voted into being by practically 100 per cent. of producers in some instances, and are controlled by boards elected by producers. It is also true to say that they are based on the experiences of the agricultural co-operative movement in marketing over a long period of years and that their trading statistics might quite rightly be added to those of co-operatives. Moreover, as we are dealing with the marketing of Scottish natural resources, it is pertinent to point out that Mr. Williamson has overlooked the fact that there are three milk marketing boards in Scotland. I have only to add, Mr. Chairman, that the National Farmers' Union of Scotland and my Society may wish to submit a separate paper on this subject.

Mr. P. Johnson Marshall, *International Centre of Regional Planning and Development*

May I say a few words on the mechanics of resource development as a member of the Executive Committee of the International Centre for Regional Planning and Development. One of the most difficult problems is that we have had, and still have, a major unplanned population movement, first to urban areas and then to metropolitan urban areas, but I think that this can only be planned and redirected with very drastic and radical new approaches at both political and economic levels. Earlier this year I had the opportunity of visiting the Tennessee Valley Authority and talking to its Manager, Mr. Wagner. Now, Mr. Chairman, both you and Dr. King mentioned the Tennessee Valley Authority, which many of us still feel to be one of the world's greatest achievements of comprehensive regional planning and development, but perhaps we should remember it was a nationally financed effort as part of the New Deal. The Tennessee Valley Authority has been going on long enough for us to see not only the dams in operation with the water controlled, the reafforested areas developed, and a fascinating new landscape with a tourist industry well under way, but also a significant new achievement in the development of industry. I think everybody knows about Bowaters, and there are many other major new industries, such as, for instance ALCOA and DuPonts. It is because of these enterprises that they have discovered their Achilles heel, and that is the lack of really comprehensive planning to enable them to integrate their urban development into regional development. What I saw in Tennessee made me sure that unless the resource development is comprehensively planned, it is going to lead us into very great difficulties.

May I just say a few words on the effect of this kind of thinking on Scotland. Because we have to begin with the British Isles if not with Europe, we must all have noted a recent report by the Royal Commission on London Government in the papers. If we also refer back to the Barlow Report, may I suggest that there is some basic thinking needed at the British Isles level on a re-orientation of economic and industrial policy. If there was a real Scottish Development Plan it might well take the form of a series of T.V.A.s; some kind of planned redevelopment programme, but essentially on a comprehensive basis, this could then be followed by a reassessment of our urban planning problems, on which a great deal of thought has already been spent. May I finish by saying we are proposing in fact to develop a major programme of planning research in the University of Edinburgh, that we have already started one post-graduate course in urban planning, and we hope soon to start another on regional planning.

Mr. Booth, *Institute of Seaweed Research*

I wonder if I may be bold enough to actually suggest a strategic area plan for Scotland at this stage. As I see things at the moment, the last year has seen considerable developments in the central lowland area, to quote but two, the Strip Mill on the West and the B.M.C. factory at Bathgate, and it has struck me during these last three days that there could be great effort placed in another area of Scotland which would do immeasurable good in particular to the area and also to the crofting counties.

I refer to the Great Glen. I started this line of thought when the paper on the location of the fifth university was mentioned, and it struck me then that were this university to be situated at Inverness we then have an area where at the other end of the Glen is the expanding aluminium works, there is the promise or the hope of a pulp mill which will naturally, I think, bring in its train paper and board mills. The area too is a great cattle-producing area, it is a centre of a great sheep industry, the sheep naturally means wool, weaving and a dyeing which could well be done there as well as it is in Langholm or Bradford. It might also mean this great cattle area, that we should introduce veterinary medicine, manufactured sheep-dips and so on and create in the Great Glen a smaller edition of the central lowland area of Scotland. Owing to the time I do not wish at this stage to elaborate this theme at all, but I do throw it forward as a suggestion and I feel that there is bound to be some study group formed to collate the suggestions and things to follow up from this Conference so I do with respect, sir, suggest that the study group give some attention to the scheme I have just suggested.

Mr. Swan, *National Farmers' Union of Scotland*

First of all on behalf of the National Farmers' Union of Scotland I would like to support Mr. Cadzow's remarks on marketing and I would like to say at the present time Mr. Cadzow's organisation and the Farmers' Union are considering very actively ways and means of further improving co-operative marketing in Scotland. Our aim is to try to produce better presentation of our agricultural products and to improve our distributive and sales methods.

I would now refer to a problem which is concerning the Farmers' Union today, and that is the question of the transport of agricultural goods to urban areas in Scotland and, perhaps even more important, across the border into England, because it is an interesting fact that today farm products from Scotland are exported annually to England to the value of some £37 million. These comprise meat £16 million, sheep £5 million, seed potatoes £6½ million and pigs approximately £4 million. The movement of farm goods emphasises a great problem in Scotland, and that is the high cost of transport from our remote areas.

Agriculture depends on the land for its output and cannot concentrate its productive capacity near urban areas without loss of output, and it is very significant that the cost of transporting frozen or chilled meat from the Argentine and New Zealand to the U.K. is not substantially higher than the cost of transporting fresh meat from our production areas in the North of Scotland to the London market, and we understand too that it is likely to cost more to consign oats from Aberdeenshire to Lancashire than wheat from the St. Lawrence to parts of the U.K.

I have mentioned specifically the agricultural side, but this is indeed a problem which affects the whole of our economy, and I think another point which should be remembered is that the real cost of the price of road transport to users is heavily inflated by the incidence of taxation on fuel and vehicles, and it is a fact that the further goods have to be taken by road the more taxation requires to be paid. In the Farmers' Union we feel that there is a real need to alleviate the burden of transport on outlying producers.

We heard this morning that about three-quarters of the population in Scotland are now concentrated in approximately a seventh of the area. There is a constant converging of the population on the urban parts, and we feel that there is an urgent need to develop the economy of the outlying areas. We believe that the Government should initiate a complete survey into this problem in all its aspects from which we would hope very much that it would be possible to introduce measures to mitigate this running sore in Scotland's economy.

Mr. W. A. W. Krebs, *Massachusetts, U.S.A.*

As one of the few visitors from abroad I feel that I might take this opportunity to attempt to repay in some small measure the debt I have incurred by being allowed to participate in the Conference. As I consider with what currency I can repay, I recognise that my principal capital is my ignorance of Scotland. However, having had some contact with programmes of economic development in other countries I believe it might be useful to capitalise my ignorance by giving you my perspective.

To me what is most impressive is that things are really as good as they are. If one compares Scotland today with other countries in which my organisation has worked—East Pakistan, Peru, Haiti, even Puerto Rico—one cannot but be impressed with the tremendous wealth of material and human resources that lie ready here to your hands to be shaped into a programme of economic development, a programme which can have untold significance for this country. I look at the skills and literacy of this population compared to the literacy of, say, East Pakistan—1 per cent. I think. I look at the financial and institutional resources which appear on every side here. I look at what the development economist today calls the infra-structure, the roads, the rail transport, the power grid, the enormously complex development of the marketing system and all of the institutions which go to make it up and, from the point of view of one comparing that with the underdeveloped economies elsewhere in the world (to borrow an expression from Mr. Moscoso), I "drool" at the magnificence of your resources. Finally, the concentration of technological talent in this country represents a resource which most of the emerging nations of this world can only dream about and scarcely can hope to assemble in the lifetimes of many generations ahead.

With all these resources at hand—again from the perspective of one coming here from the outside—what is the great missing element? I think I sense that a description of the missing element has been almost on the lips of many who have spoken here these last few days. In fact, it was on the lips of Dr. King when he spoke of the need for a national development strategy—I think he used the term "an integrated approach". Here lies the key which can unlock the resources and power of this society for growth and development. What, I wonder, are the principal elements of such an integrated approach? No one yet has attempted to voice them, and I would be presumptious to attempt to lay down an outline of what they might consist of, but there are two or three important parts of such an integrated approach that—again from my perspective from the outside—it might be worth while my mentioning. One, and perhaps the key one, is the need for a programme with truly quantitative goals and objectives, goals and objectives in terms of money, numbers of jobs, of national income and of time, the kind of measurements that are expressed in the appendices to Moscoso's paper, where year by year and decade by decade accomplishment can be measured, efficiencies can be gauged and a discipline for accomplishment can be erected, because of the existence of specific, quantitative goals. A second element that such a strategy of development might include would be a system of priorities, a means for identifying the more important and distinguishing it from the less important, the kind of measure that Professor Peacock referred to here this morning when he spoke of alternative demands for capital. Where can one most effectively place his scarce resources in order to achieve most in the least possible time? Such a system of priorities becomes an important part of a development programme A third element occurs to me—a reliance on economic research, on a programme of economic research, in order to be able to establish the priorities and to define the goals and then to carry the measures, looking toward accomplishment of those goals, to a level of definition which will permit decision-making by persons considering investment. It is all good and well to talk about desirable projects, but unless those projects have been characterised in sufficient detail so that from an investment point of view a realistic—at least a preliminary—appraisal can be made, it is unlikely that the project can be brought to fruition in a reasonable time. Thus there needs to be a mechanism for applying the skills of economic research to the formation of project objectives.

Finally, and the element that is perhaps crucial, and may even be present today at least in early form, is an organisation to carry these measures into effect. A visitor to this country is struck by what I may call the unusual nature of your Governmental arrangements. I perhaps hear the rustle of Scottish Nationalism in the wings! In any event, the absence of a national organisation or indeed of a sub-national Governmental organisation which is competent to carry such a programme into effect seems to me, again begging your pardon as a visitor, to make unusually important the role of private organisations in forming such a programme. In this respect I commend to your attention some of the private efforts which have been organised and carried out in the U.S., when time permits you to study these; for example, the programme of the New England Council, a private organisation built upon the decline of the New England textile industry, which has resulted in the emergence in New England of an electronic industry second to none.

Some of them have included measures which might be appropriate in a programme here. I hope that out of this meeting will come that kind of action.

Certainly to me it has been an inspiration to be here and I am proud to be associated with what I hope will be the genesis of a great new effort for economic development in Scotland.

Mr. FERGUS WILLIAMSON, *Balfour, Williamson & Co., Ltd.*

Mr. Cadzow, you are perfectly right, I must apologise for not giving adequate attention to the achievements which have been made in agricultural marketing. When I took on this job, which I am afraid was only a short time ago, it struck me that agricultural marketing was one of the most important things to be mentioned. If you look through any trade journals or the various publications, technical publications, of the various industries of Scotland, when you get into the agricultural ones you find yourself into marketing problems straight away, and they are very complex as you know and probably a lot better than I do. I felt they deserved a mention and in mentioning them I had intended to include a lot of statistics which you gave us some indication of. Unfortunately the statistics turned up at the last moment and were not comparable because they covered varying years such as the wool year, the milk marketing board's year and in comparing them with national statistics done on a calendar year basis it was quite unthinkable that one could include them in a paper like this and so regrettably they were left out, but maybe we can put them together for an addition to this paper because only by comparing the statistics could one see the achievements of agricultural marketing. I will say that the marketing of agricultural produce appears to me to be very much more complex than a lot of other industries and trades. I did try to bring out the various facts here—the milk marketing board, the egg-marketing board; I am sorry I left out the potatoes, generalisation on these marketing boards is sometimes a little bit difficult—and at the same time give due regard to co-operative marketing. You did pick me up for leaving out Fat Stock Marketing Corporations. I must apologise; as you know there are quite a few other organisations that did not even get a mention here.

Dr. WOODWARD

Thank you, Mr. Fergus Williamson. In all fairness I should mention to Mr. Cadzow and Mr. Swan, Mr. Williamson filled the breach at very short notice—we are very much obliged to him. He and I had a session in London only two or three days ago bringing the last things together. Now, Mr. Chairman, there is nothing left but to bring this meeting to a conclusion and in so doing may I on your behalf thank the authors of the papers in general, Mr. Moscoso in particular, and Dr. King for coming so far and giving so much of his time from a very busy life to give us the value of his experience.

RESOURCE ADMINISTRATION AND DEVELOPMENT

ADMINISTRATIVE REQUIREMENTS FOR OPTIMUM RESOURCE DEVELOPMENT

Resource Development—Central Administration

SCOTTISH OFFICE, EDINBURGH

The paper describes the existing Government administration in its relation to resource development in Scotland.

The Secretary of State acts through four Departments with a wide range of functions.

The Department of Agriculture and Fisheries for Scotland administers all Government schemes for the promotion and development of agriculture in Scotland; owns large agricultural properties; is responsible for agricultural research in conjunction with the Agricultural Research Council; takes measures for the conservation and development of fisheries including research; and is concerned with the activities in Scotland of the Herring Industry Board and the White Fish Authority.

The Department of Health for Scotland deals with water supplies and other public services, housing and planning, including questions arising out of the location of industry and movements of population.

The Scottish Home Department represents the Secretary of State's general interest in the development of industry in Scotland and exercises his functions in relation to the Scottish Electricity Boards.

The Scottish Education Department supervises all Scottish education including technical education, but not universities.

The relevant functions of the following United Kingdom Departments are also briefly described; the Board of Trade; the Ministry of Labour; the Ministry of Power; the Office of the Minister of Science (covering the Department of Scientific and Industrial Research and the Nature Conservancy); and the Forestry Commission (for whose activities in Scotland the Secretary of State is responsible).

The subject of this paper is the present Government administration machinery in Scotland that deals with aspects of the problems involved in "Resource Development".

GENERAL

Public administration in Scotland is conducted partly by departments under the direct charge of the Secretary of State for Scotland, or of the Lord Advocate, and partly by departments of other Ministers of the Crown whose responsibilities extend over the whole of Great Britain. There are four main departments of the Secretary of State. These are:

the Department of Agriculture and Fisheries for Scotland;
the Department of Health for Scotland;

the Scottish Education Department;
the Scottish Home Department.

Through these is discharged the bulk of the functions for which the Secretary of State is directly responsible to Parliament. In addition he shares with a number of other Ministers responsibilities for the administration of certain services which are organised on a Great Britain basis. For example, the functions of the Forestry Commission and the Crown Estate Commissioners extend throughout Great Britain; but for their activities in Scotland the Secretary of State bears full Ministerial responsibility.

Great Britain departments exercise functions in the spheres of trade, industry, employment, transport and defence. They include, among others, the Board of Trade; the Ministries of Labour, Works, Power, Transport, Aviation, and Pensions and National Insurance; the Post Office; and the three service departments. All these departments have offices in Scotland.

Day-to-day contacts are maintained between all the departments in Scotland, and there are Scottish inter-departmental committees on, e.g., distribution of industry, physical planning and building. Contacts are also maintained between officers of the Scottish departments and the headquarters of other Government departments in London.

While direct responsibility for administration in some of these spheres has thus been assigned to other Ministers, the Secretary of State is necessarily concerned as "Scotland's Minister" in all matters affecting Scottish economic planning and development.

Apart from Government departments, there are a number of organisations which play an important part in Scottish development and which combine independence with close relations with Government administration. On industrial and economic questions the Secretary of State receives independent information and advice from the Scottish Council (Development and Industry), and the Scottish Board for Industry provides another link between the Government and industry in Scotland. The Scottish Tourist Board helps to promote the well-being of the important tourist industry. Since 1947 the Advisory Panel on the Highlands and Islands appointed by the Secretary of State has kept under review the carrying out of the approved programme of Highland development. The Panel also, in consultation with the Secretary of State, arranges for the investigation of further means of promoting both the economic use of capacity and resources and the welfare of the Highlands and Islands. The Crofters' Commission has the duties of reorganising, developing and regulating crofting in the Highland counties. In each of the Scottish departments a senior officer has been made responsible for general oversight of the department's work in the Highlands and for its co-ordination at official level with that of other departments and agencies. In addition an inter-departmental committee meets to review progress and to promote concerted action on Highland affairs.

This brief summary indicates the general form of central administration in Scotland. The Secretary of State and his departments form a key part of that administrative structure and so far as concerns the use of natural resources are directly responsible for many factors affecting the use in Scotland of land—as regards agriculture and forestry in particular—and of water, in connection with fisheries, industry (including hydro-electricity) and public health. They are also responsible for physical planning and, to take natural resources in the human sphere, for education, welfare and public order.

This paper describes only the main functions exercised by the Secretary of State through each of the principal Scottish departments in so far as they concern natural resources.

DEPARTMENT OF AGRICULTURE AND FISHERIES

Agriculture

The Department is responsible on behalf of the Secretary of State for the management of over 800,000 acres of land throughout Scotland. Of this area, most of which is let, more than half comprises smallholding estates. The Department also administers almost all Government schemes for the promotion and development of agriculture in Scotland.

Among the production grants and subsidies provided by the Department are ploughing grants, which have for their object the maintenance of the area of land under cultivation, primarily as a source of home-produced feeding stuffs for the production of livestock and livestock products; and hill cattle subsidy, whose aim is to encourage hill farmers to increase their breeding herds and thereby improve the productivity of their land and the fertility of their grazings.

Grants are given for the drainage of agricultural land; for the control of bracken; for the provision of water supplies to fields and buildings; and for the application of lime and fertilisers. Grants for other improvement works such as land reclamation and the erection of shelter belts are provided for under hill farming schemes and farm improvement schemes. In addition, farms classified as "marginal" may receive grants on the net cost of certain operations which could not reasonably be undertaken without assistance.

Through its scientific services the Department provides for testing of seeds (for purity, germination and weed seed content), trials of new varieties of potatoes and certification of growing crops of seed potatoes, seed oats, seed barley and soft fruits. The Department also controls the import and export of potatoes, plants and trees, and its Inspectors check consignments to ensure that destructive insects or disease organisms have not been brought in from abroad.

The Department is responsible for measures to prevent damage to crops or stored food by animal, bird or insect pests. The major pest in Scotland was until recently rabbits and has been reduced but not eliminated by myxomatosis. The Department from time to time designates districts as clearance areas within which there is a legal obligation on occupiers of land to destroy rabbits. Grants are given towards the expenses of rabbit clearance societies and fox destruction clubs.

The Department's livestock improvement work includes the formulation and administration of grant and service schemes relating to horses, ponies, cattle, sheep, goats, pigs and poultry; the control of artificial insemination; the licensing of bulls, boars and stallions; and consideration of application for permission to export and import livestock.

Apart from the control of operational measures against epidemic disease, e.g. foot-and-mouth disease, which remains the responsibility of the Ministry of Agriculture, Fisheries and Food, the Department controls all matters of animal health administration including the campaign for ridding Scotland of bovine tuberculosis. The whole of Scotland is now an attested area.

The Department is closely associated with the work of the three agricultural colleges and eight agricultural research institutes in Scotland. It is responsible for their general administration and provides financial assistance for their work, including the provision to farmers of a free advisory service based upon the three colleges and staffed by college officers.

In connection with the research institutes the Department have scientific advice from the *Agricultural Research Council* which functions under a Committee of the Privy Council consisting of the Minister for Science, the Secretary of State for Scotland and the Minister of Agriculture, Fisheries and Food, and co-ordinates the development of agricultural research in Great Britain.

The development plans of local authorities and proposals involving the diversion of agricultural land to non-agricultural purposes are referred to the Department or to the appropriate agricultural executive committee and are critically examined. The loss of the land is frequently unavoidable but agricultural interests are safeguarded as far as possible. The Department joins with the Forestry Commission in making agriculture/forestry land use surveys of various areas in the country. It also examines all proposals by the National Coal Board to prospect for coal and to extract it by opencast methods. After coal has been extracted and the surface of the land reinstated, the Department, acting as agents for the Board, undertakes the agricultural restoration of sites.

The Department collaborates with the Scottish Peat Committee in investigating the use of peat for industrial and agricultural purposes. The Department also assists the Institute of Seaweed Research, which operates an information and advisory service to assist local development of the seaweed industry and co-ordinates certain fundamental chemical research on seaweed at Universities.

FISHERIES

The Department is responsible for fisheries administration in Scotland and deals with deep sea and inshore fisheries and with salmon and freshwater fisheries. Its duties range from international relations on fishery matters to domestic matters affecting fish catching including subsidy payments to the industry. Both national and international recognition has been given for many years to the need for some conservation policy to secure the rational exploitation of stocks and fish. Before the war, the fish stocks in the North Sea and other waters adjacent to the British Isles had become heavily overfished. They revived during the war when many of the principal fishing grounds were rested, but overfishing has again become a serious problem. An international Convention regulating the size of mesh of fishing nets and prescribing minimum sizes for the landing of certain of the more important species of fish came into operation in 1954. The measures for which this Convention provides are, however, very limited and a new North-East Atlantic Fisheries Convention was signed in 1959 which, when it comes into force, will enable more comprehensive measures to be taken, provided that the signatory countries are prepared to co-operate more effectively in their enforcement. Fishing in inshore waters is further controlled, particularly for the protection of fish nurseries, by statutes and byelaws which regulate fishing methods, sizes of boats and species which may be caught in different areas. To enforce these regulations the Department maintains a fleet of fishery cruisers. It is also responsible for fisheries research in Scotland which is carried out at its Marine Laboratory at Aberdeen and at the Freshwater Laboratory at Pitlochry;

a fleet of four research vessels is maintained. The Department also assists by grant and loan the provision, improvement and maintenance of fishery harbours and piers.

The Department maintains close contact with the White Fish Authority and Herring Industry Board, who are responsible for regulating and developing the white fish and herring industries throughout Great Britain. The members of both bodies are appointed by the Fisheries Ministers—the Secretary of State for Scotland, the Minister of Agriculture, Fisheries and Food and (in relation to Northern Ireland) the Home Secretary. The White Fish Authority has a Committee for Scotland and Northern Ireland, with an office in Edinburgh, to whom wide powers are delegated by the Authority; and the Herring Industry Board has its office in Edinburgh.

DEPARTMENT OF HEALTH FOR SCOTLAND

The Department of Health is responsible for the general supervision of the National Health Service in Scotland and for many other measures designed to maintain and improve health and welfare. These include the hygiene of food and milk supplies, the provision of houses, the welfare of aged and handicapped persons, the improvement of sanitation, and water supplies. The Department is also responsible for town and country planning. It is the last two functions that most closely concern natural resources in Scotland.

Town and Country Planning

The Department's work under this head involved the approval of development plans by local authorities, including proposals for comprehensive redevelopment, the determination of appeals against the decisions of the local planning authorities on development proposals, including the display of advertisements, and the determination of claims for compensation for planning restrictions on the development of land.

The Department is responsible for co-ordinating at official level proposals by Government departments and local authorities for the use and development of land and for the listing of buildings of special architectural or historic interest, as well as for planning research and surveys and the preparation of national planning maps.

A fuller statement of the scope of town and country planning, with particular reference to natural resources, is contained in the Appendix.

Water Supplies

The Department has the duty of promoting the conservation of the water resources of Scotland and the provision by local authorities of adequate water supplies throughout Scotland. This includes the making of orders, without which no new sources of water can be tapped, the authorisation of new headworks and distribution systems, with the assistance of special Exchequer grants where applicable (rural localities, development districts and town development schemes), and the amalgamation of water authorities (all of which in Scotland are local authorities or combinations of local authorities) voluntarily or compulsorily where necessary to secure economy and efficiency in the use and distribution of resources. The provision of water supplies by water authorities includes provision not only for domestic needs but also in so far as it is reasonably practicable for commercial, industrial and other non-domestic needs. It is now the general practice for non-domestic users, except in some specialised fields, to look to the water authorities for their supplies instead of seeking supplies for themselves.

It is also the Department's duty to promote the cleanliness of the rivers and other inland waters and the tidal waters of Scotland. It is responsible for the constitution and general supervision of river purification boards or other river purification authorities on whom rests the local responsibility for controlling the discharge of sewage and trade effluents to streams, including such tidal waters as may be brought, by order of the Secretary of State, within their jurisdiction. It also acts as appeal authority from the decisions of these authorities in relation to applications for consent to make new discharges or outlets to streams.

SCOTTISH HOME DEPARTMENT

The functions of this Department are exceptionally diverse. So far as natural resources are concerned its interests are twofold.

Industry

The Department advises the Secretary of State with regard to his general interest in the development of industry in Scotland, and although it exercises no statutory powers, it works in the closest co-operation with the Board of Trade, the Ministry of Labour and other appropriate departments in this sphere. A report on industry and employment in Scotland is presented to Parliament each year. The Department has a particular interest in the development of the tourist industry and maintains close contact with the Scottish Tourist Board.

Electricity

The Department is responsible for the central administration in respect of both the Scottish electricity boards and is thus concerned in a vitally important industry which uses two of the main natural resources of Scotland—coal and water—for the generation of power. It is closely concerned in the scope of the generation, main transmission and distribution programmes of these Boards, the siting of power stations, and, principally in the case of the North of Scotland Hydro-Electric Board, the utilisation of water power for the production of electricity.

SCOTTISH EDUCATION DEPARTMENT

This Department is responsible for the general control and direction of the national system of education exclusive of the universities. Locally the provision and management of schools and of further education establishments (which are subject to inspection by H.M. Inspectors of Schools) is the responsibility of 35 Education Authorities in accordance with schemes approved by the Secretary of State. In addition, seven Colleges of Education which provide teacher training under the control of independent governing bodies come within the general administrative oversight of the Department. So also do 13 colleges (known as central institutions) for advanced instruction in various technologies, in art and in domestic science. These again are conducted by independent governing bodies, and receive substantial financial grants from the Department. Typical examples are the

Royal College of Science and Technology, Glasgow, the Heriot-Watt College, Edinburgh, the Dundee Institute of Art and Technology and Robert Gordon's Technical College, Aberdeen.

FORESTRY COMMISSION

The Forestry Commission is responsible for promoting the interests of forestry and the development of afforestation and the production and supply of timber in Great Britain. In carrying out its functions in Scotland the Commission acts under the directions of the Secretary of State. In particular, the power of acquiring land in Scotland required for forestry purposes, and of disposing of any land not required for such purposes, is exercised by the Secretary of State.

The functions of the Commission include the management and planting of land, the protection of young trees and the establishment and maintenance of forests; the construction of forest roads; the building of houses and the establishment of holdings for forest workers; the sale of forest produce; the administration of the forestry dedication scheme for private woodland; the making of grants for afforestation purposes; and the formation and administration of national forest parks.

The Forestry Act, 1951, charged the Commission with the additional duty of promoting the establishment and maintenance in Great Britain of adequate reserves of growing trees. The felling of trees is controlled by licence and the re-stocking of felled areas is assured by the inclusion in the licence of replanting conditions in appropriate cases.

The Commission's plantations in Scotland total 532,000 acres. The planting programme for Forest Year 1960 was 29,000 acres; the planting programmes for the next three years are 32,000 acres in Forest Year 1961, 34,000 acres in Forest Year 1962 and 32,000 acres in Forest Year 1963. Thereafter the rate will be reduced as the plantations come into full production. In deciding where planting will take place, special attention is paid to the upland areas where expansion of forestry should provide needed diversification of employment and important social benefits.

GREAT BRITAIN DEPARTMENTS

Four Great Britain departments have particularly important functions relating to natural resources in Scotland.

The *Board of Trade* deals with the internal and international aspects of general matters affecting the conduct, regulation or welfare of United Kingdom industry and trade as a whole, including raw material and supply problems. It is the "sponsoring" authority for most manufacturing industries (and some others such as films and tourism), i.e. it is the point of contact in the Government to which most manufacturing industries go for discussion or representation of their affairs. The Board is also concerned with encouraging and assisting the provision of additional employment in districts where there is high local unemployment.

The *Ministry of Labour* is primarily the department concerned with manpower and as such is responsible for the administration of the Employment and Training Act, 1948. The Ministry's functions include the placing of persons in employment (including unemployed persons and persons in employment who wish a change of job) and the vocational training of fit and disabled persons. It is also responsible for the administration of the National Service Acts, the Disabled Persons (Employment) Act, 1944, and the Youth Employment Service (except in so far as this service is operated by local education authorities). Other functions include questions of industrial relations and the operation of a Personnel Management Advisory Service, the payment of unemployment benefit and national assistance as agents, respectively, of the Ministry of Pensions and National Insurance and the National Assistance Board, and the administration of the Wages Council Acts.

The *Ministry of Power* has a general responsibility for securing the effective and co-ordinated development of coal, petroleum and other minerals and sources of fuel and power in Great Britain; its staff includes a Chief Scientist's Division. The nationalised coal, electricity and gas industries (except electricity in Scotland) are required by statute to settle their research programme with the Minister; he refers these for advice to his Advisory Council on Research and Development, who also see the programmes of related research organisations. Where the Ministers considers that some important project is not being followed up he can invite one of the nationalised industries to undertake it, or may himself arrange for it to be investigated. The Minister is also required by statute to promote research into safety and health in coal mines; this is done in the Ministry's research laboratories at Sheffield and Buxton.

The *office of the Minister of Science* has a general responsibility for Government scientific policy, including the application of scientific methods to the conservation and development of natural resources. Advice on these matters is provided by the Advisory Council on Scientific Policy. The Minister is responsible, as Chairman in each case of a Committee of the Privy Council, for the Agricultural Research Council (see above, p. 758), the Department of Scientific and Industrial Research, the Nature Conservancy (see below) and the Medical Research Council; and has important functions in relation to the promotion and development of atomic energy.

The *Department of Scientific and Industrial Research* conducts and supports fundamental and applied research in the national interest and encourages research and the application of scientific knowledge in industry. In Scotland, the Department maintains a Liaison Office, a National Engineering Laboratory, branches of the Road Research, Building Research and Warren Spring Laboratories, a Food Investigation (Fisheries) Research Station, a Geological Survey and a Radio Research Station sub-laboratory.

These laboratories, together with the other D.S.I.R. establishments located in the United Kingdom, provide advice to local authorities, industrial firms and other *bona fide* enquirers on problems which come within the orbit of their research activities. Research work of specific importance to Scotland may be undertaken, within its field of competence, by any D.S.I.R. laboratory. The Department supports research work in Scottish universities and technical colleges through grants for training research students and for special research investigations and makes contributions to the industrial research associations, of which one (Jute) has its headquarters in Scotland.

The *Nature Conservancy* is responsible for providing scientific advice on the conservation and control of the natural flora and fauna of Great Britain; for the establishment and maintenance of nature reserves including the maintenance of physical features of scientific interest; and for the organisation and development of research and scientific services related thereto. Under Part III of the National Parks and Access to the Countryside Act, 1949, the Nature Conservancy may enter into agreements with the owners and occupiers of land, and may, where necessary, acquire land for the establishment of national nature reserves. The Conservancy may also make bye-laws under the Act for the protection of nature reserves and is responsible for advising local authorities about the establishment and maintenance of local nature reserves.

APPENDIX

Town and Country Planning
(Department of Health for Scotland)

Introduction

Town and country planning has the general function of co-ordinating and controlling, in the local and national interest, all development affecting the use of land, the settlement of population and amenity. This note gives a broad outline of the basis of planning control, with particular reference to natural resources.

Historical

The first step taken to establish planning as a national responsibility was the appointment, in 1943, of a Minister of Town and Country Planning for England and Wales. The Minister and the Secretary of State for Scotland (who was already responsible for town and country planning in Scotland) were assigned the function of ensuring "that the translation of agreed national policy into terms of land use is conceived as a single and consistent whole", and they were charged with the duty of "securing consistency and continuity in the framing and execution of a national policy with respect to the use and development of land" throughout the country. The aims of physical planning were set out in further detail in a White Paper published in 1944 (The Control of Land Use, Cmd. 6537). In 1944 the Government of the day also announced its acceptance of the main recommendations of the Barlow Report on the location of industry, designed to decentralise the very congested areas and to encourage a reasonable balance of industrial development as between various regions in the country and suitable diversification of industry in each region.

Planning Legislation

Since 1943 several important statutes, reflecting the established aims of national planning policy, have been enacted by Parliament. These include the New Towns Act, 1946 (which applies to the whole of Britain), the Town and Country Planning Acts of 1947 (separate parallel Acts for England and Wales and for Scotland) and the Town Development Acts of 1952 (England and Wales) and 1957 (Scotland). In Scotland the main governing statute is the Town and Country Planning (Scotland) Act of 1947, which established a positive and flexible system of planning and a comprehensive and continuous system of control of land use and development. Subsequent legislation has been concerned mainly with the basis of compensation for planning restrictions, and the 1959

Planning Acts restored market value as the basis of compensation where land is acquired by public authorities.

Surveys by Local Planning Authorities: Development Plans

The Acts require every local planning authority (in Scotland the county councils and the town councils of the large burghs and the two small burghs of St. Andrews and Thurso) to make a comprehensive survey of the physical, social and economic conditions, factors and resources of their district, and on the basis of a critical analysis of the survey to prepare a development plan to show the manner in which they propose that land in their district should be used (whether by the carrying out of development on it or not) and the stages by which any development should be carried out. The plan has to be approved by the Secretary of State before it comes into operation. Flexibility is secured by the provision that amendments may be submitted for approval at any time, and to prevent the plans becoming out of date fresh surveys and plans are required to be submitted periodically. The general object is to define the sites for proposed roads, public and other buildings and works, airfields, parks, pleasure grounds, nature reserves and other open spaces, and allocate areas of land for use for agricultural, residential, industrial or other purposes.

In addition, the development plans may designate as subject to compulsory acquisition land allocated by the plan for the functions of any Minister, local authority or statutory undertaker, land in an area of comprehensive development and any other land which the local planning authority consider ought to be acquired for the purpose of securing its use in accordance with the plan. In this connection local planning authorities may acquire land compulsorily and dispose of it to private developers, or develop it themselves.

Although all development is required to conform to the approved development plan, the plan is not intended to impose an inflexible pattern of development but rather to serve as a guide to the local planning authorities in the exercise of their functions of planning control under the Acts. Development is defined in the Acts as "the carrying out of any building, engineering, mining or other operation in, on, over or under land, or the making of any material change in the use of any buildings or other land", and planning permission is required for all development so defined: for minor kinds of development planning permission is given under the General Development Order without the need for a specific application to the local planning authority.

By the end of 1959, 47 of the 57 local planning authorities in Scotland had submitted 39 full development plans, 16 part plans and 63 amendment proposals, making a total of 118. Of these 85 had been approved and one amendment had been withdrawn. Up to the end of July 1960, 12 further plans or amendments were approved. A number of local planning authorities whose development plans were approved some years ago have since undertaken fresh surveys and have prepared revised or substantially amended development plans. In July 1960, for example, Glasgow Corporation submitted a revised plan, accompanied by a detailed survey report.

Functions of the Central Planning Department

Particular activities of the Department in the field of land use and the development of natural resources include:

(i) Co-ordination of the land use and development requirements of Departments and statutory bodies.

The general purpose is to harmonise these requirements with local, regional and national planning requirements.

(ii) Issue of guidance and advice to local planning authorities in the preparation of their surveys and development plans, and the examination of development plans, when submitted for approval.

These tasks require, among other things, close collaboration with local planning authorities in the course of their preparatory work and the issue of explanatory memoranda and other advisory information in the form of handbooks, broadsheets and circulars.

(iii) Co-ordination of background information necessary for planning administration.

This requires the Department (*a*) to evolve planning techniques, principles and standards by research, study and experience; (*b*) to collect and collate all necessary information concerning physical, social and economic conditions and resources that have a bearing on local, regional and national planning; (*c*) to initiate or promote *ad hoc* local or regional surveys and regional advisory plans; (*d*) to co-ordinate and relate information derived from (*b*) and (*c*) with requirements for agriculture, forestry, industry, mineral working, power, transport, the settlement of population, recreation, etc.

Paper by an Industrialist

J. O. Blair Cunynghame, O.B.E., M.C.
Deputy Chairman, The Royal Bank of Scotland, Edinburgh

At the outset it is necessary to define what is meant by "Optimum Resource Development", and it is suggested that this can only be the distribution of resources amongst various uses in such a way as to provide in the long term for the increasing happiness of mankind. Reasons are given for preferring this type of definition, in terms of people, and certain limits to the field of discussion are laid down.

The resources to be adminstered are recapitulated with reference to other papers and the several broad types of instruments for developing resources are described as private enterprise, public enterprise, the State itself, local authorities and many voluntary organisations. The importance of the last mentioned is stressed.

Certain assumptions are made regarding the likely part to be played by certain of the instruments in developing resources, including the State's responsibilities and the probable continuance of a predominantly free price economy.

The apparent conflict between the development of resources by free enterprise on the one hand and by an increasing measure of State or State-authorised control on the other is discussed and shown to be less serious than at first sight seems to be the case. The increasing sense of social responsibility in industry—particularly big industry—is showing a significant coincidence of immediate material results and long term benefits for mankind.

The Administrative Requirements are suggested as changes of emphasis rather than striking innovations. These include:

(*a*) Further education of young men and women through schools, places of further education and universities (where an amount is already being done) in the facts of resource development and use.

(*b*) Most important of all, greater attention in Scottish industry and commerce to the training and development of managerial and executive skills to produce dynamic leadership with a clear objective and highly adaptable to change: in this way, it is suggested, with sound planning and the best possible use of human material—perhaps Scotland's most valuable resources—there will be wider appreciation of the coincidence of efficiency and social responsibility in resource use and development.

(*c*) Greater assistance to research and development, particularly in smaller concerns.

(*d*) Finally, as regards the position of central and local government, a warning is sounded that unless Scotland can show on merit (which it is suggested can be done) that it is worth expanding new and existing industries there, serious damage will be done to her reputation and economy by too ready a use of special concessions and Government help.

DEFINITION OF OBJECTIVE

Before attempting to suggest the nature of the "Administrative Requirements for Optimum Resource Development", it is necessary to establish in broad terms the yardstick by which the approximation to the optimum is measured.

Broadly and simply, there would seem to be compelling grounds upon which to define Optimum Resource Development as the disposition and use of resources, now available and to be developed, in such a way as to ensure the present and future happiness of the men and women comprising the society with which we are concerned. This can be variously described as a continuously rising material standard of well-being coupled with aesthetic and other deeper satisfactions, or, more simply, as in the best long-term interests of mankind. This is not the context, however, in which to attempt any further analysis of meaning and motive: the conception is clear enough in broad terms.

This definition is just as valid for the industrialist or commercial man as for the moralist or the public servant. It is more than likely that by no means all would necessarily accept it at first sight, but this should not reduce its validity.

In discussing this broad objective of attaining the optimum so defined, it is necessary to impose certain limitations or else the field would become too wide: accordingly the particular structure of the political framework is excluded, except that an essential degree of democratic liberty is assumed, as also is the possibility of war. Both these considerations do, of course, affect resource development materially and human happiness fundamentally, but it is perfectly practical, having registered the point, to assume them as non-variables, in much their present form, for the purpose of this discussion.

The reasons for defining optimum in this way include the following:

(*a*) Unless strong and proper emphasis is laid upon the long-term happiness of the individual in this way, there is a real danger of "Resource Development" becoming a kind of purposeless juggernaut, driving the community on to all kinds of decisions and situations many of which may be basically unacceptable in terms of the significant needs of men and women.

(*b*) Only by expressing the optimum in terms of ultimate human satisfaction can one avoid the pitfalls inherent in dealing, as we are here, with one part—Scotland—of a national economy, which in its turn certainly cannot consider its resource development in isolation but must pay proper regard to the consequences of any change in this field upon the interrelationship with the whole pattern of the world economy of which it forms a significant part.

THE RESOURCES TO BE ADMINISTERED

Just as it is necessary to define the objective, it is similarly well to be clear what is meant by natural resources. The subjects of the previous papers and the programme of the Symposium give us these. They comprise:

Land. Including the products of land in its various uses as well as the greater problem of conflict between these uses.

Water. To include the conflicts in use, both short and long term, and related problems in marine waters where relevant.

Fuel and Energy (both domestic and imported). This is particularly topical at present.

Human Resources. Including the whole complex of the satisfaction of various values.

In the language of the classical economists, these natural resources include at least most of the first two of the three factors of production—land, labour and capital—while the third, comprising excess of income over current consumption, can, in strictly practical terms, also embrace many of the resources under discussion. It is, of course, true that the term land, in the classical economist's definition, included all raw materials, while in this Symposium it means land in Scotland and the resources available from it since the larger part of raw materials in the accepted industrial sense come from overseas. Nevertheless, the field for discussion is wide enough and it is evident that only the broadest suggestions regarding administrative requirement will be possible within this framework.

THE MECHANICS OF RESOURCE DEVELOPMENT

The actual mechanics of Resource Development very properly has a section of the Symposium to itself, but in order to bring the essential administrative requirements into focus it will be well to repeat here, in outline only, the principal methods under this heading. Precise definition here is difficult, partly because there is considerable overlapping between the different methods, but, perhaps principally, because as regards human resources there is virtually no section of society from family to the Government itself, which is not concerned with some aspect! Roughly, however, the following ways of developing resources seem to be relevant:

(*a*) Private industry, including agriculture, commerce and the professions, where the major objective—but by no means the sole one—is commonly accepted as being the maximum excess of revenue over all costs of production, including reasonable provision for the future.

(*b*) Nationalised industries in coal, gas, electricity, transport and airways, where an obligation is laid upon the Board to cover costs by revenue from the sale of the product, "taking one year with another and paying due regards to the public interest".

(*c*) Public Corporations such as the British Broadcasting Corporation, the Atomic Energy Authority, the Port of London Authority, etc.: where revenue cannot specifically be related to—and certainly will not cover—costs.

(*d*) The State itself directly—in a multitude of ways. These include the formal and constitutional expression of society's wishes as regards minimum standards of physical well-being and education, security against violence, rights of ownership and above all, the fundamental rights of a free citizen, but also direct ownership of land in various uses, and a measure of responsibility for power and energy.

(*e*) Local authorities—not only by way of interpreting and applying State legislation in relevant fields but also in certain cases by direct ownership and development of resources.

(*f*) Voluntary and professional bodies and associations. These cover a very wide field indeed, but are nevertheless of very great importance in our society. Apart from those of national repute and responsibilities there are the smaller, sometimes strictly local, gatherings of quite small numbers of people with a common interest or purpose, perhaps in preservation of a particular part of the country or of a kind of bird or animal. These smaller bodies may not individually appear very significant, but in the aggregate, some declining and others growing to take their places, they do in fact represent a vital part of the expression of our society's views upon the development of our resources—and very often taking a longer view than central or local government or industry or commerce can ever do.

These various instruments of society will of course require for the normal pursuit of their aims, in varying degrees, the provision of suitable finance and the application of research and development techniques. Both these factors are considered in separate papers.

ASSUMPTIONS REGARDING STRUCTURE OF SOCIETY

Underlying the argument so far there have been certain implicit assumptions. It is as well that these should be explicitly stated. Firstly, they are the present framework within which functions our society in general and industrial society in particular. Secondly, should they not prove to be eternal and, in changing, thus alter some of the ways of achieving optimum resource development, then at least it will be clear why certain methods which were perfectly sound before are then no longer valid.

Firstly, it is assumed that the wishes of the society to which we belong will continue to be expressed statutorily in the following fields in the form of minimum standards:

(*a*) Physical well-being (this covers hunger, illness, housing, safety at work, etc.).
(*b*) Education.
(*c*) Useful work for adults who so wish.
(*d*) Certain basic freedoms for the individual covering thought, speech, religion and matters of the family which add up to what is generally meant by the democratic way of life.

The minimum standards are currently much more clearly expressed under the first two headings—physical well-being and education—than under the latter two, where precise classification is much harder. Indeed, society hasn't yet really given statutory effect to a growing general acceptance of the view that all adults should have the opportunity of useful work. As regards well-being and education—particularly the latter—the standards are constantly moving forward.

Secondly, it is assumed that a free price economy will continue to predominate, where the expectation of a surplus of revenue over costs will be the principal motivating force in determining not only the present use of resources but also their planned development and thus their use in the future, because, taken overall, the excess of current real income over real consumption of goods and services will determine the amount of investment.

Thirdly, it is assumed that even in those quite sizeable sectors of the economy controlled by nationalised industry or where direct State or local authority ownership or responsibility must be exercised (such as in matters of defence or roads) the yardstick used will still be those of the free price economy—i.e. interest rates, comparisons of money cost and any revenue earned. These yardsticks will, in fact, broadly be used to determine how far beyond the point which would be justified on grounds of profit and loss (where practicable) investment of resources in any particular use should be pushed.

THE APPARENT CONFLICT IN RESOURCE USE

In this way there has emerged over recent years a puzzling conflict in the use and development of natural resources in the broadest sense. On the one hand there is the view that in a predominantly free price economy the wishes of society will be given the best expression by allowing expectation of maximum excess of revenue over costs to determine the distribution of resources between different uses. Here it is argued, with fair justification, that the most efficient industrial and commercial concerns make the biggest provision for research and development of new techniques and, in fact, take a long view of the availability of natural resources and possible substitutes.

Against this, it is pointed out that the long-term interests of the men and women in the community are best served by a continual extension of State and voluntary limitations to the logical application of the driving forces of a free price economy, which, left to itself, it is argued, would in the main, take too short a view and land the whole of society in real trouble before long.

There are, of course, a number of perfectly valid arguments on either side. It can be demonstrated that to continue to use water at presently increasing rates per head of population will result in grave shortages before new industrial processes can be developed to do with less. It can certainly be strongly argued that to allow the free development of land to industrial and urban use would quite shortly make significant inroads into the structure of domestic agriculture. It could hardly be contested that while the short-term needs of industry and commerce might be served by a big increase in the supply of relatively cheap juvenile labour by lowering the school leaving age, the longer term interests of the community—and indeed of industry—would almost certainly be damaged by the consequent loss of skill and balanced judgment.

Against these it can be strongly pressed that lengthy and leisurely discussions of proposed developments by industry and commerce in the use of national resources (particularly land) amongst central and local government experts, who have no sense of urgency and are naturally bound by the negative attitude of ensuring that no relevant clause of a statute or order is contravened, is likely to end in no development at all and consequent suffering to the people.

CONFLICT MORE APPARENT THAN REAL

In fact, the measure of conflict between free development of resources by industry, commerce and agriculture and their planned use by society, operating through central or local government or some other authority, must be much smaller, in principle anyway, than is often described by vested interests on both sides.

There are many reasons for this. Firstly, the quite quickly spreading knowledge of the facts of the situation by means of wider and better technical education, use of radio, television, journals, learned societies, discussions and the like, is resulting in an awareness that it is not a conflict of *negative conservation* against *positive use*, but of current rates of use against longer term interests. (This is just as true of human beings as of other resources.)

Secondly, the very proliferation of public bodies and authorities has meant that many of them are in large part composed of men and women who in the ordinary way of earning their living include not only those who manage the free price economy, but others and their representatives drawn from all levels of responsibility in workshop, factory, office, shipyard, mine, or the farm. This is very important and is a healthy sign of a constantly developing society.

Thirdly, the striking increase in attention paid to the human element in industry and commerce in latter years has resulted in some progress in research, continuous experiment in every aspect of man management, organisation and training and above all in a very general appreciation both by employees and by Trade Unions that poor human relationships, from whatever the cause, in factory or office mean inefficiency and wasted effort.

Finally, what can only be described as the consequence of a continually evolving society in the shape of a growing sense of responsibility on the part of men and women in authoritative positions in industry and commerce for the longer term consequences of their decisions upon the communities of which they form a part, has meant that the dividing line between immediate private interest and longer term public benefit will become progressively blurred as the years roll by.

THE REQUIREMENTS

It will readily be seen that to formulate a set of clear and specific recommendations in the administrative field as the only way to proceed at the best pace towards the optimum use and development of natural resources as defined in this paper is no easy task. Furthermore, since the structure of society itself is necessarily dynamic and continuously evolving—and this is no less true of industrial society in particular—any such recommendations must at best be explicitly tied to very broad assumptions which may well be valid only for a decade or two at the most.

The matter is further complicated by our primary concern with one part—Scotland—of a closely integrated national economy which for very evident and practical reasons is itself becoming increasingly interrelated with the complex and ever developing pattern of the economic, social and political structure of the world as a whole.

Nevertheless, there are certain practical suggestions which can be made, rather in the way of points upon which greater emphasis should be placed than cut and dried requirements for new procedures or organisational change. These would fall into various fields in the following way:

EDUCATION

At schools it should be possible to introduce lessons on the basic facts of the natural resource situation, with proper emphasis on the current rates of consumption and likely consequences, if this is not carefully watched.

At centres of further education similar steps should be taken with, naturally, greater detail and some account also of the current problems of conflict in use of the resources in question and the possible consequences of various alternative decisions in this respect.

So far as universities are concerned, aspects of this problem do, of course, already feature in certain faculty studies, but it would be interesting to try and stimulate research into the issue as an integrated whole, particularly related to the human resources and the factors in terms of which some measurement of the satisfaction of groups of men and women in the long term could be attempted.

The foregoing is concerned with education of the individual within the framework of the educational system. There is, of course, the much wider field of educating society as a whole, both as to the facts as set out by a survey such as this and the possible consequences of disregarding the problem. This can best continue to be tackled by conference and discussion, making use of public bodies and of the existence and enthusiasm of the many voluntary organisations to which reference has already been made.

INDUSTRY AND COMMERCE

Here, perhaps, there is the greatest immediate potential for satisfying certain of the requirements. By laying all possible emphasis on the importance of developing executive skill in Scottish industry it should be possible both to widen and deepen the understanding of the long-term coincidence of actual efficiency and increased social responsibility.

Better management with its attendant techniques of sound measurement, planning, co-ordination of specialists and, above all, of obtaining the best results from subordinates while co-operating fully with colleagues and superiors, will help to clarify for many the objective towards which they are working as well as being justified by results.

This process, as has already been described, will go a long way towards resolving the apparent conflict between the shorter term motives of a free price economy and the longer term demands of optimum resource development. Furthermore, and perhaps most important of all, the learning and practice of continuously better management in the widest sense will inevitably focus attention on what may well be the most important of all our natural resources in Scotland—the men and women now forming adult society and the generations which will succeed them.

There has been until comparatively recently very little reliable research into what is sometimes rather sententiously called the human factor. But in fact, in a rapidly changing society, where adaptation to change and the re-learning of perhaps three or four skills in a lifetime, is clearly likely to become more and more important, we know really very little of the conditions or the techniques which will assist, or hinder, this process.

We really must not waste more time and we in Scotland should not let pride in our tradition of education in the past dull our perception now of our comparative backwardness in certain of these respects. Scotland is, for instance, a long way behind even England, let alone certain countries overseas, in willingness and encouragement on the part of industry and commerce to give generous part-time day release, or make longer term sandwich course arrangements, for young men and women to follow course of study related to this work.

RESEARCH AND DEVELOPMENT

Much is already being done in this field, not only by the larger firms exclusively but by groups of smaller ones, with some Government help through the medium of research associations. There is also valuable work carried out by Government agencies centrally, such as the Department of Scientific and Industrial Research.

It should be sufficient to say here that the more encouragement that can be given to the technical men in smaller concerns to keep themselves currently in touch with the latest developments in this particular field the better. This can be achieved in many ways, most of which are already being employed, but conferences well run and well documented in advance, with top men taking part, are always helpful.

More and better qualified scientifically and technically trained young men and women would also help smaller firms to recruit easily the kind of assistance to the overworked holders of key technical posts which would go a long way to keeping them better informed.

CENTRAL AND LOCAL GOVERNMENT ADMINISTRATION

With the developing awareness throughout our society of the progressive integration of industry, commerce and agriculture with the communities of which they form a part and the growing sense of responsibility for the future well-being of the men and women of which they are composed—for all the reasons adduced in the earlier part of this paper, in fact—central and local government permanent servants are inevitably becoming more closely concerned with decisions which in earlier days would have been taken quite independently of their help or views.

It is true that the precedents and procedure which the public servant must observe and above all, the comparative detachment from the consequences of the final decision which he enjoys, may sometimes make him appear to be less forward looking and flexible than he might ideally be. It is, however, extremely important before passing such a judgment to bear in mind at least one major consideration which is highly relevant. The public servant is of necessity the instrument by which effect is given to such wishes of our democratic society as have been given statutory effect by society, legally organised as the State. This process is, fortunately, not often a rapid one, and on the way, plenty opportunity is given for discussion and even modification of the orginal proposals.

This means that by the time the public servant is dealing with the resultant legislation or statutory instrument, society has very probably moved forward a little in its informal thinking on the particular issue. This will often make the public servant, than whom there are few harder working or more loyal employees in the land, appear to be less flexible and forward looking than his natural ability and inclinations would otherwise dictate.

But this is just as well, for our society is very properly always ready to pounce immediately upon any public servant who in any way exceeds his statutorily authorised powers.

The lesson here is quite different and most important to Scotland. Industry must carry itself the major share of the responsibility for so arranging matters along the lines described in the preceding paragraphs, by developing management skills and efficiency generally and thus ensuring the coincidence of optimum resource development and the expectation of sound economic results.

If the burden is thrown instead on the public servant, either of central or local government, this is tantamount to demanding more and more legislation to ensure the development of Scotland's resources. This could result in an over emphasis on special treatment for Scotland over so wide a field, that industrialists and commercial leaders would cease to judge the possibility of expansion or development on its merits—of which there are plenty if realistically measured and planned—and await instead, the granting of maximum concessions before taking any action at all. Some measures of this kind have, of course, been necessary and valuable, but if extended too far, would very soon start to distort quite seriously the very distribution of resources between different uses which it would be in the best long-term interests of Scotland to secure.

Some General Observations on Scotlands Resources

N. S. MAIN, D.L., M.A., LL.B.
Glen & Henderson, Linlithgow

What people want is the fruit of employment. There is a natural limit to the useful production of essentials, such as food—man does not eat more food because it is available; to non-essentials such as cars, accessories and ladies hats there is no natural limit of production. The most promising sphere of production would seem to be to provide desirable non-essentials, and here is the opportunity for enterprise.

By tradition, the burghs were active in developing industry and trade on behalf of their local industries and nowadays local authorities have full justification for following this tradition by being active in developing local resources.

It is probably a mistake to leave the attraction of industry to the Council, since the Council cannot attend to the needs of over two hundred local authorities in Scotland.

There might be room for local authorities to help and guide local people more: in finance, in sponsoring trade, in providing recreation, or in advertising local industries.

Facts about our good climate might be more widely published. It is quite arguable on statistics that the climate of most of Scotland is as good as, if not better than, that of England.

"In the sweat of thy face shalt thou eat bread." Few people take Genesis literally today, but this sentence has been so dinned into generations of Scotsmen that it forms part of the mental background of most of them and is a factor to be reckoned with in their outlook on the development of our natural resources. In a way it is reflected in the idea of work, implied in the use of the word "unemployment" which is really a very abstract term. It is a double abstraction, for its positive, "employment", is also an abstract conception. In dealing with these abstractions one is apt to forget all that they involve. Work or employment by itself is not what most people are really wanting—what they are after is the fruit of employment. If these fruits can be obtained without employment or work, so much the better. The fruits of employment are basically the saleable products of work with our natural resources, although the connection between many kinds of employment and the products themselves may not be obvious. The importance of this point is illustrated by the fact that most local authorities generally think about unemployment in terms of factories and work, and ignore products and profits.

It is desirable therefore, in considering what resources should be looked for and developed, to reflect first on some elementary points about work and employment that have materially changed in recent years. In early times our forefathers had to sweat to produce foodstuffs in a way that their descendants do not. Owing to mechanisation or its modern synonym "automation", there is not only far less sweat required in the production of food but far less manpower, and modern men don't eat any more than their fathers so that a lower proportion of the population is required for the production of essential food. In self-supporting countries such as France and the United States, the proportion of the population so engaged is about 25 per cent., and even with that one of the problems of America is the over production of wheat and other foodstuffs. In this country it is to be observed that the largest cereal crop is not wheat but barley, and instead of that being used for food it is broken down and turned into luxury drinks of whisky and beer. It is not suggested that there is anything wrong in this, only that it shows that even farmers are not solely engaged in the production of essential foodstuffs. This too applies to a lesser extent to their production of meat, which, from an economic point of view, is a very extravagant way of utilising the vegetable product of the farm. The same reduction of manpower is found in the production of other essentials of life, clothing and shelter, so that we have to face the fact that there is not work for half the population in producing the essentials of life. What are the remainder to do? Clearly if they are to find remunerative employment it must be in producing non-essentials. If the community is running as a well-balanced economic machine, then part will be engaged in producing essentials and part in producing non-essentials—each will exchange its surplus and the whole community will enjoy a supply of both essentials and non-essentials.

A further observation falls to be made before trying to deduce any line of action from this. As already indicated, a man does not eat more food just because it is available, so that there is a natural limit to the useful production of essentials, but to non-essentials there is no natural limit. There is no natural limit to the number of cars or sports accessories a man will buy nor to the number of hats a woman will purchase. The important deduction to be drawn from this is that the most promising sphere of production to provide further employment is the production of desirable non-essentials. Of course, there is an overlap in production between essentials and non-essentials, not only in regard to food as already indicated but also in the production of clothing and houses and even in the primary industries. Steel is required both for cargo boats and luxury liners, for ploughs and cinema houses, but nevertheless the principle holds true that it is the luxury side of business that holds out the best prospect of development. There is, of course, the danger in regard to the non-essential trades that they are the first to suffer in a recession of trade. The essentials may suffer too, but not to the same extent, for man must always get his essentials; but the fact remains that non-essential production is the only promising scope for future development so that this danger must be faced and guarded against by cautious development and by building up reserves or some other form of insurance against recessions of trade. Another point we should keep in mind is that the production of essentials has engaged the world-wide activities of able and energetic men for centuries so that improvements on present methods of production are not likely to be discovered or developed by men outside these fields of work. For the same reason we can also leave very much to them the location and development of all the resources of the country likely to help their particular industries.

A survey of the resources of Scotland is more likely to be of value to men looking for new developments in the field of non-essentials. While the Industrial Council, the

Board of Trade and the Government Departments and local authorities may help to some extent, yet such development as a rule must be left to the enterprise of an individual Scotsman. We may try to encourage such men and supply them with information, but in the last resort it is their imagination, initiative and energy that we must rely on. Assistance is often suggested not only in the way of information and encouragement but by means of subsidies and loans. But subsidies and loans for new industries constitute a delicate and difficult problem. In many cases new industries are competitive with other established industries and the unfairness of taxing old industries to provide funds for new ones hardly requires stating. Many sickly old-fashioned industries also might well be stimulated or revived into thriving new concerns with the aid of loans or subsidies and they have accordingly an equal claim to consideration. But one is entering here an even more dangerous field as the claims for such assistance would likely be manifold and urged not so much in proportion to the soundness of the proposition as in proportion to its unsoundness, so that one would hesitate to advocate that any more should be done in this direction than is already being done by Government.

One matter which is worthy of special consideration is how far local authorities can contribute to the development of our resources. In considering how far it is the business of local authorities to deal with such matters it is worth while glancing at their constitutional powers and duties so far as affecting this.

The original local authorities were, of course, our burghs and towns. County councils are perhaps the most prominent local authorities today, but they are of recent origin and they are bodies set up to carry out specific statutory duties. These duties did not originally include the development of industry within their district. Their powers and duties in this respect, therefore, are to be found in recent Acts of Parliament which apply both to burghs and counties, and one is apt to assume that the powers and duties of the councils of our cities and burghs are limited to such powers and duties as are to be found in Acts of Parliament. But this is not so. In addition to their statutory powers and duties, the burghs have certain rights and privileges which have come down to them from ancient times and which were expressly preserved to them by the Act of Union in 1707. These rights and privileges were nowhere specifically defined, but can be gathered from the many records of the burghs as to the duties and powers regularly exercised by the magistrates and councils, and as practised down to the Union of the two countries they certainly covered much control over the commerce and trade of the burghs. Long after the Union, too, the burghs took an active interest in the development of the industry and trade of the country as distinct from the needs of each individual burgh. The Convention of Burghs for long maintained a staple port in Holland and negotiated directly with Holland about its trade there. Two rather quaint items of the Convention's activity are worth mentioning not only to illustrate the scope of their activities but to show that they could expend burghal funds on it. They paid Allan Ramsay, the poet, £100 for writing a poem boosting the merits of the herring and they sent £100 worth of Scottish linen as a present to the Speaker of the House of Commons and when the Speaker (perhaps rather embarrassed by this gift) sent them a present of 100 guineas in return they used it as a prize for improved designs in the linen trade.

One has no hesitation, therefore, in maintaining that our local authorities have full justification for taking an active part in doing what they can to help the development of local resources. Their present activities in this direction are well known. It is doubtful if there is a single local authority in Scotland which has not taken some steps towards bringing industries to its bounds, and the Convention of Burghs had a large part in the original setting up of the Council of Industry itself. The question is whether our local authorities can do anything more than they are already doing. This question applies more particularly to the smaller local authorities than to the cities and large towns, because in these areas the units of industry are usually much larger and abler to look after their own advertising and their own finance and these larger authorities have usually Chambers of Commerce helping to deal with this problem. Many burghs know that the attempt to attract new industries is a rather frustrating problem and are inclined to leave it to the Council of Industry, who has already so many successes to its credit in this sphere and who has much wider contacts. But this is probably a mistake. The Council of Industry cannot attend to the individual needs of over two hundred local authorities in Scotland, and there is something besides the attracting of new industries which deserves attention, and that is assisting in the expansion and development of existing industries. If one asks how they can do this, there are two suggestions that may be made: (1) to help to advertise their wares and (2) to try to aid new or expanding local concerns in getting local finance. Many of the smaller burghs have set up Industrial Committees which, after doing something in the way of getting out a brochure expounding the advantages of the area for new development, have died of inanition. They have no agenda for regular meetings and the meetings cease to be called. It might be more effective to set up a Committee (with co-opted members) who would be charged to have one regular meeting only per annum to review and report on the industry of the locality. In doing so they might come across some particular industry which could be helped and, if so (or if some particular prospect emerged at any other time of the year), they could have special meetings to deal with it. They could also issue an annual advertisement of all industries willing to co-operate with them. For instance, they might sponsor the issue of an annual calendar with some genuinely attractive picture of some feature of the burgh which would appeal to all the sons and daughters of the burgh in far parts and which would have on its back some well-written advertisements of local industries. Using one's imagination a little, one can visualise a son of Auchterfechan in some distant part of our far-flung Commonwealth assuring a local farmer that at Auchterfechan there was a factory engaged in beating bits of old battleships into the best and cheapest ploughshares in the world—nay more, that he had written the factory and had a catalogue in his pocket and he could accept an order there and then and share the commission. You may say that is pure nonsense. But is it? Is that or some other advertising idea not worth following up? With reference to the local financing of new concerns, it is not suggested, for reasons already indicated, that anything in the nature of subsidies or loans should be given, but there is many a man with a good small business though short of capital who would benefit much by turning his business into a private limited company but who does not attempt to do so because he is intimidated by the procedure of forming a company and is not in touch with persons who might be prepared to invest in it. A fine new factory with a high rent does not appeal to him. He wants his available finance for tools, material and wages. Could he not be helped by a Committee who (as a result of previous efforts) might be able to put him in touch with local people who would be willing to invest in a small local company and who (the Committee) could also assist by advice or otherwise in the flotation of a Company which would make such investment more feasible?

In a broader field, can our local authorities through their central organisations not do more for the development of Scotland's resources as a whole? If what has been said to begin with is correct, and future development of industry is to be found more and more in the provision of the amenities of life, do we devote anything like sufficient attention to a survey of our recreational potentialities and to developing the amenities of Scotland? Our local authorities give a support to the Tourist Board which can fairly be described as lukewarm only and nothing like what is deserved. We can sell the scenery of Scotland—we cannot export it, but we can do better—we can bring our customers here and charge them for travel and board; but people will not come and stay only to admire scenery. We must develop and provide recreational facilities, and we must advertise our wares. The reluctance to tackle the development and sale of recreational facilities as a serious industry is an inheritance which the modern Scotsman must discard. One other bugbear at the back of many Scotsmen's minds is that they can hardly advertise Scotland as a holiday resort on account of the climate. This is a bugbear that needs rooting out. It is high time that we published the facts about our climate. It has been quite unjustly and universally damned since the time of Tacitus, and very largely by Scotsmen too. Stamp in his most recent book in the Pelican Series says that despite opinions to the contrary, the climate in Britain is not very far from the ideal, neither too hot nor too cold, neither too wet nor too dry. It is quite arguable on statistics that the climate of the most of Scotland is as good as, if not better than, that of England. The average winter temperature of Wick for the months of December, January and February is almost identical with that of Kent. The south is hotter in summer, but who wants London heat in August. In our mountainous districts we have too much rain for amusement, but in our lowland districts we have just about the ideal amount for agriculture. We may not have so much sun as in the south, but we have longer daylight in the growing months of the year and a longer twilight all the year round. Is there any other place in the world where one can play golf in comfort on so many days of the year as at St. Andrews and our other resorts? One curious fact which is not well known is that owing to the precipitation of the moisture in the air through its passage over our mountains, the air in Scotland is on the average drier than that in England. The statistics of the daily average of moisture content for many years past published by the Meteorological Office show that of the forty-four stations in the British Isles only three show a less amount than seven centimetres per cubic metre, and these stations are Eskdalemuir, Dalwhinnie and Fort William.

Recreational potentialities cover much more than golf courses and swimming-pools. There is cultural recreation both for the retired person and the active worker, and the development of such a thing, for example, as a good bookshop in a town of any size is an industry which benefits the community as a development of one of its resources. The theatre at Pitlochry is more than a venture affecting Pitlochry alone. It is or should be a stimulant to other communities to show what can be done. Housing, health, education and other public services are all very important, but all of them depend ultimately on industry and on the efficient development of our natural resources.

INTRODUCTION TO DISCUSSION

T. G. Waterlow, C.B.E.
Deputy Chairman and Director, William Thyne Ltd.

We have three papers this afternoon and in accordance with practice I will ask the authors to stand up when I introduce them. It is not for me to assume the responsibilities of the reporter, and we have a very excellent reporter in Mr. Robertson this afternoon. But I would just like to say that I cannot believe that with all the thought that has gone into this Conference and the trouble that has been taken by the Committee that it did not occur to them that we might have had a paper from the Trade Unions. I would like to have heard a paper from the Trade Unions, possibly in this session, or whatever the appropriate session was—I imagine this was the most appropriate one—because I think they have a point of view which would have been of interest to us and we would like to have heard it. It may be if there are any Trade Unionists with us this afternoon that they will be good enough to contribute to the discussions afterwards. I think it is very important that we should know what Scotland's Trade Unions think and to be quite certain that they are not dominated by English Trade Unions, but it may be that we will hear something when the discussion arises. We have, as I say, three excellent papers. The first one is factual, the second one raises a number of points. Two particular points I would like to mention are the theme of training which runs through Mr. Blair Cunynghame's paper which, I think, is so frightfully important and on which subject some of us in industry in Scotland are a little bit weak in our factories. Another point which Mr. Blair Cunynghame makes towards the end of his paper is that we cannot just turn to the Government and expect them to get us out of all our evils. We have got to help ourselves. The point that interested me purely horticulturally in Mr. Main's paper—he commented on the good Scottish climate which sometimes people don't appreciate, as he says. I live at Dunbar, which is reputedly a cold place, and I have never had mimosa flower better outside than it did in the early part of this year, so that we have some quite interesting climate and quite good climate. I think he was right to make that point. I will now call on Mr. Robertson, Chief Executive Officer of the Scottish Council (Development and Industry) as reporter for this session.

STATEMENT BY REPORTER

W. S. Robertson, C.B.E., B.SC.
Chief Executive Officer, Scottish Council (Development and Industry)

Until this afternoon the Symposium has been primarily concerned either with natural resources individually or with the machinery associated with their use. This afternoon, on the home straight, we have three papers which set out to consider which forms of administration, either national or local, private or public, will provide the best conditions for the development of natural resources. With your permission, I shall take first the paper by Mr. Blair Cunynghame as providing perhaps the widest perspective on the administration of natural resources. At the outset he defines "optimum resource development" as that use which makes for the present and future happiness of the people in our society. He stresses that this definition of purpose is an essential part of successful administration and that without it resource development could readily, all too readily, become an end in itself, not necessarily related to the real needs of men and women. This theme he does not develop, but he recommends strongly that it should be kept in the forefront of all thinking and action about resource development. After a review of the various forms of public and private administration, the paper refers to the controversy which exists between those who believe that a continued extension of State influence and State control is necessary to the best long-term use of our natural resources and those, on the other hand, who believe that efficient private concerns, acting on consideration of profits, take an equally long view and may give better short-term results. The author draws the conclusion that the real element of conflict between these two forms of administration of natural resources is, in fact, much less than it is often made out to be. He points out that the continually growing knowledge of the value and of the nature of our natural resources is leading to a corresponding growth in the sense of responsibility for their use on the part of many people within industry. This means in turn that the dividing line between private interest and public benefit will continue to become more blurred as time goes on. Mr. Blair Cunynghame also enumerates several factors of administration on which greater stress should be laid on the interest of supporting resource development. They are, I think, so important that they are worth repeating briefly. First, lessons should be introduced in schools about the basic facts of our natural resource situation, and more advanced material should be provided at centres of further education. Second, an attempt should be made at universities to institute research on resources as an integrated whole. Third, various means should be adopted of educating the public as a whole about the issues involved. Fourth, in industry itself, as the Chairman has said, much more should be done to develop executive skill as a means of making clearer the direct relationship between efficiency and social responsibility. Also within industry ever-increasing attention must be given to the proper use of human beings within the industrial framework. Finally, Mr. Blair Cunynghame reviews the relationship between the administrative activities of central and local government on the one hand, and of industry and of the many voluntary and professional bodies associated with industry on the other. He comes to the conclusion that industry should continue to carry the primary initiative for the administrative measures required for the best development of our resources, that industry has to carry the major share of this responsibility; otherwise too great a danger of distortion of the normal and sound economic forces might result. The second paper is that by the Scottish Office on "Resource Development —Central Administration". This is a description by the Scottish Office of the responsibilities in this sphere which the Government already exercises in Scotland. It is perhaps characteristic of its authors and of their modesty not only that they are anonymous, as the Chairman remarked, but that their paper does not conclude, as some others have done, with any proposals for major extension of Government activities in this field. Indeed, it contains no proposals at all, being purely descriptive and factual in its nature. It is no less an impressive statement on this account. Faced with the task of reporting on such a wide-ranging review, I could hardly improve on the words of the Chairman at a recent function at which the Secretary of State for Scotland was present as a guest. Referring to the multifarious responsibilities and activities of the Secretary of State, the Chairman advised his audience in these words, "Count your blessings, count them one by one; you'll be surprised at what the Secretary of State has done". And indeed, I think the predominant impression made by this highly condensed account of the functions of the Secretary of State and of other Ministers, whose writ runs in Scotland, is that to some degree, and often to a large degree, the Scottish Office and other departments of Government are already intimately concerned in the administration of virtually every natural resource discussed at this Symposium. Within their embrace (although it is doubtful whether embrace is a word which would be appreciated by all those who have spoken and who are involved) fall land and agriculture; the planning of land use; peat; fisheries; national health; town and country planning; housing and water supplies; crofting; river purification; the development of industry and tourism; the generation of power; education; forestry; labour; scientific research; national parks; and a variety of others. In all this, moreover, the Secretary of State for Scotland is concerned not only with his executive responsibility for the four Scottish Departments but also as "Scotland's Minister" who is generally and popularly regarded as being responsible directly or indirectly for all issues affecting the Scottish economy. Although the paper is factual and confines itself strictly to present arrangements, I think it may not be unfair to make explicit one central issue which is implicit in the survey. I think it is evident from a reading of the paper that the Government is already up to the neck in the natural resources business. The principle that Departments should provide the administrative equipment necessary for resource development has obviously been accepted on a large scale. It would, therefore, seem not unreasonable to infer that to the extent that *further* needs for official administrative support for resource development are specified and demonstrated and urged, the Government will continue on the road along which it has already proceeded so far. In this sense, although not explicitly, the paper may be taken as pointing clearly to the future and as giving some assurance that if a firm initiative is taken and maintained by those outside the Government then the necessary official administrative provisions for natural resource development may be expected to follow on. Finally, the third paper by Mr. N. S. Main is concerned principally with the administrative responsibilities of local authorities for resource development. At the outset he makes the point that local authorities incline to use unemployment as a yardstick in considering the best use of resources. In this, I think, he reflects back to the importance laid in the first paper on purpose as an element of effective administration. In the present context it means that resource use should be related to the growth of employment for the people of an area, through the use of resources in the manufacturing industry, and the paper goes on to show that this points to an ever-increasing production of non-essentials. The consumption of essentials is limited by such physical factors as the capacity of our stomach or as the fact that one roof keeps out rain as well as twelve. On the other hand, there is no limit to the human appetite for luxuries, because their consumption requires only time—and the time devoted to the use of any one can be indefinitely reduced. Even now, Mr. Main points out, much of our agricultural effort is devoted to the production of what might be called luxury liquids rather than essential solids. From this Mr. Main proceeds to consider how local authorities can best contribute to the increased development of our resources in this sense. His paper shows that there is much room for the exercise of initiative by local authorities, for example by advertisement of the facilities which a town or a county can offer; or by taking steps (and this from experience I believe to be a particularly valuable suggestion) to arrange for local finance to be put at the disposal of local men of enterprise who wish to establish new units or to expand existing ones. Beyond this he suggests local authorities could be more active in their participation in national efforts directed towards developing Scottish recreational resources. Following in Mr. Moscoso's footsteps or preceding them, Mr. Main develops a rousing attack—and as some may think a timely attack—upon the misplaced energy with which many Scots seek to conceal from themselves and from others the undoubted fact that Scotland has one of the most ideal living climates in the world. The paper goes on to propose a positive and vigorous approach by local authorities to the many possibilities offered by our physical situation for increased recreational facilities. Along with the use of our resources by industry, these must form the foundation of all our social services and material advance. These three papers, then, provide an extensive view of administration on various planes, as it now exists in its relationship to resource development at any rate, and propose various extensions to the equipment of public and private administration. I have done them very much less than justice, but they speak for themselves. I believe that they illustrate very well the leap-frog form of progress which obtains in this field. In some areas of work and at some times the administrative element may lag behind others, sometimes it will lead—either in setting of goals or in the provision of the necessary working support. But one thing we may be sure of: that is, the increased pace of resource development in this country will require an increasing scale of administrative action, both public and private. Much of the science fiction which was written by Jules Verne we have seen come true in our generation; this is a process which will no doubt continue at an accelerating pace. Some of you may recall in connection with natural resources development a forecast which was made a few years ago by an American engineer, who drew attention to the fact that even in common rock there is contained uranium along with all the other elements. He pointed out that if a number of technological difficulties could be overcome in the extraction of this uranium, the energy which could be derived from it, even from common rock, would be sufficient to drive the extractive processes for getting it out and for getting out all the other elements and would still leave enough energy over in order to process all of them into finished products; so that he draws a picture of a sort of double-ended cornucopia sitting at one end of the Grampians putting in rock at one end, producing its own power somewhere in the middle and pouring out an endless flood of all the goods that we might wish at the other end. Now this may be a fanciful picture. His own estimate was that this was about forty years in the future. But, nevertheless, I think it is necessary to have this sort of perspective in mind as well as the immediate and pressing needs of the time when we consider the degree of the adequacy of our existing administrative machinery for the development of our natural resources.

DISCUSSION

Dr. Woodward

I apologise for taking the floor so soon after appearing on the platform this morning, but I want to raise a subject which is of great concern to me in view of all that we have heard the last three days and which I think is of very real moment to the future development of Scotland, namely the subject of research and development north of the border. My remarks will be confined solely to that type of research which receives financial support from H.M. Government, either entirely or in part. Mr. R. H. S. Robertson mentioned in his paper that only 2 or 3 per cent. of the money spent by the Government on research in this country is spent in Scotland and he suggested quite reasonably that at least 10 per cent. should come here in direct proportion to the ratio of population. The 2 or 3 per cent. figure, of course, is not quite as bad as it sounds, because much of the work that is undertaken in national laboratories located south of the border is of very direct value to Scotland, but nevertheless it is indicative of a weakness in our operations here—a very real weakness to my way of thinking and I am being deliberately provocative in the hope that somebody will get up to refute what I say. As I see it, there is no body, official or otherwise, in Scotland which is concerned with its research needs as a whole. The Secretary of State for Scotland, of course, as we have heard, officially takes this under his wing, but I submit with all deference to my friends in St. Andrew's House that he is not very well qualified to undertake this task, nor does he appear to do it particularly well.

Let us look at some of the facts. For example, of the fifteen or sixteen D.S.I.R.-controlled research laboratories in Britain, we only have two in Scotland, namely the National Engineering Laboratory and the Torry Station, which, until quite recently, was part of the food investigation group of D.S.I.R. For those who do not know how and why the National Engineering Laboratory came to East Kilbride, a word of explanation will not be out of place. It was the intention of the D.S.I.R. Executive Committee of the day to locate it within fifty miles of London, as had been done with all its laboratories previously, and it was only because of the intervention of the Scottish Council and its Chairman of the time, Lord Bilsland, and after a terrific effort that it was brought here. It is a matter of interest that the then D.S.I.R. Executive body was faced with threats of resignation on this issue. I mention this quite deliberately because when I was at the opening of the Warren Spring Laboratory two years ago I could not see, nor can I see now, why that laboratory, which is concerned with chemical engineering, should be stationed in Stevenage of all places. There are no chemical works within miles and I submit, with all deference, that we, north of the border, missed an opportunity of submitting a case for it to be stationed in the Grangemouth area.

Of the fifty D.S.I.R. Research laboratories in Britain there is only one with its headquarters in Scotland, namely that concerned with jute.

Now, when I come to the non-D.S.I.R. research stations deriving sustenance from the public purse, I find that they have grown rather like Topsy and are definitely in imbalance. If my figures are correct, there are eight excellent Research Institutes connected with agriculture and two with fish. There was one concerned with food science, but that is now in process of being closed down; there was one for seaweed—that has disappeared as an experimental unit—and there is none concerned with such matters of moment to Scotland as mineral beneficiation, forest products and non-fish marine resources.

In conclusion, I would like to make one further point, namely, that I do not think we have been particularly clever or particularly outspoken in endeavouring to retain what we have got. As some of you know, I was concerned actively with the Institute of Seaweed

Research which received world-wide acclaim for its work, and yet after ten years' operation and on the advice of a sub-committee of the Advisory Council on Scientific Policy (on which no Scotsman sat nor anybody who had much knowledge of this country or of the technical and sociological problems involved) it was recommended that it be closed down. This despite the fact that at that time there was a need for research on peat, and a peat research station was built less than thirty miles away from where we already had the skilled personnel, the know-how and much of the equipment for such work. To finish the sad story, we have the Ministry of Agriculture, Fisheries and Food Laboratory at Aberdeen which again is being closed down with hardly a voice raised in protest. I submit, sir, that this sort of thing need not have happened had there been somebody responsible for looking at Scotland's research requirements in an integrated and overall capacity. It does not need a lifetime's experience of scientific endeavour to appreciate that the problems given to these three short-lived research groups—the chemical and physical properties, including dehydration, of seaweed, peat and fish, meat and vegetables—had a common theme and required for their solution almost identical types of staff, know-how and equipment. Had these problems been tackled successively at a single Scottish biological resources laboratory—as well there could have been had a little foresight been used—we would have been in an infinitely better position than we are today. Significant sums of taxpayers' money would have been saved and instead of three groups of disillusioned scientists, now dispersed throughout the world, we would have had a well-equipped laboratory with a record of achievement of which anyone could be proud, and an experienced and enthusiastic staff capable of undertaking any of the biological resource problems with which Scotland is faced.

My final remarks are again, I must admit, an admission of failure as to why this has happened. I think that all of us here are partly to blame. We have a lassitude in the matter: we are not sufficiently outspoken, and we do not make our views felt. Also, and I hope my friends at St. Andrew's House will forgive me, there is, in my opinion, all too great an eagerness there to leave matters concerned with official research to D.S.I.R. and the other bodies like A.R.C. and M.R.C. My recommendation, sir, therefore is that this is a matter of considerable moment and one which should receive attention in the follow-up action to this Symposium. I am not going any further at this stage or say who should do it or how it should be done, but that is my recommendation.

Mr. WATERLOW

I would just like to say, in my limited experience of one industry with which I am connected, the difficulty of extending the research work of the research association is due to the fact that members of the industry will not subscribe liberally towards the research association and thereby get their D.S.I.R. grant very often increased. In one particular industry (I do not like to disclose these figures here) you would be absolutely appalled at the lack of support in Scotland for the research organisation. I admit it is a research organisation in England, but we can't get any people brought up to Scotland because we support it so badly in Scotland.

Professor R. H. MATTHEW, *Department of Architecture, Edinburgh University*

I would like to support very strongly what has been said about research or lack of research resources in Scotland. I am speaking in relation to the building industry. Now, nobody calls the building industry in Great Britain outstandingly efficient, but I think anyone that knows building in Scotland would recognise that we are several degrees less efficient here. I have been on the Board for some years of a building research station and I know well that the outpost in East Kilbride is, in fact, little more than a Post Office, and if there is one thing we need in Scotland it is a considerable amount of resources directed to all the problems of the building industry at the present time. I would like to support what has just been said very strongly indeed.

Mr. ROBINSON, *Water Research Association*

The support accorded and the location of Research Associations in England cannot be dismissed as a consequence of the backwardness of the Scots in the matter of research.

The severity of the water problems of south-east England and of Scotland are very different; this I think is the prime cause of the paucity of Scottish support for the Water Research Association.

The location of a Research Association does not nor should always coincide with the industry it serves. There are other factors to consider.

Dr. A. PARKER, *formerly Director, Fuel Research*

The question has been asked why the Warren Spring Laboratory of the D.S.I.R. was erected at Stevenage. It was recognised some years ago, before the nationalisation of the fuel industries, that the facilities for the Fuel Research Station at Greenwich were inadequate and that a new research station on a new site was required. Eventually, the site at Stevenage was selected. Later, it was decided that with the development of the research organisations of the fuel industries, the programme of work on fuel by the D.S.I.R. could be curtailed and that the station at Stevenage could take on other work of importance, including sponsored research. Any research organisation of the D.S.I.R. is there to help the whole country, including Scotland. The Fuel Research Station had a branch at East Kilbride, and it is still there, associated with the Warren Spring Laboratory. There are also other D.S.I.R. establishments at East Kilbride, and there is a liaison officer in Edinburgh. If there are any special problems in Scotland within the ambit of the D.S.I.R., all that is necessary is to bring them forward and to press for energy to be applied in efforts to solve them.

Mr. J. O. BLAIR CUNYNGHAME, *Deputy Chairman, The Royal Bank of Scotland*

Mr. Chairman, Ladies and Gentlemen: I have been enjoying the last few minutes because the last two or three speakers have made it abundantly clear that one of my principal charges—that responsibility lies fairly and squarely on the shoulders of Scottish industry to improve its own standards—is only too true.

I did mention research and development in my paper as one of the things that I thought opened up possibilities in this respect.

To obey your request, Mr. Chairman, to widen the discussion, it has struck me, listening to parts of this Conference, that the factual catalogue of resources has been more practically and effectively presented than the arguments which deal with this rather nebulous business of utilisation and the application of human skill and ingenuity to making something of them. This is, of course, because it is to do with people.

As Professor Peacock has said, resources in themselves do not have a finite value until the demand pattern of society makes this clear. Professor Macrae, also, has said all this so clearly that if I had read his paper before I had started mine, I would not have written mine at all. He suggests that culture is what man makes of himself and of nature.

Now I shall recapitulate or emphasise three points which I made in my paper, and give you one new one:

Firstly, I did suggest that it would be very difficult to come to clear decisions about the application of new techniques and the like. That is, of course, because, as Peacock and Macrae pointed out, it is largely a question of people—human skill and ingenuity and human opinion—and you will never get clear-cut answers in this field. It will be compromise, argument, discussion, pull and push.

Secondly, I strongly believe that it is up to Scottish industry to place all possible emphasis on the development and training of executive skill, to produce that adaptability and flexibility of mind which will cope with changing technological processes and indeed possibly even changing relationship between the State, or society legally organised that way, and industrial society over the next twenty or thirty years. There, I think, we have a heavy responsibility and in that I include helping the scientist and the technologist to be more closely integrated with general management.

Lastly, I suggested, rather daringly, in my paper, and I am going to say it again, that I am bothered at finding Scotland a bit like a poor relation always pleading for help. We seem to me to expect special concessions so often, that it just brings me in mind of a small boy who is lame through a temporary bruise. If you keep telling him that he is lame he thinks he'll never be able to walk again without a stick. There is, in my opinion, a little bit about that in Scotland. I can say this myself, since, although only one's best friends can say this sort of thing, I was, you see, born in Edinburgh. I'd hate anybody from outside to say this, but I think there is something in it.

Finally, here is the new point which has emerged in my mind as I was listening to the Conference. It seems to me that this integration of human endeavour and natural resources is something like this:

Firstly, it rests with industrial society, and I think the major responsibility does lie with us.

Secondly, society organised legally as the State ensures certain minimum standards —physical standards, health and all the rest, and, of course, assistance—up to a point—in research and development.

Thirdly, there are the voluntary societies, representing the voluntary expression of what people really care and feel about, which spills over eventually, very often into State action. It is the integration of these three, and above all the reliance upon human ingenuity and skill and their application to our difficulties against the background of our developing culture and tradition that I think really holds out hope for the future. I do not believe it is as bad as all that—I am really quite an optimist.

Mr. CRANNA, *Meteorological Office, Edinburgh*

Might I just say a few words in support of Mr. Main's section on climate. It is a subject on which I am liable to get a little talkative, but I'll try to keep it short. About the first thing that struck me in looking at the skeleton of this Symposium, when I saw it some time ago, was that nowhere was climate mentioned as a resource; and it is quite fantastic that it requires someone from Puerto Rico to tell us that we have a good climate in Scotland. I am not quite sure where the responsibility lies, but I think it probably started with the Victorians—the fashion at the time was that Caledonia should be stern and wild, and they insisted that it should be that way. I have in mind Landseer and all his school. Scotland became associated with a wild-eyed stag bracing itself against a gale of wind, in torrential rain, with a background of beetling crags and swirling mists. We have all looked at those pictures for so long that we have begun to believe that they represent Scotland.

It is absolute nonsense, of course, and we have got the statistics to prove it. But if you are the type who does not believe in statistics I can only suggest that you go and look for yourself—say round the Moray Firth area, where you will see figs and nectarines growing—and peaches—at something like 58° N.; or, on the other side, look at the Inverewe Gardens. Or if you consult some of the authorities on human environment about the most suitable conditions either for physical output or mental activity, you can pick out the figures for yourselves and then look around and see where you can find them —and the answer, of course, is in Scotland. I don't think I'll say any more at this point, sir, but I feel that we should realise the truth, and get away from this idea, lay this bogey, that the Scottish climate is a bad one, not only from the tourist point of view but from the industrial point of view. It has got a lot to offer. Perhaps you can say Scotland is a little windy; on the other hand, you can say it is well ventilated—that applies particularly to the north-west coast. There are processes for which a reasonably cool climate is an advantage; someone mentioned cool rivers—the same thing applies to the atmosphere. If you have got de-humidifying problems, the cooler the outside air is in summer, before you start to heat it, the better off you are. There is an awful lot to this, sir. I won't say any more, but I would like people to think about this climate a little, and realise that it is not a handicap—it is a resource.

Mr. Bruce

Do you mind if I speak again, but on a rather different subject? I would heartily endorse what has been said about climate. I am going to put the blame on the Meteorological Office. They have no idea what Scottish weather is like. However, that's by the way. Two papers that particularly interested me were Mr. Moscoso's and the last paper. This is guidance that I think many areas would like. In planning, now, Dundee is a development area, we have acquired in the past ten years some very fine industries indeed. Occasionally we do hit problems on the skilled and semi-skilled labour. This is referred to in the last paper. Can this be planned beforehand to avoid these bottle-necks and problems between a newer starting industry and the older existing one, because it is possible for an older industry to become short of skilled men because they go to the new industry and then unemployment can result in the old industry. Is it possible to plan as fine as that?

Mr. R. A. Main, *Glen & Henderson, Linlithgow*

As one of the authors of these papers who had the temerity to put forward ideas among so many experts, one thing I have enjoyed is the amount of information and knowledge that I have obtained by listening to the criticisms, and I think that the authors of these papers (I would not speak for the other ones as much as for myself) are rather grateful for having heard these criticisms and we might want to modify our ideas and put forward any supplementary notes afterwards, but I would like to take this opportunity of thanking our critics for the information that they have supplied, with most of which I find I am in agreement.

Professor WATSON, *Department of Geography*

One thing I have been impressed by in listening in this afternoon has been the claim that Scotland has not fared too well compared with England. That may or may not be the case—but it is not as serious a case as that some regions of Scotland fare very poorly compared with Scotland as a whole. I do think that we have got to look at Scottish problems regionally as well as nationally. For I assure you, sir, that if Scotland feels at times neglected in face of the needs of England, I think that there are some regions of Scotland that feel neglected compared with Scotland. In terms of the special issue before us—educational resources—I would like to put forward the plea for some regional associations of research, and for the regional integration of research in Scotland. I would not like to see everything being handled on a national scale, or treated from a national centre. I would like to see strong regional associations for the northern islands, the western islands, the West Highlands, for north-east Scotland, for south-west Scotland, and for the Midland Valley. I think that this is just as important as trying to press for some kind of integration on a national scale. (Interruptions.) In a few words, is there not a plea for groups of Scotsmen in their own region, as well as for Scotland as a whole?

Dr. LAMONT

Mr. Chairman: I wish to be very blunt. My name is Lamont and I have written pamphlets on Scottish resources which have been completely neglected by Professor Wreford Watson and by the people at this Conference. I therefore wish to challenge Professor Watson's attempt to divide Scotland into regions in order to establish more firmly here the rule of London, which takes half our revenue and does not return it to us, which takes £200 million a year out of Scotland to be squandered on atomic weapons and such like nonsense when we in Scotland really want to be a small nation again with the prosperity which nations with far less resources than ours, like Denmark, have. I challenge Professor Wreford Watson as a good example of a Scottish quisling.

Professor PEACOCK

I hesitate to rise to my feet once again, because I was very well treated this morning, but I thought that, in view of the minority position held by economists at this Conference about economic problems, I might make a similar plea for economic research. Perhaps it is not necessary to say more, but I do want to make one or two points about the Scottish economy in particular.

The first is that in the absence of official data about the Scottish economy, particularly its economic development, irrelevant information was used. For example, Sir Alexander Fleck's paper suggests that you can measure economic progress, or the lack of it, by figures of industrial stoppages. There is some unpublished information which gives a much clearer idea of economic development which has been prepared by Glasgow economists. Broadly speaking it shows that industrial productivity in Scotland in individual industries does not differ from industrial productivity in individual industries for the U.K. as a whole. It is the pattern of industry which is the problem; Scotland has a greater preponderance of industries which have grown at relatively slow rates since the war. Measuring economic progress should be done by taking an indicator such as income per head after allowing for price changes. But we have no continuous figures of income per head in Scotland and no regional price index to deflate them. The general point is that we do not possess the usual economic indicators which discipline our thoughts about the relationship between the use of resources and economic advance.

The second point is the corollary of the first. If we need more information, more resources need to be used to produce it. There are many practical difficulties in compiling these statistics, notably the fact that transactions as between regions cannot be traced, as they can be across national frontiers. This is not necessarily an argument for Customs at Berwick! A good deal could be done at the official level, although this involves a point of principle—what you do for Scotland, you may have to do for Northern Ireland, Lancashire and Wales. The difficulty at the official level is the dislike of producing "guesstimates" and of "processing" the statistics so as to make a particular economics point. This is a reasonable point of view. However, we want relevant, if approximate, figures and not simply accurate and irrelevant ones. A good deal could be done by private organisations, by the Scottish Council or by the universities, relying on private finance. There is little money being put into economic research of this kind, highly important for the Scottish economy, by Scottish industry. There may be a healthy scepticism about the probable results, but it would be worth trying to see what could be produced.

A Strategy for Making and Using Resources

Mr. L. A. Elgood

Your Grace, My Lord, Ladies and Gentlemen: Last week, up to the end of the week, I was quite a happy man. I began to worry about Monday morning—the start of this Symposium. I have been very happy until 3 o'clock this afternoon. The Symposium seemed to be going quite well. After each session I altered the remarks that I was going to make as Chairman of the Symposium and I lost all my happiness. Here I am now to try and give a summary of all that has gone on in the Papers that were presented in the discussions, and I assure you it is not an easy task. I am not really a scientific man or a technical man. I suppose I am an industrialist, but I will do my best to give a summary as I saw the Symposium, and to go on to give you an idea of what I see emerging from these very happy three days.

The Committee of which I am Chairman assembled a pattern of subjects on which to hinge discussion at a fact-finding meeting on resources—which turns out to be this Symposium. Authors of papers have presented something of the existing knowledge on these subjects, and have provided the hard core for the meeting, and we are all most indebted to them; but even with the pattern and the hard core, the subjects cover so wide a field that this approach alone could only be piecemeal. Over 250 people have come to this Symposium. They have provided, through discussion, the substance—the missing parts—without which it would not be possible for a fully rounded assessment of our resources to be made.

May I remind you that when it was decided to hold this meeting we had three main points before us: that the rate of change of technology tends to leave all countries in arrears of their development potential; that there are particular fields in which Scotland lags; and that a review in which resources are regarded as an integrated whole is particularly required.

There were further important points which were put to you in our letter of invitation. I had intended to elaborate a little on these points, but I cannot do better than quote from the Annual Report of the Advisory Council on Scientific Policy which was published a few weeks ago:

> "If advance is to be made with economy of effort, it is important to ensure that the growing points of scientific knowledge should from time to time be reviewed to ensure that there is maximum contact and interaction between different fields of activity, and that the greatest range of professional skill is brought to bear on them. We have paid particular attention to the frontiers of traditional disciplines; and have noted the need to organise many 'hybrid' studies which cut across customary educational patterns or organisations, in order to attack a central or particularly resistant problem. It has become increasingly clear that the growing points in science are found most frequently in areas lying between the traditional disciplines and involve the participation of several of them. The rigid separation of these disciplines has proved awkward; but the solution to such problems is not always to be found in the creation of new university departments and new disciplines."

In essence we have considered in the past two days, and today, what resources we have, how they are being used, and how to use them more effectively.

The process of planning the use of natural resources is no innovation to Scotland. It began formally with Adam Smith. The opportunities which were opened up by the combination of his thinking with the experience of Glasgow merchant venturers laid the lines of much economic development in Scotland in the eighteenth and nineteenth centuries.

Much of this momentum was later lost. Scotland suffered as a result. But as long as thirty years ago the Scottish Development Council was formed to grapple with the complicated causes and results of the great depression. Its work was effective not only in Scotland: much legislation on the distribution of industry in Britain as a whole derived from its analyses.

This tradition has been maintained. Most post-war development in fact derives from studies of the kind which has been advocated by some speakers. Quantitative targets have been set up, technical and geographical enquiries have been instituted and acted upon, and some notable results have been achieved.

But the pace of developments requires a continuing extension and refinement of this integrated approach. It was for this reason that the Scottish Council warmly welcomed the proposals which were formulated by my Committee and which led to this Symposium We see this as a new and a large step forward on a familiar road. I know from Lord Polwarth how much the Council is looking forward to having the views of the Symposium, about the next steps which should be taken.

There has been no lack of proposals to advance.

In Scotland our resources include people, climate, soil, minerals and geographical location. I agree with at least two authors who pointed out that our climate is excellent; it is—for recreation as well as for industry.

On minerals I feel that a contradiction in views between Dr. A. MacGregor and Professor Neville George was apparent only. In fact, their points were complementary, each being related to different basic circumstances of approach. There is room for a much more persistent and imaginative approach to mineral utilisation.

It is often said that water is the limiting factor in the development of biological and material resources—the major single raw material required in industry, in agriculture, in maintaining fish and wildlife, and in recreation. This we have in plenty, although it is clear from the presentation on the first two days of this meeting that there are certain inadequacies in the measurement and control of fresh water; in particular, water gauging must be tackled effectively at the earliest date; soil, of perhaps equal importance to water to our way of life, may require to be surveyed at a greater pace, and in the marginal areas—not only the areas where good soil is known to be.

It has also been shown yesterday how we can improve and protect our soil through forest growth practices, and how necessary it is for us in Scotland to do this. It is surprising, and yet perhaps not surprising, that lack of facts about materials which we have in relative abundance—such as water and grass—should still exist as a handicap for users, or potential users.

I have been informed that Scotland is a wealthy nation. I agree entirely. In Scotland no industrial facility need be far from a port through which to send the products of a resourceful people, and through which to receive the resources of the world to complement their own. Geographically, Scotland is at a hub in trans-world airline communication, connecting with 90 per cent. of the world's population. Comprising only 30,000 square miles, with 260 miles between mainland extremities, its internal communications can be close-knit and efficient.

Sometimes we may not make the most of the potential for creating resources, and a continuing conscientious study of our assets (bearing in mind Professor Peacock's standards of economic assessment) will be of value to us. Some of our resources must be developed better, and in co-ordination with other resources.

Generally throughout the world there has been a tendency (by the standards now required) to squander resources which appear to be in abundance. The squandering appears in different forms—in Los Angeles it might be in fuel and motor cars; here it might be in water usage. I am informed, for instance, that if irrigation developed into a general practice in the United Kingdom, the whole pattern of water husbandry, supply and drainage, would change. A change of this kind would be making use of a resource in a dynamic way; resources become static when we cease to be resourceful.

So many other authors referred strongly to education that I have more than a suspicion that there *is* something amiss with our educational system. I am particularly in agreement with Professor Macrae when he says in his paper ". . . the best specialist is not the man who knows his own subject and nothing else, but the man who knows his own subject supremely well, and the more 'besides' the better, because all knowledge bears upon, illumines, and fortifies all other knowledge". As an industrialist I am glad that Professor Bruce Williams has tackled the problem of the management of innovation. This is a major problem throughout industries, and at the same time is the spring of opportunity for new activity and business life. The inflexibility of traditional practices and institutions resists guidance into paths where poise, through technical competence, is vital in a rapidly changing technical atmosphere.

As education is the stimulant for the human resource, in energy is the means to multiply strength. The availability of energy for our needs must anticipate the pace set by advances in production techniques. Yesterday afternoon's papers and discussion clearly show that energy is available in Scotland when required. *There was also a case put for some sort of co-ordination of energy authorities in Scotland.* Perhaps the most spectacular development has been the rapid rise of the complex of petroleum chemical plants at Grangemouth stemming from petroleum. It is in the "by-products" of main production that new, valuable and profitable goods can often be found. Thus electricity is a by-product from Chapelcross nuclear factory; high-pressure gas is a by-product from coal fields, refineries and steel plants; and by-products can be found from hitherto unworthy bings. On the latter point there has been shown at this meeting that there is something of worth to be found from a different and more persistent approach to using our waste materials, including sewage. Sewage might well be a subject on its own account. I am well aware of the excellent waste disposal plant used by the City of Edinburgh. At the same time, some of our seaside resorts are polluted by sewage discharges through pipes which in some cases do not even reach the low tide mark.

I am most grateful to Sir Robert Urquhart for reminding us that there are more than one million acres in crofting areas which, I understand, are prevented from being used well by the Crofters' Act of 1886. Sir Robert asked for a verdict from a meeting of this kind.

It has been said that the main agricultural effort is to increase productivity on existing farmlands, and there has not seemed to me to have been enough drive towards increasing productive areas—mainly because agricultural production and markets seem to be generally in balance. Surely however, rather more can be done in selling and in creating new markets. Perhaps a main unexplored new market lies in biological materials being used in industrial processes. It is a pity, I think, that we could give no more time for "Developing Uses of Biological Resources" since I am sure there is room for new industrial developments based on biological materials.

It has been shown at this meeting that one of our tasks must be to reconstitute efficient biological systems and also meet the present-day requirements of man as a town dweller and a worker. This means a multicultural approach to the use of land. I feel that if a philosophy is developed and accepted to that end, problems involving the interrelated resources will be progressively more easy to solve.

The United Kingdom is a major importer of food and raw materials, in return for which it exports the products of its brains applied to manufacturing industry. As these brains show the way, other countries rapidly follow, equalise and then lead. We must maintain the ability to maximise on all our resource opportunities, internal and external. Industrial leadership can take us so far and our excellent Civil Service can administer and co-ordinate the development of our resources up to a certain point. I think there is a field, however, where thoughts on the interrelated development of our natural wealth must be guided by others than the industrialist as such, or by the Civil Service as such. Others might regularly assemble as a Council, perhaps industrialists, Civil Servants, and scientists—under another hat—whose thoughts are geared to the alertness required by the rate of technical change in all countries, and to the hard competition for markets, and whose thoughts cross the boundaries between traditional educational patterns and scientific disciplines.

In saying this, and in arranging a meeting of this kind, I have been reinforced by the strong interest shown in this kind of thinking and operation by our own Government, by people in Canada, in America, and by organisations concerned in the development of other countries, and by the United Nations Organisation as such.

I am led to the conclusion that it would be of service to our country if in due course there were to be established a centre set up with certain objectives such as:

1. co-ordinating the interests of those concerned with the conservation and use of resources;
2. promoting high level co-operation between those concerned with the conservation and use of resources;
3. educating the social body in the attitudes of conservation and use so as to help Governmental administration;
4. educating the individual in leadership having regard to an integrated approach to resource development.

Such a body would form a centre for resource development transactions and authoritative information. At the same time it would not interfere with established schools and disciplines, but might form a complementary function.

It is clear to me that change in attitude is required in our approach to some resource problems, and a strategy is required which, if it existed, would help those concerned with different resources to tend to pull better in the same direction.

I find considerable food for thought in Mr. Blair-Cunynghame's warning, contained in his paper, that unless Scotland can show on merit that it is worth while to expand new or present industries "serious damage will be done to her reputation and economy by too ready a use of special concessions and Government help".

And now where do we go? I suppose there are some 260,000 words in the papers submitted and to this we must add say another 200,000 words in the discussions. My Committee are not out to practice magic—they are unable to bring rabbits out of a hat. Ever since I was given the remit from the Scottish Council I have looked upon it as a long-term investigation covering as a start four or five years, possibly more. First we had to know the facts. These have been established in this study group. Now the Committee must join with me and others in hard but interesting and worthwhile work. We must go over all these words. We must do some sifting. Possibly some will have to be discarded altogether. Some will be put on one side for longer-term consideration, whilst the rest will be closely examined and weighed up, with the view to framing a report with such recommendations as seem necessary or desirable, to be sent to the authority which we feel is the right one. I think that in two years time we shall convene another Conference, possibly with a much larger audience than this, to give consideration to those findings and to those recommendations.

Mr. Elgood continued:

Your Grace, My Lord, Ladies and Gentlemen: There is luckily perhaps for me no discussion about what I have said. I have no doubt I have tried to be and I hope you have taken it as provocative, and I hope and I am sure it is right that you will wish my Committee and others whom we bring in to go over these papers and discussion the very best of luck.

My duty is now a rather pleasant one, and that is to try and pay tribute to a whole lot of people in one sort of rounded vote of thanks: first of all there are those who came from abroad, some without expense to the Scottish Council: to the authors of the papers: those who came to the study group to take part in the discussions: the Chairmen and Deputy Chairmen and Reporters: to my Committee who did really wonderful work—and their names are listed on the first page of your programme; there are the officials of the Scottish Office who have sat in at our meetings and give us wonderful advice and I have reason to believe that they will continue to do so; there is Professor Frazer for organising work in connection with this Symposium; there are Mr. Wilson, Mr. McNab, and members of the staff of the Scottish Council, and there is the Royal Society of Edinburgh who have made us welcome in their Rooms here for the last three days. Finally, perhaps, I would be allowed to say how much we have all appreciated the hospitality given to us by the Lord Provost in the Civic Reception, and by Dr. Woodward and his organisation—the Arthur D. Little Research Institute. To them, to all of you, I give my very deep thanks.

I believe that we have started something here. As I have said before in connection with this, if we cannot take this farther after this Symposium, then we have completely failed in our job. I believe we will not fail. I believe we will take it farther, and I look forward to giving out in due course information regarding the work on Natural Resources in Scotland set up by the Scottish Council. Thank you very much.

Vote of Thanks

Mr. E. P. Hudson, *Managing Director, Scottish Agricultural Industries Ltd.*

Mr. Chairman, Your Grace, My Lords, Ladies and Gentlemen: Mr. Elgood has just said that he had a pleasant duty to perform. I think the rest of us all have a duty we would wish to perform to pay tribute to him. I have been privileged to act as a spokesman of this and I would suggest that we could perhaps look at it this way. Your programme this afternoon, page 13, ends with "Conclusions", but we did start after lunch with the "Administrative Requirements for Optimum Resource Development". We now come at this stage in the evening to "administrative requirements for optimum Symposium development" and you will find that listed on page 1, as Mr. Elgood said, and there you will see a list of people who are specialists. If you have had time to read your newspapers the last two or three days you will find 150 or 250 experts or specialists here, but we must have one General, and there he is at the top of the page—Mr. Elgood. He is the General who has been in charge of this operation, and surely we must all agree that he has indeed won a signal victory. In his quiet, and if I may say so, kindly way, he has watched the various people, on whom he has evolved responsibility, from Monday morning until Wednesday afternoon, and then if I can change the metaphor in a horrible way—like a jolly good miler he has come in with a fine performance on his own account with an excellent summary of the whole of these proceedings which has tied everything together for us very nicely indeed. So without further ado I think we should express our appreciation to Mr. Elgood and our thanks to him for everything he has done, and through him to the Scottish Council (Development and Industry), whom he epitomises this afternoon. I suggest there are two ways in which we can express thanks and appreciation.

The first is not to leave it to him and his Committee to work away at the things we have been talking about these three days. Surely we all owe it to ourselves as well as to Mr. Elgood and his Committee that we should ponder these matters and see what we can do about it each in our own different ways, and thus provide a greater body of practical support and moral support to the Scottish Council, to Mr. Elgood, and his Committee. That, I suggest, is the best way we can show our thanks and appreciation.

The second way is the conventional way, but I am sure it will be entirely heartfelt if we now, here and now, accord an expression of our thanks to him in the usual way.

Mr. Elgood

Mr. Hudson, . . . Ladies and Gentlemen: Thank you very much indeed. I have no more to say. At 3 o'clock I was unhappy. At 4 o'clock I am very happy.

FINIS